W9-ADQ-444

PULPING PROCESSES

ERIK HÄGGLUND [*1887–1959*]
Pioneer of modern pulping chemistry

Contents

Introduction vii

Part I.   Wood
1. Forests of the world 3
2. Species, anatomy and physical properties of wood . . 42
3. Fiber morphology 69
4. Wood chemistry 90

Part II.   Preparation of Unbleached Pulp
5. Preparation of wood for pulping 257
6. General principles of pulping 277
7. Mechanical pulping 368
8. Semichemical pulping 401
9. Chemical pulping 439
10. Further treatment of unbleached pulp 715
11. Preparation of cooking chemicals and treatment of waste liquors 764

Part III.   Preparation of Bleached Pulp
12. General principles of bleaching 839
13. Lignin-bleaching methods 885
14. Lignin-removing methods 916
15. Carbohydrate-removing methods 992
16. Removal of impurities 1024
17. Multistage bleaching 1061
18. Further treatment of bleached pulp 1081
19. Preparation of bleaching chemicals 1089

Part IV.   Pulp Properties and Uses
20. Characterization of pulp properties 1107
21. Pulp properties and uses 1133
22. Pulp industry of the world 1186

Author Index 1205
Subject Index 1231

Introduction

Like every art which is steadily developing into a science, pulping has been studied in many ways from different angles; practical and theoretical, mechanical and chemical, technical and economic, empirical and scientific. The collected knowledge obtained in the pulp mills and research laboratories is vast, but published information, although rapidly increasing, is scattered and heterogeneous. The need to summarize and organize them is felt by anyone working in the field. This has been extensively done from a mechanical and operational point of view (16), with little stress on the chemical reactions. Some textbooks deal with the chemistry of pulping, but either as a prelude to the chemistry and technology of paper manufacture (3), or as an addendum to the chemistry of wood (6, 20) or cellulose (11). There are also shorter direct treatments of the subject (e.g. 8, 12, 15) but few extensive up-to-date accounts which correspond to the size and importance of the pulp industry (9).

In trying to fill this gap in the literature, I have found it necessary to cover a wide variety of fields, and as the work progressed I felt increasingly that on studying this book an expert in any one of these fields will find errors, neglect of important facts, and unsatisfactory ways of approach. Suggested changes for the next edition will be appreciated, as I feel that with the present speed of publication and also of the development of pulping processes, revision will soon be needed. I have tried to select for reference only the more important of the vast number of publications in each field, and sometimes have filled in with my own experimental results where published information is scanty. For a more complete bibliography on pulping processes, the reader is referred to *Pulp and Paper Manufacture* (19).

In treating the subject of 'Pulping Processes', it has been found necessary to include a none-too-brief description of the chemistry of wood and wood components, in spite of the satisfactory and fairly recent treatments of these subjects elsewhere (1, 6, 10, 11, 20). However, this is done with direct reference to the pulping processes, with no claim to complete citation of literature and leaving out most of the historical background. The same is true of the description of the structure and properties of wood and fibers, where satisfactory monographs can also be found (4, 5, 7, 17, 18). Likewise, in describing the pulping processes some treatment of the operations and machinery used is unavoidable. However, no complete or detailed description is attempted, but reference is made to Britt (2), Nepenin (9) and Stephenson (16). It has been found desirable to describe the methods of characterization of different types of pulp as well as their end uses, but here again connection with the pulping processes is stressed, leaving details and complete literature references to standard works published on pulp analysis (14), the production of paper (3, 16) and cellulose derivatives (11, 13).

Thus, the book begins with surveys on the forests of the world, the various wood species, the gross and minute structure of the tree and of the fiber, and the chemical composition and reactions of their components. After touching the operations in the forests and at the mill involved in the preparation of wood for pulping, the processes for preparation of unbleached and bleached pulp are treated extensively, ending with a survey on pulp properties and uses as well as on the pulping industry.

I think that I should mention here that the metric system has been used throughout, and that apart from the normal abbreviations, two rather frequent ones are: ptw = per metric ton of bone dry wood; ptp = per metric ton of bone dry pulp.

I wish to express my gratitude to Billeruds AB, Säffle, Sweden, which with its activities in most fields of the pulping industry has given me the opportunity of becoming acquainted with the multitudinous aspects of pulping. I am especially grateful to the previous Research Director of the company, Dr. Leif Jörgensen, for his advice, and regret that his extended professional responsibilities prevented his active contribution to the book.

As a late but reverent acknowledgement, I have asked the publisher to include on one of the front pages a portrait of my late professor of cellulose technology and wood chemistry, Erik Hägglund, whose pioneering work on the chemistry of wood and pulping processes is cited on almost every page of this book. His educational work, as well as that of Professors Holger Erdtman, Börge Steenberg and others, was aimed at giving my generation of students at the Royal University of Technology in Stockholm a solid basis for their various tasks in the cellulose industry, and their stimulating tradition is carried on by Professors Bengt Lingberg and Lennart Stockman, with whom I have had the benefit of many interesting discussions. They have also encouraged me to carry on with this manuscript on occasions when the rapid progress of the pulping science to be described seemed out of proportion to the time available for writing. Numerous friends at their institutions and in many other places of the world, including my colleagues at Billerud, have also stimulated my efforts in many ways. I am grateful to them all, and also to my family, who tolerantly put up with me during this trying period.

SVEN RYDHOLM

GENERAL REFERENCES

1. Brauns, F. E., *Chemistry of Lignin*, Academic Press, New York, 1952.
2. Britt, K. W., *Handbook of Pulp and Paper Technology*, Reinhold, New York, 1964.
3. Casey, J. P., *Pulp and Paper, Chemistry and Chemical Technology*, 2nd Ed., Interscience, New York, 1960.

4. Esau, K., *Plant Anatomy*, Wiley, New York, 1953.
5. Frey-Wyssling, A., *Die pflanzliche Zellwand*, Springer, Berlin, 1958.
6. Hägglund, E., *Chemistry of Wood*, Academic Press, New York, 1951.
7. Jane, F. W., *Structure of Wood*, Black, London, 1956.
8. Libbey, C. E., ed., *Pulp and Paper Science and Technology*, McGraw-Hill, New York, 1962.
9. Nepenin, Y. N., *Chemie und Technologie der Zellstoffherstellung*, Akademie-Verlag, Berlin, 1960.
10. Nikitin, N. I., *Die Chemie des Holzes*, Akademie-Verlag, Berlin, 1955.
11. Ott, E., H. M. Spurlin and M. W. Grafflin, *Cellulose and Cellulose Derivatives*, 2nd Ed., Interscience, New York, 1955.
12. Sandermann, W., *Grundlagen der Chemie und Chemischen Technologie des Holzes*, Geest–Portig, Leipzig, 1956.
13. Schildknecht, C. E., ed., *Polymer Processes*, Interscience, New York, 1956.
14. Sieber, R., *Die Chemisch-Technischen Untersuchungsmethoden der Zellstoff und Papierindustrie*, 2nd Ed., Springer, Berlin, 1951.
15. Stamm, A. J., and E. E. Harris, *Chemical Processing of Wood*, Chemical Publ., New York, 1953.
16. Stephenson, J. N., *Preparation and Treatment of Wood Pulp*, McGraw-Hill, London, 1952.
17. Treiber, E., *Die Chemie der Pflanzenzellwand*, Springer, Berlin, 1957.
18. Trendelenburg, R., *Das Holz als Rohstoff*, 2nd Ed., Hauser, München, 1955.
19. West, C. J., W. B. Weber and J. Weiner, *Pulp and Paper Manufacture*, Bibliography, Tech. Assoc. Pulp Paper Ind., New York, yearly publication.
20. Wise, L. E., and E. C. Jahn, *Wood Chemistry*, 2nd Ed., Reinhold, New York, 1952.

PART I

WOOD

1

FORESTS OF THE WORLD

The principal raw material of pulp is wood. Table 1.1 shows that at present only 5% of pulp production originates from other sources—mainly from bagasse, straw and bamboo. It is therefore appropriate to start a book on pulping processes with a survey of the forests of the world, in order to give an idea about the location and relative importance of the wood-producing areas. At the end of the book, a similar survey is given of the pulping industry of the world at present. It should be remembered, however, that on agricultural land fiber materials are produced in quantities of the same order of magnitude as those produced by the forests.

Table 1.1. World production of pulp by
raw materials, M t, 1960

Softwood pulp	47
Hardwood pulp	9.5
Other pulps	3.5
Total	60

I. Climate and Vegetation

Nearly one-third of the earth's total land area is covered by forests; these occur wherever conditions are not too dry, too cold, or too barren to permit their growth. The climate and the soil conditions also greatly influence the type of forest, and consideration of a few basic climatological facts is helpful in order to understand both the past and present distribution and composition of the forests.

The temperature gradient from the equator to the poles, acting in conjunction with the earth's rotation, sets up a fairly standard pattern of atmospheric circulation and humidity conditions. If the surface of the earth were uniform, there would be three parallel zones of a precipitation higher than the average, one at the equator and the other two around the two 60° parallels. Four zones would get less than average of precipitation, namely the polar regions and around the two 30° parallels. The rotation of the earth and the unequal distribution of continents and oceans alter this theoretical pattern considerably.

Figures 1.1 and 1.2 show the principal distribution of climates and of vegetation in the present state of general continental elevation—the

3

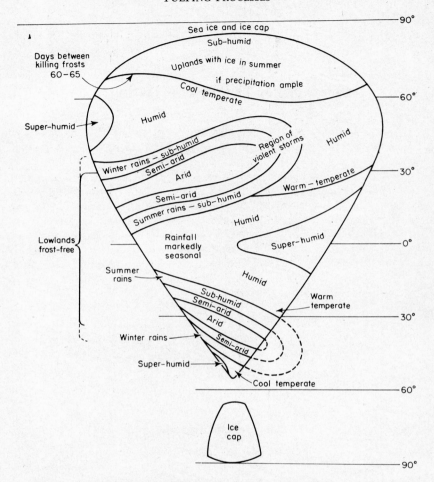

Fig. 1.1. Theoretical world distribution of climates, no account being taken of factors introduced by local features, such as mountain ranges, etc. The land area indicated is roughly similar to the combined land masses of either the eastern or the western hemisphere (Haden-Guest, Wright and Teclaff)

unequal distribution of land masses at the northern and southern hemispheres is indicated diagrammatically. These illustrations reflect the close correlation between vegetation and effective precipitation, i.e. water available to plants, considering not only the total precipitation, but also its seasonal distribution.

The arid and semi-arid zones contain no forests. The sub-humid areas are transition zones of the scrub and woodland type, with trees along streams or in scattered colonies, although the tundra and ice fields bordering on the ice caps of the poles are also sub-humid. The real forest land

4

is in the humid zones, with the forest type changing with temperature from the cooler coniferous belts over the mixed broadleaf–coniferous zones to the light tropical broadleaf forests. The tropical rain forests correspond to the super-humid zones.

Figure 1.3 illustrates the actual distribution of these vegetation types, as modified by the shapes of the land masses. A striking circumstance is the much greater concentration of coniferous forests in the northern than in the southern hemisphere, owing to the absence or scarcity of land in the latter at the particular latitudes in which conifers flourish.

The coniferous forests thus cover a vast part of Siberia, Scandinavia,

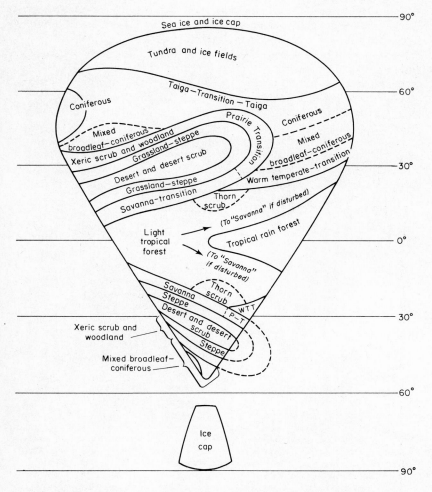

Fig. 1.2. The present vegetation types, correlated with the climates of Figure 1.1. Secondary effects caused by mountain ranges and the relation of particular areas of land and ocean are not indicated (Haden-Guest, Wright and Teclaff)

5

Canada and Alaska. Mixed broadleaf–coniferous forests extend over Central Europe, the eastern states of the U.S.A., Japan and eastern China, as well as over New Zealand, Tasmania, southernmost Africa and southern Chile. Tropical forests cover western central Africa, northern South America and south-eastern Asia.

Obviously not only climate and soil, but also the actions of man influence the forest pattern. In areas where man has burnt or logged the virgin stands and—often after a period of agricultural use—left the regrowth to nature, a different type of vegetation may have developed. Thus, jungle has succeeded the virgin tropical forests in many regions, and thorn forest and scrub is formed in other regions with longer dry seasons. Hardwoods may replace original coniferous forests, and scrub vegetation may succeed softwood or hardwood forests in regions of lower humidity. Accelerated erosion often occurs at such areas.

Large forest areas have of course also been converted to permanent agricultural land. During the last few millennia, the forest area has thus been reduced by from 30 to 50%, predominantly through human activity. On the other hand, big afforestation and reforestation programmes are being carried out on all continents after the establishment of definite forestry policies by many countries, which have realized the beneficial influences of forests on the climate and the soil, and the economic value of a well-managed forest industry. In this way large areas are being covered with forests containing both indigenous and often also exotic species or hybrids; scientific, silvicultural principles having been applied.

Fig. 1.3. The forests of the world. 1–6: Major Forest Regions. 1. *Coniferous forests*. Northern portion (*taiga*) mainly spruce–fir; at lower latitudes spruce and fir with other conifers and some broadleaf hardwoods. Timber, pulpwood. 2. *Mixed broadleaf-coniferous forests*. Broadleaf forests usually on better soils, coniferous types on poorer soils or in special habitats. Timber, forest products; general farming on better soils after clearing; pome and stone fruits. 3. *Tropical rain forests*. Important timbers, special tree crops, shifting agriculture. Includes unmapped areas of light forest, especially in Africa, and undifferentiated montane forest, as in Indonesia. 4. *Light tropical forest*. Timbers, important woods, special tree crops; often supports intensive tropical agriculture after clearing. 5. *Undifferentiated montane forests*. Regionally variable and complex, altitudinal tree line usually present. Timber, plateau agriculture and grazing. 6. *Thorn forest and scrub*. A few special woods and other products; seasonal grazing. 7–8: Transition Types. 7. *Xeric scrub and woodland* ("Mediterranean scrub" forest). Local lumber, fuel, other products; specialized horticulture, winter pasture. 8. *Gallery forest and groves*. Grasslands with gallery forest along streams and scattered upland groves. Local lumber, fuel. Clearing and repeated fires produce aspect of treeless grassland. Two types may be distinguished: (a) *Prairie*: temperate regions above 30° N and S latitude; the great grain-raising regions of the world. (b) *Savanna*: tropical latitudes; partly natural but often follows disturbance of light forest; grazing semisedentary to shifting agriculture. 9–11: Areas With No Forests. 9. *Steppe*. Bunch-grass, low shrubs and herbage; sometimes a few trees along main watercourses. Cattle and sheep ranching. 10. *Desert and desert scrub*. As mapped, includes some uplands with steppe and small areas of sparse forest. 11. *Tundra*. Low vegetation (Haden-Guest, Wright and Teclaff)

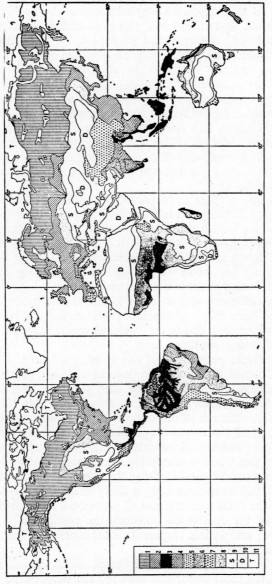

Fig. 1.3. The forests of the world (for key to numbers see facing page)

II. Global Distribution of Forests

Tables 1.2 and 1.3 show the size of the forested land in different regions. Of the 13,000 M ha (million hectars) land area of the world, about 4,000 M ha are forested. More than half this is considered inaccessible in an economic sense, i.e. uneconomical to exploit for industrial purposes because of difficult terrain, distance from markets, or lack of transportation. This area cannot justifiably be considered as a forest reserve, equivalent to the accessible forests in other than economical respects, because a large part consists of very slow-growing or thin forests with a much lower production per area than the commercial forests.

There are, however, still fairly large areas of potentially productive forests untouched. Not all of the accessible forests are being exploited; for various reasons about one-third is not used for timber production— for example immature forests, national parks, or forests in under-developed countries.

This leaves about 1,200 M ha of forests under exploitation, half of which are softwood stands and half hardwood stands. This area is mainly situated in the northern hemisphere, in North America, Europe and the U.S.S.R., whereas Latin America, Africa and the Pacific area contain relatively small forest areas and the Asiatic forests (excluding the U.S.S.R.) are predominantly hardwood. When figures for growing stock volume are considered instead of areas the picture is similar.

So far, the softwood species have attracted the greatest industrial interest. More than 90% of the softwood stands are located in the U.S.S.R., North America and Scandinavia, whereas the greatest hardwood resources are found in southern Asia.

To get the correct perspective of the pulping industry, which will be described in Chapter 22, it must be pointed out that about half of the roundwood fellings are still used for fuel purposes, and that lumber predominates for industrial purposes, as seen from Table 1.4. Thus, the pulping industry, although its importance is rapidly increasing, consumes less than 15% of all the roundwood which at present amounts to about 1,600 Mm^3. Fuel wood is predominantly hardwood, except in the U.S.S.R. where the large fuel wood consumption must consist mainly of softwood. At present Russian softwood is therefore relatively unimportant in the industrial field and constitutes only a fairly small—though increasing— proportion of the total consumption of pulpwood. It is obvious that at present, part of the fuel wood consumption constitutes a reserve for industrial wood, and in this respect Russian coniferous fuel wood is of considerable potential value.

The forests in Canada, the United States, U.S.S.R. and Scandinavia are at present the most important ones for the pulping industry of the world; of minor but increasing importance are forests in Central Europe, Japan, South Africa, South America, Australia and New Zealand.

Table 1.2. Forest resources of the world, 1953

Country or region	Total land area, M ha	Forested area Total, all types M ha	Softwood portion %	Accessible forests M ha	Forest under exploitation All types M ha	Soft-wood M ha	Hard-wood M ha	Growing stock (with bark) on areas under exploitation All species Mm³	Soft-wood Mm³	Hard-wood Mm³
North America										
U.S.A. (excl. Alaska)	770	262	52	196	196	93	103	15,500	10,500	5,000
Alaska	148	55	78	10	10	10	0	510	510	0
Canada	900	385	75	150	77	58	19	7,200	5,600	1,600
Mexico	197	26	14	15	4	2	2	450	400	50
Total	2,015	728	65	371	287	163	124	23,660	17,010	6,650
Latin America	2,050	865	3	314	78	10	68	8,050	1,000	7,050
Europe (excl. U.S.S.R.)										
Western	378	110	60	106	105	64	41	7,800	5,080	2,720
Eastern ('red')	101	27	52	27	26	13	13	2,120	1,130	990
Total	479	137	58	133	131	77	54	9,920	6,210	3,710
U.S.S.R.	2,190	742	78	425	351	301	50	33,150	30,000	3,150
Asia (excl. U.S.S.R.)										
Northern ('red')	1,690	99	75	44	36	27	9	3,450	2,720	730
Southern	970	426	11	268	196	13	183	20,300	880	19,420
Total	2,660	525	23	312	232	40	192	23,750	3,600	20,150
Africa	2,980	800	1	284	108	2	106	8,000	110	7,890
Pacific Area	860	86	9	20	17	2	15	1,000	200	800
Total, world	13,240	3,883	33	1,859	1,204	595	609	107,500	58,100	49,400

Table 1.3. Summary of forest resources, relative importance of regions

Country or region	Total land area, %	Forested area %	Accessible forest area %	Forests under exploitation			Growing stock on exploited areas		
				All types %	Softwood %	Hardwood %	All species %	Softwood %	Hardwood %
North America	15	19	20	23	27	20	22	29	13
Latin America	15	22	17	7	2	11	8	2	14
Europe (excl. U.S.S.R.)	4	3	7	11	13	9	9	11	8
U.S.S.R.	16	19	23	29	51	8	31	52	6
Asia (excl. U.S.S.R.)	20	14	17	19	7	32	22	6	41
Africa	23	21	15	9	0	17	7	0	16
Pacific Area	7	2	1	1	0	3	1	1	2
Total, world	100	100	100	100	100	100	100	100	100

10

Table 1.4. Roundwood fellings by use, species groups and regions, 1958.
Per cent of 1.584 Mm³

| Region | Species group | Use | | | | | |
		Lumber, veneer, sleepers	Pulp, pit-props	Other industr. wood	Total industr. wood	Fuel wood	Total wood
North America	Softwoods	10.8	5.0	0.5	16.4	0.9	17.3
	Hardwoods	2.4	1.0	0.5	4.0	2.6	6.6
	Total	13.2	6.0	1.0	20.4	3.5	23.9
Latin America	Softwoods	0.7	0.1	0.0	0.8	1.6	2.3
	Hardwoods	0.9	0.0	0.1	1.0	8.3	9.3
	Total	1.5	0.1	0.1	1.8	9.9	11.6
U.S.S.R.	Softwoods	7.2	3.5	3.2	13.9	5.1	19.0
	Hardwoods	1.3	0.1	0.6	2.0	2.7	4.7
	Total	8.5	3.6	3.8	15.9	7.8	23.7
Europe (excl. U.S.S.R.)	Softwoods	5.1	3.9	0.7	9.7	1.2	10.9
	Hardwoods	1.5	0.4	0.6	2.5	5.2	7.7
	Total	6.6	4.3	1.3	12.2	6.4	18.6
Asia (excl. U.S.S.R.)	Softwoods	1.6	0.6	0.3	2.5	0.2	2.7
	Hardwoods	1.7	0.2	0.2	2.1	8.4	10.5
	Total	3.3	0.8	0.5	4.6	8.6	13.2
Africa	Softwoods	0.0	0.0	0.0	0.0	0.1	0.2
	Hardwoods	0.5	0.0	0.1	0.6	7.0	7.6
	Total	0.5	0.0	0.1	0.6	7.1	7.8
Pacific Area	Softwoods	0.3	0.1	0.0	0.4	0.0	0.4
	Hardwoods	0.5	0.0	0.0	0.5	0.4	0.9
	Total	0.7	0.1	0.0	0.9	0.4	1.3
All regions	Softwoods	25.7	13.2	4.7	43.6	9.2	52.8
	Hardwoods	8.7	1.8	2.1	12.7	34.5	47.2
	Total	34.4	14.9	6.8	56.3	43.7	100.0

III. Regional Forest Description

1. CANADA

Figure 1.4 shows a forest classification of Canada. Of the 900 M ha land area, 385 M ha is forest land, of which 215 M ha is classified as commercial and still less, 150 M ha, is accessible. The map shows the changing forest type. In the north, a sparsely forested land borders the tundra. South of it, an important conifer region, the 'Boreal Forest', extends from east to west, consisting principally of white and black spruce (*Picea glauca* and *P. mariana*), balsam fir (*Abies balsamea*), jack pine (*Pinus banksiana*), and of the hardwoods aspen (*Populus tremuloides*) and white birch (*Betula papyrifera*). Together with the tundra-bordering region, which is also included in the concept of the Boreal Forest, it constitutes 80% of the Canadian forest area, although a large part of it is inaccessible or slow-growing.

South of this is a belt of more varying forest types, beginning in the east with the 'Acadian Forest Region' in the favourable maritime climate of Nova Scotia, Prince Edward Island and New Brunswick. Red spruce (*Picea rubens*) is the dominant feature, associated with balsam fir, some white and black spruce, white and red pine (*Pinus strobus* and *P. resinosa*), and in the southern districts also yellow birch (*Betula lutea*) and maples (*Acer rubrum* and *A. saccharum*).

West of this region is the 'Great Lakes–St. Lawrence Forest Region', where white and red pine, eastern hemlock (*Tsuga canadensis*) and some spruce occur, associated with yellow birch and maples.

In the south, the hardwoods become accentuated in a small region called the 'Deciduous Forest', which is now completely settled, and its species, beech (*Fagus grandifolia*), maples and oaks (*Quercus alba, Q. borealis*), occur only in small wooded areas.

West of the grassland regions in Saskatchewan and Alberta and bordering the Boreal Forest, the 'Sub-alpine Forest Region' extends towards the Northwest Territory, with dominant species Engelmann spruce (*Picea engelmanni*), alpine fir (*Abies lasiocarpa*) and lodgepole pine (*Pinus contorta* var. *latifolia*).

The adjacent 'Montane Forest Region' contains ponderosa pine (*Pinus ponderosa*) and lodgepole pine, Douglas fir (*Pseudotsuga taxifolia*) and aspen.

The 'Columbia' and 'Coast Forest Regions' have a similar composition: western hemlock (*Tsuga heterophylla*), western red cedar (*Thuja plicata*) and Douglas fir are the principal common species, with Engelmann spruce in the former region and Sitka spruce (*Picea sitchensis*) in the latter region.

Table 1.5 shows the distribution of standing timber volume by species on commercial forest land in Canada. Obviously the conifers dominate, and among them spruces and balsam fir constitute about half of the volume, and the western species—hemlock, cedar, Douglas fir and lodgepole pine—the other half, in spite of the fact that the Boreal Forest Region, spruces

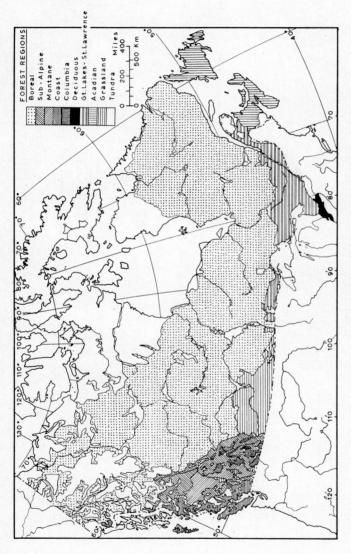

Fig. 1.4. Canada: forest regions (Haden-Guest, Wright and Teclaff; based on a map by the Department of Resources and Development, Forestry Branch, Canada)

13

Table 1.5. Volume of merchantable timber on commercial forest land in Canada, by species and accessibility class, 1953

Species	Total Mm³	%	Accessible Mm³	%	Inaccessible Mm³	%
Softwood:						
Spruces		38		36		41
Jack and lodgepole pine		11		11		13
Balsam fir		16		15		18
Hemlock		7		7		7
Cedar		5		5		4
Douglas fir		4		4		4
Other softwood		2		2		1
Total		83		80		88
Hardwood:						
Aspen		9		10		9
White birch		5		7		3
Yellow birch		1		1		–
Maple		1		1		–
Other hardwood		1		1		–
Total		17		20		12
All species	11,300	100	7,800	100	3,500	100

and balsam fir, constitutes 80% of the forested area. The western forests, especially in the coastal districts, are obviously denser than average.

Table 1.6 demonstrates that about half of the standing timber volume grows in the east—Quebec, Ontario and the Maritime Provinces—and the other half in the west, particularly in British Columbia. This distribution corresponds fairly well with that of the species just mentioned. The hardwoods are predominantly found in the eastern provinces. The

Table 1.6. Volume of merchantable timber on accessible forest land in Canada, by region, 1953

Region	All species Mm³	%	Softwood Mm³	%	Hardwood Mm³	%
Maritime Provinces*		6		6		7
Quebec		23		21		32
Ontario		27		25		35
Prairie Provinces†		9		6		20
British Columbia		32		40		2
Yukon and Northwest Terr.		3		2		4
Total	7,800	100	6,200	100	1,600	100

* Newfoundland, Prince Edward Island, Nova Scotia, New Brunswick
† Manitoba, Saskatchewan, Alberta

yearly consumption of wood amounts to about 100 Mm³, of which about a quarter is used for fuel. The consumption corresponds to less than 1.0 m³/ha.year, which is the average growth rate.

Because of its abundant coniferous forests, Canada has always been an important pulp producer, and the high proportion of spruces and balsam fir has made sulfite pulping and particularly mechanical pulping the traditional methods in the industry. In British Columbia, a kraft pulping industry based on the western wood species is rapidly developing in connection with the saw-mill industry.

2. THE UNITED STATES OF AMERICA

The United States' pulping industry is the largest in the world, and a description of the American forests is fully justified. Of 925 M ha land area, including Alaska, 318 M ha are forested of which 214 M ha are commercial forests. They extend over large areas of widely varying climate and therefore display a correspondingly wide variation in type and species. Figure 1.5 shows their location, excepting the Alaskan forests, of which especially those of the coastal areas have recently become of industrial importance. In the interior of Alaska there are spruce–birch forests similar to those of the Boreal Forest Region of Canada, whereas Coastal Alaska represents an extension of the British Columbian western hemlock–Sitka spruce belt.

This belt also extends into the U.S. west coast in the states of Washington and Oregon, where it is used intensively as a source of lumber and pulpwood. Adjacent to the hemlock–spruce belt, the important Douglas fir region covers the western part of Washington, Oregon and northern California, where growing conditions are ideal. Long growing seasons, heavy rainfalls and suitable soils favor rapid growth and dense stands, and these are among the most economically important forests in the United States. Douglas fir occurs here in pure stands, or mixed with western hemlock and western red cedar to the north and with redwood in California. Much of this wood is old and of immense dimensions but fairly slow-growing, in spite of the favorable growing conditions. An important lumber industry is located here, combined more recently with an expanding pulp industry. Further south along the coast of California, redwood (*Sequoia sempervirens*) becomes dominant. Although an important raw material for the lumber industry, it is not yet used for pulping.

In the vast western inland, with its very much lower rainfall, the drought-resistant ponderosa pine covers large areas, often intermixed with other species, such as sugar pine (*Pinus lambertiana*). Ponderosa pine is the most important lumber wood after Douglas fir and the southern pines, but is less important for pulping. In the more moist parts of the western inland to the north, western white pine (*Pinus monticola*) and western larch (*Larix occidentalis*) occupy limited areas, intermixed with western red cedar and the mountain type of Douglas fir. At higher elevations in the Rocky

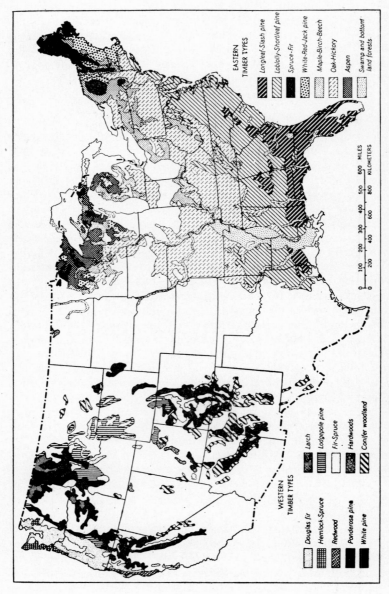

Fig. 1.5. United States: major forest types (Haden-Guest, Wright and Teclaff; based on a map by U.S. Department of Agriculture, Forest Service)

16

Mountains, a spruce–fir zone exists, consisting of Engelmann spruce, true firs (*Abies* spp.) and mountain hemlock (*Tsuga mertensiana*), and at middle altitudes lodgepole pine occurs in pure stands. Hardwoods are scarce in the western United States. Most common are alder (*Alnus rubra*), cotton-wood (*Populus trichocarpa*) and aspen.

The forests described above are commonly classified as those of the West. East of the unforested great plains, large forest areas extend from the Mississippi River system to the Atlantic, classified as the forests of the North and the South. To the North belong the Lake, Middle Atlantic, and New England states, and the sub-regions of the South are called South Atlantic, Southeast and West Gulf states. In the north large coniferous forests were long dominant, but as a result of logging and fire only remnant areas in the Northeast and the Lake states remain today. These are of two types, the spruce–fir forests, containing black and red spruce, balsam fir, eastern hemlock and tamarack (*Larix laricina*), and the northern pine forests, with white, red and jack pine, both types increasingly inter-mixed with hardwoods, such as maple, birch and aspen. Of these hard-woods, aspen is particularly common in the Lake states region, whereas the maple–birch–beech forests occur both there and in the New England states. The forest industry of these regions, important and long-estab-lished, was originally based on softwoods, but has now been forced partly to change its methods and production pattern to adapt itself to the changed raw material situation.

A broad belt of forests extends across the eastern United States, about equally shared by the North and the South regions. This is characterized by various species of oaks and hickories. The oak–hickory forest was originally continuous, and although a large part of it has been cleared for agriculture it still covers the largest area of all American forest types—more than one-fifth of the entire commercial forest land. The forest is far from homogeneous and merges imperceptibly into the northern hard-woods and the southern pine belts. In the western parts, white and black oak (*Quercus alba and Q. velutina*) and hickory (*Carya* spp.) are dominant species, associated with black walnut (*Juglans nigra*), elm (*Ulmus americana*), white ash (*Fraxinus americana*) and post oaks (*Q. stellata*). Towards the east, chestnut oak (*Q. prinus*), hickory and yellow poplar (*Liriodendron tulipifera*) are the most common species. The wood of the oak–hickory region was formerly of only limited importance for the pulping industry, but new methods and new products have contributed to change this.

Another hardwood forest type of increasing interest for pulping is the oak–gum forest of the Mississippi swamp and bottomlands and some other isolated areas in the South. Black, swamp and tupelo gum (*Nyssa sylvatica, N. biflora* and *N. uniflora*) and on better drained soil sweetgum (*Liquid-ambar styraciflua*) dominate together with cottonwood, over-cup oak (*Q. lyrata*), water oak (*Q. nigra*), white and red oak (*Q. falcata*), post and blackjack oak (*Q. marilandica*).

Some of these hardwoods are also intermixed in the most important

17

forest belt of the South, namely the southern pines region, extending from eastern Texas to the Atlantic and supplying more than half of the pulpwood used in the United States. Actually there are two different belts—the loblolly–shortleaf pine belt (*Pinus taeda* and *P. echinata*) is to the north of the coastal longleaf–slash pine belt (*P. palustris* and *P. elliottii*). In the former, Virginia and pitch pine (*P. virginiana* and *P. rigida*) are also found, and in addition pond pine (*P. serotina*) is found in the latter. The pines of the latter belt are of a heavier type than those of the former. The kraft pulp industry based on southern pines is the biggest of its kind in the world. There is also an important saw-mill industry in this region.

To give a more quantitative picture of the complex forest pattern in the United States, Table 1.7 shows the distribution of commercial forest land by species and regions. It can be seen that if Alaska is included in the West the forest area is about equally distributed on the West, North and South. Softwood and hardwood forest areas are about equal but not uniformly distributed among the regions: whereas hardwood forests are rare in the West, they exceed the softwood forest area in the South and dominate entirely in the North. There are so many common species, that their relative importance is not very clearly seen unless they are grouped in more general categories as in Table 1.8. Unlike Canada, where the softwoods, including spruces and firs, dominate, the United States' forest areas contain a good deal of hardwood and pines. This is also reflected in the production pattern of the pulping industry. Whereas there are more sulfite and, particularly, groundwood pulp mills in Canada, in the United States the kraft pulping industry is the largest one since Douglas fir, the pines and the heavier hardwoods are best suited to kraft pulping. The peculiar forest pattern has also caused the manufacture of pine groundwood pulp and the process of neutral sulfite pulping of hardwoods to be developed in the United States.

Table 1.8 shows two further aspects of the relative importance of species and regions. Although the forest area is equally divided between soft-woods and hardwoods, two-thirds of the standing timber volume are soft-woods. This change is mainly caused by the heavy coniferous stands of the Pacific coast, so that Alaska and the West contain more than half of the timber volume on less than a third of the forest area. Since part of these stands is old and slow-growing, a comparison of the annual growth again changes the picture, restoring the balance between softwoods and hard-woods and emphasizing the importance of the South as a timber-producing region. The average annual growth is about 2 m^3/ha.year, but in several districts in the West and the South much higher figures are quoted, and with improved silvicultural methods, a decided increase in wood produc-tion can be expected. The question of industrial importance is still another one, and will not be discussed here. It should only be pointed out that for both saw-mills and pulp mills, softwood is still the preferred raw material, emphasizing the importance of the West and the South.

18

Table 1.7. Distribution of commercial forest area in the United States by species and region, 1953

Per cent of 214 M ha

	Alaska			West						North						South				All regions
Forest type	Interior	Coastal	Total	Pacific Northwest Douglas fir sub-reg.	Pacific Northwest Pine sub-reg.	California	Rocky Mountains North	Rocky Mountains South	Total	New England	Middle Atlantic	Lake States	Central	Plains	Total	South Atlantic	Southeast	West Gulf	Total	
Softwoods:																				
Spruce–fir	5.46	–	5.46	0.31	0.34	0.52	0.51	0.90	2.58	2.00	0.16	1.92	–	–	4.08	–	–	–	–	12.12
Hemlock–Sitka spruce	–	0.81	0.81	–	0.67	–	–	–	0.67	–	–	–	–	–	–	–	–	–	–	1.48
Douglas fir	–	–	–	3.46	0.35	0.83	1.18	0.19	6.01	–	–	–	–	–	–	–	–	–	–	6.01
Redwood	–	–	–	–	–	0.30	–	–	0.30	–	–	–	–	–	–	–	–	–	–	0.30
Larch	–	–	–	–	0.22	–	0.62	–	0.84	–	–	–	–	–	–	–	–	–	–	0.84
Ponderosa pine	–	–	–	0.13	2.41	1.15	1.49	1.91	7.09	–	–	–	–	0.08	0.08	–	–	–	–	7.17
White pine	–	–	–	0.05	0.06	0.43	0.48	–	1.02	–	–	–	–	–	–	–	–	–	–	1.02
Lodgepole pine	–	–	–	0.04	0.35	0.06	1.83	0.47	2.75	–	–	–	–	–	–	–	–	–	–	2.75
Piñon pine–juniper	–	–	–	–	–	–	0.16	–	0.16	–	–	–	–	–	–	–	–	–	–	0.16
White–red–jack pine	–	–	–	–	–	–	–	–	–	0.65	0.31	0.84	–	–	1.80	0.04	0.02	–	0.06	1.86
Longleaf–slash pine	–	–	–	–	–	–	–	–	–	–	–	–	–	–	–	0.30	4.22	0.49	5.01	5.01
Loblolly–shortleaf pine	–	–	–	–	–	–	–	–	–	0.03	0.53	–	0.11	0.04	0.71	3.08	4.29	2.96	10.33	11.04
Total, softwoods	5.46	0.81	6.27	3.99	4.40	3.29	6.27	3.47	21.42	2.68	1.00	2.76	0.11	0.12	6.67	3.42	8.53	3.45	15.40	49.76
Hardwoods:																				
Alder–cottonwood	–	–	–	0.17	0.03	–	0.14	0.41	0.75	–	–	–	–	–	–	–	–	–	–	0.75
Oak–pine	–	–	–	–	–	–	–	–	–	0.01	0.11	–	0.33	0.02	0.47	1.04	1.65	1.18	3.87	4.34
Oak–hickory	–	–	–	–	–	–	–	–	–	0.60	3.52	1.22	5.50	0.25	11.08	2.82	4.55	2.76	10.13	21.21
Oak–gum–cypress	–	–	–	–	–	–	–	–	–	–	0.52	–	0.24	0.17	0.93	1.40	3.02	2.27	6.69	7.62
Elm–ash–cottonwood	–	–	–	–	–	–	–	–	–	0.16	0.27	0.87	1.45	0.44	3.19	–	0.08	0.19	0.27	3.46
Maple–beech–birch	–	–	–	–	–	–	–	–	–	2.00	2.02	1.76	0.39	0.02	6.17	0.05	0.10	–	0.15	6.32
Aspen–birch	2.09	–	2.09	–	–	–	–	–	–	0.36	0.55	3.48	0.02	0.03	4.44	–	–	–	–	6.53
Total, hardwoods	2.09	–	2.09	0.17	0.03	–	0.14	0.41	0.75	3.13	6.99	7.33	7.93	0.91	26.28	5.31	9.40	6.40	21.11	50.23
All species	7.55	0.81	8.36	4.16	4.43	3.29	6.41	3.88	22.17	5.81	7.99	10.09	8.04	1.03	32.96	8.73	17.93	9.85	36.51	100.00

Table 1.8. Summary of U.S. forest area, timber volume and annual growth, distribution by species and region, 1953

Species	Alaska	West	North	South	Total
	Area, % of 214 M ha of commercial forests				
Softwoods					
Spruces, firs and hemlocks	6.3	3.2	4.1	0.0	13.2
Douglas fir, redwood, larch	0.0	7.2	0.0	0.0	7.2
Pines	0.0	11.0	2.6	15.4	29.0
Total softwoods	6.3	21.4	6.7	15.4	49.8
Hardwoods					
Oaks, gums, hickory, etc.	0.0	0.0	12.5	20.7	33.2
Maple, beech, birches, aspen, etc.	2.1	0.7	13.8	0.4	17.0
Total hardwoods	2.1	0.7	26.3	21.1	50.2
All species	8.4	22.1	33.0	36.5	100.0
	Timber volume, % of 14,600 Mm^3 on commercial forests lands				
Softwoods	4	50	5	10	69
Hardwoods	0	2	17	12	31
All species	4	52	22	22	100
	Annual growth, % of 406 Mm^3 on commercial forests lands				
Softwoods	5	16	6	25	52
Hardwoods	2	0	26	20	48
All species	7	16	32	45	100

3. THE U.S.S.R.

The largest forest areas in the world are found in the U.S.S.R., which occupies a major portion of north-eastern Europe and of northern and central Asia. The total land area is about 2,230 M ha, with 510 M ha in Europe and 1,720 M ha in Asia. From the vegetation point of view, it is divided into four broad parallel zones, stretching from east to west: tundra to the north, then, coming southwards, forest, steppe and finally desert, as seen in Figure 1.6.

The forest zone embraces about 1,100 M ha, or half of the entire land area. However, not all of the forest zone is solid forest but includes also vast swamps, meadows and forest land of low productivity. About two-thirds is considered to be productive timber land, or 630–740 M ha according to different estimates, which report the accessible forest area to be 425–485 M ha, of which 137 M ha is in European Russia. The distribution of the forest area by regions and by species is seen in Tables 1.9 and 1.10. The conifers thus dominate by area and also constitute 85–90% of the standing timber volume. The latter is immense, about 75,000 Mm^3, of which about 40,000 Mm^3 are considered accessible. As the average

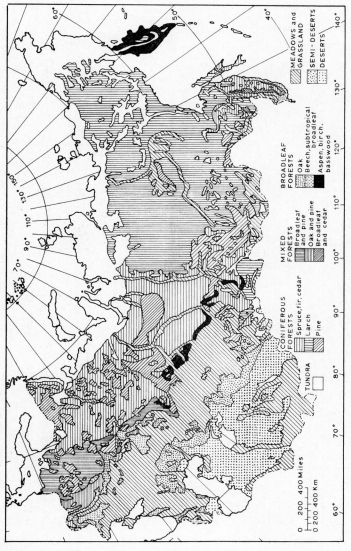

Fig. 1.6. U.S.S.R.: major forest regions (Haden-Guest, Wright and Teclaff; based on a map in the Great Soviet Encyclopedia)

Table 1.9. Distribution of U.S.S.R. forests by
species. Per cent of 630 M ha

Softwoods		
Larch	40	
Pine	16	
Spruce	12	
Cembra pine	5	
Fir and other	5	78
Hardwoods		
Birch	14	
Aspen	2	
Oak	1	
Beech–maple–basswood	1	
Other	4	22

Table 1.10. Distribution of accessible and productive U.S.S.R.
forests by regions.

Region	Area		Timber volume	
Per cent of 450 M ha or 42,000 Mm³				
European Part:				
North	13		12	
West	2		1	
Central	5		4	
South	2		1	
Ural	9		26	
Caucasus	1	32	1	45
Asiatic Part:				
Western Siberia	6		8	
Eastern Siberia	61		46	
Central Asia	1	68	1	55
Per cent of 680 M ha or 75,000 Mm³				
European Part:				
North	10		9	
West	2		2	
Central	4		4	
South	5		2	
Ural	4	25	4	21
Asiatic Part:				
Western Siberia	10		12	
Eastern Siberia	50		51	
Far East	15	75	16	79

rate of growth is low, about 1 m³/ha.year (as in Canada), the total timber produced per year amounts to about 850 Mm³ of which 450 Mm³ is accessible, or about the same as that of the U.S.A. Furthermore, of the accessible forests only about three-quarters are at present under exploitation. On the other hand, the predominance of softwoods makes the area of enormous industrial interest, in spite of the very large problems involved in its utilization. These are mainly transportation problems arising from the uneven geographical distribution of forests and consumption centres and the lack of adequate means of water and land transportation. Hence 75% of all stands are ripe or over-aged.

As seen in Table 1.10, the largest forests are located in Eastern Siberia, east of the Lake Baikal. They are composed mainly of Siberian larch (*Larix sibirica*), apart from hardwood districts in the far east (the Maritime Territory and the Khabarovsk region, where a quarter of all the hardwood forests of the U.S.S.R. are located). The species include birches, maples, basswoods, oaks and aspens.

In Western Siberia, in addition to Siberian larch, spruce (*Picea abies*), fir (*Abies sibirica*) and pine (*Pinus silvestris*) also occur over large areas, and substantial stands of high-quality Cembra pine (*Pinus cembra*).

To the south there is a hardwood zone of birch and aspen. Around Lake Baikal an important pulping industry is now developing. Otherwise, the main forest industry of the U.S.S.R. is still found in the European part, in connection with the large spruce and pine forests in the North and Central regions.

In the West region and the southern part of the Central region, pine forests are mixed with a great deal of hardwood, such as oak and beech. The important Ural region occupies a unique position among the forest regions of the country, with comparatively dense stands of pine and hardwoods, in a district of great industrial activity.

The southern regions of European and Central-Asiatic U.S.S.R. are agricultural districts or steppe and of little interest from a forestry point of view. On both sides of the Caucasus Mountains, some hardwood forests containing oak, beech, etc., and some conifer stands, such as Caucasian fir (*Abies nordmannia*), support a local lumber industry.

An important part of the wood produced, or nearly 50%, is consumed for fuel. The principal industrial use is lumber, but the pulp and paper industry of the U.S.S.R. is now growing rapidly.

4. EUROPE

Excluding the U.S.S.R., Europe has a comparatively small land area—about 470 M ha, of which only about 130 M ha, or one-quarter, is forested. However, the region deserves attention, partly because of its easily accessible coniferous forests in the northern region, and also because of its high industrialization, which includes an important forest industry.

Figure 1.7 shows the distribution of the forest areas. Europe has a similar forest pattern to North America, although its climate is on average

23

more maritime and its Northern region, Scandinavia and Finland, benefits from the influence of the North Atlantic Drift. The western winds carry warm, moisture-laden air to Scandinavia, and the Norwegian forests thus correspond to the coastal forests of Alaska, although most of the mountain sides towards the Atlantic are now barren because of over-cutting. The main coniferous forests are found in south-eastern Norway, in Sweden and in Finland.

Moving eastwards, the climate becomes increasingly influenced by the Russian land mass, and the forest vegetation is similar to that of North-European Russia. Norway spruce (*Picea abies*) and Scots pine (*Pinus silvestris*) are the main species, with spruce predominating in Norway, pine in Finland and the two species having about equal importance in Sweden. Together with these conifers a little aspen (*Populus tremula*) and considerable quantities of birch (*Betula verrucosa* and *B. pubescens*) are intermixed, of which Norway has the smallest portion—about 7%, Sweden having 15% and Finland 22%. The forest land is largely accessible and operated on a sustained yield basis, with an average annual growth of about 2 m³/ha.year. This region is by far the most important wood-producing part of Europe and has developed an advanced lumber and pulp

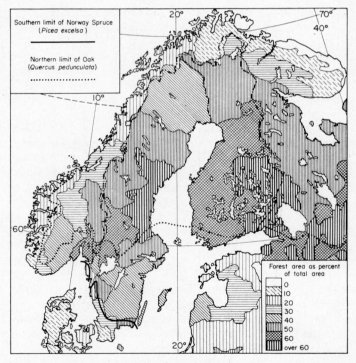

Fig. 1.7. (above and facing page) Europe: distribution of forest areas (Haden-Guest, Wright and Teclaff, based on Weltforstatlas, Hamburg)

24

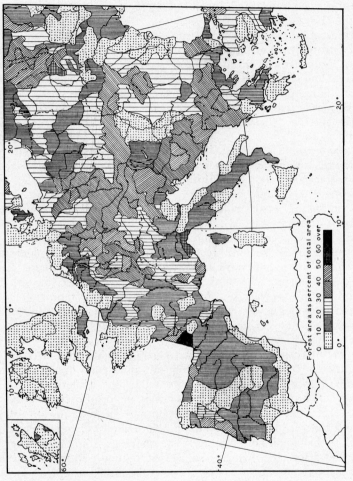

Fig. 1.7. (see facing page)

Forest area as percent of total area

0 10 20 30 40 50 60 over

industry, the structure of which follows the forest pattern. Thus in Norway mechanical and sulfite pulping predominate, in Finland kraft pulping, whereas in Sweden the three branches are of equal importance.

Southern Sweden and especially Denmark have a milder climate and form a transition to the Western region of Europe, which has about the same total land area but only half as much, and far less useful, forest area. Only half of these forests are softwoods, and much of the remaining hardwood area is no longer high forest but coppice, particularly in France and Belgium.

Two forest zones may be recognized. One is the western extension of the North-European plain, including the north-western half of France, the Benelux countries and north-western Germany. These plains are densely populated and the forests have had to yield for cultivation and settlements. The remaining forests, 10% of the land, contain less than 50% softwoods, mainly pines (*Pinus silvestris* and *P. pinaster* var. *maritimus*), and of the hardwoods, oaks (*Quercus petraea, Q. robur*) and beech (*Fagus silvatica*) dominate.

The second zone is an extension of the central European coniferous belt, comprising south-eastern France, Switzerland and south-eastern Germany. These forests grow at higher altitudes and are largely coniferous—pines (*Pinus silvestris, P. nigra, P. cembra*), spruce (*Picea abies*) and fir (*Abies alba*) dominating, mixed with larch (*Larix decidua*). They continue into the East-Central region with the forests of Czechoslovakia, Austria, northern Yugoslavia and Poland, which in turn borders on the East-European U.S.S.R. region. East-Central Europe, however, contains on the average somewhat more hardwood than softwood forest, because hardwoods dominate in Albania, Bulgaria, Hungary, Rumania and Yugoslavia. Oak forests (*Quercus robur, Q. petraea, Q. cerris*, etc.) often mixed with elm (*Ulmus glabra*), maple (*Acer campestre*, etc.) and linden (*Tilia europaea*) occur at low altitudes in these countries, and beech forests at somewhat higher elevations.

The Mediterranean region of Europe, in which Portugal is included, has a different type of vegetation from the other parts of Europe because of its entirely different climate, with mild, wet winters and hot, dry summers. The summer drought is a limiting factor of extreme importance to the vegetation. It makes regeneration and reforestation difficult, and has contributed to the catastrophic results of careless logging already performed by the peoples of antiquity. The search for ship timber, the steady use of fuel wood, the disturbances caused by many wars, as well as the spreading cultivation of the land, stripped the mountain forests of Greece five centuries B.C. and the plains and hills of Italy and Spain only a few centuries later. A serious drought that prevailed over southern Europe around the year A.D. 1000 was especially detrimental to the remaining forests. The typical scrub vegetation of the Mediterranean, the 'macchia' or 'maquis', took over the forest areas not utilized for cultivation, and serious soil denudation has occurred.

The remaining forests consist mainly of mixed hardwoods, with about

Table 1.11. Distribution of European forests by regions and species

Region	Total land area, M ha	Forest area, M ha	Timber volume, Mm³	Annual growth, Mm³	Softwoods, in % of forest area
Scandinavia and Finland					
Denmark	4.2	0.4	60	1.8	61
Finland	30.5	21.8	1,491	45.0	78
Norway	30.9	6.1	390	12.0	85
Sweden	41.1	22.9	1,820	51.5	93
Total	106.7	51.2	3,761	110.3	85
Western Europe					
Belgium	3.1	0.6	46	2.3	37
Netherlands	3.2	0.2	15	0.6	69
Luxemburg	0.2	0.1	10	0.2	
France	55.1	11.4	805	32.4	30
West Germany	24.0	6.7	625	25.0	65
East Germany	10.8	2.8	253	5.4	80
Switzerland	4.0	1.0	200	3.3	80
United Kingdom	24.5	1.5	100	2.0	48
Ireland	7.0	0.1	10	0.2	64
Total	131.9	24.4	2,064	71.4	49
East-Central Europe					
Albania	2.9	1.1		2.5	21
Austria	8.4	3.2		7.4	84
Bulgaria	11.1	3.7		4.0	13
Czechoslovakia	12.8	4.0		10.4	65
Hungary	9.3	1.2		3.0	6
Poland	31.2	7.5		11.0	88
Rumania	23.8	6.3		15.0	25
Yugoslavia	25.7	8.7		15.0	20
Total	125.2	35.7	ca. 3,000	68.3	45
Mediterranean Region					
Greece	13.0	0.5	44	1.0	41
Italy	30.0	5.6	300	11.6	19
Portugal	8.9	2.5		4.8	47
Spain	50.3	7.3		5.0	37
Total	102.2	15.9	ca. 1,000	22.4	33
All Europe	466	127	9,900	270	62

one-third of pines. The hardwoods on the lower altitudes are frequently of the *sclerophyllous evergreen* type, such as *Myrtus*, *Erica* spp. and *Quercus ilex;* at somewhat higher elevation thin oak forests (*Q. robur*, *Q. suber*, etc.); and still higher up beech and chestnut (*Castanea vesca*). Most of these hardwood forests are of little value to the pulping industry, whereas an increasing number of areas are being planted with industrially important poplar (*Populus* × *euramericana*) and eucalyptus species (*Eucalyptus globulus, E. camaldulensis*).

Table 1.11 shows in figures the distribution and composition of the European forests in the various regions. In addition to the Scandinavian and Finnish pulping industry, the importance of which has already been stressed, there is a considerable amount of pulp and paper making on the continent, relying partly on imported wood—Scandinavian, Russian or sometimes even Canadian. Of the local wood, spruce, fir and pine have been used for a long time, but the abundant beech is gaining importance as a pulp raw material, especially in France, Germany, Yugoslavia and Italy, poplar in Poland, Germany, and especially in Italy, and eucalyptus in Spain, Portugal and Italy. The pulping industry of continental Europe will much rely on France for its raw material. Here systematic efforts are being made to transform the large hardwood coppice areas into useful forests. The large maritime pine plantations in south-western France should also be mentioned in this connection. In the British Isles, once extremely well forested, and now having a forest coverage of only 6%, considerable efforts at reforestation are also made, mainly Scots pine, Sitka spruce and Norway spruce being planted.

The rate of growth in Europe, excepting Scandinavia, is on average somewhat more than 3 m³/ha.year, a higher average than the forest regions previously described. The planted poplar and eucalyptus forests especially grow fast, averaging 15 m³/ha.year for eucalyptus in Portugal and Spain, and on favourable sites twice as much. Similar figures are also quoted for poplar hybrids in Italy. However, eucalyptus requires a special climate and poplar a favorable soil, which limits the possible areas considerably. Beech will therefore probably remain the most important European hardwood for pulping, together with the Scandinavian birches.

5. EAST ASIA

Asia, excluding the U.S.S.R., should be discussed in two sections, one covering the region of East Asia, including China, Korea and Japan, the other covering South Asia, and including the Philippines, Indonesia and the Indias. Each of these two regions has a land mass of more than 1,000 M ha, or about the same as that of the U.S.A. South-western Asia is of little interest from a forestal point of view, and will not be described.

The forests of East Asia, though the sub-regions vary widely in type, are mainly situated in temperate or cool climate zones, and hence do not differ in principle from the American or European forests already described. The forests of southern Asia, on the other hand, are mainly of the tropical type, more similar to those of Africa and South America, and will be treated subsequently.

China, once well covered with forests, has now, after five to six thousand years of destructive action of man, a forested area covering only 9% of the country. As seen in Table 1.12, this still constitutes a considerable

Table 1.12. Forests of East Asia by regions and species

Region	Total land area M ha	Total forest area M ha	Productive forest area M ha	Softwoods hereof, %	Standing timber volume of productive forests, Mm³		
					Softwoods	Hardwoods	Total
China							
North-east	158	35.7	32.1	65	3,502	968	4,470
North-west	438	11.4	6.9	10	450	288	738
North	72	1.0	0.2	2	31	6	37
East	60	6.2	5.3	75	290	315	605
Central South	116	11.2	7.7	35	252	546	798
South-west	145	23.4	15.2	28	1,656	457	2,113
Total	989	88.9	67.4	45	6,181	2,580	8,761
Japan							
Hokkaido	7.8	5.4					
Honshu	23.0	15.6					
Shikoku	1.9	1.4					
Kyushu	4.1	2.6					
Total	36.8	25.0	15.7	24			
Korea							
North	10.6	9.2	7.2				
South	9.4	6.8	4.8				
Total	20.0	16.0	12.0	*ca.* 25	*ca.* 80		
All regions	1,046	130	95	40			

forest area, of which three-quarters is productive forest land. Half of this is covered by coniferous forests, mainly concentrated in the north-eastern part of the country (the Manchurian forests). Based on the volume of standing timber, the softwoods constitute 70% of productive forests. The Central, South and South-west regions contain a considerable part of the hardwood forests.

There are three main forest zones in China, namely the sub-tropical, the warm–temperate and the cool–temperate. The sub-tropical zone includes Taiwan, Hainan and the southern part of the southern provinces. Evergreen broadleaf trees, such as several species of oak, occur, together with banyans, palms, tree ferns and bamboos.

The warm–temperate zone includes the rest of China south of the provinces along the Yangtse river. Its forests contain deciduous broadleaf species such as oak, maple, poplar, *Albizzia*, etc., and even some conifers, such as pine, *Cryptomeria* and *Cunninghamia*.

The cool–temperate zone to the north is the most important one. It comprises forests of pine, spruce, hemlock, fir, larch, birch, maple, etc. The most valuable conifer in China is the sha mu (*Cunninghamia lanceolata*), growing in the warm–temperate zone, and a larch (*Larix gmelini*), in Manchuria. The most important of all lignified plants in China are, however, the bamboos, or 'chu', of which there is a great number of genera and species. The most common are *Phyllostachys edulis*, *P. puberula*, *P. bambusoides*, *Bambusa arundinacea*, *B. aspinosa* and *Dendrocalamus giganteus*. Bamboo is very fast-growing and flourishes in all the southern provinces, sometimes in the form of vast jungles. It has a wide variety of uses and is an indispensable part of the every day life of the Chinese. Its usefulness and potential possibilities as a pulping raw material are well realized.

Korea, a much smaller country than China, is in comparison well forested, nominally to about 80%. However, heavy demand and lack of control have, as in China, resulted in great devastation and the remaining forests are very thin. The rate of cutting is twice that of growth, and the standing timber volume is rapidly decreasing. In the north, a cool–temperate zone contains spruce (*Picea koyamai*), fir (*Abies holophylla*), larch (*Larix gmelini*) and pines (*Pinus densiflora* and *P. koraiensis*). A narrow coastal strip in the south has sub-tropical vegetation, with evergreen oaks, etc., and some pines, but the main part of the country has a temperate zone of deciduous forest, containing oaks (*Quercus glandulifera*, etc.), maples and birches as well as some conifers.

The highly industrialized Japan has also a growing pulp and paper industry of considerable capacity. Nominally about two-thirds of the land area is forested, but as a result of demand from the heavy population, only about 25% of the forests are capable of yielding industrial wood today, and only 15% are accessible conifer forests. The climatic zones are similar to those of China and Korea. The sub-tropical, evergreen–broad-leaf forests occur at lower altitudes on southern Honshu and the islands south thereof. Live oaks (*Quercus* and *Lithocarpus* spp.), laurels (*Machilus* spp.) and camphor (*Cinnamomum* spp.) grow in this zone, together with pine, momi fir (*Abies firma*), Japanese hemlock (*Tsuga sieboldii*), etc. The warm–temperate zone with its deciduous hardwoods is the most important one for timber production and occurs at higher altitudes and further north. Sugi (*Cryptomeria japonica*), hinoki (*Chamaecyparis obtusa*), Japanese red pine (*Pinus densiflora*), larch (*Larix kaempferi*), fir (*Abies sachalinensis*), spruce (*Picea ajanensis*) and hemlock are the conifers in this zone, where beech, oak, maple, ash, etc., represent the hardwoods. At the highest altitudes and northern-most islands the cold, conifer zone prevails, with fir, spruce, yew (*Taxus cuspidata*), birch (*Betula japonica*), alder, aspen and willow.

In general composition, the Japanese forests resemble those of Europe or eastern North America, though genera are represented by different species and some indigenous trees have no generic counterparts in the two other regions. Ambitious forestry programs are now in active progress, and it is estimated that 75% of the entire productive forest area could be usefully developed for industrial timber production, preferably softwoods. This would be of great importance not only to Japan but to the entire east Asiatic and Pacific world. Bamboo, particularly *Phyllo-*

stachys reticulata and *P. mitis*, is grown primarily by farmers in small patches for domestic use as well as for the export of a large number of bamboo articles, and it is also of interest as a raw material for pulping.

6. SOUTH ASIA

In central and south-western Asia, large areas are nothing but desert, desert scrub, steppe or barren high-mountain regions. The only noteworthy forests are in Iran. The remaining Asiatic forest land to be described therefore commences in India, extends over Burma, Thailand and Indo-China to the Indonesian islands and the Philippines. Except for comparatively large, dry areas in India and Pakistan, this region is covered with *tropical forests*, which will be described now.

As seen from Table 1.13, the region consists of more than 1,000 M ha, of which 350–400 M ha can be called forest land, about 250 M ha productive forests and approximately 100 M ha accessible productive forests. All the main countries of the region are about equally important as regards forest area, although the extent of forestation and accessibility varies.

Temperature, and especially rainfall determine the type of vegetation. The annual rainfall varies from about 50 cm in the drier regions to 500 cm

Table 1.13. Forests of South Asia by regions

Region	Total land area M ha	Total forest area M ha	Accessible forests M ha	Accessible and productive forests M ha
Iran	163.6	19.0	3.6	
Afghanistan	60.0	1.0	0.7	
Pakistan	94.4	9.3	4.2	
India, Nepal, Bhutan	341.3	75.5	53.2	
Ceylon	6.4	3.5	1.1	
Burma	67.3	39.0	36.2	(25.4)
Thailand	41.6	32.1	15.7	
Cambodia	17.4	8.8	6.0	
Laos	23.6	15.0	4.0	
Vietnam	32.0	8.8	5.0	
Malaya	13.1	10.4	5.2	
Northern Borneo	20.3	15.4	12.8	
New Guinea (Australia)	47.4	33.0	3.0	
Indonesia				
Java	13.2	3.1		
Sumatra	47.4	29.2		
Borneo	53.9	41.6		
Eastern	75.9	49.9		
Total	190.4	121.0	70.0	(11.0)
Philippines	29.7	21.5	15.9	(11.4)
All regions	1,150	410	240	*ca.* 120

or more in the mountains. The rainfall is largely directed by the monsoons. The west coast of India as well as the west coast of Burma and their western mountains intercept the south-west monsoon and hence receive an abundant precipitation, particularly during the season July to October. The inland plains of India, Burma, Thailand and Indo-China, leeward of the mountains, get far less rain, whereas on the east coast of India and Indo-China the rainfall again is heavier, owing to the influence of the Bay of Bengal and the South China Sea respectively. Also the southern slopes of the Outer Himalayas receive heavy precipitation from the south-west monsoon. The central parts of the Indonesian archipelago and Malaya lie in the sphere of alternating monsoons and get abundant rains during the whole year, whereas to the north and south thereof the typical monsoon climate prevails, with a rain season alternating with a drier period. Also the climate and vegetation are influenced by the mountain ranges. The Philippines also have a monsoon climate, modified by mountains.

The tropical forests in these regions have a pattern varying with the temperature and rainfall. The main types are the tropical evergreen rain forest, with lowland and montane modifications, the tropical deciduous rain forest or monsoon forest, with montane modifications, and finally dry and xerophytic forests at the lower humidity extreme. The tropical evergreen forest is as a rule typically three-storied, the highest story containing lofty trees, often buttressed, having a height of 40–50 m or more, the intermediate story with trees 20–30 m in height, and on the ground an intense bush vegetation. In all regions, the typical species of this forest type are dipterocarps, of the genera *Dipterocarpus*, *Hopea*, *Pentacme*, *Shorea*, *Parashorea*, as well as members of the families *Myrtaceae* and *Lauraceae*, but there are thousands of species represented.

In India the montane modifications are the shola forests, which have a different composition. In south-east Asia, the corresponding montane forests may also contain conifers, such as *Podocarpus* species, sometimes in pure stands. With a somewhat less rainy climate, the evergreen forest becomes increasingly admixed with deciduous species, in which the leaves fall during the dry season. In the more typical monsoon climate, this vegetation becomes dominant, forming the monsoon forest. *Terminalia*, *Pterocarpus* and *Xylia* species are typical, in some forests dominant; in the Philippines, the molave (*Vitex parviflora*) has lent its name to these forests. However, in most regions, teak (*Tectona grandis*) is the most valuable species of this forest type. At higher altitudes, tropical montane conifer forests appear, such as pines (*Pinus merkusii* and *P. khasya*) in Burma and Thailand, and *Pinus merkusii* and *P. insularis* in the Philippines and Indonesia. Hoop pine (*Araucaria cunninghamia*) occurs in New Guinea.

In the Himalayas, the dry, monsoon and rain forests deviate in type from those of the other regions, with a stronger accent on conifers. The western Himalayas, which include Kashmir, form the driest part, with almost pure conifer forests, containing a juniper (*Juniperus macropola*) and a pine (*Pinus gerardina*), deodar cedar (*Cedrus deodara*) and silver fir

(*Abies pindrow*). The central Himalayas (Garhwal, Kumaun and western Nepal) have a moister type of vegetation, corresponding to the monsoon forest. Typical conifers of this region are silver fir, spruce (*Picea morinda*), cedar, hemlock (*Tsuga brunoniana*) and pines (*Pinus longifolia* and *P. excelsa*). However, hardwoods occur to a considerable extent, represented by the genera *Acer, Betula, Carpinus, Quercus*, etc. The eastern Himalayas have the highest rainfall and the slopes are covered with semi-evergreen (in Nepal) and evergreen (in Sikkim and Bhutan) rain forests. The former contain hardwoods of the genera mentioned above with some different species, as well as some hemlock and a fir (*Abies densa*), whereas the evergreen forests, depending on altitude, have laurel, buk-oak or high-level oak as the characteristic species.

A special type of tropical vegetation, the mangrove forest, is also worth comment. It occurs on tidal flats at the mouths of streams and on the shores of protected bays throughout the region from India to the Philippines. The stands are composed mainly of *Rhizophoraceae* members, predominantly of the genera *Rhizophora* and *Bruguiera*.

Although the tropical forests of southern Asia contain an enormous variety of species and a large quantity of timber, the industrial value should not be exaggerated. Because of the great distances and high costs of transport, only the most valuable species such as teak, ebony (*Diospyrus* spp.), rosewood (*Dalbergia latifolia*) and sandalwood (*Santalum album*) from the Indias and Indonesia, and lauans (*Pentacme contorta* and *Shorea* spp.) from the Philippines (Philippine mahogany), can be considered for export to Europe and America. These wood species are used for particularly beautiful cabinet woods and other qualified lumber purposes, as well as for veneer production. The forestry costs and the logging costs also become abnormally high because of the selection of only a few, scattered species for industrial purposes. The extreme variability of the tropical forests thus makes their industrial exploitation difficult, in spite of favourable growing conditions. Only exceptional cases, such as the *Pinus merkusii* forests, have been considered as a base for a pulping industry. It is more likely that the bamboos will form the future pulping raw material of many of these regions, in some cases together with exotic tree species from commercially run plantations. The latter will be considered in some detail after the other forest regions of the world have been described.

7. AFRICA

Africa, apart from its equatorial tropical forests, is poorly forested. Vast deserts, steppes and savannas extend north and south of that forest belt, leaving fairly narrow coastal districts to the extreme north and south, with limited forested areas.

Man and nature have both contributed to this vegetational pattern. The forests in the regions bordering on the deserts have to combat a hot and dry climate, and once removed by human action, such as the shifting cultivation of burnt-over clearings, they find it extremely difficult to recover lost ground. In the tropical region the same type of cultivation likewise leads to destruction of the primary forest type, which is replaced by a brush jungle. Reconstitution of the virgin forest is even there a slow process. Thus, also within the tropical region, only a fraction of the land area is actually covered with rain forests. They are virtually confined to western equatorial Africa, on the Atlantic watershed of the continent. Eastern Africa is much drier, and its dense forests are concentrated along the coast where the rainfall is heaviest, and on the upper slopes of the higher mountains that intercept the wet winds of the Indian Ocean.

Table 1.14 thus shows that the forests are concentrated mainly on the western part of the tropical region, with about 140 M ha of productive forests, another 80 M ha being potentially productive were the vegetation not disturbed by the system of shifting agriculture. Most figures for

Table 1.14. Forests of Africa by regions

Region	Total land area M ha	Forest area M ha	Productive forest area M ha
North Africa			
Morocco	41.2	3.9	2.8
Algeria	220.5	3.1	1.6
Tunisia	15.6	0.9	0.9
Libya	176.0	0.2	0.0
Egypt	100.0	0.0	0.0
Total	553.3	8.1	5.3
Tropical Africa (not counting 'dry forests')			
Guinea Forest		33	17
Nigerian Forest		16	4
Equatorial Forest			
Cameroons–Congo–Angola		63	43
Central Congo–Ruanda Urundi		106	75
Total western		218	139
Madagascar			6.0
Kenya			1.4
Uganda			0.6
Tanganyika			1.5
Nyasaland			0.1
Mozambique			0.6
Total eastern			10.2
Total region		ca. 225	153
South Africa and Rhodesias		70	2
Total Africa	2,980	300	160

African forest land are still very approximate because of the lack of reliable maps and forest surveys. Large areas of 'dry forests' have not been included, since they are generally very open and to a large extent appear to be condemned to degradation into savannas because of the custom of dry land burning.

The tropical rain forests in Africa have similar characteristics to those of Asia. Abundant rainfalls and very short dry seasons give rise to an evergreen vegetation, often with three distinguishable stories, with trees 40–50 m high, 25–30 m high, and brush vegetation on the ground. Buttresses and aerial roots are frequent with the high trees and make felling difficult.

The biological composition of the forests is extremely complex, and varies by regions. Only comparatively few species have so far proved to be of commercial interest, making, as in the case of the Asiatic rain forests, general exploitation of the African forests difficult and expensive. The early fame of the African forest was based on its 'African mahoganies', which term includes the *Khaya* (e.g. *K. ivorensis*) and *Entandrophragma* (e.g. *E. utile*) species, thus differing botanically from South-American mahogany. Other red timbers, such as 'makoré' (*Mimusops heckelii*) and 'bossé' (*Guarea cedrata*) are also exported. Species of importance for the veneer industry are 'okoumé' (*Aucoumea klaineana*) and 'afara' (*Terminalia superba*). Altogether about forty species are exported, but only fifteen are in regular demand.

In view of the vast forest area in tropical Africa, the log and lumber exports are still comparatively small. As a raw material for pulping, these hardwoods present certain technological as well as economic problems and are not likely to achieve any great importance. Apart from a few isolated cases, such as the Mlanje cedars, there are practically no conifers. However, these areas may become of interest to the pulping industry if suitable species and uniform plantations are introduced, because of the favorable growing conditions. Such plantations are being established in several districts in the tropical region as well as in North and South Africa. They consist of eucalyptus and pines.

8. LATIN AMERICA

As seen in Table 1.15, South America has a land area of about 1,800 M ha, half of which is forested. About one-third of the forests, or 300 M ha, are classified as accessible. These figures are on the whole rather similar to those of North America, but the latter region is far more important from an industrial point of view. Whereas North America has an annual production of about 400 Mm³ roundwood, of which only 60 Mm³ are used for fuel, South America's roundwood production is only about 140 Mm³, of which 125 Mm³ are consumed as fuel wood, leaving a quantity of industrial wood of only about 5% of that of North America.

These discrepancies are partly explained by the difference in general industrial development of the two regions, but a very important reason

Table 1.15. Distribution of forest land in Latin America by regions

Region	Total land area, M ha	Total forest area, M ha	Accessible forests, M ha
South America			
Argentina	280.8	70.0	60.0
Bolivia	109.9	47.0	6.0
Brazil	851.6	480.2	120.0
British Guiana	19.8	18.1	3.6
Chile	74.2	16.4	6.9
Colombia	113.9	69.0	62.0
Ecuador	27.5	12.0	2.5
French Guiana	8.9	8.5	1.5
Paraguay	40.7	20.9	6.3
Peru	131.1	70.0	15.0
Surinam	13.6	11.7	1.0
Uruguay	18.7	0.5	0.5
Venezuela	91.2	36.5	12.0
Total	1,782	860	297
Central America			
Mexico	197.0	25.9	24.6
Total	273	61	43

is the heterogeneous composition of the South-American forests and their lack of conifers—only 8%. Central America, covering about 270 M ha, is still less important, although it was originally well forested. The reduction of the forests has been largely caused by agricultural expansion. The remaining forests are mainly tropical. The most abundant and widespread forest type of South America is the tropical evergreen rain forest, which is similar to those of Africa and Asia already described. It extends from the Amazon basin, through most of the Guianas, and westward past the mouth of the Orinoco in Venezuela. A smaller area lies in the coastal districts of Brazil, Venezuela, Colombia and Ecuador. This type of forest has only been accessible for exploitation on the coast and along the rivers, and it constitutes the greatest untapped natural resource of the continent. Nearly all the mahogany (*Swietenia macrophylla*), the world's most important cabinet wood, grows in the rain forest.

Where there is a well-defined annual dry season the evergreen forest gives way for the tropical deciduous forest, such as in Brazil behind the maritime belt of rain forests. To a large extent this forest area has been cleared, since the soil and climate of these regions are favorable for agriculture. A montane form of the evergreen forest appears in the Andes from Bolivia to Venezuela. It is largely inaccessible.

In southern Chile, a temperate zone of softwood and hardwood forests extends from 35 to 55°S along the Pacific Ocean. For geographical reasons, the importance of this zone is much more limited than its northern hemisphere counterpart. *Nothofagus* species, corresponding to the northern hemisphere beech, is dominant, together with several conifers. Sparse population and transport problems have so far limited the exploitation of these forests.

The *Araucaria* forests form an industrially important part of the South-American forests. They are located in south-eastern Brazil and in a small area in Chile. The former area, which is the important and exploited one, contains the species *Araucaria angustifolia*, or paraná pine. Its wood resembles that of North-American yellow pine, and forms the base of a modern saw-mill industry. It is also of potential interest as a pulpwood. These forests have been heavily logged and may not be able to meet future demands unless the forestry policy is changed.

Mangrove swamp forests occupy shallow salt water belts on the Pacific and especially Atlantic coast at low latitudes. Their type is similar to that of other regions of the tropics. The main species is red mangrove (*Rhizophora mangle*).

Although attempts are being made to utilize the tropical rain forest species as a pulping raw material, the future interests of the pulping industry in South America are likely to be connected with the *Araucaria* forests and with the plantations of exotic tree species, mainly pine plantations in the temperate zone, particularly in Chile and eucalyptus plantations in the tropical regions, especially in Brazil.

9. PACIFIC AREA

The flora of this botanically interesting part of the world has developed in comparative isolation. The most typical example is the eucalyptus forests of Australia, which cover more than 90% of the forest land in that region but do not occur in the natural state in any other country of the world but New Guinea, which had formerly a land connection with Australia. The podocarp–southern beech forests of New Zealand are likewise very characteristic, though not as unique. However, the land area of the Pacific region is comparatively small and its main part, Australia, forested to only 6%, as the main inland is either steppe or desert.

Table 1.16 gives an indication of the relative importance of the various regions. It must be observed that the quality of the so-called productive forests, 20 M ha, varies greatly. The Australian forest flora consists predominantly of evergreen hardwoods, mainly eucalyptus. A limited area, about 3% of the forest land, has favorable soils and rainfall and contains a rain forest of the Indonesian type, and a forest area of similar size is covered by conifers, mainly cypress pine (*Callitris cupressiformis*) and hoop pine (*Araucaria cunninghamii*). The conifer forests are very depleted and do not meet the domestic demand for lumber, and large quantities have to be imported from New Zealand and North America. To some extent this deficit will be covered by large-scale plantations of exotic pines, such as *Pinus radiata*. Of the eucalyptus forests, the karri (*Eucalyptus diversicolor*) and jarrah (*E. marginata*) are the principal species used, but also other species such as *E. regnans*, *E. gigantea*, *E. sieberiana* and

Table 1.16. Distribution of forest land in the Pacific area by regions

Region	Total land area, M ha	Total forest area, M ha	Productive forests, M ha
Australia			
Queensland		7.0	2.8
New South Wales		12.1	4.9
Victoria		7.0	4.9
South Australia		2.7	0.1
Western Australia		15.8	3.2
Tasmania		2.8	2.0
Capital territory		0.1	0.0
Total Australia	770.4	47.6	17.9
New Zealand	26.4	5.5	1.0
Oceania (not incl. New Guinea)	8.3	4.5	0.7
All regions	805	58	20

E. obliqua. The wild eucalyptus forests form the base of an important lumber and pulping industry. They are mostly old and on the average rather slow-growing. On good sites, however, many of the eucalyptus species are capable of very high production on short rotations, and some have become important for plantations in other parts of the world.

The climate of New Zealand varies from sub-tropical to cold–temperate, and is thus favorable to forest vegetation. In the past the two islands were heavily forested, but here also the action of man has resulted in considerable deforestation. During the last hundred years the forest area has been reduced from 12 to 5 M ha, the main loss being of accessible forests. Today, the commercial forests of indigenous species only occupy about 0.5 M ha, with an almost equal area of plantations of mainly exotic species. The indigenous forests consist of both hardwoods and softwoods, in pure stands and mixed. The hardwoods are *Nothofagus* species, or southern beech, which cover about 3 M ha and grow at a comparatively normal rate. The conifers are *podocarps*, with *Dacrydium cupressinum* as the normal dominant, mixed with *Podocarpus spicatus*, *P. totara* and *P. dacrydoides*. These appear to be postclimax forests, growing slowly and regenerating poorly. Since the present stands constitute excellent lumber, the podocarp forests are being heavily exploited and are likely to diminish rapidly. One further conifer, the kauri (*Agathis australis*) has in the past formed distinct forests, but a very small area now remains. Nevertheless, it is believed that under proper management kauri may again play the rôle of an industrial timber.

Exotic softwoods have for a comparatively long time been planted to substitute the vanishing podocarp forests. Northern hemisphere softwoods, especially Douglas fir (*Pseudotsuga taxifolia*), ponderosa and monterey pines (*Pinus ponderosa* and *P. radiata*), have become well established and the planted area is now as large as that of the accessible indigenous forests, with a much higher production since the annual growth of the planted species is extremely high, in some cases allowing rotations of only thirty years for lumber, compared with an estimated three hundred year rotation for the podocarp forests. The future raw material for both saw-mills and pulp mills will thus be drawn from the exotic forests, and exploitation has already begun.

IV. Forest Plantations

In the forests of the northern hemisphere, the planting of conifers as a means of forest regeneration or afforestation has been practised for a long time, in parallel with other methods. Seedlings from nurseries are planted at regular intervals, normally between 2×2 m and 3×3 m. This form of forest regeneration is the most expensive one and requires favorable growing conditions to be economically feasible. Normally, the same species are used as those indigenous to the district. However, a great deal of experimentation has been carried out to introduce exotic species, in order to improve the rate of growth or to change the softwood–hardwood balance. This has been particularly motivated in the warmer regions of the northern hemisphere, and in most southern hemisphere regions.

There are two essential types of hardwood plantations for industrial and fuel wood purposes, those of eucalyptus and of poplar hybrids. Other hardwood plantations with different principal objects, such as wattle (*Acacia mollissima*) for tannin extracts and *Hevea* for rubber, may also achieve a limited importance as a source of industrial wood. Table 1.17 gives an indication as to the present areas planted with eucalyptus and poplar. Thus, the eucalyptus plantations have been carried out mainly in South America, South Africa and the Mediterranean region, whereas poplar has been planted mainly in Southern and Central Europe. As yet, the planted areas are fairly small, but the rate of planting is considerable and the growth rates often enormous, so that these plantations have already achieved industrial importance, especially as a source of pulpwood.

Many of the numerous Australian species of eucalyptus have been tried in other countries, especially Brazil. Only a few are being extensively used, and three should be mentioned specially, namely *Eucalyptus saligna* (or possibly *E. grandis*) in South Africa and South America, *E. globulus* in Portugal and northern Spain, and *E. camaldulensis* in North Africa, southern Spain and Italy. *E. saligna* is extremely fast-growing in hot and wet districts, where its annual production is 10–15 t/ha. It regenerates by coppices from the stumps, and normal rotation periods are eight years. As it is well suited to pulping, such plantations are expected to be the most satisfactory solution to the wood supply problem of large districts in the tropical and sub-tropical regions, instead of the use of a complex mixture of indigenous hardwoods. *E. globulus* endures a somewhat cooler climate than does *E. saligna*, and *E. camaldulensis* is drought-enduring but less

39

Table 1.17. Plantations of exotic species for industrial wood

Species	Region	Area, M ha	
Eucalyptus	Brazil	0.5	
	Total South America		0.7
	Republic of South Africa	0.2	
	Madagascar	0.1	
	Total South Africa		0.5
	Portugal	0.2	
	Spain	0.1	
	Total Mediterranean region		0.4
	All regions		1.6
Poplars and willows	Argentina	0.1	0.1
	Spain	0.2	
	Italy	0.2	
	France	0.1	
	Poland	0.1	
	Total Europe		0.8
	All regions		1.0
Pines	Chile	0.2	
	Total South America		0.3
	Republic of South Africa	0.4	0.4
	Portugal	0.1	
	Spain	0.1	
	Total Mediterranean region		0.4
	New Zealand	0.5	
	Australia	0.2	
	Total Pacific region		0.7
	All regions		2.0

productive. None of them will survive repeated frosts. In the temperate regions, therefore, poplar hybrids are more suited for hardwood plantations. After considerable experiment, certain clones of a hybrid between European and American poplar, called *Populus × euramericana*, have been found to be most suitable for plantations and are now being introduced especially to France and northern Italy. Annual production is also high, 7–10 t/ha, especially on good sites, but it has to compete there with agricultural crops. Often combinations of cereal crops and poplar growing are used. Poplar wood is suitable—and is also used—for pulping.

Of the softwood plantations pines are normally preferred. The large area (over 1 M ha) planted in Les Landes in south-western France is not a true exotic plantation, since the species used, maritime pine (*Pinus pinaster*, var. *maritimus*), once covered large areas in the district. The same species is one of the more important pines used for planting in Portugal and Spain, and it yields pulpwood for some mills there as well as in France. The exotic conifer plantations of South America, South Africa and New Zealand, already mentioned, are more typical. The most important pines introduced are *Pinus radiata*, *P. pinaster*, *P. longifolia*, *P. patula* and

P. ponderosa. Some of them are already used as pulpwood. *P. radiata* and *P. patula* especially have been shown to grow very fast, 5–10 t/ha.year, when conditions are favorable.

An estimate of the present areas of conifer plantations is given in Table 1.17. The figures give only an idea about the order of magnitude of the exotic plantations, since these areas continually increase and since the borderline to afforestation with indigenous species is often vague. An estimated total area of 5 M ha of fast-growing exotic hardwood and softwood species shows that this type of forest corresponds to less than 0.5% of the exploited forest area. However, because of their high productivity such plantations have a proportionately much greater importance as a source of pulpwood.

GENERAL REFERENCES

Algvere, K. V., *Development of Forest Economy in the Soviet Union according to the Seven-Year Plan 1959–1965*, Skogsind. Samarbetsutskott, Stockholm 1961.

F.A.O., *Eucalypts for Planting*, Rome 1958.

F.A.O., *Pinus Radiata*, Rome 1960.

F.A.O., *Poplars in Forestry and Land Use*, Rome 1958.

F.A.O., *Yearbook of Forest Products Statistics*, Rome 1955–1960.

Haden-Guest, S., J. K. Wright and E. M. Teclaff, Eds., *A World Geography of Forest Resources*, Ronald Press Co., New York 1956.

Streyffert, T., *World Timber, Trends and Prospects*, Almqvist-Wiksell, Uppsala (Sweden) 1958.

U.S. Forest Service, Dept. of Agriculture, *Timber Resources for America's Future*, Washington, D.C. 1958.

2

SPECIES, ANATOMY AND PHYSICAL PROPERTIES OF WOOD

Valuable monographs (4, 6, 9, 11, 23, 27, 44, 46) and surveys (3, 13, 16, 28) have been written on these subjects, and the purpose of this chapter is only to give some fundamental facts—botanical, physiological and physical—on the tree and the wood, which are necessary for an understanding of the pulping processes.

I. Species

It has been estimated that of the roughly 150,000 plant species in the world, there are above 20,000 species of woody plants. Only a few are of commercial value today, but as the demand for wood is rapidly increasing new species are taken into consideration, both in the forests which today are considered as commercially available and in the potentially available areas, such as most of the tropical forests (11). Table 2.1 gives a survey of the most common wood species for *pulping* and their origin. Some annual species are also used as raw materials for pulping, such as bamboo and sabai grass in India, esparto grass from Spain and North Africa, *Arundo donax* straw in Italy, reed and cereal straws in various countries, e.g. Holland, and flax straw and bagasse in America. These are, however, of only minor importance compared with wood, cf. Chapter 9.IV.

The coniferous woods, or softwoods, are still the most important, but the deciduous or hardwood, are increasingly used, partly by methods specially developed for hardwood pulping. There are several reasons why hardwoods have not been used for pulping to greater extent. Often they do not, as do many softwoods, occur in pure stands, but in a mixture of several species with greatly differing properties which do not give a uniform pulping. Further, many hardwoods take up water more easily than softwoods, and are therefore almost impossible to transport by river driving, which has been the most economic means of wood transportation in several parts of the world. The chemical composition of a hardwood, e.g. its content of extractives, sometimes renders it less suitable for pulping, and sometimes its structure is so dense that it is difficult to penetrate by pulping liquors. The most important reason why hardwoods have been considered less suitable for pulping than softwoods is, however, that shorter and less uniform pulp fibers are obtained, and fiber length has for a long time been considered of primary importance for the quality of paper pulps. Even among the softwoods there are great differences in

42

properties, making them more or less suitable to the different pulping processes. The demand and therefore the price for the different wood species thus varies with the properties of the wood, and these properties are determined by the structure and the structural elements of the wood, and their chemical composition.

Table 2.1. Species of wood, used for pulping (cf. Chapter 1)

Latin name	English name	Origin
Coniferous species (softwoods)		
Abies alba Mill.	European silver fir	Europe (continental)
A. amabilis Loud.	Pacific silver fir	Western North America
A. balsamea Mill.	Balsam fir	North-eastern North America
A. concolor Lindl. and Gord.	Western white fir	Western North America
A. grandis Lindl.	Grand fir	Western North America
A. lasiocarpa (Hook.) Nutt.	Alpine fir	Western North America
A. procera Rehd.	Noble fir	Western North America
Larix decidua Mill.	European larch	Europe
L. laricina K. Koch.	Tamarack	North-eastern North America
L. leptolepis Gord.	Japanese larch	Japan
L. occidentalis Nutt.	Western larch	Western North America
L. sibirica Lebed.	Siberian larch	Russia, Siberia
Picea abies (L.) Karst. (*Picea excelsa*)	Scandinavian spruce or Norway spruce	Europe
P. engelmannii (Parry) Engelm.	Engelmann spruce	Western North America
P. glauca (Moench) Voss.	White spruce	North-eastern North America
P. mariana B.S. et P.	Black spruce	North-eastern North America
P. rubens Sarg.	Red spruce	North-eastern North America
P. sitchensis (Bong.) Carr.	Sitka spruce	Western North America
Pinus banksiana Lamb.	Jack pine	North-eastern North America
P. contorta Dougl. v. *latifolia* S. Wats.	Lodgepole pine	Western North America
P. cembra L. v. *sibirica* Loud.	Siberian pine	Siberia and Eastern Asia
P. echinata Mill.	Shortleaf pine	Southern North America
P. elliottii Elliott (*P. caribaea* Morelet)	Slash pine	Southern North America
P. palustris Mill.	Longleaf pine	Southern North America
P. patula Schlecht. et Cham.	Patula pine	North America, planted in South Africa
P. pinaster Ait. v. *maritimus*	Maritime pine	Southern Europe, planted in South Africa
P. ponderosa Dougl.	Ponderosa pine	Western North America
P. radiata D. Don.	Monterey or radiata pine	Western North America, planted in Europe, South America, South Africa, New Zealand
P. resinosa Ait.	Red pine	Eastern North America
P. silvestris L.	Scots pine	Europe
P. strobus L.	Yellow pine	North America
P. taeda L.	Loblolly pine	Southern North America
Pseudotsuga taxifolia Britt.	Douglas fir	Western North America
Taxodium distichum Rich.	Bald cypress	Western North America
Thuja plicata D. Don.	Western red cedar	Western North America
T. occidentalis L.	White cedar	Eastern North America
Tsuga canadensis Carr.	Eastern hemlock	Eastern North America
T. heterophylla Sarg.	Western hemlock	Western North America

Table 2.1. Species of wood, used for pulping (cf. Chapter 1)—*continued*

Latin name	English name	Origin
Deciduous or evergreen–broadleaf species (hardwoods)		
Acer pseudoplatanus L.	Sycamore	Europe, Asia, North America
A. saccharum Marsh.	Sugar maple	Eastern North America
Alnus glutinosa Gaertn.	Alder	Europe
A. rubra, Bong.	Red alder	Western North America
Betula japonica	Japanese birch	Japan
B. lutea Michx.	Yellow birch	Eastern North America
B. papyrifera Marsh.	Paper (White) birch	Eastern North America
B. pubescens Ehrh.	European birch	Europe
B. verrucosa Ehrh.	Silver birch	Europe
Eucalyptus camaldulensis Dehn. (*E. rostrata*)	Murray red gum	Australia, planted in Mediterranean areas
E. gigantea Hook	Tasmanian oak	Australia
E. globulus Labill.	Southern blue gum	Australia, planted in Mediterranean areas
E. gomphocephala A.DC.	Tuart	Australia, planted in Morocco
E. marginata Sm.	Jarrah	Australia
E. regnans F. v. M.	Mountain ash (giant gum)	Australia
E. saligna Sm.	Sydney blue gum	Australia, planted in South Africa, Brazil
Fagus grandifolia Ehrh.	American beech	Eastern North America
F. silvatica L.	European beech	Europe
Fraxinus americana L.	White ash	North America
F. excelsior L.	European ash	Europe, India
Liquidambar styraciflua L.	American red or sweet gum	Southern North America
Liriodendron tulipifera L.	Yellow poplar	Southern North America
Magnolia acuminata L.	Cucumber magnolia	Southern North America
Morus nigra L.	Mulberry	Asia
Nyssa aquatica L.	Tupelo gum	Southern North America
N. silvatica Marsh.	Black gum	Southern North America
Populus deltoides v. *monilifera* Henry	Cottonwood	Western North America
P. nigra L.	European poplar	Europe
P. tremula L.	European aspen	Europe
P. tremuloides Michx.	American aspen	North America
P. × *euramericana*	Poplar hybrid	Europe
Quercus alba L.	White oak	North America
Q. borealis Michx.	Red oak	North America
Q. robur L.	European oak	Europe
Tilia americana L.	Basswood	North America
T. vulgaris Hayne (*T. europaea*)	Lime (linden)	Europe
Ulmus americana L.	White elm	North America
U. glabra Huds.	Elm	Europe, Asia

II. Anatomy

1. GROSS STRUCTURE OF THE TRUNK

The main part of the tree which is used for pulping is the trunk. It has three main physiological functions, to carry the crown aloft, to transport water and mineral salts from root to crown, and to store some reserve food, and it is constructed accordingly. The trunk is composed histologically of three parts, the *xylem* or *wood*, the *cambium*, and the *bark*, as shown schematically in Figure 2.1. In the core of the wood is the *pith*, and in older trunks the wood is of denser structure in the inner parts, the *heartwood*, than in the outer *sapwood*. Cambium is a thin, green layer of growing cells between the bark and the wood. The bark is composed of a white, inner bark, called *phloem* or the *bast zone*, and a darker, outer bark, or *cork*. Apart from the cambial zone there is another zone of growth on the tree, the *apical zone*, located at the tips of the stems and roots. During the dormant season it is enclosed within the buds, and during the growth period the apical zone is responsible for the growth in length of the tree.

As a cambial cell divides, one of the daughter cells remains a cambial cell, whereas the other forms a phloem cell or a xylem cell, depending on

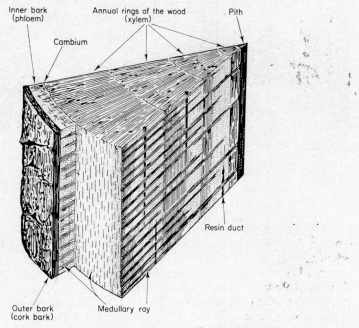

Fig. 2.1. Schematic section of four-year-old pine trunk (Hägglund after Strasburger)

which side it was split off. Most of the xylem cells are longitudinal, and are formed from the cambium in concentric layers outside the older wood. Figure 2.2, shows transverse and longitudinal sections. In springtime, when growth is rapid, cells with thin walls and wide cavities are formed, whereas towards the fall growth is slower, producing cells with thicker walls and narrow cavities. The former wood cells are called *springwood*, or *earlywood*, the latter *summerwood*, or *latewood*, and a year's growth is, especially in softwoods, easily seen and is called a *growth ring*. With

Fig. 2.2. Transverse (above, ×54) and longitudinal (below, ×108) sections of spruce and birch (Öhrn)

Scandinavian softwoods which have a growth season of three to four months, a growth ring contains some twenty to fifty fairly concentric layers of cells, which means that the cambium on average splits off two to three layers a week. The growth rings vary in thickness from 0.1 to 10 mm, according to climate, soil, age of the tree, species, etc. A thin growth ring often means dense wood. Therefore, density variations are frequent both within a stand and within one single trunk. This, as well as the phenomena of heartwood and sapwood, springwood and summerwood, greatly influences the pulping reactions and the pulp properties.

46

2. STRUCTURAL ELEMENTS OF WOOD

A. Classification, functions and occurrence

Several different types of cells, with different functions, are formed from the cambium, which together make it possible for the trunk to fulfil its three above-mentioned main functions. There are four main elements, *parenchyma cells*, *fibers*, *tracheids* and *vessel elements* (see Figure 2.3). The parenchyma cells serve as storage and transport cells for food and water. The fibers are supporting elements, giving rigidity to the wood structure. The tracheids and the vessels function as water conductors, and also give mechanical support to the structure. There are several forms of gradations between *libriform fibers*, which have only mechanical functions, and the tracheids, which have well developed conductive functions. The intermediate elements are called *fiber tracheids*. Although the term 'fiber' in its strict, botanical sense is confined to cells with mechanical functions only, in pulp technology the word is used for all sorts of structural elements in wood and in other pulping raw materials.

All wood contains parenchyma cells, but need not contain all the other types of structural elements. In softwoods the tracheids dominate, with few if any libriform fibers and no vessels, whereas tracheids are scarce in hardwoods, and the corresponding functions instead are performed by the more specialized libriform fibers and vessels. This difference is due to the more pronounced need of rapid water transport in the case of hardwoods, which develop their leaf crowns during a very short period in springtime. Table 2.2 gives the approximate relative proportions of different structural elements in some technically important pulpwoods.

B. Fiber dimensions

As demonstrated in Figure 2.3, the form and size of the different structural elements vary widely. Tracheids and libriform fibers, after being split off from the cambium, extend longitudinally and become stretched to a length of approximately fifty to a hundred times their diameter. The length of the softwood tracheids varies from 1–11 mm, and is usually 2–5 mm in the commercially important species. The hardwood libriform fibers are shorter, about 1–2 mm. The vessel elements are very often wide and short, with thin walls. Their diameter may be as small as 0.02 mm and sometimes as large as 0.5 mm, and their length shows similar variations. The parenchyma cells are generally small, 0.02–0.2 mm.

Because of their influence on pulp quality, the dimensions of the tracheids and libriform fibers especially have been studied intensely, with regard to length, diameter and wall thickness. Table 2.3 gives fiber length figures for some commercially important pulpwoods. It is seen that some softwoods of the western United States have fibers considerably longer than with most softwoods, but the length differences between the common pulpwood species are rather insignificant and hardly important for the

47

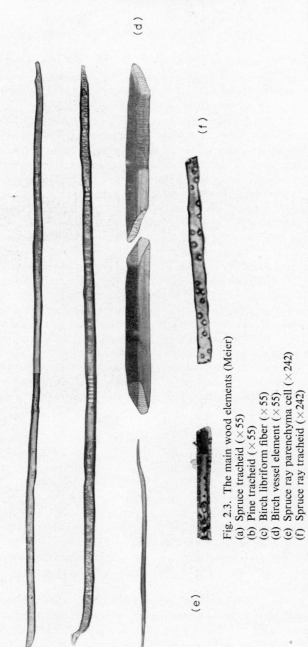

Fig. 2.3. The main wood elements (Meier)
(a) Spruce tracheid (×55)
(b) Pine tracheid (×55)
(c) Birch libriform fiber (×55)
(d) Birch vessel element (×55)
(e) Spruce ray parenchyma cell (×242)
(f) Spruce ray tracheid (×242)

Table 2.2. Volume per cent of structural elements in some wood species (4, 20, 34).
Weight per cent in brackets (36)

Species	English name	Tracheids and fibers	Parenchyma cells	Vessel elements
Abies alba	European fir	90	10	—
Abies balsamea	Balsam fir	94	6	—
Larix decidua	European larch	91	9	—
Larix occidentalis	Western larch	90	10	—
Picea abies	Scandinavian spruce	95 (99)	5 (1)	—
Picea engelmannii	Engelmann spruce	94	6	—
Picea glauca	White spruce	93	7	—
Picea rubens	Red spruce	95	5	—
Picea sitchensis	Sitka spruce	93	7	—
Pinus elliottii	Slash pine	88	12	—
Pinus palustris	Longleaf pine	92	8	—
Pinus ponderosa	Ponderosa pine	93	7	—
Pinus silvestris	Scots pine	93 (98)	7 (2)	—
Pinus strobus	White pine	93	7	—
Pseudotsuga taxifolia	Douglas fir	93	7	—
Tsuga canadensis	Eastern hemlock	94	6	—
Tsuga heterophylla	Western hemlock	92	8	—
Average, softwoods		93	7	—
Betula lutea	Yellow birch	—	11	—
Betula papyrifera	Paper birch	—	11	—
Betula verrucosa	Silver birch	65 (86)	10 (5)	25 (9)
Castanea vesca	Chestnut	57	17	26
Fagus grandifolia	American beech	—	20	—
Fagus silvatica	European beech	37	32	31
Fraxinus americana	White ash	—	12	—
Fraxinus excelsior	European ash	62	26	12
Liquidambar styraciflua	Red gum	26	18	55
Musanga smithii	Umbrella tree	70	24	6
Populus tremula	European aspen	61	13	26
Populus tremuloides	American aspen	—	10	—
Quercus pedunculata	Oak	44	16	40
Rhizophora mangle	Mangrove	64	19	17
Average, hardwoods		ca. 50	ca. 20	ca. 30

Table 2.3. Weight average fiber lengths and basic densities of some commercial pulpwoods (4, 27, 28, 32, 44)

Species	English name	Fiber length, mm	Basic density o.d. weight green volume
Abies alba	European fir	3.7	0.38
Abies balsamea	Balsam fir	3.5	0.34
Larix decidua	European larch	3.5	0.48
Larix laricina	Tamarack	3.5	0.49
Larix occidentalis	Western larch	5.0	0.48

Table 2.3. Weight average fiber lengths and basic densities of some commercial pulpwoods (4, 27, 28, 32, 44) (continued)

Species	English name	Fiber length, mm	Basic density o.d. weight / green volume
Picea abies	Scandinavian spruce	3.5	0.41
Picea engelmannii	Engelmann spruce	3.5	0.31
Picea glauca	White spruce	3.5	0.37
Picea mariana	Black spruce	3.5	0.40
Picea sitchensis	Sitka spruce	5.5	0.37
Pinus banksiana	Jack pine	3.5	0.39
Pinus contorta var. latifolia	Lodgepole pine	3.5	0.38
Pinus echinata	Shortleaf pine	3.5	0.46
Pinus elliottii	Slash pine	3.5	0.56
Pinus palustris	Longleaf pine	3.5	0.54
Pinus ponderosa	Ponderosa pine	3.6	0.38
Pinus resinosa	Red pine	3.5	0.44
Pinus silvestris	Scots pine	3.0	0.41
Pinus strobus	White pine	3.5	0.34
Pinus taeda	Loblolly pine	3.5	0.47
Pseudotsuga taxifolia	Douglas fir	3.5	0.47
Sequoia sempervirens	Redwood	7.0	—
Taxodium distichum	Bald cypress	6.0	0.42
Thuja plicata	Western red cedar	3.8	0.35
Tsuga canadensis	Eastern hemlock	3.5	0.38
Tsuga heterophylla	Western hemlock	4.0	0.38
Acer saccharum	Sugar maple	1.0	0.56
Acer pseudoplatanus	Sycamore	1.7	0.46
Acer rubrum	Red maple	0.7	—
Betula lutea	Yellow birch	1.5	0.55
Betula papyrifera	Paper birch	1.2	0.48
Betula verrucosa	Silver birch	1.2	0.51
Eucalyptus camaldulensis	Murray red gum	0.8	0.68
Eucalyptus globulus	Blue gum	1.1	0.60
Eucalyptus marginata	Jarrah	0.9	0.71
Eucalyptus saligna	Sydney blue gum	1.0	0.51
Fagus grandifolia	American beech	1.2	0.56
Fagus silvatica	European beech	1.3	0.58
Fagus silvatica var. purpurea	Red beech	1.0	0.90
Fraxinus americana	White ash	1.2	0.55
Fraxinus excelsior	European ash	1.1	0.60
Liquidambar styraciflua	Red gum	1.6	0.44
Liriodendron tulipifera	Yellow poplar	1.8	0.38
Nyssa silvatica	Black gum	1.7	0.46
Populus balsamifera	Balsam poplar	1.2	—
Populus deltoides	Cottonwood	1.3	0.37
Populus × euramericana	Poplar hybrid	0.9	0.43
Populus grandidentata	Bigtooth aspen	1.1	—
Populus tremula	European aspen	1.0	0.37
Populus tremuloides	American aspen	1.2	0.35
Tilia americana	Basswood	1.2	0.32
Tilia vulgaris	Linden	1.0	0.45
Ulmus americana	Elm	1.5	0.46

differences in paper properties of the corresponding pulps. Similarly, it is clearly seen that the average length of softwood tracheid is always much greater than that of hardwood libriform fibers, which is one of the reasons why softwood pulps are preferred for most papers. In Chapter 21 it will be shown that other fiber dimensions—i.e. the lumen width and the wall thickness—are almost as important as the length with regard to paper properties. Table 2.4 gives the results of extensive investigations on length and wall thickness of tracheids and libriform fibers for a large number of species, including tropical woods. It is seen that dimensions

Table 2.4. Fiber dimensions of various wood species (15, 22, 25, 32, 39, 41)

Species	English name	Length, mm Range	Length, mm Av.	Width, μ Range	Width, μ Av.	Wall thickness, μ Range	Wall thickness, μ Av.	Wall fraction, % (av.)
European and North-American woods:								
Picea abies	Scandinavian spruce	—	3.5	24–59	36	1.3–13	6	33
Pinus silvestris	Scots pine	—	3.5	—	38	—	—	—
Pinus taeda	Loblolly pine	—	4.0	—	43	—	—	—
Pseudotsuga taxifolia	Douglas fir	3.00–6.00	4.0	—	44	1.0–10	7	—
Tsuga heterophylla	Western hemlock	—	4.0	—	41	1.0–7	4	—
Salix	Willow	0.43–1.05	0.73	10–29	20	1.2–3.6	2.4	26
Populus tremula	Aspen	0.50–1.35	0.95	13–37	21	1.3–5.3	4.3	39
Populus × euramericana	Poplar hybrid	0.82–1.42	1.12	—	30	—	3.7	24
Tilia vulgaris	European lime	0.45–1.80	1.00	17–37	28	2.9–5.7	4.7	35
Betula verrucosa	European birch	0.56–2.00	1.25	10–29	18	2.4–7.2	3.7	42
Quercus robur	European oak	0.40–1.90	1.10	10–35	21	2.5–10	6	55
Fagus silvatica	European beech	0.40–2.30	1.30	25–35	29	2.5–15	5.2	59
Fagus silvatica var. *purpurea*	European red beech	0.40–1.93	1.03	10–27	19	2.5–12	7.5	84
Fraxinus excelsior	European ash	0.49–1.61	1.05	10–29	16	2.4–6	3.8	48
Abies lasiocarpa	Alpine fir	—	3.0	—	29	—	2.0	25
Picea abies	Scandinavian spruce	—	3.5	—	27	—	2.9	33
Picea engelmannii	Engelmann spruce	—	3.0	—	30	—	2.9	35
Pinus contorta v. *latifolia*	Lodgepole pine	—	3.0	—	32	—	2.4	33
Pinus elliottii	Slash pine	—	2.3	—	36	—	3.8	38
Pinus pinaster v. *maritimus*	Maritime pine	—	3.1	—	40	—	3.7	33
Pinus silvestiis	Scots pine	—	2.9	—	28	—	3.2	41
Pseudotsuga latifolia	Douglas fir	—	3.4	—	37	—	4.0	39

51

Table 2.4. Fiber dimensions of various wood species (15, 22, 25, 32, 39, 41) (continued)

Species	English name	Length, mm Range	Av.	Width, μ Range	Av.	Wall thickness, μ Range	Av.	Wall fraction, % (av.)
Bambusa arundinacea	Dowga bamboo	—	2.8	—	16	—	3.1	62
Betula verrucosa	Silver birch	—	1.1	—	20	—	1.9	34
Eucalyptus camaldulensis	Red gum	—	0.8	—	11	—	—	—
Eucalyptus globulus	Blue gum	—	1.0	—	13	—	1.6	43
Eucalyptus saligna	Sydney blue gum	—	1.0	—	13	—	1.4	40
Fagus silvatica	European beech	—	1.5	—	14	—	3.3	73
Populus × euramericana	Poplar hybrid	—	0.9	—	16	—	1.2	28
African tropical woods:								
Albizzia falcata		0.62–1.38	1.01	32–69	43	—	<1	<10
Diospyros sp.	Ebony	—	1.05	—	23	—	6.5	56
Guajacum sanctum	Pockholz	—	0.60	—	12	—	5	80
Musanga smithii	Umbrella tree	0.77–2.25	1.44	32–58	43	—	1.5	<10
Pycnanthus kombo		0.90–2.50	1.60	20–40	28	2.7–9.4	3.5	25
Rhizophora mangle	Mangrove	1.21–2.56	1.74	16–29	25	6.3–13	11	87
American tropical woods:								
Cordia alliodora	Laurel blanco	0.3–2.4	1.34	10–60	27	—	3.5	26
Couratari pulchra	Tauari	0.6–2.3	1.49	10–40	22	—	3.3	30
Dicorynia paraensis	Angelique	0.6–2.3	1.39	10–40	23	—	4.5	39
Eschweilera sagotiana	Kakeralli	0.8–2.4	1.59	10–30	19	—	7.3	77
Hymenaea courbaril	Courbaril	0.4–1.9	1.12	10–30	20	—	4.5	45
Licaria cayennensis	Kaneelhart	0.9–2.3	1.54	10–40	21	—	7.7	73
Manilkara bidentata	Bullet wood	0.4–2.0	1.33	10–40	22	—	9.2	84
Ochroma lagopus	Balsa tree	—	1.30	19–55	40	—	1.5	<10
Ocotea rodiaei	Greenheart	0.4–1.6	1.04	10–40	26	—	7.5	58
Ocotea rubra	Determa	0.6–2.8	1.89	10–60	34	—	9.6	56
Pseudosamanea guachapele	Frijolillo	0.3–1.5	0.92	10–40	22	—	3.8	35
Swietenia macrophylla	Mahogany	0.7–2.3	1.42	10–60	28	—	3.3	24
Tabebuia guyacan	Guyacan	0.4–1.5	0.95	10–30	16	—	5.0	63
Burma:								
Tectona grandis	Teak	0.6–2.0	1.29	20–50	30	—	6.0	40
Australian (origin) woods:								
Eucalyptus saligna	Sydney blue gum	—	1.00	—	19	—	—	—
Eucalyptus camaldulensis	Murray red gum	0.5–1.4	0.97	—	17	—	3.6	44
Eucalyptus globulus	Blue gum	0.6–1.4	0.99	—	19	—	5.9	64
Eucalyptus gomphocephala	Tuart	0.7–1.4	1.06	—	19	—	7.4	80

vary considerably within each sample, and the causes will be discussed below. However, the average width of softwood tracheids is about 40 μ, or twice that of the libriform fibers of most hardwoods. As the average length of the tracheids is about three times that of the libriform fibers, the latter are generally less fine. The wall thickness varies especially for the softwood tracheids, because of the occurrence of springwood and summerwood fibers (see below). The average wall thickness varies widely in different species. Thus some North American softwoods have much thicker tracheid walls than others, and the denser hardwoods have libriform fibers with much thicker walls than the lighter hardwoods. In the paper-forming process the thickness of the wall must be correlated to the total fiber diameter, as the width of the lumen will vary in the different species. One way of expressing this is in terms of *wall fraction*, i.e. the percentage of the fiber radius which consists of fiber wall. This is considered to indicate the plasticity of the fiber (32). As seen from the table, this figure varies from below 10% to almost 90%, the former being very thin-walled fibers with a wide lumen, which collapse to double-walled ribbon structures on delignification; the latter are rod-like fibers which do not show much plastic deformation on pulping and paper formation and offer little surface contact for interfiber bonding. Softwood summerwood tracheids belong to the latter category with a wall fraction of above 60%, whereas the springwood fibers have a wall fraction around 20% or below. The average wall fraction should not exceed 50% in pulpwood of good quality and preferably should be below 40%. Although the wall fraction is naturally related to the density of the wood, especially in the case of softwoods, there is no generally valid clear-cut correlation, among other things because of the varying volume fraction of vessel elements in the hardwoods.

Thus, the wood species has been shown to be a very significant factor for the fiber dimensions. Other important variables are the age of the tree, the trunk height, the growing conditions, the proportions of spring-wood and summerwood, etc. An early work (40) on Scots pine made the following generalizations: at any height of the trunk, the fiber length increases from the centre outwards to a maximum and then remains constant; at any growth ring the fiber length increases up the trunk to a maximum and then decreases. Subsequent work has disclosed many exceptions to these rules, and shown the great variability of the material with a large number of influential factors, but on the whole the generalizations have been confirmed. An often-cited investigation (16, 28, cf. 42) on a black spruce trunk showed a variation in average fiber length from 0.9 mm in the first growth rings, 2.7 mm after ten years, 3.1 mm after twenty and around 3.7 mm from seventy-five to one hundred years. The fiber length variations up the trunk were much smaller, on average 3.5 mm at the base, 3.8 mm at 5 m from the ground and 3.2 mm at 17 m from the ground. Within a growth ring, fiber length generally increases somewhat from springwood to summerwood (1, 2), only about 10% in the case of softwoods, whereas in some hardwoods larger differences occur, in some eucalyptus species up to 50–100% difference. The increase in fiber length during the juvenile period is of industrial importance, since increasing forest areas consist of plantations on short rotation periods, from six to twenty years, and because of the increasing use of thinnings as pulpwood. Figure 2.4 (47) shows the increase in fiber length during the growth of a pine belonging to the group of species used in short rotations. Obviously, the maximum fiber length will not be reached before felling. Furthermore, one tree displays longer fibers throughout in comparison with another tree of the same species. The difference is apparently genetic and makes it possible to improve the fiber length by selecting the proper trees for seed production. Heredity factors as well as growing conditions may be the cause in a case where a slow-growing spruce (*Picea abies*) with about

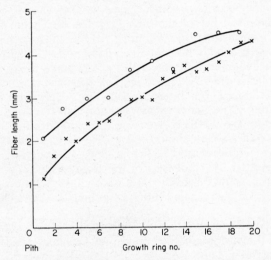

Fig. 2.4. Fiber length of successive annual rings, sampled from two pine trees (Wardrop)

twenty annual rings per cm showed an average fiber length of 3.4 mm and width of 0.040 mm, whereas a fast-growing sample with less than two annual rings per cm had an average length of 2.6 mm and a width of 0.050 mm (18).

It is obvious, that with the variations mentioned, fiber length has a fairly wide distribution curve even within a single trunk. In softwoods, with their fairly homogeneous composition of structural elements, a sample with an average fiber length of 3 mm has a standard deviation around 0.5 mm, i.e. two-thirds of the fibers fall in the range of 2.5–3.5 mm and 90% within 2.0–4.0 mm. Hardwood vessels with an average length of 0.5 mm have a standard deviation of 0.1 mm and hardwood libriform fibers and fiber tracheids with an average length of 1.2 mm show a standard deviation around 0.2 mm (3).

The thickness of the cell walls varies within the ranges $2-8\,\mu$ for most tracheids, $1.5-3\,\mu$ for vessels, $3-7\,\mu$ for libriform fibers and $2-5\,\mu$ for parenchyma cells (46). Scandinavian spruce and Scots pine tracheids are $2-4\,\mu$ thick in springwood and $6-8\,\mu$ in summerwood (32, 34, cf. 25). Sitka spruce tracheids were found to be $2.5\,\mu$ thick in springwood and $4.6-6.7\,\mu$ in summerwood (26). Some softwoods of the warmer zones develop a high percentage of thick-walled summerwood fibers, $50-75\%$, whereas the softwoods of the temperate zones contain only about $20-30\%$ summerwood in slow-growing and $5-15\%$ in fast-growing trees (19). The decrease in fiber width and increase in wall thickness within an annual ring was studied for four North American softwoods and found to be on the average from 40 to 20 μ respectively from 2 to 5μ, with individual deviations reflecting the just-mentioned differences in summerwood development (32a). The cross-sectional area of the fiber wall substance is accordingly considerably higher in summerwood than in springwood tracheids. For loblolly pine, the former was found to have a cross-sectional area of about 600 μ^2 the latter about 400 μ^2 (29). It is interesting to note that the specific strengths after delignification are also different, with a tensile strength of about 80 kp/mm^2 for summerwood and 40 kp/mm^2 for springwood holocellulose fibers. (The corresponding tensile strength of wood for a similar species is about 40 kp/mm^2.) The individual fiber strength is therefore much higher for a summerwood fiber. In the case of loblolly pine tracheids, it was found to be about 50 p/fiber for summerwood and 15 p/fiber for springwood holocellulose. Similar results have been obtained for other softwoods (24), as shown in Table 2.5.

Table 2.5. Cross-sectional area and strength of earlywood and latewood fibers from some softwood species

Ref.	Species	Fiber type	Cross-sectional area, μ^2	Tensile strength, kp/mm^2	Strain at failure, %
29	*Pinus taeda,* Loblolly pine	Earlywood Latewood	400 600	40 80	— —
24	*Taxodium distichum,* Bald cypress	Earlywood Latewood	290 460	56 102	3.4 3.2
24	*Pseudotsuga taxifolia,* Douglas fir	Earlywood Latewood	350 530	35 97	2.1 2.5
24	*Picea glauca,* White spruce	Earlywood Latewood	200 290	53 58	2.5 1.9

C. Water-conducting system

As the cambial cells divide, a middle lamella between the daughter cells is formed, and the xylem cell then develops a thicker cell wall around the central cavity, the *lumen*. The lumina of adjacent structural elements are

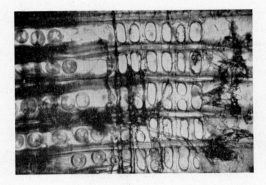

Fig. 2.5. Pits. (a) Bordered
and unbordered pits of pine
tracheids. Radial cut also
showing horizontal ray cells
(vertical in this particular
figure) ($\times 192$) (Bucher)

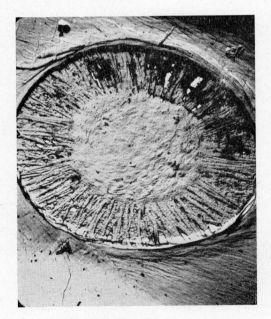

(b) Torus of a bordered pit of
a pine tracheid, originating
from the heartwood ($\times 4740$)
(Stemsrud)

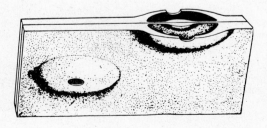

(c) Schematic longitudinal section and view of a bordered
pit (Preston)

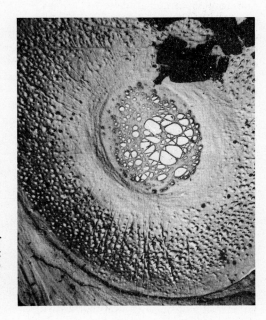

(d) Torus of a bordered pit of a pine tracheid, originating from the sapwood (×5680) (Stemsrud)

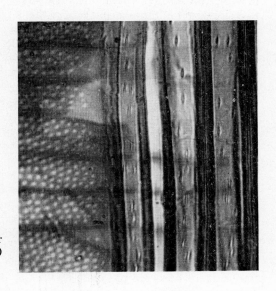

(e) Slitlike pits of birch fiber (×590) (Öhrn)

therefore separated by cell walls, and a shared middle lamella. For the detailed structure and composition of these walls and lamellae, see Chapter 3. However, quite often this structure is interrupted by so-called *pits* or other cell wall perforations, where no thicker walls have been formed and only a thin, perforated membrane separates the lumina. Here water exchange is possible, and the main sap transport occurs in the wood through the lumina and these membranes. In the softwoods the tracheid pits of several types are frequent, and in hardwoods the vessel elements are joined in vertical rows, with the parting cell walls heavily perforated in several different ways.

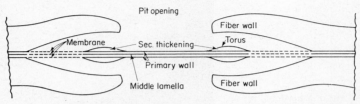

Fig. 2.5 (*continued*) Pits. (f) Schematic longitudinal section of a bordered pit. (Stemsrud)

As the liquid-conducting elements are of extreme importance for the penetration of pulping liquors, they will be considered here at some length. Figure 2.5 shows the most common type of softwood pits, the *bordered pit*, in detail. They occur most frequently in springwood, whereas summerwood contains small bordered pits or slitlike pits. Most pits occur on the radial walls of the tracheids, usually in one single row, but in some species in two or three rows. Often, but not always, the pit in one cell corresponds to a similar pit in the adjacent cell, so that a *pit pair* is formed. A bordered pit consists of a crater in the cell wall, with a small opening towards the lumen and a wider one towards the outside. Over the wider opening a membrane is spanned, consisting of the middle lamella and primary wall of the cell (13a, cf. Chapter 3). The central part of the membrane is thicker and in the shape of a plano-convex lens, or according to recent investigations a disk with a ring-shaped thickening (43a), called the *torus*, which is somewhat larger in diameter than the inner pit opening. The torus is compact, whereas the rest of the membrane is perforated. The size of a pit membrane varies, from about $2\,\mu$ up to the width of the tracheid, 30–$50\,\mu$, in the case of one-row bordered pits. The diameter of the torus is about half that of the membrane. The perforations vary in size from 0.03 to $1.0\,\mu$ and exert the main resistance to liquid flow through the trunk. It is believed that the tori act as sort of back-pressure valves, to counteract sudden pressure changes. If the pressure increases too much on one side of a bordered pit pair, the torus is pressed against the opposite pit opening, thus preventing flow. When the tree grows older and the trunk wider, the inner parts of the wood are not needed for sap transport. In such tracheids the bordered pits close by the tori becoming attached to the cell walls, probably to prevent fungal attacks. For the same reason different types of extractives, some with fungicidal properties, are deposited. In some wood species certain extractives are colored and the heartwood thus formed is easily distinguished from the sapwood. From a pulping point of view, these changes are important, as they affect the penetrability of pulping liquors. The extractives sometimes are not only difficult to remove in the pulping, but may also give rise to undesirable side reactions. The relative proportions of sapwood and heartwood in different wood species of different age has therefore been studied. At fifty years old a Scandinavian spruce is found to contain 30% and a Scots pine 20% of heartwood, and at one hundred years old they contain 50% and 40% respectively (8). Heartwood formation starts in Scots pine in northern Sweden at seventy years old and in southern Sweden at twenty-five (18). The latter figure is also found to be operative for softwoods grown in sub-tropical regions.

In the case of hardwoods water transportation occurs mainly through the vessels. Recent electron microscopic studies (30) have shown no evidence of pores through the pit membranes of hardwood fibers. The cell wall openings between the vessel elements do not usually resemble tracheid pits. The end walls of the elements are oblique to transverse, joining cells together into vessels which may become several meters long and from 20 to 500 μ in diameter. The end walls and their separating middle lamella may disappear—simple perforation—but remain often as bars in gridlike or netlike perforations. The vessels also contain pits on their longitudinal walls. As the hardwood tree grows old, and the inner parts of the trunk are not needed for water conduction, the vessels there may lose their water content. Due to pressure differences which then

Fig. 2.6. Vessels with tyloses (Jane)

arise, the content of adjacent parenchyma cells is pressed through the pits into the empty vessels together with the elastic pit membranes. These ingrowths, *tyloses*, Figure 2.6, finally block the vessels, and serve thereby the same purpose as the tori in the heartwood tracheids of softwood. It has much the same effect on pulping—the penetrability of pulping liquors is decreased, and undesirable extractives are produced from the tyloses.

D. Food-conducting system

The parenchyma cells are the only living cells in the xylem. In contrast to the others, they contain not only water but also proteins, starch and fats. They serve as food storage for the tree. There are three kinds of parenchyma cells, *ray*, *longitudinal*, and *epithelial*. The ray cells form the rays, which extend from the inner bark tissues, through the cambium, into the wood, in a horizontal, radial direction, and in young trees reach the pith, which also consists of parenchyma cells. Usually several rows of ray cells run parallel to each other and form ribbonlike structures. They serve as roads for food transportation. Food, such as starch, is produced in the leaves and conducted down the trunk through the inner bark tissues and further through the rays into the trunk for storage in the parenchyma cells. Towards the fall the storage is complete. In the early days of spring the food is transported in the opposite direction, and the starch is used up in the new hectic development of life activities. Some of the ray cells have pits and are classified as *ray tracheids*. This structure of horizontal elements naturally disturbs the regularity of the main, vertical structure of the wood. In some cases the vertical elements are intercepted by ray cells, as is easily seen in the vessels of hardwoods, and also recently noticed in softwood tracheids as a local weakening of the cell wall, which has technical consequences (12).

The longitudinal parenchyma cells are arranged in vertical rows, of size and shape similar to tracheids and fibers. Several strands are often grouped together.

The epithelial parenchym enters into intercellular passages, which often occur in connection with the rays, in both radial and longitudinal direction, to form *resin ducts*, into which resin is excreted by the osmotic pressure built up in the parenchyma cells. The ducts are probably caused by the disturbance in the wood structure, which occurs when the horizontal and vertical structural elements meet. The sheathing with epithelial parenchym and excretion of resin serves to prevent fungal attack. The extractives in the resin ducts have different composition from those in the rays (cf. Chapter 4), but both types create problems in pulping.

E. Reaction wood

When a tree is exposed to abnormal stress, i.e. if due to gravity, persistent winds (38), or some other cause, it is pulled out of its original direction, the structure of the wood and the composition of its elements change through the action of plant hormones, *auxins* (5, 35, 48). In softwoods the fibers in the pressure zone (on the *lower* side) become shorter, the fiber walls thicker and more heavily lignified, and the structure stiffer, denser and darker, see Figure 2.7. Characteristic are the round cross-sections of the tracheids, leaving intercellular spaces, see Figure 2.8. This type of wood is called *compression wood* and is present in all trees, although it is most

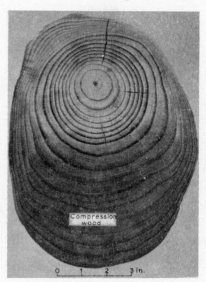

Fig. 2.7. Compression wood, cross-section of *Pinus radiata* trunk (Dadswell)

Fig. 2.8. Compression wood, cross-section of *Pinus radiata* tracheids (Dadswell)

61

frequent in those growing under hard climatic conditions. *Tension wood* is a similar type of abnormal wood structure, which occurs on the *upper* side of branches of hardwoods (5, 23a). It may be dark but is often brighter and more silvery than normal wood, and frequently has longer fibers. Both abnormalities are also called 'reaction wood', and affect pulping, having inferior fibers and giving a lower pulp yield than normal wood.

3. BARK AND ITS STRUCTURAL ELEMENTS

The bark is not used for pulping but is yet of very great interest in connection with the production of pulp, because it has to be removed as completely and as economically as possible. Bark impurities lower the pulp quality; bark contains extractives which after diffusion into the wood may cause undesirable side reactions on pulping; and it can be utilized in the pulp industry as fuel or in some instances as a raw material for useful products. Therefore some of its main structural features should be mentioned.

As does the xylem, the *phloem* or inner bark contains both vertical and horizontal cells. The latter are known as *phloem rays*, and form extensions of the xylem rays. The vertical elements are the *sieve tubes* (in hardwoods), or *sieve cells* (in softwoods), *companion cells* (in hardwoods only), parenchyma cells, and fibers. The sieve tubes and sieve cells correspond to xylem vessels and tracheids and are conductive elements. The companion cells are cut off from the sieve tubes by longitudinal cell division. As in the xylem, the parenchyma cells are used for food storage and the fibers have mechanical functions. The sieve tubes and sieve cells transport food, produced in the leaves, down the trunk, for storage in the phloem parenchyma cells or for further transport through the phloem rays and xylem rays to the xylem parenchyma cells.

Beyond the phloem the *cork* or outer bark is formed. In contrast to the fairly thin phloem tissue, cork can form quite a substantial portion of the trunk. In spruces it is only around 10 mm thick, whereas Douglas fir bark is usually 10–25 cm and sometimes half a meter in thickness. In some instances the cork is quite brittle, whereas in others, especially in some hardwoods, it is tough but flexible. Barking methods have to be suited to these variations.

Soon after their formation, cork cells die as they become impregnated with *suberin*, a substance which makes the cork gasproof, waterproof and resistant to fungi. As the girth of the trunk increases, the cork bark cracks and the outer layers are shed, in several different ways, characteristic for each species.

Although the bark substance constitutes around 10–15% of the trunk, it contains a comparatively low proportion of useful fibers and a high proportion of other substances which either will not dissolve in pulping liquors or else consume a great deal of pulping chemicals. It is therefore removed as completely as possible before pulping. Sometimes, pockets of bark occur embedded in the wood. When a certain area of cambium dies for some reason, the surrounding cambium continues to produce xylem cells, which finally wall over the dead parts with their bark and bury them in the trunk. Such bark pockets give rise to impurities in the pulp, as they cannot be removed in the barking procedure.

In the same way that bark pockets are formed, the ends of broken branches and twigs become embedded in the wood, often together with bark remnants. Living branches have a cambium layer in organic continuity with the cambium of the trunk, and both branch and trunk add new growth rings at the same time. The earlier points of branching thus will become embedded into the trunk and leave a *knot* structure with an increasing diameter. In this case, however, bark will be absent, as the phloem moves with the living cambium layer in both branch and trunk. The knot, containing the narrow growth rings of the branch, forms a denser structure than the surrounding trunk wood. Therefore, it is more difficult to penetrate with pulping liquors and shows up usually in the unscreened pulp as unpulped residues, which have to be removed from the pulp.

4. DECAY OF WOOD

Fungal attack on wood is of two types, *sap stains* and *rot*. The sap stains fungi preferentially grow on the food stored in the parenchyma cells, into which they send their hyphae. Little damage to the wood substance is caused by them, although discoloration may reappear in the pulp and lower its quality.

In contrast the rotting fungi attack the cell walls. The *brown rots* consume the carbohydrates and leave a brown residue of lignin, whereas *white rots* seem to attack all cell wall constituents with some preference for lignin (10). In both cases the value of the wood as a pulping raw material is seriously impaired, as the resultant pulp is obtained in lower yields, is darker and more difficult to bleach, and has inferior strength properties. However, wood in early stages of rotting is still a usable raw material for many grades of pulp. Decay occurs in the living tree especially in those cells which are dead and partly air-filled, i.e. the heartwood. In the felled logs after some drying the sapwood cells also are partly filled with air and subject to fungal attack. As the sapwood structure is less dense than that of heartwood, less dry, and less rich in fungicides, sapwood is preferentially attacked in felled logs. When the wood is drier, fungal damages occur less frequently and therefore all handling and storing of wood in the forests or in the wood yards of the pulp mills tries to effect a rapid drying through the critical moisture range. Debarking is a prerequisite for rapid drying.

III. Physical Properties of Wood

In this section some physical properties of wood will be treated. The mechanical properties, although very important in wood technology, are of less importance for the understanding of the pulping processes, and will not be discussed. In Chapter 6.II, the strength of the interfiber bonds will be treated, as an introduction to the pulping problems. The chemical properties are dealt with in Chapter 4.

1. DENSITY

Pulpwood is generally bought by volume, and pulp or paper is sold by weight. Hence the *specific gravity* or *density* of wood and its variations is of great interest. The density of wood *substance* is about 1.53 (43) and shows little variation with species, type of growth or chemical composition. As the porosity of the wood varies very much with the proportions of different structural elements and their type, the density variations of dry wood are great, from 0.04 in the case of the pith tree (*Aeschynomene*) or 0.14 for balsa wood (*Ochroma*), to 1.42 for axemaster (*Krugiodendron*) wood. The volumetric proportion of wood substance in these woods are 3, 9 and 93 % respectively. The commercial pulpwoods have densities in the range 0.3–0.6, or 20–40 % of their volume occupied by wood substance. The remaining 60–80 % of the volume are void spaces, the lumina of the fibers as well as vessels and ducts. If this volume is filled with water, the wood becomes heavier. Also the wood substance itself adsorbs water, whereby it adds to both its weight and volume. Obviously, some definitions have to be made. Apart from the *density of the actual wood substance*, which is of theoretical interest, the *density of wet wood* often determines the transportation costs for a volume unit of pulpwood, whereas the *density of dry wood* determines the amount of wood substance obtained from a volume unit. As the shrinkage of wood on drying is around 10–15 %, and as the volume of green (living or freshly felled) wet wood is usually measured when the pulpwood is bought, the density of interest in this case should be defined as oven-dry weight per volume of green wood. This magnitude is called the *basic density of wood* and is tabulated in Table 2.3 for the more important pulpwoods. The values are averages, and there are large variations, not only for different species, but also for trees of the same species, within one single trunk at varying height and distance from the centre, and within a growth ring. The densities for 2,000 different samples of a spruce with an average density of 0.45 ranged from 0.3–0.6, and similar results were obtained for other softwoods and hardwoods (45). Within a 170-year-old pine trunk, densities were shown to vary from 0.30 in central parts to 0.49 in the outer, lower parts of the trunk (15). In general, softwood summerwood is of higher density than springwood, 0.6 as against 0.3 in the case of Scandinavian spruce (25), and slow-growing trees of higher density than fast-growing ones. The variations in density with age, geographic location, etc., for some southern pines have been studied in detail (e.g. 31, 37, 49). The juvenile period was found to last for at least ten years, during which there is a steady increase in density (49), and even later on the density increased with age, although at a slower rate (31). There is a definite geographical trend in average density, decreasing westwards (49) and northwards (14a). No significant difference in the basic density was found for slash pine trees growing two to three times as fast as the average (37), indicating that the property is a pronounced heredity factor (cf. also 43b, 45a). Similar studies have been performed on Scandinavian wood species (33). It was found that the density of Scandinavian spruce decreases slightly with increasing latitude and altitude, whereas fiber length and chemical composition are hardly influenced, Table 2.6.

Table 2.6. Wood density, fiber length and chemical composition of Scandinavian spruce as a function of latitude and altitude (33)

Latitude	Altitude, m	Wood density o.d. weight/o.d. volume	Fiber length, mm	Lignin, %	Pentosan, %
55	100	0.444	2.90	28.3	7.5
57	100	0.480	3.18	27.4	7.6
59	100	0.478	3.21	27.1	7.5
61	100	0.450	3.13	27.2	7.8
63	100	0.448	3.23	27.9	7.8
65	100	0.435	2.94	28.5	7.7
61	0	0.465	3.13	27.2	7.5
61	100	0.450	3.13	27.2	7.8
61	200	0.463	3.15	27.6	7.6
61	300	0.455	3.07	27.8	7.9
61	400	0.444	3.04	27.4	7.7
61	500	0.443	3.65	27.7	8.1
61	600	0.446	3.17	27.6	8.2

2. HYGROSCOPICITY

The water is held by the wood by *adsorption* in the wood substance, and by *capillary forces* in the cavities. The adsorbed water is in equilibrium with the relative humidity of the surrounding atmosphere and is in the order of 10% of the wood at around 60% relative humidity. At 100% relative humidity the moisture content approaches 25%, counted on the wet wood, or around 30% on the dry wood. This is called the *point of fiber saturation*. Up to this moisture content, all water is adsorbed in the wood substance and the cavities are air-filled. The maximum amount of water which can be taken up by the wood is then determined by its porosity. It can be calculated according to the formula

$$u_{max} = u_{sat} + \frac{1.53-r}{1.53 \cdot r} \cdot 100$$

where u_{max} and u_{sat} are respectively maximal water uptake and uptake at fiber saturation, and r the density of the wood. 1.53 is the density of the wood substance. u_{sat} varies for different species between 23 and 33%. For a spruce with a basic density of 0.40, the amount of water in a completely soaked piece of wood is around 215% calculated on the weight of dry wood or 68% of the weight of wet wood. Green wood contains so much water, that the whole wood substance is saturated and the cavities of the sapwood almost filled, whereas the heartwood cavities are almost exclusively air-filled. Thus, it has been shown (44) in the case of a growing spruce tree, that the outer twenty growth rings were almost completely water-filled, the next fifteen rings constituting a transition volume of partly and decreasingly filled cavities, where the inner twenty rings were almost entirely air-filled. Hence the average moisture content must have been above 50% of the weight of wet wood, and accordingly a land transport has to carry a load twice the weight of the wood. The density of the wet wood must have been around 0.90, or dangerously near the point where river transportation is impossible. On storing in the forest after felling, part of the water is lost, especially if the log has been barked. Scandinavian spruce, felled and barked in the beginning of April was found (17) to be completely air-dry towards the end of June, whereas unbarked logs required almost eighteen months to reach equilibrium with the atmosphere, and only did so because the bark was lost during that period. The speed of drying *hardwoods* in the forest can be increased by leaving the crown attached to the trunk for some time (14).

Air-dry wood contains 10–15% moisture. On removing the capillary bound water, the volume of the wood is not appreciably changed. From the fiber saturation point to the state of air-dryness, the shrinkage is about 8% of the green volume, and nearly as much shrinkage occurs from air-dryness to oven-dryness.

At contact, wood takes up water through the capillary system. The air in the capillaries exerts a certain back-pressure which prevents the system being filled completely. Therefore wood floats on water, and river transportation is possible for most softwoods. Hardwoods, with their somewhat higher density and more elaborate water-conducting structural system, soon sink if special precautions have not been taken (cf. Chapter 5).

The behavior of wood in contact with water is of the greatest importance for the pulping reactions and will be further treated in Chapter 6.III.

3. SPECIFIC HEAT

Another physical property of interest for the pulping reactions is the *specific heat* of wood, which enters into calculations of heat consumption, steaming condensate quantities etc. This magnitude is fairly constant for different species, as might be expected from their relatively similar chemical composition, and also the density of the wood has little influence. It varies with temperature according to the equation

$$x = 0.266 + 0.00116\,t \qquad (t \text{ in degrees centigrade})$$

and is accordingly 0.266 at 0°C and 0.382 at 100°C (7).

REFERENCES

1. Bisset, I. J. W., and H. E. Dadswell, *Australian For.*, **13**, 86 (1949); **14**, 17 (1950); **15**, 17 (1951).
2. Bisset, I. J. W., *et al.*, *Nature*, **165**, 348 (1950).
3. Brown, H. P., *Origin and Anatomy of Wood*, in L. E. Wise and E. C. Jahn, eds., *Wood Chemistry*, 2nd Ed., Reinhold, New York 1952, Chapter 1.
4. Brown, H. P., *et al.*, *Textbook of Wood Technology*, McGraw-Hill, New York 1949 and 1952.
5. Dadswell, H. E., and A. B. Wardrop, *Australian For.*, **13**, 22 (1949); *Holzforschung*, **9**, 97 (1955); *Australian J. Botany*, **3**, 177 (1955).
6. Desch, H. E., *Timber, its Structure and Properties*, New York 1953.
7. Dunlop, F., *The Specific Heat of Wood*, *U.S. Dep. Agr. Bull.* 110 (1912).
8. Eneroth, O., *Handbok i Skogsteknologi*, Stockholm 1920, p. 25.
9. Esau, K., *Plant Anatomy*, Wiley, New York 1953.
10. Falck, R., *Ber. Deut. Botan. Ges.*, **44**, 652 (1927).
11. F.A.O., *Tropical Woods and Agricultural Residues as Sources of Pulp*, Forestry and Forest Products Studies No. 3, Rome, Italy 1952.
12. Forgacs, O. L., *Tappi*, **44**, 112 (1961).
13. Forsaith, C. C., *The Mechanical and Physical Properties of Wood*, in L. E. Wise and E. C. Jahn, eds., *Wood Chemistry*, 2nd Ed., Reinhold, New York 1952, Chapter 2.
13a. Frey-Wyssling, A., and H. H. Bosshard, *Holz Roh Werkstoff*, **11**, 417 (1953).
14. Gibbs, R. D., *Can. J. Res.*, **12**, 727 (1935).
14a. Goddard, R. E., and R. K. Strickland, *Tappi*, **45**, 606 (1962).
15. Graff, J. H., and I. H. Isenberg, *Tappi*, **33**, 94 (1950).
16. Hägglund, E., *The Chemistry of Wood*, Academic Press, New York 1951, Chapters 1–2.
17. Hägglund, E., *The Chemistry of Wood*, Academic Press, New York 1951, p. 33.
18. Hägglund, E., *Svensk Papperstid.*, **37**, 133 (1934); **38**, 454 (1935).
19. Hägglund, E., *Papierfabrikant*, **33**, 73 (1935).
20. Huber, B., and G. Prütz, *Holz Roh Werkstoff*, **1**, 377 (1938).
21. Huber, B., and E. Schmidt, *Wochbl. Papierfabrik.*, **71**, 125 (1940).
22. Hyland, F., *Paper Trade J.*, **135**, No. 20, 85 (1952).
23. Jane, F. W., *The Structure of Wood*, Black, London 1956.
23a. Jayme, G., *et al.*, *Das Papier*, **5**, 411, 445, 504 (1951); *Holzforschung*, **7**, 39 (1953).
24. Jayne, B. A., *Tappi*, **42**, 461 (1959).
25. Johansson, D., *Holz Roh Werkstoff*, **3**, 73 (1940).
26. Koehler, A., *U.S. Dep. Agr. Tech. Bull.*, 342 (1933).
27. Kollman, F., *Technologie des Holzes*, Berlin 1936.
28. Lee, H. N., and J. D. Hale, *Structural, Microscopical and Physical Characteristics of Wood*, in J. N. Stephenson, ed., *Preparation and Treatment of Wood Pulp*, McGraw-Hill, London 1952, Chapter 1.
29. Leopold, B., and D. C. McIntosh, *Tappi*, **44**, 235 (1961).
30. Liese, W., *Holz Roh Werkstoff*, **15**, 449 (1957).
31. Mitchell, H. L., *U.S. Dep. Agr.*, *Forest Prod. Lab. Rep.* No. 1993 (1954); *Pulp Paper*, **33**, No. 5, 144 (1959).
32. Mühlsteph, W., *Wochbl. Papierfabrik.*, **72**, 201, 219 (1941); *Papierfabrikant*, **36**, 341 (1938), **38**, 109 (1940); *Holz Roh Werkstoff*, **5**, 95 (1942); *Cellulosechem.*, **18**, 132 (1940).

32a. Murray, C. E., and B. B. Thomas, *Tappi*, **44**, 625 (1961).
33. Nylinder, P., and E. Hägglund, *Medd. Statens Skogsforskningsinst.*, **44**, No. 11 (1954).
34. Omeis, E., *Forstl. Naturwiss. Z.*, **4**, 137 (1895).
35. Onaka, F., *Wood Res. Kyoto*, **1**, (1949).
36. Perilä, O., *J. Polymer Sci.*, **51**, 19 (1961).
37. Perry, T. O., and W. C. Wu, *Tappi*, **41**, 178 (1958).
38. Phillips, E. W. J., *Emp. For. J.*, **19**, 282 (1940).
39. Runkel, R. O., *Wochbl. Papierfabrik.*, **71**, 93 (1940); *Holz Roh Werkstoff*, **5**, 305 (1942); *Zellstoff Papier*, **21**, 133 (1941); *Tappi*, **35**, 174 (1952).
40. Sanio, K., *Jb. wiss. Bot.*, **8**, 401 (1872).
41. Scaramuzzi, G., in A. de Philippis, ed., *Publicazioni del Centro di Sperimentazione Agricola e Forestale*, Vol. I–II, Rome 1957–1958.
42. Schultze-Dewitz, G., *Holz Roh Werkstoff*, **17**, 319 (1959).
43. Stamm, A. J., and L. A. Hansen, *J. Phys. Chem.*, **41**, 1008 (1937).
43a. Stemsrud, F., *Holzforschung*, **10**, 69 (1956).
43b. Squillace, A. E., *et al.*, *Tappi*, **45**, 599 (1962).
44. Trendelenburg, R., *Das Holz als Rohstoff*, 2nd Ed., München 1955.
45. Trendelenburg, R., *Das Bayerland*, **47**, 513 (1936).
45a. Van Buijtenen, J. P., *Tappi*, **45**, 602 (1962).
46. Vorreiter, L., *Holztechnologisches Handbuch*, Wien 1949.
47. Wardrop, A. B., and R. D. Preston, *Biochim. Biophys. Acta*, **6**, 36 (1950).
48. Wershing, H. F., and I. W. Bailey, *J. Forestry*, **40**, 411 (1942).
49. Zobel, B. J., and R. L. McElwee, *Tappi*, **41**, 167 (1958).

3

FIBER MORPHOLOGY

I. Cell Formation and Growth

The primary organic compounds, which eventually build up the wood substance, are produced in the leaves by photosynthesis out of carbon dioxide and water. They are then conducted down the trunk through the inner bark tissues and further through the rays into the trunk, where they are stored in the parenchyma cells, or consumed by growth reactions in the production of new cells of the cambium zone. The reactions leading from carbon dioxide to carbohydrate are now understood in some detail (8), and considerable progress has also been made toward understanding the nature of the energetic linkage between respiration and growth (6). Both respiration and, in a certain sense, photosynthesis are considered to be exergonic processes ($\triangle F < 0$), whereas growth is an endergonic one, requiring energy. The common reactant coupling the exergonic and endergonic reactions is probably adenosinetriphosphate, which is formed during the exergonic processes and stores energy to be used in the endergonic processes such as muscle contraction or growth. Respiration processes involve the oxidation of carbohydrate to carbon dioxide via pyruvic acid, under conservation of most of the released energy as adenosinetriphosphate. The photosynthesis in addition to energy also supplies building blocks for the formation of cellulose and hemicelluloses, as well as of lignin and minor components involved in the growth. The rate of the growth reactions seems to be controlled by plant hormones such as indole-3-acetic acid, causing changes of the physical properties of the cell wall. The chemical details of lignification are likewise beginning to be understood, as further discussed in Chapter 4.IV.

The process of cell formation has been followed in detail by microscopic examination (e.g. 5, 7). There are two principal types of growth, *apical* or bud growth, and *cambial* or growth of the trunk circumference. As the latter process is the one forming the dominating part of the cells, the discussion will be limited to the growth of the cambium layer. In dormant condition this consists of 1–4 cell tiers, the outer of which is the *initiating layer* and the remainder called *xylem mother cells*, which have been formed by successive cell divisions of the initiating layer. The xylem mother cells are in turn capable of division and redivision to produce wood-destined cells, as schematically illustrated in Figure 3.1 (7). This happens when the cells are activated in the spring. There is first a radial expansion because of considerable water uptake. Then follow division

69

of the chromosomes and formation of a longitudinal partitioning wall. In the beginning, the generation of new cells is a fairly slow process, the interval between the first and second divisions being up to two weeks, but the tempo increases and there may be as many as 10–30 cell layers taking an active part in the generative process of the xylem upon formation of springwood. Occasionally there is also a formation of phloem mother cells from the initiating layer, and a further division of these, but the activity on the bark side is considerably smaller. After midsummer, cell division proceeds at a decreasing rate in the initiating layer, whereas the xylem mother cells eventually cease to divide, thereby diminishing the active cambium zone to a few cell rows, and consequently the rate of wood production. The bark production, on the other hand, continues at an unchanged rate.

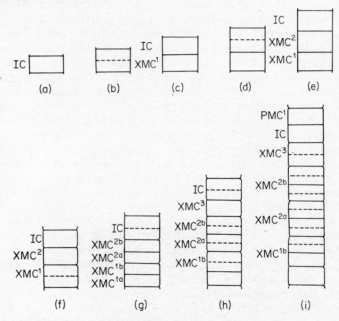

Fig. 3.1. Diagrams illustrating sequence of cell divisions in the cambium. IC initial cell, XMC xylem mother cell, PMC xylem mother cell. Successive divisions of the initial cell yield xylem mother cells internally and occasional phloem mother cells externally. The xylem mother cells undergo extensive division and redivision to produce wood-destined cells (Bannan)

As the diameter of the trunk grows, an increase in the cell number along the periphery, *multiplicative* division is necessary. This initially occurs in the cambium layer, for a few species by a simple radio-longitudinal cell division, but for most species by a semitransverse (or pseudotransverse) division. An obliquely oriented, sigmoidal wall is laid down across

70

the center of the cambial cell, whereby two daughter cells are formed, each somewhat more than half the length of the original cell. Each subsequently elongate by tip growth to almost normal size. In some cases, due to insufficient ray-cell contact for food supply, one of the daughter cells dies at an early stage, leaving space for the one remaining to elongate to a size larger than the average. A high frequency of multiplicative division will tend to bring about a decrease in fiber length, whereas selection of the longest cambial cells for survival acts in the opposite direction. The former mechanism is likely to cause the differences in average fiber length between the juvenile wood of the core and the mature wood of older trees.

The xylem cells formed by longitudinal division of xylem mother cells have very thin *primary walls*, consisting of cellulose and some pectic substances, and a largely pectic *middle lamella*. As the growth proceeds, they eventually become increasingly remote from the cambium layer and lose their capacity for division. Then they enlarge and maturate as tracheids or libriform fibers. Length growth is not more than about 10% in softwoods and up to 500% in hardwoods, but expansion in radial direction may be as high as fourfold. Towards the end of this expansion there is a thickening of the cell walls by deposition of a *secondary wall*, containing cellulose and hemicelluloses. During the final phases of secondary wall formation, lignification completes the maturation of the xylem cell. The transition from springwood to summerwood formation, producing more thickwalled fibers, does not seem to be influenced by environmental factors (12) but rather by an internal auxin nutrient balance (36). It is accompanied by a marked decrease in bud growth.

II. Fiber Structure

The chemical nature of the constituents of the cell wall will be discussed in detail in Chapter 4. Most are macromolecules, of which only cellulose is entirely linear and possesses a certain stiffness also in molecular solution. In contrast to the hemicelluloses and lignin, which form amorphous structures encrusting the cell wall, the cellulose molecules form a framework of linear and partly crystalline aggregates. The hemicelluloses, being structurally more related to the cellulose and deposited at an earlier stage than lignin, are somewhat more intimately admixed with the cellulose structure. The cellulose aggregates are of indefinite length and varying width. Structures 250 Å wide are called *microfibrils* (18), which in turn seem to be aggregated from *elementary fibrils* (38) about 100 Å wide and 30 Å thick and separated by zones of less crystalline order, cf. Chapter 4.II. The arrangement of this fibrillar framework is different in different parts of the fiber and contributes to the changes in physical properties displayed in the various layers of the fiber wall. Another contributing factor to these variations is the varying proportions of chemical components, which will be further examined in the last section of this chapter.

The gross structure and dimensions of the various types of cells was described in Chapter 2, and shown to vary considerably with species, growth conditions and cell type. As the softwood tracheids and the hardwood libriform fibers are the two cell types of dominating importance from the pulp- and paper-making standpoint, the discussion on the detailed fiber structure will be limited to them. There is a surprising concordance in the structure of their cell walls, in spite of the differences in gross dimensions. Figure 3.2 shows a schematic representation of the various layers of a tracheid or libriform fiber wall. Surrounding the fiber, and heavily lignified and stiff is the *middle lamella* (M), shared with adjacent fibers. The outermost layer of the fiber is called the *primary*

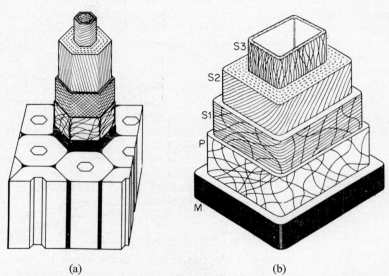

(a)   (b)

Fig. 3.2. Cell-wall architecture, schematically. M middle lamella, P primary wall, S1 transition lamella, S2 main layer of secondary wall, S3 tertiary wall, or tertiary lamella of secondary wall (Wardrop (a), Meier (b))

wall (P), which was formed on the cambial cell division. The *secondary wall*, formed during the maturation of the fiber, is not homogeneous but subdivided into the *outer secondary wall* or *transition lamella* (S1), the *main secondary wall* (S2), and the *inner secondary wall* (S3), sometimes called the *tertiary wall* or *lamella*. Recent surveys on the detailed structure of the layers have been given (e.g. 1, 11, 14, 19, 20, 23, 29, 30, 32, 39, 41). The relative thicknesses of these layers have been measured for spruce tracheids, and were: P 7–14%, S1 5–11%, S2 74–84% and S3 3–4% (25). In *compression wood*, cf. Chapter 2.II, the primary wall is thicker than it normally is, and the tertiary wall is lacking. In *tension wood*, an inner, gelatinous layer is formed, sometimes in addition to the other lamellae, sometimes substituting the S3 or even S2 and S3 layers.

72

The middle lamella is intimately connected to the primary walls of two adjacent fibers and the concept of 'compound middle lamella' includes the primary walls. The true middle lamella is about $1-2\,\mu$ thick (27), varying with species and growing conditions. Its structure is amorphous, with a pattern of discontinuities of about 60 Å, Figure 3.3 (1), and membraneous and dense, Figure 3.4 (41). Still, it is somewhat more porous than the fiber wall, the packing density being about 80–90% of that of the secondary wall (28). Its high lignin content makes the middle lamella a hard and hydrophobic sheathing around the fibers, which has to be removed to allow their separation. In the cambial zone it is mainly made up of pectic material, but becomes heavily lignified during the phase of fiber maturation.

The primary wall forms the original wall of the fibers and merely grows

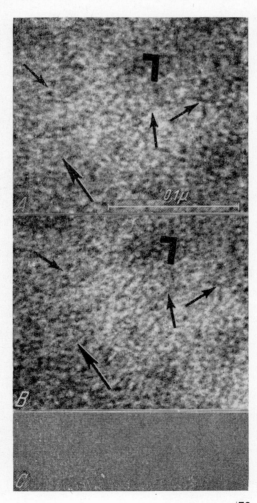

Fig. 3.3. Fine structure of middle lamella of sprucewood, degraded by *Polyporus*. A and B stages of a series of varied focussing, C grain of photographic plate (Asunmaa)

Fig. 3.4. Electron micrographs of lignin from the primary wall and middle lamella, isolated from a longitudinal section of *Nothofagus cunninghamii* with 72% H_2SO_4 (Wardrop)

Fig. 3.5. Electron micrograph showing microfibrils of the primary wall of *Eucalyptus elaephora* (Wardrop)

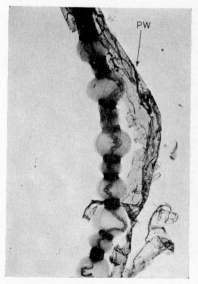

Fig. 3.6. Swelling of a radiata pine tracheid. The primary wall bursts, it forms a sheet and is still attached to the fiber at certain points. The transition lamella constricts the swelling secondary wall, which is ballooning. The tertiary wall is seen within the balloons (Bucher)

in area, in contrast to the secondary wall, which grows in thickness. The primary wall is therefore very thin, in the native state about 0.1μ (2, 15) and in the dry state only 300 Å, corresponding to the width of three elementary cellulose fibrils. Cellulose fibrils form a thin framework of a woven or felted texture with little orientation, Figure 3.5 (41), embedded in an amorphous substance of pectic hemicelluloses and much lignin. Being so thin, the primary wall is not very easily studied. Because of its lignin content, as well as its woven fibrillar texture, the primary wall has a very limited swelling capacity and bursts on treating the fiber with swelling agents, Figure 3.6 (11), whereby it splits like a pea pod and forms a spiralling, flat ribbon, on which the four edges of the fiber are easily recognizable as dark lines, Figure 3.7 (23). The primary wall is removed in

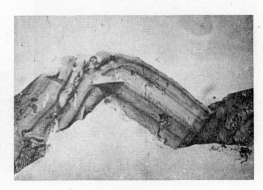

Fig. 3.7. The primary wall of a strong sulfite spruce tracheid after dissolution of the secondary wall in cuam solution upon staining with Victoria blue. Longitudinal dark zones indicate residual middle lamella substance from the edges of the fiber (Dymling and Giertz)

the early stages of beating a paper pulp, and is considered to have some influence on the paper properties (23). In general it is thought to be too weak to remain long enough in the pulping and beating processes to be of considerable importance, attention instead being focused on the various layers of the secondary wall.

The secondary wall, as pointed out previously, is not a morphologically homogeneous layer and should be considered as a collective term for all fiber layers formed in the secondary process of fiber maturation. As shown in Figure 3.6, the substances enclosed by the primary wall behave heterogeneously on swelling. There is the well-known phenomenon of balloon formation, caused by the extensive swelling of the middle layer of the secondary wall, which is restricted at certain points by the non-swelling outer layer, which at the same time becomes pushed together to cuffs between the balloons. The inner secondary wall in the same way is only slightly swollen. Even varying optical properties (birefringence of the outer and inner layers) show the different nature of the various layers, Figure 3.8 (41). These differences in behavior are explained by the submicroscopic arrangement of each layer, especially of the cellulose microfibrils.

The outer secondary wall or *transition lamella* has a thickness of about

75

0.15 μ (15) and consists of two counter-rotating helices of cellulose micro-fibrils, of which the Z helix appears to dominate in thickness and strength (9, 14, 15, 17, 31). The helix angle (with the longitudinal fiber axis) is for hardwood fibers $\pm35°$ to $\pm55°$ and for softwood tracheids $\pm55°$ to $\pm75°$, generally about $\pm65°$ (15, 17). When subjected to swelling pressure from the main secondary wall, the weaker fibrillar system is ruptured, and the action of the remaining one is not sufficient to restrict swelling. The whole outer layer glides over the main one to form prominent gatherings at the nodes between the balloons, with clearly visible fibrillar connections,

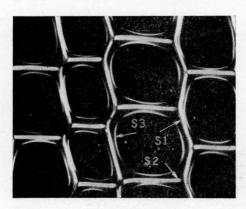

Fig. 3.8. A transverse section of *Pinus radiata* photographed between crossed nicols showing the three layers of the secondary wall (Wardrop)

winding as a single thread on the surface of the balloon, cf. Figure 3.6. That there is a distinct discontinuity between these two layers is further indicated by the frequent failure of wood between the transition lamella and the main secondary wall when subjected to a tensile load, especially at high temperatures or after preswelling in alkali (22, 26). The transition lamella is shown in detail in Figure 3.9 (15). Besides microfibrils it contains lignin and hemicelluloses, some of which seems to form a thin outer layer (39).

The main secondary wall forms the bulk of the fiber, with a thickness of 1–10 μ, varying with species and growing conditions. Its relatively high content of cellulose is present in microfibrils in helical arrangement, at a fairly low angle to the axis, 10–20° for softwood tracheids (15, 37, 39) and 15–35° for libriform fibers (13). The angle will vary slightly from lamella to lamella in the layer, and also from fiber to fiber within a single trunk. The latter phenomenon has been shown to be related to the elongation growth of the fiber, since there is a close correlation between fibrillar angle and fiber length (37). The lamellated structure of the main secondary wall, seen in Figure 3.10 (41), does not seem to be related to daylight variations but to some internal fluctuation in the growth mechanism. The lamellae are only a few microfibril sheets thick, but their individuality is not very pronounced, and the microfibrils lie virtually parallel in the whole structure of the main secondary wall. Occasionally, so-called *slip planes* are observed, where the structure has been mechanically distorted,

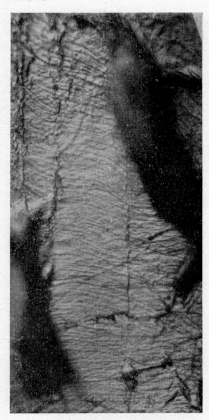

Fig. 3.9. Crossed fibrillar structure of the transition lamella, S1, of slash pine kraft pulp ($\times 1013$) (Emerton)

Fig. 3.10. Lignin distribution in the secondary wall, with concentric pattern. *Tetramerista glabra* cross-section after treatment with 72% H_2SO_4 ($\times 1000$) (Wardrop)

77

Figure 3.11 (20). Thereby dislocations are formed between the micro-fibrils, where chemical attack is facilitated. The decrease in the pulp quality observed where the wood chips have been subjected to mechanical damage (cf. Chapter 6) may have a connection with such slip plane formation, as well as with the previously mentioned slipping between the transition lamella and the main secondary wall. Similar weaknesses in the fiber wall occur at the crossings between tracheids and ray cells in softwoods. These lead to preferential bending and even to fragmentation at about 0.3 mm intervals on processing (pulping and beating) (16). The

Fig. 3.11. 'Slip planes' in the parallel texture of the secondary wall (Mühle-thaler)

Fig. 3.12. Electron micrograph of the secondary wall of Douglas fir (Wardrop)

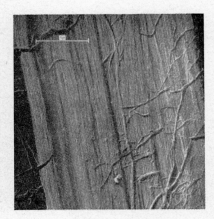

Fig. 3.13. Electron micrograph of the secondary wall of Douglas fir after removal of lignin (Wardrop)

microfibrillar framework of cellulose in the secondary wall is encrusted with amorphous hemicelluloses and lignin to a dense structure, Figure 3.12 (41). Figures 3.13 and 3.14 (41) demonstrate the structure of carbohydrates and lignin respectively in the main secondary wall after removal of the opposite component. It is seen that the encrusting lignin is amorphous but intimately mixed with the framework, the pores visible being of the same order of magnitude as the width of the microfibrils. On the removal of both types of encrustants by successive holocellulose preparation and hydrolysis, the remaining cellulose microfibrils associate to coarser structures, Figure 3.15 (41), in the same way illustrating the intimate admixture of the components in the original tissue.

Fig. 3.14. Electron micrograph of the secondary wall lignin from a longitudinal section of *Notofagus cunninghamii*, isolated by 72% H_2SO_4 (Wardrop)

Fig. 3.15. Electron micrograph of the secondary wall of *Eucalyptus elaeophora* after delignification and acid hydrolysis (Wardrop)

The inner secondary wall, even called the *tertiary wall* (10, 30a, 31), is the structure limiting the fiber wall toward the lumen, and is hence of particular interest from a pulping point of view, since it is the first part of the fiber wall to come in contact with the cooking liquor. It consists of one single lamella, $0.07–0.08\,\mu$ thick. It is remarkably resistant to chemicals, which may be a result of its dense morphological structure. The tertiary wall contains a framework of cellulose microfibrils, arranged in a Z helix at an angle varying with the species. In European spruce and birch the helix angle is fairly low, about 30° (11, 31), whereas for most species, such as pines, larch, Douglas fir, and North-American spruces and firs, a steep angle, 70–90°, has been measured for the tertiary wall helix (11). The different fibrillar arrangement in the three secondary layers, S1, S2 and S3, is clearly seen in Figure 3.16 (14). The inner surface of the tertiary wall is varying in texture. In some species, such as *Picea*, *Larix* and *Pseudotsuga*, the surface is smooth, whereas in *Abies*, *Betula* and some *Pinus* species it is full of warts, Figure 3.17 (10, 21, 24, 32), or has a grainy texture. The chemical resistance of the tertiary wall, especially towards alkaline reagents, may be a consequence of its dense structure as well as its special chemical composition, where glucuronoarabinoxylan is believed to dominate.

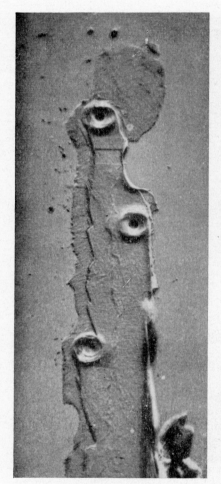

Fig. 3.17. Warts on tertiary wall occurring in some species (Mühlethaler)

Fig. 3.16. Wall fragment of Scots pine tracheid ($\times 467$). S3 overlies S2, the fracture line of which may be seen sweeping round the pits. Underlying S2 is S1, which has a quite different fracture line. The bordered pits have collapsed during drying (Emerton)

III. Chemical Composition

1. LIGNIN DISTRIBUTION

The average lignin content of wood is somewhat less than 30% for softwoods and about 20% for hardwoods, cf. Chapter 4.I. In the previous section it has been shown that this lignin appears in concentrated, compact form in the middle lamella, and in more scattered and porous form in the cell wall. The gross distribution of lignin and carbohydrates is demonstrated in Figures 3.18 and 3.19 (31, 32), where cross-sections of wood treated with selective rotting fungi show the dominance of lignin in the middle lamella and of carbohydrates in the cell wall. A quantitative chemical microanalysis has been tried (4), by which the middle lamella of Douglas

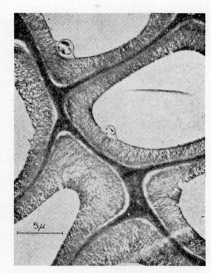

Fig. 3.18. Cross-section of sprucewood, degraded by *Merulius domesticus*, leaving predominantly lignin (Meier)

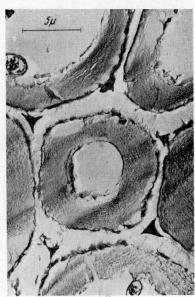

Fig. 3.19. Cross-section of birchwood, degraded by *Trametes pini*, leaving predominantly carbohydrates (Meier)

81

fir was found to contain 72 % lignin and 14 % pentosan. A different method used the selective absorption of ultraviolet light by lignin to determine the relative distribution of lignin throughout the middle lamella and cell wall in ultra-thin cross-sections of spruce and some hardwoods. Figures 3.20 and 3.21 (27) give two examples of the photomicrographs obtained, and Figure 3.22 (27) the photometration curves of such a photomicrograph as well as the corrections necessary. The concentration of spruce lignin was found to be 10–20 % in the cell wall near lumen and 60–90 % in the middle lamella, with the main decrease in concentration in the outer secondary wall and an average concentration of 16 % lignin in the cell wall and 73 % in the middle lamella (27, 29). In hardwoods, the concentration of lignin in the cell wall is decidedly lower, and higher in the middle lamella, although no quantitative data are available. Compression wood of spruce

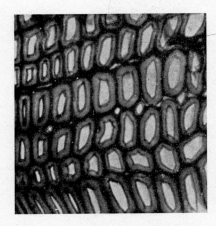

Fig. 3.20. Photomicrograph at 2,750 Å of a cross-section of sprucewood, illustrating the lignin distribution (dark) (Lange)

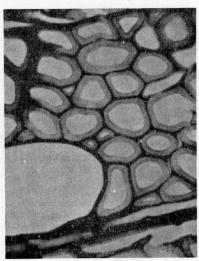

Fig. 3.21. Photomicrograph at 2,750 Å of a cross-section of birchwood (Lange)

and tension wood of red beech were likewise shown to accentuate the concentration of the lignin to the middle lamella (27). Interference microscopy can also be used as a method of estimating the relative concentrations of lignin and carbohydrate, by embedding the specimen in a number of media with varying refractive indices and measuring the optical path difference for various parts of a cross-section. The method gave similar values for the lignin distribution as did the UV method (29), or 10 and 66% as the average values for the lignin concentration in the cell wall and middle lamella respectively. Using the above average values of 16 and 73%, and assuming a total average lignin content of 27% in the spruce wood, it can be calculated that the middle lamella contained 20% of the entire wood substance and 53% of the entire lignin in the wood. If the interferometric values cited are used, the middle lamella contained 30%

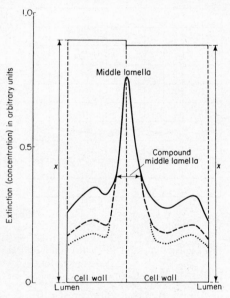

Fig. 3.22. Relative distribution of lignin in middle lamella and cell wall, as measured by ultraviolet light absorption of a thin spruce-wood section. *Solid curve:* measured extinction at 2,750 Å. *Dashed curve:* extinction corrected for non-absorptive light losses. *Dotted curve:* extinction further corrected for the convergence of incident light, and representing the relative lignin distribution. In the present case this corresponds to an absolute distribution of 85% lignin in the middle lamella and 15% lignin close to lumen (Lange)

of the wood substance and 75% of the lignin. Obviously, a large material has to be collected in order to achieve a higher degree of accuracy in the estimation of how much of the wood lignin is located in the middle lamella. It is likely to vary a good deal with the species and growing conditions. For spruce it would be from half to three-quarters of the lignin and for hardwoods considerably more. A further limitation of the methods used so far is the resolving power, which does not discriminate details below 0.5 μ. Therefore, they are not able to tell the lignin content of the primary, outer and inner secondary walls, as their thickness is of the order of magnitude of 0.1 μ. However, the lignin concentration appears to decrease sharply in the neighbourhood of the outer secondary wall (27). It is doubted that the inner secondary, or tertiary, wall contains any lignin at all (31), whereas the primary wall is heavily lignified.

2. CARBOHYDRATE DISTRIBUTION

In the middle lamella, cellulose is virtually absent (35, 42). In addition to the 14% pentosans and 72% lignin found (4), the remainder is largely hemicelluloses of the pectin type (33).

Although the absolute concentration of lignin in the fiber wall appears to decrease from the outer layers and toward lumen, thus increasing the relative concentration of carbohydrates in the same direction, the absolute mass distribution of carbohydrate matter remains approximately uniform throughout the fiber wall, Figure 3.23 (3), as evidenced by microspectrographic studies on holocelluloses from spruce and birch, colored by esterification with *p*–phenylazobenzyl chloride. The interesting question

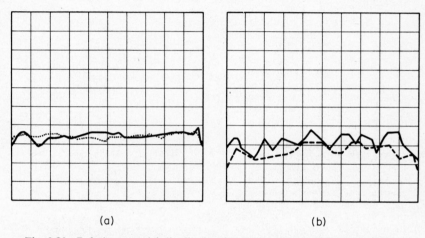

(a)   (b)

Fig. 3.23. Relative material distribution (expressed as extinction) for cell walls of spruce (a) and birch (b) holocellulose. Lumen to the right, as in similar subsequent figures (Asunmaa and Lange)

of the relative distribution of cellulose and hemicelluloses in the cell wall has been examined by the same esterification technique but using fibers in different states of hemicellulose removal. Thus cold alkali extracted as well as hot alkali extracted holocellulose was studied, further holocellulose after a short acid hydrolysis followed by cold alkali extraction as well as holocellulose hydrolyzed for a longer time with acid at more severe conditions. In all these cases, it is to be expected that a preferential hemicellulose removal will take place, although some quantities of easily accessible cellulose will also be dissolved. Figures 3.24–3.27 (3) show that in all cases most of the substance removed was located in the outer parts of the fiber wall and comparatively little near lumen. The conclusion was therefore drawn, that the hemicelluloses, although penetrating the entire fiber wall, are located predominantly in its outer regions, whereas an increasing concentration of cellulose is found towards lumen. It must be

84

stressed at once, that these conclusions refer to the main secondary wall, since the microspectrographic methods used do not discriminate details below about 0.5 μ.

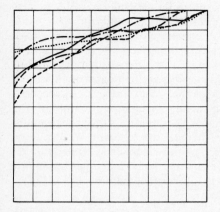

Fig. 3.24. Relative material distribution curves within a single cell wall for cold-alkali-treated spruce holocellulose (Asunmaa and Lange)

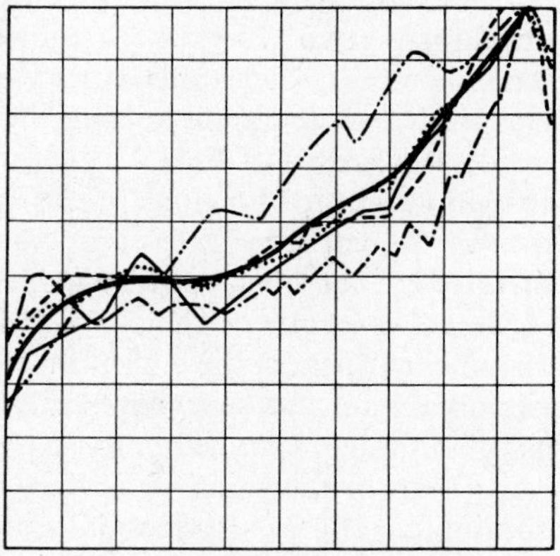

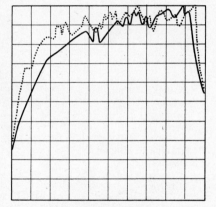

Fig. 3.25. Relative material distribution curves within a single cell wall for hot-alkali-treated spruce holocellulose (Asunmaa and Lange)

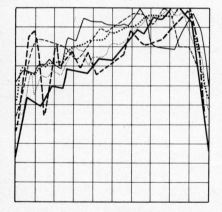

Fig. 3.26. Relative material distribution curves within a single cell wall of cold-alkali-treated spruce holocellulose after a short prehydrolysis (Asunmaa and Lange)

Fig. 3.27. Relative material distribution curves within a single cell wall of spruce holocellulose after 0.5 h of Nickerson hydrolysis (Asunmaa and Lange)

Information on the carbohydrate composition of the various other layers of the pine tracheid wall, as well as the distribution of the various hemicellulose components, has been acquired by a combined microscopic and microchemical technique (33). The various cell layers close to the cambium and in different stages of maturation were isolated with the aid of a micromanipulator and their carbohydrate composition determined by micro-chromatography after hydrolysis. In the microscope the birefringence of the outer and inner secondary walls facilitated the identification of the various stages of cell maturation. Some fibers contained only the middle lamella and primary wall, in others the outer secondary wall was also developed, two further categories contained in addition the main secondary wall, incompletely as well as completely developed, and finally, mature wood fibers containing the tertiary wall also were analyzed. The results are shown in Table 3.1 (33), together with a recalculation assuming certain weight proportions of the various layers and giving a rough estimation of the carbohydrate composition of the various layers. In the first-mentioned category, polygalacturonic acid, galactan and araban constituted two-thirds of the carbohydrates. These pectic substances rapidly disappear during the maturation, whereas the content of cellulose, glucomannan and glucuronoarabinoxylan increases. The content of the last-mentioned hemicellulose is higher in the outer and inner secondary walls than in the main secondary wall, where glucomannan and cellulose dominate. The inner secondary, or tertiary, wall consists to a very large

Table 3.1. The distribution of the carbohydrate components in the cell wall (pine summerwood tracheid) (33)

Cell wall layers	M+P	M+P +S1	M+P +S1 (+S2)*	M+P+ S1+S2	M+P+ S1+S2 +S3	M+P	S1	S2	S3
Number of cell rows, approx.	12	2	5	8	15				
Sugar analysis, %									
Galactose	20.5	9.6	3.1	4.5	3.2				
Glucose	38.0	60.5	71.0	68.6	64.5				
Mannose	6.2	11.8	18.4	19.0	20.1				
Arabinose	30.8	8.6	2.6	2.1	3.2				
Xylose	4.6	10.6	5.0	6.0	9.0				
Polysaccharide content, %									
Galactan	20.2 (0)†	8.3 (0)†	3.0	4.2	3.1	20	6	4	0
Cellulose	35.8 (71.3)	54.7 (64.6)	65.0	62.3	57.5	35	61	64	22
Glucomannan	7.6 (15.1)	14.3 (16.8)	22.6	23.2	24.2	8	16	25	14
Arabinan	29.7 (0)	7.2 (0)	2.0	1.4	2.0	30	0	0	0
Glucuronoarabino-xylan	6.8 (13.6)	15.4 (18.3)	7.4	8.8	13.1	7	17	7	64
Weight fractions of cell wall carbohydrates assumed						2	10	78	10

* S2 only partially developed.

† Composition excluding pectic substances such as arabinogalactan and galacturonic acid, the latter of which was found to an extent of 20% in the compound middle lamella.

86

extent of glucuronoarabinoxylan together with some cellulose, a conclusion which was reached also from earlier microscopic observations on the presence or absence of the tertiary wall in pulps of high or low pentosan content (34), and is further substantiated by the fact that springwood tracheids with their thin main secondary walls contain proportionally more xylan and less glucomannan than do the thick-walled summerwood fibers (33). A similar microchemical examination of the distribution of the carbohydrate constituents in the various parts of the fiber layers has also been carried out on spruce and birch (33). Those species have less pronounced tertiary wall, and the composition of the latter could not be deduced with the same certainty as for pine. In Table 3.2, the data are therefore given in terms of S2 outer part and S2 inner part plus S3. It is seen that in spruce as well as in pine, cellulose and glucomannan dominate in S2 and xylan in S3. For birch, cellulose is enriched in the innermost part of the fiber wall.

Table 3.2. The distribution of the carbohydrate components in the cell wall of birch, spruce and pine (33)

Cell wall layers Wood species component		M+P	S1	S2 Outer part	S2+S3 Inner part
Betula verrucosa	Galactan	17	1	1	0
	Cellulose	41	50	48	60
	Glucomannan	3	3	2	5
	Arabinan	13	2	1	0
	Glucuronoxylan	25	44	48	35
Picea abies	Galactan	16	8	0	3
	Cellulose	33	56	63	58
	Glucomannan	8	19	24	24
	Arabinan	30	0	1	0
	Glucuronoarabinoxylan	13	18	12	15
Pinus silvestris	Galactan	20	5	2	3
	Cellulose	36	61	67	48
	Glucomannan	8	17	25	27
	Arabinan	29	1	0	2
	Glucuronoarabinoxylan	7	16	7	19

3. MINERAL CONSTITUENTS AND EXTRACTIVES

The ash content of wood, about 0.3%, indicates a certain amount of mineral constituents, such as metals and silica. By micro-incineration methods, it was shown that they are predominantly deposited in the compound middle lamella (30).

The extractives, i.e. water-soluble and organo-soluble constituents of the wood, are virtually concentrated in the medullary rays and other parenchymatic cells, as well as in the resin ducts. They have two main functions, namely as a reserve food and as a protective substance at those parts of the xylem which become exposed to the atmosphere. As a reserve food, both carbohydrates, mainly starch, and organo-soluble substances function. The organo-soluble extractives, which consist of fatty and resin acids and esters, as well as phenolic compounds and neutral components such as fatty alcohols, terpenes and sterols, dominate in some species, whereas in others starch is the main reserve food. Whereas starch presents no pulping problems, the 'resin' components, because of their hydrophobic character, do so very much. Investigations have shown some of the resin constituents, such as the resin acids and esters, to be enriched in the resin ducts, indicating their physiological destination as a protective substance, which is under pressure and will migrate to parts of the xylem subjected to mechanical damage or to parts which dry up during the later stages of the tree life, the heartwood formation. The parenchyma cells are richer in the fatty acid esters and neutral substances, which constitute the reserve food supply.

The detailed chemical composition of these substances is dealt with in Chapter 4.V.

REFERENCES

1. Asunmaa, S., in E. Treiber, ed., *Die Chemie der Pflanzenzellwand*, Springer, Berlin 1957, p. 181.
2. Asunmaa, S., *Svensk Papperstid.*, **58**, 308 (1955).
3. Asunmaa, S., and P. W. Lange, *Svensk Papperstid.*, **57**, 501 (1954).
4. Bailey, A. J., *Ind. Eng. Chem., Anal. Ed.*, **8**, 52 (1936).
5. Bailey, I. W., *Am. J. Botany*, **7**, 417 (1920).
6. Bandurski, R. S., *Tappi*, **40**, 217 (1957).
7. Bannan, M. W., *Tappi*, **40**, 220 (1957).
8. Bassham, J. A., and M. Calvin, in D. E. Green, ed., *Currents in Biochemical Research 1956*, Interscience, New York 1957.
9. Bosshard, H. H., *Ber. Schweiz. Botan. Ges.*, **62**, 482 (1952).
10. Bucher, H., *Die Tertiärlamelle von Holzfasern und ihre Erscheinungsformen bei Coniferen*, Attisholz (Schweiz) 1953; *Holzforschung*, **11**, 1, 97 (1957).
11. Bucher, H., in F. Bolam, ed., *Fundamentals of Papermaking Fibres*, Tech. Sect. Brit. Paper and Board Makers' Assoc., Kenley (England) 1958, p. 7.
12. van Buijtenen, J. P., *Tappi*, **41**, 175 (1958).
13. Correns, E., *et al.*, *Faserforsch. Textiltech.*, **7**, 565 (1956).
14. Emerton, H. W., in F. Bolam, ed., *Fundamentals of Papermaking Fibres*, Tech. Sect. Brit. Paper and Board Makers' Assoc., Kenley (England) 1958, pp. 35, 431.
15. Emerton, H. W., and V. Goldsmith, *Holzforschung*, **10**, 108 (1956).
16. Forgacs, O. L., *Tappi*, **44**, 112 (1961).
17. Frei, E., *et al.*, *J. Exp. Botany*, **8**, 139 (1957).
18. Frey-Wyssling, A., *Science*, **119**, 80 (1954).
19. Frey-Wyssling, A., *Die Pflanzliche Zellwand*, Springer, Berlin 1959.
20. Frey-Wyssling, A., in F. Bolam, ed., *Fundamentals of Papermaking Fibres*, Tech. Sect. Brit. Paper and Board Makers' Assoc., Kenley (England) 1958, p. 1.
21. Frey-Wyssling, A., *et al.* *Holz Roh Werkstoff*, **13**, 245 (1955).
22. Garland, H., *Ann. Missouri Botan. Garden*, **26**, 1 (1939).

23. Giertz, H. W., in F. Bolam, ed., *Fundamentals of Papermaking Fibres*, Tech. Sect. Brit. Paper and Board Makers' Assoc., Kenley (England) 1958, p. 389.
24. Harada, H., *J. Japan Forestry Soc.*, **34**, 350 (1952), **35**, 393 (1953).
25. Jayme, G., and D. Fengel, *Holz Roh Werkstoff*, **19**, 50 (1961).
26. Lagergren, S., *et al.*, *Svensk Papperstid.*, **60**, 632, 664 (1957).
27. Lange, P. W., *Svensk Papperstid.*, **57**, 525 (1954).
28. Lange, P. W., *Svensk Papperstid.*, **57**, 533 (1954), Norsk Skogsind., **11**, 425 (1957).
29. Lange, P. W., in F. Bolam, ed., *Fundamentals of Papermaking Fibres*, Tech. Sect. Brit Paper and Board Makers' Assoc., Kenley (England) 1958, p. 147.
30. Lange, P. W., *Pulp Paper Mag.*, **59**, No. 10, 210 (1958).
30a. Liese, W., *Naturwiss*, **44**, 240 (1957); *Holz Roh Werkstoff*, **18**, 296 (1960).
31. Meier, H., *Holz Roh Werkstoff*, **13**, 323 (1955).
32. Meier, H., in E. Treiber, ed., *Die Chemie der Pflanzenzellwand*, Springer, Berlin 1957, p. 213.
33. Meier, H., *Svensk Papperstid.*, **62**, 687 (1959); *Holzforschung*, **13**, 177 (1959); *J. Polymer Sci.*, **51**, 11 (1961).
34. Meier, H., and S. Yllner, *Svensk Papperstid.*, **59**, 395 (1956).
35. Mühlethaler, K., *Histochemie*, **38**, 299 (1953).
36. Oppenheimer, H. R., *Palestine J. Botany*, Ser. **R 5**, 22 (1945).
37. Preston, R. D., and A. B. Wardrop, *Biochim. Biophys. Acta*, **3**, 585 (1949), **6**, 36 (1950).
38. Rånby, B. G., *Fine Structure and Reactions of Native Cellulose*, Diss., Uppsala (Sweden) 1952; *Svensk Papperstid.*, **55**, 115 (1952); and in F. Bolam, ed., *Fundamentals of Papermaking Fibres*, Tech. Sect. Brit. Paper and Board Makers' Assoc., Kenley (England) 1958, p. 55.
39. Svensson, A. Å., *Arkiv Kemi*, **10**, 239 (1956).
40. Treiber, E., in E. Treiber, ed., *Die Chemie der Pflanzenzellwand*, Springer, Berlin 1957, p. 167.
41. Wardrop, A. B., *Tappi*, **40**, 225 (1957).
42. Wardrop, A. B., and H. E. Dadswell, *Australian J. Sci. Res.*, **B 5**, 223 (1952).

4

WOOD CHEMISTRY

I. Chemical Composition of Wood

1. DEFINITIONS

Wood consists of *carbon, hydrogen* and *oxygen*. Neglecting small amounts of nitrogen, below 0.1 %, and the ash content, about 0.3 %, the elementary composition of dry wood substance is about 50 % C, 6 % H and 44 % O, with astonishingly small variations with species, including both softwoods and hardwoods. This corresponds to an empirical formula of about $C_{1.5}H_{2.1}O_{1.0}$. However, even with simple chemical reagents such as acids, alkalis, oxidants and organic solvents it is easily demonstrated that wood is no uniform substance but consists of many chemical components, varying in quantity with species, within the species, within the tree trunk and within the cell wall. In order to reach some sort of systematic order in describing the composition of wood, the components were classified according to available analytical methods, which will be further discussed in Chapter 20. This was necessary, since the exact nature of the components was not known, and in many cases is still not. However, the analytical concepts thus formed have lingered even in such cases where chemical concepts have emerged and constitute a better description, and a certain confusion has been unavoidable in cases where an originally analytical term has been applied to a chemical compound. Such important terms as *cellulose, hemicelluloses* and *lignin,* which today, together with the minor categories of *extractives* and *mineral constituents,* are used to describe the wood composition, have varied in meaning during the last century of wood chemistry.

Cellulose was originally defined as a carbohydrate based on glucose and isomeric with starch (603), and present in all plant cells. This chemical definition, which virtually coincides with the present-day concept, was later often disregarded, and the term cellulose used for the more resistant part of the carbohydrates, as defined by various chemical reagents, sometimes with a prefix, such as Cross and Bevan cellulose, alphacellulose, etc. In most plant tissues non-cellulosic carbohydrates occur, which are similar in composition to cellulose but behave differently towards alkali and acids. The most frequent term for these is hemicellulose (708), today preferably designated hemicelluloses to mark their heterogeneity. To draw the boundaries between cellulose and hemicelluloses and hence their quantitative determination in the wood has been a difficult analytical problem, since the more resistant hemicelluloses remain in the cellulose residue even at isolation conditions so severe that cellulose degradation products appear in the removed hemicellulose fraction. It serves to underline the confusion that the term hemicellulose is still frequently used in the viscose industry to describe the alkali solubles, whether cellulose degradation products or hemicelluloses in the modern terminology of wood chemistry. A further difficulty is that glucose is a component not only in the cellulose but also of some hemicelluloses, the glucomannan, and still worse, might in some species exist even as a non-cellulosic homopolymer glucan. Among the hemicelluloses there are also such components as methyl-uronic acids, which are not carbohydrates in the strict sense of the term, but are still counted as such. The total carbohydrate fraction is defined as the *holocellulose*, although the practical methods of isolation give slightly different yields and never quite reach the theoretical yield at theoretical purity, and these holocellulose preparations thus have to be further defined by a prefix.

The third category of compounds, the lignin, was originally designed to mean the compounds removed by an oxidative mixture of nitric acid and potassium chlorate (709). Since this treatment also removes some hemicelluloses, the definition has had to be changed, which was easier since it had become clear that the main component removed was of aromatic structure, in contrast to the carbohydrates. That small quantities of low-molecular compounds were also aromatic was no real difficulty, since these compounds can be extracted with organic solvents. However, a small amount of lignin has a low enough molecular weight to be extractable with ethanol, and for some hardwoods there are compounds of still lower molecular weight, which are structurally closely related to lignin.

Thus, the terms used are still somewhat undefined, but will be used in the following sense in this book:

Cellulose, the linear polysaccharide, of sufficient chain length to be insoluble in water or dilute alkali and acids at room temperature, containing only anhydroglucose units linked together with $1:4$-β-glucosidic bonds and possessing a well-ordered structure.

Hemicelluloses, the non-cellulosic polysaccharides of wood, including the related substances, such as uronic acids, etc., and their substituents.

Lignin, the aromatic polymer of wood, consisting of four or more substituted phenylpropane monomers per molecule.

Extractives, the low-molecular compounds of various types, extractable from the wood with water or organic solvents, excluding components which by definition belong to the hemicelluloses or lignin.

The fibrous substance isolated from wood will invariably be called *pulp*, and the term cellulose in this sense is considered a misuse. The analytical concepts will be reserved for the products as defined by the analysis, thus *alphacellulose* is the portion of a pulp resistant to strong lye under the conditions of the alphacellulose analysis, and is by no means equivalent to the chemical concept of cellulose. Other terms of more recent date which have partly turned out to be misnomers are *polyuronides, mannan, galactan, xylan* and *arabinan*, as in most cases there are no homopolymers of these types. They are therefore used mainly to express the quantity of anhydromonose units present, disregarding their combinations in the hemicelluloses. The corresponding chemical terms are *glucomannan acetate, arabinogalactan, 4-O-methylglucuronoxylan acetate* and *4-O-methyl-glucuronoarabinoxylan*. In view of the length of the last-mentioned terms it may be excusable to use the term xylan, especially as the arabinose and acetate substituents easily disappear on chemical treatment. The term *pentosan* includes both anhydroxylose and anhydroarabinose units, as contrasted to *hexosans*, composed of hexose monomers.

2. COMPOSITION

There is not much data available on the composition of wood in terms of the chemical components defined above. A large amount of analytical material exists describing ash, extractives, lignin, uronic acid and pentosan content, cf. Tables 4.1–2 (132, 826). Although these data allow an estimation of the total carbohydrate fraction and its proportions of pentosans and hexosans, and have been useful in the evaluation of various pulpwood species, they do not tell how much of the hexosans is cellulose. The estimation of the cellulose content is fairly intricate, as discussed in the previous section, and is usually carried out as a holocellulose preparation by a mild lignin removal, subsequent preparation of alphacellulose through a cold alkali extraction of the holocellulose, and by finally subjecting the alphacellulose to a chromatographic analysis. The alphacellulose yield is then corrected for non-glucose constituents and often also for glucose of glucomannan origin, assuming a certain proportion of glucose to mannose in the residual glucomannan. This has been done for thirteen North-American wood species, together with complete analysis of the other wood components, Table 4.3 (764), and studies on Scandinavian wood species (267, 392, 403, 472, 751) have been compiled in a similar manner in Table 4.4. Analysis of two cereal straws are shown for comparison in Table 4.5 (765). In agreement with the previous tables, it is observed that the pentosan content is higher and the lignin content lower in the hardwoods than in the softwoods. The variations between the species within these two groups are appreciable, especially for the hardwoods. Calculated on extractive-free dry wood, average values would be for softwoods about 43% cellulose, 28% hemicelluloses and 29% lignin, and for hardwoods about 43% cellulose, 35% hemicelluloses and 22% lignin. Of the hemicelluloses, *arabinogalactan* occurs in small amounts, 1–3%, in all species, *glucomannan* in small amounts, about 3%, in hardwoods, *(galacto-)glucomannan acetate* in large quantities in softwoods, about 15–20%, *4-O-methylglucuronoarabinoxylan*, about 10%, in softwoods and the corresponding *4-O-methylglucuronoxylan acetate* in very large amounts, 20–35%, in hardwoods. The substituted xylans are therefore next to cellulose the most important carbohydrate. The exact nature of the non-cellulosic *glucan*, indicated for hardwoods, in amounts of 0–3%, remains to be investigated. In some cases it is likely to be starch, in other

Table 4.1. Chemical analysis of some North-American wood species (unextracted, dry wood basis) (826)

Species	Ash content, %	Extractives, %, in Alcohol– benzene	Ethyl ether	1% NaOH	Hot water	Lignin content, %	Pento- sans, %
Western White pine							
Pinus monticola	0.3	8.3	5.6	15.6	3.7	25.4	7.9
Red pine							
Pinus resinosa	—	3.5	2.5	13.4	4.4	26.2	10.0
Jack pine							
Pinus banksiana	0.3	3.7	2.3	11.2	2.9	26.7	9.7
Slash pine							
Pinus elliottii	0.2	2.6	2.0	9.9	2.5	28.0	8.6
Lodgepole pine							
Pinus contorta v. *latifolia*	0.2	3.5	2.3	12.6	3.6	25.0	9.2
Tamarack							
Larix laricina	0.3	2.0	0.7	11.5	4.8	26.4	8.3
Western larch							
Larix occidentalis	0.4	1.4	0.4	13.4	4.9	26.8	7.8
Engelmann spruce							
Picea engelmannii	0.2	2.8	1.4	12.2	3.7	26.3	9.2
Douglas fir							
Pseudotsuga taxifolia	0.2	4.4	1.2	15.1	5.6	27.2	6.8
Western hemlock							
Tsuga heterophylla	0.3	1.6	0.8	9.2	0.4	27.8	9.2
Mountain hemlock							
Tsuga mertensiana	0.5	4.6	1.0	11.6	4.8	27.0	7.0
Noble fir							
Abies nobilis	0.4	2.7	0.6	9.6	2.3	29.3	9.0
Trembling aspen							
Populus tremuloides	—	2.9	1.1	18.0	2.1	19.3	18.8
Yellow birch							
Betula lutea	0.8	2.6	0.8	15.4	2.7	22.7	22.6
White birch							
Betula papyrifera	0.4	2.8	1.3	14.1	1.5	20.0	22.6
Beech							
Fagus grandifolia	0.5	1.8	0.7	14.7	1.5	21.0	20.2
Chestnut oak							
Quercus montana	0.4	4.7	0.6	21.1	7.2	24.3	19.2
White elm							
Ulmus americana	0.4	2.0	0.5	14.3	1.6	20.5	16.2
Red maple							
Acer rubrum	0.7	2.5	0.8	17.9	4.4	22.8	17.1
Basswood							
Tilia glabra	0.7	4.1	2.1	19.9	2.4	20.0	16.6

cases an artefact derived from the analytical procedure. The determination of Klason lignin tends to give too low values with hardwoods, and a quantity corresponding to the acid-soluble lignin will in the calculations show up as 'non-cellulosic glucan'. *Arabinogalactans* are present in particularly

Table 4.2. Chemical analysis of some Canadian wood species (unextracted, dry wood basis) (132)

Species	Ash content, %	Extractives, %, in Ethyl ether	Extractives, %, in 1% NaOH	Extractives, %, in Hot water	Extractives, %, in Cold water	Acetyl, %	Methoxyl, %	Lignin, %	Pentosans, %	Uronic acid anhydride, %
Balsam fir										
Abies balsamea	0.4	1.8	13.4	3.6	2.7	1.5	5.47	27.7	7.0	3.8
White spruce										
Picea glauca	0.2	2.1	12.5	2.2	1.4	1.1	5.07	27.0	8.0	4.5
Black spruce										
Picea mariana	0.2	1.0	12.3	2.5	1.4	1.1	5.07	27.3	7.6	3.7
Jack pine										
Pinus banksiana	0.2	4.3	16.3	3.7	2.2	1.1	4.97	27.4	10.1	3.7
White pine										
Pinus strobus	0.2	5.9	19.1	4.4	3.3	1.1	5.17	25.6	5.8	3.3
Eastern hemlock										
Tsuga canadensis	0.3	0.7	13.7	3.4	2.2	1.3	5.67	29.6	5.1	3.5
White birch										
Betula papyrifera	0.3	2.4	20.1	2.7	2.0	4.9	5.93	18.5	22.0	4.9
Trembling aspen										
Populus tremuloides	0.4	1.9	19.3	2.8	1.5	3.4	5.47	18.1	17.2	5.0

large amounts in *Juniperus* and *Larix* species, as also seen from Table 4.6 (267), describing the polysaccharide composition of a large number of species. As often pointed out (e.g. 764), galactose values were earlier difficult to determine accurately in the presence of glucose, and therefore the galactan figures especially vary for different investigators. Another reason for this is that some of the galactan belongs to the water-soluble polysaccharide fraction and will thus vary according to the wood sample preparation. A comparison of the non-glucose polysaccharide constituents of a large number of species, also including annual ones, is given in Table 4.7 (649). In most of the latter cellulose must be more dominant than in wood, especially considering the lower lignin content of these substances.

The largest variations in wood composition are between species. Comparatively small variations occur within the species and within the tree. Table 2.6 (591) demonstrated this for sprucewood, grown at varying latitudes, Tables 4.8–9 (267, 539) for earlywood and latewood and Table 4.10 (663) for sapwood and heartwood. For earlywood a somewhat high lignin content was found as compared to latewood, Table 4.11 (32), presumably because the middle lamella forms a larger proportion of the total substance in earlywood. But at reaction wood there are more definite changes in the chemical composition, *compression* wood giving an enormous increase in lignin and a corresponding decrease in cellulose and glucomannan as compared to normal wood (271), and *tension* wood giving the opposite effect (130, 813), Table 4.12 (130, 271, 813). The

Table 4.3. Chemical composition of some North-American wood species (extractive-free wood basis) (764)

Species	Analysis									Estimation					Gross composition		
	Ash %	Lignin %	Acetyl %	Uronic acid anhydride %	Glucan %	Galactan %	Mannan %	Araban %	Xylan %	Cellulose %	Non-cellulosic glucan? %	Gluco-mannan (acetate) %	Arabino-galactan %	4-O-methyl-glucurono (arabino) xylan (acetate) %	Cellulose %	Hemicelluloses %	Lignin %
Trembling aspen *Populus tremuloides*	0.2	16.3	3.4	3.3	57.3	0.8	2.3	0.4	16.0	53	3	4	1	23	53	31	16
White elm *Ulmus americana*	0.3	23.6	3.9	3.6	53.2	0.9	2.4	0.6	11.5	49	2	4	2	19	49	27	24
Beech *Fagus grandifolia*	0.4	22.1	3.9	4.8	47.5	1.2	2.1	0.5	17.5	42	4	4	2	25	42	36	22
White birch *Betula papyrifera*	0.2	18.9	4.4	4.6	44.7	0.6	1.5	0.5	24.6	41	2	3	1	34	41	40	19
Yellow birch *Betula lutea*	0.3	21.3	3.3	4.2	46.7	0.9	3.6	0.6	20.1	40	3	7	1	28	40	39	21
Red maple *Acer rubrum*	0.2	24.0	3.8	3.5	46.6	0.6	3.5	0.5	17.3	41	2	7	1	25	41	35	24
Sugar maple *Acer saccharum*	0.3	22.7	2.9	4.4	51.7	—	2.3	0.8	14.8	—	—	4	1	22	—	—	—
Hardwoods, average										45	3	5	1	25	45	34	21
Balsam fir *Abies balsamea*	0.2	29.4	1.5	3.4	46.8	1.0	12.4	0.5	4.8	44	0	18	1	8	44	27	29
Eastern white cedar *Thuja occidentalis*	0.2	30.7	1.1	4.2	45.2	1.5	8.3	1.3	7.5	44	0	11	2	12	44	25	31
Eastern hemlock *Tsuga canadensis*	0.2	32.5	1.7	3.3	45.3	1.2	11.2	0.6	4.0	42	0	17	1	7	42	26	33
Jack pine *Pinus banksiana*	0.2	28.6	1.2	3.9	45.6	1.4	10.6	1.4	7.1	41	0	16	2	12	41	30	29
White spruce *Picea glauca*	0.3	27.1	1.3	3.6	46.5	1.2	11.6	1.6	6.8	44	0	17	2	10	44	29	27
Tamarack *Larix laricina*	0.2	28.6	1.5	2.9	46.1	2.3	13.1	1.0	4.3	43	0	18	3	7	43	28	29
Softwoods, average										43	0	16	2	9	43	28	29

Table 4.4. Chemical composition of three Scandinavian wood species. Compiled from data in (267, 392, 403, 472, 751)

	Analysis (unextracted dry wood basis)											Estimation (extractive-free wood basis)					Gross composition		
Species	Ash, %	Extractives,* %	Protein and undet., %	Lignin, %	Acetyl, %	Uronic acid anhydride, %	Glucan, %	Galactan, %	Mannan, %	Araban, %	Xylan, %	Cellulose, %	Non-cellulosic glucan? (acetate), %	Glucomannan (acetate), %	Arabinogalactan, %	4-O-methyl-glucurono (arabino) xylan (acetate), %	Cellulose, %	Hemicelluloses, %	Lignin, %
Spruce Picea abies	0.4	1.8	1.3	28.6	1.4	2.5	44.3	1.9	10.3	0.5	7.6	43	0	15	2	10	43	27	29
Pine Pinus silvestris	0.4	5.3	1.2	27.8	1.6	2.4	44.8	1.3	7.6	0.6	7.2	44	0	14	2	10	44	26	29
Birch Betula verrucosa	0.3	3.1	2.5	19.5	4.8	5.9	37.5	1.0	0.5	0.5	24.6	40	0	1	1	37	40	39	21

* Ethanol–benzene.

Table 4.5. Chemical composition of two cereal straws (765)

	Analysis (extractive-free dry basis)									Estimation (extractive-free basis)					Gross composition		
Species	Ash, %	Lignin, %	Acetyl, %	Uronic acid anhydride, %	Glucan, %	Galactan, %	Mannan, %	Araban, %	Xylan, %	Cellulose, %	Non-cellulosic glucan? %	Glucomannan, %	Arabinogalactan, %	4-O-methyl-glucurono-xylan (acetate), %	Cellulose, %	Hemicelluloses, %	Lignin, %
Cornstalks Zea mays	1.2	14.0	4.6	5.6	47.6	1.0	0	2.8	23.3	43	5	0	1	36	43	43	14
Wheat straw Triticum sativum	1.6	22.0	2.9	2.7	44.8	0.9	0	2.0	22.6	42	4	0	1	30	42	36	22

96

Table 4.6. Polysaccharide composition of some European wood species (relative amounts, excluding uronic acid and acetyl) (267)

Species		Glucose, %	Galactose, %	Mannose, %	Arabinose, %	Xylose, %
Scandinavian spruce	Picea abies	65.5	6.0	16.0	3.5	9.0
Scots pine	Pinus silvestris	65.0	6.0	12.5	3.5	13.0
Juniper	Juniperus communis	61.0	13.3	14.0	0.5	11.0
Siberian larch	Larix sibirica	63.0	17.5	7.5	3.0	9.0
Aspen	Populus tremula	64.5	1.5	3.0	1.0	30.0
Poplar	Populus balsamifera	68.0	3.5	2.5	2.5	23.5
Birch	Betula verrucosa	58.5	1.5	0.5	0.5	39.0
Birch	Betula pubescens	55.0	1.0	2.5	2.5	39.0
Hazel	Corylus avellana	69.5	2.0	2.0	2.0	24.5
Basswood	Tilia cordata	58.5	1.5	3.5	2.0	34.5
Maple	Acer platanoides	60.5	2.0	4.0	1.0	32.5
Beech	Fagus silvatica	65.0	4.0	1.5	1.5	28.0
Oak	Quercus robur	68.5	2.5	2.0	1.0	26.0
Ash	Fraxinus excelsior	60.0	3.0	2.5	2.5	32.0
Willow	Salix alba	74.0	3.0	2.5	1.0	19.5
Elm	Ulmus scabra	68.5	2.5	2.0	1.0	26.0
Alder	Alnus incana	67.0	3.5	1.5	1.0	27.0
Alder	Alnus glutinosa	73.5	2.5	3.5	1.0	19.5
Bird-cherry	Prunus padus	65.5	2.5	2.5	1.0	28.5
Rowan-tree	Sorbus aucuparia	66.5	1.5	2.5	2.0	27.8

Table 4.7. Non-glucan carbohydrates for some wood and herbaceous species (based on dry wood or herb substance) (649)

Species		Galactose, %	Mannose, %	Arabinose, %	Xylose, %
Scandinavian spruce	Picea abies	1.5	10.5	1.6	4.5
Scots pine	Pinus silvestris	1.8	11.4	1.4	6.2
Loblolly pine	Pinus taeda	1.7	10.2	1.0	6.5
European beech	Fagus silvatica	0.9	1.3	0.8	11.3
European poplar	Populus alba	0.5	1.4	0.6	13.2
European birch	Betula verrucosa	0.7	0.8	0.3	17.2
European willow	Salix alba	1.3	1.4	0.4	11.3
Chestnut	Castanea sativa	0.8	1.0	0.6	9.7
Australian gumwood	Eucalyptus globulus	1.3	0.8	0.6	9.4
Mangrove	Xylocarpus sp.	0.7	1.0	2.1	12.3
Red gum	Liquidambar styraciflua	0.7	1.0	0.1	14.2
Bamboo	Phyllostachys puberula	0.5	0.0	1.2	10.9
Wheat	Triticum vulgare	0.7	0.2	2.3	17.0
Flax	Linum usitatissimum	2.3	1.8	0.8	9.2
Hemp	Cannabis sativa	2.3	5.8	1.0	1.2
Ramie	Boehmeria nivea	0.9	1.0	0.3	0.3
Rice	Oryza sativa	1.4	0.0	2.9	14.2
Alpha grass	Stipa tenacissima	0.8	0.0	2.6	16.0
Bagasse	Saccharum officinarum	0.5	0.0	1.7	16.5

Table 4.8. Carbohydrate composition of spruce and pine, earlywood and latewood (267)

Species		Glucose, %	Galactose, %	Mannose, %	Arabinose, %	Xylose, %
Picea abies	Earlywood	64.5	4.5	17.0	3.0	11.0
	Latewood	62.0	8.0	19.5	2.0	8.5
Pinus silvestris	Earlywood	63.5	4.0	19.0	3.5	10.0
	Latewood	64.5	5.5	17.5	3.0	9.5

Table 4.9. Carbohydrate composition of spruce (*Picea abies*), earlywood and latewood (539)

	Cellulose, %	Glucomannan, %	Glucurono-arabinoxylan, %	Galactan and arabinan, %
Earlywood	63	20	15	2
Latewood	60	24	13	3

Table 4.10. Analysis of heartwood and sapwood of some North-American wood species (663)

Species		Ash, %	Ether extract, %	Lignin, %	Pentosans, %
White pine	Sapwood	0.2	5.5	26.5	9.3
	Heartwood	0.4	3.6	26.1	8.6
Yellow cedar	Sapwood	0.3	1.0	29.0	8.5
	Heartwood	0.2	1.3	28.7	8.7
White birch	Sapwood	0.3	0.5	24.7	21.4
	Heartwood	0.4	0.8	24.6	20.4
Yellow poplar	Sapwood	0.5	0.3	23.1	18.4
	Heartwood	0.4	0.4	22.2	18.5

Table 4.11. Analysis of earlywood and latewood of various wood species (32)

Species	Type of wood		Lignin, %	Pentosans, %
Douglas fir	Heartwood,	earlywood	32.6	12.0
		latewood	29.2	9.9
Western white pine	Heartwood,	earlywood	26.3	10.0
		latewood	25.3	9.8
Loblolly pine	Sapwood,	earlywood	28.1	11.6
		latewood	26.8	11.1
	Heartwood,	earlywood	26.8	12.8
		latewood	24.2	12.1
Red alder	Heartwood,	earlywood	24.7	22.4
		latewood	23.0	23.4
White ash	Sapwood,	earlywood	25.6	20.3
		latewood	23.5	19.4
Average		Earlywood	27.3	14.8
		Latewood	25.3	14.3

Table 4.12. Chemical composition of reaction woods

Ref.	Species	Type of wood	Cellulose, %	Hemicelluloses, % Gluco-mannan	Glucu-rono-xylan	Galac-tans	Total	Lignin, %	Minor compo-nents, %
271	*Picea abies*	Normal	42				26	28	4
		Compression	27				30	38	5
86	*Picea abies*	Normal	41	17	10	2	29	27	3
		Compression	35	8	8	11	27	39	
813	*Pinus radiata*	Normal			10			24	
		Compression			7			34	
266	*Betula*	Normal	40	3	30	2	35	*ca.* 20	4
	verrucosa	Tension	55	1	15	8	24	*ca.* 17	4
393	*Populus*	Normal	41		36			23	
	canadensis	Tension	49		29			22	
130	*Populus*	Normal	46		20		24	18	4
	tremuloides	Tension	52		19		22	17	4
130	*Ulmus*	Normal	38		19		24	29	4
	americana	Tension	42		18		22	27	4
813	*Eucalyptus*	Normal			18			22	
	regnans	Tension			12			16	
813	*Eucalyptus*	Normal			17			21	
	nitens	Tension			11			15	
813	*Eucalyptus*	Normal	44		20			25	
	goniocalyx	Tension	57		11			10	
715	*Eucalyptus*	Side	44		27	1.5		23	
	goniocalyx	Tension	57		17	7.4		14	
		Opposite	37		31	2.5		26	

wood opposite to the reaction woods has a composition deviating from that of normal wood in an opposite manner to that of the reaction wood. A new type of hemicellulose, a *galacturonogalactan* (cf. Chapter 4.III), has been found in the reaction wood in appreciable quantities (86). These changes, together with the corresponding changes in fiber structure, greatly influence the result of pulping and make reaction wood a less desirable raw material. The deposition of certain extractives in the heart-wood, such as pinosylvin in pines and taxifolin in Douglas fir, have a still greater influence on the pulping (acid sulfite process), cf. Section V of this chapter.

The chemical composition of the various parts of the fiber wall was dealt with previously in Chapter 3.III, Tables 3.1–2. The composition of outer and inner bark as compared to wood is shown in Table 4.13 (32) for black spruce and Table 4.14 (131) gives the analytical composition of bark from some Canadian wood species. The lignin content of bark is quite high, and most characteristic is the high proportion of compounds extractable with organic solvents and water. Obviously, the cellulose content is quite low and bark is unsuitable as a pulping raw material. A large proportion of the bark is left undissolved after cooking, especially in the acid sulfite process, and has to be removed in screening, cleaning

Table 4.13. Analysis of black spruce fractions unextracted (dry basis) (32)

	Ash, %	Protein, %	Pento-sans, %	Uronic acid anhydride, %	Methoxyl, %	Lignin, %	Tannin, %
Outer bark	1.2	2.1	11.8	8.6	4.0	33.9	1.9
Inner bark	3.2	3.8	12.0	10.0	2.2	6.6	7.6
Cambium	3.6	7.1	6.3	4.6	0.7	1.8	0
Young sapwood	0.4	1.7	8.1	3.8	4.7	24.9	0
Sapwood	0.3	0.3	12.0	3.7	4.9	26.3	0
Heartwood	0.3	0.4	12.5	3.9	4.8	26.1	0

Table 4.14. Analysis of bark from some Canadian wood species (unextracted, dry basis) (131)

				Extractives			Sum of last two columns, %
Species	Ash content, %	Ethyl ether, %	Hot water, %	Successive extractions, %*	Successive extractions, %†	Lignin, %	
Balsam fir	2.0	23.6	26.7	36.2	58.7	20.6	79.3
Black spruce	2.4	25.5	32.3	38.7	58.8	16.7	75.5
White spruce	3.1	22.9	41.8	47.7	70.7	14.3	85.0
Douglas fir	0.9	34.4	29.2	42.9	68.3	26.1	94.4
Eastern hemlock	1.0	23.9	30.0	40.2	59.7	31.5	91.2
Western red cedar	0.9	6.3	6.4	11.5	51.3	36.7	88.0

* Ethanol: benzene, ethanol, hot water.
† Ethanol: benzene, ethanol, hot water, 1% NaOH.

and bleaching operations. Another connection between the bark components and the pulping processes is the tannin-damage occurring when tannins of unbarked, water-driven logs diffuse from the bark into the wood. This causes discoloration and in sulfite pulping also lignin condensation and shives in the unbleached pulp. The chemistry of bark is otherwise outside the scope of this book and reference is made to an exhaustive literature review on bark and its utilization (521).

II. Cellulose

1. FORMATION AND LOCATION IN THE CELL WALL

The net reaction for the formation of a hexose molecule from carbon dioxide and water is $6\,CO_2 + 6\,H_2O \longrightarrow C_6H_{12}O_6 + 6\,O_2$. The complicated mechanism behind this reaction, the *photosynthesis* of carbohydrates, which takes place in the leaves and needles of the tree, involves the following elements and mechanism (69, 626, 732). The chloroplast of the leaves appears to be laminar, with very thin layers of chlorophyll alternating with thicker layers of proteins and lipoproteins, the latter probably acting as a semi-conducting material. Thus a biological photoelectric battery exists,

100

which by absorption of light quanta creates mobile charges to form a potential. On one side of this battery, the photolysis of water and formation of oxygen takes place, possibly over hydrogen peroxide, on the other side certain components, such as thioctic (α-lipoic) acid, are reduced to reductants which in turn are capable of producing *adenosine triphosphate* (ATP), a reductant which is a vital component in the production of carbohydrates from carbon dioxide. The essential steps involved in that conversion are (1) the carboxylation of a sugar phosphate, *ribulose diphosphate*, to give two three-carbon bodies, probably phosphoglycerate, (2) reduction of the phosphoglycerate by more ATP, (3) rearrangement of most of the reaction product, phosphoglyceraldehyde, to yield more ribulose diphosphate with the aid of more ATP, with some of the sugar (hexose, pentose and triose) phosphates being withdrawn from the system as end products, as shown in Figure 4.1 (69) and by the carbon balance shown below:

$$3\ C_5 + 3\ CO_2 \xrightarrow{\ 3\ ATP\ } 6\ PGA\ (phosphoglycerate)$$
$$6\ PGA + 12\ [H] \xrightarrow{\ 6\ ATP\ } 6\ C_3$$
$$2\ C_3 \longrightarrow C_6$$
$$C_6 + 2\ C_3 \longrightarrow C_5 + C_7$$
$$C_5 + C_3 \longrightarrow 2\ C_5$$

$$12\ [H] + 3\ CO_2 \xrightarrow{\ 9\ ATP\ } C_3$$

The sugars formed appear as *starch* (as well as *saccharose, sugar alcohols*

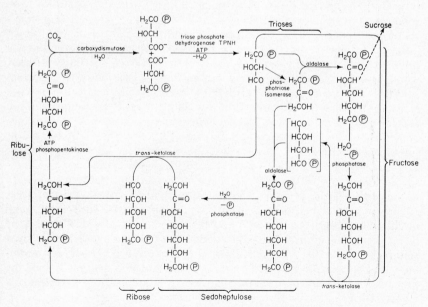

Fig. 4.1. Photosynthesis of carbohydrates (Calvin)

and *glucosides*) which is stored in the parenchymatic cells and used in the metabolism of the tree. *Cellulose* is formed at the very place it is deposited, at the interface between the protoplast and the cell wall of the living cells, whereas there is a possiblity that the *hemicelluloses* may diffuse short distances in the cell wall. The building stones in the polymerization do not seem to be the respective monoses but rather their phosphates, which in turn originate from smaller molecules, which at least partly have formed by degradation of the previously formed carbohydrates (e.g. 102, 235, 338, 560).

The deposition of the cellulose molecules occurs in an ordered structure, the elementary fibril, which will be further dealt with in a subsequent subsection (3B). The location of these fibrils in the cell wall was described in Chapter 3.II–III, showing that cellulose occurs in all the layers of the wall, but is concentrated in the main secondary wall, probably with increasing concentration of cellulose towards the lumen of that layer and more hemicelluloses located in the outer parts of it.

2. ISOLATION

The isolation of cellulose, which is simple in the case of some plant products, where it occurs in a fairly pure form, is rather complicated in the case of wood. It is not possible to extract cellulose from the wood in unchanged form and the usual procedure is to carry out a selective delignification followed by an extraction of the hemicelluloses, to leave a more or less pure and undegraded residue of cellulose. There is no ideal procedure, as there are always some small losses and degradation of the cellulose, and never a complete separation from the most resistant hemicelluloses. The isolation of cellulose has both analytical and industrial interest. In order to investigate the properties of native cellulose and the cellulose content of the wood, resin is extracted from the finely divided wood by organic solvents, lignin removed by oxidation with chlorine, acidified chlorite or chlorine dioxide, and finally the hemicelluloses are extracted by alkali (cf. Section III of this chapter). The remaining cellulose preparation is then analyzed by chromatography to determine the amount of hemicellulose impurities and the true cellulose content of the wood subsequently calculated, as also described in Section I.2 of this chapter. The cellulose preparation may be subsequently studied by microscopical methods to describe its super-molecular structure and location in the cell wall, and by physico-chemical methods to investigate the molecular weight distribution as well as the possible presence of foreign functional groups, etc. Another method of isolation of wood cellulose is by direct nitration of the wood and extraction of the cellulose nitrate by a suitable solvent (108, 704, 779). Such preparations are likewise contaminated by hemicelluloses (in the nitrate form) but less degraded than the preparations previously described, and have therefore been preferred for investigations of the chain length distribution.

The industrial preparation methods are those known as pulping processes, which are the main subject of this book. They involve both pressure treatments with chemicals known as cooking, and bleaching and purification operations at atmospheric pressure. These processes are carried out with less expensive chemicals than those involved in the previously described isolation methods, but on the other hand tend to degrade the cellulose more severely and lose more of it. The purity obtained also depends on the methods and conditions chosen and the desired product. In some cases the purity of the cellulose is about 99%, in others the composition of the product approaches that of wood. To avoid confusion with the chemical concept of cellulose, all these industrial products should be called *pulps*.

3. STRUCTURE

A. Molecular constitution

As defined in the previous Section I, cellulose is the linear and largely crystalline or paracrystalline glucan found in most vegetable and some animal tissues. The qualitative relationship between cellulose and glucose was early recognized (91), but it was not until a hundred years later that the nearly quantitative yield of glucose on the acid hydrolysis of cellulose was established (567, 824), according to the reaction

$$(C_6H_{10}O_5)_n + n\ H_2O \longrightarrow n\ C_6H_{12}O_6$$

The manner of coupling was examined by determining the number and nature of the free hydroxyl groups of cellulose. Reaction with metallic sodium in liquid ammonia (697, 704) as well as acetylation (324, 597) and methylation (156, 204, 383, 800) showed that there are three hydroxyl groups capable of reaction. Acid hydrolysis of the methyl cellulose gave nearly quantitative yields of 2,3,6-trimethylglucose (384), together with small quantities of 2,3,4,6-tetramethylglucose (314), indicating that in practically the entire molecule the free hydroxyls are in the 2-, 3- and 6-position, whereas positions 1, 4 and 5 are blocked but for the end monomers, where the 4-hydroxyl groups are also present.

On acetylation and acetolysis of cellulose, a crystalline octaacetate of the disaccharide cellobiose is obtained (617, 727, 838). After hydrolysis of the acetate, cellobiose is obtained, which can be further hydrolyzed to two molecules of glucose. Hydrolysis of the cellobiose can also be achieved by the enzyme emulsin, proving it to be a glucosyl-β-glucoside. Further characterization of the cellobiose (206, 313) showed its exact constitution as 4-O-glucopyranosyl-β-D-glucopyranoside. After establishing the same type of linkages in the polymer-homologous series of cellotriose (78, 206, 312, 382, 598), cellotetraose (206), cellopentaose (747), cellohexaose (157) and celloheptaose, all obtained by acetolysis of cellulose and subsequent hydrolysis, it was fairly well proven that the cellulose molecules contained one type only of linkages, namely 1,4-β-D-glucosidic bonds, between the anhydroglucose monomers, Figure 4.2. That not even a few linkages of different type are present, was ascertained from studies on the kinetics of the hydrolysis and acetolysis of cellulose (205). More recently, kinetical studies on the heterogeneous as well as homogeneous acid hydrolysis of cellulose have again brought about a discussion on the possible presence of a few linkages of different type in the cellulose molecule, as will be discussed in a subsequent section. It has also been suggested, that especially in wood cellulose there are occasional monomers of non-glucose type, especially mannose (2), but it is now generally agreed and rather convincingly proven (645), that cellulose in its unmodified, native state consists of linear molecules of anhydroglucose monomers only, linked in the manner shown by the previous figure. The question of the average molecular weight and the molecular weight distribution remains to be discussed, as well as the super-molecular structure of cellulose. In connection with the latter, the question arises in which conformation the cellulose chain appears in the fiber wall and in molecular solution, since it seems possible that there are several conformations at about the same energy level.

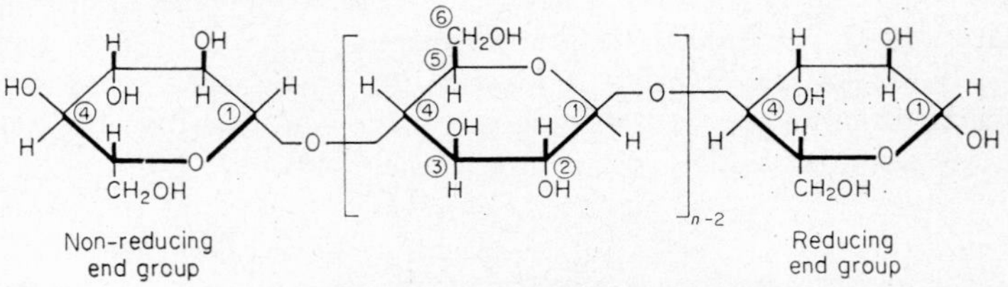

Non-reducing end group

Reducing end group

Fig. 4.2. Molecular structure of cellulose, schematic

In the determination of the average molecular weight of cellulose, the usual methods for polymers have been applied, such as end-group determinations (e.g. 311, 575), osmometry (e.g. 158, 417), light scattering measurements (160), ultracentrifugation (e.g. 454, 757), and above all the convenient viscometric determinations (e.g. 374, 453, 744). The aldehydic end-group determinations give too low values because of the presence of a few similar groups along the chains. The osmometric methods give *number* average molecular weights,

$$\overline{M_n} = \frac{\Sigma n_i . M_i}{\Sigma n_i}$$

light scattering methods the *weight* average,

$$\overline{M_w} = \frac{\Sigma n_i . M_i^2}{\Sigma n_i . M_i}$$

and ultracentrifugation the *weight* or Z average,

$$\overline{M_z} = \frac{\Sigma n_i . M_i^3}{\Sigma n_i . M_i^2}$$

whereas the viscometric methods give an average

$$\overline{M_\eta} = \frac{\Sigma n_i . M_i^{\alpha+1}}{\Sigma n_i . M_i}$$

which is not far from the weight average (α being close to 1).

104

In the viscometric methods, the *intrinsic viscosity*, $[\eta]$, is determined by measuring the specific viscosity of the sample at several, low concentrations (0.02–0.10 g/dl) and extrapolating to zero concentration. The rate of shear in the determination will affect even intrinsic viscosity in particularly high-molecular samples, and a standardized rate of shear, 500 sec.$^{-1}$, is preferably used (766). The average molecular weight is calculated according to the equation

$$[\eta] = K_m . M^a \quad (370, 453, 749)$$

where K_m and a are constants which vary for varying solvents and cellulose derivatives. Table 4.15 (319, 634) gives the constants of this equation for various cellulose preparations and solvents, as obtained by comparing the viscometric measurements with ultracentrifugation data. The exponent a is close to 1 in most cases, especially for cellulose trinitrate in acetone or ethyl acetate, which are also for other reasons the most preferred combinations. It is interesting to note, that according to theory (cf. 786), chain molecules with unrestricted rotation (a random coil) should give an a value of 0.5, whereas stiff, rod-like molecules should give 1.5–2.0, which shows that cellulose molecules in solution display a fairly low flexibility, although they are far from being rod-like.

Table 4.15. Parameters in the modified Staudinger equation, $[\eta] = K_m \overline{M}_v^a$ for cellulose and cellulose derivatives (Mark–Houwink)

Polymer	Solvent	$K_m.10^5$	a	Method	Ref.
Cellulose	Cuoxam	6.8	0.9	SD	(530)
	Cuoxen	9.8	0.9	SD	(530)
	Cuoxen	13.3	0.90	SD	(380)
	Cuoxen	29.0	0.80	OS	(802)
	Cadoxen	56.0	0.75	SD	(319)
	Cadoxen	36.0	0.77	LS	(319)
	EWNN	4.0	1.01	SD	(127)
Cellulose acetate	Acetone	9.0	0.90	SD	(624)
Cellulose trinitrate	Acetone	17.0	1.00	SD	(364)
	Ethyl acetate	25.0	1.01	SD	(374, cf. 581)
	Ethyl lactate	12.2	0.92	SD	(380)

SD = sedimentation-diffusion, OS = osmometry, LS = light scattering.

It is vital to avoid degradation during the isolation of the cellulose, conversion to the nitrate and determination of the molecular weight. The isolation has proved to be a problem, especially for wood cellulose. Of the various methods tried, a direct nitration of the wood has been the most successful (779), whereas holocellulose preparation, for example, seems to involve some degradation (cf. below). Nitration is carried out in a mixture of nitric acid, phosphoric acid and phosphorus pentoxide (e.g. 29), or nitric acid and acetic anhydride (298), whereby practically no degradation occurs. Corrections of the viscosity measurements have to be made not only for kinetic energy losses (705), but also for variations in the degree of nitration (503). Since complete nitration is seldom reached, correction is preferably done to correspond to 13.6% N.

Because of the degradation during the isolation and conversion of cellulose to a soluble derivative when using less suitable methods, and not observing all precautions necessary at the viscometric determination, the data published on the molecular weight are somewhat contradictory. Table 4.16 (779) compiles some of these data for wood cellulose in terms of degree of polymerization (DP), or average number of anhydroglucose

Table 4.16. Degree of polymerization and polymolecularity of various types of wood cellulose, isolated by different methods (cf. 779)

Method of isolation	Wood species	Average DP	Number of maxima in frequency weight distribution	Ref.
Direct nitration of wood	Picea glauca	1,000	–	141
	Pinus taeda	2,400	2	561
	Tsuga heterophylla	2,000	–	561
	Picea mariana	2,200	–	341
	Picea abies	1,400	2	101
	Picea glauca	4,000	2	779
	Abies balsamea	4,400	2	779
	Tsuga canadensis	3,900	2	779
	Larix laricina	4,350	2	779
	Pinus banksiana	5,000	2	779
	Thuja occidentalis	4,250	2	779
	Populus tremuloides	2,900	1	341
	Eucalyptus regnans	2,400	2	175
	Betula papyrifera	3,000	2	781
	Betula papyrifera	5,500	1	779
	Populus tremuloides	5,000	1	779
	Fagus grandifolia	4,050	1	779
	Acer rubrum	4,450	1	779
Chlorination and alkaline extraction	Picea mariana	1,600	2	56
	Betula papyrifera	2,850	2	781
Oxidation with chlorite or chlorine dioxide	Pinus silvestris	1,500	–	745
	Pinus strobus	1,200	–	140
	Picea abies	1,200	–	506
	Picea abies	1,650	3	269
	Pinus silvestris	1,300	3	837
	Populus tremula	1,200	–	745
	Fagus silvatica	1,000	–	745
	Fraxinus, Fagus, Tilia	2,000	–	442
	Populus tremuloides	2,800	–	341
	Betula papyrifera	2,500	–	781
Extraction with cuoxam	Pinus silvestris	1,500	–	745
	Populus sp.	1,000	–	745
Sulfite pulping (mild)	Picea mariana	2,750	–	341
	Picea abies	3,100	2	107
	Picea abies	3,500	–	107
	Picea abies	3,600	–	107
	Picea abies	3,300	2	707

Table 4.17. Degree of polymerization of cellulose from various sources, determined by identical methods of isolation and viscosimetry (779, 780)

Cotton	4,700
Flax	4,700
Hemp	4,700
Jute	4,700
Milkweed floss	5,800
Ramie	5,800
Kapok	3,300
Cornstalk	2,700
Wheat straw	3,000
White spruce	4,000
Balsam fir	4,400
Eastern hemlock	3,900
Tamarack	4 300
Jack pine	5,000
Eastern white cedar	4,200
White birch	5,500
Trembling aspen	5,000
Beech	4,000
Red maple	4,400

Table 4.17a. Degree of polymerization of cellulose from various sources, determined by identical methods of isolation and light scattering measurement (259a)

Material	Species	Cellulose $\overline{DP}_w$
Seed hairs	Coastland cotton, *Gossypium*, opened	9,400
	California cotton, *Gossypium*, opened	8,100
	California cotton, *Gossypium*, unopened	15,300
	Kapok, *Ceiba pentandra*	9,500
	Milkweed floss, *Asclepias syriaca*	8,000
Bast fibers	Flax, *Linum usitatissimum*, oil	7,100
	Flax, *Linum usitatissimum*, textile	8,800
	Hemp, *Cannabis sativa*	9,300
	Jute, *Corchorus capsularis*	8,600
	Ramie, *Boehmeria nivea*	10,800
Wood	Trembling aspen, *Populus tremuloides*	10,300
	White birch, *Betula papyrifera*	9,400
	Red maple, *Acer rubrum*	8,300
	Amabilis fir, *Abies amabilis*	7,500
	Jack pine, *Pinus banksiana*	7,900
	Engelmann spruce, *Picea engelmannii*	8,000
Bark	White birch, *Betula papyrifera*	7,500
	Amabilis fir, *Abies amabilis*	7,200
	Lodgepole pine, *Pinus contorta* v. *latifolia*	10,300
	Engelmann spruce, *Picea engelmannii*	7,100
	Gingko, *Gingko biloba*	8,800
Ancient plants	Cinnamon fern, *Osmunda cinnamonea*	8,300
	Psilotum nudum	2,300
	Equisetum arvense	2,400
	Lycopodium clavatum	4,400

monomers per molecule. Obviously, a mild sulfite pulping, or especially direct nitration of the wood, gives the least degraded cellulose samples (108). The more recent data employing the latter technique (779) gives an average DP of about 4,000–5,000 for both softwood and hardwood cellulose. The uniformity is still more apparent in Table 4.17 (779, 780), where it is shown that most other sources of cellulose give a similar average. Similar or even higher values have been obtained for cotton, ramie and wood celluloses employing slightly different methods (707). Adjustment of the viscosity–DP constants to fit data obtained from light scattering measurements (774a), as well as direct light scattering data (259a), resulted in still higher DP values for native cellulose, Table 4.17a. It appears that cellulose from ferns, gymnosperms and angiosperms has a weight-average DP of about 10,000, sometimes even 15,000.

Table 4.16 also indicates the number of maxima in frequency weight distribution of molecules within the sample. Hardwoods, seed hairs and bast fibers contain cellulose which displays one maximum only, whereas two or more are found for softwood and straw cellulose, Figure 4.3 (341, 707, 779, 780). The latter may be a consequence of degradation during the fractionation procedure, as considerable degradation seems to be unavoidable with these extremely high-molecular celluloses (cf. 394). Furthermore, the nitrates also contain some hemicellulose, which has been shown to produce irregularities in the chain length distribution curves (779). There are some indications, however, that the two maxima found

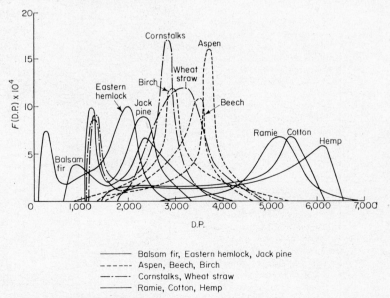

Fig. 4.3. Molecular weight distribution of cellulose from eleven different sources. The softwood cellulose preparations somewhat degraded during isolation and subsequent fractionation procedures (Timell)

are real. The reason for the difference between softwood and hardwood celluloses might be related to the differences in the morphological structure, such as the more pronounced formation of springwood and summerwood in the softwood species, or the different manner of substance distribution in the cell wall. While no information is available as to the DP of spring-wood and summerwood cellulose, there is an indication that heartwood cellulose may be somewhat lower in DP than sapwood cellulose, values of 5,000 and 5,600 having been found for white birch (779). The vessels of a beech pulp were found to contain a cellulose of decidedly lower DP than did the libriform fibers (44), but in this case obviously both types of cellulose were degraded, suggesting the possibility of preferential degradation of the more accessible vessel cellulose. A lower DP of the cellulose of the primary wall than that of the secondary wall has also been indicated (337, 707).

B. Supermolecular structure

The hydroxyl groups of the cellulose molecule tend to form hydrogen bonds with hydroxyls of adjacent chains, giving the cellulose a super-structure of considerable lateral order. Celluloses from various sources and treatments differ noticeably in their degree of crystallinity, as evidenced by a large number of investigation methods. Since the super-structure of cellulose has important consequences for the pulping processes as well as for the cellulose reactions and properties in the ultimate use, these investigations will be dealt with at some length. They have involved: (1) electron microscopy, (2) x-ray and electron diffraction measurements, (3) hygroscopicity determinations, (4) infrared absorption spectrophotometry, (5) measurements of double refraction and optical rotation in visible light, and (6) density determinations. Many of these methods have been used for the study not only of isolated cellulose from various sources but also its derivatives as well as cellulose treated with hydrolyzing or swelling agents.

Cellulose gives an x-ray diffraction diagram, which is more diffuse than those of pure crystals but still indicating definite crystalline regions (322, 586, 698). Figure 4.4 (635) shows the x-ray diffraction patterns for cellulose from four different sources, displaying a distinct crystallinity in all cases but to a varying degree. A distinction is made between the discrete reflections and the background scattering, the former indicating the crystalline material and the latter the amorphous part (320). Estimations of the proportions of crystalline and amorphous material (320) give 50–90%, generally about 70%, crystallinity for native celluloses, and somewhat lower values for wood cellulose than for cotton and ramie. Similar results have been obtained with density measurements (100, 320), deuterium exchange kinetics 55–60% (238), and hygroscopicity measurements (371, 413), whereas most chemical methods, such as hydrolysis (136, 371, 413, 584, 667, 767), periodate oxidation (767), substitution reactions (767), etc., give much higher values, generally 90–95%. The latter methods have been considered to measure only chemical *accessibility*, a concept thought to differ from that of *non-crystallinity*, especially as it was demonstrated that, e.g. a hydrolytic treatment caused a secondary crystallization of amorphous material (320, 371). However, that pheno- menon was later shown to involve only 2–5% of the material (495, 720), thus far from explaining the whole discrepancy between the figures for crystallinity and non-accessibility. It has been suggested (e.g. 636) that the surface layer of the crystallites might give a diffuse x-ray scattering, and because of the small size of the crystals, this layer will amount to at least 20% of the entire crystalline material, which would bring about a general agreement in the results of the physical and chemical methods of estimating the degree of lateral order. Disregarding 10–15% of less ordered material, the entire structure of native cellulose would therefore be microcrystalline according to this concept, and obviously some of this amorphous portion is able to crystallize after the removal of some other material. Infrared absorption spectra also indicate that almost

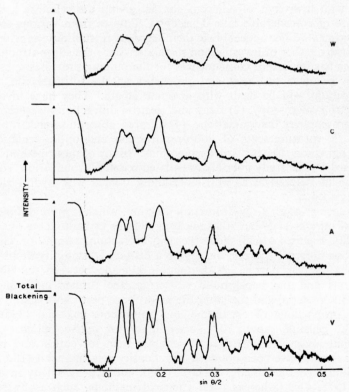

Fig. 4.4. X-ray powder diagrams of four cellulose preparations of different origin (W wood, C cotton, A animal, V algal (Valonia)), showing sharper reflections, i.e. increased lattice order, in the given order. Photometer curves with intensity vs. sin $\theta/2$ (Rånby)

all cellulose hydroxyls are engaged in hydrogen bonding (143, 174, 523, 537, 669), Figure 4.5.

The super-structure of native plant cellulose, involving this high degree of lateral order, has been studied intensely by means of electron microscopy (54, 235, 429, 570, 635, 643, 650, 758, 812). The structure of cellulose in the fiber wall with no, partial or complete removal of the other constituents was shown in Figures 3.12–15, where the principal fibrillar shape is clearly seen. By subjecting purified cellulose preparations to ultrasonic irradiation, the *microfibrils* and *elementary fibrils* are separated from each

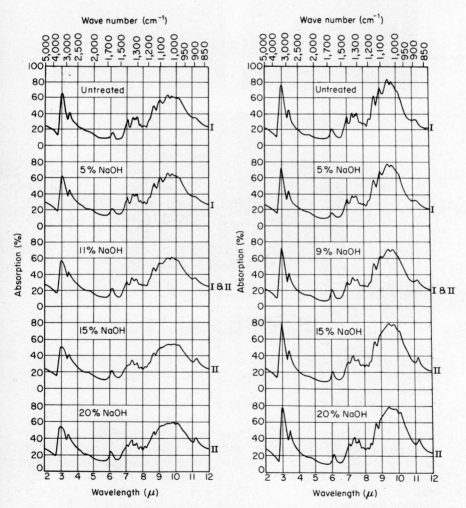

Fig. 4.5. Infrared spectra of (a) cotton and (b) eucalypt wood cellulose, untreated and treated with alkali of varying concentration, giving the spectra of cellulose I and II and a mixture of both (McKenzie–Higgins)

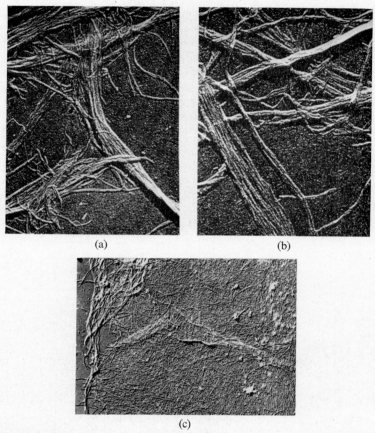

(a)   (b)

(c)

Fig. 4.6. Electron micrographs of cellulose microfibrils and elementary fibrils, from (a) purified sprucewood pulp and (b) cotton, disintegrated by ultrasonic irradiation of the fibers in water suspension (×27,000) (Rånby) (c) As occurring in the primary wall of eucalypt fibers (×9,000) (Wardrop)

other to an extent which permits an evaluation of how far these fibrils constitute structural entities, Figure 4.6 (635). Although the values of the average width of the elementary fibrils have tended to decrease with improved resolution of the electron microscope, it is now fairly well established, that they are about 100 Å wide, 30 Å thick and of infinite length. The elementary fibrils of wood cellulose may be less wide than those of cotton, whereas animal and algal cellulose elementary fibrils may be a little wider, possibly accounting for the differences noted in the corresponding x-ray diagrams. These structural units are often intimately aggregated to microfibrils about 200–250 Å wide by means of hydrogen bonding between the respective surface layers, Figure 4.7 (235). On hydrolysis, the elementary fibrils first tend to aggregate still further (812) and then eventually disintegrate into short fragments, *micelles*, of the

112

same width as the elementary fibrils (570, 635, 643), Figure 4.8 (570).
The average length of these fragments depends on the pretreatment, those
pulps which have been alkali-treated yielding shorter micelles on hydrolysis
than those which have not (414). In the former case, the micelles are about
500–1,000 Å long, corresponding to the length of molecules of DP
100–200, which is also the average DP of the hydrolyzed pulp (70). Thus
the hydrolysis of cellulose suspensions is pronouncedly heterogeneous, and
it is assumed that the amorphous regions form the starting points of this

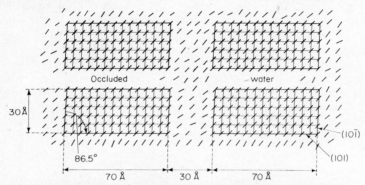

Occluded — water

30 Å

86.5°

70 Å   30 Å   70 Å

(10$\bar{1}$)
(101)

Fig. 4.7. Diagrammatic representation of a cross-section of a microfibril as an aggregation of elementary fibrils (Frey-Wyssling)

Fig. 4.8. Micelles from hydrolysed ramie
cellulose, deposited on a glass surface
(× 47,000) (Morehead)

attack. The degradation of the more crystalline regions first occurs in the
vicinity of the amorphous regions. After the initial phase of the hydrolysis,
which removes the amorphous matter and degrades the crystalline portion
to a more or less constant level of DP 100–200, a second phase follows, in

113

which the crystalline material is removed in a first order reaction, twice as fast for wood cellulose as for cotton. During that phase, the micellar length and DP of the residue from the latter material remains almost constant, whereas that from wood cellulose gradually decreases in micellar length and DP (559, 582). This indicates a higher degree of crystalline perfection in the cotton cellulose micelles (378, cf. 719). Not only alkali treatment but also drying of the original cellulose induces changes in the course of subsequent hydrolytic degradation and results in a lower DP level (378, 502), thus reflecting changes in the super-structure of cellulose. Mechanical influence, such as crushing or bending of the fibers, which is known to introduce slip planes and irregularities in the association of the elementary fibrils to larger structures, cf. Chapter 3, may cause similar disturbance within the fibrils and lead to phenomena of the same type as those previously mentioned for alkaline swelling or drying.

The detailed arrangement of the crystalline regions has been deduced from x-ray data (34, 265, 325, 550, 629, 739). An elementary cell with a rhombic symmetry was originally proposed (629), later modified (550) to a monoclinic cell with the dimensions:

$$a = 8.3 \text{ Å}$$
$$b = 10.3 \text{ Å}$$
$$c = 7.9 \text{ Å}$$
$$\beta = 84°$$

as illustrated in Figure 4.9 (550). The cellulose chains are arranged parallel to the b axis and have the symmetry of a digonal screw axis (a modification suggests a distortion of every second monomer (83, 590)). The chains are parallel to each other and are considered to hold together in the a–b plane

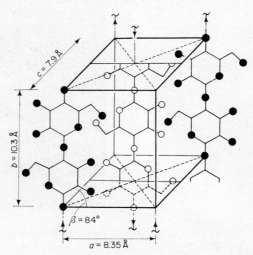

Fig. 4.9.   The monoclinic elementary cell of cellulose (Meyer–Misch)

114

by hydrogen bonding (a modification suggests hydrogen bonding between the *a–b* planes in the 101 direction (234)). The chains of adjacent *a–b* planes run in opposite directions and are staggered as to their vertical arrangement by the length of half a monomer. Figures 4.10–12 show the

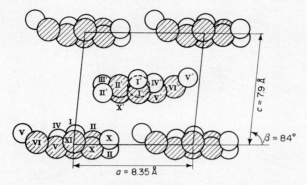

Fig. 4.10. Projection of the elementary cell of cellulose on the *a–c* plane perpendicular to the *b*-axis (Wise–Jahn)

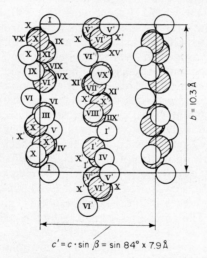

$$c' = c \cdot \sin \beta = \sin 84° \times 7.9 \, \text{Å}$$

Fig. 4.11. Projection of the elementary cell of cellulose on the *b–c* plane perpendicular to the *a*-axis (Wise–Jahn)

detailed arrangement of the atoms of the elementary cell in the three projections. The hydroxyl oxygen of two adjacent chains are at a distance of only 2.5 Å in the direction of the *a* axis, allowing complete hydrogen bonding. The closest distance between the atoms belonging to different *a–b* planes is about 3.1 Å (cf. however (234)), allowing only weaker forces, i.e. the attraction of the OH-dipoles and the permanent electric moment

115

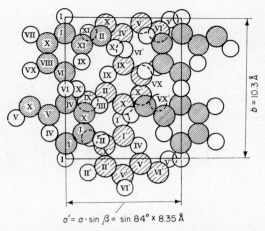

$a' = a \cdot \sin \beta = \sin 84° \times 8.35 \, \text{Å}$

Fig. 4.12. Projection of the elementary cell of cellulose on the $a–b$ plane perpendicular to the c-axis (Wise–Jahn)

of the C–O–C groups. The strongest forces, of covalent bonds, operate in the direction of the b axis. Recent work (83, 590, 618) indicates, that the glucose units have the C1 *conformation* (chair form) and every second unit slightly twisted (20–30°). Infrared analysis further suggests, that all hydroxyls are engaged in hydrogen bonding, and that an *intrachain* hydrogen bond is present between the 3-hydroxyl and the ring oxygen of the adjacent monomer (488, 524, 797). If that bond prevails also after mercerization, it would probably decrease the reactivity of the 3-hydroxyl in substitution reactions (143), cf. the subsequent section. These recent observations cause only relatively small adjustments of the classical model. A more radically new concept has also been advanced for discussion (787). Work on other polymers, such as polyethylene, nylon, etc., has indicated that chain *folding* can occur to give crystals of uniform thickness (197, 430), and it was suggested (787) that similar folding of cellulose chain molecules in the 101 plane occurs, giving discontinuities for every 500 Å. The comparative rigidity of the cellulose molecules in solution (e.g. 319) is an argument against such a super-structure, but investigations on steric models indicate a U-turn diameter of only about 10 Å (644), and cellulose derivatives and even cellulose have been obtained from very dilute solutions in the form of regular, compact, lamellar crystals of microscopic size, similar to the single crystals of linear synthetic polymers mentioned above (644).

The crystalline structure described is valid for native cellulose. There are several polymorphous forms, of which that of *regenerated cellulose* is the most important. This form is also designed *cellulose II*, in contrast to *cellulose I*, native cellulose. Cellulose II is formed upon regeneration of cellulose from its solid addition compounds, such as the acid, water or alkali celluloses (cf. below), as well as from solutions of addition compounds (cuam or cuen solutions) or unstable substitution compounds, predominantly cellulose xanthate. Its x-ray diffraction diagram is shown in Figure 4.13 (635) in comparison to that of cellulose I. The x-ray studies have revealed (34, 114, 550) that cellulose II has a monoclinic elementary cell of the dimensions:

$$a = 8.1 \text{ Å}$$
$$b = 10.3 \text{ Å}$$
$$c = 9.1 \text{ Å}$$
$$\beta = 62°$$

which contains four glucose monomers as in the case of cellulose I. The spatial arrangement of the chains is shown in Figure 4.14 in comparison with cellulose I. It is seen that the transformation involves a slight dis-

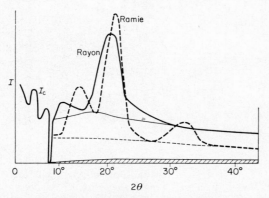

Fig. 4.13. X-ray scattering diagrams from cellulose I (ramie) and cellulose II (rayon). I_c is a reflection from a standard sample (Hermans)

tortion of the chains out of the a–b plane to form new hydrogen bonds in the $10\bar{1}$ direction. It is thereby noticed that the chains thus interconnected run in an opposite direction to the situation in cellulose I. Cellulose II seems to be the thermodynamically more stable form. On heating cellulose II to high temperatures in glycerol or alkali, it is converted to a new crystalline form which closely resembles cellulose I (68, 139, 326, 459, 551), but is probably a separate type, called high-temperature cellulose or cellulose IV (327, 372, 416), with an orthorhombic symmetry and the approximate dimensions:

$$a = 8.1 \text{ Å}$$
$$b = 10.3 \text{ Å}$$
$$c = 7.9 \text{ Å}$$
$$\beta = 90°$$

indicating a denser packing than both cellulose I and II (corresponding to a density of 1.62 as compared to 1.59 for cellulose I and II and about 1.50

117

for amorphous cellulose). Its formation is not complete at temperatures normally used in pulping processes and is therefore of little importance, as is cellulose III, observed to form on the decomposition of ammonia cellulose (326).

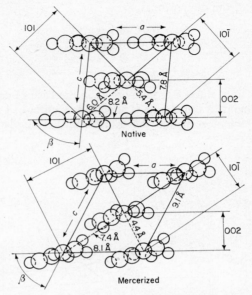

Fig. 4.14. Cross-sections of the unit cells of cellulose I and II lattices, cut at right angles to the *b*-axis, i.e. at right angles to the cellulose chains

The importance of the super-molecular structure of cellulose for its properties and its heterogeneous reactions is obvious. Only a limited fraction of its hydroxyl groups is available for interaction with water, and cellulose hence remains insoluble in water in spite of its polarity. Likewise most of its hydroxyl and acetal groups are comparatively inaccessible to chemical reagents unless the super-structure is influenced by treatment with strong swelling agents. The physical properties are influenced not only by the average molecular length and the length distribution, but also by the degree of crystallinity.

4. REACTIVITY

As just indicated, the influence of the super-molecular structure on the reactivity of cellulose is profound and has to be considered in all cellulose reactions of heterogeneous type. However, obviously the various possibilities of cellulose reactions are determined by its molecular constitution. Like all carbohydrates, the cellulose molecule is capable of reactions at its hydroxyl and acetal groups, as well as at the aldehydic end groups. The reactions now described for cellulose will be principally possible also for the hemicelluloses, and in the section on hemicelluloses therefore only those deviations will be pointed out which result from the different carbohydrate structure of those compounds.

The hydroxyl groups react with *addition, substitution* and *oxidation* agents and the acetal groups undergo *hydrolysis* in acid as well as in alkaline medium. The aldehydic end groups can be *reduced* to alcohol groups, *oxidized* to carboxyl groups or *rearranged* under the influence of alkali to form either alcohol or carboxyl end groups. Since the redox and rearrangement reactions all influence the ease of hydrolysis of the glucosidic bonds, they will be treated together with hydrolysis under the heading of chemical *degradation reactions*. This category of reactions include those of importance for the pulping processes, whereas the addition and substitution reactions are of interest mainly in connection with the use of dissolving pulps. A special variant of the substitution reactions, called *grafting*, involves the incorporation of copolymers, e.g. of the polyvinyl type, usually by reacting cellulose with the monomer in a redox system, such as ceric ions (379, 710a). A radical mechanism is involved. One addition reaction, that of carbohydrates and water, is of predominant importance in the use of paper pulps. To facilitate the understanding of the various reactions, the analogous reactions with low-molecular compounds will first be treated, followed by a discussion of the reaction of cellulose in homogeneous solution, and finally the corresponding reaction in the heterogeneous two-phase system will be described.

A. Degradation reactions

(*a*) *Degradation of low-molecular model compounds.* Hydrolysis of glycosidic bonds occurs in both acid and alkaline medium, although much faster at low pH. The rate of reaction also varies with the type of sugar and aglycone. Table 4.18 (161, 831) gives the relative rates of hydrolysis of various methyl glycopyranosides, showing the relative stability of glucosides in acid medium and of mannosides in alkaline medium. Glycofuranosides are much more easily hydrolyzed in acid medium than

Table 4.18. Relative rates of hydrolysis of various methyl glycopyranosides (161, 831)

	Acid hydrolysis	Alkaline hydrolysis
Methyl-α-glucoside	1.0	1.0
Methyl-β-glucoside	1.9	10.0
Methyl-α-mannoside	2.4	11.0
Methyl-β-mannoside	5.7	4.4
Methyl-α-galactoside	5.2	3.9
Methyl-β-galactoside	9.3	23.0
Methyl-α-xyloside	4.5	4.8
Methyl-β-xyloside	9.0	23.0

119

are the glycopyranosides. Acid hydrolysis is very pH-dependent, and its rate becomes appreciable even below 100°C if the acid concentration is high, whereas alkaline hydrolysis proceeds with a remarkable velocity only above 150°C even in fairly concentrated lyes. Therefore, hydrolytic degradation takes place even at relatively mild acid sulfite cooks, e.g. at 120°C, whereas at hot alkali purification of pulps at the same temperature no hydrolysis of unactivated glucosidic bonds occurs. At the temperature of the alkaline kraft or soda cooks around 170°C, however, hydrolytic degradation is appreciable. At a similar high temperature, water pre-hydrolysis is efficient, although the acidity developing is only slight, pH being 3–4. On the other hand, chlorination at room temperature, and chlorine dioxide bleaching at 60–70°C do not cause appreciable acid hydrolysis of unactivated glucosidic bonds, in spite of their relatively low pH, 2–3.

The mechanism of alkaline hydrolysis has been investigated at 170°C in 10% NaOH for methylglycosides (161). It was demonstrated that those glycosides having the aglycone and the adjacent hydroxyl group in *trans* position reacted much faster than the corresponding *cis* forms (such as the β-methyl mannoside). This indicates that the cleavage of the glycosidic bond of the *trans* compounds, e.g. cellulose, is preceded by a formation of the 1,2-anhydro-configuration, I.

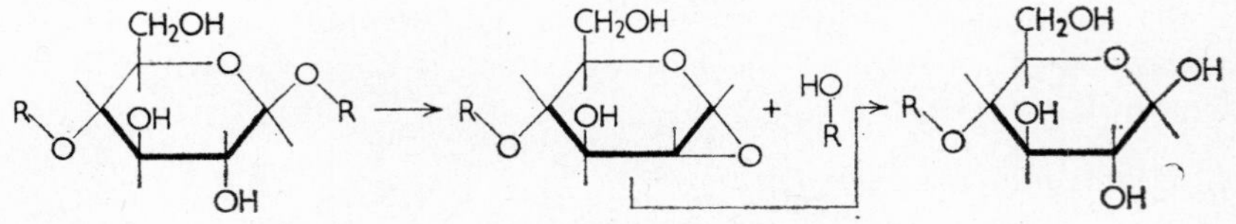

I

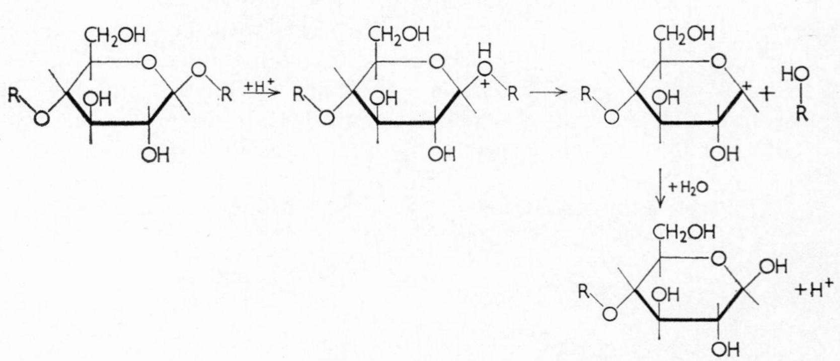

II

The mechanism of acid hydrolysis of an acetal bond is considered to be the following (133). A proton is added to the acetal oxygen, heterolysis results in an intermediate carbonium ion, which finally reacts with water under re-formation of the proton, II.

120

The rate of hydrolysis is considerably influenced by the presence of electrophilic groups introduced into the sugar monomer, or into the aglycone. Carboxyl groups in the molecule will stabilize the molecule to hydrolysis, as e.g. 2-O-(4-O-methyl-α-D-glucopyranosyl uronic acid)-D-xylose, III, is hydrolyzed by acids at a rate of only about 6% of that of

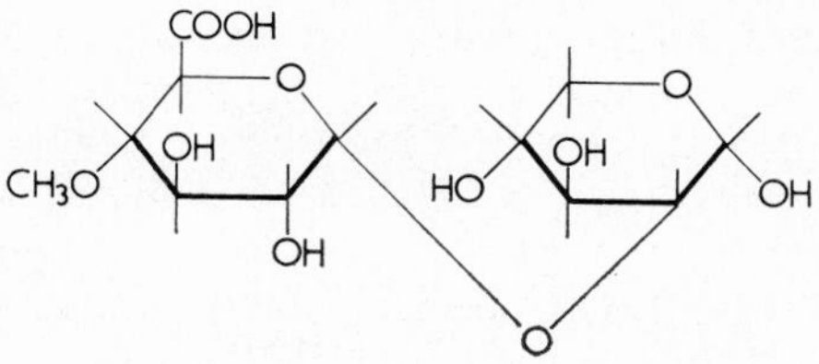

III

2-O-(4-O-methyl-α-D-glucopyranosyl)-D-xylitol, IV, or maltose (651).

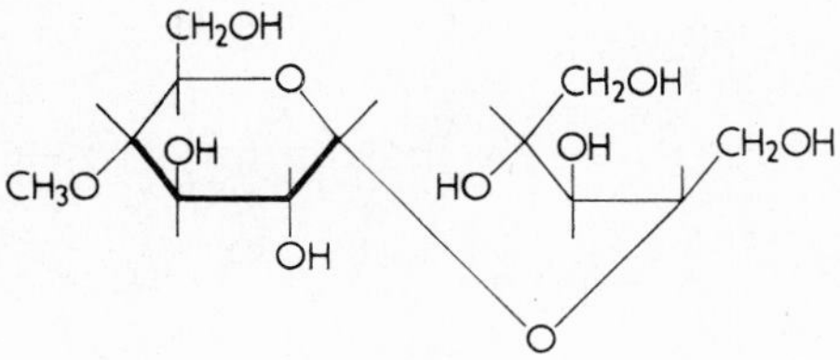

IV

Carbonyl groups on the other hand enhance the rate of hydrolysis in both acid and alkaline medium, especially in alkaline. The 2-oxo- and 3-oxo-methyl-β-glucosides, V, VI, have been shown to hydrolyze only slightly

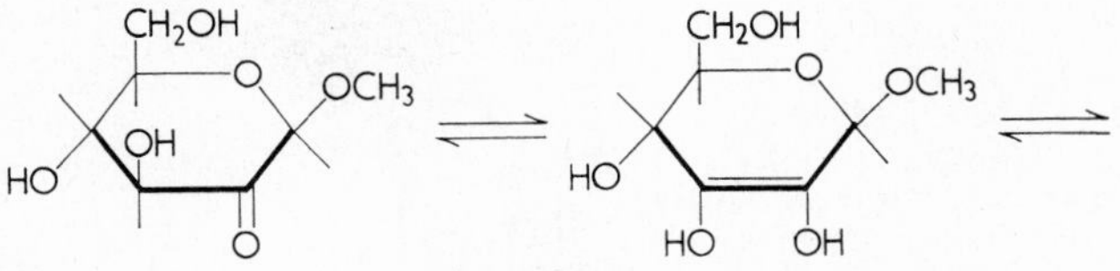

V

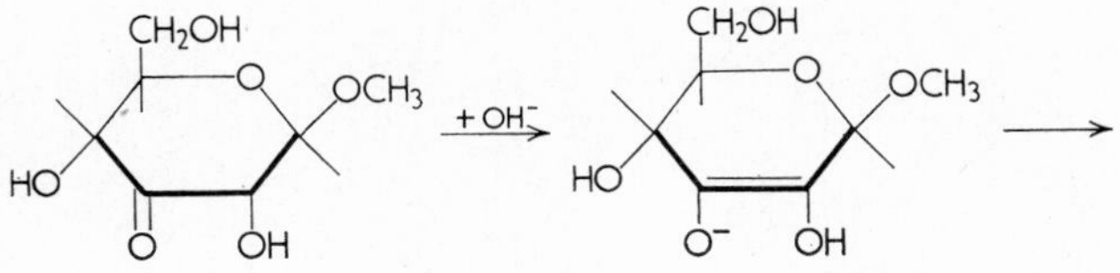

VI

more rapidly than methyl-β-glucoside at pH 4 and pH 7, but extremely rapidly in alkaline medium (761). The hydrolysis leads to the formation of a dioxo compound, VII, which in turn rapidly rearranges at all pH conditions with formation of a hydroxy acid.

The behavior of these oxo compounds also agrees with the degradation

121

mechanism of low-molecular sugars as well as of polysaccharides in alkali at temperatures below that needed for unactivated alkaline hydrolysis of glycosidic bonds (cf. above). The degradation at lower temperatures starts at the aldehydic end groups of the molecules, and involves the formation and ionization of an enediol, elimination of the β-hydroxyl, alkoxyl or glycosyl group, rearrangement to an α-dicarbonyl intermediate and finally a benzilic acid type rearrangement to give a saccharinic acid, VIII (385). The reaction sequence may thus lead to the hydrolysis of a

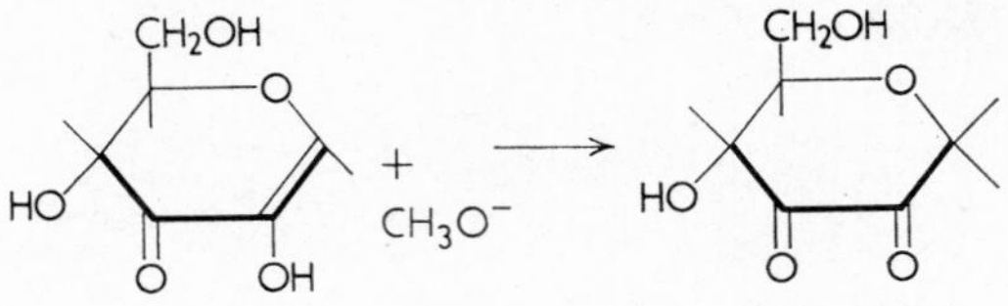

VII

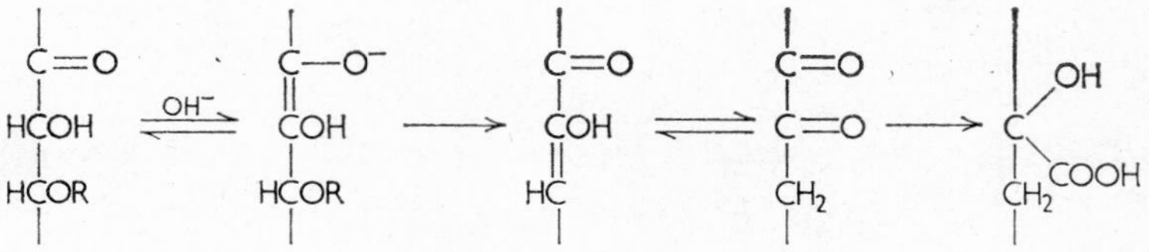

VIII

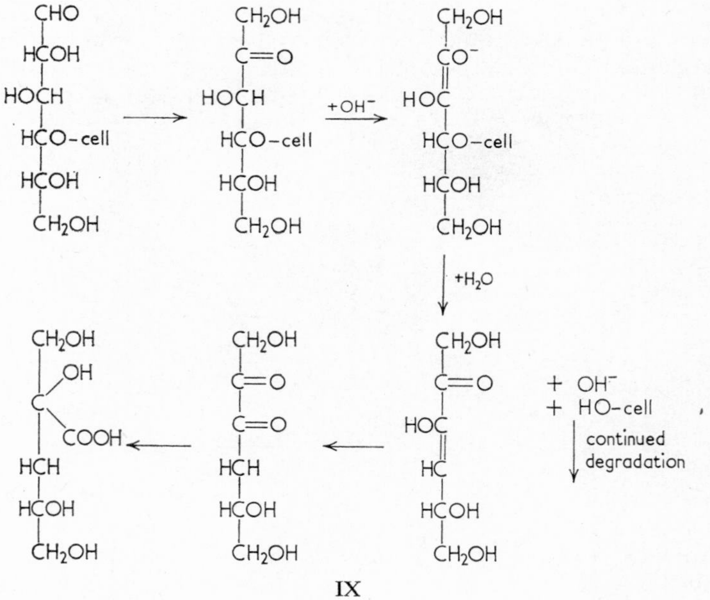

IX

disaccharide not substituted in the 2-position, with contemporary formation of an isosaccharinic acid and a monosaccharide, IX (431).

122

Similarly, for a polysaccharide, the reaction will give an isosaccharinic acid and a new end-group in a chain, one monomer shorter than the original. The degradation therefore can proceed with the same mechanism from the end of the molecules, by '*peeling-off reaction*', until finally the reaction is brought to an end by means of a '*stopping reaction*' of similar mechanism, whereby a metasaccharinic end group is formed, X (507).

$$
\begin{array}{ccccc}
\text{CHO} & \text{HCO}^- & \text{CHO} & \text{CHO} & \text{COOH} \\
| & \| & | & | & | \\
\text{HCOH} & \text{COH} & \text{COH} & \text{C}=\text{O} & \text{HCOH} \\
| & | & \| & | & | \\
\text{HOCH} & \text{HOCH} & \text{CH} & \text{CH}_2 & \text{CH}_2 \\
| \quad \xrightarrow{+\text{OH}^-} & | & | & | & | \\
\text{HCO-cell} & \text{HCO-cell} & \text{HCO-cell} & \text{HCO-cell} & \text{HCO-cell} \\
| & | & | & | & | \\
\text{HCOH} & \text{HCOH} & \text{HCOH} & \text{HCOH} & \text{HCOH} \\
| & | & | & | & | \\
\text{CH}_2\text{OH} & \text{CH}_2\text{OH} & \text{CH}_2\text{OH} & \text{CH}_2\text{OH} & \text{CH}_2\text{OH} \\
\end{array}
$$

X

Obviously, hydrolytic degradation of a long polysaccharide chain such as cellulose is therefore influenced by the presence of oxidized groups even at only a few monomers, and the formation of such groups by oxidative treatment has been studied also for low-molecular compounds, such as methylglucosides. Chlorine water gives D-gluconic acid, 5-oxo-D-gluconic acid and D-glucosaccharic acid (165). Methyl α- and β-D-galactosides, -mannosides and -xylosides (493) as well as methyl β-cellobioside (166) gave similar products, all indicating scission of the glycosidic bonds under conditions where little direct hydrolysis of methyl glycosides occurs. The hydrolysis is in this case believed to be induced by the polarized chlorine molecule. Chromic acid oxidation in water or chromium trioxide oxidation in acetone of methyl glucosides gave the 2-oxo, 3-oxo, 4-oxo- and 6-oxo-derivatives, the 3- and 6-oxo compounds being the main reaction intermediates, followed by hydrolysis of the glucosidic bonds and further oxidation (761). Nitrogen dioxide treatment gives primarily oxidation of the primary hydroxyl to carboxyl (531) and on further treatment glucosaccharic acid as the main reaction product together with 2-oxo-, 3-oxo- and 4-oxo-methyl glucosides (761). Periodate oxidation of 1,4-substituted monosaccharides gives a dialdehyde (2,3-dialdo) structure, which on alkalization yields glycolic acid and α,γ-dihydroxybutyric acid after cleavage of the semiacetal bond (596). Treatment with hypochlorous acid at varying pH gives in addition to glucose also arabinose, 2-oxo-, 3-oxo- and 6-oxo-methyl glucosides as well as gluconic, erythronic and glyoxylic acids (761). Maximal amounts of neutral oxidation products occur at pH 4, where hypochlorous acid has its maximal concentration. Maximal overall rate of oxidation occurred at pH 7, possibly because the oxo compounds, including the free sugars, are more readily attacked at higher pH. Further oxidation of 2-oxo- or 3-oxo-methyl glucosides gives a dicarboxylic acid (XI), which is considered to yield erythronic (XII) and glyoxylic (XIII) acids by subsequent hydrolysis (761, 817).

The formation of glucose from methyl glucoside on hypochlorite oxidation indicates a cleavage of the glucosidic bond after an initial oxidation of the aglycone and demonstrates that an oxidative attack on either of the two members joined by the acetal linkage will accelerate its hydrolysis (165, 761).

XI   XII   XIII

The oxidation of the aldehydic end groups to carboxyls by chlorite (401) or hypoiodite (402) is selective and fast. The glycol grouping of the 2- and 3-hydroxyls is likewise selectively oxidized by lead tetraacetate or sodium periodate with cleavage of the carbon–carbon bond and formation of a dialdehyde (e.g. 316). Both reactions are utilized as analytical tools for the study of carbohydrates and their derivatives, but have less direct industrial importance. Dialdehyde *starch*, analogously produced, has found some technical application, however.

Chlorine dioxide treatment of alcohols and low-molecular carbohydrates gives little oxidation (699, 700, 736a), whereas carbonyl compounds are more readily oxidized (736a).

(*b*) *Degradation of cellulose in homogeneous solution.* Cellulose is readily dissolved in certain concentrated acids and quaternary ammonium bases, which allows the study of its homogeneous hydrolysis. The homogeneous *acid* hydrolysis especially has been investigated and compared with the results of the corresponding heterogeneous hydrolysis. The first investigations used sulfuric acid, such as 51 % H_2SO_4 at 18°C, following the course of hydrolysis by end-group determinations or polarimetry (218). The reaction was found to be of the first order, $dn/dt = -K.n$, where n is the molar concentration of bonds capable of undergoing scission, t the time of degradation and K the rate constant. The latter can be expressed as

$$K = \frac{1}{t} \ln \frac{1 - 1/DP_1}{1 - 1/DP_2}$$

where DP_1 and DP_2 are the *number* average DP's at the start and after the time t. Table 4.19 (218) gives the rate constants found for cellulose, cellotetraose, cellotriose and cellobiose. It is seen that the hydrolysis is accelerated by the influence of the terminating aldehyde group. Because of the slower rate of hydrolysis in phosphoric acid, this solution has

124

subsequently been preferred to sulfuric acid, and a large number of investigations have been carried out in 80–86% H_3PO_4, preferably after preswelling in 73% H_3PO_4, which facilitates subsequent dissolution (172, 413). Some of these investigations (172, 742) by using weight average DP methods of following the reaction, gave less correct results than those using the number average DP (413, 642, etc.), since only the latter give data for direct use in the kinetic calculations. Table 4.20 (413) gives the hydrolysis constants of three cellulose samples in

Table 4.19. Rate of (homogeneous) hydrolysis
in 51% H_2SO_4, 18°C (218)

	Velocity constant, $min^{-1} \times 10^4$
Cellobiose	1.07
Cellotriose	0.64
Cellotetraose	0.51
Cellulose (ramie)	0.31

Table 4.20. Rate of (homogeneous) hydrolysis in 86.4% H_3PO_4, 25°C (413)

Cellulose sample	Time of hydrolysis, min.	Number average DP	Velocity constant, $min^{-1} \times 10^6$
Cotton	0	1,245	
(weight average DP 3,930)	15	1,080	8.2 ⎫
	60	785	7.8 ⎪
	135	530	8.1 ⎪
	210	410	7.4 ⎬ 8
	330	300	7.4 ⎪
	750	152	7.7 ⎪
	1,140	104	7.8 ⎪
	2,100	54	9.3 ⎭
Spruce sulfite pulp	0	550	
(weight average DP 1,980)	15	485	16.2 ⎫
	60	359	16.0 ⎪
	135	252	15.7 ⎬ 16
	210	195	15.4 ⎪
	330	142	15.8 ⎪
	690	74	18.0 ⎭
	1,335	30	30.0
	1,710	20	40.0
Aspen neutral sulfite pulp	0	670	
(weight average DP 2,000)	15	597	12.2 ⎫
	45	522	8.1 ⎪
	135	381	7.9 ⎬ 9
	195	314	9.3 ⎪
	255	269	8.8 ⎪
	405	191	10.1 ⎭
	525	148	12.7
	1,185	60	15.0

125

86.4 % H$_3$PO$_4$ at 25°C and varying times, and Table 4.21 (642) the constants of three samples in 81.3 % H$_3$PO$_4$ at different temperatures. The energy of activation calculated (172, 642) is of the same order of magnitude as that obtained for low-molecular sugars (566). The rate of hydrolysis is virtually constant over a broad DP interval but tends to increase at very low average DP's (below 100), probably owing to end-group effects. Earlier investigations, mainly those using weight average DP values for the calculations, seemed to indicate the presence of weak linkages distributed along the chains, in order to explain the higher initial rate of hydrolysis found (172, 375, 599, 706). Semi-acetal bonds were among other things suggested (599), and the frequency considered to be 1 out of 250 or 500 bonds. A careful investigation (718) could detect the presence of one acid-sensitive bond out of 2,900 for cotton, much fewer such bonds than was previously assumed, and gives a more correct interpretation of the actual constitution of the cellulose molecule.

Table 4.21. Rate of (homogeneous) hydrolysis in 81.3 % H$_3$PO$_4$, 20–40°C (642)

Cellulose sample	Velocity constant, min^{-1} × 10^6			Activation energy kcal/mole
	20°C	30°C	40°C	
98 % alpha cotton linters	0.55	4.1	20	32
94 % alpha hardwood preh.-kraft pulp	1.0	8.9	38	34
96 % alpha softwood sulfite pulp				
untreated	0.85	7.1	37	35
chlorite oxidized	0.83	6.8		
borohydride reduced	0.51	5.1		

It is also seen in the tables that the rate of hydrolysis for wood pulps is almost twice that of cotton. Since the solutions can be considered as molecular-disperse, this discrepancy must be caused by deviations in the molecular structure. It seems likely that the weak linkages thus indicated in the wood pulps are glucosidic bonds labilized by the presence of oxo groups along the chains, since reduction with borohydride but not oxidation with chlorite gave a reduction in the rate of hydrolysis to the same level as for cotton cellulose, Table 4.21 (642). This is in agreement with the behavior of low-molecular oxo-methyl glucosides.

Several mathematical expressions have been deduced to describe the partial degradation, starting from various assumptions regarding chain length and uniformity of the hydrolyzable bonds (162, 461, 522, 568, 569, 681, 723). The general case gives highly involved expressions, unless approached by the method of moments (72). The latter theory was tested against the experimental result from the homogeneous and heterogeneous hydrolysis of cotton and wood celluloses (413). It was found, that the molecular weight distribution of cotton cellulose subjected to both homogeneous and heterogeneous hydrolysis could be computed from kinetical data with rather satisfactory accuracy, as was also the case with homogeneous but not heterogeneous hydrolysis of wood cellulose. This indicates that the heterogeneous hydrolysis degradation of wood cellulose does not involve random cleavage of the glucosidic bonds in contrast to the other three cases.

(*c*) *Heterogeneous degradation of cellulose.* The heterogeneous degradation of cellulose is of much greater industrial importance than the homogeneous one. Homogeneous degradation mainly occurs in the manufacture of cellulose acetate, whereas heterogeneous degradation takes place in the pulping processes, cooking as well as bleaching, and further in the aging of alkali cellulose in the viscose process and manufacture of cellulose ethers, as well as in the production of low-viscosity cellulose nitrate. The degradation involves hydrolysis in acid and alkaline medium of the glucosidic bonds, unactivated or labilized by the presence of oxo groups, which may have been introduced by oxidants prior to the hydrolysis.

As indicated in the previous section, heterogeneous hydrolysis, especially of wood cellulose, is influenced by the supermolecular structure, as was also pointed out in Section II.3B. First of all the amorphous or para-crystalline material, which is most easily accessible, is not only degraded but also dissolved (136, 371, 413, 584, 667, 767). The dissolved matter amounts to about 5% of cotton and 10% of wood cellulose (rayon pulp grade), to which should be added 2–5% of material which seems to crystallize during the hydrolysis (495, 720). The degradation has to proceed to a DP below 10 before solubility in the hydrolyzing medium is obtained (719). The DP of the main fraction decreases more rapidly in the beginning of the hydrolysis and eventually achieves a more or less constant value, varying for different materials and pretreatments, but quite often around a (weight average) DP of 100–200 (70, 414, 582, 634), which corresponds to the average length, 500–1,000 Å, of the elementary fibril fragments, the micelles, obtained by the hydrolysis (70). Drying of the sample was found to increase the rate of hydrolysis for hot-alkali purified holocellulose, whereas it was without effect on the unextracted holocellulose (634). The latter was found to be more hydrolysis-resistant. The initial phase of the degradation is more rapid for wood pulps than for cotton, whereas the rate constant during the subsequent hydrolysis is often lower for wood pulps (413), as shown in Table 4.22 (413) for the same materials for which the velocity constants of homogeneous hydrolysis were given in Table 4.20. Hydrolysis of the micelles after having reached the 'limit' D.P. values of 100–200 (weight average) proceeds according to a slow first-order reaction. Here again, the degradation of wood cellulose is about twice as fast as that of cotton (559), and whereas the DP of the cotton hydrocelluloses remains fairly constant down to a rather low yield, the DP of the wood cellulose residue shows a gradual decrease (414, 559). The results are interpreted to reflect the differences in supermolecular structure between cotton and wood cellulose. The initial fast drop in wood cellulose DP as well as the intermediate relative resistance may be caused by heterogeneities in the structure as well as the protecting influence of non-cellulosic material. The difference in the final phase of hydrolysis

127

reflects the fact that cotton cellulose contains less amorphous material and hence less interruptions of the ordered regions (longer and more well-defined micelles). It has also been demonstrated (414), that alkali treatment in the concentration range causing intramicellar swelling results in a decrease in the limit DP on subsequent acid hydrolysis. The drying of the sample prior to hydrolysis likewise decreases the limit DP level (502). The degradation of the micelles has been shown to involve end attack, since there is an inverse relation between the micellar length and the rate of hydrolysis (719). The wood cellulose micelles with their lower lattice order may to some extent be attacked also from their side surfaces (378). The higher rate of hydrolysis because of the presence of oxo groups as evidenced by the results of the homogeneous hydrolysis should be observed also in connection with heterogeneous hydrolysis.

Table 4.22. Rate of (heterogeneous) hydrolysis in $0.5M$ KHSO$_4$, 47°C (413)

Cellulose sample	Time of hydrolysis, hours	Number average DP	Velocity constant, hours^{-1} × 10^6
Cotton	0	2,860	
(weight average DP 3,930)	2	2,300	42.5
	8	1,800	20.1
	22	1,525	7.2
	35	1,160	15.8
	54	1,080	3.5 ⎤
	84	980	3.3 ⎟
	126	870	3.1 ⎬ 3.4
	222	645	4.2 ⎟
	558	410	3.0 ⎦
Spruce sulfite pulps	0	875	
(weight average DP 1,980)	2	665	181.0
	8	575	39.2
	53	510	4.9
	115.5	475	2.3 ⎤
	212	430	2.1 ⎟
	455	350	2.2 ⎬ 2.2
	1,031	240	2.3 ⎦
Aspen neutral sulfite pulp	0	1,500	
(weight average DP 2,000)	2	1,305	50.0
	22	1,145	5.4
	35	1,020	8.2
	54	910	6.2
	84	830	3.5 ⎤
	126	775	2.0 ⎟
	222	670	2.1 ⎬ 2.1
	558	605	0.7 ⎦

Although very useful in revealing the fine structure of the cellulose fibers, the limit DP represents a state of degradation which is seldom reached in the technical processes. (A highly degraded cellulose, dispersible in water, has been recently introduced on the market, however.) The preceding phases of hydrolysis are of more direct technical interest.

128

Figures 4.15–16 (413) show the approximate weight frequency distribution curves for cotton and wood cellulose and their changes on heterogeneous hydrolysis. Whereas the degradation of cotton cellulose appears to proceed in a fairly uniform manner, with the maximum gradually moving to lower DP values contemporarily with the average DP, the degradation of wood cellulose (a softwood sulfite pulp from a mild cook) results in maintaining the original three maxima at about the same DP's, so that even a fairly degraded cellulose preserves a high-molecular portion together with much low-molecular material. This phenomenon, which occurs to about the same extent in the acid sulfite cooking of rayon pulps, cf.

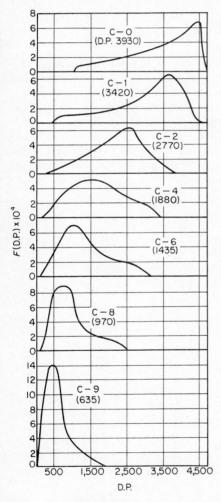

Fig. 4.15. Molecular weight frequency distribution of cotton linters during heterogeneous hydrolysis (Jörgensen)

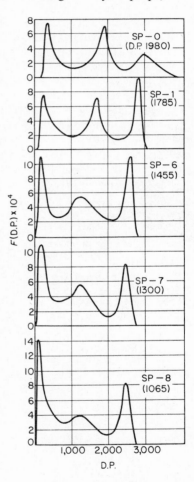

Fig. 4.16. Molecular weight frequency distribution of mildly cooked spruce sulfite cook during heterogeneous hydrolysis (Jörgensen)

129

Chapter 9, indicates regions which are less accessible to hydrolysis than the main part of the material. In contrast, degradation of wood cellulose by alkaline hydrolysis gives a more uniform chain-length distribution, and therefore prehydrolyzed-kraft pulps are preferred to degraded sulfite pulps for uses (cord manufacture) where the low-molecular portion gives less desirable characteristics to the end product, cf. Chapter 9. Another method is to use high-molecular sulfite pulps, which are subsequently degraded by an increased aging of the alkali cellulose in the viscose process, where a more uniform degradation of the swollen cellulose is obtained, cf. below. As indicated by the behavior of low-molecular model compounds, the alkaline hydrolysis proceeds much slower than acid hydrolysis. The temperature dependence of cellulose degradation at various pH levels has been investigated (565). A decrease in pH from 7 to 5 gives the same effect as a temperature increase of 30°C.

An important type of heterogeneous degradation in the pulping processes is the oxidative degradation during hypochlorite bleaching, cf. Chapter 14. This reaction is undesirable in the bleaching of paper pulps, since it leads to a deterioration of the strength properties, and special precautions are taken to avoid degradation when aiming at maximal bleaching action on the impurities. In the case of rayon pulps, the hypochlorite oxidation is used as a process controlling the average DP of the pulp to give a uniform product. For both reasons, the oxidative degradation of cellulose has been thoroughly studied.

$$
\begin{array}{ccc}
\text{CHO} & & \text{COOH} \\
| & & | \\
\text{HCOH} & & \text{HCOH} \\
| & & | \\
\text{HOCH} & \xrightarrow[\text{or HIO}]{\text{HClO}_2} & \text{HOCH} \\
| & & | \\
\text{HCO-cell} & & \text{HCO-cell} \\
| & & | \\
\text{HCOH} & & \text{HCOH} \\
| & & | \\
\text{CH}_2\text{OH} & & \text{CH}_2\text{OH}
\end{array}
$$

XIV

The heterogeneous oxidation of cellulose has been studied especially for the following oxidants: *halogen hypohalite* at various pH (e.g. 152, 291, 670, 716, 741, 815), *dichromate* (e.g. 151, 577, 630), *nitrogen dioxide* (e.g. 432, 532, 578), *periodate* (e.g. 151, 390, 395, 631), *chlorite* (401, 686a) and *hypoiodite* (376, 528). The resulting product, *oxycellulose* or better *oxidized cellulose*, contains oxidized groups of varying *amounts*, *nature* and *distribution*, depending on the type of oxidant used and the reaction conditions. The functional groups, attacked by oxidation, are the aldehyde end groups and the hydroxyl groups, forming aldehyde, ketone and carboxyl groups. As stated in the previous section on the oxidation of low-molecular compounds, some oxidants are specific, attacking and forming only certain groups, whereas others are non-specific. To the former category belong hypoiodite and chlorite, which under carefully chosen conditions only oxidize aldehyde groups to carboxyls, XIV, and periodate, which converts the glycol configuration at the carbon atoms 2 and 3 to a dialdehyde structure, XV (or possibly the hydrated form or a cyclic semiacetal configuration). Somewhat less specific is nitrogen dioxide–tetroxide, which with some preference converts the primary 6-hydroxyl to a carboxyl group, XVI, but likewise introduces carbonyl groups at the 2- and 3-hydroxyls. Unspecific are chlorine-hypochlorite, and chromic acid, which oxidize aldehydic end groups as well as all three hydroxyl groups to carbonyls and carboxyls, XVII. The reaction mechanism is believed to involve an esterification of the hydroxyl group, decomposition of the ester and rearrangement of the decomposition product, XVIII.

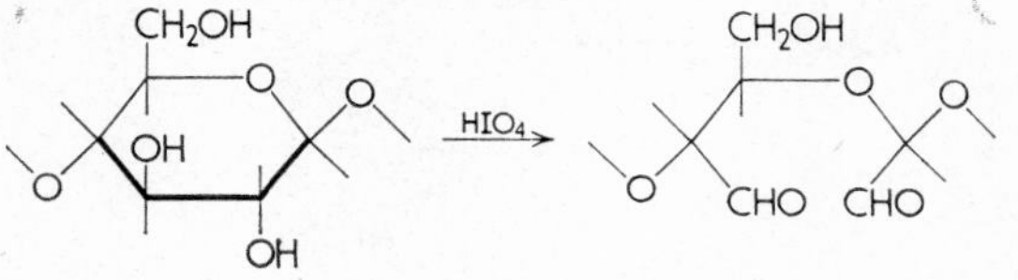

XV

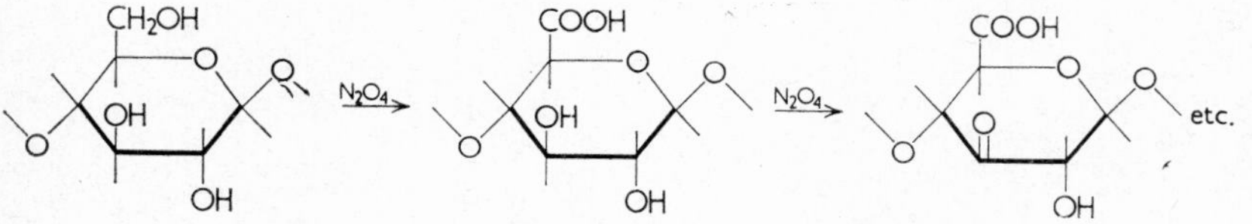

XVI

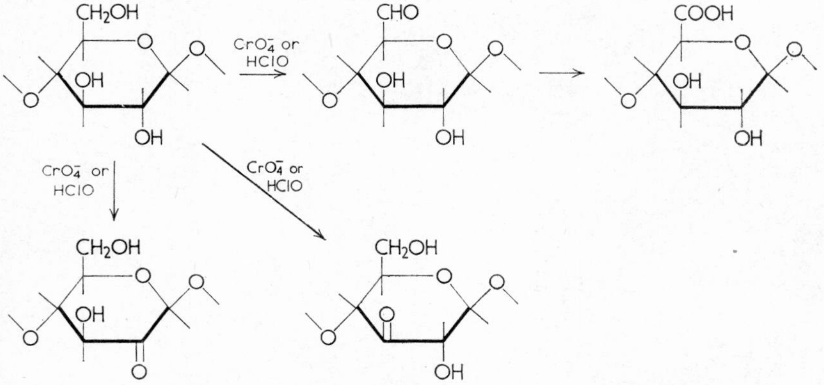

XVII

Chlorine dioxide, in contrast to most other oxidants, was found to be little reactive towards cellulose (699, 700), an observation which was to become of great importance in the non-degradative bleaching of pulp.

Of special interest is the question of the distribution of the oxidized groups and the extent of oxidation. Periodate oxidation is initially fast and subsequently proceeds at a slower rate (256, 767), Figure 4.17 (767), in

131

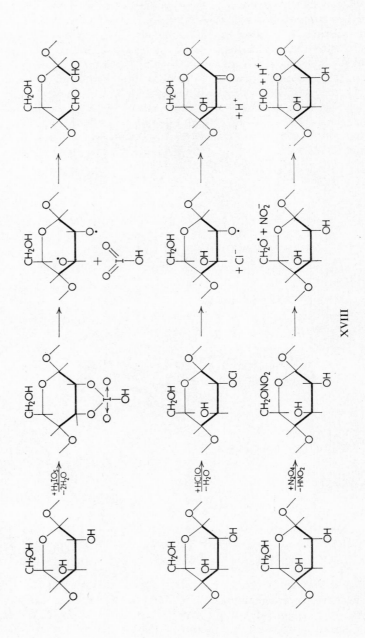

XVIII

132

a manner analogous to the heterogeneous acid hydrolysis of cellulose. The crystalline regions are therefore considered to react more slowly than the amorphous parts, but eventually react to completion. Periodate therefore has access to the entire cellulose structure. The same is true for nitrogen dioxide–tetroxide, as virtually complete oxidation of the primary hydroxyls to carboxyl groups can be achieved. Periodate (151) as well as nitrogen dioxide (578) oxidation have accordingly been found to make the x-ray diagram of cellulose more diffuse, whereas chromic acid oxidation (151) does not change the x-ray pattern and is considered to involve only the amorphous regions. Hypochlorite is likely to be able to penetrate the

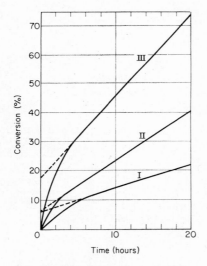

Fig. 4.17. Periodate oxidation of cotton linters (I), sulfite wood pulp (II), and viscose rayon (III) (Timell)

crystalline regions as well as periodate, but degradation by hypochlorite oxidation has been found to give non-uniform chain length distributions (682, 722), showing that the more accessible regions are preferentially attacked.

The rate of reaction as well as the type of oxidized groups formed on chlorine-hypochlorite treatment depends on the pH of the solution, as shown by Figures 4.18–19 (660, 685, cf. 761). Obviously, the maximal rate of reaction occurs at pH 7, whereas the maximal amounts of carbonyl groups are formed in acid solution and of carboxyl groups in alkaline solution, in agreement with the low-molecular model reactions mentioned in a previous section. In all cases, hypochlorous acid is likely to be the active oxidant. Because of chlorine formation at low pH and ionization to hypochlorite ion at high pH, maximal concentration of hypochlorous acid occurs at pH 4. The higher rate of oxidation at pH 7 indicates an

133

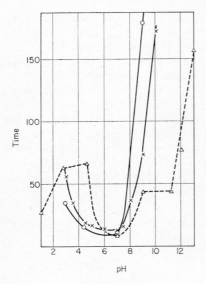

Fig. 4.18. Rate of oxidation of methyl glucoside and cellulose by hypochlorous acid at varying pH
× : Methyl-β-glucoside, time (minutes) for the consumption of 0.05 eq. oxidant per mole (Theander)
△ : Cotton, time (hours) for the consumption of 50% of HClO charge (Clibbens–Ridge)
○ : Sulfite pulp, time (minutes) for degradation to 12.5 cP (Samuelson–Ramsel)

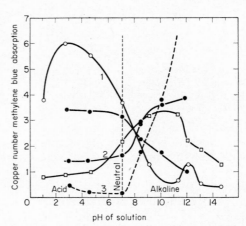

Fig. 4.19. Type of oxidation of cellulose by hypochlorous acid at varying pH
1: copper number (carbonyl groups)
2: methylene blue absorption (carboxyl groups)
3: time to constant degree of degradation
Open circles: Cotton (Birtwell, Clibbens and Ridge)
Black circles: Wood pulp (Samuelson–Ramsel)

intermediate mechanism, possibly an esterification of the hydroxyls with hypochlorous acid. Hydroxyl ions facilitate further reaction to yield carboxyl groups. This effect is probably connected with the degradation reaction occurring at carbonyl-containing monomers in alkaline medium.

The alkali lability of oxidized celluloses follows the reaction pattern shown previously for the low-molecular compounds in formula VIII. Regardless of the position of the introduced carbonyl group, the adjacent glucosidic bond is labilized to alkaline hydrolysis, as 6-oxo and 2-oxo group are in β-position to the glucosidic bond at carbon atom 4, and 3-oxo groups to that of carbon atom 1. The alkali lability of oxidized celluloses is demonstrated by the fact that their nitrate viscosity generally indicates a much higher DP than does their cuoxam viscosity, whereas nitrate viscosity of an alkali-treated sample shows the lower DP level (150). These phenomena are most pronounced at oxidized cellulose containing oxo groups, upon oxidation by periodate (596), chromic acid or acidic-to-neutral solutions of hypochlorous acid. Oxidants giving predominantly carboxyl groups, such as alkaline hypochlorite or hypo-bromite, do not impart a corresponding alkali lability to cellulose, and the relation between nitrate and cuoxam viscosities of such samples shows a similar relation as that of celluloses degraded by acid hydrolysis, which display no alkali lability at room temperature. Furthermore, alkali-labile periodate-oxidized cellulose can be made alkali-resistant by further oxidation of the aldehyde groups to carboxyls (546) by sodium chlorite. On the other hand, mild chlorite oxidation does not convert non-aldehydic carbonyls to carboxyls, and therefore such treatment cannot render an ordinary oxidized cellulose completely alkali-stable, whereas that is the case for reduction of oxo groups to hydroxyls by e.g. sodium borohydride (546, 659). The degradation of oxidized cellulose is a rapid reaction, as readily demonstrated with nitrogen dioxide-oxidized cellulose, containing carboxyl groups at carbon atom 6 and a considerable amount of oxo groups at carbon atoms 2 and 3. On dissolution of this product in alkali, for a moment a highly viscous solution is obtained, resembling that of polymannuronic or polygalacturonic acid salt solutions. However, within a few seconds the solution will lose most of its viscosity, even at room temperature, owing to the fast degradation.

As the oxidation of cellulose with alkaline hypochlorite also results in considerable degradation, it is likely that the oxidation initially involved the formation of carbonyls, which were partly further oxidized to car-boxyls but predominantly disappeared in the alkaline degradation reaction under rearrangement to saccharinic acid configurations according to formula VIII.

Oxidative degradation of cellulose also occurs in bisulfite pulping at pH 4–6, as indicated by viscosity reduction and presence of carbonyl groups (303a). At these conditions, mannitol has been shown to be oxidized to the sugars mannose and fructose (492). Bisulfite is con-temporarily reduced to thiosulfate.

The degradation of non-oxidized cellulose by alkali proceeds only at

135

elevated temperature. The peeling-off reaction, mentioned previously for the low-molecular compounds, proceeds according to formula IX (547, 652, 659). The initial rearrangement of the end monomer to the alkali-labile β-alkoxycarbonyl configuration obviously requires a higher temperature than the subsequent degradation. Therefore 70–120°C is used in *hot alkali purification*, the pulping process utilizing this reaction. Still higher temperature, 150–180°C, is necessary to give unactivated alkaline hydrolysis of glycosidic bonds, such as occurs in *kraft cooking*, according to the mechanism indicated by formula I. The peeling-off reaction of course also occurs during the kraft cook.

Another oxidative cellulose degradation is the *aging of alkali cellulose*. In contrast to hypochlorous acid oxidation this reaction occurs readily in crystalline as well as amorphous regions, yielding a comparatively uniform DP distribution (682, 722, 758a). Aging of alkali cellulose is an autoxidation, initiated by an absorption of molecular oxygen. It has been found that the initial rate of oxidation is a function of the copper number of the pulp, i.e. of its carbonyl content, Figure 4.20 (184). Comparatively little of the oxygen absorbed appears as carbonyl or carboxyl groups, Figure 4.21 (184). The reaction mechanism is assumed to involve a hydroperoxide, free-radical mechanism. Positive catalysts are cobalt and manganese ions, whereas metallic silver, known to decompose peroxides, is a negative catalyst which nearly prevents degradation. Aging catalysts are sometimes used in the viscose process to increase the capacity of the aging room or to allow the processing of slowly aging or high DP pulps.

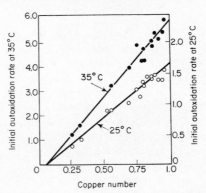

Fig. 4.20. Relation between initial autoxidation rate of alkali cellulose and the copper number of the cellulose regenerated from it (Entwistle, Cole and Wooding)

There are other cellulose degradation reactions, which do not occur during the pulping processes but in the final product, the paper or the viscose rayon. Light, especially in the ultraviolet range, will cause depolymerization, either by direct *photolysis* of covalent bonds on short-wave irradiation, or over an energy transfer, *photosensitization,* caused by the presence of a pigment or a dye, which can absorb energy from light of higher wavelength. In the former case, the presence of oxygen is unimportant (171) and water vapor exerts an inhibiting effect (475). Photosensitization also involves the action of atmospheric oxygen and water vapor (170) and consequently has a hydroperoxide radical mechanism, initiated by the irradiation energy absorbed by the sensitizer. *Thermal degradation* of the cellulose does not occur on drying at normal temperature. When a DP reduction is experienced on drying, or subsequent storage of the hot, dried pulp, this is usually caused by hydrolysis from acidic impurities. On heating above 140°C, degradation of pure cellulose will also occur, whereby the presence of air oxygen and moisture greatly accelerate the degradation (137, 809). Such conditions may occur in the use of rayon tire cord. The degrading effect of repeated launderings for cellulose textiles also involves oxidative degradation, caused by the bleaching agent of the detergent, as well as the air oxygen on subsequent drying, especially in light. *Microbiological degradation* of cellulose is an important process in nature and may also occur during the ultimate use of the cellulosic products. This appears to involve an enzymatic hydrolysis of the β-glucosidic bonds (647).

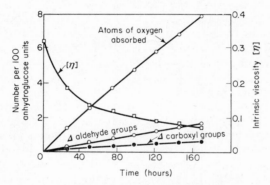

Fig. 4.21. Functional group development during autoxidation of alkali cellulose (Entwistle, Cole and Wooding)

B. Reactions forming addition compounds

The preparation of cellulose derivatives forms an important industrial aspect of cellulose chemistry, as several million tons of wood pulp are consumed for this purpose every year. The conversion processes involve the substitution of the cellulose hydroxyls to esters or ethers, which are either used as such (cellulose nitrate, acetate, propionate or acetobutyrate, methyl, ethyl, carboxymethyl, hydroxyethyl or benzyl cellulose) or further converted to regenerated cellulose by elimination of the substituents (cellulose xanthate). The purpose of the preparation is in all cases to convert the cellulose to a more useful form by dissolving the native fiber structure and extruding the solution to form filaments, sheets, foils, rods, etc., or molding the derivative together with a plasticizer to plastics of useful shape, or sometimes as a dissolved ingredient in glues, sizes, paints or detergents.

As shown in the previous Section II.3 of this chapter, most of the cellulose hydroxyls are engaged in hydrogen bonding, giving the cellulose chains a dense, ordered structure, which is not easily accessible to the esterifying or etherifying agents. In order to make the hydroxyls accessible to the reagent, cellulose is treated with strongly alkaline or acid solutions, either as a pretreatment or in the same operation in which the main reaction is performed. Thereby *addition compounds* are formed between the cellulose and both solute and solvent molecules. In some cases, with one industrial application, that of the *cuprammonium process*, the addition compound goes into solution and is then used directly for the conversion of cellulose into filaments or films, whereby cellulose is regenerated. Generally, however, the addition compounds remain in the fibrous state of the original pulp, although the fibers are greatly swollen by the entering molecules.

The most characteristic features of these compounds are that:

(1) They exist only in equilibrium with the reagent and decompose more or less rapidly when the excess reagent is removed or diluted with water beyond a certain limit.

(2) Their formation is accompanied by fiber swelling.

(3) Their formation involves a transition into a new lattice in the crystalline parts of the cellulose, as evident from the change in diffraction patterns, etc.

(4) The reagents are absorbed by the cellulose in certain, stoichiometric proportions.

The lability of the addition compounds and the influence of the super-structure have made the study of the exact composition of these compounds difficult. They are well defined only in the crystalline regions of the cellulose, and most information regarding their structure has been obtained by x-ray studies. Table 4.23 (641) gives the data for most of the addition compounds of cellulose, which can be subdivided into four main groups, *alkali celluloses, acid celluloses, amine celluloses* and *salt celluloses*. The reagents listed are all *polar* compounds. Whereas the periodicity along the *b* axis of 10.3 Å is usually unchanged, the *a* and *c* dimensions of the unit cell of cellulose increase, mainly because of an increase in the (101) interplanar distance, whereas the (10$\bar{1}$) and (002) spacings are almost identical with those of cellulose II, as illustrated by Figure 4.22 (cf. Figure 4.14). Evidently the cellulose lattice is attacked and expanded mainly in one direction, indicating that the chains are pushed apart to allow the reagent to enter between the hydroxyl groups of adjacent chains. Thereby the hydrogen bonds between the hydroxyl groups must be broken and new ones formed with the reagent, since the structure is only swollen and still kept together by cohesive forces.

In principle a hydrogen bond is composed of two atoms (O, N or F)

138

Table 4.23. Addition compounds of cellulose (642)

Type and name	Reagent	Appr. reagent conc. at fully developed comp. %W/W	Mole H$_2$O Mole reag.	Suggested composition mole/monomer Reagent	Water	X-ray data, Å 101	10ī	002	Unit cell dimensions, Å a	b	c	d	β°	Ref.
Celluloses (for comparison)														
Cellulose I	—	—	—	—	—	6.1	5.4	4.0	8.4	10.3	7.9	8.4	84	1974, 552
,, II	—	—	—	—	—	7.4	4.5	4.0	8.1	10.3	9.1	7.5	62	552
,, IV	—	—	—	—	—	5.8	5.3	4.05	8.1	10.3	7.9	8.1	90	377, 423
Water celluloses														
Water cellulose	H$_2$O	—	—	—	1–1.5	9.0	4.5	4.0	10.0	10.3	10.0	9.1	52	321, 679
Alkali celluloses														
Lithia cellulose	LiOH + H$_2$O	10	13	0.5–1	0–3	18.0	4.7	4.3	12.8	10.4	13.2	12.5	40	328
Soda cellulose I	NaOH + H$_2$O	15	13	0.5–1	0–3	12.3	4.4	4.0		10.3	17.5	10.0	(60)	328, 736
,, II	,,	25	7	1–1.5	0–1	8.8	5.0	4.4	12.0	15.2	14.0	12.5	40	329, 736
,, III	,,	15	13	0.5–1	0–2.5	12.3	4.4	3.9	12.0	10.3	10.0	9.1	52	329, 736
,, IV	,,	(6)		0–1	2–5	9.0	4.5	4.0	10.0	15.3	26.1	13.9	(42)	321, 736
,, Q	,,	25	7	1–2	much	13.0	5.0	4.0	9.9	10.3				736
Potash cellulose I	KOH + H$_2$O	8	25	0.5–1	—	12.0	4.5	4.0		10.3				736
,, II		15	18	0.5–1	—	15.0	10.4	4.4		10.3				328, 795
Quaternary ammonium base cellulose (I)	(CH$_3$)$_4$NOH + H$_2$O	33	6			13.0		4.0	14.3	10.3	13.0	13.1	38	795
celluloses (II)	(CH$_3$)$_3$(C$_2$H$_5$)NOH + H$_2$O	20	20			15.0			14.8	10.3	13.4	13.5	37	726
(III)	(CH$_3$)$_3$(C$_6$H$_5$CH$_2$)NOH + H$_2$O	22	21			16.1	4.3	4.0	18.0	10.3	16.1	16.6	30	726
(I)	(CH$_3$)$_2$(C$_6$H$_5$CH$_2$)$_2$NOH + H$_2$O	29	23			13.0	4.5	4.1	14.3	10.3		13.1	38	726
Cuproxam cellulose	Cu(NH$_3$)$_4$(OH)$_2$ + H$_2$O	31	30	0.5(0.5)*		16.7	4.4	4.0	18.5	10.3	16.5	17.1	29	789
Sodium cupricellulose	Cu(OH)$_2$ + NaOH + H$_2$O			1.0(0.5)†						10.3				330, 789
Cupriethylenediamine cellulose	Cu(en)$_2$(OH)$_2$ + H$_2$O													330, 339, 666, 405
Acid celluloses														
Knecht compound	HNO$_3$ + H$_2$O	67	1.5	0.5–1	0–1	12.2	4.6		12.2	10.3	10.3	10.1	53	35, 125, 447, 794
Perchloric acid cellulose	HClO$_4$ + H$_2$O	61	3.5	0.5–1										36
Sulfuric acid cellulose	H$_2$SO$_4$ + H$_2$O	57.6	4	1	4									172
Hydrochloric acid cellulose	HCl + H$_2$O	33.6	4	1	4									172, 173a
Phosphoric acid cellulose	H$_3$PO$_4$ + H$_2$O	73.2	2	1	2									172
Amine celluloses														
Ammonia cellulose I	NH$_3$	100	0	1	0–1	10.3	4.6		12.0	10.3	11.2	10.7	46	68, 128, 326, 331
,, II	,,	65		2		10.3			14.5	15.2	14.5	15.0	60	68
Hydrazine cellulose	N$_2$H$_4$ (+ H$_2$O)	78	1	1–1.5		10.3	4.7	4.3	10.5	10.3	10.5		52	124, 796
Ethylenediamine cellulose	NH$_2$CH$_2$CH$_2$NH$_2$ (+ H$_2$O)	100	1			12.2	4.7	4.4		10.3				796
Tetramethylenediamine cellulose	NH$_2$(CH$_2$)$_4$NH$_2$ (+ H$_2$O)	100	0			14.6	7.3	4.6		10.3				796
Methylamine cellulose	CH$_3$NH$_2$					14.7	4.3	4.0	16.4	10.3	14.8	15.0	33	796
Ethylamine cellulose	C$_2$H$_5$NH$_2$					15.7	4.6	4.2						154
Propylamine cellulose	C$_3$H$_7$NH$_2$					18.5	4.4	3.9						154
Butylamine cellulose	C$_4$H$_9$NH$_2$					19.7–	4.5							154
Amyl- to heptylamine cellulose	C$_5$H$_{11}$NH$_2$ to C$_7$H$_{15}$NH$_2$					21.9–28.7			20.8	10.3	19.8	19.8	25	154
Salt celluloses														
Lithium thiocyanate cellulose	LiSCN	75	1						10.3					426

* 0.5 Cu (NH$_3$)$_4$(OH)$_2$ + 0.5 Cu (OH)$_2$ † 1.0 NaOH + 0.5 Cu (OH)$_2$

sharing one hydrogen atom. One of them acts as a proton donor and the other as a proton acceptor. Sometimes both atoms may function alternatively as donor and acceptor, as is the case with the hydrogen bond between two hydroxyl groups, XIX. A competing proton donor or

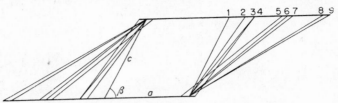

Fig. 4.22. Projection on the *a–c* plane of the elementary cells of cellulose and various cellulose addition compounds. I, cellulose II; 2, water cellulose; sodium cellulose IV; 3, ammonia cellulose; 4, nitric acid cellulose (Knecht compound); 5, sodium cellulose I and III; 6, tetramethylammonium cellulose, trimethylbenzylammonium cellulose II; 7, trimethylethylammonium cellulose, dimethyldibenzylammonium cellulose II; 8, trimethylbenzylammonium cellulose I; 9, dimethyldibenzylammonium cellulose I (Rånby–Rydholm)

acceptor can destroy a hydrogen bond. Figure 4.23 illustrates what happens when cellulose is treated with concentrated solutions of strong acids or bases, i.e. with proton donors (the hydronium ions) or proton acceptors (the hydroxyl ions). First the hydrogen bond between two cellulose hydroxyls is destroyed and a new one formed between the reagent and one of the hydroxyl groups. The reagent then probably forms a hydrogen bond with the other hydroxyl group as well, either directly or via another molecule or ion. By cautious neutralization, 'water cellulose' is formed from both alkali and acid celluloses. Thus one or more oxygen atoms form a connecting bridge between the cellulose hydroxyls in the alkali, acid and water celluloses. Similarly, in the ammonia and amine celluloses, nitrogen is the bridge-forming atom.

$$R{-}O{-}{-}H{-}{-}{-}O{-}R'$$
$$|\ \ \ \ \ \ \ \ \ \ \ H$$
$$R{-}O{-}{-}{-}H{-}{-}O{-}R'$$
$$|$$
$$H$$

XIX

In the case of the alkali and acid celluloses, water plays an important role. A certain amount of water should be present in the mineral acids to allow the formation of hydronium ions. On the other hand, too high a water content in the acid or base prevents the formation of the addition compound. This results from the competition for the reagent (the hydronium or hydroxyl ion) between the water molecules and the cellulose hydroxyls. Figures 4.24 (794) and 4.25 (678, 714) show the formation of an acid cellulose (the 'Knecht compound') and two alkali celluloses. In a

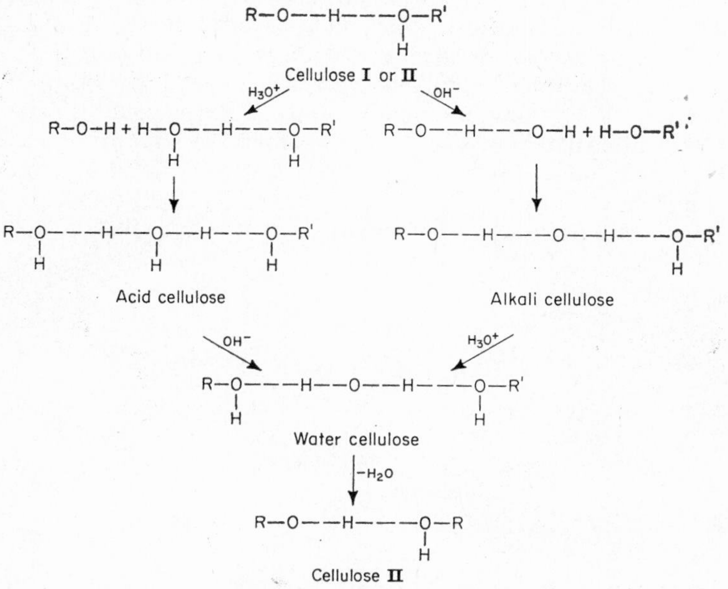

R—O——H————O—R'
$\quad\quad\quad\quad\quad$ |
$\quad\quad\quad\quad\quad$ H

Cellulose **I** or **II**

H_3O^+ $\quad\quad\quad\quad\quad\quad\quad\quad$ OH^-

R—O—H + H—O——H————O—R' $\quad\quad$ R—O——H————O—H + H—O—R'
$\quad\quad\quad\quad$ |$\quad\quad\quad$ |
$\quad\quad\quad\quad$ H$\quad\quad\quad$ H

R—O————H——O——H————O—R' $\quad\quad$ R—O——H————O——H————O—R'
| $\quad\quad\quad$ | $\quad\quad\quad$ | $\quad\quad\quad\quad\quad\quad\quad\quad\quad\quad\quad\quad\quad\quad\quad\quad$ |
H $\quad\quad\quad$ H $\quad\quad\quad$ H $\quad\quad\quad\quad\quad\quad\quad\quad\quad\quad\quad\quad\quad\quad\quad\quad\quad\quad$ H

$\quad\quad$ Acid cellulose $\quad\quad\quad\quad\quad\quad\quad\quad\quad\quad\quad\quad$ Alkali cellulose

$\quad\quad$ OH^- $\quad\quad\quad\quad\quad\quad\quad\quad\quad\quad$ H_3O^+

R—O————H——O——H————O—R'
| $\quad\quad\quad\quad\quad\quad\quad\quad\quad\quad$ |
H $\quad\quad\quad\quad\quad\quad\quad\quad\quad\quad$ H

Water cellulose

$-H_2O$

R—O——H————O—R
$\quad\quad\quad\quad\quad$ |
$\quad\quad\quad\quad\quad$ H

Cellulose **II**

Fig. 4.23. Formation of cellulose addition compounds of different proton content. R indicates the glucose residue (Rånby–Rydholm)

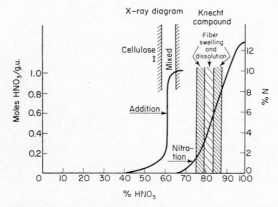

Fig. 4.24. Formation of the Knecht addition compound and of cellulose nitrate on the treatment of cellulose with nitric acid of varying concentration (Trogus)

certain concentration range the x-ray pattern changes to that of the addition compound, and in that interval the main uptake of chemical occurs. The critical concentration range varies with the type of reagent, the type of cellulose and the temperature. As shown in the previous Table 4.23, a smaller number of water molecules is allowed in the formation of acid celluloses than alkali celluloses. It has also been stated that

141

for the different alkali hydroxides more water can be tolerated, the smaller and more hydrated is the alkali metal ion (340). Thus it is evident that not only the hydronium and hydroxyl ions but also the counter ions are of importance. The hydration tendency of the latter is probably the factor that determines how much water can be tolerated, cations immobilizing more water molecules than anions (309). This concept also accounts for the temperature dependence in the formation of alkali celluloses, where lower temperatures allow higher water content of the alkali as the hydration tendency of the cation increases.

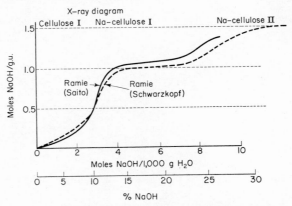

Fig. 4.25. Formation of alkali celluloses on the treatment of cellulose with sodium hydroxide solutions of varying concentration (Saito and Schwarzkopf)

When the water content of the acid or base is sufficiently high to cause ionization and sufficiently low to let the cellulose hydroxyls compete for the hydronium or hydroxyl ions, the reagent enters into the cellulose structure. The hydronium and hydroxyl ions, and sometimes water also, form hydrogen bonds with the hydroxyl groups, and the counter ions with their water shells follow by electrostatic attraction. This causes not only the expansion of the crystal lattice but also intermicellar swelling. If the counter ions are sufficiently bulky, they will push adjacent cellulose chains so far apart that the connecting forces become too weak and dissolution of the cellulose occurs. That is the case in quaternary ammonium bases, as well as in copper ammonia and copper amine hydroxide solutions. In the latter, copper is also complexed by the cellulose hydroxyls, adding to the decrease in hydrogen bonding between the molecules. This is also the case for some other hydroxides containing complexed multivalent ions Co, Ni, Zn and Cd (159, 319, 396) or for two ferritartrate-hydroxide complexes (397). The solvents mentioned are usually abbreviated as follows: *Cuoxam* (or *cuam*), *Cuoxen* (or *cuen* or *CED*), *Cooxen*, *Nioxen*, *Zincoxen*, *Cadoxen* and *EWNN* (German abbreviation for Eisen-Weinsäure-Natrium-Natron-Lauge). Similarly, dissolution occurs in the case of strong, non-aqueous mineral acids, sometimes also when containing a small quantity of water (36, 172, 450). The excess of non-hydrated protons probably saturates the cellulose hydroxyls, giving no possibility of bridge-forming atom complexes, XX. Apart from the cuprammonium process, none of these methods of bringing cellulose into solution has found industrial application, but several are used in production-controlling viscosity determinations or in research to study the homogeneous degradation or substitution of cellulose.

$$R-O--H----O-R' + 2H^+ \longrightarrow R-\overset{+}{O}--H + H--\overset{+}{O}-R'$$

XX

The most important cellulose addition compound is that with sodium hydroxide, and the formation of alkali cellulose at various conditions has been thoroughly investigated. Figure 4.26 (725, cf. 332) shows that complete alkali cellulose formation occurs within a limited concentration and temperature interval, a low temperature favoring the reaction also at low alkali concentrations. On regeneration, cellulose II is formed from the alkali cellulose (725, 735), which facilitates the study of the addition compound formation. The phase transition can be followed by changes in x-ray diffraction (37, 635, 637, 640), electron diffraction (635, 637), moisture regain (37, 635, 637, 640) and infrared absorption (537). It has

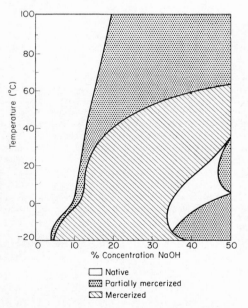

□ Native
▨ Partially mercerized
◩ Mercerized

Fig. 4.26. The effect of sodium hydroxide solutions on cotton cellulose at various temperatures and concentrations (Sisson and Saner)

143

been frequently observed, that the critical lye concentration interval is not only dependent on the temperature but also on the type of cellulose, Figure 4.27. Thus, at 0°C, the point of 50% transition is at 6.8% NaOH for sulfite pulps, 7.8% NaOH for prehydrolyzed-kraft pulps and 8.7% NaOH for cotton cellulose (635, 637, 640). Straw cellulose behaves like wood pulps, but ramie and bacterial cellulose, like cotton and animal cellulose (tunicin), requires 10% NaOH at 0°C for 50% transition (635,

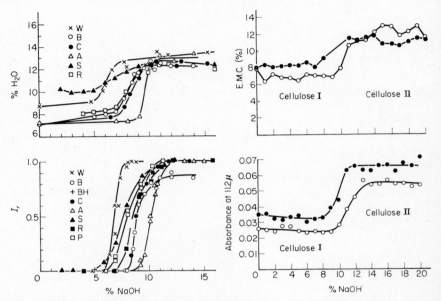

Fig. 4.27. (a) Phase transition diagrams for mercerization of different celluloses with caustic soda solutions at 0°C. W, wood sulfite; B, bacterial; BH, bacterial hydrolyzed with hot sulfuric acid; C, cotton: A, animal; S, straw; R, ramie, and P, prehydrolysis–kraft wood cellulose. The upper graph shows increases of water absorption (at 65% relative humidity) by the cellulose after alkali treatment, and the lower graph shows intensity ratios, Ir, of selected x-ray reflections (Ir = 0.0 for native and 1.0 for completely mercerized cellulose) (Rånby)

(b) Phase transition diagrams for mercerization of cotton (open circles) and eucalypt wood cellulose (closed circles) with caustic soda solutions at 20°C. The upper graph shows increases of water absorption by the cellulose after alkali treatment, and the lower graph absorbance at 11.2 μ (McKenzie–Higgins)

637, 640). The formation of alkali cellulose, or *mercerization*, starts at a certain, well-defined concentration and is complete within an interval of 2% NaOH. Prior to the intramicellar swelling there is an intermicellar swelling at lower concentrations of alkali, which reaches a maximum at a concentration just preceding the mercerization interval, at room temperature at about 10% NaOH. It is likely that the phenomenon of intermicellar swelling is related to the amount of less ordered material, including residual hemicelluloses, between the elementary fibrils, as well as to the state of hydration of the entering sodium hydroxide, whereas the critical concentration of intramicellar swelling is related to the dimensions and lateral order of the elementary fibrils.

Depending on the conditions of mercerization, various types of alkali celluloses are formed, cf. the previous Table 4.23, with various amounts of chemicals absorbed and with various cell dimensions (332). The most important of them is soda cellulose I, considered to consist of 1 NaOH and 3 H_2O per glucose unit (332, cf. 623, 678, 714). At room temperature, its formation is completely ensured at a concentration of 18% NaOH, which is the customary concentration at the alkali steeping operation of the viscose process and in the production of carboxymethyl cellulose. At concentrations above 25% NaOH and room temperature, soda cellulose II dominates and is of some importance in the preparation of other cellulose ethers.

C. Substitution reactions

The industrial aspects of these reactions will be treated in Chapter 21.III. Only the reaction principles and some special features connected with the cellulose structure will be described here.

(a) Reaction mechanisms. Once the original hydrogen bonds have been broken and intramicellar swelling achieved, the cellulose hydroxyls are capable of reacting like an ordinary aliphatic hydroxyl group. Consequently, they may be esterified and etherified according to classical methods. Table 4.24 (641) gives a survey of the best known cellulose derivatives.

Esterification is generally carried out in strongly acid medium and requires the absence of water for completion, as it is a reversible reaction. The most important commercial acid esterification reactions are nitration, acetylation and sulfation. The first two give two important cellulose derivatives, whereas sulfation occurs in both nitration and acetylation as an undesirable side reaction. Furthermore, sulfation as a main reaction was developed to the pilot plant stage for the manufacture of cellulose sulfate (788). These three reactions will therefore be discussed as type reactions for acid esterification of cellulose.

Nitration is carried out in a nitration medium consisting of nitric acid, sulfuric acid and water, the sulfuric acid acting as a dehydrating agent. The molar proportions of the components are approximately 1:2:2 (after reaction) in the bath giving maximum nitration (76).

Acetylation is performed in a mixture of acetic acid, acetic anhydride and an acid catalyst, usually sulfuric acid. The latter is added in relatively small amounts, about 1% of the cellulose, and thus the dehydrating agent in this case is the anhydride. The acetic acid merely acts as a diluent and solvent and could be replaced by methylene dichloride (354).

Sulfation as the main reaction is performed in a mixture of sulfuric acid and an alcohol such as ethanol, propanol or butanol (201, 788). The molar proportions should be about 3:2.

Nitration and sulfation are very rapid reactions, whereas acetylation is somewhat slower. In sulfuric acid-catalyzed acetylation the total amount

Table 4.24.   The substitution derivatives of cellulose (641)

Type and name	Reagent	Substituent	Ref.
Esters			
Nitrate	HNO_3	$R-ONO_2$	76, 556, 557
Sulfate	H_2SO_4	$R-OSO_3H$, $R-OSO_3Na$	
Phosphate	H_3PO_4	$R-OPO_3H_2$	788, 790
Formate	HCOOH	$R-OCHO$	648, 759
Acetate	$(CH_3CO)_2O$	$R-OCOCH_3$	583
Propionate	$(C_2H_5CO)_2O$	$R-OCOC_2H_5$	509
Butyrate	$(C_3H_7CO)_2O$	$R-OCOC_3H_7$	198, 510
Acetate-propionate	$CH_3COOCOC_2H_5$		198, 510
Acetate-butyrate	$CH_3COOCOC_3H_7$		511
Other aliphatic esters	$R'COOH + (ClCH_2CO)_2O$	$R-OCOR'$	511, 512
Alkyl succinates	$R'OCOCH_2CH_2COOH + (ClCH_2CO)_2O$	$R-OCOCH_2CH_2COOR'$	198, 510
Alkyl phthalates	$R'OCOC_6H_4COOH + (ClCH_2CO)_2O$	$R-OCOC_6H_4COOR'$	513
p-Toluenesulfonate	$CH_3C_6H_4SO_2Cl$	$R-OSO_2C_6H_4CH_3$	514, 768
Phenylurethane	C_6H_5NCO	$R-OCONHC_6H_5$	134
Xanthates			
Dithiocarbonate	$CS_2 + NaOH$	$R-OCS_2Na$	260, 398
Thiocarbonate	$COS + NaOH$	$R-OCOSNa$	333
Ethers			
Methyl	CH_3Cl, $(CH_3)_2SO_4$	$R-OCH_3$	834
Ethyl	C_2H_5Cl	$R-OC_2H_5$	834
Propyl	C_3H_7Cl	$R-OC_3H_7$	769
Isopropyl	$i-C_3H_7Cl$	$R-OC_3H_7$	769
Butyl	C_4H_9Br	$R-OC_4H_9$	769
Isobutyl	$i-C_4H_9Br$	$R-OC_4H_9$	769
Amyl	$C_5H_{11}Br$	$R-OC_5H_{11}$	769
Methyl-ethyl	$(CH_3)_2SO_4 + C_2H_5Cl$		809a
Methyl-hydroxyethyl	$CH_3Cl + C_2H_4O$		733
Ethyl-hydroxyethyl	$C_2H_5Cl + C_2H_4O$		418, 737
Methyl-hydroxypropyl	$CH_3Cl + C_3H_6O$		263
Hydroxyethyl	C_2H_4O, $ClCH_2CH_2OH$	$R-OCH_2CH_2OH$	254
Carboxymethyl	$ClCH_2COONa$	$R-OCH_2COONa$	126, 355
Sulfoethyl	$ClCH_2CH_2SO_3Na$	$R-OCH_2CH_2SO_3Na$	770
Allyl	$CH_2=CHCH_2Br$	$R-OCH_2CH=CH_2$	771
Cyanoethyl	$CH_2=CHCN$	$R-OCH_2CH_2CN$	297
Benzyl	$C_6H_5CH_2Cl$	$R-OCH_2C_6H_5$	504
Trityl	$(C_6H_5)_3C\,Cl$	$R-OC(C_6H_5)_3$	318

of sulfuric acid combines very rapidly with the cellulose and remains combined during the main acetylation period (510). Sulfation also occurs to some extent in the nitration medium and prevents complete nitration even at optimal composition of the mixture.

The general esterification reaction in media of low water content is believed to proceed in the following manner for a carboxylic acid, the reverse reaction being that of acid hydrolysis of the ester (381, 664), XXI.

$$RCOOH + H^+ \rightleftharpoons RCO\overset{+}{O}H \rightleftharpoons R\overset{+}{C}O + H_2O$$
$$\qquad\qquad\qquad H$$

$$R\overset{+}{C}O + HOR' \rightleftharpoons RCO\overset{+}{O}R' \rightleftharpoons RCOOR' + H^+$$
$$\qquad\qquad\qquad H$$

XXI

For aqueous and alcoholic solutions a similar mechanism is assumed, where the life of the acylium ion is limited to the time of a collision period (381). In a mixture of two different alcohols and their esters, ester interchange proceeds according to a very similar mechanism, and a similar

146

general reaction scheme, XXII, is valid for anhydrides and inorganic acid esters and anhydrides.

$$ROR' + H^+ \rightleftharpoons R\overset{+}{O}R' \rightleftharpoons R^+ + HOR'$$
$$\quad\quad\quad\quad\quad\quad H$$

$$R^+ + HOR'' \rightleftharpoons R\overset{+}{O}R'' \rightleftharpoons ROR'' + H^+$$
$$\quad\quad\quad\quad\quad\quad H$$

$$ROR' + HOR'' \overset{H^+}{\rightleftharpoons} ROR'' + HOR'$$

XXII

Thus, in the nitration bath, the following compounds are present: H_2SO_4, HSO_4^-, HNO_3, (NO_3^-), H_3O^+, $NO_2OSO_3^-$, NO_2OSO_3H, SO_3 and NO_2^+. The existence of the last two compounds has been demonstrated in non-aqueous sulfuric and nitric acid (251, 373).

The following are present in the acetylation bath: CH_3COOH, $CH_3COOH_2^+$, $(CH_3CO)_2O$, H_2SO_4, HSO_4^-, $CH_3COOSO_3^-$, CH_3COO-SO_3H, SO_3 and CH_3CO^+. The existence of the acetylium ion has been proved (115, 250). In the sulfation bath there are: H_2SO_4, HSO_4^-, H_3O^+, $C_2H_5OH_2^+$, $C_2H_5OSO_3^-$, $C_2H_5OSO_3H$, $(C_2H_5^+)$ and SO_3.

The reaction of cellulose hydroxyls follows (after the hydrogen bonding structure has been opened by the hydronium ions), probably with NO_2^+, CH_3CO^+ and SO_3, XXIII–XXV. Furthermore, ester interchange takes place between the same reagents and the ester groups formed. As shown in the formulas, the cellulose hydroxyl oxygen is not eliminated (443).

$$NO_2^+ + HO\text{-cell} \rightleftharpoons NO_2\text{—}\overset{+}{O}\text{-cell} \rightleftharpoons NO_2\text{—O-cell} + H^+$$
$$\quad\quad\quad\quad\quad\quad\quad\quad\quad\quad H$$

XXIII

$$SO_3 + HO\text{-cell} \rightleftharpoons SO_3\text{—}O\text{-cell} \rightleftharpoons SO_3^-\text{—O-cell} + H^+$$
$$\quad\quad\quad\quad\quad\quad\quad\quad\quad H$$

XXIV

$$CH_3CO^+ + HO\text{-cell} \rightleftharpoons CH_3CO\overset{+}{O}\text{-cell} \rightleftharpoons CH_3CO\text{—O-cell} + H^+$$
$$\quad\quad\quad\quad\quad\quad\quad\quad\quad\quad H$$

XXV

Strictly, reaction might not occur with cellulose, but with the addition compound. Thus nitration could be described in the following way, XXVI.

$$NO_2^+ + \text{cell-}O\overset{+}{H}OHO\text{-cell} \longrightarrow \text{cell-O—}NO_2 + H_3O^+ + HO^+\text{-cell}$$
$$\quad\quad\quad\quad H\ H\ H \quad\quad\quad\quad\quad\quad\quad\quad\quad\quad\quad H$$

XXVI

Note that, in the case of mixed anhydrides and esters, the formation of the acylium ion in the general equation XXII determines which ester group is formed in the subsequent reaction. Both ions R^+ and R'^+ are formed to a certain extent, but one usually predominates, to an extent depending on their relative electrophility. The strength of the corresponding acids may be taken as a measure of the latter. In actual cases this decreases in the order $H_2SO_4 > HNO_3 > HSO_4^- > CH_3COOH > C_2H_5OH$. Nitration, as it is usually carried out, implies the reaction with the anhydride $NO_2OSO_3^-$, corresponding to the acids HNO_3 and HSO_4^-, and should consequently lead mainly to nitration. However, with increasing sulfuric acid content and decreasing water content (after passing the optimum composition), there is probably an increasing formation of NO_2OSO_3H, corresponding to HNO_3 and H_2SO_4. This leads to sulfation and prevents maximum nitration. Nitration in a bath, where sulfuric acid has been exchanged with the weaker phosphoric or acetic acids and anhydrides, leads to the most complete nitration (77, 85, 298, 562). Sulfation occurs with preference in mixtures of sulfuric acid with either acetic acid or the alcohols.

Thus, in principle, there is nothing uncommon in the esterification reactions of cellulose from the point of view of the esterifying agent. The special features of these reactions arise from the chemical and physical structure of cellulose and will be dealt with later.

Etherification, the other principal reaction of the cellulose hydroxyls, also follows the general pattern. This reaction is carried out in alkaline medium, and the etherifying agents are alkyl halides or, less often, sulfates. The general reaction is termed aliphatic, nucleophilic substitution, and employed under normal conditions it is of the bimolecular type, XXVII. The radical R may be cellulose or H. If the former, etherification occurs, if the latter, hydrolysis of the etherifying agent, which is an undesirable side reaction.

$$RO^- + R'Cl \longrightarrow ROR'Cl \longrightarrow ROR' + Cl^-$$

XXVII

The cellulose hydroxyl thus reacts in its alcoholate form, as it occurs in the alkali cellulose equilibrium XXVIII. Therefore, the acidity of the cellulose hydroxyl relative to water determines its etherification reactivity.

$$ROH + OH^- \rightleftharpoons RO^- + HOH$$

XXVIII

As the acidity of the hydroxyl groups is approximately the same as that of water, there is about equal chance for etherification and hydrolysis. However, usually one hydroxyl ion activates more than one hydroxyl group, and that may increase the chance of etherification.

To suppress the hydrolysis and favor the etherification it is desirable that there are no hydroxyl ions in excess of those activating the cellulose

148

hydroxyl groups, i.e. as little alkali per weight of cellulose as possible. The lower limit is drawn by the amount necessary to form the alkali cellulose. As the latter requires a certain concentration of the alkali, it is important to keep the amount of water per weight of cellulose as low as possible. Therefore, several water-removing diluents have been suggested (446, 762).

The most common etherifying agents are methyl chloride or dimethyl sulfate giving *methyl cellulose* (MC), ethyl chloride giving *ethyl cellulose* (EC), chloracetic acid or sodium salt giving *carboxymethyl cellulose* (CMC), and ethylene chlorohydrine or oxide giving *hydroxyethyl cellulose* (HEC). The last reaction follows a pattern similar to those given above, XXIX.

$$CH_2CH_2O + HO\text{-cell} \xrightarrow{OH^-} HOCH_2CH_2O\text{-cell}$$

XXIX

A special type of alkaline reaction of an aliphatic hydroxyl group is *xanthation*, and xanthation of cellulose is one of its most important reactions. Formally, xanthation is an esterification of an alcohol with dithiocarbonic acid. However, the xanthation has most features in common with etherifications. The net reaction in treating alkali cellulose with carbon disulfide is XXX. There is, however, some indication that

$$CS_2 + HO\text{-cell} + OH^- \longrightarrow {}^-CS_2O\text{-cell} + H_2O$$

XXX

carbon disulfide itself is not the reactant but its hydrated form, $CS_2 . H_2O$ or HOCSSH. Thus it is difficult to obtain xanthation of cellulose mercerized at high caustic concentrations with little free water, although the formation of most cellulose ethers occurs readily under such conditions. As a side reaction, the hydrolysis of the xanthating agent occurs, XXXI, to yield bidithiocarbonate ions, which react further with alkali to sulfide, carbonate, trithiocarbonate, etc.

$$CS_2 + OH^- \longrightarrow HOCS_2^-$$

XXXI

In contrast to the ethers, cellulose xanthate is not stable in alkaline solution. Acetylation and xanthation are equilibrium-controlled reactions, normal etherifications kinetically controlled. Therefore, in the *viscose*, which is a solution of the xanthate in lye, there is a continual hydrolysis and re-xanthation, causing both a more uniform distribution of the xanthate groups and a steadily decreasing substitution due to side reactions. Because of their instability the xanthates are not used as such. They are, however, important as intermediates in the manufacture of different kinds of regenerated cellulose in the viscose process. In principle, the regeneration reactions consist of the acid hydrolysis of an ester according to the general equation XXI or XXII.

Summing up, the reactions involved in the preparation of cellulose substitution derivatives follow the mechanisms of esterification and etherification of low-molecular aliphatic alcohols. Owing to the physical structure of cellulose, however, the reactions have to be carried out in concentrated acid and alkaline solutions without free water molecules.

(b) *Distribution of substituents.* The discussion of the reaction mechanisms in the preceding section was based on the esterifying and etherifying agents. Now the reactions and properties of the cellulose hydroxyl groups will be treated in comparison with those of an ordinary low-molecular alcohol. There are three main factors influencing the distribution of their substitution: (1) the supermolecular structure of cellulose, (2) the nature of cellulose as a linear polymer molecule, and (3) the properties of the three different types of hydroxyl groups.

The variations in the accessibility of cellulose molecules to reagents and the dominant hydrogen bonding in the whole native structure have been described above, and it was pointed out that very drastic conditions must be chosen to make this structure accessible to reaction. In some cases, as in the treatment with quaternary ammonium bases of sufficient strength, cellulose is brought into molecular solution, where it can be etherified or xanthated. In that case a homogeneous reaction takes place. With all technical processes, however, the fiber structure is retained, although in a swollen state, during the first part of the reaction, and in most cases throughout the entire process. The reactions are necessarily heterogeneous, with a definite influence from the fiber structure, not only on the rate of the process, but also on the location of the reacting areas and the distribution of the substituents. The long-chain nature of the cellulose molecules makes it important that the reactions take place along the entire chain in order to produce a homogeneous end product. The third factor of importance, the different nature of the three hydroxyl groups in the glucose unit, raises the question of the extent to which there is a preference for one type of hydroxyl, which may be of importance in determining the properties of the final derivative.

When the fibrous cellulose, either in the native state or in the form of fibrous addition compounds, is mixed with chemicals for the substitution reaction, it is important that each individual fiber be equally treated as regards both chemical and thermal access. Otherwise from the beginning there will be a *macroheterogeneity* which will impair the final product. This aspect must not be neglected in the discussion on the nature of cellulose reactions, as it is one of the most important factors for the producer of cellulose derivatives. It is therefore necessary to exercise care in the choice of raw material as well as in carrying out the mixing operations. If cellulose is used in sheet form, as in the alkaline steeping preceding xanthation and some etherifications, the sheet should have certain wetting characteristics to ensure an even penetration of the alkali.

150

If cellulose is mechanically disintegrated in the dry state, as before nitration, acetylation and certain etherifications, the sheets should possess such a structure that disintegration results in easily penetrable flocks.

Assuming that the distribution of reagents among the fibers is perfect, there remains the question of ensuring their penetration of the fibers and microfibrils, preferably before the reaction has begun. This is the question of accessibility, and of diffusion rates versus reaction rates. If the cellulose is in a swollen state, permitting diffusion in all directions of the fiber, the diffusion paths and times are very short from one elementary fibril to another, and assuming the crystalline parts are accessible, the diffusion is also rapid within the swollen elementary fibril, as in alkali cellulose (684). Therefore, in the case of the ethers, the acetate and xanthate, where reaction times are of the order of one to several hours, this competition between diffusion and reaction rates should not be too important a cause of heterogeneity. In the case of nitration, which is a very rapid reaction even at low temperatures, there might be an appreciable reaction even during diffusion into the fiber, although this possibility seldom causes difficulties in actual practice. The initial rapid sulfation in the acetylation process, as well as in nitration, may also occur in this way.

In recent research on cellulose reactions it has been more and more evident that most cellulose reactions are of the permutoid type, i.e. there is complete accessibility of the hydroxyl groups to the reagent. This makes the reaction proceed, on the whole, as if it were a homogeneous one, although it actually occurs in the boundaries between solid and liquid phase and consequently should be regarded as heterogeneous. Exceptions from the permutoid type of reaction involve bulky reagents, which find it difficult to penetrate the cellulose lattice even in its swollen state. Benzyl chloride has proved such a compound (504), but there are also indications that ethyl chloride and dimethyl sulfate tend to give a more heterogeneous reaction than does the smaller methyl chloride molecule (143).

In the earlier years of cellulose research, the concept of *micellar-heterogeneous* reactions was advanced, with the micelles considered to react first in the outer parts, the reagent thereafter slowly penetrating the micelles, converting layer after layer to trisubstituted derivatives before reaching the core. This theory was advanced because all derivatives of medium degree of substitution (D.S.) yielded upon hydrolysis some unsubstituted glucose, as well as mono-, di- and trisubstituted glucose derivatives. From a statistical analysis, however, it was concluded that such distributions are expected also in the permutoid type of reaction (740).

If all the hydroxyl groups are assumed to be accessible and equally reactive, the distribution of the substituents on the different glucose units with increasing D.S. should be that indicated by the curves of Figure 4.28 (740). The D.S. is defined as the *average* degree of substitution per glucose unit of the derivative and may assume any value from 0.0 to 3.0, trisubstitution being the maximum obtainable. It is seen from the figure,

151

that even at D.S. about 2 there is an appreciable amount of monosubstituted glucose units and even some unsubstituted ones. If one of the hydroxyl groups should be somewhat more reactive than the two others, the deviation from the curves in the figure will not be very great as illustrated with the broken lines. Surely the influence of the superstructure and macroheterogeneity in the distribution of reagents and heat will affect the distribution along the chains to a greater extent. The experimental data from the cellulose ethers investigated (143, 334, 696, 767, 772, 782, 791) agree on the whole with the permutoid concept, as indicated by the plots in Figure 4.28. Nitration and sulfation are also permutoid reactions, whereas it is still a matter of debate if acetylation could be regarded as permutoid.

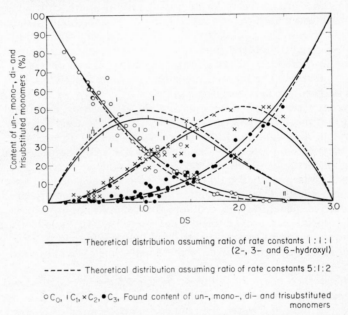

———— Theoretical distribution assuming ratio of rate constants 1 : 1 : 1
(2-, 3- and 6-hydroxyl)

------ Theoretical distribution assuming ratio of rate constants 5:1:2

○ C_0, ı C_1, × C_2, ● C_3, Found content of un-, mono-, di- and trisubstituted monomers

Fig. 4.28. Theoretical and found distribution of substituents in cellulose ethers, expressed as content of un-, mono-, di- and trisubstituted monomers (Croon, Timell and Spurlin)

Since the three hydroxyl groups of the glucose unit in cellulose are all of different types, much work has been devoted to investigating their relative reactivities. Figure 4.29 shows a structural comparison of the three hydroxyls. It is sometimes stated that the 6-hydroxyl, being primary, should be more reactive than the secondary ones. These statements are based on the well-known facts that in substituting the hydrogen atoms attached to carbon in methanol or ethanol with *alkyl* groups, there is a decrease in reactivity of the hydroxyl, both for esterification (6) and etherification. However, it should be pointed out that if a secondary

152

hydroxyl is less reactive than a primary, it is not because it is *secondary*, but because the group substituting one of the hydrogen atoms at the α-carbon represents either a steric hindrance for the reaction or gives an unfavorable electron effect. It is therefore necessary to consider the kind of substituent on the α-carbon in order to decide whether the primary hydroxyls could be expected to be less or more reactive than the primary hydroxyl. It is seen from Figure 4.29 that the 3-hydroxyl differs

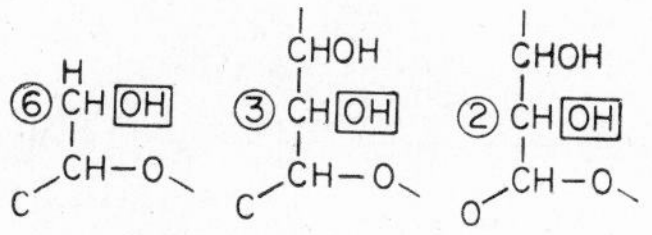

Fig. 4.29. Structural comparison of the different hydroxyl groups in cellulose to illustrate their different acidity (Rånby–Rydholm)

in configuration from the 6-hydroxyl in that one hydrogen atom has been substituted by a CHOH group. The 3-hydroxyl should thus be compared to the 6-hydroxyl as the methanol hydroxyl to a glycol hydroxyl, or a glycol hydroxyl to the secondary hydroxyl in glycerol. Similarly, the 2-hydroxyl differs from the 3-hydroxyl in that the β-carbon atom is bound to two oxygen atoms, instead of one oxygen and one carbon atom. From the assumed electron configurations and from comparisons with model compounds it is evident that there should be a slight *increase* in acidity in the order 6-, 3- and 2-hydroxyl, disregarding interaction effects. However, with the 2-hydroxyl ionized, the acidity of the 3-hydroxyl is likely to decrease, in analogy with normal dibasic acids containing adjacent carboxyl groups such as oxalic acid. Thus, the 2-hydroxyl should have the strongest acidity, whereas the 3-hydroxyl might be weaker than the 6-hydroxyl unless the adjacent 2-hydroxyl has been eliminated by substitution. The differences are probably not very great, and all hydroxyl groups should have an acidity of the order of that of glycerol, glycol or water, i.e. pK_a about 14. Determinations indicate an acidity for cellulose corresponding to a pK_a of 13.4–13.7 (118a, 575a, 671, 691a), with calculations assuming only one acid group per glucose unit. Recalculated to correspond to the acidity of each hydroxyl group, the acidity will be about pK_a 14 on average, with the 2-hydroxyl probably a little stronger.

As acidity should be one of the dominant factors for *etherification* reactivity, no great difference is to be expected in the relative reactivities of the different hydroxyl groups. The analytical problems involved have caused some discrepancies in opinions (164, 366, 508, 672, 767, 773), but recent improvements in the technique of quantitative determination of the various substituted glucose monomers, employing separation on carbon columns in conjunction with paper chromatography and paper electrophoresis (143), have finally solved the problems. For methylations and ethylations the 2-hydroxyl is the most reactive one, followed by the 6-hydroxyl and the 3-hydroxyl, with the approximate ratio of rate constants of 4:2:1, there being indications for the 3-hydroxyl to increase in reactivity after substitution of the adjacent 2-hydroxyl has occurred. The resultant distribution of substituents is indicated in Figure 4.30. *Carboxymethylations* occur at a corresponding rate-constant ratio of 2:2.5:1, the reason for the decreased reactivities of the secondary hydroxyls as compared to the primary being electrostatic effects at the glycol grouping, which prevent substitution of both secondary hydroxyls in the

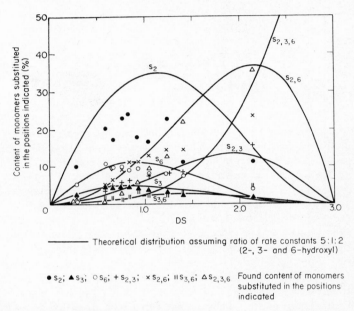

Theoretical distribution assuming ratio of rate constants 5:1:2 (2-, 3- and 6-hydroxyl)

● s_2; ▲ s_3; ○ s_6; + $s_{2,3}$; × $s_{2,6}$; ‖ $s_{3,6}$; △ $s_{2,3,6}$ Found content of monomers substituted in the positions indicated

Fig. 4.30. Theoretical and found distribution of substituents in cellulose ethers, expressed as content of monomers substituted in the positions indicated (Croon)

same monomer. *Hydroxyethylations* with ethylene oxide seem to involve a somewhat different mechanism, giving some preference to the primary hydroxyl. When hydroxyethyl groups have been thus introduced, further substitution can occur at the hydroxyl group of the substituent, which has proved to be more reactive than the original cellulose hydroxyls. Further, in the case of sodium cupricellulose, an addition compound corresponding to an alkali cellulose also containing 0.5 Cu per glucose unit in chemical combination, it has been found that the primary hydroxyl and some 3-hydroxyls are deactivated by the copper atoms or possibly the reactivity of the 2-hydroxyl increased (143, 774, 791).

Esterification of alcohols in general favors primary hydroxyls, even in comparison with secondary alcohols derived from the primary by substitution of hydrogen with hydroxymethyl groups (422). The differences are not very great, the primary hydroxyl in general being 1.5–3.5 times as reactive. The relative reactivities seem, however, to depend greatly on such factors as temperature and amount of water present.

The relative reactivities of the hydroxyl groups in *acetylation* have been investigated by several workers (350, 509, 514, 515, 516, 517, 680). In a commercial acetate with a D.S. of about 2.5 usually 30–40% of its remaining hydroxyl groups are primary. This is of course no measure of the relative esterification reactivities of the hydroxyl groups but rather of the relative rates of hydrolysis, since it is the result of the hydrolysis of the triacetate, which is initially formed in the technical process and subsequently hydrolyzed (cf. Chapter 21). It has been shown, that those rates are dependent on the conditions of hydrolysis, especially the water content of the hydrolytic medium. This is illustrated in Figure 4.31 (516). If the hydrolysis is carried out in acetic acid containing more than 20% water, the proportion of free primary hydroxyls increases, whereas lower water content causes a decrease. The amount of unsubstituted hydroxyl groups

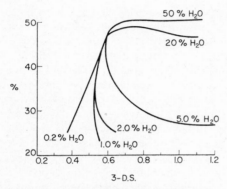

Fig. 4.31. Percentage of primary hydroxyls among the free hydroxyl groups in the esterification and de-esterification of a commercial cellulose acetate in reaction media of different water content (Malm *et al*)

in a partially hydrolyzed acetate may even decrease if the water content in the hydrolysis bath is low, and even then there is a reduction in the proportion of unsubstituted primary hydroxyls. It is therefore evident that during the hydrolysis treatment there are two competing reactions, hydrolysis and esterification, and that in both the primary hydroxyl seems to be the most reactive. An investigation of the esterification of a commercial hydrolyzed acetate to triacetate in homogeneous solution (515) has shown that the primary hydroxyl is more reactive than the secondary ones, but that the differences are greatest at conditions which give a slow over-all reaction, and that they decrease when temperature

155

is raised and catalysts added. However, in no case was the relative reactivity ratio of primary to secondary less than 2.5:1. These investigations have shown that the primary hydroxyl is also the most reactive one in the sulfation reaction taking place during acetylations. Investigations of a series of cellulose nitrates (572) also pointed to a preference for the 6-hydroxyl in *nitration* equilibria.

Summing up, the investigations on the relative reactivities of the cellulose hydroxyl groups have shown that in *esterifications* the 6-hydroxyl is the most reactive, whereas in most *etherifications* the relative reactivities of the hydroxyl groups follow the order of relative acidities, with the 2-hydroxyl as the most reactive. As regards *xanthation*, there is as yet inconclusive evidence, but it is probable that the distribution of substituents on the different hydroxyls resembles that of the cellulose ethers.

III. Hemicelluloses (51, 292, 352, 353, 489, 765a, 778)

1. CLASSIFICATION AND LOCATION

A considerable part of the wood polysaccharides is not cellulose but occurs in close association, and in the previous section on cellulose the definition of the borderline between cellulose and the non-cellulosic constituents was left to this section. It was discovered fairly early, that there are other carbohydrate monomers than glucose. The borderline cannot be drawn between glucosidic and non-glucosidic components, however, as some glucose is chemically combined with other sugars, whereas the major part makes up the cellulose. In the beginning, the definition was based on empirical methods rather than on theoretical grounds. The term *hemicellulose* was assigned to those carbohydrates which were degraded by acid hydrolysis more rapidly than cellulose (708). Hemicellulose was also found to be extractable with alkaline solutions to a larger extent than is cellulose. Further studies revealed that some non-glucosidic components were quite resistant to hydrolysis and alkali extraction, which made it evident that a sharp definition could not be made on such grounds. As the heterogeneity of the hemicellulose fraction became evident, the plural term of *hemicelluloses* has become increasingly used. The use of this collective term is still practical, in spite of the fact that there are now definite chemical terms for the compounds thus covered. It is, however, becoming increasingly evident that these compounds react differently to the pulping chemicals and have different properties, and many discussions on pulping problems would gain if each of the hemicelluloses were considered separately.

Although even recently doubts have been expressed, it is now generally agreed, that cellulose as it occurs also in wood is constituted entirely of glucose monomers, linked with 1:4-β-glycosidic bonds. From that ground, the hemicelluloses are defined as all other cell wall polysaccharides, with the exception of substances which occur only occasionally, e.g. during the sapping period or not in close association with cellulose (51). Pectic

156

substances and starch are thus not considered as hemicelluloses. The definition may be further complicated if the 1: 4-β-linked glucan of DP 150–200, which has been indicated in some wood species (562), should turn out not to be degraded cellulose.

The *location* of the hemicelluloses to the various morphological elements and within the cell wall is of great technical interest, as it will influence both the pulping reactions and the final pulp properties. Table 4.25 gives the approximate carbohydrate composition of the morphological elements of three important pulpwoods (614a). It is seen that cellulose constitutes between 50 and 60% of the carbohydrates in all cells but the hardwood parenchyma cells, where the cellulose content is as low as about 20%. In all parenchyma cells, the xylan content is higher than in the fibers and tracheids, and in birch parenchyma it dominates entirely and has been found to possess a definite crystalline structure (540). As was described in more detail in Chapter 3.III on the relative distribution of cellulose and hemicelluloses (55, 469), it has been found that the cell wall towards lumen contains matter which is more resistant to acid hydrolysis and cold and hot alkali treatment than are the outer parts of the cell wall, although the total concentration of carbohydrate matter seems to be constant over the entire cross section. Thus, the hemicelluloses are likely to be located throughout the cell wall, as well as in the middle lamella (62), but predominantly in the outer parts of the cell wall. The location of the different constituents of the hemicelluloses (541) was also described in Chapter 3.III, Tables 3.1–2. Pectic substances appear in the primary wall, glucomannan

Table 4.25. Approximate carbohydrate composition of pine, spruce and birch cells (recalculated after 614a)*

Wood species and cells	Cellulose, %	Glucomannan, %	Glucurono-(arabino) xylan, %	Galactan and arabinan, %
Pinus silvestris				
Wood	56	26	14	4
Holocellulose	53	30	15	2
Tracheids (98% by weight)	53	30	15	2
Ray cells (2% by weight)	52	21	24	2
Picea abies				
Wood	59	22	16	2
Holocellulose	56	24	18	1
Tracheids (99% by weight)	59	23	17	1
Ray cells (1% by weight)	51	17	32	0
Betula verrucosa				
Wood	53	4	40	2
Holocellulose	54	4	41	1
Fibers (86% by weight)	56	5	38	1
Vessels (9% by weight)	62	—	38	—
Parenchyma cells (5% by weight)	19	2	79	—

* Approximate calculation from chromatographic data (614a), assuming 0.2 glucuronic acid units in softwood xylan and 0.1 in hardwood xylan, and a glucose : mannose ratio of 1 : 3.5 in softwood glucomannan and 1 : 1 in hardwood glucomannan. All arabinose in softwood included in the xylan figure, all galactose in galactan. No acetate groups included in the calculation.

predominantly in the secondary wall (S2) and xylan to a large extent in the tertiary wall (S3). Further it seems to be established, that hemicellulose components may change their location during the pulping processes and become more intimately associated with the cellulose, e.g. xylan in kraft pulping (833) and glucomannan in some types of sulfite cooking (38). It is unlikely that any covalent bonds between cellulose and the hemicelluloses exist, either in the wood or in the pulps. There is considerable evidence, however, in favor of a chemical combination between lignin and hemicelluloses, especially in softwoods (496), but only with relatively few and easily hydrolyzable bonds. These bonds also seem to link the various types of hemicelluloses together via lignin (146).

The hemicelluloses *in situ* are probably largely amorphous in character but some tend to crystallize upon chemical modification and isolation (82, 368, 378, 491, 638, 835), and it is probable that the above-mentioned more intimate association with the cellulose which occurs for part of the hemicelluloses during pulping depends on this tendency. Recent results also indicate a certain degree of orientation *in situ* (488, 519, 540).

2. ISOLATION AND CHARACTERIZATION

The hemicelluloses are isolated from the wood by means of alkali extraction. Only in exceptional cases, such as for arabinogalactans of larch, water extraction yields substantial quantities (411). In the case of hardwoods, alkali extraction of a considerable portion of hemicelluloses can be successfully carried out directly without previous delignification (576), as the hardwood lignin is predominantly located in the middle lamella. Softwood lignin is present to a considerable extent also in the cell wall, and restricts swelling of the latter. To isolate the bulk of the softwood hemicelluloses it is necessary to delignify the wood, whereby mild methods have to be applied to avoid degradation of the hemicelluloses. The isolated mixture of polysaccharides is called *holocellulose* (662). There are mainly two methods of holocellulose preparation, one applying repeated acid chlorite (398, 441, 825) or chlorine dioxide oxidations (292, 699) at elevated temperature, the other repeated alternating treatments with chlorine and ethanolamine (801). Alkali extraction of the holocellulose then gives the main part of the hemicelluloses. Lower alkali concentrations remove fractions enriched on xylan, whereas glucomannan predominates in successive extractions with stronger lye. Some components, mainly part of the glucomannan, are extractable only when borate has been added to the alkali, whereby a complex is formed which facilitates extraction (810).

It cannot be avoided, that the hemicelluloses change on the holocellulose preparation and the subsequent alkali extraction. The chlorite method of lignin removal has recently been criticized (781) because of the hydrolytic conditions and fairly high temperature applied, and chlorine dioxide or chlorine–ethanolamine methods are sometimes preferred, although the latter is rather tedious. Chlorite oxidation at lower temperature for prolonged periods improves the result (441). To characterize some details in the hemicellulose structure, such as the location of ester-bound acetyl groups, the alkaline conditions of the extraction must be avoided. Swelling and extraction of the holocellulose in organic compounds, such as dimethyl sulfoxide, must then be used (272, 490). This is particularly useful in characterizing pulp hemicelluloses containing acetate groups (593).

From the extracts, the crude hemicelluloses can be isolated by means of neutralization and alcohol precipitation. For further purification, elaborate fractionation methods have been worked out, making use of the slightly different behavior of these chemically related components (498). Thus, xylose- and mannose-containing carbohydrates can be precipitated by Fehling's solution, negatively charged components (containing uronic acid) are precipitated by cation active soaps (575b), arabinogalactan by borate with cation active soaps (90) and glucomannan by barium hydroxide (544).

The complicated characterization of the hemicelluloses has involved conventional methods as well as others, specially developed (731). The monomeric constituents of the crude hemicelluloses and of the separated fractions are determined by means of quantitative paper chromatography, completed by uronic acid, methoxyl and acetyl analysis. Chromatographic and electrophoretic methods are also used to separate and characterize fragments from a partial hydrolysis of the carbohydrates, containing two or more monomers, in order to determine the mode of interlinking. Methylation, followed by hydrolysis and chromatographic identification of the methylated sugars, serves the same purpose. Infrared spectra of hemicellulose preparations have been recorded in the study of the possible orientation of hemicelluloses in wood (488, 519).

3. STRUCTURE

Tables 4.3–9 show the analytical composition of the carbohydrates of some typical pulping raw materials. *Glucose*, XXXII, is the dominating sugar, as long as the cellulose is included in the figures. In the softwood hemicelluloses, *mannose*, XXXIII, is the most important monomer, whereas *xylose*, XXXIV, dominates in the hardwood hemicelluloses.

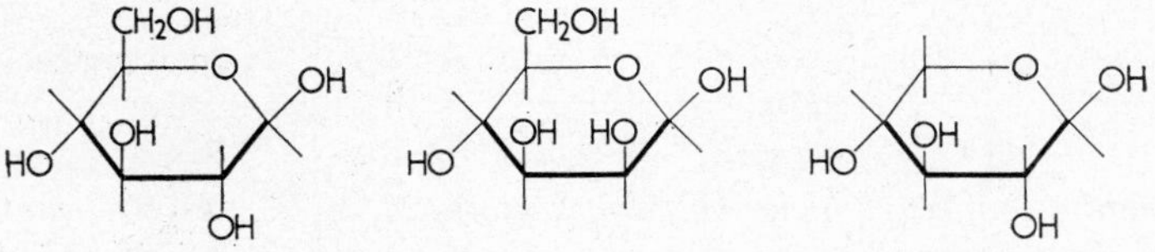

XXXII   XXXIII   XXXIV

Non-cellulosic glucose is fairly common in both softwoods and hardwoods, *galactose*, XXXV, occurs to some extent in hardwoods and is fairly important in softwoods, especially in some species, such as larch. *Arabinose*, XXXVI, occurs in small quantities in hardwoods and somewhat more in softwoods. *Rhamnose*, XXXVII, has been found in minor amounts

159

in hardwoods. *Glucuronic acid*, **XXXVIII**, *methoxyl* and *acetyl* groups are found in both softwoods and hardwoods in considerable quantities. The formulae show the configuration of these monomers in the forms that are believed to occur in the hemicelluloses.

XXXV   XXXVI

XXXVII   XXXVIII

Although there is some work to be done on structural details of the hemicelluloses, investigations in recent years have given a fairly clear picture of their composition (49, 51, 489, 765a). Table 4.26 gives a qualitative description and a gross comparison between softwood and hardwood hemicelluloses (292), and Tables 4.3–5 a quantitative estimation. The

Table 4.26. A qualitative comparison of the hemicelluloses of softwoods and hardwoods (cf. 292)

Polymer	Hardwoods	Softwoods
4-O-methylglucuronoxylan acetate	Very large	Small, if present
4-O-methylglucuronoarabinoxylan	Trace	Medium
Glucomannan acetate	Small	Large
Galactoglucomannan acetate	Trace, if present	Small
Arabinogalactan	Trace, if present	Trace to medium
Other galactose-containing polymers	Trace	Trace, if present
Pectins	Very small	Very small
Starch	Trace	Trace
Glucan other than cellulose or starch	Very small	Trace, if present

polymers *4-O-methylglucuronoxylan acetate*, **XXXIX**, and *4-O-methylglucuronoarabinoxylan*, **XL**, commonly called *xylans* (3, 31, 47, 48, 88, 93, 163, 252, 253, 259, 292, 293, 310, 549, 579, 592, 668, 676, 691, 750, 778, 803, 828), have a straight-chain backbone of xylose monomers (252, 352, 778), connected with 1 : 4-β bonds similar to the linking of the glucose units of cellulose (310). To these chains are attached, in contrast to cellulose, substituents at the hydroxyl groups, preventing crystallization. The substituents are 4-O-methylglucuronic acid (3, 39, 93, 252, 293, 549, 579,

160

592, 676, 691, 750, 803), arabinose (48, 310, 409, 558, 803) and acetate (489, 699) groups. The glucuronic acid is attached predominantly at the 2-hydroxyl (93, 252, 292, 778) and possibly at the 3-hydroxyl (28) groups in a pyranosidic linkage, which strongly resists hydrolysis. There is approximately 0.2 glucuronic acid per xylose unit in softwood xylan and around 0.1 in hardwood xylan. These are average values, and fractionation studies have shown that there is a molecular spectrum of xylan molecules with considerable variation in the uronic acid content (147). The position of the acetate groups has not yet been fully ascertained (88), but there is some evidence of their substituting both 2- and 3-hydroxyls, with about 0.7–0.8 acetate groups per xylose unit in hardwood xylan. The softwood acetate groups belong to the glucomannan, which contains about 0.3 per monomer (452, 542, 672), cf. below. In softwood xylan there are further 0.1–0.3 arabinose units per xylose monomer attached with easily hydrolyzable furanosidic bonds at the 3-carbon atom (65, 239). Therefore, 20–50% of the hydroxyl groups of the xylan chains are blocked by substituents. For the carbohydrate reactions in alkaline pulping and purification, it is important that the glucuronic acid substituents at the 2-hydroxyl, although not very stable to alkali at high temperature (293), at lower temperature to a considerable extent block the degradation reaction known as 'alkaline peeling' from the aldehydic end group of a polysaccharide chain. The acetate groups are rapidly hydrolyzed in alkaline processes but are surprisingly stable to acid hydrolysis (593). Arabinose is rapidly removed, especially in the acid processes, whereas the glucuronic acid substituents are fairly resistant to acid hydrolysis. The removal of substituents will increase the crystallization tendency of the xylan chains. The degree of polymerization of the hardwood xylan chains ranges from 80 to 270 with an average of around 190, whereas the average DP of isolated softwood xylan is around 100, with some reservation for degradation during the holocellulose preparation.

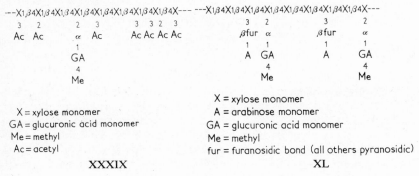

The *glucomannan* and *galactoglucomannan*, XLI, constituents of hemicellulose likewise contain monomers linked with 1 : 4-β-pyranosidic bonds (39, 45, 64, 80, 92, 144, 146, 253, 294, 295, 296, 335, 378, 409, 480, 491, 549, 628, 639, 730, 783, 803). The molecules are generally considered to be linear, although in softwood glucomannan about 3–5 branches per molecule have been indicated (144, 549). The DP is 70–140 for softwood (491) and about 70 for hardwood glucomannan (775). The branches probably extend from the glucose units, substituted in 3-position (cf., however, 80). Also the branches seem to contain 1:4-β-pyranosidic bonds. Probably all mannose of the wood is contained in these compounds, and the proportions of glucose to mannose are about 1:3–1:4 in softwood glucomannan and 1:2–1:1 in the less studied and less important hardwood glucomannan. The acetate groups of softwood glucomannan were mentioned above, and as with xylan acetate, the ester groups are easily hydrolyzed by alkaline pulping liquors and less easily by acidic ones (673), and their removal will increase the degree of order and hydrolytic resistance of the glucomannan. Galactoglucomannan, which has mainly been found in softwoods (4, 64, 293, 400, 543, 776), has been less studied, or studied as a glucomannan. It appears altogether possible that most of the so-called glucomannan in the native state is present as galactoglucomannan, about one tenth to one third of which is water-soluble and contains almost 20% galactose and the remainder alkali-soluble with only 3% galactose, in both cases linked to the glucomannan chain in terminating 1:6-α-pyranosidic units (559a, 776). From the present investigations on hemicelluloses, it does not seem altogether clear, whether all non-cellulosic glucose has been accounted for with the glucomannan, especially for some hardwoods, as was pointed out earlier, but relatively small additional amounts remain to be explained, and practically nothing in softwoods.

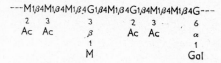

M = mannose monomer
G = glucose monomer
Gal = galactose monomer
Ac = acetyl

XLI

The *arabinogalactans* (5, 31, 46, 50, 79, 87, 89, 99, 120, 199, 410, 564, 608, 750, 806, 819), XLII, abundant in larch and less so in other softwoods, are believed to have a fairly complicated structure, and to contain two different structural types. To a galactan backbone, containing 1:3-β-pyranosidic bonds, are attached branches from almost all 6-carbon atoms. The branches seem to consist of single or double galactose units in 1:6-β-pyranosidic linkages, or single or double arabinose units, in furanosidic linkages to the backbone but interlinked with 1:3-β-pyranosidic bonds. Altogether, there are around 0.25 arabinose units per galactose monomer. The DP of arabinogalactan is about 50–100 for most softwoods and 100–600 for larch (90, 571). There is probably also a pure *galactan* (765a).

From what is known today it can be concluded that softwoods generally contain, in addition to 40–45% cellulose, about 12–20% glucomannan and galactoglucomannan acetate, 10–14% methylglucuronoarabinoxylan and about 2% galactan or arabinogalactan, whereas hardwoods, in addition to about the same quantity of cellulose contain 20–35% methylglucurono- xylan acetate, 2–5% glucomannan, 1–2% arabinogalactan and possibly some non-cellulosic glucan. As is the case with cellulose and lignin, the amounts and proportions of hemicelluloses greatly vary with the wood species, and probably also from tree to tree.

```
----Gal1β3Gal1β3Gal1β3Gal1β3Gal1β3Gal1β3Gal1β3Gal1β3Gal1β3Gal---
       6      6     6      6      6      6      6      6      6
       β      β     β     βfur    β      β     βfur    β      β
       1      1     1      1      1      1      1      1      1
      Gal    Gal   Gal     A     Gal    Gal     A     Gal    Gal
       6            3             6      3             6
       β            β             β      β             β
       1            1             1      1             1
      Gal           A            Gal     A            Gal
```

Gal = galactose monomer
A = arabinose monomer
fur = furanosidic bond (all others pyranosidic)

XLII

The nature and proportions of the hemicelluloses in *reaction wood* are somewhat different from those of normal wood. In tension wood (266) as well as in compression wood (751), there is an increase in the content of galactose units, which is probably caused by the occurrence of a *galacturo- nogalactan*, having a backbone of about 50 1:4-β-linked galactose mono- mers, some of which have galacturonic acid substituents (86, 544a). Both types of reaction wood are likely to contain about 10% of this hemicellu- lose, whereas the content of glucomannan in compression wood and of glucuronoxylan in tension wood is considerably reduced as compared to normal wood.

4. REACTIVITY

As the hemicelluloses are structurally related to the cellulose, their reactions are very similar. Like cellulose, the hemicelluloses form *addition* compounds at their hydroxyl groups, which also can be *substituted* to ester and ether groups. Like cellulose, the hemicelluloses can undergo *oxidation* to keto- and aldo- compounds, which are *degraded* by alkali already in the cold, whereas further oxidation eventually leads to alkali- stable carboxyl-containing compounds. As with cellulose, hypochlorite oxidation of xylan is most extensive around neutrality, yielding carbon dioxide and after hydrolysis glyceric acid (818). *Hot alkaline degradation* starts at the aldehydic end groups or at oxidized groups along the chain, and proceeds as a peeling reaction. At especially high temperature, *alkaline hydrolysis* of the glycosidic bonds occurs, producing new starting-points of alkaline peeling. *Rearrangements* during alkali cooking produce alkali-stable carboxyl end groups. In *acid* medium, *hydrolytic degradation* at the glycosidic bonds is the dominating reaction. Action of the bisulfite or sulfite ions causes formation of polymers containing sulfonate and carboxyl groups, the 'sugarsulfonic acids', as well as the low-molecular aldonic acids. Therefore, the conditions chosen for the pulping processes in many respects could consider the carbohydrate reactions as a whole and contrast them to the reactivity of lignin, in order to achieve a selective delignification which leaves a paper pulp where the entire carbohydrate fraction is left undegraded to the highest possible extent.

However, there are important differences in spite of the similar pattern of reaction of cellulose and the hemicelluloses, and on these differences depend not only the methods of modifying the paper pulp properties, but also the principles of dissolving pulp manufacture, where a selective removal of the hemicelluloses is desired to leave a relatively pure and not too degraded cellulose. These differences in reactivity to a large extent have physical causes rather than chemical ones, and are better described as differences in accessibility. The hemicelluloses are *in situ* largely amorphous, in contrast to cellulose. Most chemical agents therefore reach the hemicelluloses much more easily than the crystalline regions of the cellulose. The oxidation and degradation reactions will thus hit the hemicelluloses more rapidly than the cellulose. There are, however, strong indications that xylan (833, 836) as well as glucomannan (82, 368, 638) may undergo secondary crystallization (38, 833, 836), probably after losing some substituents. This is not only the case on precipitation of dissolved hemicellulose fractions, but also in the course of cooking, whereby the crystallization may also take the form of adsorption to the cellulose crystallites. This is indicated from the behavior of xylan in the kraft cook and of glucomannan in the acid sulfite cook, in the latter particularly when the cook is kept for some time at low temperature or for a shorter time at higher temperature and lower acidity. In both cases, *deacetylation* is likely to be the main prerequisite to obtain a well-ordered structure. Glucomannan molecules are then almost entirely linear, and investigations on the x-ray pattern of glucuronoxylan (520) and glucoxylan (777) show that the glucuronic acid side chains do not form an integral part of the unit cell of the former.

Some chemical differences also give rise to varying reactivity. The 2- and 3-substituents of xylan serve to improve its resistivity to hot alkali. Glucuronic acid groups check peeling in hot alkali purification and arabinose groups facilitate the metasaccharinic acid end-group stabilization in the kraft cook. Similarly, some glucomannan is fairly resistant to hot alkali, although a smaller amount than in the case of xylan. In the glucomannan there are probably no substituents in the 2-position to explain the alkali-resistance of the glucomannan molecules remaining after a kraft cook. Location and degree of order are probably important factors to decrease their accessibility. However, the stopping reaction discussed in the previous section on cellulose, which by means of intramolecular rearrangement of the end monomer to *meta*-saccharinic acid makes the polysaccharide molecule stable to alkali, will occur also for glucomannan. The only way of further alkaline degradation of such a stabilized chain is hydrolysis of glycosidic bonds, by which new aldehyde end groups are exposed. Such a hydrolysis will occur also in alkali at kraft cooking temperature. It has, however, been demonstrated by model experiments (161), that these glycosidic bonds having the aglycone and the 2-hydroxyl in *cis* position are considerably more stable to alkaline hydrolysis than the corresponding *trans* configurations. Therefore, it is to be expected that the mannosidic bond in a polysaccharide chain will be more resistant to alkaline hydrolysis than the glycosidic bonds of glucose, galactose and xylose. A glucomannan, ending with a *meta*-saccharinic acid monomer should thus be subjected to further alkaline degradation largely at the glucosidic bonds, which are only around 25% of the total glycosidic bonds originally, and eventually considerably less. The remarkable resistance of glucomannan in a kraft cook charged with borohydride (303) to reduce the aldehydic end groups is likewise explained by the slow alkaline hydrolysis of mannosidic bonds.

There are also certain differences of reactivity in substitution, compared with that of cellulose. That is of considerable interest when pulps containing hemicelluloses are reacted with chemicals in the dissolving pulp processes. Some of these differences may be of physical rather than chemical nature. Minor amounts of hemicellulose are likely to improve the swelling of the fibers in lye and thereby cause a greater accessibility of the entire fiber wall to the chemical reagents, such as carbon disulfide of the viscose process. Excessive amounts of amorphous hemicelluloses cause 'hornified' structures on drying which decrease the reaction rate on chemical processing. Hemicelluloses have thus been accused of causing non-uniform xanthation of the pulp (116, 270). Xylan, having only two hydroxyl groups per monomer, exhibits some chemical differences on chemical processing. It gives a carboxymethyl ether similar to that of cellulose (701), but in the investigated D.S. range of 0.1–0.9 practically none of the monomers were doubly substituted. This is in agreement with the behaviour of cellulose on carboxymethylation, where contemporary substitution of both secondary hydroxyls is scarce (145, 782), whereas the primary hydroxyl group is readily substituted. A similar behavior might be expected in the case of xanthation, and both xylan and mannan have been found to xanthate readily in alkaline solution (399, 622). In the acid processing of pulps to nitrate and acetate some disadvantages occur, such as haze, color and 'false viscosity', which are ascribed to the presence of hemicelluloses (92, 594, 734, 748), since purification of the pulp cellulose will improve the properties, and since the addition of mannan (but not of xylan) to cotton gave 'false viscosity' phenomena upon acetylation (814). The persistence of glucomannan through nitration (563), and acetylation (814, 830) is remarkable and higher than that of xylan, and is probably caused by the secondary crystallization mentioned earlier. The haze-producing matter of cellulose acetate solutions is considerably enriched in xylan (148, 738). The haze occurring in the nitrate is possibly caused by xylan because of the poor solubility of xylan dinitrate (378).

The greater accessibility to water of the amorphous hemicelluloses in mildly isolated pulp fibers causes a higher tendency of these pulps to water retention and swelling. This greatly facilitates another important processing of pulps, the beating for paper production. In contrast to most of the effects mentioned above, where the hemicelluloses of the pulp are detrimental to the quality of dissolving pulps, the rôle of the hemicelluloses in paper production is positive and very important, as they contribute to the paper strength, cf. Chapter 21.

IV. Lignin

The third main component of wood is lignin, which occurs in amounts between 20 and 35% of the wood. In fact, wood is defined by the presence of lignin in the cell wall structure, which by the lignification receives its stiff woody appearance. The lignin content varies with species, rate of growth, amount of reaction wood, etc. Tables 4.1–5 show the lignin content of some typical pulpwoods, as well as of some annual plants used for pulping. The chemistry of lignin is to a very large extent involved in most pulping reactions, since lignin is the less desirable of the three main wood components and therefore has to be removed or bleached to an extent varying with the grade of pulp desired. Furthermore, as lignin constitutes so great a part of the wood weight and has no immediate use, it has long attracted interest for conversion into useful chemicals. For these two reasons lignin chemistry has grown to a separate and important branch of organic and physical chemistry during the efforts of almost a century. It would be futile to try to reduce all the work done to a few pages in this chapter. Reference must be made to the standard works and excellent surveys of lignin chemistry (7, 94, 95, 273). This section will instead take advantage of the knowledge collected, present the stand-point of lignin chemistry today, and dwell on the aspects of interest for pulping reactions.

After a presentation of our knowledge of the formation of lignin and its distribution in the cell wall, of the methods of isolation from the other wood constituents, the present concept of the lignin structure will be given. Finally the reactivity of lignin towards chemicals used in the preparation of pulp is described.

1. FORMATION AND DISTRIBUTION IN THE CELL WALL

Several workers have followed the formation of lignin in young plants, preferably annual ones, such as rye (73), barley and oats (103, 625). They found that both lignin content and the methoxyl content of the lignin increased during the growth. This was interpreted as a rapid lignin formation followed by a somewhat slower methylation of the lignin, but

166

could possibly also mean that other substances than those defined as lignin in mature wood contaminated the isolated lignin in the earlier samples. If methoxyl content is taken as a measure of the true lignin content, lignification occurred for winter rye after approximately 200 days of growth. The period of lignification coincided with the main growth and the disappearance of the green color of the plant. Also, in wood, lignification occurs contemporarily with the main growth period, and cell maturity is reached after more than two years. Proportionally more lignin than carbohydrates is added during the second year, whereas the youngest tissues are comparatively little lignified (756).

The precursors of lignin and its formation in the wood are still not completely elucidated, although recently considerable progress has been made. Earlier it was generally believed that lignin is formed from carbohydrates and it has been pointed out that the proportions of lignin and hemicellulose in wood are interrelated, so that a high lignin content goes with a low hemicellulose content and the reverse (646, 712). Quite early, however, another hypothesis was advanced (435), namely that lignin is formed from coniferyl alcohol or coniferyl aldehyde. This was indicated by the presence of coniferin, the glucoside of coniferyl alcohol, in the cambial sap of conifers (763), and later supported by the established fact that native lignin has an aromatic structure (cf. below). The most representative lignin preparation (81) has a chemical composition of $C_9H_{8.83}O_{2.37}(OCH_3)_{0.96}$, whereas coniferyl alcohol has the formula $C_9H_9O_2OCH_3$. Assuming the somewhat higher oxygen content to be caused by hydration, deduction of 0.37 H_2O will give a lignin composition of $C_9H_{8.09}O_{2.00}(OCH_3)_{0.96}$. This is practically one hydrogen atom less than in coniferyl alcohol. It was suggested (189), that p-hydroxyphenylpropane compounds, unsaturated in the middle of the side chain, on oxidation would give rise to coupling reactions not only in the o-position to the phenolic hydroxyl, but also at the β-carbon atom of the side chain. This gives the possibilities for coniferyl alcohol shown in XLIII.

The dimers indicated, coupled as β–$aryl$, β–β (lignan) or β–$aroxyl$, could be further dehydrogenated and polymerized to lignin. This was shown experimentally (208, 209) by treatment of coniferyl alcohol with mushroom peroxidase in the presence of air (and later on also with a peroxidase extracted from the cambium and adjacent cell layers (210), whereby an amorphous polymer was obtained. The polymerization could be interrupted on the dimer stage. When the solutions of coniferyl alcohol and enzyme were directly mixed, the β–aryl coupling dominated, whereas by drop-wise addition of the coniferyl alcohol to the enzyme, the β–aroxyl coupling was the main reaction. The latter is in conformity with the indications of structural analysis of lignin (cf. below). In addition, lignin has been found to contain small amounts of $diphenyl$ couplings, the fourth possibility (57, 224, 620). The α–β coupling is also a probable polymerization reaction (226, 228). The dimers, considered as the secondary building stones of lignin, could also be isolated in the cambial sap of living trees (209). Further, injection of D-coniferin, labelled with C^{14} at

167

XLIII

the terminal carbon atom of the side chain, into a young spruce twig was found to be deposited in the wood as a high-polymer product, which gave the lignin reactions (207). L-coniferin was not assimilated, showing the presence of only β-glucosidase and proving that hydrolysis of the glucosidic bond yielding coniferyl alcohol is a prerequisite for the polymerization. The presence of glucosidase was demonstrated by using indican, a colorless glucoside of indoxyl, which after hydrolysis gives blue indigo in the presence of air. It was found that the glucosidase is present in about ten cell rows close to the cambium, in those cells where the lignification is not complete, Figure 4.32.

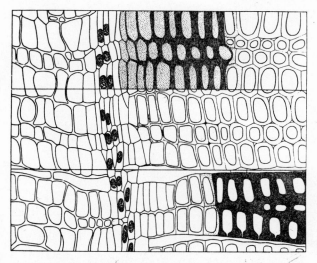

Fig. 4.32. Cross-section of the cambial zone and adjacent wood tissue.
Top: β-glucosidase, made visible by indican treatment.
Middle: untreated.
Bottom: lignin, made visible by treatment with phloroglucinol-hydrochloric acid (Freudenberg)

Additional information has been gathered from further experiments with addition of labelled model compounds to tissues *in vitro* or *in vivo* (102, 168, 452, 518, 588, 721, 804). Phenylpyruvic acid, cinnamic acid and phenylalanine were all shown to be rapidly assimilated in grass and hardwoods (102), giving a lignin which could be subsequently degraded by oxidation to the aromatic aldehydes vanillin, syringaldehyde and p-hydroxybenzaldehyde, which are typical oxidative degradation products of grass and hardwood lignin (XLIV). Further evidence indicates that the aromatic molecules are first hydroxylated (799), possibly by oxygen in the presence of ascorbic acid and ferro ions, and subsequently methylated (117, 167), possibly in a reaction with methionine (XLV).

The biosynthesis of aromatic amino acids, such as phenylalanine, has

169

been shown to occur via the following route (153). Glucose is degraded to C_4 and C_5 fragments, which recombine to C_7 molecules such as sedoheptulose-7-phosphate (XLVI). Cyclization gives hydroaromatic products such as shikimic acid, which possibly on reaction with pyruvic acid yields an intermediate compound, prephenic acid. The latter is unstable and yields by decarboxylation and dehydration the first aromatic compound, phenylpyruvic acid, which may be aminated to phenylalanine. Thus, a possible sequence of reactions has been established for the full biosynthesis of lignin.

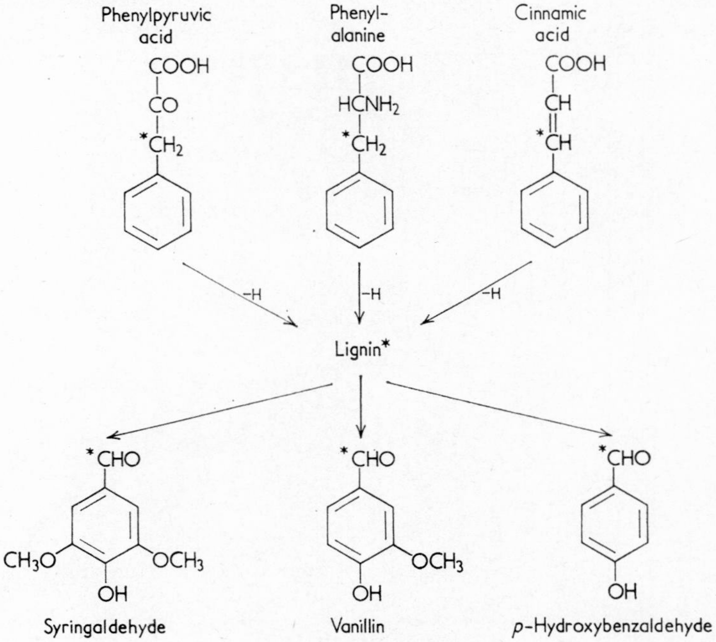

Syringaldehyde   Vanillin   p-Hydroxybenzaldehyde

XLIV

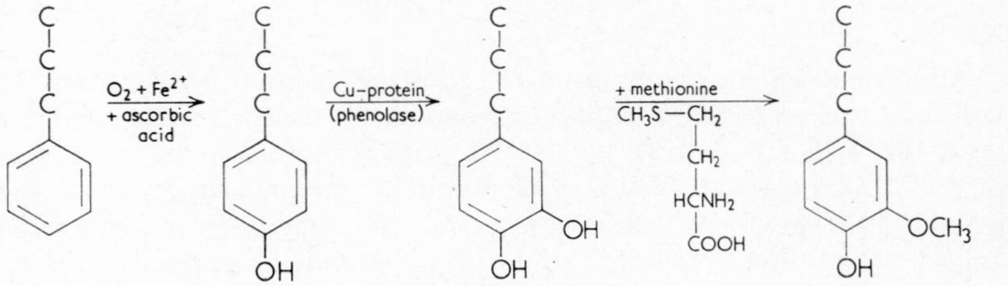

XLV

As the cell walls grow, carbohydrates develop predominantly in the secondary wall and lignin mainly in the middle lamella and primary wall (470). With micromanipulator and chemical microanalysis the middle lamella of Douglas fir was found to contain around 71 % lignin and the remaining fiber substance about 15% lignin (62), whereas measurements of the ultraviolet light absorption of ultrathin spruce wood sections gave values of 60–90%, average 73%, lignin content of the middle lamella plus primary wall and 10–20%, average 12%, lignin content in the remainder of the cell wall (470). Interference microscopy (471) gave an average of 68% lignin in the middle lamella and 10% lignin in the secondary wall. The lignin content dropped very sharply in the outer parts of the secondary wall (470). Other studies seem to indicate a still sharper border-line between the lignin-rich middle lamella and the rest of the fiber (53). There is no great difference in the lignin distribution of springwood and summer-wood cell walls but the cells of reaction wood show a marked differenti-ation (470). How much of the total lignin is concentrated to the lignin-rich parts of the fiber is not quite clear, since it depends on the thickness of these parts relative to the total cell wall, and their density, but it seems likely, that at least two-thirds of sprucewood lignin is situated in the outer parts of the fiber, and in the middle lamella. In hardwoods probably

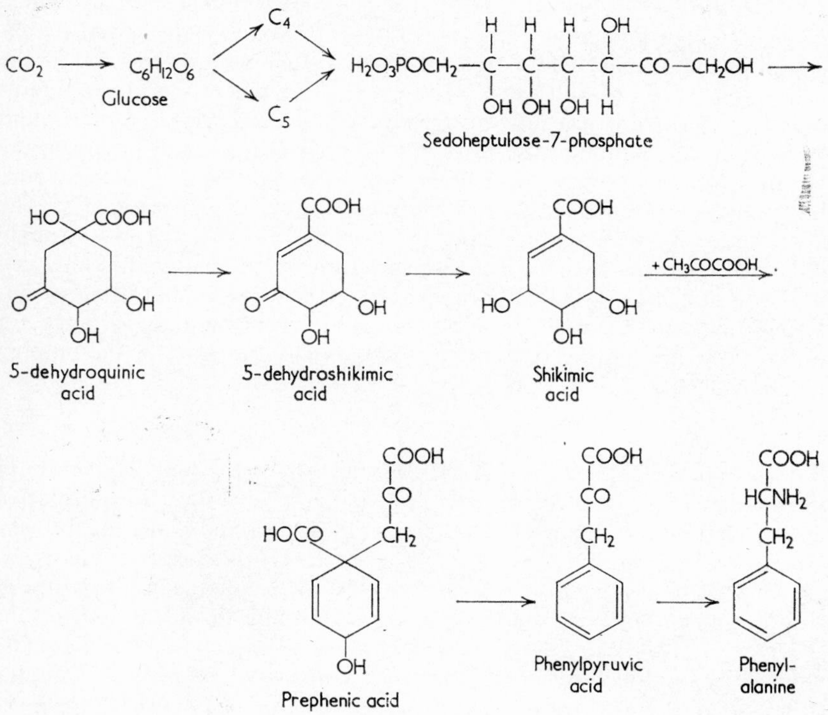

XLVI

still more of the lignin is outside the main part of the fiber. Although the recent work thus seems to develop a picture of a stiff lignin enamel sur-rounding the fibers and binding them together (cf. 369), the occurrence of minor amounts of lignin penetrating the whole structure of the cell wall

171

must not be overlooked. Lignin isolated from the region of the primary wall and intercellular layer has a membraneous and dense structure, whereas that isolated from the secondary wall is porous, with pores 200–300 Å in width, corresponding to the coarse microfibril structure, Figures 3.4 and 3.14 (811). This indicates an intimate structural association with the cellulose and shows that lignin, together with the hemicelluloses, constitutes an amorphous phase in which the microfibrils are embedded. The relation between cell wall formation, i.e. carbohydrate deposition, and lignification has been closely investigated (811). The latter begins in the primary wall adjacent to the corner thickenings of the intercellular substances and then extends to the intercellular layer and the rest of the primary wall. In the first phase, the carbohydrates have completely formed the S1 layer. Before the formation of the main part of the secondary wall is completed, lignification of S1 has begun, and on the formation of S3, S2 was rapidly becoming lignified. However, lignification considerably lags behind the carbohydrate deposition, and has the character of filling in the regions between the microfibrils to a compact structure which gives the rigidity of wood, Figure 3.12 (811). Possibly the initial lignification in the primary wall is related to the progressive withdrawal of the cytoplasm from the wall (811). The question of where the precursors of lignin are formed is not fully answered. The occurrence of coniferin and syringin in the cambium sap does not necessarily mean that lignin in the xylem arises only from the cambium components diffusing into the wood, but similar substances may also be formed within the lignifying cells. The occurrence of lignin–carbohydrate bonds (cf. below) is further strongly indicated, showing that the intimate structural relation with the other cell wall components is partly a chemical one. It is obvious that the distribution of lignin in the wood structure is of great interest and importance not only for the mechanical properties of wood (440) but also for the pulping reactions.

2. ISOLATION OF LIGNIN

Some studies of lignin have been made directly on wood. However, in most cases it is necessary to isolate the lignin, e.g. for its quantitative determination and for most structural studies. Because of the interwoven structure of wood and the sensitivity and reactivity of lignin, this is no easy matter, and it has still not been possible to isolate the total amount of wood lignin in an unchanged form, corresponding to the 'protolignin' of the wood. This has caused many workers to conclude that lignin is chemically combined to some other wood constituent, whereas others refer to topochemical difficulties. The isolation of lignin has many problems in common with pulping, although the purpose of pulping is the reverse, to isolate the remainder of the wood after removal of the lignin. Isolation of lignin is achieved in two principally different ways: (1) dissolution or destruction of the carbohydrates leaving a lignin residue, and (2) dissolution of the lignin either in a more or less unchanged form or as a derivative. In both cases removal of the wood components extractable with alcohol or benzene–alcohol mixtures is essential to avoid contamination of the lignin.

A. Isolation of lignin as a residue after chemical treatment of wood

This category of methods makes use of selective solubility or reactivity of the carbohydrates, and thus involves mainly carbohydrate chemistry. Carbohydrates can be *dissolved* by mineral acids of certain concentration ranges, as well as by copper ammonia or amine hydroxide and quaternary ammonium bases (cf. Chapter 3.II). Carbohydrates can be broken down to fragments by hydrolysis of the glycosidic bonds, or by periodate oxidation of its glycol groups. None of these treatments leaves the lignin unaffected, since condensation occurs in acid medium and some oxidation of lignin by periodate also takes place. In concentrated alkalis unknown changes occur, and some lignin dissolves. Furthermore, in contrast to pure carbohydrates, wood will not dissolve directly in copper ammonia hydroxide or phosphoric acid solutions, where little or no hydrolysis takes place, but has to be prehydrolyzed, whereby lignin is changed at the same time. There is also danger of contamination by carbohydrates, if the lignin preparation is not carefully hydrolyzed, and also part of the lignin dissolves together with the carbohydrates.

Four main preparation techniques with many variations are known, namely *sulfuric acid* or *Klason* lignin, *hydrochloric acid* or *Willstätter* lignin, *cuproxam* lignin and *periodate* lignin. Related to these methods is the liberation of lignin by destruction of the carbohydrates by *brown-rot fungi* (485, 587).

Sulfuric acid lignin is obtained by treatment of wood meal with sulfuric acid in a concentration around 70% for a certain period, followed by dilution and reflux cooking (436). This method is generally accepted as a standard method for the quantitative determination of lignin in wood (123, 760) although modifications in the concentration from about 65–75% seem to be necessary to obtain correct values for all species of wood (212, 404). Some lignin dissolves in the acid, only little from softwoods (104, 505) but as much as 15–20% of hardwood lignin goes into solution (606, 749). Sulfuric acid lignin is dark brown from extensive condensation, has a low reactivity toward most lignin reagents and is of little value for research on lignin structure.

Hydrochloric acid lignin is isolated by treatment of wood with fuming hydrochloric acid, 40–43%, at below room temperature (425, 823, 824). After dilution and prolonged hydrolysis, the lignin is filtered off. It is lighter in color and less condensed than Klason lignin and has been used for some structural research, but is still considered to be more condensed than both the protolignin and several lignin preparations.

Cuproxam lignin remains when wood flour has been 'degummed' with 5% sodium hydroxide solution, prehydrolyzed with boiling dilute sulfuric acid, and after washing shaken with cuprammonium hydroxide solution in repeated sequences (213, 214). This lignin is either contaminated with carbohydrates or obtained in lower yields than would correspond to the protolignin content, but has a high reactivity and is believed to be less condensed than the former two preparations.

Periodate lignin is the residue after oxidation of wood flour with sodium periodate at room temperature and pH 4 (661, 807). Although these conditions will permit isolation of a lignin with little or no acid condensation, it is obvious from its analytical figures that some part of it has been oxidized, thereby decreasing its value for structural research.

Enzymatically liberated lignin with the aid of brown-rot fungi is considered to be one of the most unchanged lignin preparations, according to spectral evidence (587), etc., although it has a slightly low methoxyl content, especially for hardwood lignin, similar to the so-called Brauns' native lignin, cf. below and Table 4.28.

B. Isolation of lignin by dissolution

(1) *Extraction with neutral solvents.* Although lignin from its chemical nature would be expected to dissolve in neutral organic solvents, the bulk of the lignin in the wood does not. This is usually explained in two ways: that lignin is chemically combined with the carbohydrates, or that lignin is high-molecular and forms a three-dimensional network in the wood. A small fraction of the lignin in wood flour (about 1.6% of sprucewood and 0.4% of beechwood (229)) can be dissolved by aqueous ethanol at room temperature (96) and is called *Brauns' native lignin.* Although this preparation has long been used as a reference substance coming closest to protolignin because of the mild conditions of its isolation, it has been doubted whether it may be considered as representative for the protolignin, since it has been shown to differ analytically from the latter in some respects, especially in methoxyl content. Still, its value for lignin structural research has been considerable.

To overcome the inhibitory influence of the wood structure on the dissolution of lignin in neutral solvents, attempts have been made to grind and mill the wood to finer particles together with the solvent (97, 264, 336). No appreciable quantities of lignin in excess of Brauns' native lignin were, however, recovered until it was discovered that grinding small amounts of wood flour in a vibrational ball mill together with a non-swelling diluent, followed by extraction in neutral solvents, gave substantial quantities of lignin and lignin–carbohydrate complexes (81). These preparations, called *Björkman* or *milled wood lignin,* isolated in a chemically mild way in quantities which could be considered representative for the protolignin, are now being extensively investigated (e.g. 7, 229, 607).

(2) *Extraction with acidified solvents.* In contrast to the two methods previously mentioned, addition of small amounts of acids to the organo-solvents at elevated temperature has been used to extract lignin from wood. In the case of the *alcohol lignins* (236, 299, 437) the isolation obviously involves a chemical change in the lignin, as an increase in the alkoxyl content has been found (119, 274, 357). In similar cases, as with *dioxane lignin* (419, 616), where no such group can be introduced, it is still probable that a chemical change has occurred, namely hydrolysis, at the

same groups where alcoholysis occurs. Particularly mild is a special variant of dioxane lignin isolation in dioxane with a low water content and small additions of hydrochloric acid at room temperature (755). In contrast to the alcohol lignins, which are obtained in fairly small amounts calculated on wood, dioxane lignin (176) and *polyglycol lignin* extractions have been suggested as technical pulping methods. *Phenol lignins* are isolated by heating wood in phenols together with an acid catalyst (129, 304) and contain phenol radicals condensed to the lignin, probably at the same place as the alkoxyl groups are bound in the alcohol lignins.

Mercapto lignins are obtained by treatment of wood with alkyl mercaptans (98, 358). The highest yield, above 90 % of the lignin in the wood, is obtained with thioglycolic acid in boiling absolute alcohol, that is $1N$ with respect of hydrochloric acid (356). After extraction with alcohol and alkali, a thioglycolic acid lignin is obtained, containing considerable amounts of combined thioglycolic acid groups. The same groups in lignin seem to react as in the isolation of alcohol lignins, since the alkoxyl groups in alcohol lignins can be replaced by thioglycolic acid groups.

Thiolignin can also be regarded as a mercapto lignin. It is formed in the reaction between hydrogen sulfide and wood at elevated temperature (275, 276) and can be isolated after pyridine extraction (180, 181). This reaction is also important in the kraft pulping process.

(3) *Extraction with hydrotropic solutions.* Certain salts of high solubility in water change the properties of water so that organic compounds become increasingly soluble, so-called hydrotropic solutions. Concentrated solutions of sodium xylenesulfonate and related compounds have been used to dissolve lignin from wood at elevated temperature and pressure (536, 610). Hardwood lignin dissolves almost completely (673, 793), whereas a large part of the softwood lignin remains undissolved (673). The lignin can be precipitated from the solution by dilution with water. This method has been suggested for pulping (536).

(4) *Extraction with aqueous alkaline solutions.* Lignin can be extracted from wood by digestion at high temperature and pressure in aqueous alkali, which method is applied by the alkaline pulping processes. The *alkali lignin* can be precipitated from the cooking liquor on acidification (526, 538) and has been used for several structural investigations, although it is quite dark in color and has undergone considerable structural changes during the isolation procedure. If the alkaline solution has contained sulfide, sulfur is bound to the alkali lignin (28, 33, 438).

(5) *Extraction with aqueous sulfite–bisulfite solutions.* Lignin can be extracted from wood by the action of sulfite–bisulfite solutions at various pH's, preferably on the acid side. Some extraction occurs already at room temperature on prolonged treatment, but usually elevated temperature and pressure are used. This method is applied by the sulfite and neutral sulfite pulping processes. A lignin derivative, *lignosulfonic acid* or its corresponding salt, *lignosulfonate*, is formed (437, 609, 784), which is soluble in water and can be isolated by different methods (187, 215, 433). Lignosulfonic acids of different degrees of sulfonation have been much

used for structural investigations, particularly the low-sulfonated type which is obtained by sulfonation in nearly-neutral solution and subsequent extraction of the 'solid' lignosulfonic acid from the wood by mild hydrolysis (462). Sulfonation seems to involve the same group in lignin as do alcoholysis and hydrolysis.

3. STRUCTURE

With the aid of the lignin preparations just described, as well as with direct investigations on the wood, the lignin chemists have tried to elucidate the chemical structure of lignin. This has turned out to be very complicated, often compared in this respect to the phenol–formaldehyde plastics, and is still obscure on many points. However, much progress has been made during the past six decades, and although now and then some workers have questioned the existence of lignin in wood (351, 710), there is today fairly general agreement about the main structural features of lignin.

The methods used for the structural research have been the following:

(*a*) Careful analysis of the elementary composition of lignin preparations of different types and from different plant species.

(*b*) Determination of characteristic functional groups.

(*c*) Comparison of lignin reactions and reaction kinetics with model substances.

(*d*) Comparison of lignin light absorption spectra with those of model substances.

(*e*) Degradation of lignin *in situ* or isolated, by various methods, and analysis of the degradation products.

(*f*) Synthesis of lignin-like polymers from monomers believed to be the precursors of lignin in the wood.

A. *Elementary composition*

Only carbon, hydrogen and oxygen are present in lignin. The elementary composition determined on analysis of various lignin preparations varies considerably, carbon content from 63 to 67% and hydrogen from 5 to 6% (softwood lignin), showing structural changes during the isolation, mainly hydration and dehydration. Calculated from analysis of holocellulose and the corresponding wood, the lignin removed contains 67.5% carbon and 6% hydrogen (807). Anyway, the high carbon content indicates the aromatic nature of the lignin. Hardwood lignin has a somewhat lower carbon content, 59–60%, and higher oxygen content, 33–34%. Table 4.27 (81) gives the elementary composition of some milled wood lignin preparations from various 'species'.

B. *Functional groups*

The most characteristic functional group in lignin is its *methoxyl* group. Although hemicellulose contains some methoxyl, cf. Section III, over 90% of the methoxyl content of softwood, and almost as much of the

176

hardwood methoxyl, belongs to lignin (277). Therefore this group is often used to trace lignin in various connections. The actual methoxyl content of lignin is also somewhat uncertain, as it varies with the mode of preparation, but the most probable values are around 16% for softwood lignin and almost 22% for hardwood lignin (7, 81, 273). This would correspond to 0.95 and 1.4 methyl groups per phenylpropane monomer respectively (cf. below).

Table 4.27. Elementary composition of some milled wood lignin preparations from various species (81)

Wood species	C %	H %	O %	OCH₃ %
Picea abies	63.8	6.0	29.7	15.8
Picea mariana	63.7	6.3	29.4	15.4
Pinus silvestris	64.0	6.1	29.8	15.7
Tsuga heterophylla	63.4	6.3	29.8	15.7
Thuja plicata	63.8	6.1	30.1	16.1
Betula verrucosa	58.8	6.5	34.0	21.5
Populus tremula	60.4	6.2	33.0	21.4
Fagus silvatica	60.3	6.3	33.4	21.4

Hydroxyl groups are indicated in several ways, by methylation (215, 800), acetylation (188), etc. Total amount of hydroxyl groups is around 10%, or about 1.1–1.2 per monomer, for both hardwood and softwood lignin (81, 216). It must be kept in mind that especially the hydroxyl content of the protolignin is likely to be changed on isolation, since these groups are formed by hydrolysis and lost by condensation and other reactions. The hydroxyl groups are of varying nature, *phenolic* as well as *primary*, *secondary* and *tertiary aliphatic* hydroxyls (207, 225) are present, in roughly equal amounts. The phenolic groups of spruce, hemlock and pine milled wood lignin are 0.30 per monomer, and those of the corresponding Brauns' native lignins 0.4–0.5 (8, cf. 57, 182, 224, 257, 554, 695). Their acidity corresponds to a pK_a value of 10.5–11.0 (387).

Ether bound oxygen, aromatic as well as aliphatic, besides that of the methoxyl groups, is present in considerable amounts, 0.7 aromatic and 0.3 aliphatic bonds per monomer (81). Aliphatic ether oxygen must also be dependent on the mode of isolation of the lignin, since hydrolysis may convert it to hydroxyl groups.

Carboxyl groups appear in the protolignin to an extent of <0.05 per monomer (529).

Carbonyl groups have been estimated by the hydroxylamine method to occur with about 0.10 (9) or 0.20 per monomer (16, 23, 81), of which a very small fraction belongs to coniferyl aldehyde groupings, about 0.04 per monomer (9, 23), about 0.10 to the β-carbon and about 0.07 to the α-carbon of the side chain.

Aliphatic *double bonds* are present in small amounts, corresponding to the 0.04 coniferyl aldehyde and 0.03 coniferyl alcohol (501) groupings.

177

Methylene dioxy groups have been assumed to be present but later shown to be lacking. *C-methyl* groups are very few, about 0.04 per monomer (81).

Ester groups have been found to occur in certain hardwood lignins, such as poplar. They seem to constitute bonds between α-carbon atoms of lignin monomers and *p*-hydroxybenzoate groups (574, 605, 728).

C. Structure of degradation products

In order to determine still larger fragments of the lignin structure, several degradation methods have been applied to lignin preparations as well as to lignin *in situ* in wood meal, mainly *alkali cooking, alkali fusion, oxidation, hydrogenation, ethanolysis* and *acidolysis*. Alkali cooking of lignosulfonic acids (e.g. 289, 367, 457, 785) or lignin (19) from softwoods yields *vanillin*, XLVII, in limited amounts, 3–8 %, as well as *acetaldehyde*. Alkali cooking of hardwoods yields many aromatic low-molecular compounds, such as *vanillin, syringaldehyde*, XLVIII, *p-hydroxybenzaldehyde*, XLIX, *vanillic*, L, *syringic*, LI, *p-hydroxybenzoic*, LII, *ferulic*, LIII, and *p-coumaric*,

LIV, (605) acids. Significant amounts of *p*-hydroxybenzaldehyde and *p*-hydroxybenzoic acid appear to distinguish willow and aspen from other hardwoods. The *p*-hydroxybenzoic acid may occur esterified with the aliphatic hydroxyl groups of lignin (728). Alkali fusion gave 10–20% *protocathecuic acid*, LV (278, 342), from softwood lignin, and alkali fusion of methylated wood gave degradation products, from which after methylation and permanganate oxidation could be isolated as much as 20% *veratric*, LVI, and 10% *isohemipinic acid*, LVII, calculated on the lignin of the wood (217). Smaller amounts of *dehydrodiveratric acid* and more than 10 other acids have been found as well (231). Oxidation of softwood lignin in alkaline medium by air (463), nitrobenzene (218) or copper and silver oxides (477, 604) yields *vanillin*, of up to 25% (218, 481), whereas nitrobenzene oxidation of hardwood lignin in addition to *vanillin* gives also *syringaldehyde* (344, 481, 580, 605, 753) and very little *p-hydroxy-benzaldehyde* (481, 588). The latter has also been found on the oxidation of softwood lignin (588). The total aromatic aldehyde yield of nitro-benzene oxidation of hardwoods has been as much as 52% (427) of the lignin, corresponding to about 0.6 aromatic aldehydes per phenylpropane monomer. Monocotyledones, such as grasses, contain lignin yielding considerable quantities of *p-hydroxybenzaldehyde*, 10% being found for bagasse lignin, in addition to 17% *vanillin* and 13% *syringaldehyde* (588), which indicates a fairly equal importance for these structural types in the lignin of monocotyledones. Silver-oxide catalyzed oxidation gave in addition to *vanillin* also *vanillic acid*, *vanillin-5-carboxylic acid*, LVIII, and

LVII   LVIII

acetoguaiacone, LIX (604). Catalytic hydrogenation using copper chromite of methanol (300) or ethanol lignin (346) as well as of wood (346) gave a total yield of up to 42% of the three hydroaromatic products *4-n-propylcyclohexanol*, LX, *4-n-propylcyclohexanediol-1,2*, LXI, and *3-(4-hydroxycyclohexyl)-1-propanol*, LXII. Hydrogenation using Raney

LIX   LX   LXI   LXII

nickel gave lower yields of products preserving the aromatic nucleus and some of which contained only two carbon atoms in the side chain (261, 347, 613). Ethanolysis of spruce wood with hydrochloric acid in ethanol at elevated temperature gave aromatic compounds, containing carbonyl groups in the side chain (348), *1-(4-hydroxy-3-methoxyphenyl)* derivatives of *2-ethoxy-1-propanone*, LXIII, *1-ethoxy-2-propanone*, LXIV, *1-2-propanedione*, LXV, and *2-propanone*, LXVI. Maple wood gave the same products together with corresponding monomers with a methoxyl group also in the 5-position. Each of these compounds contain both carbonyl

and C-methyl groups, which occur in lignin only to a limited extent, showing a rearrangement of the side chain, possibly from the compound LXVII. However, also *veratrylglycerol*, LXVIII, and its *β-guaiacyl ether*, LXIX, have been shown to yield these ketones (17), and especially the latter is considered to be structurally related to one of the configurations

in lignin. Acidolysis with hydrochloric acid in dioxane at elevated temperature was found to yield similar products as does ethanolysis (18). A specific degradation for estimation of the *p-hydroxybenzylalcohol groups* of lignin is obtained with *quinone monochlorimide*, which reacts with the former groups under indophenol formation, LXX (242). About 0.07 such groups per monomer have been found (81).

180

D. *Spectrochemistry of lignin*

The absorption spectra of lignin preparations in the ultraviolet, visible and infrared regions are seen in Figures 4.33–35 (387, 408, 445). Some characteristic features are observed, which have been utilized for structural investigations. They can be mainly classified as studies on the *aromatic structure* of lignin, the *phenolic groups* of lignin, and the presence of *carbonyls or other double bonds conjugated with the aromatic system.* Since the initial studies (279, 323, 601), extensive investigations have been carried out on the ultraviolet spectrum of a large number of dissolved lignin preparations and low-molecular model compounds (57) in order to

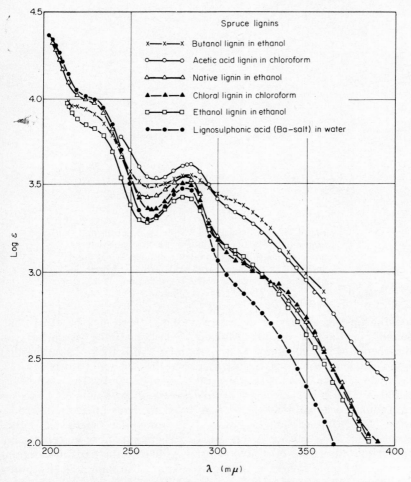

Fig. 4.33. Ultraviolet light spectrum (log molar absorbency) of various spruce lignin preparations (Aulin–Erdtman)

181

establish a solid basis for structural conclusions. These investigations conclusively show that all lignin preparations have an aromatic structure, and corresponding measurements of the absorption spectrum of ultra-thin wood preparations (470) gave final evidence for the aromatic structure also of the lignin *in situ*. The characteristic peak at 280 mμ can be taken as a measure of the lignin concentration in a solution, since the molar absorbency index (a_M or ϵ) is fairly constant for most mildly isolated lignin preparations, with its logarithmic value in the vicinity of 3.50 (57). However, it has been argued that in impure preparations, such as in sulfite

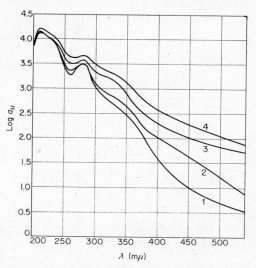

Fig. 4.34. Ultraviolet and visible light spectrum (log molar absorbency index) for uncondensed and condensed lignosulfonates, measured at pH 2 and pH 12. 1, uncondensed pH2; 2, uncondensed pH 12; 3, condensed pH2; 4, condensed pH 12 (Ivancic and Rydholm)

cooking liquors of varying degree of cooking, there may be other compounds, such as dehydration products of carbohydrates, which have an absorbency at 280 mμ (445). Still more important is the observation, that lignin condensation considerably increases the 280 mμ absorbency (57, 387), which is the case towards the end of a sulfite cook. The absorbency at 200–210 mμ is less affected by condensation of the lignin (387) and has been found to agree much better with other methods of lignin determination (445). Figure 4.36 (81) shows the ultraviolet spectra for milled wood lignin from various wood species. There is a close agreement not only within the group of softwood lignins, but also the hardwood lignins have spectra quite similar to the former group. The same was also found for Brauns' native lignin of oak, maple and beech (588), whereas one aspen native lignin showed no maximum at 280 mμ (111), in contrast to aspen

182

milled wocd lignin, which definitely does (607), and bagasse lignin a plain at 280–300 mμ and a peak at 315 mμ (588) in conformity with the spectra of some dominating structural units, ferulic and coumaric acid (605).

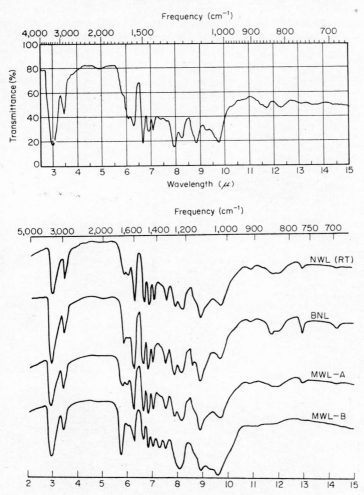

Fig. 4.35. Infrared light spectrum (transmittence) of spruce milled wood lignin (Croon), aspen milled wood lignin and Brauns native lignin preparations (Pearl) respectively

Other spectrochemical investigations on Brauns' native lignin showed no differences between two *Picea* species, whereas a *Tsuga* lignin displayed minor deviations (57). Sulfonation of Brauns' native lignin decreased the absorption in the 300–350 mμ region, but further sulfonation of a low-sulfonated product did not change the spectrum appreciably (57), which

183

excludes any deep changes in the lignin structure on sulfonation. Dia-zomethane methylation and catalytic hydrogenation had a similar effect on Brauns' native lignin as had sulfonation, i.e. a decrease in the 300–350 mμ absorption (57). Based on the bathochromic shift in the ultraviolet absorption band of phenols on increasing the pH of the solution, a method was worked out for the estimation of phenolic hydroxyls in lignin, the $\triangle\epsilon$ method, measuring the change in molar absorbency on increasing the pH from acid solution to pH 12 (57). Studies on the $\triangle\epsilon$ curves for various preparations indicated that the phenolic hydroxyl content is about 0.5–0.6 per monomer for Brauns' native lignin and its sulfonated product and considerably less, maximally 0.3 for low-sulfonated wood lignin, in fair agreement with the periodate method for determination of

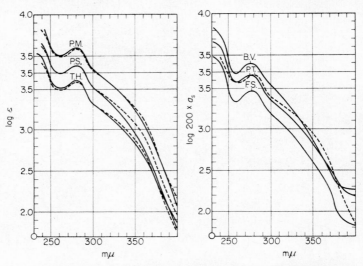

Fig. 4.36. Ultraviolet light spectrum (log molar absorbency) of various softwood and hardwood lignin preparations, milled wood lignin type. Broken lines *Picea abies.* PM *Picea mariana,* PS *Pinus silvestris,* TH *Tsuga heterophylla,* BV *Betula verrucosa,* PT *Populus tremula,* FS *Fagus silvatica* (Björkman)

phenolic groups (8). The phenolic hydroxyl content increased only little or not at all on further sulfonation. Most of the phenolic groups were not conjugated with chromophors outside the aromatic ring. Further information gained concerns the *coniferyl aldehyde,* LXXI, *4-ketoguaiacol,* LXXII, and *o-dihydroxydiphenyl,* LXXIII, groupings, all found to be present in small amounts, 0.01–0.05 per monomer, as judged from the changes in spectrum at 325–355 mμ (57). Measuring the change in molar absorbency on reduction with borohydride has given valuable information on the location of the carbonyl group (23).

The *visible absorption spectrum* of lignin has no peaks but a uniform slope from higher to lower values at increasing wavelength. This means that lignin has a light-brown hue, which becomes more intense on drastic treatments involving condensation. The spectral changes in visible light on condensation, reduction and oxidation have been studied (387). Reduction decreases absorption and drastic oxidation does so still more. The ionization constant of the phenolic hydroxyls was estimated by observing the increase in absorbency, to correspond to a pK_a value of about 10.8. The changes of the visible spectrum of lignin are of considerable technical interest, e.g. in connection with the bleaching of pulp or in determining the end point of a sulfite cook. The spectral changes on chlorination of lignin both in ultraviolet and visible light were found to yield valuable information on the chlorination process (387) and are treated in more detail in Chapter 14.

LXXI   LXXII   LXXIII

The *infrared spectrum* of lignin displays bonds arising from hydroxyl groups (at 3400 cm^{-1}), aliphatic C–H bonds (at 2900 cm^{-1}), aromatic C–H bonds (at 1600 and 1510 cm^{-1}) as well as from carbonyl groups (at 1668 cm^{-1}) (408, 460, 588, 607). The spectra for Brauns' native lignin from pine, birch, oak and maple were found to be surprisingly similar, and aspen native and milled wood lignin had also similar spectra. Acid or ester carboxyl groups have been indicated for the latter (607) and for pine thiolignin (406, 494) at 1720 cm^{-1}. The spectrum of protolignin in spruce-wood, as measured by a differential technique, was found to agree well with that of isolated milled wood lignin (448).

E. Structure of lignin

The evidence of elementary analysis (the high carbon content), of some of the functional groups determined (phenol and phenolic ether groups), of the degradation experiments (high percentages of aromatic compounds obtained), of the spectral results (aromatic absorption indicated in both ultraviolet and infrared light), as well as of the biogenetical investigations proves without a doubt that lignin is of predominantly aromatic structure. Further, the fragments of degradation as well as the biogenetical considerations make it likely that the lignin macromolecule is built of *monomers of phenylpropane type*, containing a varying amount of methoxyl groups. The results of the elementary analysis and the determination of the functional groups therefore are calculated on the C_9 basis, excluding all methoxyl carbon. The following comparison of the elementary analysis

185

Table 4.28. Comparison of the empirical formulae of various lignin preparations

Wood species	Preparation	Ref.	Empirical formula
Spruce	Milled wood lignin	(81)	$C_9H_{8.83}O_{2.37}(OCH_3)_{0.96}$
,,	Brauns' native lignin	(94)	$C_9H_{8.7}O_{2.6}(OCH_3)_{0.9}$
,,	Thio acids lignin	(362)	$C_9H_{8.90}O_{2.85}(OCH_3)_{0.92}$
,,	Cuproxam lignin	(216)	$C_9H_{7.88}O_{2.50}(OCH_3)_{0.92}$
,,	Dioxane lignin	(755)	$C_9H_{8.7}O_{2.6}(OCH_3)_{0.98}$
,,	Lignosulfonic acids	(188)	$C_9H_{8.2}O_{2.6}(OCH_3)_{0.94}$
,,	Ethanol lignin	(40)	$C_9H_{7.6}O_{2.6}(OCH_3)_{0.95}$
Pine	Enzymatically liberated lignin	(587)	$C_9H_{8.5}O_{2.6}(OCH_3)_{0.86}$
,,	Thiolignin (kraft process)	(406)	$C_9H_{8.5}O_{2.0}(OCH_3)_{0.75}$
Birch	Milled wood lignin	(81)	$C_9H_{9.03}O_{2.77}(OCH_3)_{1.58}$
,,	Enzymatically liberated lignin	(587)	$C_9H_{8.1}O_{3.0}(OCH_3)_{0.92}$
,,	Brauns' native lignin	(587)	$C_9H_{8.0}O_{3.1}(OCH_3)_{0.93}$
Beech	Milled wood lignin	(81)	$C_9H_{8.50}O_{2.86}(OCH_3)_{1.43}$
,,	Milled wood lignin	(229)	$C_9H_{7.10}O_{2.41}(OCH_3)_{1.36}$
,,	Cuproxam lignin	(216)	$C_9H_{7.46}O_{2.72}(OCH_3)_{1.52}$
Aspen	Milled wood lignin	(81)	$C_9H_{8.35}O_{2.83}(OCH_3)_{1.43}$
,,	Thio acids lignin	(363)	$C_9H_{8.94}O_{2.72}(OCH_3)_{1.32}$
,,	Thio acids lignin	(363)	$C_9H_{9.19}O_{2.87}(OCH_3)_{1.21}$
,,	Lignosulfonic acids	(473)	$C_9H_{8.8}O_{3.8}(OCH_3)_{1.5}$
,,	Lignosulfonic acids	(473)	$C_9H_{14.0}O_{6.3}(OCH_3)_{1.3}$
,,	Brauns' native lignin	(111)	$C_9H_{7.89}O_{2.45}(OCH_3)_{1.24}$
,,	Milled wood lignin	(607)	$C_9H_{7.95}O_{3.00}(OCH_3)_{1.36}$

of various lignin preparations is of interest, Table 4.28. A fair general agreement is shown. Accepting milled wood lignin as the most representative preparation, determination of its functional groups has the following result (81) for spruce, LXXIV. Possibly some of the dialkyl ether oxygen,

$$C_9H_{7.68}(OCH_3)_{0.96}$$
$$(phenol\ OH)_{0.30}$$
$$(aliphatic\ OH)_{0.85}$$
$$(carbonyl\ O)_{0.18}$$
$$(alkylaryl\ ether\ O)_{0.70}$$
$$(dialkyl\ ether\ O)_{0.34}$$

LXXIV

determined by difference, should instead be ascribed to a somewhat higher carbonyl figure, or semiacetal oxygen. With this formula, the lignin structure is far from clear. The combinations of the different monomers must now be considered, in a manner which agrees with the analytical composition, the amounts of functional groups as well as the principles of biogenetical coupling. Commencing with the fact that sprucewood lignin predominantly contains phenylpropane monomers substituted in the 3-position with a methoxyl group and in the 4-position with either a phenolic hydroxyl or ether group, it follows that there must be 0.70 phenolic ether groups per monomer since there are 0.30 phenolic hydroxyls. As there is no evidence so far of aryl–aryl ethers, these 0.70 groups must

186

be alkylaryl ethers. The next problem is which of the three carbon atoms in the side chain is engaged in this ether bond. Substantial amounts of α-alkylaryl ether, although acceptable from a biogenetical stand-point (230), are unlikely from several respects, such as the insignificant amounts of phenolic hydroxyl groups formed on sulfonation (8, 57). Spectral evidence indicates the presence of maximally 0.08 phenylcoumarane systems per monomer, LXXV (24). For other reasons, γ-alkylaryl ether

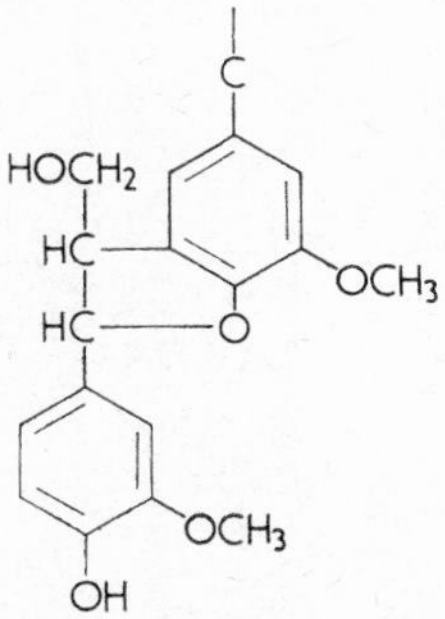

LXXV

configurations are less likely, which leaves the main part, 0.62 alkylaryl ether bonds, to the β-carbon atom. This is in accordance with the bio-genetical coupling principles, XLIII, and evidenced by the formation of phenolic groups and Hibbert ketone monomers, LXIII–LXVI, on ethan-olysis of both lignin and the model compound veratrylglycerol-β-guaiacyl ether, LXIX (17). However, acidolysis in dioxane–hydrochloric acid indicates that only about 0.3 such configurations per monomer occur in lignin, i.e. β-alkylaryl ethers containing a hydroxyl group or hydrolyzable ether group in the α-position, LXXVI. Obviously, the remaining 0.3 β-aryl ethers must involve configurations with α-carbon atoms engaged in carbon–carbon bonds, LXXVII. Small amounts of stilbene fragments isolated on oxidative degradation of lignin (604) indicate the presence of α–α carbon–carbon bonds, LXXVIII. Also α–β carbon–carbon bonds are

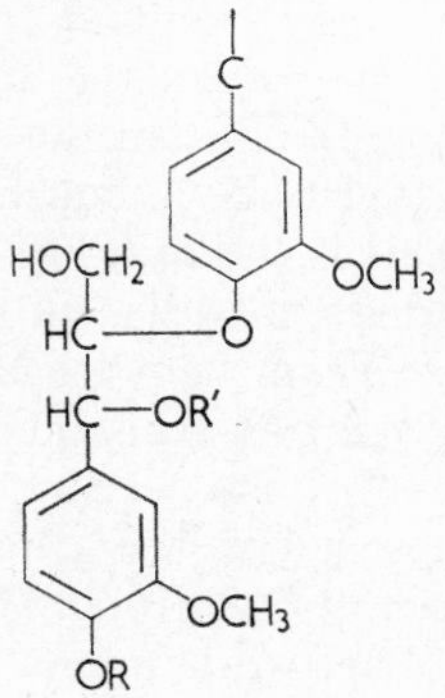

LXXVI

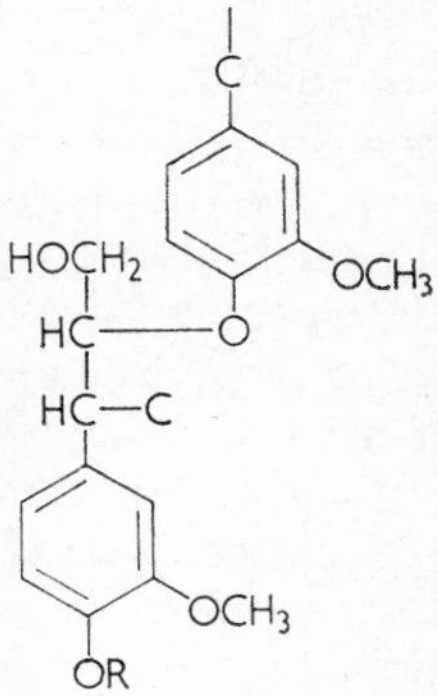

LXXVII

187

indicated (226), LXXIX and may form an important biogenetical coupling principle. Alkylaryl carbon–carbon bonds are believed to involve the aromatic nucleus in the 5-position, as indicated by the presence of isohemipinic acid and absence of metahemipinic acid in the oxidation products of methylated wood (656). Some of these bonds may involve the β-carbon of the side chain, LXXX, with an adjacent phenolic hydroxyl.

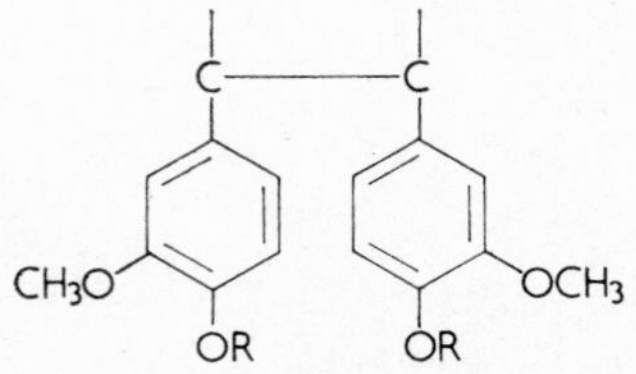

LXXVIII

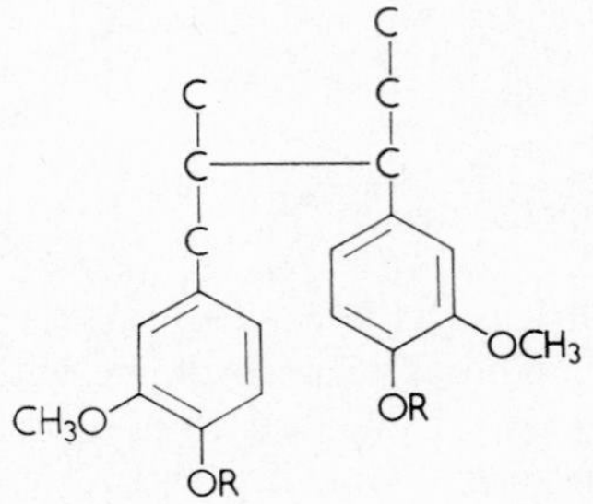

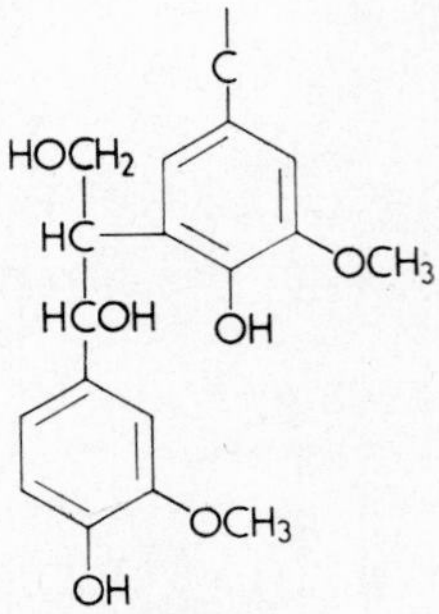

LXXIX

LXXX

The increased yield of isohemipinic acid on alkali cooking of the wood prior to methylation and oxidation indicates similar couplings, although adjacent to a phenolic ether structure, i.e. the phenylcoumarane structure mentioned above, LXXV. Additional carbon–carbon bonds are possibly present in pinoresinol structures, LXXXI, and in diphenyl derivatives, LXXXII (483, 620), according to the two remaining possibilities of coupling, XLIII. Both can only occur in limited amounts. The total amount of 'condensed' monomers, with a carbon–carbon bond either in the 5- or the α-position, has been estimated to be as much as 50% (232, 483), or possibly only 30–40% (620). This is the order of magnitude required to explain the β-alkylaryl ether bonds not adjacent to an α-carbon with a hydroxyl or dialkyl ether group. From dehydrogenation experiments with labelled coniferylalcohol 45% of the monomers are likely to be condensed at the C_5 atom (233).

Having thus discussed the oxygen attached to the aromatic ring, the aliphatic oxygen remains to be considered. Of the total oxygen, 2.37 per monomer, excluding methoxyl groups, of softwood lignin, 1.0 is attached to the aromatic ring in the 4-position, leaving 1.37 aliphatic oxygen.

Some of this is in the form of hydroxyl groups, some as carbonyl or semiacetals, and some as dialkyl ether bonds. Of the total amount of hydroxyl groups, 1.15 per monomer, 0.30 are phenolic hydroxyls, leaving 0.85 for aliphatic hydroxyls. Thus, 1.37–0.85 or 0.52 oxygen per monomer remain for dialkyl ether, carbonyl and semiacetal groups. Accepting the figure of 0.20 for the sum of the two latter (16, 23), 0.32 dialkyl ether

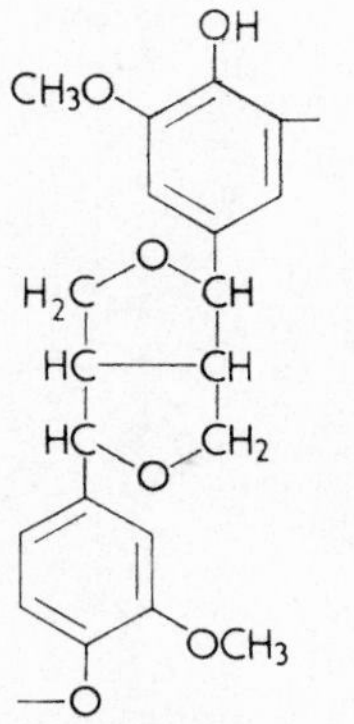

LXXXI

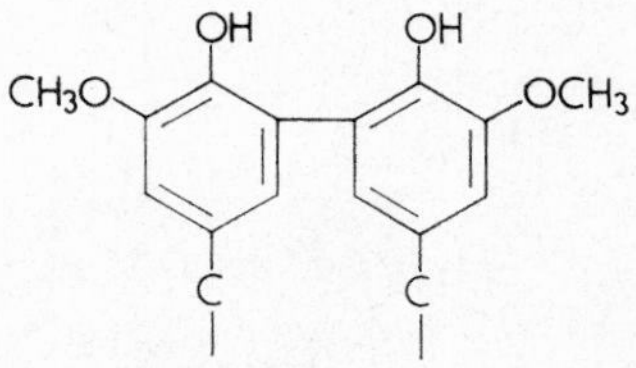

LXXXII

oxygen per monomer or 0.64 shared ether groups will remain. Further evidence on amount and nature of the aliphatic hydroxyl and ether groups is gained from sulfonation in liquors of various pH levels (497), as well as from methylation experiments at room temperature in methanol–hydrochloric acid (25). About 0.5 OCH_3 per monomer are introduced by the latter treatment, which cannot involve alkylaryl ether bonds nor dialkyl ethers of the pinoresinol type (α–γ) nor γ-hydroxyl groups. Some 0.07 ω-hydroxyguaiacylacetone structures also react in this way. The remaining 0.43 therefore indicate α-hydroxyls, α–α dialkyl ethers and possibly α-carbohydrate ether bonds, and is in fair agreement with the evidence of sulfonation, which indicates the presence of about 0.15 p-hydroxybenzyl alcohol and alkyl ether (or semiacetal) groups, LXXXIII, 0.15 p-alkoxybenzyl alcohol, LXXXIV, and possibly 0.30–0.35 p-alkoxy-benzyl alkyl ether groups, LXXXV. The amount of the last-mentioned

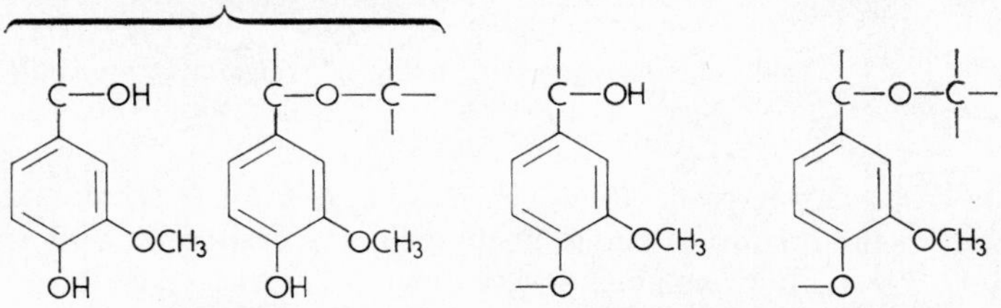

LXXXIII   LXXXIV   LXXXV

category is in some doubt, since the behavior of some sulfonate groups does not correspond to such a structure (243, 244). In addition, about 0.10 monomers are engaged in the pinoresinol structure, with less reactive cyclic

189

a–γ dialkyl ether groups. Figure 4.37 (7), including most of the configurations mentioned, has no pretention of being quantitative. On the contrary some of the elements indicated are present only in fairly small amounts. The insufficient knowledge on the nature and distribution of the aliphatic oxygen and of the condensed structures makes a more quantitative

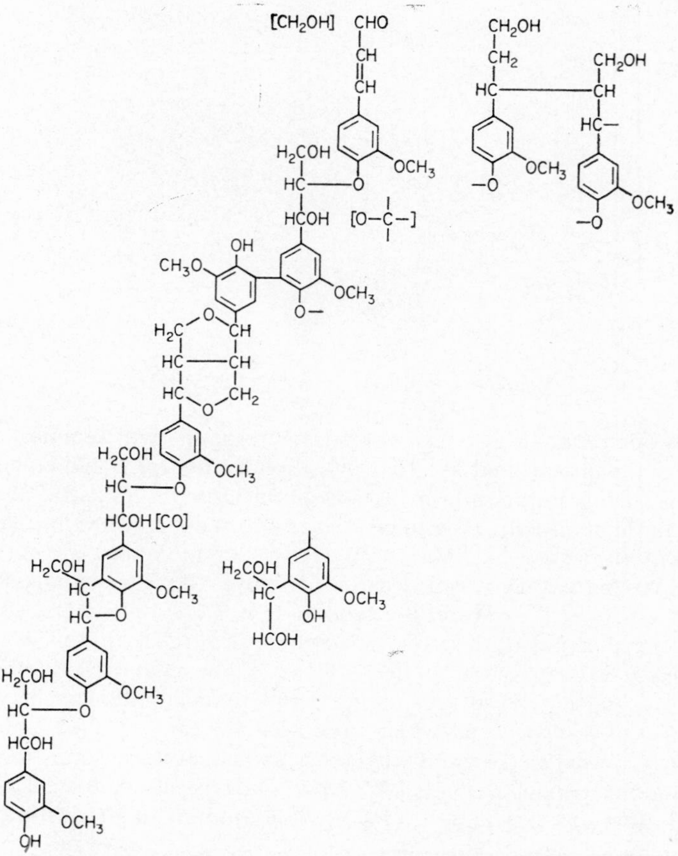

Fig. 4.37. Molecular structures occurring in softwood protolignin
(Adler)

formula still a future goal. Figure 4.38 is an attempt to summarize what is known in the form of a single phenylpropane monomer, although it is definitely felt that it includes several inconsistencies, e.g. its empirical formula will be $C_9H_{7.8}O_{2.5}(OCH_3)_{0.96}$, which is on the low side for hydrogen. For angiosperme lignin it is necessary to superimpose on the formula monomers with the syringyl configuration, about one for every two guaiacyl nuclei (229), and for certain species, especially monocotyledones, the p-hydroxyphenyl nucleus as well. It is also questionable whether

Formula   Configuration

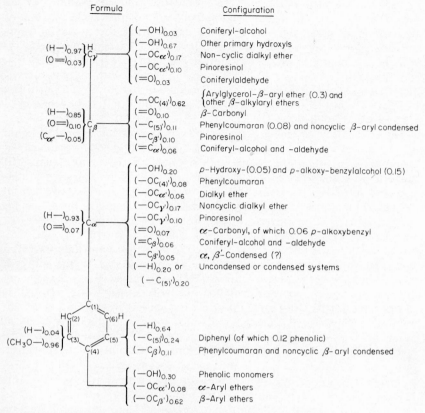

Fig. 4.38. The approximate substitution of the phenylpropane monomer of softwood lignin

angiosperme lignin can be regarded as homogeneous with respect to the different types of monomers. The ratio of syringaldehyde to vanillin obtained by nitrobenzene oxidation of aspen lignin dissolved from the wood by cooking in dioxane–hydrochloric acid or sulfite–bisulfite solutions (527, 752) changed appreciably during the cooking. In the former case the ratio was appreciably higher for the dissolved fraction than for the wood during the first cooking stages and then decreased towards the end of the cook, at the same time as a marked decrease in total aldehyde yield. The reverse was true for sulfite–bisulfite pulping, and the results could be interpreted to show the existence of a lignin enriched in syringyl monomers in the middle lamella as compared to that of the cell wall. However, the possibility of a difference in the influence of the cooking on the vanillin and syringaldehyde yields must not be disregarded as a cause of the effects noted. In any case, lignin is definitely polymolecular, and especially for hardwood lignin the border-line between lignin and low-molecular

191

extractives is diffuse (605), and the localization and composition of the molecules of different size is still largely unknown. The structure of *reaction wood lignin* deviates to some extent from the normal. Compression wood contains a softwood lignin which has a low methoxyl content, indicating a certain amount of *p*-hydroxybenzyl monomers (84, 813), and tension wood contains a hardwood lignin with more coniferyl-aldehyde monomers than in normalwood lignin (84, 813). The quantity of lignin is considerably increased in compression wood and decreased in tension wood, cf. Section I.

The *molecular weight distribution* and *average molecular weight* of lignin has been the subject of some investigations. Difficulties are naturally encountered in obtaining representative preparations, to an extent still higher than in the structural elucidation work. On isolation both degradation and secondary condensation may occur, and it is also necessary to isolate the main part of the lignin in the wood. The results of the molecular weight determinations therefore vary from a few hundred to 20,000 (63, 81, 135, 180, 195, 280, 359, 388, 439, 534, 545, 595, 602, 612, 711, 746, 816), corresponding to a DP of 2–100, taking the phenylpropane monomer as a unit. To some extent this variation may also be due to the different methods used for the determination. However, most values for isolated lignin preparations are below 10,000, whereas milled wood lignin (81) shows values of 10,000–12,000 in the case of spruce, which must represent minimum values for the protolignin, since some degradation is likely to occur also in the mechanical disintegration of the wood. For most methods of isolation, degradation therefore seems to dominate condensation, and by mild hydrolysis in dioxane or formic acid containing hydrochloric acid (219, 220) lignin preparations with molecular weights around 800–1,000 are obtained, i.e. 4–5 monomers. This corresponds to the molecular weight of Brauns' native lignin (407), the small fraction extractable from wood with neutral solvents even without excessive mechanical treatment. The ultracentrifuge sedimentation curves for milled wood lignin (81) also indicated the heterogeneity in molecular weight. This is also indicated from the fact that a comparatively large fraction of lignin is more easily extracted from the wood on alcoholysis or sulfonation (1, 482). This fraction, about a third of softwood lignin, has a molecular weight of 2,000–4,000, whereafter lignosulfonate molecules of increasing size pass into solution, up to around 100,000, giving an average of 10,000 at nearly complete delignification (534, cf. also 73a). In contrast, the main part of maple lignin was found to be fairly homogeneous and low in molecular weight, 1,000–2,000 throughout the sulfite cook. The lignin molecules have been found to be neither linear nor spherical but possessing a slightly ellipsoidal form (81, 595) or irregularly shaped microgels (258a).

It is concluded, that lignin is a polymer forming a three-dimensional network, each polymer molecule containing 5–500, average 60, monomers in softwood lignin and 5–10 in hardwood lignin, where some of the monomer linkages are sensitive to acids and others, which are not, join

192

the monomers together to building blocks of at least 4–5 monomers (497). The acid sensitive linkages are dialkyl ether bonds, presumably between α–α and α–γ carbon atoms of adjacent monomers, whereas the non-hydrolyzable linkages connecting monomers to the larger building units are alkylaryl ether bonds between the 4- and β-carbons of adjacent monomers as well as carbon–carbon bonds in a number of combinations, mainly involving the 5-, α- and β-carbon atoms. The alkylaryl ether bonds may be opened up with alkali cooking, whereas the carbon–carbon bonds require oxidative treatment. Lignin is insoluble in water but soluble in alkali due to its content of phenolic groups. It can be made water-soluble by the introduction of hydrophilic groups, such as sulfonate groups. Its compact location in the fiber wall, and possible chemical bonds to the carbohydrates, makes it insoluble in alkali *in situ*.

Lignin–carbohydrate complex has been much discussed (81, 213, 237, 496, 500, 548, 589, 611, 658, 800) in order to explain the difficulties in extracting the different wood components by solvents in which they are normally soluble as isolated products. Lignin preparations are soluble in alkali or dioxane but cannot be extracted from ordinary wood by these solvents. Carbohydrates are soluble in cuproxam solutions but extraction of the total carbohydrate fraction from the wood with cuproxam solution is possible only if the extraction is repeated several times, with intermediate hydrolytic treatments. That wood behaves differently from its constituents is therefore obvious, but the question remains whether the reason is a mechanical or chemical association. Electron micrographs show that the lignin of the fiber wall is amorphously deposited together with the hemicelluloses, whereas the cellulose microfibrils constitute a separate crystalline phase. A chemical association lignin–cellulose is therefore unlikely, whereas lignin–hemicellulose bonds are not excluded. The extraction with dioxane of a large portion of the lignin from finely divided wood, milled in toluene (81), may indicate both that the physical structure of the wood is an important hindrance, and possibly also that some of the chemical bonds between lignin and hemicellulose are broken. Further extraction of the dioxane-extracted wood residue with dimethyl formamide gave a substance containing both lignin and hemicelluloses in the proportion 1:3 or 1:4 (81). Electrophoresis showed that part of the components were probably chemically combined to a homogeneous product with the proportions lignin:hemicelluloses 1:1 (496, 500). Further milling of the dried dimethylformamide extract gave more carbohydrate-free lignin soluble in dioxane, showing the effect of mechanical degradation. Similar experiments with enzymatic degradation of dry-milled wood (619) or with chlorination of poplar wood followed by extraction (792), in the same way gave preparations indicating a chemical lignin–hemicellulose combination. Mild sulfonation at pH 5 (658) of wood gave a residue which to a considerable part could be dissolved in cuproxam solution. From the dissolved portion a water-soluble lignosulfonate could be isolated, which contained an inseparable hemicellulose component in an amount of about 12%. Smaller amounts of

193

carbohydrates normally contaminate most lignosulfonate preparations (187), and an investigation involving chromatographic purification of such preparations from beech showed the inseparable sugars to consist of xylose and xylobiose (428). Methylation of such preparations and subsequent analysis showed the presence of 2,3,4-trimethyl xylose, indicating that the linkage to the lignin had been a glycosidic one. The nature of the lignin–carbohydrate bond has been discussed, and two main possibilities are considered, a phenylglycosidic bond at the 3-carbon atom of the lignin (349) or a benzyl ether bond (21), the latter being the most likely one.

A further evidence for lignin–hemicellulose bonds is the observation (544) that even small amounts of lignin in soluble hemicellulose preparations make the separation of some of the hemicellulose components impossible, whereas a light chlorite oxidation eliminates this difficulty. The possibilities of lignin–hemicellulose complexes must vary in the different parts of the wood, as the lignin concentration is highest in the middle lamella and decreases towards the lumen. For the same reason, the possibilities of lignin–carbohydrate complexes in hardwoods must be different from that in softwoods, as the location of the lignin to the middle lamella is more pronounced in the former.

4. REACTIVITY

The reactivity of lignin has been investigated mainly for two purposes, the elucidation of its chemical structure, and the understanding of its reactions in the pulping processes. In most cases, these lines of investigation coincide, and the treatment here will mainly apply the latter points of view. For the understanding of the sulfite and neutral sulfite processes it is necessary to know the fundamentals of lignin *sulfonation*, its *hydrolysis* and *condensation in acid medium*, as well as some of its *color reactions*. For the understanding of the alkaline processes, similarly the *mercaptation*, *alkaline condensation* and *alkaline hydrolysis*, as well as some other color reactions should be known. The bleaching of pulps involves the principles of *halogenation, alkaline degradation* of halogenated lignin as well as the *degradative* and *non-degradative oxidation* of lignin. That the color reactions of lignin are also of interest in bleaching is obvious.

Many of these reactions, such as sulfonation, mercaptation, condensation and acid hydrolysis, involve the *benzyl alcohol* or *benzyl alkyl ether* (or possibly semiacetal) groups, others, such as alkaline hydrolysis, the *phenol ether groups*, whereas halogenation, oxidation and to some degree condensation involve reactions at the *benzene nucleus* and the color reactions various parts of the molecule, *coniferyl aldehyde*, *phenol* and *carbonyl* groups.

A. Sulfonation

When wood is treated with solutions containing bisulfite and sulfite ions, sulfur is chemically combined with the lignin which under suitable conditions goes into solution as a derivative, which has been found to be

194

a sulfonate (609, 784) and is called *lignosulfonate,* in acid form *lignosulfonic acid.* Isolated lignin preparations can also be sulfonated, although sulfonation becomes more difficult, the more drastic the conditions of the isolation have been, or if other functional groups have been introduced during the process of isolation. The groups in the protolignin, which can be sulfonated, can obviously react in many other ways, such as condensation with phenolic compounds, to which lignin itself can be counted, alkylation with alcohols in acid medium, and alkyl esters of mineral acids in alkaline medium, mercaptation with hydrogen sulfide or thioglycolic acid, all of which have been found to check subsequent sulfonation (128, 181, 191, 281, 476). Sulfonation has been one of the most convenient reactions for the study of these groups, and has played an important role in the structural research on lignin. It is also the most important reaction in sulfite pulping, and will therefore be treated here at some length.

The sulfonate groups in lignosulfonates are not all of the same nature. Two main categories exist with respect to their different stability towards alkali. A minor part is classified as *loosely combined SO_2* and is split off, already at room temperature, on alkalization. This part probably consists of α-hydroxysulfonic acids of the type formed between bisulfite and a carbonyl group (10) according to the reaction

$$R_2CO + HSO_3^- \rightleftharpoons R_2C(OH)SO_3^-$$

and is therefore combined with the carbonyl groups of lignin, and have been found in an amount of about 0.12 per monomer (22). A special type of loosely combined SO_2 occurs at the coniferyl aldehyde groups (one for 40–60 monomers), where bisulfite is added at the double bonds (11), a second bisulfite ion later being added at the aldehyde group to an α-hydroxysulfonate, LXXXVI. The main part of the sulfonate groups are,

LXXXVI

however, combined with the α-carbon atom of the phenylpropane monomers, after a reaction with benzyl alcohol or benzyl alkyl ether groups. These sulfonate groups are split off by alkali only at elevated temperature, but also within this category there is a varying alkali lability (169), corresponding to the different structure of the various phenyl-propane monomers. These differences are also noted in the reaction

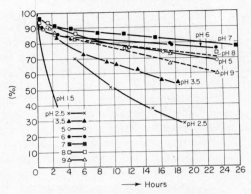

Fig. 4.39. The rate of delignification of sprucewood
by bisulfite solutions of various pH, judged by the
dissolution of methoxyl at 135°C (Lindgren *et al*)

between lignin and bisulfite at different pH. Figure 4.39 (497) illustrates
the pH dependence of the rate of *dissolution* of lignin from sprucewood
with bisulfite solutions. The rate decreases considerably at an increase in
pH, and above pH 3–4 no complete dissolution of the lignin is achieved.
Figure 4.40 (497) shows the pH dependence of the rate of *sulfonation* of
lignin, expressed in S/OCH_3 (192, 282, 283, 497), which approximately
equals the average degree of sulfonation per phenylpropane monomer. At
low pH the degree of sulfonation rapidly reaches the range of 0.3–0.5,
where dissolution occurs, whereas above pH 4 there seems to be a maximal
degree of sulfonation about 0.30 S/OCH_3, and these lignosulfonates remain
chiefly undissolved in the wood unless fairly high temperatures are applied.
It is obvious, that about half of this sulfonation, to about 0.15 S/OCH_3
occurs very rapidly, and the following sulfonation more slowly.

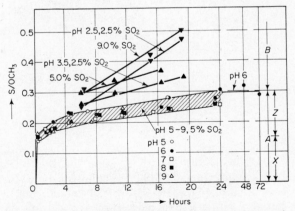

Fig. 4.40. The ratio of sulfur atoms per methoxyl group in
sprucewood, treated with bisulfite solutions of various pH at
135°C (Lindgren *et al*)

196

Wood, sulfonated in neutral or slightly acid solution, behaves like a cation exchanger, and the sulfonate groups are converted to sulfonic acids on treatment with mineral acids. After washing, the lignosulfonic acids still remain attached to the wood, but on subsequent treatment with hot water they dissolve to so-called low-sulfonated lignosulfonic acids (192, 462). This lignin preparation, often called *Kullgren acid*, has been much used for research work as a mildly isolated lignin. The dissolution is obviously a hydrolysis, induced by the acidity of the solid phase, and it is much retarded by the presence of cations in the hydrolysing hot water, as they lower this acidity according to the usual Donnan equilibria.

Low-sulfonated lignosulfonates can be further sulfonated in bisulfite solutions (192, 282, 283), and even in neutral ones (482) to a fairly high degree of sulfonation, normally to about 0.7 S/OCH_3 and for certain fractions even as much as 1.0 S/OCH_3. (Neutral sulfite sulfonation may also involve the pinoresinol structures.) During this further sulfonation, aliphatic hydroxyl groups disappear at a rate corresponding to the sulfonation (188). The degree of sulfonation in commercial sulfite cooks ranges from 0.4–0.7 S/OCH_3 (187), and can for the lower degrees of sulfonation be brought to above 0.7 S/OCH_3 on further sulfonating treatment (388).

These observations have been compared to model reactions between bisulfite at various pH's and low-molecular compounds. Some of these have contained structures which are not present in lignin, and which are likely to affect their reactivity. Others on sulfonation formed groups, e.g. phenolic hydroxyls, which are evidently not formed in the sulfonation of lignin. The category of compounds which have led to the most fruitful comparisons are benzyl alcohols and benzyl alkyl ethers. It has long been known that triphenylmethanesulfonate (71) is formed on reaction of triphenylcarbinol, LXXXVII, with bisulfite ions, and it was later shown that bisulfite reacts analogously with diphenylcarbinol, LXXXVIII, and α-phenethylcarbinol, LXXXIX, to sulfonic acids (360). It was therefore

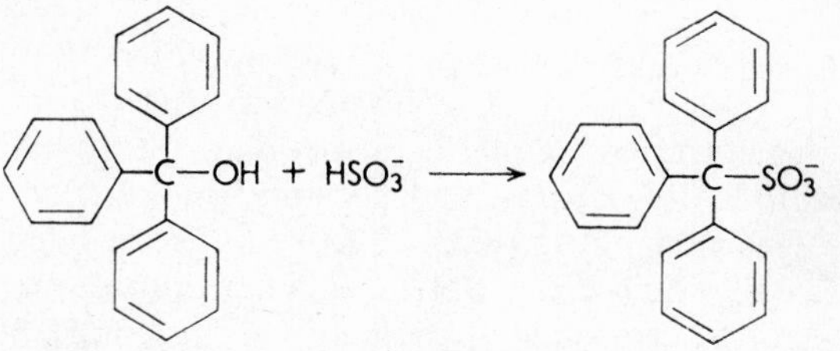

LXXXVII

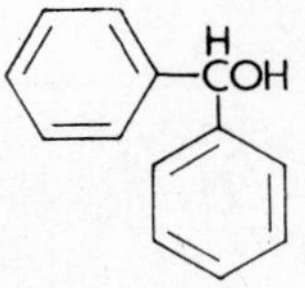

LXXXVIII

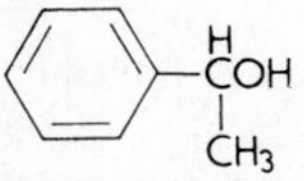

LXXXIX

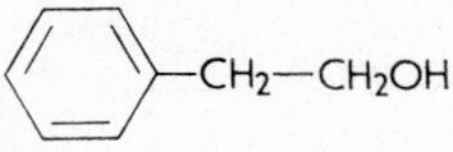

XC

197

suggested that a benzyl alcohol group is the active group of lignin on sulfonation as well as on mercaptation (361). In contrast, β-phenethyl alcohol, XC, was shown to be non-sulfonatable in this way. However, also α-phenethyl alcohol reacted much slower than does lignin, and the hypothesis needed support by experiments with benzyl alcohols, substituted to more 'lignin-like' models. Such were found in the following compounds (17, 190, 498), XCI–XCIV. All these compounds, as well as their alkyl ethers rapidly react with bisulfite ions in acid solution to form sulfonates, whereas the alkyl ethers having no activating phenol group in the 4-carbon position are not sulfonated in neutral bisulfite solutions (360, 499, 654).

The stand-point of lignin chemistry until recently (7, 194, 497) with regard to the sulfonatable groups of lignin, was that the groups reacting with bisulfite in neutral or weakly acid medium, the so-called A-groups (191), are benzyl alcohol groups, and possibly benzyl alkyl ether groups activated by a free phenolic group in the benzene nucleus, whereas the so-called B-groups, which react only in acid medium, are benzyl alkyl ethers with phenol ether groups at the benzene nucleus. These B-groups may after hydrolysis to B'-groups (482), accordingly benzyl alcohol groups, be sulfonated in neutral bisulfite solutions. The difference in reactivity within the A-groups, about half of which, called X-groups (553), react very fast in neutral medium, whereas the remainder, the Z-groups, react more slowly, is compared to the difference in reactivity between benzyl alcohol groups activated by phenolic hydroxyls and those activated by phenol ether groups (497). Formulae LXXXIII–LXXXV therefore illustrate the concept of the sulfonatable groups of lignin.

The X-groups, LXXXIII, thus correspond to about 0.15 groups per monomer, the Z-groups to about 0.15, LXXXIV, and the B-groups to approximately 0.4–0.7, LXXXV, making a total of 0.7–1.0 sulfonatable groups per monomer. In some cases, still more sulfur has been shown to combine with lignin (221), but it is doubtful whether all sulfur was bound as sulfonate. Lignosulfonate, on reaction with thiosulfate, takes up considerable amounts of sulfur without a corresponding increase in sulfonate groups, and towards the end of a sulfite cook, such excess sulfur combination has been shown to appear (258, 686). It is also of interest to note, that the phenolic groups of lignin, around 0.30 per monomer, correspond to the number of A-groups of lignin. However, it is now believed that about half the monomers containing phenolic groups are condensed at the α-carbon atom and thus do not contain sulfonatable groups. This is compensated for by the amount of the benzyl alcohol groups with a phenol ether group in the nucleus, i.e. the Z-groups. The part of the X-groups which consists of phenol-activated benzyl alcohol groups can be estimated by the indophenol color reaction (cf. above), and is in the case of spruce lignin about 0.05–0.07 per phenylpropane monomer (81, 242). Consequently, the remainder of the X-groups, i.e. the phenol-activated benzyl alkyl ether groups, are about 0.08–0.10 per monomer. Phenol-activated benzyl alcohol and alkyl ether groups are considered to react in the methylene quinone (quinone methide) form with bisulfite (389) as well as with hydrosulfide (245, 308, cf. CII below) and with water, hydrolysis (474). The methylene quinone formation is activated by hydrogen ions as well as by hydroxyl ions and has a minimum at pH5.

There are certain recent objections to, or at least uncertainties in the structural concept just given on the sulfonatable groups of lignin. One is that the conclusions are based on comparisons between the model substances and wood lignin *in situ*, and ascribing all effects to various chemical configurations. However, as the sulfonation of wood is a decidedly heterogeneous reaction, some of the phenomena could as well be ascribed to varying accessibility of the lignin (674). For instance, in reaching an average degree of sulfonation of 0.3 S/OCH_3 in neutral medium, does not mean that the lignin is homogeneously sulfonated to this level. Less accessible portions are sulfonated to a considerably less extent. In fact, milled wood lignin, sulfonated in neutral medium, takes up as much as 0.5 S/OCH_3 (81), which should indicate a decidedly higher proportion of alcohol groups and less alkyl ether groups than earlier assumed. Furthermore, lignin or wood after borohydride reduction yielded only little water-soluble lignosulfonate in acid sulfite cooking (243). This indicates that the role of the carbonyl (or semiacetal) groups is much more essential than hitherto assumed and suggests that either semiacetal hydroxyls are sulfonated at normal sulfite cooking conditions (cf. 58), or that carbonyl groups activate γ-hydroxyl groups, a reaction previously suggested to explain the quantity of acetoguaiacol formed on severe alkali cooking of lignosulfonates (444, 457), XCV. The reduction of lignosulfonates by a mixture of HI, HCl and H_3PO_2 causes formation of

199

hydrogen sulfide from benzyl-bound sulfur (244). However, only about half the sulfonate groups in lignosulfonates were found to react in such a manner (243, 244), which would indicate (unless there are unknown stabilizing influences on the sulfonate groups in α-position) that a considerable part of the sulfonate groups are in other positions, presumably at the γ-carbon atom.

XCV

Finally, it must be emphasized, that most of the investigations on lignin sulfonation have been carried out on softwoods. Although the main structure of hardwood lignin is likely to be similar to that of softwood lignin, differences may exist in the sulfonation reaction. Anyway, the localization of hardwood lignin, its lower tendency for condensation through the blocking of the 5-carbon at several monomers, and the lower lignin content of hardwoods make them more suitable for neutral sulfite pulping than softwoods. It has been shown, that for hardwoods the sulfonation reactions are essentially the same with sulfite as with bisulfite solutions, although the rate of reaction is slower in the former case (527), and defibrable chemical pulps can be obtained in both cases. The delignification of softwood in neutral sulfite cooking liquor (pH 9) is extremely slow for the main part of the lignin.

The nature of the sulfonating agent is discussed in Chapter 9.

B. Acid hydrolysis

As has been stressed in previous sections, the molecular weight of the protolignin in the wood seems to exceed that of most lignin preparations isolated under mild acid conditions, such as alcohol and dioxane lignin as well as low-sulfonated lignosulfonic acids. The probable reason is scission of benzyl alkyl ether bonds through acid hydrolysis or alcoholysis. Hydrolysis also occurs at the bonds of the lignin–hemicellulose complex. In both cases hydrolysis is a reaction which aids the dissolution of lignin, e.g. in the sulfite pulping process. However, hydrolysis alone is not sufficient, as the lignin units themselves do not have sufficient hydrophility to pass into solution but have to be converted to sulfonates. It is also open to question how many of the benzyl alkyl ether bonds are broken by hydrolysis and how many by *sulfitolysis* (674, cf. 173, 290), i.e. the direct sulfonation in acid medium of benzyl alkyl ether bonds (cf. Chapter 9). In the case of hardwoods, some of the low-molecular portions of lignin may dissolve by hydrolysis even without sulfonation, as in the

200

prehydrolysis process. It should also be stressed, that acid treatment of wood in the absence of bisulfite ions will cause not only hydrolysis but also condensation, and that the net result is not necessarily a decrease in molecular weight.

Hydrolysis of the β-alkylaryl ether bonds does not occur in the technical acid cooking processes to any great extent, as there is no great increase in phenolic hydroxyl groups. However, acidolysis of lignin in dioxane–hydrochloric acid containing only small quantities of water has been found to split about 0.3 such bonds per monomer (18).

C. Condensation

The activated benzyl alcohol structure of lignin resembles that of low-molecular condensation products of phenol and formaldehyde, which are inclined to further condensation in both acid and alkaline medium. The *alkaline* condensation of lignin is little investigated, although there is little doubt of its occurrence (118, 284). The *acid* condensation of lignin is of greater technical importance, as it may disturb the dissolution of lignin in the sulfite pulping process far more than does alkaline condensation in the kraft pulping process. Acid self-condensation of lignin, as well as condensation between lignin and other phenolic compounds has therefore been subjected to considerable research.

Acid self-condensation occurs between phenylpropane monomers at moderate (458) to high acidity, especially in the early stages of the sulfite process, when the solid lignosulfonic acids in the wood under unfavorable conditions may give rise to local high acidity (cf. Chapter 9). It will also take place to quite an extent during the mild acidic conditions of a water prehydrolysis cook at pH about 3 (cf. Chapter 9), and also during the various processes of making wallboard (458). The reaction has also been considered as a possibility of making thermosetting plastics out of lignin (743), with or without the aid of extra additions of phenols and formaldehyde. However, most isolated lignin products are already rather condensed and therefore fairly unreactive in this respect. There is little doubt that the same functional groups react as in sulfonation, especially the *A*-groups and the *B'*-groups, that is all benzyl alcohol groups and possibly some of the benzyl alkyl ether groups. The other carbon atom involved in the condensation is the 6- and especially 5-carbon of the aromatic nucleus.

There is some difficulty in distinguishing between the condensed monomers of the protolignin and those subsequently formed. As discussed in the section on lignin structure, the condensed units in the protolignin involve the 5-position of the aromatic ring and probably the β-carbon of the side chain. This has been demonstrated by enzymatic condensation of coniferyl alcohol labelled at the β-carbon (227). After methylation and permanganate oxidation isohemipinic acid, LVII, containing radioactive carbon in the 5-position was isolated. The problem is further illustrated by comparing the oxidative degradation products from methylated wood and from various methylated lignin preparations (215, 217, 656), Table 4.29.

Table 4.29. Absolute and relative amounts of products isolated from the oxidative degradation of wood and lignin preparations (656)

Preparation	Absolute amounts, lignin basis, %					Relative amounts, %				
	Veratric acid	Dehydrodiveratric acid	Isohemipinic acid	Metahemipinic acid	Total acids	Veratric acid	Dehydrodiveratric acid	Isohemipinic acid	Metahemipinic acid	Total acids
Wood, methylated	4.9	0.0	0.9	0.0	5.8	85	0	15	0	100
Hydrochloric acid lignin, methylated	2.9	0.2	1.9	1.3	6.3	46	4	30	20	100
Hydrochloric acid lignin, methylated and alkali cooked	7.8	1.5	3.4	0.9	13.6	57	11	25	7	100
Lignosulfonic acid, methylated	3.2	0.0	1.2	0.8	5.2	62	0	23	15	100
Thiolignin, methylated	10.2	3.8	6.65	0.0	20.7	49	18	32	0	100
Ethanol lignin, dissolved, methylated	9.2	0.5	0.95	1.3	12.0	77	4	8	11	100
Ethanol lignin, in wood residue isolated as HC1 lignin, methylated	4.9	0.0	1.85	1.2	8.0	62	0	23	15	100

There are two main features to be noticed in these results. One is the *absolute* amounts of oxidation products isolated. For wood, hydrochloric acid lignin and lignosulfonic acid, the sum of the oxidation products is around 6%, calculated on lignin, whereas hot alkali pretreatment prior to methylation and oxidation more than doubles that figure. This means that whereas the untreated lignin samples yield oxidation products from those monomers only, which contain phenol groups, the hot alkali treatment also shows the condensation of those monomers which are joined by phenolic ether linkages, as these are split by alkaline hydrolysis. The high yield of oxidation products from thiolignin reflects the high phenol group content formed in this preparation on even mild treatments. The results from the ethanol lignins dissolved and remaining in the wood illustrate a possible heterogeneity of the wood lignin. The other feature of interest is the *nature* and *relative* amounts of the oxidation products. Metahemipinic acid, XCVI, is not found in the oxidation products from

XCVI

methylated wood, and its presence in the other preparations but thiolignin shows that some condensation in 6-position takes place during the isolation, mainly in monomers containing a phenolic hydroxyl. The increase in isohemipinic acid yields from the isolated lignins as compared to that of wood indicates that condensation in 5-position also occurs during the isolation.

Another technique, alkaline permanganate oxidation followed by boiling nitric acid oxidation and isolation of the benzenecarboxylic acids formed, has shed some light on lignin condensation (118). The yield of these oxidation products is very low from wood, whereas lignin preparations give higher yields, especially after acid or alkaline condensation.

A third technique of studying lignin condensation arises from the fact that vanillin formation on alkaline oxidation of dioxane lignin or ligno-sulfonates is decreased by condensation (285). A lignosulfonate was heated for various times in calcium bisulfite cooking acid, and the yield of vanillin on subsequent oxidation was shown to decrease on prolonged heating. A coloration of the lignin runs parallel to this decrease, which has long been considered an indication of lignin condensation and has also been studied quantitatively (387).

Finally, the formation of 2,4-dinitroguaiacol, XCVII, from uncondensed guaiacyl nuclei on nitric acid treatment in ether has been used for a study on lignin condensation (268). Heating in buffer solutions of varying pH of spruce and birch wood prior to the treatment indicated minimal condensation at pH 4–5, which coincides with the conditions for minimal methylene quinone formation from phenol-activated benzyl alcohol and alkyl ether groups (474).

Condensation with other phenolic compounds occurs, besides on the isolation of phenol lignins, in the sulfite cooking of tannin-damaged sapwood and of the heartwood of certain species. In the first case the phenolic compounds originate from the bark and have diffused into the wood, and in the second case they are normal constituents of the heartwood of pines and Douglas fir and may be either tannins or other types of extractives, cf. Chapter 4.5. These compounds are all of the resorcinol type, XCVIII which makes them highly reactive to condensation with the benzyl alcohol groups of lignin (193, 621). Tannins of the phlobotannin group often contain the principal structure XCIX. Pinosylvin or its monomethyl ether, C, are found in the heartwood of most pines, sometimes together with extractives of the flavanone type.

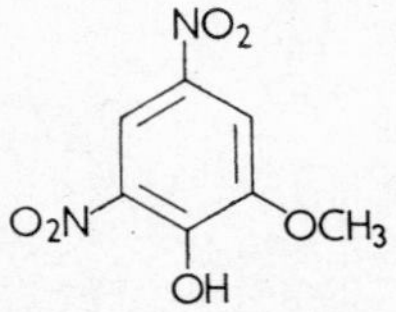

XCVII

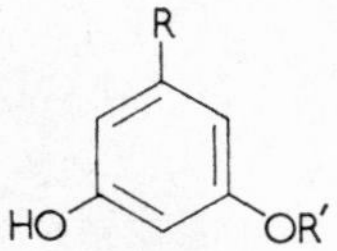

XCVIII

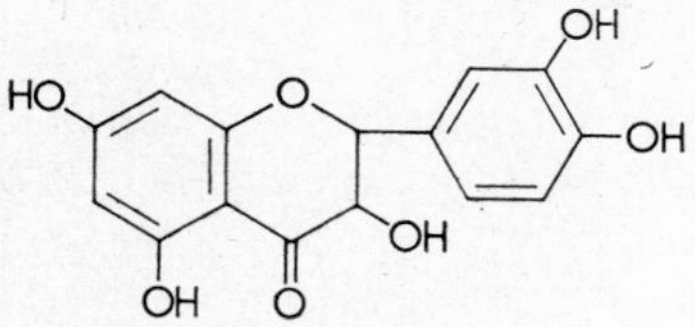

XCIX

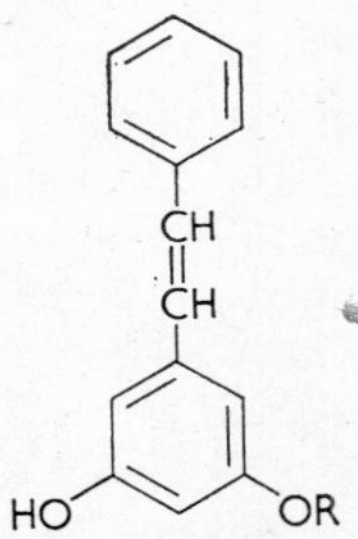

C
(R = H or CH₃)

As has been shown in experiments with simpler phenols as well as with these compounds (193, 805), lignin condenses under acidic conditions with all these phenols, and especially rapidly with resorcinol structures. It is the *A*-groups which react, if not previously sulfonated in neutral medium. Also the *B'*-groups have been shown to react (498), i.e. the *p*-alkoxybenzyl alcohol groups developed on acid hydrolysis. As sulfonation prevents condensation, the reverse is also true, and excessive condensation with phenols, as well as self-condensation, renders lignin insoluble in the sulfite pulping process. This not only necessitates a cautious cooking schedule, to allow for ample penetration of the wood by the sulfonating agent before self-condensation is given a chance to occur, but also limits the applicability of the *conventional* sulfite process to wood and wood species substantially free from such phenolic compounds (cf. Chapter 9).

D. Mercaptation

The mercaptolysis with alkylmercaptans (98, 356), and the formation of thioglycolic acid lignin (356) seems to involve the same reactive groups as sulfonation, i.e. benzyl alcohol or benzyl alkyl ether groups, up to at least 0.8 groups per monomer introduced, CI. Besides these reactions, lignin

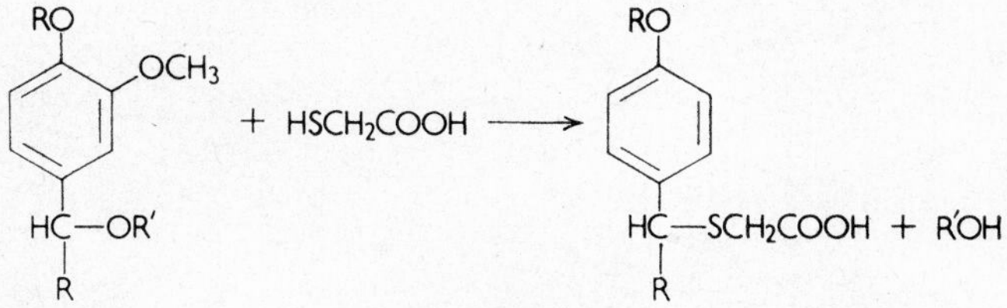

CI

also reacts with hydrogen sulfide or hydrosulfide ions to sulfur-rich compounds, so-called thiolignins, containing from 7–17% S, or from 0.4 to more than 1 S per monomer (180, 275, 286). Of the thiolignin sulfur 50–75% has been shown to be attached to the α-carbon atom (245). This reaction is believed to be a mercaptation, at least in its initial phase, whereby a benzyl alcohol or benzyl alkyl ether group, activated by a phenolic hydroxyl, reacts with the hydrosulfide ion (181) to a mercaptan, which in alkaline medium reacts further to sulfide (245) or disulfide

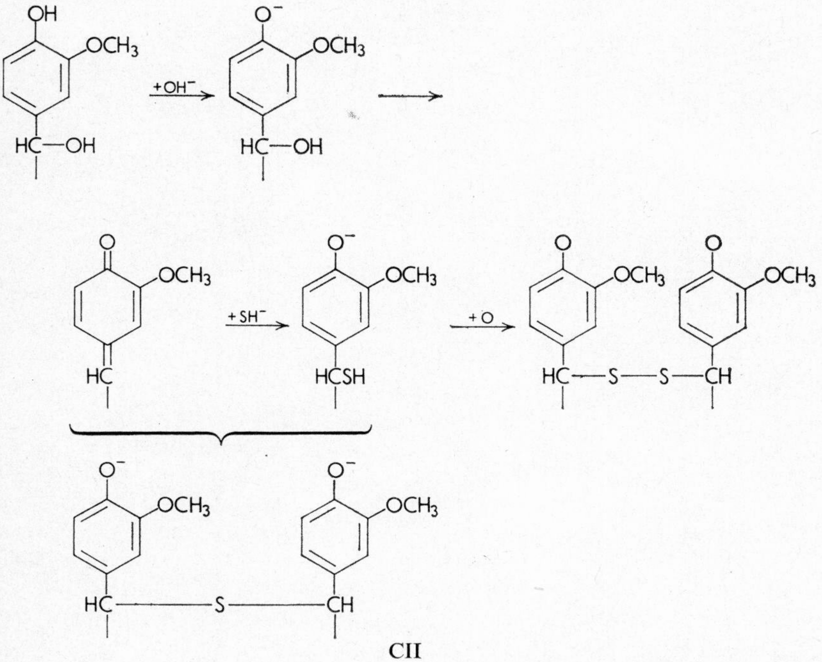

CII

compounds, which in their turn can be split under regeneration of hydrosulfide ions (181). This sequence of reactions, CII, is based on model reactions with vanillyl alcohol, etc. (181, 245, 308, 420), and is of particular interest for the understanding of the chemistry of the kraft cook. A more recent alternative is the formation of thiols and episulfides (43), CIII.

CIII

Lignin isolated from kraft black liquors contains 1–3% sulfur (33, 406) or 0.07–0.2 S per monomer, has a lower methoxyl content, more phenolic and carboxyl groups, and a lower molecular weight than the protolignin. A slight treatment of wood with hydrogen sulfide renders it difficult to pulp by the conventional sulfite process (181), whereas a neutral sulfite cook does convert the sulfide bond between two monomers to two sulfonate groups, provided the monomers contain free phenolic hydroxyls (246). Thiolignin does not methylate under conditions when methanol lignin is formed from wood. Also, lignosulfonic acid and alcohol lignin take up little sulfur on treatment with hydrogen sulfide under conditions which form thiolignin from wood. Therefore, the same groups of lignin as in sulfonation and alcoholysis seem to react (181). However, some additional phenomena are connected with the formation of thiolignin, namely the labilization of the phenolic ether bonds, as thiolignin, at least after a fairly mild alkali treatment, contains a large number of phenolic groups. A more complete discussion on the lignin reactions of the kraft cook is given in Chapter 9. Similar to thiolignin formation is the reaction of the guaiacyl groups with thiosulfate in acid medium. This reaction, which is important for the stability of the cooking acid during the sulfite cook, involves first the formation of guaiacylthiosulfate groups and subsequently sulfide groups between the two lignin monomers (258). Another similar reaction is that of lignin and thiocyanic acid (666a), which has been found to prevent sulfonation.

E. Alkaline hydrolysis

When lignin is treated with alkaline solutions at elevated temperature, scission of the phenol ether bonds occurs, a reaction which seems to be facilitated by the presence of hydrosulfide. The formation of phenol groups is of great importance in the alkaline pulping processes, since they render the lignin alkali soluble. Determination of the equivalent weights of alkali and kraft lignin indicates that they contain an acid group for every two monomers (182) or 0.7–0.9 per monomer (406). Even if some of these acid groups may be carboxylic (183, 406), about 0.16 per monomer according to recent investigations (529), most are phenolic, and lignin is precipitated from alkaline solutions by carbon dioxide or barium chloride. Determination of phenolic groups in thiolignin from a hydrogen sulfide cook and from a kraft cook respectively indicates that the former contains little more than the protolignin, whereas the latter contains up to almost 1 per monomer (181,182). Most phenol groups are formed by cleavage of the phenol ether groups between the monomers, but the methoxyl content of most alkali lignins is also appreciably lower than that of protolignin, indicating a splitting of every three to four methoxyl groups. An investigation on various thiolignins and one alkali lignin revealed the presence of 0.7–1.0 acidic groups per monomer, of which 0.25–0.3 were weaker than the remainder (240). Some of the latter are likely to correspond to 3-carbon-phenolic groups formed on demethylation, whereas the others may be 4-carbon-phenolic hydroxyls of which 0.3 were present in

207

the protolignin and 0.2–0.6 formed by hydrolysis of the alkylaryl ether bonds between the monomers. Consequently, determination of the molecular weight of thiolignin from kraft cooking of pine gave 500–1,800 (181, 406, 555), as compared to an approximate value of 10,000 for the protolignin. Alkali cooking of the model compound XCIII (484) at 170°C showed cleavage of the alkylaryl ether bond. The compound XCIV is hydrolyzed, provided that the phenolic hydroxyl is originally etherified (R = CH$_3$) (247). The reaction is considered to involve epoxide formation at the α- and β-carbon atoms, CIII. In monomers with free phenolic groups, there is instead a methylene quinone formation followed by elimination of the γ-carbon as formaldehyde and stabilization of the β-alkylaryl ether bond (247). The greater ease of splitting of these alkylaryl bonds in the thiolignin by alkali, as well as certain model experiments (43) indicate, however, that the cleavage of the alkylaryl ether bonds in the kraft cook is facilitated by the episulfide formation shown in formula CIII (182a), which also shows the reactions in the absence of sulfide.

F. Halogenation and nitration

In contrast to the reactions already described, which mainly involve the aliphatic part of lignin and mostly occur with appreciable rate only at elevated temperature, halogenation and nitration are electrophilic reactions with the aromatic part of lignin, and they proceed rapidly also at room temperature or below. In principle, the reactions proceed in a way typical for the halogenation of phenols and phenol ethers, with a substitution at the benzene ring and simultaneous formation of hydrogen halide and of water respectively. The location of the substituents is not entirely clear and will be influenced by the degree of condensation and by the substituents of the side chain. Furthermore, accompanying reactions, such as demethylation and oxidation very much depend on the amount of reagent charged as well as the reaction medium and the solubility of the product therein. Bromination in aqueous hydrobromic acid of hydrochloric acid and cuproxam lignin lead to substitution in the 6-position only (222, 478), chlorination was considered to occur in the 5- and 6-positions (345), or in the 6- and 1-positions under scission of the side chain from the aromatic ring (155). The latter reaction, CIV–CV, only occurs at monomers with

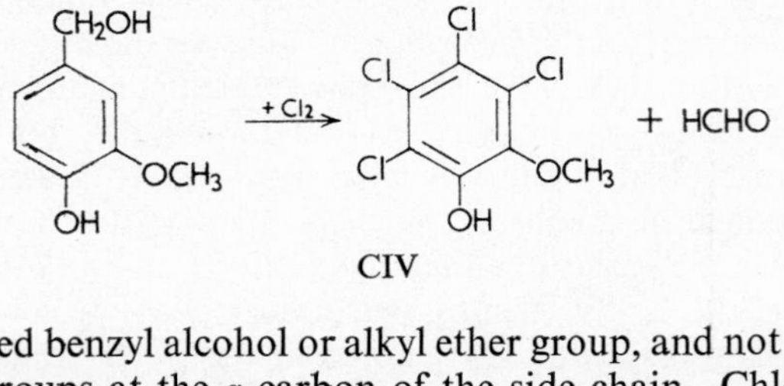

CIV

an unsubstituted benzyl alcohol or alkyl ether group, and not with carbonyl or sulfonate groups at the α-carbon of the side chain. Chlorination also induces demethylation of the methoxyl groups (345) and of some of the phenolic ether bonds between the monomers. This reaction is hydrolytic cleavage of the ether bonds catalyzed by the polarized chlorine molecule (693, 694). Chlorolignin therefore has a reduced molecular weight, and dissolves in organic solvents such as ethanol, as well as in alkali. Cautious chlorination of Klason softwood lignin in carbon tetrachloride (299) to avoid oxidation resulted in chlorolignin of 25–30% Cl and removal of about every third methoxyl group. This corresponds to a degree of substitution of about 2 Cl/monomer and possibly to the removal of the methyl groups adjacent to a free phenolic hydroxyl. In the chlorination of lignin in aqueous solutions, much more methoxyl is removed (301), possibly preceded by a scission of the phenolic ether bonds between the monomers. Then kraft lignin is demethylated to an extent of nearly 90% and sprucewood meal and lignosulfonate to about 75% (693). The pyrocatechol configurations formed are then readily oxidized to o-quinone derivatives and turn yellow or orange. The chloroquinone may be further oxidized with destruction of the ring structure (345). This is clearly indicated by the spectral changes in visible and ultraviolet light, which show the presence of a maximal amount of quinoid structures upon consumption of about 5–6 Cl/OCH_3 (387), corresponding to the introduction of nearly 2 Cl/monomer, and subsequent oxidation of all monomers to quinones. The measurements also show that the quinoid structures are rapidly degraded by larger chlorine charges, the main chromophors having disappeared after an additional consumption of about 8 oxidation equivalents per monomer, corresponding to the oxidation of 1–2 double bonds per monomer. The proportions of substitution to oxidation reactions on chlorination of pulps have been investigated by several workers for a variety of conditions and pulp types (248, 262, 317, 455) and will be further discussed in Chapter 14. Oxidation is depressed and substitution favored by a higher acidity in the reaction medium, which lowers the concentration of hypochlorous acid (122, 222). The quinoid chlorolignin formed on chlorination in aqueous medium is unstable and will decompose slowly, as evidenced by the spectral changes (387). It is a neutral compound, but comparable to any acyl chloride, as the hydroxyquinones, such as the chloranilic acid, are fairly strong acids (pK_a about 2.5) (387). The removal of about 1 Cl/monomer by aqueous alkali already in the cold, therefore need not be interpreted as a reaction with aliphatically combined chlorine (387, cf. 627).

CV

In a way similar to halogenation, lignin reacts with nitric acid or nitrogen tetroxide under formation of *nitrolignin* containing around 10% nitro groups attached to the aromatic ring, or less than 1 NO_2/monomer,

209

probably in the 6-position (223, cf. 820). About a third of the methoxyl groups are removed on the treatment. Uncondensed guaiacyl groups have been found to yield 2,4-dinitroguaiacol, XCVII, involving 1,5-substitution of the phenylpropane monomers and scission of the side chain (268). Nitration is somewhat slower than halogenation and is carried out at slightly elevated temperature. Considerable oxidation takes place, and the reaction products are alkali- and even water-soluble. Nitration of lignin has been commercially utilized in the nitric acid pulping process (cf. Chapter 9).

G. Oxidation

The following oxidizing agents are of interest in the pulping processes: *hypochlorite* or *hypochlorous acid, chlorite* or *chlorous acid, chlorine dioxide, sodium* and *hydrogen peroxide, permanganate* and *periodate*. The latter two are not used in pulping reactions but in the characterization of the lignin or the isolation of a lignin preparation. Generally speaking, oxidation leads to considerable degradation, although periodate, and peroxide under alkaline conditions primarily react with some functional groups without causing much degradation. Under the same conditions the carbohydrates are little affected by chlorite, chlorine dioxide and peroxide, somewhat more by hypochlorite and permanganate, and are fundamentally changed by periodate. These facts are of principal interest in the choice of pulp bleaching agents.

(a) *Hypochlorite oxidation.* From the work on the chlorination of lignin (345) it is known that hypochlorous acid oxidizes lignin, or at least chlorolignins. Chlorination followed by demethylation is, however, the dominating reaction in acid medium. In alkaline media, elemental chlorine concentration is low, most of the chlorine being present in the form of hypochlorite ion or hypochlorous acid. This ought to favor oxidation. Hypochlorite treatment of various lignin preparations, lignosulfonates, ethanol lignin, hydrochloric acid lignin, Brauns' native lignin, and kraft lignin at pH 11 (657), showed an initial rapid hypochlorite consumption followed by a slower reaction. The lignosulfonates, and similarly the other preparations excepting kraft lignin, consumed 3–4 moles of hypochlorite per phenylpropane monomer at 45–75°C and 6–8 moles at 95°C, most of the consumption occurring during the first ten minutes. Kraft lignin behaved similarly but with almost double hypochlorite consumption. After methylation of the lignin preparations with diazomethane, which blocks the phenol groups and the most reactive aliphatic alcohol groups, a very noticeable reduction in the hypochlorite consumption occurred, with only 1–3 moles of hypochlorite per monomer reacting at 95°C.

At 20°C the rapid reaction consumed 2 moles hypochlorite per monomer in the case of lignosulfonates and 2.7 moles in the case of kraft lignin. Only 0.2 and 0.25 moles chlorine per monomer respectively were found to be attached to the lignin, and 80% were accordingly consumed in oxidation. No appreciable degradation took place, as the preparations were still undialysable and their ultraviolet absorption spectra almost unchanged.

However, a third of the methoxyl was split off from the lignosulfonate and somewhat less from the kraft lignin. Further consumption, to a total of about 7 moles per monomer, causes a definite change in the absorption spectrum and makes most of the lignin preparation dialysable.

In an attempt to use these results for structural conclusions, a great number of model substances were treated with hypochlorite for comparison (657). It was found that phenols, but not phenyl alkyl ethers, react as rapidly as the lignin preparations, and to about the same hypochlorite consumption. Theoretically, guaiacol should consume 6 moles of hypochlorite and yield methanol, oxalic acid and maleic acid, and the consumption was found to be 6 moles. With a side chain, sensitive to oxidation, as in the case of isoeugenol or guaiacylglycerol-α-sulfonic acid, the consumption increases to 10 moles. The first reaction is with these phenols a chlorination, even at pH 11.

It is of interest to note that lignin reacts as rapidly and as completely with hypochlorite as do phenols, although free phenolic groups are present at only about a third of the monomers in the case of protolignin and all lignin preparations except kraft lignin, which is likely to contain one phenol group on every second monomer. It has therefore been suggested that hypochlorite oxidation starts at the monomers containing free phenolic groups, after the insignificant initial chlorination. After degradation of these monomers, the oxidation continues at the adjacent ones, which are likely to become activated by the degradation of the first ones, possibly by cleavage of the phenyl alkyl ether bond and formation of new phenolic groups. This has been shown to be the case (657) for model compounds such as the β-guaiacyl ether of guaiacylglycerol and related compounds, which are considered to be structurally similar to lignin (12). They consume 14 moles of hypochlorite per mole at 90°C, corresponding to about 8 moles per phenylpropane monomer, as was found to be the hypochlorite consumption of the lignin preparations.

The hypochlorite oxidation of lignin can thus be considered as a peeling reaction, starting at the phenolic groups and proceeding throughout the molecule, cf. Chapter 14, Figure 14.27, in a manner somewhat analogous to the alkaline degradation of carbohydrates (cf. Chapter 4.II).

(b) *Chlorite and chlorine dioxide oxidation.* Chlorite and chlorine dioxide are important bleaching agents because of their strong oxidizing action on lignin and small effect on the carbohydrates. The inorganic chemistry involved will be treated in connection with the bleaching theory, Chapter 14. It is sufficient to mention here, that both are used at temperatures around 60–70°C, and that both bleaching agents are present after a short bleaching time, regardless of the starting chemical, although in different concentration. However, their oxidizing action differs in some respects. Thus, chlorite will oxidize aldehyde groups to carboxyl groups, whereas chlorine dioxide will not (401, 687). This is of interest in their action on the carbohydrates, but applies to lignin only for its coniferyl aldehyde end groups and for the aldehyde groups formed on degradation. Investigation of chlorine dioxide oxidation of wood, carbohydrates and a wide range of low-molecular compounds revealed (700) that carbohydrates are not attacked, whereas the lignin is degraded and dissolved. Mono-saccharides, amines, amides, alcohols, acids, esters and aromatic compounds containing no phenolic groups are indifferent towards chlorine dioxide, whereas aliphatic double bonds, mercaptanes, dialkyldisulfides and phenols are readily oxidized. Phenols immediately form colored quinoid compounds, which are further oxidized to mainly carbon dioxide, oxalic and maleic acid. Phenolic ether groups are fairly stable to chlorine dioxide oxidation (632).

The reaction between chlorine dioxide and vanillin, vanillyl and veratryl alcohol has been studied as a model reaction (633, 692). It is likely that to some extent the side chain is oxidized leaving methoxybenzoquinones, to some extent also the benzene ring oxidized to muconic acid methyl esters, which are demethylated in alkali. Indeed, studies on chlorine dioxide treatment of lignosulfonate (729) indicate that the aromatic nature of the latter is lost. The reactions following upon the initial oxidation are still not elucidated, but it does not seem unlikely that the degradation takes place in a similar peeling reaction as that assumed for hypochlorite oxidation of lignin, whereby a new phenolic hydroxyl is formed for every monomer destroyed, giving a new starting point. However, as even veratrol was found to react with chlorine dioxide (692), it is also conceivable that chlorine dioxide oxidation may occur at other lignin monomers than those containing phenolic groups. It is also worth mentioning, that only in exceptional cases does a bleaching sequence start with chlorine dioxide, and when applied towards the end of the bleaching, it may never meet an unchanged lignin monomer. Then 60–70°C are required to get appreciable oxidation, whereas an initial chlorine dioxide treatment is already effective at room temperature. The most remarkable property of chlorine dioxide is, however, that it does not appreciably react with carbohydrates at low pH, which makes it an excellent bleaching agent.

Chlorite, or rather chlorous acid, on the other hand, seems to be fairly unreactive even towards phenols (241, 249), and it is concluded that the bleaching action of chlorite only starts after the formation of chlorine dioxide and hypochlorite, or hypochlorous acid. On the other hand, chlorite rapidly oxidizes aldehydes, and differs in this respect from chlorine dioxide.

(c) *Peroxide oxidation.* Under the technical conditions chosen, low temperature and pH about 10, sodium peroxide oxidation has a very mild action on both lignin and carbohydrates. In groundwood bleaching (412) about half the peroxide is consumed by lignin, which thereby is bleached, but not appreciably degraded. Bleached lignin preparations showed essentially the same composition as the unbleached ones. Although Brauns' native lignin, extracted from unbleached eastern spruce ground-wood pulp, consumed around 0.12 g Na_2O_2/g, most of which in a fairly rapid reaction, the same material extracted from peroxide bleached groundwood pulp consumed only about 0.01 g Na_2O_2/g less, giving the approximate limits of 0.30 and 0.03 moles of peroxide consumption per phenylpropane monomer. Methylation by diazomethane or by methanol and hydrochloric acid checked peroxide oxidation, and both treatments caused a similar brightening as obtained in the peroxide bleach. They also prevent the color reaction which is obtained with lignin on treatment with phloroglucinol–hydrochloric acid, and which has been shown to be caused by the coniferyl aldehyde groups (11). On the assumption that the decrease in peroxide consumption on diazomethane methylation prior to oxidation is to be ascribed to lignin only, a peroxide consumption of 0.07 moles per monomer was calculated (412). Anyway, it seems probable that lignin reacts with peroxide at the coniferyl aldehyde groups, and possibly with other carbonyl groups, e.g. those in α-position, and phenolic groups as well, on technical groundwood peroxide bleaching. The lignin thereby becomes less colored but not much degraded. On the super-bleaching of bleached kraft or sulfite pulp more severe conditions are used, in order to destroy highly condensed residual lignin. The reactions involved are likely to be similar to those of the oxidation of lignin with hydrogen peroxide under more severe conditions, which causes degradation to formic, acetic, oxalic, succinic and malonic acids (33, 287, 655, 800).

(d) *Periodate and permanganate oxidation.* Periodate oxidation is of interest in connection with the isolation of lignin by periodate degradation of the carbohydrates at room temperature and pH 4 (661, 807). It has been shown (8) that the lignin is attacked at the phenolic groups under splitting of the adjacent methoxyl group, which can then be determined as methanol. Therefore, periodate lignin cannot be considered as unchanged lignin, but periodate oxidation of lignin preparations can be used to measure their content of phenolic groups. Diazomethane methylation prevents the reaction.

The reaction occurs rapidly, the whole release of methanol being complete after 1–5 minutes at 4°C. It is therefore believed (8) that it belongs to the large groups of oxidation reactions involving an ionic rather than a radical mechanism, CVI (486). The initial attack by the periodonium ion, IO_3^+, or its hydrate, $H_2IO_4^+$, would result in the formation of a periodate ester with the phenolic group, from which the iodate ion is removed with the formation of a mesomeric aroxyl cation. The latter would decompose to yield the corresponding o-quinone and methanol, followed by subsequent additional oxidation of the quinone by excess oxidant.

Permanganate oxidation is carried out on the determination of the so-called permanganate number of pulps (cf. Chapter 20). This is correlated to the lignin content of the pulp, although some oxidation of the carbohydrates occurs simultaneously. The lignin is degraded to water-soluble products. The oxidation is likely to start at the phenolic groups, although permanganate oxidation also takes place with such lignin, in which the phenolic groups have been methylated with diazomethane. The degradation products of the methylated lignin are somewhat larger molecules as the aliphatic acids mentioned above for peroxide oxidation, such as

213

veratric, isohemipinic and metahemipinic acids, as already described in the section on lignin structure and on condensation reactions.

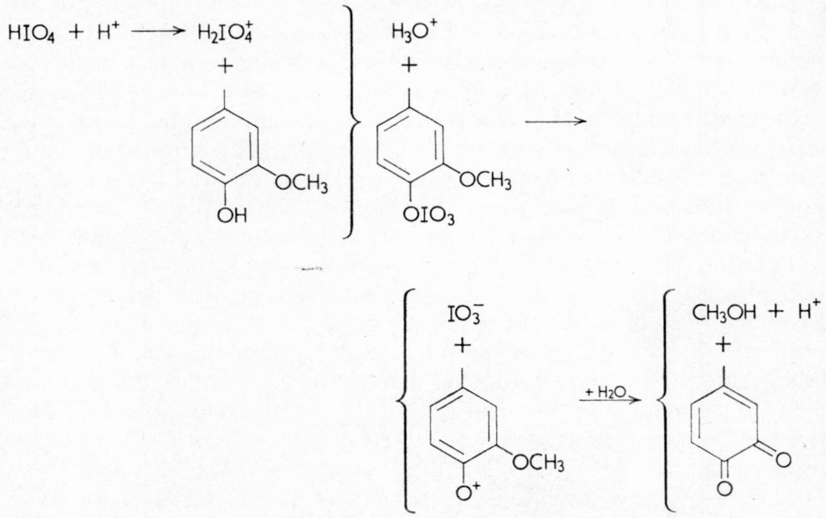

$$HIO_4 + H^+ \longrightarrow H_2IO_4^+$$

CVI

H. Color reactions

Lignin in wood is light yellow or cream-colored, but owing to its reactivity and tendency to form chromophoric configurations, it will easily impart objectionable color to the pulp, and in fact, a large part of the pulp processing deals with the color reactions of lignin and the removal of lignin chromophors. To the more important color reactions of lignin encountered in the pulping processes or pulp use belong:

(1) The yellowing of groundwood pulp and newsprint paper.

(2) The reddening of unbleached sulfite pulps on storage.

(3) The darkening of lignin-rich shives, e.g. of tannin-damage origin or similar, on storage.

(4) The darkening of lignin on condensation at sulfite cooks of higher acidity and temperature, causing in extreme cases the dark-brown color of 'burnt chips', and in more normal cases the darkening of the cooking liquor used for the determination of the end point of rayon cooks.

(5) The darker color of pulps and cooking liquors on ammonium-based sulfite cooks in comparison to other bases.

(6) The dark-brown color of the alkaline, especially the kraft pulps and papers.

(7) The yellowing of pulp on chlorination, reddening or darkening on subsequent alkalization, and the yellow tone of insufficiently bleached pulps.

(8) The yellowing, or part of the yellowing of bleached pulps on long storage or shorter heat treatment.

214

(9) The fluorescence of unbleached pulps.

These color reactions of industrial interest should be compared to those used in the microscopical staining technique of wood preparations believed to be typical for lignin, because the latter color reactions have been more extensively investigated and are sometimes better defined. It is not possible here to review the vast literature but reference is made to a survey (273). Four types of color reactions of wood and mildly isolated lignin preparations, namely with (a) phenols, (b) aromatic amines, (c) hydrogen sulfide and strong sulfuric acid, and (d) concentrated hydrochloric acid, have all been shown to be connected with the coniferyl aldehyde groups of lignin (273). One of the best defined reactions, that with phloroglucinol in acid medium, has even been used for a quantitative determination of these groups in lignin, one on every 40 phenylpropane monomers (9). The reaction is thought to proceed as shown by CVII. Coniferyl aldehyde or

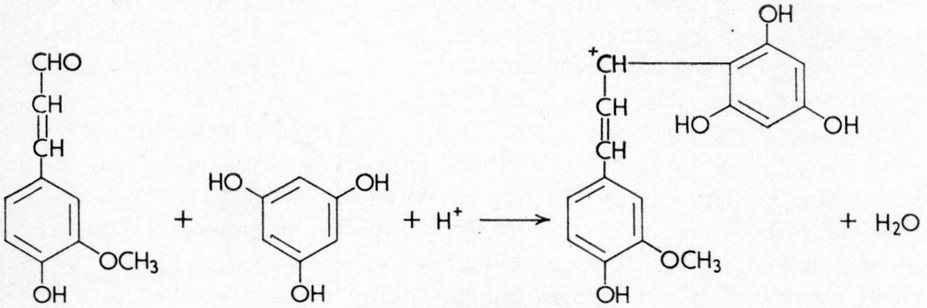

CVII

lignin, treated with dimedone, do not give the phloroglucinol reaction, the aldehyde groups being blocked. Treatment with bisulfite solutions, which give a hydrosulfonic acid with the coniferyl aldehyde groupings, blocking the double bond, likewise prevent the color reaction. Mild treatment with alkali at room temperature removes the sulfonic groups and restores the color reaction.

Another configuration in lignin leading to color reactions are the p-hydroxybenzyl alcohols or ethers. They yield on treatment with hydrogen bromide and subsequent increase in pH a colored quinone methide structure, CVIII (14). The alcohols also give the specific indo-

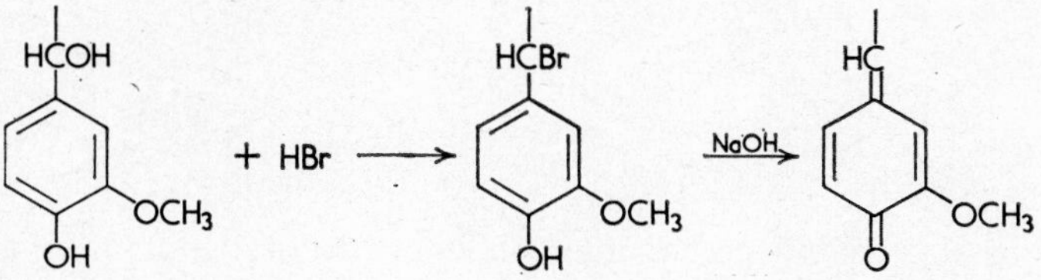

CVIII

phenol color reaction with quinone monochlorimide (242), mentioned in the section on lignin structure. Phenolic guaiacylpropane monomers

215

further react with potassium nitrosodisulfonate to red and comparatively stable o-quinones, CIX, provided the monomers are uncondensed (26).

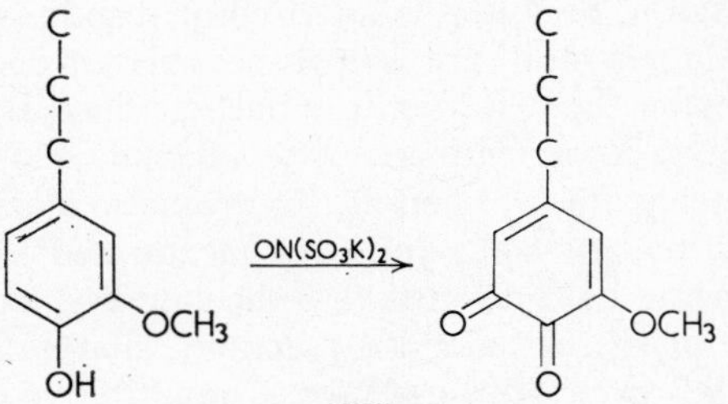

CIX

They can thus be spectrophotometrically determined. Spectrophotometric methods have also been worked out for the determination of monomers containing α-carbonyls (574), and these are also useful for the determination of benzyl alcohols after their oxidation to carbonyls with dichloro-dicyano-p-quinone (27).

The color reactions mentioned all proceed at low temperature. The treatment of wood or lignin at elevated temperature in acid solution with phenols or amines causes further combination with these substances, probably with benzyl alcohol or ether groupings, but these reactions are not responsible for the development of color.

The results of the investigations on lignin color reactions with low-molecular, well-defined compounds, also throw some light on some of the industrially important color reactions. Lignin, containing phenolic groups, may undergo condensation corresponding to the reaction with phloroglucinol, CX. Whereas phloroglucinol gives a violet-red color

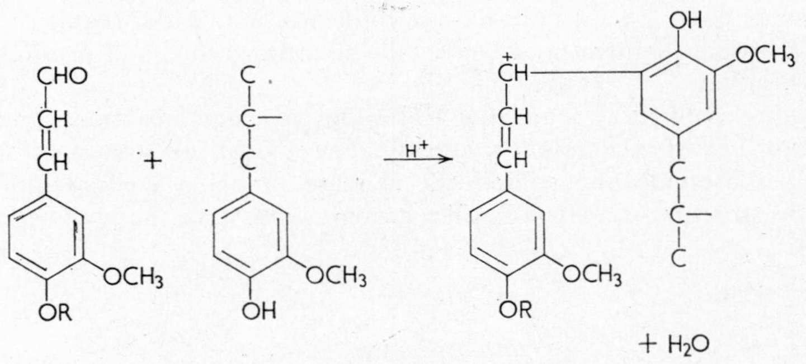

CX

and guaiacol a yellow-green, intercondensation of lignin units gives a yellow-green color only with cold, concentrated mineral acids, whereas with hot acidic cooking liquors a color develops, which changes from yellow and orange to reddish brown and finally very dark brown. Part of this color can be removed by treatment with bisulfites and regenerated by

216

mild alkali treatment, which decomposes the unstable sulfonic acids formed. However, far from all the color disappears on bisulfite treatment, especially with more highly condensed samples. Therefore, other structures than that indicated above are likely to add to the brown color of condensed lignin, possibly of the following type, CXI, in the formation of which

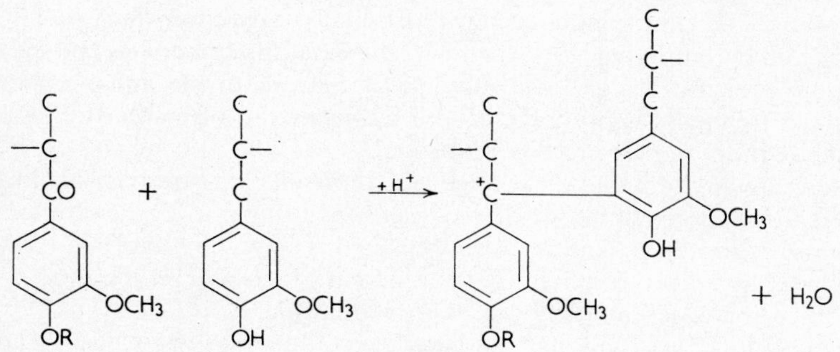

CXI

the carbonyl groups at the α-carbon atom may be involved, or possibly benzyl alcohol groups if subsequent oxidation of the condensed configuration is assumed (387). It should also be pointed out, that the ability to give the phloroglucinol reaction disappears with increasing condensation of lignin. The tendency of ammonium-based sulfite cooks to give darker pulps and cooking liquors has apparently a connection with these condensation reactions, and the higher viscosity of the ammonium-based waste liquors as compared to calcium- or sodium-based ones indicates that condensation is impelled by the presence of ammonium ions, possibly by formation of imino groups with lignin carbonyls.

The development of this brown color occurs in the acid cooking processes, such as sulfite cooking and prehydrolysis. The darkening of shives in pulp from tannin-damaged wood might depend on air oxidation of condensation products with phenolic tannin compounds further increased by the presence of iron contaminants. The reddening of unbleached sulfite pulps has been shown to involve an oxidation mechanism (13), which is obtained by acid peroxide treatment of the pulp, or by air oxidation in the presence of multivalent ion catalysts such as copper or iron. It is believed that oxidation causes formation of stilbene quinones with a spectral absorption very similar to that of CXII. This implies that in this case the α–α-con-

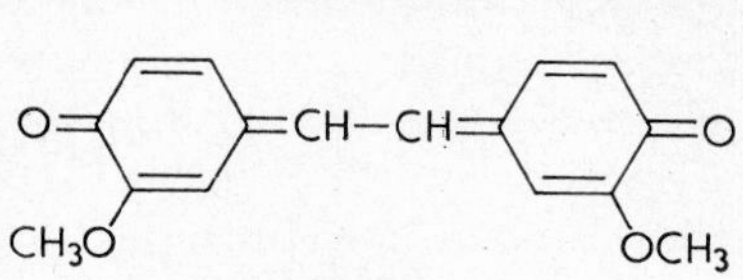

CXII

densed monomers of lignin are involved. On further storage the red color changes to brown. Especially pronounced is the reddening of unbleached

217

hardwood sulfite pulps, which nearly prevents their use in the unbleached state.

The lignin discoloration developed upon alkali cooking is very little studied from a fundamental point of view, although it may be called the most important industrial color reaction of lignin. It has obviously close connection with the large amounts of phenolic groups formed by alkaline hydrolysis. Alkaline condensation is also likely to be important.

The yellow color developed during chlorination of unbleached pulps or lignin preparations and the subsequent changes to red and brown on the alkali treatment is probably caused by formation of *o*-chloroquinones (cf. the section on chlorination reactions).

The yellowing of lignin on storage, e.g. in newsprint paper, is also likely to be caused by oxidation of phenolic groups in lignin. The oxidation is more pronounced in alkaline medium, which is shown by the yellow color developed by a drop of alkali lye on a newsprint paper. In the same way this oxidation is accelerated by heat or irradiation.

Lignosulfonic acid as well as unbleached sulfite pulps show fluorescence by irradiation with ultraviolet light in the dark (288, 434, 487). After alkali treatment at room temperature the fluorescence disappears, and reappears after acid bisulfite treatment. Therefore the coniferyl aldehyde or carbonyl groups of lignin must be involved. However, coniferyl aldehyde does not behave in the same manner (15).

V. Minor Components

1. EXTRACTIVES

This concept covers a wide variety of compounds, and the subsequent treatment will concentrate upon those extractable with *organic solvents*, including also some which are ordinarily classified as volatiles. Extraction with water or alkali removes additional compounds which are related to the hemicelluloses or lignin, and which have been mentioned in previous sections of this chapter, and the alcohol-soluble lignin fraction called Brauns' native lignin has also been discussed there.

More complete treatments on the wood extractives are found in books on wood chemistry (e.g. 827). As the subject is very wide, only those aspects will be dealt with here which have any bearing on the pulping processes, such as by-product value or adverse influence on the processes or on the final quality of the pulp. With those limitations, the wood extractives can be crudely divided into three groups: *terpenes*, '*resins*' and *phenols*. From a physiological stand-point, the classification into the following groups is more justified: (1) food reserves (fats, fatty acids), (2) protectants (terpenes, resin acids, phenols) and (3) plant hormones (phytosterols).

A. Formation and location in the wood structure

All the widely varying types of compounds belonging to the category of extractives are formed from carbohydrates originating from photosynthesis. The places of formation and subsequent location in the wood (615a) depend on their function. The seasonal variations of the extractives content of both softwoods and hardwoods, with a maximum sometimes found in the autumn and a minimum in the springtime (585, 614), sometimes a maximum in May and a minimum in the winter (2), are likely to be connected with the food reserve function. The food reserves, mainly fatty acids and esters, are located at the parenchymateous cells, especially the ray cells, where they are formed in the sequence shown in CXIII (451, 754), with acetoacetate, CXIV, as an important intermediate.

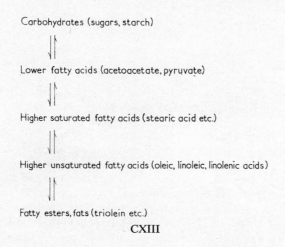

Carbohydrates (sugars, starch)

Lower fatty acids (acetoacetate, pyruvate)

Higher saturated fatty acids (stearic acid etc.)

Higher unsaturated fatty acids (oleic, linoleic, linolenic acids)

Fatty esters, fats (triolein etc.)

CXIII

The neutral components (138) as well as the resin acids (42, 689) are formed in a similar manner, two- and three-carbon molecules coupling to isoprene building units, such as β-methylcrotonic acid, CXV, which form mono-, sesqui- and diterpene structures (cf. below, subsection B).

$$CH_3COCH_2COOH \qquad\qquad CH_3-\underset{\underset{CH_3}{|}}{C}=CHCOOH$$

CXIV   CXV

The terpenes and resin acids have wood-preserving functions and are produced by parenchymateous epithelial cells, surrounding the resin ducts in coniferous woods. Of the *Pinaceae* subfamily, the genera *Abies, Tsuga, Pseudolarix* and *Cedrus* only occasionally contain resin canals, mostly indicating a direct response to wounding, whereas *Picea, Larix, Pseudotsuga* and especially *Pinus* contain frequent vertical and radial resin ducts scattered within the entire wood. Already before the canal lumen is originally formed, resin droplets appear in its epithelial cells (200), and are subsequently extruded into the lumen of the resin duct to build up an osmotic pressure (702) which causes a flow of resin to wounded parts of the tree. The terpenes thereby function as a viscosity-reducing component in the secrete, and volatilizes when the secrete reaches the open wound, leaving a viscous gum of resin acids to cover it, called *oleoresin*. In those parts of the wood, where all living functions have ceased and the moisture content goes down, i.e. in the heartwood, the protective function of the resin is emphasized. During the heartwood formation, the epithelial cells of pine resin ducts swell to occupy the lumen completely and extrude its resin into the surrounding wood. The spruces have a less pronounced heartwood formation and display a more gradual loss of the living functions of the epithelial cells, and the *Abies* and *Tsuga* species develop a secondary thickening of the wall of the epithelial cells as early as within a year of their formation, which prevents further secretion of resin (66). In many deciduous woods, heartwood formation is accompanied by intrusion of tyloses into the vessels from adjacent ray cells according to a similar mechanism, although the excreted substances do not consist of resin acids but of fats.

The protective function of the resin acids is mainly a physical one. However, the heartwoods of many trees display a remarkable resistance to fungal attack because of the presence of a certain class of fungicidal compounds of phenolic character. Although some of them are ether soluble, they cannot be directly extracted by this solvent, indicating that they are inaccessibly deposited. Acetone extraction is successful to remove the phenols. Other phenolic substances in other conifers are less toxic and may have different functions. Species of the genus *Thuja* contain a unique class of compounds with phenolic properties but a tropolone structure and a biogenetic relation to the terpenes (185). Other phenols of importance are the tannins, which in most species are mainly located in the bark, from where they may diffuse into the wood on storage or transportation of the logs in water, as happens in the case of water driving of unbarked spruce logs. Some species, such as oaks, quebracho and redwood, do contain large amounts of tannins, 2–20%, in the wood (827), which is thus preserved from insect and fungal attack.

B. Chemical classification

The crude classification of the wood extractives according to their technical importance, although omitting many less abundant compounds, still includes a large number of substances, mainly of low molecular weight.

The *terpenes* (464, 626a, 724) are hydrocarbons of the elementary composition $C_{10}H_{16}$ (monoterpenes), $C_{15}H_{24}$ (sesquiterpenes) or $C_{20}H_{32}$ (diterpenes), all to be regarded as isoprene polymers. The monoterpenes are most abundant and are recovered in several industrial processes for the production of turpentine: (1) steam distillation of the oleoresinous exudate from living trees, (2) steam distillation or solvent extraction of stumps, (3) destructive distillation of wood and (4) relief gas condensation of kraft cooking. The terpene content of the wood varies with species, generally from 0–2%, preferentially in the conifers. Some *Cedrus, Juniperus* and *Pinus* species are exceptionally rich in terpenes, as much as 6% volatile oils being found in *Cedrus libani* Barr. Related to the terpenes are terpene alcohols and ketones, which occur together with the hydrocarbons in limited amounts.

There are *acyclic, monocyclic* and *bicyclic* terpenes, the two last-mentioned groups being more frequent. Dominating among the bicyclic terpenes are α-*pinene*, CXVI, β-*pinene*, CXVII, and △³-*carene*, CXVIII, and

| CXVI | CXVII | CXVIII |

the most important monocyclic terpenes are *limonene* (racemate *dipentene*), CXIX, and *sylvestrene* (racemate *carvestrene*), CXX. The proportions of these terpenes vary with the species, with the pinenes (especially α-pinene) usually dominating, 50–100%. Carene is lacking in spruce turpentine but amounts to about a third of some pine turpentines. The monocyclic terpenes are generally limited to 20% or less of the turpentine and are partially formed by isomerization of the bicyclic terpenes during the recovery. *Terpineol*, CXXI, is an example of a terpene alcohol, and *cadinene*, CXXII, and *cedrene*, CXXIII, both occurring in wood of *Juniperus* species and other members of *Cupressaceae*, may exemplify the sesquiterpenes.

| CXIX | CXX | CXXI |

| CXXII | CXXIII |

221

The *'resins'*, as defined in the chemistry of pulping processes, include a wide variety of compounds, less inter-related than the various terpenes. They are the non-volatile components of wood, which are extractable with organic solvents. Frequently some of the more polar components such as phenolic compounds, are excluded and the term resin restricted to non-volatile ether solubles. These are *fats, fatty acids, fatty alcohols, resin acids, phytosterols* and some less known neutral substances in small amounts. The proportions of these compounds vary, as well as the total amount of resin. In principle, the resin acids occur only in conifers, where they amount to about 25–50% of the ether solubles. The fatty acids, mainly esterified to fats, dominate in the hardwood species, 50–90% of the ether solubles, and occur in appreciable quantities, 25–50%, also in the ether solubles of the conifers. Fatty alcohols and phytosterols (the *'unsaponifiable fraction'*) amount to 10–33% of the ether solubles of both softwoods and hardwoods, usually somewhat more in the latter. The total quantity of ether soluble extractives varies from 0.2–4.0% of the wood for most species, some pines containing as much as 25% and linden up to 13%. Table 4.30 gives a compilation of the extractives content of some softwood and hardwood species. There is more resin in the heartwood than in the sapwood, especially in the pines. The extractives removed by alcohol–benzene are at least 1% of the wood more than what is obtained with ether, because they also contain phenols, some lignin and other polar compounds. Table 4.31 shows the composition of the ether extractives from a number of wood species. Obviously, the resin acids are confined to softwoods, where they are especially abundant in the heartwood. Spruce and the sapwood of pine contain less resin acids and, instead, much fatty acids, mainly esterified. Particularly dominating are the fatty acids in the extractives of some hardwoods, where they have been found to be mainly esterified in birches and less so in other species. The method of analysis, as well as a tendency for fats to hydrolyse on the storage of wood may

Table 4.30. Alcohol–benzene and ether soluble extractives content of some softwoods and hardwoods

Species	Alcohol–benzene solubles, % of wood	Ether solubles, % of whole wood	% of sap-wood	% of heart-wood	Ref.
Abies amabilis, Pacific silver fir	1.6	0.2			121
balsamea, balsam fir	2.2–2.9	0.9–1.2			67
concolor, western white fir	2.1	0.2			121
grandis, grand fir	1.6	0.2			121
procera, noble fir	2.5	0.2			121
Larix laricina, tamarack	2.0	0.6–0.7			106
occidentalis, western larch	1.4	0.4			106
Picea abies, Scandinavian spruce	2.3	0.8–1.5			178, 713
engelmannii, Engelmann spruce	2.8	1.4			106
glauca, white spruce	0.8	0.4			67
mariana, black spruce	0.6	0.2			67

Table 4.30. Alcohol–benzene and ether soluble extractives content of some softwoods and hardwoods—*continued*

Species	Alcohol–benzene solubles, % of wood	Ether solubles, % of whole wood	% of sap-wood	% of heart-wood	Ref.
Pinus banksiana, jack pine	3.1–4.9	2.4–3.2			67
banksiana, jack pine		2.9			109
echinata, shortleaf pine	3.3–6.3		2.6	5.7	467
echinata, shortleaf pine		3.1			109
elliottii, slash pine	2.6	2.0			106
elliottii, slash pine		2.4			109
monticola, western white pine	8.2	5.6	3.6	5.5	106, 663
palustris, longleaf pine		6.3	2.0	7–10	467, 703
palustris, longleaf pine		2.0			109
ponderosa, ponderosa pine		8–25			30, 663
resinosa, red pine	3.5	2.5			106
serotina, pond pine		2.8			109
silvestris, Scots pine	3.3	1.9			713
taeda, loblolly pine		2.5			109
virginiana, virginia pine		2.5			109
Pseudotsuga taxifolia, Douglas fir	4.4–6.8	1.0–1.3			106, 466, 703
Tsuga heterophylla, western hemlock	1.6	0.8			106
mertensiana, mountain hemlock	5.5	1.5			465
Average, softwoods	3.4	2.1			
Acer rubrum, red maple	2.5	0.3–0.8	0.2–0.5	0.2–0.3	106, 653
saccharum, sugar maple	1.2–1.3	0.2–0.9	0.1–0.2	0.3–0.9	133, 202, 663, 703
Betula lutea, yellow birch	2.6	0.4–1.4	0.4–0.9	0.3–1.2	133, 196, 202, 653, 663
papyrifera, white birch	2.8–6.4	1.5–3.5	0.8–3.0	2.2–3.9	106, 109, 133, 202, 573, 653
verrucosa, silver birch	1.5–4.5	1.1–2.7			403, 406, 615, 671, 717
Fagus grandifolia, American beech	1.0–1.4	0.3–0.9	0.2–0.3	0.4–0.6	133, 202, 653
silvatica, European beech	1.2	0.3			713
Fraxinus americana, white ash			0.9–1.2	0.4–0.5	663
Liquidambar styraciflua, sweet gum		0.2–0.5			808
Liriodendron tulipifera, yellow poplar			0.1–0.3	0.4–0.6	663
Nyssa aquatica, tupelo gum		0.3–0.9	1.0	0.9	808, 829
silvatica, black gum		0.3–0.4	0.4	0.5	386, 808, 829
Populus deltoides, cotton wood		0.3–0.4			386, 535
grandidentata, bigtooth aspen	2.1–2.4	0.9–1.0	1.0	1.0	133, 386
tremula, European aspen	2.9	1.1			713
tremuloides, American aspen		1.0–2.7			105, 109, 133, 535
Quercus alba, white oak			0.5–0.7	0.6–0.7	663
Salix nigra, black willow		0.3			386
Tilia americana, basswood		0.9–13.2			133, 386, 663
Tilia europea, linden		7–8			149
Ulmus americana, white elm		0.3			133
Average, hardwoods	2.0	0.8 (1.5)	0.7	0.8	

Table 4.31. Composition of ether extractives of some wood species

Species	Resin acids, %	Free fatty acids, %	Fats %	Unsaponifiables, %	Ref.
Picea abies, Scandinavian spruce	24	9	41	20	178
Pinus banksiana, jack pine	67	13	8	12	343
Pinus banksiana, jack pine	37	10	40	12	109
Pinus echinata, shortleaf pine (sapwood)	23	68		9	467
Pinus echinata, shortleaf pine (heartwood)	67	19		14	467
Pinus echinata, shortleaf pine	40	16	36	9	109
Pinus elliottii, slash pine	47	34		14	533
Pinus elliottii, slash pine	26	14	46	13	109
Pinus palustris, longleaf pine	36	6	49	9	109
Pinus serotina, pond pine	40	18	28	14	109
Pinus silvestris, Scots pine (tall oil)	56	34		10	421
Pinus taeda, loblolly pine	44	11	38	6	109
Pinus virginiana, virginia pine	44	9	40	7	109
Average, softwoods	42	12	35	11	
Betula papyrifera, white birch	(2)	9	52	32	573
Betula papyrifera, white birch	–	22	61	16	110
Betula papyrifera, white birch	(1)	1	59	36	109
Betula verrucosa, silver birch	–	6	58	32	424
Betula verrucosa, silver birch	–	3	92	6	717
Betula verrucosa, silver birch	–	3–12	69–87	10–19	615
Liquidambar styraciflua, sweet gum	–	57	31	11	808
Nyssa aquatica, tupelo gum	–	52	16	32	808
Nyssa silvatica, black gum	–	47	16	37	808
Populus tremuloides, aspen	(2)	72		18	105
Populus tremuloides, aspen	(2)	5	66	19	109
Average, hardwoods	–	19	55	24	

account for some of that discrepancy. The chemical differences found reflect different physiological functions. The canal resin is dominated by the resin acids and the ray cell resin by the fats (59). The former type of resin is influenced by the amount of heartwood, etc., the latter is subjected to seasonal variations, as the food reserves are increased or consumed. These phenomena will naturally influence the overall composition of the resin as found by analysis of the ether extract.

The *fatty acids* are composed of more than 10 different acids of both the saturated and unsaturated type and of different molecular size. Table 4.32 (110, 424, 717, cf. 109), shows the approximate content of the various types of fatty acids contained in the ether extract of spruce and birch. Obviously C_{16}–C_{18} acids are dominating and among them the unsaturated fatty acids, especially *linoleic*, CXXV, but also *oleic*, CXXIV, and *linolenic acid*, CXXVI. Table 4.33 (717) shows that the saturated fatty acids range from *lauric acid* to *lignoceric acid*, but with *palmitic* and *stearic acids* as the dominating ones. In addition, the fatty alcohol *lignoceryl alcohol* has been found (109, 688). The fatty acids present the main difficulties involved in deresination and pitch troubles of the pulping processes, but constitute a valuable by-product of the kraft pulping industry. The fatty acids occur predominantly esterified with *glycerol* to *triglycerides*, but a small fraction may also form phytosterol esters (109, 110, 717).

$$CH_3(CH_2)_7CH=CH(CH_2)_7COOH$$

CXXIV

$$CH_3(CH_2)_4CH=CHCH_2CH=CH(CH_2)_7COOH$$

CXXV

$$CH_3CH_2CH=CHCH_2CH=CHCH_2CH=CH(CH_2)_7COOH$$

CXXVI

Table 4.32. The fatty acid components in the ether extracts of spruce and birch.

Species	Ref.	Total fatty acids, % of ether extract	Fatty acid components, % of total fatty acids					
			Satur-ated C_{16-18}	Oleic acid	Lino-leic acid	Lino-lenic acid	Total C_{16-18}	Other acids
Picea abies, Scandinavian spruce	424	49	4	16	41	0.5	61	39
Betula papyrifera, White birch	110	72	*ca.* 8	*ca.* 3	*ca.* 75	*ca.* 6	92	8
Betula verrucosa, Silver birch	717	85	14	3	67	10	95	5
Betula verrucosa, Silver birch	424	63	14	8	54	3	80	20

Table 4.33. The detailed composition of total fatty acids, 2.5% of the wood, in ether extract of silver birch (717)

Saturated acids, %		Unsaturated acids, %	
C_{12} (lauric)	0.2	C_{16}I (palmitoleic)	2.0
C_{14} (myristic)	0.3	C_{16}IIa	0.5
C_{16} (palmitic)	8.9	C_{16}IIb	0.2
C_{18} (stearic)	4.6	C_{18}I (oleic)	3.4
C_{20} (arachidic)	1.9	C_{18}II (linoleic)	65.6
C_{22} (behenic)	1.9	C_{18}III (linolenic)	10.0
C_{24} (lignoceric)	0.5		
Total	18.3	Total	81.7

The *resin acids* occur in a number of isomeric forms of $C_{20}H_{30}O_2$ acids and some related structures, *levopimaric*, CXXVII, *neoabietic*, CXXVIII, *abietic*, CXXIX, *dehydroabietic*, CXXX, *dihydroabietic*, CXXXI, *isodextropimaric*, CXXXII, and *dextropimaric*, CXXXIII, *acids*. As seen in Table

225

4.34 (424, 615, cf. 479), levopimaric acid is the most abundant of these acids in both spruce and pine, but several of the other acids occur in appreciable amounts. The compositions of the oleoresin of spruce and pine are similar but not identical, with more emphasis on the dextro-pimaric acids in spruce. The resin acids are less troublesome from a pulping stand-point than are the fatty acids, although they contribute to the pitch troubles. They constitute a valuable by-product of the kraft pulping industry, although a more unchanged mixture of resin acids of less color is obtained by other methods.

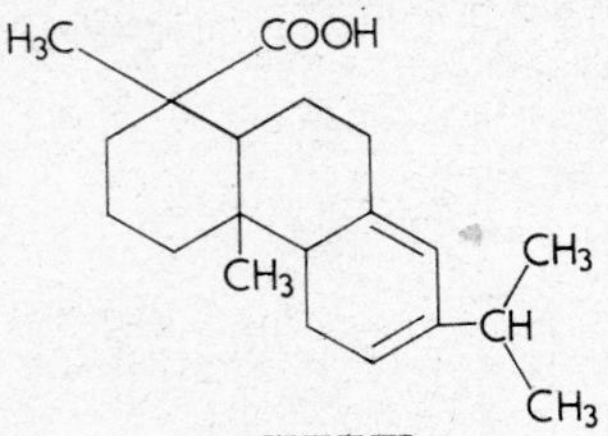

CXXVIJ

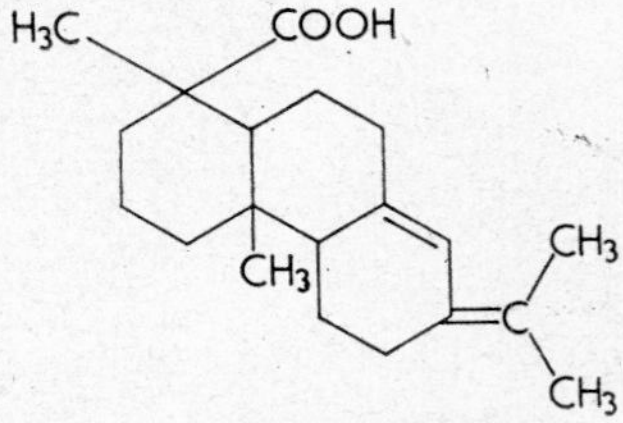

CXXVIII

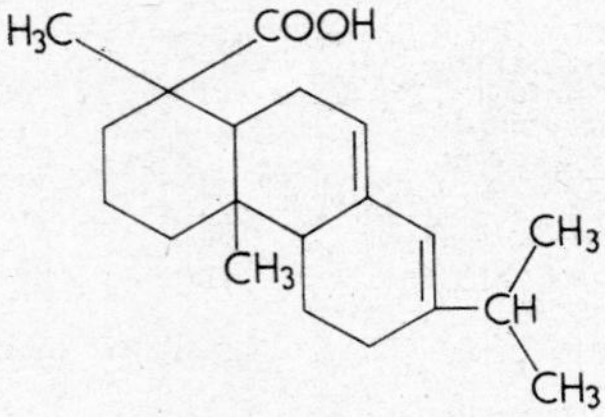

CXXIX

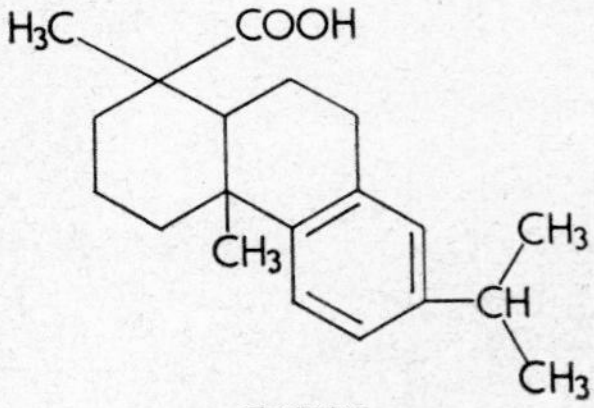

CXXX

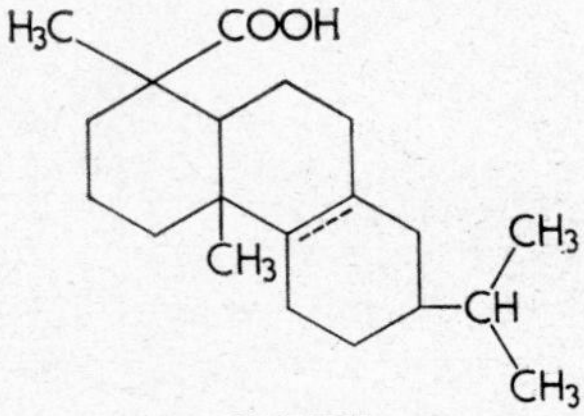

CXXXI

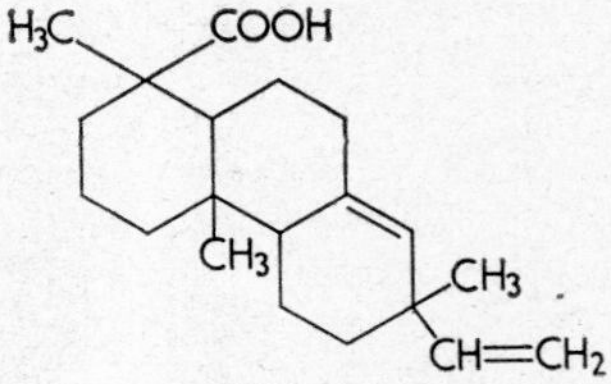

CXXXII

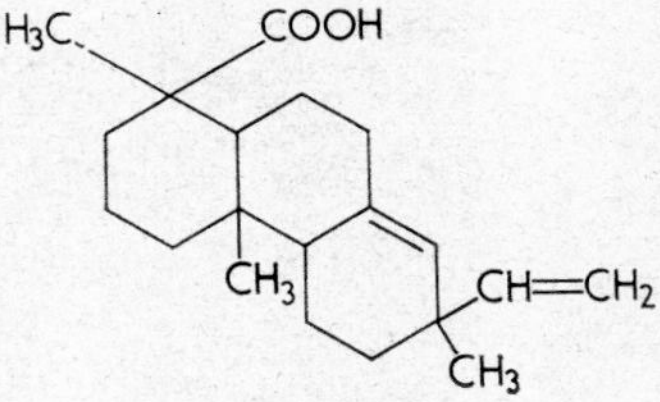

CXXXIII

The *unsaponifiable neutral substances* of the wood extractives contain higher fatty alcohols such as *lignoceryl alcohol*, as well as plant hormones,

Table 4.34. The components of oleoresin of spruce and pine

		Spruce (423)	Pine (302)
Unsaponifiables,	% of oleoresin	25	
Acids,	% of oleoresin	72	
Resin acids,	% of oleoresin	70	
Levopimaric acid,	% of resin acids	25	30–35
Neoabietic acids,	% of resin acids	10–15	15–20
Abietic acids,	% of resin acids	10–15	15–20
Dehydroabietic acids,	% of resin acids	8–9	4
Dihydroabietic acids,	% of resin acids	5–6	4
Isodextropimaric acids,	% of resin acids	⎫	8
Dextropimaric acids,	% of resin acids	⎬40	8
Others		⎭	

the phytosterols, mainly *β-sitosterol*, CXXXIV, and *β-sitostanol*, CXXXV, in the approximate proportions of 30: 63 :7 (307). The phytosterols have been demonstrated in spruce (178), pine (74, 179, 307, 690 822) as well as birch (424, 717). These substances contribute appreciably to deresination difficulties and pitch troubles, as they possess little hydrophility at all pH levels. Their utilization in the production of sex hormones has been investigated on a fairly large scale, but was not found to be competitive with the alternative source, cholosterol from wool fat.

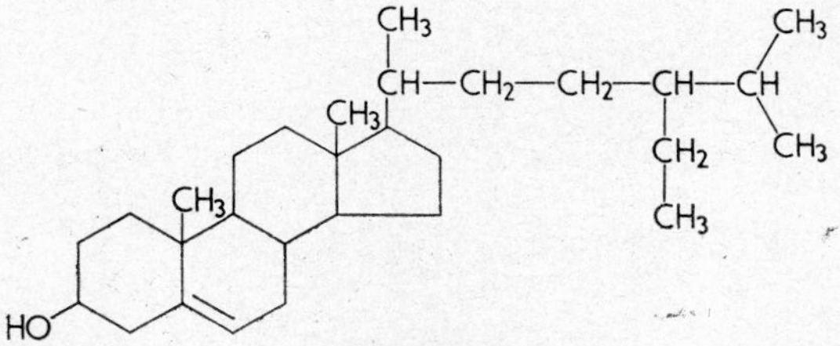

CXXXIV

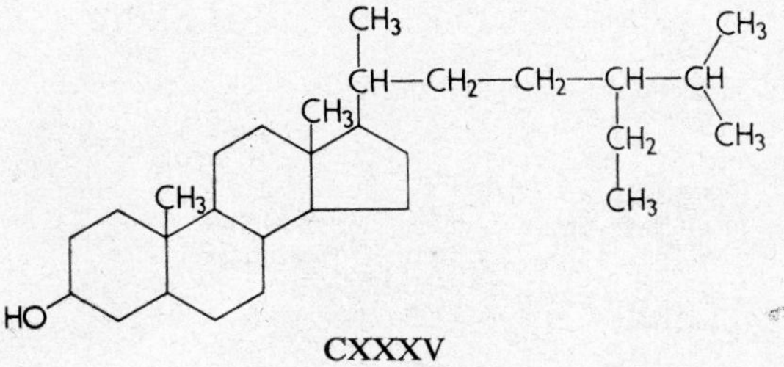

CXXXV

The important category of extractives here classified as *phenols* is less troublesome in connection with the deresination and pitch problems, although they add to the quantity of compounds extractable with alcohol or alcohol–benzene and are therefore often classified as resins. They

227

consist of a large number of insufficiently studied compounds, among which the most important are *tannins*, and *heartwood phenols* and related substances.

The *tannins* are subdivided (203, cf. 112) into *hydrolysable* and *condensed* tannins, both of which are structurally insufficiently known. They have one property in common, in that they become firmly bound by hide substance. Although there are several possibilities for the chemical combination with hide proteins, phenolic hydroxyls have been found to be the most essential functional groups for compounds used as tanning agents. The hydrolysable tannins (also called *gallotannins* and *ellago-tannins*) yield *gallic*, CXXXVI, or *ellagic*, CXXXVII, *acid* and sugars, the condensed tannins (also called *phlobatannins*) give products of still higher molecular weight, called the *phlobaphenes*. The condensed tannins contain monomers of the *catechin* type, CXXXVIII, and monomeric

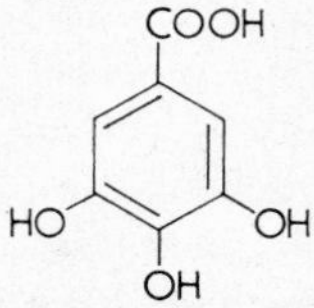

CXXXVI 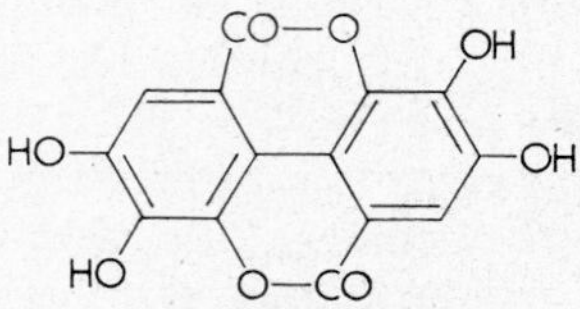 CXXXVII 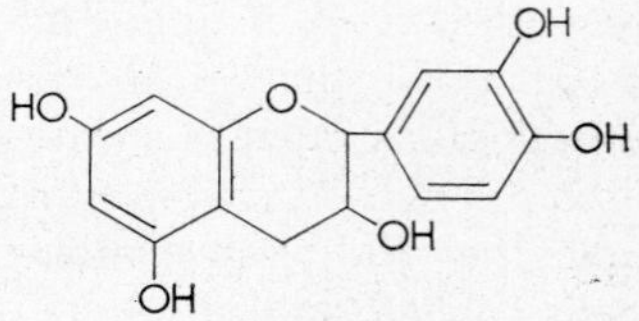 CXXXVIII

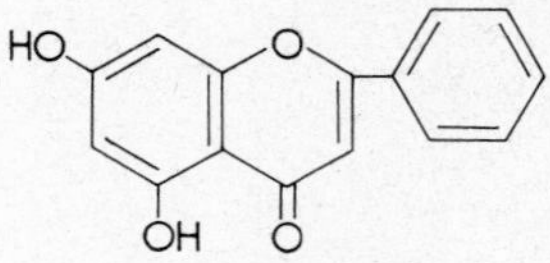

CXXXIX 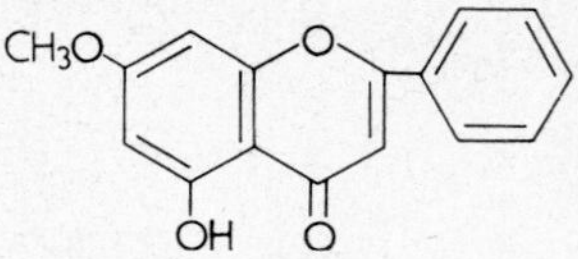 CXL

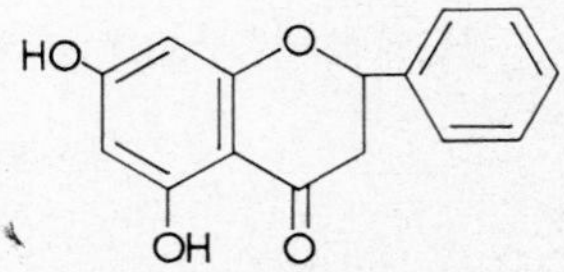

CXLI 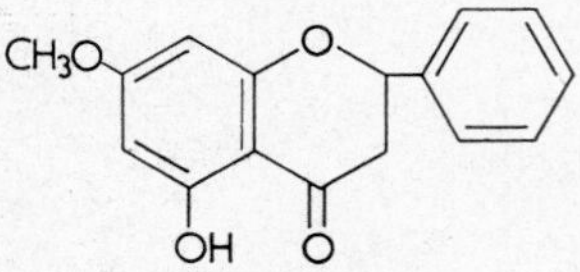 CXLII

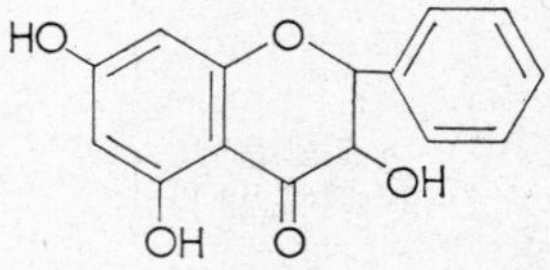

CXLIII 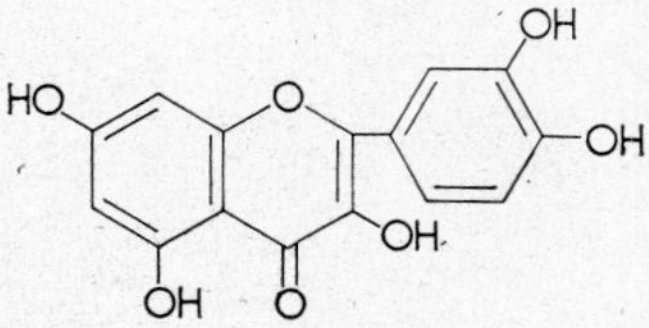 CXLIV

compounds of the same category likewise occur in bark and wood (112, 186). They are called *flavonones* and are coloring substances, such as *chrysin*, CXXXIX, *tectochrysin*, CXL, *pinocembrin*, CXLI, *pinostrobin*, CXLII, and *pinobanksin*, CXLIII, occurring in some pine heartwoods, *fisetin*, CXLIV, in quebracho and yellow cedar, and *quercetin*, CXLV, in

228

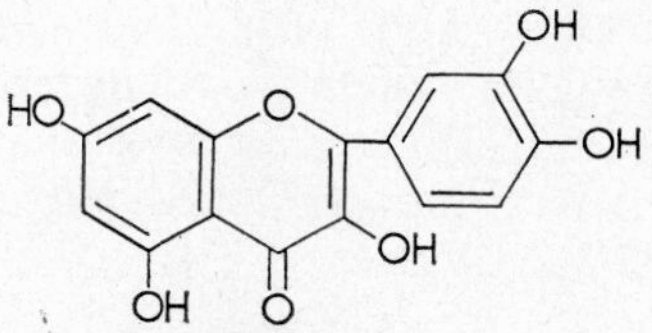

CXLV 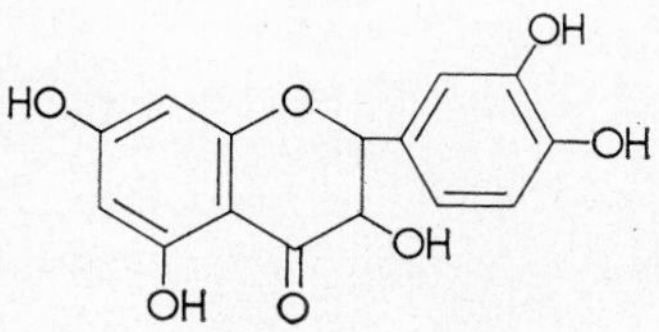 CXLVI

some oaks and chestnut, etc. *Dihydroquercetin*, CXLVI also called *taxifolin*, is found in Douglas fir heartwood in quantities of up to 2% and up to 12% in the bark. The flavanones thus constitute one type of the heartwood phenols. Another type (not limited to the heartwood) are the *lignans*, as exemplified by the *pinoresinol*, CXLVII, of some spruces and pines, *lariciresinol*, CXLVIII, of larch, *olivil*, CXLIX, from olive

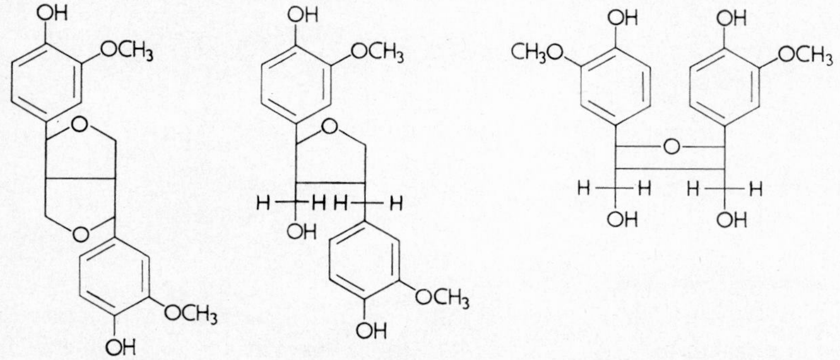

CXLVII CXLVIII CXLIX

wood, and *conidendrin*, CL from spruce and hemlock. Still another important type of heartwood phenols are stilbene derivatives, such as *pinosylvin*, CLI, which occurs in the heartwood of some pines, and *pinosylvin monomethyl ether*, CLII, occurring in most pine species. A

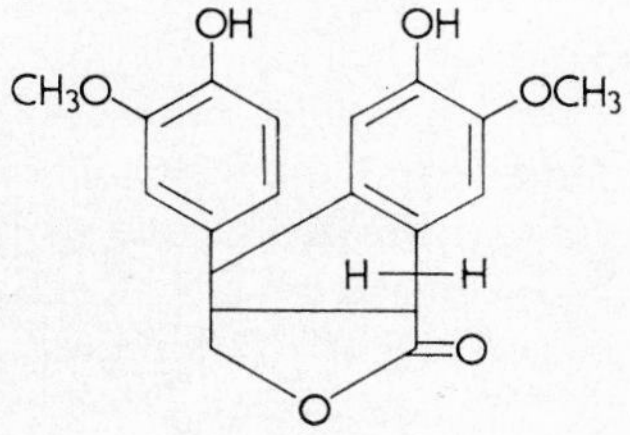

CL

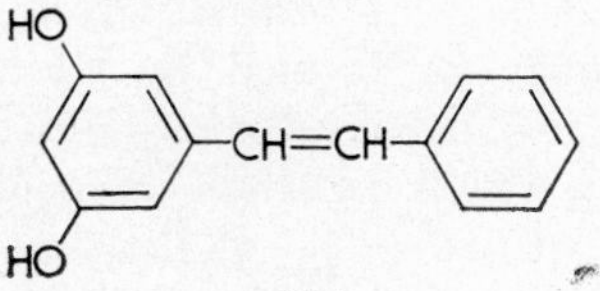

CLI 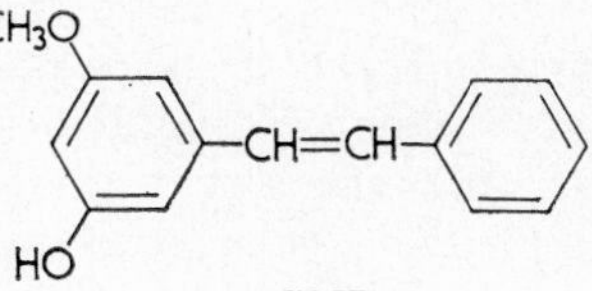 CLII

229

special category of compounds, displaying phenolic properties, although their elementary composition, $C_{10}H_{12}O_2$, suggests a relation to the terpenes, are found in the fungus-resistant woods of *Thuja plicata*, western red cedar (186). They are tropolone derivatives and are called *thujic acid*, CLIII, and *α*-, *β*- and *γ*-*thujaplicins*, CLIV–CLVI.

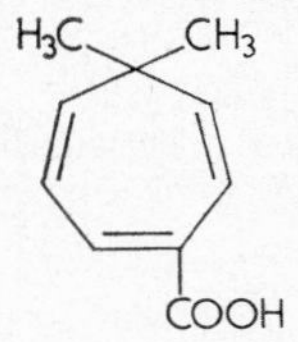

CLIII 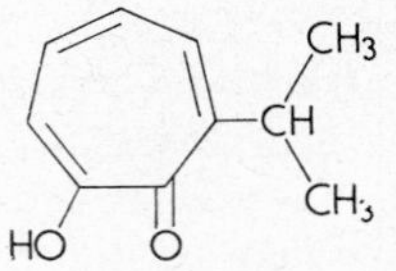   CLIV 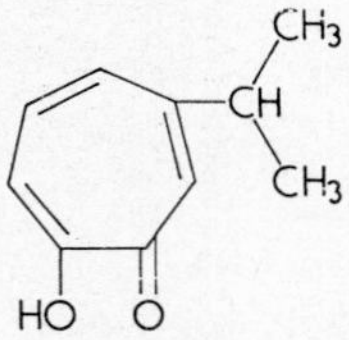   CLV

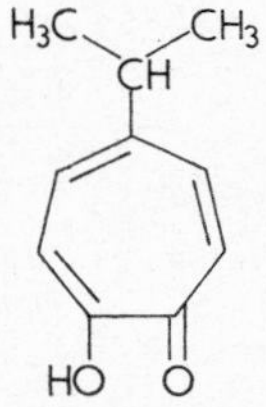

CLVI

C. *Reactivity towards pulping chemicals*

As references to the extractives will be made in the various chapters on pulping reactions, and a special chapter devoted to the problems of deresination, Chapter 16, only some general aspects on the reactivity of this heterogeneous class of compounds will be dealt with here. Obviously, reactions between most extractives and the pulping chemicals will occur at the interface of water and the less polar phase, although the latter may be dispersed in water by mechanical action, often in the presence of surfactants. The reactions are not always limited to the extractive and the pulping chemical, but other wood components may also take part in the reaction.

The *terpenes* are capable of *isomerization, polymerization, disproportionation, reduction-oxidation*, and *addition of chemicals*. As they are volatile, they usually disappear during the top or blow-down relief of the cook if unchanged, and their reaction with bleaching chemicals need not be considered. In alkaline cooking they are indeed recovered as turpentine from the relief gases, although changed to some extent. The evil smell of kraft turpentine is not entirely due to the fact that the turpentine includes some of the methyl mercaptan formed, but also arises from sulfur-containing terpene derivatives. They may be formed by addition of hydrogen sulfide, and tend to split off hydrogen sulfide on distillation. However, the reactivity of the terpenes is much higher in the acid sulfite cook, and there no terpenes can be recovered. One of the dominating reactions should be the acid-catalyzed addition of water, CLVII, with the

230

formation of *terpinol*, as well as subsequent dehydration reactions to *terpineol* and to monocyclic terpene isomers. Furthermore, bisulfite ions are known to oxidize terpenes to *cymene* under formation of thiosulfate, an undesirable reaction which, however, is of little quantitative importance. The yield of cymene is low, about 0.1 % of the wood or less. Most terpenes form *p*-cymene, but $\triangle^3$-carene yields *m*-cymene. From a pulping standpoint, the terpene reactions are of little importance.

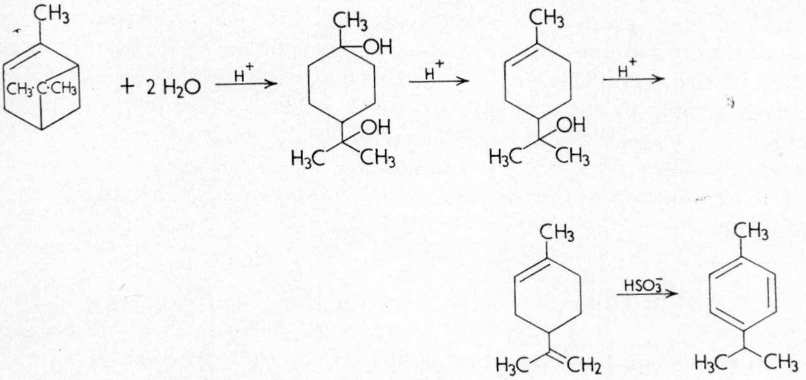

CLVII

The reactions of the '*resins*' during the pulping processes are much more important, although insufficiently investigated. As this category of extractives is non-volatile, both the cooking and bleaching operations involve reactions with these compounds. The *fats* undergo enzymatic or acid- or alkali-catalysed *hydrolysis* to glycerol and fatty acids, and the unsaturated fatty acids may *isomerize, polymerize, form adducts* with *bisulfite, chlorine* or *hypochlorous acid*, or *degrade* by oxidation, all reactions occurring at the double bonds. The *fatty acids* are *neutralized* to soaps in the pH interval of 5–7 (415), and many of the pitch troubles encountered in the mills are extremely pH-dependent. The formation of tacky soaps with multivalent ions, especially calcium, iron and copper, is thereby a contributing factor. Alkaline soaps of sufficient concentration form micelles, which aid in the dispersion of neutral extractives in alkaline cooks. In groundwood pulp production from resinous wood, such as pine, the pitch problems are controlled by the addition of alkali and alum to prevent a dispersion and subsequent agglomeration of the resin.

Most of the reactions at the double bonds and carboxyl groups of the fatty acids have their parallels in the reactions of the *resin acids*, which in addition are capable of undergoing disproportionation. The carboxyl group of resin acids is fairly weak, with a pK_a of around 5.7 (60). The *neutral, unsaponifiable components* of the resin have to be solubilized by surfactants, such as the alkali soaps of the fatty and resin acids. In the removal of resin during hot alkali purification in the bleachery, it may be essential to ensure complete saponification of fats in order to achieve

231

solubilization of the unsaponifiables by micelle formation of the soaps. The critical micelle concentration is thereby around 0.02 mol./l. for resin acid soaps (61, 305) and 0.001–0.002 mol./l. for fatty acid soaps (142, 449), and equal mixture of the two forming micelles at 0.0025 mol./l. (305). The quantity of neutral substance to be dispersed further influences the amount of surfactants required.

The reactions of the *phenols* are of two types, *reduction* of bisulfite to thiosulfate by pyrocatechol configurations, and *condensation* with the benzyl alcohol groups of lignin, especially by the aromatic systems containing resorcinol configurations. Pinosylvin is consequently very active in this respect and is one of the reasons why pine heartwood is difficult to pulp by the acid sulfite process, whereas the troubles in sulfite pulping of Douglas fir have been ascribed to the property of taxifolin to reduce bisulfite. Some of the tannins and flavanones may in addition cause discoloration of the unbleached pulps even without condensing with the lignin.

2. INORGANICS

As is shown in Tables 4.1–2, the mineral constituents of *wood* usually correspond to less than 1% of ash substances. Most of them are present in combination with organic compounds and have physiological functions. Spectrographical analysis of ashes from pine wood has revealed as many as 27 trace elements (821). Table 4.35 (28a) shows that the bark may contain more minerals than the wood, and that the differences between sapwood and heartwood are small, as well as between species, grown in the same part of the world. The dominating ash components are *alkali*

Table 4.35 (28a). The major constituents of ashes from some wood samples

Species and part of tree	Ash content, %	Ash composition, %										
		Na_2O+ K_2O	CaO	MgO	MnO_2	Fe_2O_3	Al_2O_3	SiO_2	SO_3	P_2O_5	CO_2	Sum
Pinus silvestris												
Heartwood	0.17	13.0	39.3	10.8	5.4	3.0	–	1.8	–	0.4	21.9	–
Sapwood	0.23	16.9	34.6	6.8	4.8	2.8	2.7	2.4	5.0	3.9	19.5	99.4
Bark	0.20	9.5	49.8	6.8	2.8	1.0	10.7	1.9	2.8	6.0	7.5	98.8
Picea abies												
Heartwood	0.30	13.9	39.6	7.5	3.5	1.6	1.4	2.2	3.2	0.4	25.3	98.6
Sapwood	0.26	18.0	37.3	5.5	3.2	1.2	–	2.8	–	3.4	21.8	–
Bark	0.69	5.4	47.7	3.4	3.5	0.6	3.3	1.4	0.8	2.2	30.1	98.4
Betula verrucosa												
Wood	0.27	18.6	30.8	10.3	3.5	0.9	3.4	2.0	3.9	5.1	21.3	99.8

and *earth alkali* carbonates, which constitute more than 80% of the ashes. The metals occur in the wood as *oxalates* and *carbonates* or as metals attached to the carboxyls of the carbohydrates. *Phosphate* is mainly present in ester form and takes an active part in the metabolism, and it is therefore especially concentrated in the cambium layer (75). Some of the silica is in the same way combined to carbohydrate components in ester linkages (177, 365), but is also deposited as silica crystals, and is especially abundant in cereal *straw*, 2–20% (cf. Chapter 9.IV), where it presents a serious problem in kraft pulp production and also prevents successful sulfite pulping (41). Also for rayon wood pulps, silica is a factor to be controlled. Some of the metals, such as calcium, magnesium, iron and manganese, should also be removed during the pulping operations in rayon pulp production, but pulping chemicals and mill water often introduce more metals and silica than those originating from the wood. However, during the evaporation of sulfite waste liquor from sodium-based cooks, calcium from the wood is sufficient to cause gypsum incrustation problems, and salts of the alkali metals, of which potassium dominates, tend to accumulate in the regeneration system of magnesium-based sulfite mills unless removed at a special washing stage. In this connection it should be pointed out that logs, transported in salt or brackish water, contain sodium chloride, which tends to accumulate in mills with chemicals recovery systems and give corrosion problems in sulfite digesters and an unnecessary load on the recovery furnace in kraft mills.

By micro-incineration methods it has been shown (468) that most of the mineral constituents are located at the middle lamella and primary wall, but that also the secondary wall yields ashes (600, 798). Manganese has been found to be especially located in the ray cells (832).

REFERENCES

1. Abrahamsson, B., *et al.*, *Svensk Papperstid.*, **51**, 471 (1948).
2. Adams, G. A., and C. T. Bishop, *Tappi*, **38**, 672 (1955).
3. Adams, G. A., *Can. J. Chem.*, **35**, 556 (1957).
4. Adams, G. A., *Tappi*, **40**, 721 (1957).
5. Adams, G. A., *Can. J. Chem.*, **36**, 755 (1958); **38**, 280 (1960).
6. Adkins, H., *et al.*, *J. Am. Chem. Soc.*, **57**, 193 (1935); **59**, 1694 (1937).
7. Adler, E., in E. Treiber, ed., *Die Chemie der Pflanzenzellwand*, Springer, Berlin 1957, p. 446; *Papier*, **15**, 604 (1961); *Tappi*, **40**, 294 (1957).
8. Adler, E., *et al.*, *Acta Chem. Scand.*, **9**, 319 (1955); *Svensk Papperstid.*, **61**, 641 (1958).
9. Adler, E., and L. Ellmer, *Acta Chem. Scand.*, **2**, 839 (1948).
10. Adler, E., *Svensk Papperstid.*, **50**, 261 (1947), **50**, No. 11 B, 9 (1947).
11. Adler, E., *et al.*, *Acta Chem. Scand.*, **2**, 93 (1948).
12. Adler, E., and S. Yllner, *Acta Chem. Scand.*, **7**, 570 (1953); *Svensk Papperstid.*, **57**, 78 (1954).
13. Adler, E., and S. Häggroth, *Svensk Papperstid.*, **53**, 287, 321 (1950).
14. Adler, E., and J. Gierer, Paper presented at the 13th Int. Congr. Pure Appl. Chem., Stockholm 1953.
15. Adler, E., and S. Häggroth, unpubl., cited in E. Hägglund, *Chemistry of Wood*, Acad. Press, New York 1951, p. 455.
16. Adler, E., and J. Gierer, *Acta Chem. Scand.*, **9**, 84 (1955).
17. Adler, E., *et al.*, *Svensk Papperstid.*, **55**, 238, 245 (1952); *Acta Chem. Scand.*, **9**, 34 (1955).

18. Adler, E., *et al.*, *Ind. Eng. Chem.*, **49**, 1391 (1957).
19. Adler, E., *et al.*, *Acta Chem. Scand.*, **2**, 93, 839 (1948); **3**, 86 (1949).
20. Adler, E., *Ind. Eng. Chem.*, **49**, 1377 (1957).
21. Adler, E., and B. O. Lindgren, *Svensk Papperstid.*, **55**, 563 (1952).
22. Adler, E., *Svensk Papperstid.*, **50**, No. 11 B, 9 (1947).
23. Adler, E., and J. Marton, *Acta Chem. Scand.*, **13**, 75 (1959); **15**, 357, 370, 384 (1961).
24. Adler, E., *et al.*, *Acta Chem. Scand.*, **13**, 2149 (1959).
25. Adler, E., *et al.*, *Acta Chem. Scand.*, **9**, 84 (1955), **15**, 370 (1961).
26. Adler, E., and K. Lundquist, *Acta Chem. Scand.*, **15**, 223 (1961).
27. Adler, E., *et al.*, *Acta Chem. Scand.*, **15**, 218 (1961) and in press.
28. Ahlm, C. E., *Paper Trade J.*, **113**, No. 13, 115 (1941).
28a. Åkerman, R., and C. G. Särnström, *Jernkontorets Ann.*, **43**, 261 (1888).
29. Alexander, W. J., and R. L. Mitchell, *Anal. Chem.*, **21**, 1497 (1949).
30. Anderson, A. B., *Ind. Eng. Chem.*, **38**, 759 (1946).
31. Anderson, E., *et al.*, *J. Biol. Chem.*, **135**, 189 (1940).
32. Anderson, E., and W. W. Pigman, *Science*, **105**, 601 (1947).
33. Anderzén, O., and B. Holmberg, *Ber.*, **56**, 2044 (1923).
34. Andress, K. R., *Z. Physik. Chem.*, **A 122**, 261 (1926); **B 2**, 380 (1929); **B 4**, 190 (1929).
35. Andress, K. R., *Z. Physik. Chem.*, **136**, 279 (1928).
36. Andress, K. R., and L. Reinhardt, *Z. Physik. Chem.*, **A 151**, 425 (1930).
37. Anker-Rasch, O., and J. L. McCarthy, *Norsk Skogind.*, **8**, 329 (1954).
38. Annergren, G. E., and S. A. Rydholm, *Svensk Papperstid.*, **62**, 737 (1959), **63**, 591 (1960).
39. Anthis, A., *Tappi*, **39**, 401 (1956).
40. Arlt, H. G., *J. Am. Chem. Soc.*, **78**, 1904 (1956).
41. Aronovsky, S. I., *et al.*, *Paper Trade J.*, **126**, No. 25, 78 (1948).
42. Arreguin, B., *et al.*, *Arch. Biochem. Biophys.*, **31**, 234 (1951).
43. Ashorn, T., *Soc. Sci. Fennica; Commentationes Phys. Math.*, **25**, 8 (1961); *Paperi Puu*, **43**, 655 (1961).
44. Asoka, H., *et al.*, *J. Chem. Soc. Japan*, **54**, 670 (1951).
45. Aspinall, G. O., *et al.*, *J. Chem. Soc.*, **1957**, 4444.
46. Aspinall, G. O., *et al.*, *J. Chem. Soc.*, **1958**, 593.
47. Aspinall, G. O., and M. O. Carter, *J. Chem. Soc.*, **1956**, 3744.
48. Aspinall, G. O., and J. E. McKay, *J. Chem. Soc.*, **1958**, 1059.
49. Aspinall, G. O., Paper presented at the 136th A.C.S. Meeting, Atlantic City, N.J. 1959.
50. Aspinall, G. O., and A. Nicolson, *J. Chem. Soc.*, **1960**, 2503.
51. Aspinall, G. O., in M. L. Wolfrom and R. S. Tipson, eds., *Advances in Carbohydrate Chemistry*, Vol. 14, Academic Press, New York 1959, p. 429.
52. Aspinall, G. O., *et al.*, *J. Chem. Soc.*, **1961**, 3667.
53. Asunmaa, S., *Svensk Papperstid.*, **58**, 308 (1955).
54. Asunmaa, S., *Svensk Papperstid.*, **58**, 33 (1955).
55. Asunmaa, S., and P. W. Lange, *Svensk Papperstid.*, **56**, 85 (1953); **57**, 498 (1954).
56. Atchison, J. E., *Paper Trade J.*, **116**, No. 22, 23 (1943).
57. Aulin-Erdtman, G., *Svensk Papperstid.*, **47**, 91 (1944); **55**, 745 (1952); **56**, 91, 287 (1953); **57**, 745 (1954); **59**, 363 (1956); **60**, 671 (1957); **61**, 187 (1958); *Tappi*, **32**, 160 (1949).
58. Aulin-Erdtman, G., *et al.*, *Svensk Papperstid.*, **50**, No. 11 B, 81 (1947).

59. Back, E., and O. T. Carlson, *Svensk Papperstid.*, **58**, 415 (1955).
60. Back, E., *et al.*, *Acta Chem. Scand.*, **4**, 810 (1950), **12**, 1516 (1958).
61. Back, E., *Svensk Papperstid.*, **54**, 657 (1951).
62. Bailey, A. J., *Ind. Eng. Chem.* (*Anal. Ed.*), **8**, 52, 389 (1936); *Paper Trade J.*, **110**, No. 1, 29 (1940).
63. Bailey, A. J., *Paper Trade J.*, **111**, No. 6, 27 (1940).
64. Ball, D. H., *et al.*, *Tappi*, **39**, 438 (1956).
65. Banerjee, S. K., and T. E. Timell, *Tappi*, **43**, 849 (1960).
66. Bannan, M. W., *New Phytologist*, **35**, 11 (1936).
67. Barnes, F., *Chem. Met. Eng.*, **28**, 503 (1923).
68. Barry, A. J., *et al.*, *J. Am. Chem. Soc.*, **58**, 333 (1936).
69. Bassham, J. A., and M. Calvin, in D. E. Green, ed., *Currents in Biochemical Research 1956*, Interscience, New York 1956, p. 29.
70. Battista, O. A., *et al.*, *Ind. Eng. Chem.*, **48**, 333 (1956).
71. Bayer, A., and V. Villiger, *Ber.*, **35**, 3016 (1902).
72. Beall, G., and L. Jörgensen, *Textile Research J.*, **21**, 203 (1951).
73. Beckman, E., *et al.*, *Biochem. Z.*, **139**, 491 (1923).
73a. Benko, J., *Tappi*, **44**, 766, 771, 849 (1961).
74. Bergström, H., *et al.*, *Jernkontorets Ann.*, **12**, No. 5, 507 (1911).
75. Bergström, H., *Svensk Papperstid.*, **62**, 160 (1959).
76. Berl, E., *et al.*, *Beiträge zur Kenntnis der Mischsäure*, Lehmann, München 1937.
77. Berl, E., and G. Rueff, *Cellulosechem.*, **12**, 53 (1931); **14**, 115 (1933).
78. Bertrand, G., and S. Benoist, *Compt. Rend.*, **176**, 1583 (1923).
79. Bishop, C. T., *Can. J. Chem.*, **35**, 1010 (1957).
80. Bishop, C. T., and F. P. Cooper, *Can. J. Chem.*, **38**, 793 (1960).
81. Björkman, A., *Svensk Papperstid.*, **59**, 477 (1956); **60**, 158, 243, 285, 329 (1957).
82. Björkqvist, K. J., *et al.*, *Svensk Papperstid.*, **57**, 113 (1954).
83. Björnhaug, A., *et al.*, *Norsk Skogind.*, **7**, 171 (1953).
84. Bland, D. E., *Holzforschung*, **12**, 36 (1958).
85. Bouchonnet, A., *et al.*, *Compt. Rend.*, **197**, 63 (1933).
86. Bouveng, H. O., and H. Meier, *Acta Chem. Scand.*, **13**, 1884 (1959).
87. Bouveng, H. O., and B. Lindberg, *Acta Chem. Scand.*, **10**, 1515 (1956).
88. Bouveng, H. O., *et al.*, *Acta Chem. Scand.*, **14**, 742 (1960), **15**, 96 (1961).
89. Bouveng, H. O., *Svensk Kem. Tidskr.*, **73**, 115 (1961).
90. Bouveng, H. O., and B. Lindberg, *Acta Chem. Scand.*, **12**, 1977 (1958).
91. Braconnot, H., *Ann. Chim. Phys.*, (2), **12**, 172 (1819).
92. Bradway, K. E., *Tappi*, **37**, 440 (1954).
93. Brasch, D. J., and L. E. Wise, *Tappi*, **39**, 581, 768 (1956).
94. Brauns, F. E., *Chemistry of Lignin*, Academic Press, New York 1952.
95. Brauns, F. E., in L. E. Wise and E. C. Jahn, eds., *Wood Chemistry*, 2nd Ed., Reinhold, New York 1952, Chapter III.
96. Brauns, F. E., *J. Am. Chem. Soc.*, **61**, 2120 (1939); *Paper Trade J.*, **111**, No. 14, 35 (1940); *J. Org. Chem.*, **10**, 211 (1945).
97. Brauns, F. E., and H. Seiler, *Tappi*, **35**, 67 (1952).
98. Brauns, F. E., and M. A. Buchanan, *Paper Trade J.*, **122**, No. 21, 49 (1946).
99. Brauns, F. E., *Science*, **102**, 155 (1945).
100. Brenner, F. C., *et al.*, *J. Am. Chem. Soc.*, **70**, 877 (1948).
101. Brissaud, L., and S. Ronssin, *Bull. Assoc. Tech. Ind. Papétière*, **4**, 107 (1953).

102. Brown S. A., and A. C. Neish, *Can. J. Biochem. Physiol.*, **32,** 170 (1954); **33,** 948 (1955); *Nature,* **175,** 688 (1955); *J. Am. Chem. Soc.,* **81,** 2419 (1959).

103. Browne, C. A., and M. Phillips, *J. Wash. Acad. Sci.,* **25,** 517 (1935).

104. Browning, B. L., and L. O. Bublitz, *Tappi,* **36,** 452 (1953).

105. Browning, B. L., and L. O. Bublitz, *Tappi,* **36,** 418 (1953).

106. Browning, B. L., and I. H. Isenberg, in L. E. Wise and E. C. Jahn, eds., *Wood Chemistry,* Reinhold, New York 1952, p. 1264.

107. Bryde, Ö., *et al., Svensk Papperstid.,* **50,** No. 11 B, 34 (1947); **52,** 389 (1949); *Norsk Skogind.,* **8,** 353 (1954).

108. Bryde, Ö., *et al., Norsk Skogind.,* **4,** 308 (1950); **6,** 192 (1952); **7,** 405 (1953); **9,** 399 (1955); *Tappi,* **36,** 353 (1953).

109. Buchanan, M. A., *et al., Tappi,* **42,** 578 (1959).

110. Buchanan, M. A., *et al., Tappi,* **44,** 576 (1961).

111. Buchanan, M. A., *et al., J. Am. Chem. Soc.,* **71,** 1297 (1949).

112. Buchanan, M. A., in L. E. Wise and E. C. Jahn, *Wood Chemistry,* Reinholds, New York 1952, p. 618.

113. Bunton, C. A., *et al., J. Chem. Soc.,* **1955,** 3817.

114. Burgeni, E., *et al., Z. Physik. Chem.,* **B 4,** 401 (1929).

115. Burton, H., and P. F. G. Praill, *J. Chem. Soc.,* **1950,** 1203, 1204; **1951,** 522, 529, 726.

116. Buurman, A., *Textile Research J.,* **23,** 888 (1953).

117. Byerrum, R. U., *et al., J. Biol. Chem.,* **210,** 633 (1954).

118. Cabott, I. M., and C. B. Purves, *Pulp Paper Mag. Can.,* **57,** No. 4, 151 (1956).

118a. Calkin, J. B., *Tappi,* **34,** No. 9, 108A (1951).

119. Campbell, W. G., *Biochem. J.,* **23,** 1225 (1929).

120. Campbell, W. G., *et al., Nature,* **147,** 25 (1941); *J. Chem. Soc.,* **1948,** 774.

121. Carlberg, G. L., and E. F. Kurth, *Tappi,* **43,** 982 (1960).

122. Carmody, W. R., and J. S. Mears, *Paper Trade J.,* **106,** No. 20, 38 (1938).

123. CCA5, Standard Method of Central Laboratory of Cellulose Industry, Stockholm.

124. Centola, G., *Gazz. Chim. Ital.,* **68,** 831 (1938).

125. Chedin, J., and A. Marsaudon, *Chim. Ind.,* **71,** 55 (1954).

126. Chowdhury, J. K., *Biochem. Z.,* **148,** 76 (1924).

127. Claeson, S., *et al., Svensk Papperstid.,* **62,** 141 (1959).

128. Clark, G. L., and E. A. Parker, *J. Phys. Chem.,* **41,** 777 (1937).

129. Clark, J. C., and F. E. Brauns, *Paper Trade J.,* **119,** No. 6, 33 (1944).

130. Clermont, L. P., and F. Bender, *Pulp Paper Mag. Can.,* **59,** No. 7, 139 (1958).

131. Clermont, L. P., and H. Schwartz, *Pulp Paper Mag. Can.,* **49,** No. 7, 90 (1948).

132. Clermont, L. P., and H. Schwartz, *Pulp Paper Mag. Can.,* **52,** No. 13, 103 (1951).

133. Clermont, L. P., and H. Schwartz, *Pulp Paper Mag. Can.,* **53,** No. 6, 142 (1952).

134. Coenen, M., *Papier,* **5,** 46 (1951).

135. Conner, W. P., *J. Chem. Phys.,* **9,** 591 (1941).

136. Conrad, C. C., and A. G. Scroggie, *Ind. Eng. Chem.,* **37,** 592 (1945).

137. Conrad, C. M., *et al., Textile Research J.,* **21,** 726, 841 (1951).

138. Coppens, N., *Nature,* **177,** 279 (1956).

139. Coppick, S., Diss., New York State College of Forestry, Syracuse, N.Y. 1941.

140. Coppick, S., *Paper Trade J.*, **117**, No. 26, 29 (1943).

141. Coppick, S., and E. C. Jahn, *Ind. Eng. Chem.*, **33**, 678 (1941); **35**, 890 (1943).

142. Corrin, M. L., *et al.*, *J. Chem. Phys.*, **14**, 480 (1946).

143. Croon, I., *et al.*, *Svensk Papperstid.*, **59**, 794 (1956); **60**, 82, 843 (1957); **61**, 35, 919, 963 (1958); **62**, 700, 876 (1959); **63**, 247 (1960).

144. Croon, I., and B. Lindberg, *Acta Chem. Scand.*, **12**, 453 (1958).

145. Croon, I., and C. B. Purves, *Svensk Papperstid.*, **62**, 876 (1959).

146. Croon, I., *et al.*, *Acta Chem. Scand.*, **13**, 1299 (1959).

147. Croon, I., and B. Enström, *Tappi*, **44**, 870 (1961).

148. Croon, I., and T. Krantz, unpublished.

149. Dahlén, A., *IVA*, No. 2, 73 (1940) (Stockholm).

150. Davidson, G. F., *J. Textile Inst.*, **25**, T 174 (1934); **27**, P 144 (1936); **29**, T 195 (1938); **31**, T 81 (1940).

151. Davidson, G. F., *J. Textile Inst.*, **32**, T 109 (1941).

152. Davidson, G. F., *J. Textile Inst.*, **39**, T 65 (1948); **43**, T 291 (1952).

153. Davis, B. D., *et al.*, *Biochem. Biophys. Acta*, **15**, 268 (1954); *Science*, **119**, 774 (1954).

154. Davis, W. E., *et al.*, *J. Am. Chem. Soc.*, **65**, 1294 (1943).

155. Dence, C., and K. Sarkanen, *Tappi*, **43**, 87 (1960).

156. Denham, W. S., and H. Woodhouse, *J. Chem. Soc.*, **103**, 1735 (1913); **105**, 2357 (1914); **111**, 244 (1917); **119**, 77 (1921).

157. Dickey, E. E., and M. L. Wolfrom, *J. Am. Chem. Soc.*, **71**, 825 (1949).

158. Dobry, A., *J. Chim. Phys.*, **31**, 568 (1934); **32**, 50 (1935); *Bull. Soc. Chim.*, (5) **2**, 1882 (1935); *Kolloid-Z.*, **81**, 190 (1937).

159. Donetzhuber, A., *Svensk Papperstid.*, **63**, 447 (1960); **64**, 898 (1961).

160. Doty, P. M., *et al.*, *J. Chem. Phys.*, **12**, 144, 203 (1944); **13**, 159 (1945); *J. Am. Chem. Soc.*, **68**, 159 (1946).

161. Dryselius, E., and B. Lindberg, *Acta Chem. Scand.*, **12**, 340 (1958).

162. Durfee, W. H., and Z. I. Kertesz, *J. Am. Chem. Soc.*, **62**, 1196 (1940).

163. Dutton, G. G. S., and K. Hunt, *J. Am. Chem. Soc.*, **80**, 4420, 4888 (1958); **82**, 1682 (1960).

164. Dyer, E., and H. E. Arnold, *J. Am. Chem. Soc.*, **74**, 2677 (1952).

165. Dyfverman, A., *et al.*, *Acta Chem. Scand.*, **5**, 253 (1951).

166. Dyfverman, A., *Acta Chem. Scand.*, **7**, 280 (1953).

167. Eberhardt, G., *J. Am. Chem. Soc.*, **78**, 2832 (1956).

168. Eberhardt, G., and W. J. Schubert, *J. Am. Chem. Soc.*, **78**, 2835 (1956).

169. Edhborg, A., *et al.*, *Acta Chem. Scand.*, **6**, 450 (1952).

170. Egerton, G. S., *J. Soc. Dyers Colourists*, **64**, 336 (1948); *J. Textile Inst.*, **39**, T 293 (1948).

171. Egerton, G. S., *J. Soc. Dyers Colourists*, **63**, 161 (1947); **65**, 764 (1949); *Textile Research J.*, **18**, 659 (1948).

172. af Ekenstam, A., *Über die Celluloselösungen in Mineralsäuren*, Diss., Lund (Sweden) 1936.

173. Eliaschberg, M. G., *et al.*, *Bumazha. Prom.*, **30**, No. 9, 10, 5 (1955); **31**, No. 1, 8 (1956).

173a. Ellefsen, Ö., *et al.*, *Norsk Skogind.*, **13**, 411 (1959).

174. Ellis, J. W., and J. Bath, *J. Am. Chem. Soc.*, **62**, 2859 (1940).

175. Emery, C., and W. E. Cohen, *Australian J. Appl. Sci.*, **2**, 474 (1951).

176. Engel, O., and E. Wedekind, *Ger. Pat.* 581,806 (1933).

177. Engel, W., *Planta*, **41**, 358 (1953).
178. Enkvist, T., *Paperi Puu*, **25**, No. 7 A, 108 (1943).
179. Enkvist, T., *Svensk Papperstid.*, **50**, 351, 363 (1947).
180. Enkvist, T., *Svensk Papperstid.*, **51**, 225 (1948).
181. Enkvist, T., *et al.*, *Svensk Papperstid.*, **52**, 183, 517, 587 (1949); **53**, 85 (1950); **54**, 185 (1951); **55**, 668 (1952).
182. Enkvist, T., *et al.*, *Paperi Puu*, **38**, 1 (1956).
182a. Enkvist, T., *et al.*, *Proc. Wood Chemistry Symposium, Montreal 1961*, Butterworths, London 1962, p. 177.
183. Enkvist, T., and B. Hougberg, *Paperi, Puu*, **37**, 201 (1955).
184. Entwistle, D., *et al.*, *Textile Research J.*, **19**, 527, 609 (1949).
185. Erdtman, H., *Tappi*, **32**, 305 (1949).
186. Erdtman, H., in L. E. Wise and E. C. Jahn, eds., *Wood Chemistry*, Reinhold, New York 1952, p. 661.
187. Erdtman, H., *Svensk Papperstid.*, **45**, 315, 374, 392 (1942).
188. Erdtman, H., *et al.*, *Acta Chem. Scand.*, **4**, 228 (1950).
189. Erdtman, H., *Biochem. Z.*, **258**, 172 (1933); *Ann.*, **503**, 283 (1933); *Svensk Papperstid.*, **44**, 243 (1941); *Research*, **3**, 63 (1950).
190. Erdtman, H., and B. Leopold, *Acta Chem. Scand.*, **2**, 535 (1948); **3**, 1358 (1949).
191. Erdtman, H., *Svensk Papperstid.*, **43**, 255 (1940); *Cellulosechem.*, **18**, 83 (1940).
192. Erdtman, H., *Svensk Papperstid.*, **48**, 75 (1945).
193. Erdtman, H., *Ann.*, **539**, 116 (1939); *Svensk Papperstid.*, **42**, 344 (1939); **43**, 241, 255 (1940); *Cellulosechem.*, **18**, 83 (1940); *Tappi*, **32**, 303 (1949).
194. Erdtman, H., in L. E. Wise and E. C. Jahn, eds., *Wood Chemistry*, Reinhold, New York 1952, p. 999.
195. Ernsberger, F. M., and W. G. France, *J. Phys. Colloid Chem.*, **52**, 267 (1948).
196. Feola, J. A., and C. E. Libby, *Paper Trade J.*, **123**, No. 13, 64 (1946).
197. Fischer, E. W., *Z. Naturforschung*, **14 A**, 584 (1959).
197a. Fisher, D. G., and J. Mann, *J. Polymer Sci.*, **42**, No. 139, 189 (1960).
198. Fordyce, C. R., *et al.*, *Ind. Eng. Chem.* **28**, 1310 (1936).
199. Foreman, E. L., and D. T. Englis, *Ind. Eng. Chem.*, **23**, 415 (1931).
200. Frank A., *Botan. Arch.*, **3**, 173 (1923).
201. Frank, G., *Fr. Pat.* 939,198; *U.S. Pat.* 2,559,914.
202. Freeman, R. D., and F. C. Peterson, *Ind. Eng. Chem., Anal. Ed.*, **13**, 803 (1941).
203. Freudenberg, K., *Tannin—Cellulose—Lignin*, Springer, Berlin 1933.
204. Freudenberg, K., *et al.*, *Ann.*, **460**, 288 (1928); *Ber.*, **71**, 2435 (1938).
205. Freudenberg, K., *et al.*, *Ber.*, **63**, 1510 (1930); **65**, 484 (1932); **66**, 19 (1933).
206. Freudenberg, K., *et al.*, *Ber.*, **63**, 1961 (1930); **66**, 27 (1933); **68 B**, 2070 (1935); *Ann.*, **494**, 41, 63 (1932).
207. Freudenberg, K., and F. Bittner, *Ber.*, **86**, 155 (1953).
208. Freudenberg, K., and H. Richtzenhain, *Ber.*, **76**, 997 (1943).
209. Freudenberg, K., *Angew. Chem.*, **51**, 228 (1949); **68**, 84, 508 (1956); *Fortschr. Chem. Org. Naturstoffe*, **11**, 43 (1954); *Naturwiss.*, **42**, 29 (1955); *Ber.*, **92**, LXXXIX (1959); *J. Prakt. Chem.*, **10**, 220 (1960); *Holz Roh Werkstoff*, **18**, 282 (1960); *Holzforschung*, **15**, 33 (1961).
210. Freudenberg, K., *Holzforschung*, **6**, 37 (1952).
211. Freudenberg, K., *Holz Roh Werkstoff*, **10**, 339 (1952); **11**, 267 (1953).

212. Freudenberg, K., and T. Ploetz, *Ber.*, **73**, 754 (1940).
213. Freudenberg, K., *et al.*, *Ber.*, **62**, 1814 (1929).
214. Freudenberg, K., *et al.*, *Ber.*, **61**, 1760 (1928).
215. Freudenberg, K., *et al.*, *Ann.*, **518**, 62 (1935); *Ber.*, **66**, 262 (1933).
216. Freudenberg, K., and G. Dietrich, *Ann.*, **563**, 146 (1949).
217. Freudenberg, K., *et al.*, *Ber.*, **69**, 1415 (1936); **70**, 500 (1937); **71**, 1810 (1938).
218 Freudenberg, K., *et al.*, *Ber.*, **63**, 1510 (1930); **65**, 484 (1932); **68**, 2070 (1935).
219. Freudenberg, K., and R. Kraft, *Ber.*, **83**, 530 (1950).
220. Freudenberg, K., *et al.*, *Ber.*, **83**, 533 (1950).
221. Freudenberg, K., *et al.*, *Cellulosechem.*, **22**, 97 (1944).
222. Freudenberg, K., *et al.*, *Ber.*, **62**, 1554 (1929).
223. Freudenberg, K., and W. Dürr, *Ber.*, **63**, 2713 (1930).
224. Freudenberg, K., and K. Dall, *Naturwiss.*, **42**, 606 (1955).
225. Freudenberg, K., *Ber.*, **80**, 149 (1947); **85**, 78 (1952).
226. Freudenberg, K., *Angew. Chem.*, **68**, 84, 508 (1956).
227. Freudenberg, K., and F. Niedercorn, *Ber.*, **89**, 2168 (1956).
228. Freudenberg, K., and H. Schlüter, *Ber.*, **88**, 617 (1955).
229. Freudenberg, K., and G. S. Sidhu, *Holzforschung*, **15**, 33 (1961).
230. Freudenberg, K., *Holz Roh Werkstoff*, **18**, 282 (1960).
231. Freudenberg, K., and C. L. Chen, *Ber.*, **93**, 2533 (1960); **95**, 2814 (1962).
232. Freudenberg, K., and V. Jovanovic, *Ber.*, **94**, 3227 (1961).
233. Freudenberg, K., *et al.*, *Ber.*, **94**, 3227 (1961).
234. Frey-Wyssling, A., *Biochim. Biophys. Acta*, **18**, 166 (1950).
235. Frey-Wyssling, A., *et al.*, *Experientia*, **4**, 476 (1948); *Fortschr. Chem. Org. Naturstoffe*, **8**, 1 (1951); *J. Polymer Sci.*, **1**, 172 (1946).
236. Friedrich, A., and J. Diwald, *Monatsh.*, **46**, 31 (1925).
237. Friese, H., *et al.*, *Ber.*, **62**, 2538 (1929); **70**, 1072, 1463 (1937); **73**, 1135 (1940); **74**, 308 (1941).
238. Frilette, V. J., *et al.*, *J. Am. Chem. Soc.*, **70**, 1107 (1948).
239. Garegg, P. J., and B. Lindberg, *Acta Chem. Scand.*, **14**, 871 (1960).
240. Gaslini, F., and L. Z. Nahum, *Svensk Papperstid.*, **62**, 520 (1959).
241. Gianola, G., and J. Meybeck, *Assoc. Tech. Ind. Papétière Bull.*, **1960**, 25.
242. Gierer, J., *Acta Chem. Scand.*, **8**, 1319 (1954); *Ber.*, **89**, 257 (1956).
243. Gierer, J., *Svensk Papperstid.*, **61**, 648 (1958).
244. Gierer, J., and B. Alfredsson, *Ber.*, **90**, 1240 (1957); *Svensk Papperstid.*, **63**, 201 (1960).
245. Gierer, J., and B. Alfredsson, *Acta Chem. Scand.*, **11**, 1516 (1957).
246. Gierer, J., and B. Alfredsson, *Svensk Papperstid.*, **62**, 434 (1959).
247. Gierer, J., *Paperi Puu*, **43**, 654 (1961); *Acta Chem. Scand.*, **16**, 1713, 1976 (1962).
248. Giertz, H. W., *Svensk Papperstid.*, **46**, 152 (1943).
249. Giertz, H. W., *Medd. Cellulosaind. Centrallaboratorium* (*Stockholm*), Ser. B, No. 10 (1946).
250. Gillespie, R. J., *J. Chem. Soc.*, **1950**, 2997.
251. Gillespie, R. J., *et al.*, *J. Chem. Soc.*, **1950**, 2516, 2552.
252. Glaudemans, C. P. J., and T. E. Timell, *Svensk Papperstid.*, **60**, 869 (1957); **61**, 1 (1958); *J. Am. Chem. Soc.*, **80**, 941, 1209 (1958).
253. Glaudemans, C. P. J., and T. E. Timell, Paper presented at the 136th A.C.S. Meeting, Atlantic City, N.J., 1959.

254. Gloor, W. E., *et al.*, *Ind. Eng. Chem.*, **42**, 2150 (1950).
255. Godard, H. P., *et al.*, *J. Am. Chem. Soc.*, **63**, 3061 (1941).
256. Goldfinger, G., *et al.*, *Ind. Eng. Chem.*, **35**, 1083 (1943).
257. Goldschmid, O., *J. Am. Chem. Soc.*, **75**, 3780 (1953); *Anal. Chem.*, **26**, 1421 (1954).
258. Goliath, M., and B. O. Lindgren, *Svensk Papperstid.*, **64**, 109, 469 (1961).
258a. Goring, D. A. J., *Proc. Wood Chemistry Symposium, Montreal 1961*, Butterworths, London 1962, p. 233.
259. Goring, D. A. I., and T. E. Timell, Paper presented at the 136th A.C.S. Meeting, Atlantic City, N.J., 1959.
259a. Goring, D. A. J., and T. E. Timell, *Tappi*, **45**, 454 (1962).
260. Götze, K., *Chemiefasern nach dem Viskoseverfahren*, Springer, Berlin 1951.
261. Granath, M., and C. Schuerch, *J. Am. Chem. Soc.*, **75**, 707 (1953).
262. Grangaard, D. H., *Tappi*, **39**, 270 (1956).
263. Greminger, G. K., *et al.*, *Ind. Eng. Chem.*, **47**, 156 (1955).
264. Grohn, H., *Chem. Tech.*, **3**, 240 (1951).
265. Gross, S. T., and G. I. Clark, *Z. Krist.*, **99**, 357 (1938).
266. Gustafsson, C., *et al.*, *Acta Chem. Scand.*, **6**, 1299 (1952).
267. Gustafsson, C., *et al.*, *Paperi Puu*, **33**, 300 (1951).
268. Gustafsson, C., and R. Soila, *Paperi Puu*, **38**, 9 (1956).
269. Haas, H., and D. Teves, *Makromol. Chem.*, **6**, 174 (1951).
270. Haas, H., *et al.*, *Tappi*, **35**, 116 (1952).
271. Hägglund, E., *et al.*, *Svensk Kem. Tidskr.*, **45**, 123 (1933); *Svensk Papperstid.*, **51**, 269 (1948).
272. Hägglund, E., *et al.*, *Acta Chem. Scand.*, **10**, 1160 (1956).
273. Hägglund, E., *Chemistry of Wood*, Academic Press, New York 1951, Chapter III.
274. Hägglund, E., and T. Rosenqvist, *Biochem. Z.*, **179**, 376 (1926).
275. Hägglund, E., and T. Enkvist, *Festskrift J. A. Hedvall*, 149 (1948).
276. Hägglund, E., *Tappi*, **32**, 241 (1949).
277. Hägglund, E., and O. Sandelin, *Svensk Kem. Tidskr.*, **46**, 83 (1934).
278. Hägglund, E., *Arkiv Kemi*, **7**, No. 8 (1918).
279. Hägglund, E., and F. W. Klingstedt, *Svensk Kem. Tidskr.*, **41**, 185 (1925); *Z. Physik. Chem.*, **152**, 295 (1931).
280. Hägglund, E., and H. Urban, *Cellulosechem.*, **8**, 69 (1927); **9**, 50 (1928).
281. Hägglund, E., and J. Holmberg, cited in E. Hägglund, *Holzchemie*, 2nd Ed., Leipzig 1939, p. 147.
282. Hägglund, E., and T. Johnson, *Biochem. Z.*, **202**, 439 (1928).
283. Hägglund, E., *et al.*, *Svensk Papperstid.*, **49**, 199 (1946).
284. Hägglund, E., *Chemistry of Wood*, Academic Press, New York 1951, p. 487.
285. Hägglund, E., and H. Heiwinkel, *Svensk Papperstid.*, **45**, 123 (1942).
286. Hägglund, E., *Svensk Papperstid.*, **48**, 195 (1945).
287. Hägglund, E., and C. B. Björkman, *Biochem. Z.*, **147**, 74 (1934).
288. Hägglund, E., *et al.*, *Angew. Chem.*, **40**, 1101 (1927); *Svensk Papperstid.*, **32**, 815 (1929).
289. Hägglund, E., *et al.*, *Svensk Papperstid.*, **39**, 347 (1936); **40**, 236 (1937); **45**, 123 (1942).
290. Häggroth, S., *et al.*, *Svensk Papperstid.*, **56**, 660 (1953).
291. Haller, R., and F. Lorenz, *Helv. Chim. Acta*, **16**, 1165 (1933).
292. Hamilton, J. K., and N. S. Thompson, *Pulp Paper Mag. Can.*, **59**, No. 10, 233 (1958); *Tappi*, **42**, 752 (1959).

293. Hamilton, J. K., *et al.*, *Tappi*, **41**, 803, 811 (1958); *J. Am. Chem. Soc.*, **79**, 6464 (1957).
294. Hamilton, J. K., *et al.*, *J. Am. Chem. Soc.*, **78**, 2508 (1956).
295. Hamilton, J. K., and H. W. Kirchner, in press.
296. Hamilton, J. K., and G. R. Quimby, *Tappi*, **40**, 781 (1957).
297. Happey, F., and J. H. MacGregor, *Nature*, **160**, 907 (1947).
298. Harland, W. G., *Shirley Inst. Mem.*, **28**, 167 (1955); *J. Textile Inst.*, **45**, T 678 (1954).
299. Harris, E. E., *J. Am. Chem. Soc.*, **58**, 894 (1936).
300. Harris, E. E., *et al.*, *J. Am. Chem. Soc.*, **60**, 1467 (1938).
301. Harris, E. E., *et al.*, *J. Am. Chem. Soc.*, **56**, 889 (1934).
302. Harris, G., *J. Am. Chem. Soc.*, **70**, 3671 (1948).
303. Hartler, N., *Svensk Papperstid.*, **62**, 467 (1959).
303a. Hartler, N., *et al.*, *Svensk Papperstid.*, **64**, 67 (1961).
304. Hartmuth, R., *Ger. Pat.* 326,705; 328,783 (1919).
305. Harva, O., Diss., Åbo Akademi, Åbo (Finland) 1951.
306. Haskins, J. F., and M. I. Hogsed, *J. Org. Chem.*, **15**, 1264 (1950).
307. Hasselström, T., *et al.*, *Paper Trade J.*, **118**, No. 16, 30 (1944); **128**, No. 7, 17 (1949); *J. Am. Chem. Soc.*, **63**, 111 (1941).
308. Hästbacka, K., *Soc. Sci. Fennica Commentationes Phys. Math.*, **26**, 4 (1961).
309. Hasted, J. B., *et al.*, *J. Chem. Phys.*, **16**, 1 (1948).
310. Haworth, W. N., *et al.*, *J. Chem. Soc.*, **1931**, 2850; **1934**, 1917; *Ber.*, **65 A**, 43 (1932).
311. Haworth, W. N., *et al.*, *J. Chem. Soc.*, **1932**, 2270, 2372; *Trans. Faraday Soc.*, **29**, 14 (1933).
312. Haworth, W. N., *et al.*, *J. Chem. Soc.*, **1932**, 2368; *Ber.*, **65 A**, 59 (1932).
313. Haworth, W. N., *et al.*, *J. Chem. Soc.*, **1921**, 193; **1927**, 2809.
314. Haworth, W. N., *et al.*, *J. Chem. Soc.*, **1932**, 2372; **1939**, 1899.
315. Hedlund, I., *Svensk Papperstid.*, **50**, No. 11 B, 109 (1947).
316. Heidt, L. J., *Paper Trade J.*, **121**, No. 9, 35 (1945).
317. Heiwinkel, H., and E. Hägglund, *Svensk Papperstid.*, **43**, 273 (1940).
318. Helferich, B., and H. Koester, *Ber.*, **57 B**, 587 (1924).
319. Henley, D., *Svensk Papperstid.*, **63**, 143 (1960); Diss., Uppsala Univ. (Sweden) 1961.
320. Hermans, P. H., *Physics and Chemistry of Cellulose Fibers*, Elsevier, Amsterdam 1949, p. 311; *J. Polymer Sci.*, **4**, 317 (1949); *Makromol. Chem.*, **6**, 25 (1951).
321. Hermans, P. H., and A. Weidinger, *J. Colloid Sci.*, **1**, 185 (1946).
322. Herzog, R. O., and W. Jancke, *Z. Physik*, **3**, 196 (1920); *Ber.*, **53**, 2162 (1920).
323. Herzog, R. O., and A. Hillmer, *Ber.*, **60**, 365 (1927); **62**, 1600 (1929); **64**, 1288 (1931); *Papier-Fabr.*, **29**, Festschrift, 40 (1931); **30**, 205 (1932).
324. Hess, K., and N. Ljubitsch, *Ber.*, **61**, 1460 (1928).
325. Hess, K., *et al.*, *Naturwiss.*, **18**, 437 (1930); *Ber.*, **64**, 408 (1931); *Planta*, **25**, 419 (1936).
326. Hess, K., and J. Gundermann, *Ber.*, **70**, 527, 1788 (1937).
327. Hess, K., *et al.*, *Z. Physik. Chem.*, **B 49**, 64, 235 (1941).
328. Hess, K., and C. Trogus, *Z. Physik. Chem.*, **B 11**, 381 (1931).
329. Hess, K., and C. Trogus, *Z. Elektrochem.*, **42**, 696 (1936).
330. Hess, K., and C. Trogus, *Z. Physik. Chem.*, **A 145**, 401 (1929).
331. Hess, K., and C. Trogus, *Ber.*, **B 68**, 1986 (1935).

332. Hess, K., *et al.*, *Z. Physik. Chem.*, **B 43**, 309 (1939); *Ann.*, **594**, 119 (1955); *Z. Elektrochem.*, **55**, 697 (1951).

333. Hess, K., and H. Grothjohn, *Z. Elektrochem.*, **56**, 58 (1952).

334. Hess, K., *et al.*, *Ann.*, **506**, 260 (1933).

335. Hess, K., and M. Lüdtke, *Ann.*, **466**, 18 (1928).

336. Hess, K., and H. E. Heumann, *Ber.*, **75**, 1802 (1942).

337. Hessler, L. E., *et al.*, *Textile Research J.*, **18**, 628 (1948).

338. Hestrin, S., *et al.*, *Nature*, **159**, 64 (1947); *Biochem. J.*, **58**, 345 (1954).

339. Heuser, E., and A. Brötz, *Papier-Fabr.*, **25**, 238 (1927).

340. Heuser, E., and R. Bartunek, *Cellulosechem.*, **6**, 19 (1925).

341. Heuser, E., and L. Jörgensen, *Tappi*, **34**, 57 (1951).

342. Heuser, E., and A. Winsvold, *Cellulosechem.*, **2**, 113 (1921); **4**, 49, 62 (1923); *Ber.*, **56**, 902 (1923).

343. Hibbert, H., and J. B. Phillips, *Can. J. Res.*, **4**, 1 (1931).

344. Hibbert, H., *et al.*, *J. Am. Chem. Soc.*, **66**, 32, 37 (1944).

345. Hibbert, H., *et al.*, *Tech. Assoc. Papers*, **24**, 179 (1941).

346. Hibbert, H., *et al.*, *J. Am. Chem. Soc.*, **63**, 3052 (1941); **65**, 1192 (1943).

347. Hibbert, H., *et al.*, *J. Am. Chem. Soc.*, **70**, 57, 67 (1948).

348. Hibbert, H., *et al.*, *J. Am. Chem. Soc.*, **66**, 39, 41 (1944).

349. Hibbert, H., *et al.*, *J. Am. Chem. Soc.*, **62**, 1412 (1940); **63**, 3031 (1941).

350. Hiller, L. A., *J. Polymer Sci.*, **10**, 385 (1953).

351. Hilpert, R. S., and E. Littmann, *Ber.*, **67**, 1551 (1934); **68**, 16 (1935).

352. Hirst, E. L., *J. Chem. Soc.*, **1955**, 2974.

353. Hirst, E. L., in F. Bolam, ed., *Fundamentals of Papermaking Fibres*, Kenley (England) 1958, p. 93. *Proc. Wood Chemistry Symposium, Montreal 1961*, Butterworths, London 1962, p. 53.

354. Hofmann, R., *U.S. Pat.* 2,126,190.

355. Hollabaugh, C. B., *et al.*, *Ind. Eng. Chem.*, **37**, 943 (1945).

356. Holmberg, B., *Ing. Vetenskaps Akad.*, *Handl.*, **No. 103** (1930); **No. 131** (1934).

357. Holmberg, B., *Svensk Papperstid.*, **50**, No. 11 B, 111 (1947).

358. Holmberg, B., and S. Runius, *Svensk Kem. Tidskr.*, **37**, 189 (1925).

359. Holmberg, B., and N. Gralén, *Ing. Vetenskaps Akad.*, *Handl.*, **No. 162** (1942).

360. Holmberg, B., *et al.*, *Svensk Kem. Tidskr.*, **47**, 257 (1935); **48**, 207 (1936).

361. Holmberg, B., *Papir-Journalen*, **23**, 81, 92 (1935).

362. Holmberg, B., *Ber.*, **69**, 115 (1936).

363. Holmberg, B., *Arkiv. Kemi*, **24 A**, No. 29 (1947).

364. Holtzer, A. M., *et al.*, *J. Phys. Chem.*, **58**, 624 (1954).

365. Holzapfel, L., *Z. Elektrochem.*, **55**, 577 (1951).

366. Honeyman, J., *J. Chem. Soc.*, **1947**, 168.

367. Hönig, M., and W. Ruziczka, *Angew. Chem.*, **44**, 845 (1931).

368. Horio, M., *et al.*, *Tappi*, **43**, 769 (1960).

369. Horio, M., *et al.*, cited in E. Ott and H. M. Spurlin, eds., *Cellulose and Cellulose Derivatives*, Interscience, New York 1954, p. 517.

370. Houwink, R., *J. Prakt. Chem.*, **157**, 15 (1940); Huggins, M. L., in E. Ott and H. M. Spurlin, eds., *Cellulose and Cellulose Derivatives*, Interscience, New York 1954, p. 1195.

371. Howsmon, J. A., *Textile Research J.*, **19**, 152 (1949).

372. Howsmon, J. A., and C. W. Hock, in E. Ott and H. M. Spurlin, eds., *Cellulose and Cellulose Derivatives*, Interscience, New York 1954, p. 1482.

373. Hughes, E. D., and D. A. Davenport, through C. K. Ingold, *Structure and Mechanism of Organic Chemistry*, Bell, London 1953, p. 299.

374. Hunt, M. L., *et al.*, *J. Phys. Chem.*, **60**, 1278 (1956).
375. Huseman, E., and A. Carnap, *Makromol. Chem.*, **1**, 158 (1947).
376. Huseman, E., and O. Weber, *J. Prakt. Chem.* **161**, 20 (1942).
377. Hutino, K., and I. Sakurada, *Naturwiss.*, **28**, 577 (1940).
378. Immergut, B., and B. G. Rånby, *Ind. Eng. Chem.*, **48**, 1183 (1956); *Svensk Papperstid.*, **60**, 573 (1957).
379. Immergut, E. H., and H. Mark, *Makromol. Chem.*, **18/19**, 322 (1956).
380. Immergut, E. H., *et al.*, *Ind. Eng. Chem.*, **45**, 2483, 2500 (1953).
381. Ingold, C. K., *Structure and Mechanism in Organic Chemistry*, Bell, London 1953.
382. Irvine, J. C., *J. Soc. Chem. Ind.*, **44**, 242 (1925).
383. Irvine, J. C., and E. L. Hirst, *J. Chem. Soc.*, **121**, 1585 (1922).
384. Irvine, J. C., and E. L. Hirst, *J. Chem. Soc.*, **123**, 518 (1923).
385. Isbell, H. S., *J. Res. Nat. Bur. Std.*, **32**, 45 (1944).
386. Isenberg, I. H., *et al.*, *Paper Ind. Paper World*, **28**, 816 (1946); *Paper Ind.*, **38**, 1042, 1098 (1957).
387. Ivancic, A., and S. A. Rydholm, *Svensk Papperstid.*, **62**, 554 (1959).
388. Ivarsson, B., *Svensk Papperstid.*, **54**, 1 (1951).
389. Ivnäs, L., and B. Lindberg, *Acta Chem. Scand.*, **15**, 1081 (1961).
390. Jackson, E. L., and C. S. Hudson, *J. Am. Chem. Soc.*, **58**, 378 (1936); **59**, 994, 2049 (1937); **60**, 989 (1938).
391. Jahn, E. C. *Cellulose Xanthate and the Viscose Process*, in L. E. Wise and E. C. Jahn, *Wood Chemistry*, Reinhold, New York 1952, p. 327.
392. Jayme, G., and F. Finck, *Cellulosechem.*, **22**, 102 (1944).
393. Jayme, G., and M. Harders-Steinhäuser, *Papier*, **4**, 104 (1950).
394. Jayme, G., *Papier*, **15**, 492 (1961).
395. Jayme, G., *et al.*, *Naturwiss.*, **29**, 768 (1941); *Papierfabr.*, **1944**, No. 9, 295; *Ber.*, **77**, 383 (1944).
396. Jayme, G., *et al.*, *Papier*, **5**, 244 (1951); **9**, 563 (1955); **11**, 47 (1957); *Naturwiss.*, **42**, 536 (1955); **44**, 62 (1957); *Makromol. Chem.*, **23**, 71 (1957); *Tappi*, **44**, 299 (1961).
397. Jayme, G., *et al.*, *Reyon, Zellwolle Chemiefasern*, **32**, 193, 275 (1954); **34**, 27 (1956); *Papier*, **10**, 88, 307 (1956); **11**, 280 (1957).
398. Jayme, G., *Cellulosechem.*, **20**, 43 (1942).
399. Jayme, G., and N. Nikoliew, *Angew. Chem.*, **60 A**, 15 (1948).
400. Jayme, G., and K. Kringstad, *Angew. Chem.*, **73**, 219 (1961).
401. Jeanes, A. R., and H. S. Isbell, *J. Res. Nat. Bur. Std.*, **27**, 125 (1941).
402. Jeanloz, R., *Helv. Chim. Acta*, **29**, 57 (1946).
403. Jensen, W., *Paperi Puu*, **31**, No. 7 A, 20 (1949); *Svensk Papperstid.*, **54**, 739 (1951); *Norsk Skogind.*, **7**, 254 (1953).
404. Jensen, W., *Acta Acad. Aboensis, Math. Phys.*, **16**, 3 (1948); *Paperi Puu*, **31**, No. 7 A, 20 (1949).
405. Jolley, L. J., *J. Textile Inst.*, **30**, T 22 (1939).
406. Jones, E. A., *et al.*, *Tappi*, **41**, 721, 727 (1958).
407. Jones, E. J., cited in L. E. Wise and E. C. Jahn, eds., *Wood Chemistry*, Reinhold, New York 1952, p. 444.
408. Jones, E. J., *J. Am. Chem. Soc.*, **70**, 1984 (1948); *Tappi*, **32**, 167 (1949).
409. Jones, J. K. N., *et al.*, *Can. J. Chem.*, **35**, 634 (1957).
410. Jones, J. K. N., *J. Chem. Soc.*, **1953**, 1672.
411. Jones, J. K. N., and P. E. Reid, Paper presented at the 136th A.C.S. Meeting, Atlantic City, N.J. 1959.

412. Jones, G. W., *Tappi*, **33**, 149 (1950).
413. Jörgensen, L., *Studies on the Partial Hydrolysis of Cellulose*, Diss., Oslo 1950.
414. Jörgensen, L., *Acta Chem. Scand.*, **3**, 780 (1949); **4**, 185, 658 (1950).
415. Jukes, T. H., and C. L. A. Schmidt, *J. Biol. Chem.*, **110**, 9 (1935).
416. Jullander, A., and B. G. Rånby, *Svensk Papperstid.*, **61**, 680 (1958).
417. Jullander, I., *Studies on Nitrocellulose, Including the Construction of an Osmotic Balance*, Diss, Uppsala (Sweden) 1945.
418. Jullander, I., *Svensk Papperstid.*, **55**, 197 (1952); **56**, 443 (1953).
419. Junker, E., *Kolloid-Z.*, **95**, 213 (1941).
420. Juslén, C., and T. Enkvist, *Acta Chem. Scand.*, **12**, 511 (1958).
421. Juvonen, V. V., *Suomen Kemistilehti*, **20 A**, 18 (1947).
422. Kailan, A., through Landolt-Börnstein, *Phys.-Chem. Tabellen, 2. Erg. band*, 5th Ed., Springer, Berlin 1931, p. 1418.
423. Kahila, S. K., *Paperi Puu*, **39**, 7 (1957).
424. Kahila, S. K., and A. Y. E. Rinne, *Paperi Puu*, **39**, 526, 530 (1957).
425. Kalb, L., and T. Lieser, *Ber.*, **61**, 1007 (1928).
426. Katz, J. R., and J. C. Derksen, *Rec. Trav. Chim.*, **50**, 149 (1931).
427. Kavanagh, K. R., and J. M. Pepper, *Can. J. Chem.*, **33**, 24 (1955).
428. Kawamura, I., and T. Higuchi, through *C.A.*, **46**, 9841 (1952); **47**, 309, 4079 (1953); **48**, 1675 (1954).
429. Kellenberger, E., *Experientia*, **4**, 449 (1948).
430. Keller, A., in R. H. Doremus, *et al.*, eds., *Growth and Perfection of Crystals*, Wiley, New York 1958, p. 499.
431. Kenner, J., *et al.*, *J. Chem. Soc.*, **1957**, 3019 and many earlier refs., surveyed in *Chem. Ind.*, **1955**, 727.
432. Kenyon, W. O., *et al.*, *J. Am. Chem. Soc.*, **64**, 121 (1942); **69**, 342, 347, 349, 355 (1947); **70**, 2700 (1948).
433. King. E. G., *et al.*, *Can. J. Research*, **13 B**, 88 (1935).
434. Kirmreuther, H., *Papier-Fabr.*, **24**, 106 (1926).
435. Klason, P., *Svensk Kem. Tidskr.*, **9**, 133 (1897); *Arkiv Kemi*, **No. 15**, 21 (1917); *Ber.*, **53**, 706, 1862, 1864 (1920).
436. Klason, P., *Arkiv Kemi*, **3**, No. 5, 17 (1906); *Ber.*, **55**, 455 (1922).
437. Klason, P., *Tek. Tidskr.*, **23**, 53 (1893).
438. Klason, P., and B. Segerfeldt, *Arkiv Kemi*, **4**, No. 6 (1911).
439. Klason, P., *Beiträge zur Chem. Zusammensetzung des Fichtenholzes*, Berlin 1911, p. 34.
440. Klauditz, W., *Holzforschung*, **6**, 70 (1952).
441. Klauditz, W., *Holzforschung*, **11**, 110 (1957).
442. Klauditz, W., *Papier-Fabr.*, **39**, 225 (1941).
443. Klein, R., and M. Mentser, *J. Am. Chem. Soc.*, **73**, 5888 (1951).
444. Kleinert, T., *Monatsh.*, **80**, 582 (1949).
445. Kleinert, T. N., *et al.*, *Pulp Paper Mag. Can.*, **58**, No. 5, 154; No. 6, 131; No. 7, 215; No. 11, 147 (1957); *Tappi*, **40**, 813, 827 (1957); **41**, 372 (1958).
446. Klug, E. D., *et al.*, *Brit. Pat.* 623,276; *U.S. Pat.* 2,517,577; 2,572,039.
447. Knecht, E., *Ber.*, **37**, 549 (1904).
448. Kolboe, S., and Ö. Ellefsen, *Tappi*, **45**, 163 (1962).
449. Kolthoff, I. M., and W. Stricks, *J. Phys. Colloid Chem.*, **52**, 915 (1948).
450. König, W., *Melliand Textilber.*, **32**, 290 (1951).
451. Kornberg, H. L., and H. Beevers, *Biochim. Biophys. Acta*, **26**, 531 (1957).
452. Koshijima, T., *J. Japan. Wood Research, Soc.*, **6**, No. 5, 194 (1960).

453. Kraemer, E. O., *Ind. Eng. Chem.*, **30,** 1200 (1938).
454. Kraemer, E. O., and W. D. Lansing, *Nature,* **133,** 870 (1934); *J. Phys. Chem.*, **39,** 153 (1935).
455. Kraft, F., *Papier-Fabr.*, **36,** 429 (1938).
456. Kratzl, K., *et al.*, *Tappi,* **40,** 269 (1957); **43,** 650 (1960); *Monatsh.,* **90,** 1, 526, 536, 768 (1959); *Holzforschung,* **14,** 1 (1960).
457. Kratzl, K., *et al.*, *Monatsh.,* **80,** 314 (1949); **83,** 197, 205 (1952); **85,** 1046 (1954).
458. Kratzl, K., and H. Silbernagel, *Monatsh.,* **83,** 1022 (1952).
459. Kubo, T., and K. Kanamaru, *Z. Physik. Chem.,* A **182,** 341 (1938).
460. Kudzin, S. F., and F. F. Nord, *J. Am. Chem. Soc.,* **73,** 690, 4619 (1951).
461. Kuhn, W., *Ber.,* **63 B,** 1503 (1930); *Z. Physik. Chem.,* A **159,** 368 (1932).
462. Kullgren, C., *Svensk Kem. Tidskr.,* **42,** 179 (1930); **44,** 15 (1932); *Svensk Papperstid.,* **55,** 1 (1952).
463. Kürschner, K., *J. Prakt. Chem.,* (2), **118,** 238 (1929).
464. Kurth, E. F., in L. E. Wise and E. C. Jahn, eds., *Wood Chemistry,* Reinhold, New York, 1952, p. 548.
465. Kurth, E. F., *Tappi,* **41,** 733 (1958).
466. Kurth, E. F., *Paper Trade J.,* **126,** No. 6, 56 (1948).
467. Kurth, E. F., and E. C. Sherrard, *Ind. Eng. Chem.,* **23,** 1156 (1931); **24,** 1179 (1932); **25,** 192 (1933).
468. Lange, P. W., *Pulp Paper Mag. Can.,* **59,** No. 10, 210 (1958).
469. Lange, P. W., *Svensk Papperstid.,* **56,** 807 (1953); F. Bolam, ed., *Fundamentals of Papermaking Fibres,* Kenley (England) 1958, p. 159.
470. Lange, P. W., *Svensk Papperstid.,* **47,** 262 (1944); **48,** 241 (1945); **50,** No. 11 B, 130 (1947); **57,** 525 (1954).
471. Lange, P. W., and A. Kjaer, *Norsk Skogind.,* **11,** 425 (1957).
472. Larinkari, G., Diss., Helsinki 1947.
473. Larsson, A., *Svensk Papperstid.,* **46,** 93 (1943).
474. Larsson, S., and B. Lindberg, *Acta Chem. Scand.,* **16,** 1757 (1962).
475. Launer, H. F., and W. K. Wilson, *J. Am. Chem. Soc.,* **71,** 958 (1949).
476. Lautsch, W., *Cellulosechem.,* **20,** 119 (1942).
477. Lautsch, W., *et al.*, *Angew. Chem.,* **53,** 450 (1940).
478. Lautsch, W., and G. Piazolo, *Ber.,* **73,** 317 (1940).
479. Lawrence, R. V., *Tappi,* **45,** 654 (1962).
480. Leech, J. G., *Tappi,* **35,** 249 (1952).
481. Leopold, B., *Acta Chem. Scand.,* **6,** 49 (1952).
482. Leopold, B., *Acta Chem. Scand.,* **6,** 55 (1952).
483. Leopold, B., *Acta Chem. Scand.,* **6,** 38 (1952); *Svensk Kem. Tidskr.,* **64,** 18 (1952).
484. Leopold, B., *Acta Chem. Scand.,* **4,** 1523 (1950).
485. Leopold, B., *Svensk Kem. Tidskr.,* **63,** 260 (1951).
486. Levitt, L. S., *J. Org. Chem.,* **20,** 1297 (1955).
487. Lewis, S. J., *J. Soc. Dyers Colourists,* **34,** 167 (1918); **37,** 201 (1921); **38,** 76, 99 (1922); **40,** 29, 111 (1924).
488. Liang, C. Y., and R. H. Marchessault, *J. Polymer Sci.,* **37,** 385 (1959), **39,** 269 (1959), **43,** 71, 85 (1960), *Tappi,* **43,** 1017 (1960).
489. Lindberg, B., *Svensk Papperstid.,* **61,** 675 (1958), *Proc. Wood Chemistry Symposium,* Montreal 1961, Butterworths, London 1962, p. 67.
490. Lindberg, B., *et al.*, *Acta Chem. Scand.,* **14,** 742 (1960).
491. Lindberg, B., and H. Meier, *Svensk Papperstid.,* **60,** 785 (1957).

492. Lindberg, B., and O. Theander, *Svensk Papperstid.*, **65**, 509 (1962).
493. Lindberg, B., and D. Wood, *Acta Chem. Scand.*, **6**, 791 (1952).
494. Lindberg, J. J. and T. Enkvist, *Finska Kemistsamfundets Medd.*, **28B**, 23 (1955).
495. Linderoth, J., *Svensk Papperstid.*, **59**, 37 (1956).
496. Lindgren, B. O., *Svensk Papperstid.*, **61**, 669 (1958).
497. Lindgren, B. O., *Svensk Papperstid.*, **55**, 78 (1952); *Acta Chem. Scand.*, **5**, 603 (1951).
498. Lindgren, B. O., *Acta Chem. Scand.*, **1**, 779 (1948); **3**, 1011 (1949).
499. Lindgren, B. O., *Acta Chem. Scand.*, **4**, 1365 (1950).
500. Lindgren, B. O., *Acta Chem. Scand.*, **12**, 447 (1958).
501. Lindgren, B. O., and H. Mikawa, *Acta Chem. Scand.*, **11**, 826 (1957).
502. Lindgren, B. O., and M. Goliath, *Makromol. Chem.*, **20**, 101 (1956).
503. Lindsley, C. H., and M. B. Frank, *Ind. Eng. Chem.*, **45**, 2491 (1953).
504. Lorand, E. J., and E. A. Georgi, *J. Am. Chem. Soc.*, **59**, 1166 (1937).
505. Lorås, V., and F. Löschbrandt, *Norsk Skogind.*, **10**, 402 (1956).
506. Lovell, E. L., *Ind. Eng. Chem.*, *Anal. Ed.*, **16**, 683 (1944).
507. Machell, G., and G. N. Richards, *J. Chem. Soc.*, **1957**, 4500, **1958**, 1199.
508. Mahoney, J. F., and C. B. Purves, *J. Am. Chem. Soc.*, **64**, 9, 15 (1942).
509. Malm, C. J., et al., *Ind. Eng. Chem.*, **38**, 77 (1946); **47**, 955 (1955).
510. Malm, C. J., et al., *Ind. Eng. Chem.*, **43**, 684, 688 (1951).
511. Malm, C. J., et al., *Ind. Eng. Chem.*, **34**, 430 (1942).
512. Malm, C. J., and C. R. Fordyce, in J. Alexander, ed., *Colloid Chemistry*, Vol. 6, Reinhold, New York 1946, p. 917.
513. Malm, C. J., and C. R. Fordyce, *Ind. Eng. Chem.*, **32**, 405 (1940).
514. Malm, C. J., et al., *J. Am. Chem. Soc.*, **70**, 2740 (1948).
515. Malm, C. J., et al., *J. Am. Chem. Soc.*, **75**, 80 (1953).
516. Malm, C. J., et al., *J. Am. Chem. Soc.*, **74**, 4105 (1952).
517. Malm, C. J., et al., *J. Am. Chem. Soc.*, **72**, 2674 (1950).
518. Manskaya, S. M., *Dokl. Akad. Nauk.*, *SSSR*, **62**, 369 (1948).
519. Marchessault, R. H., et al., *Tappi*, **43**, 1017 (1960).
520. Marchessault, R. H., and T. E. Timell, *J. Phys. Chem.*, **64**, 704 (1960).
521. Marian, J. E., and A. Wissing, *Svensk Papperstid.*, **59**, 751, 800, 836 (1956); **60**, 45, 85, 124, 170, 255, 348, 522 (1957).
522. Mark, H., and R. Simha, *Trans. Faraday Soc.*, **36**, 611 (1940).
523. Marrinan, H. J., and J. Mann, *J. Appl. Chem.*, **4**, 204 (1954); *Trans. Faraday Soc.*, **52**, 481, 487, 492 (1956).
524. Marrinan, H. J., and J. Mann, *J. Polymer Sci.*, **21**, 301 (1956); **27**, 595 (1958).
525. Marrinan, H. J., and J. Mann, *Chem. & Ind.*, **41**, 1092 (1953).
526. Marshall, H. B., et al., *Can. J. Research*, **13 B**, 103 (1953).
527. Marth, D. E., *Tappi*, **42**, 301 (1959).
528. Martin, A. R., et al., *J. Res. Nat. Bur. Std.*, **27**, 449 (1941).
529. Marton, J., and E. Adler, *Tappi*, **46**, 92 (1963).
530. Marx, M., *Makromol. Chem.*, **16**, 157 (1955).
531. Maurer, K., and G. Drefahl, *Ber.*, **75**, 1489 (1942).
532. Maurer, K., and G. Reiff, *Makromol. Chem.*, **1**, 27 (1943).
533. Max, K. W., *Southern Pulp Paper Mfr*, **7**, No. 9, 22 (1945).
534. McCarthy, J. L., *J. Am. Chem. Soc.*, **79**, 4495, 4499 (1957).
535. McGovern, J. N., and G. H. McGregor, *Tappi*, Data Sheet No. 118 (Dec. 1944).
536. McKee, R. H., *Ind. Eng. Chem.*, **38**, 382 (1946); *U.S. Pat.* 2,308,564 (1943).

537. McKenzie, A. W., and H. G. Higgins, *Svensk Papperstid.*, **61**, 893 (1958).
538. Mehta, M. M., *Biochem. J.*, **19**, 958 (1925).
539. Meier, H., *J. Polymer Sci.*, **51**, 11 (1961).
540. Meier, H., to be published.
541. Meier, H., *Svensk Papperstid.*, **62**, 687 (1959); *Holzforschung*, **13**, 177 (1959).
542. Meier, H., *Acta Chem. Scand.*, **15**, 1381 (1961).
543. Meier, H., *Acta Chem. Scand.*, **14**, 749 (1960).
544. Meier, H., *Acta Chem. Scand.*, **12**, 144 (1958).
544a. Meier, H. *Acta Chem. Scand.*, **16**, 2275 (1962).
545. Melander, K., *Cellulosechem.*, **2**, 69 (1921).
546. Meller, A., *Tappi*, **35**, 72 (1952); **36**, 366 (1953).
547. Meller, A., *Holzforschung*, **14**, 78 (1960).
548. Merewether, J. W. T., *Holzforschung*, **11**, 65 (1957).
549. Merler, E., and L. E. Wise, *Tappi*, **41**, 80 (1958).
550. Meyer, K. H., *et al.*, *Z. Physik. Chem.*, **B 2**, 115 (1929); *Helv. Chim. Acta*, **20**, 232 (1937); **22**, 59 (1939).
551. Meyer, K. H., and N. P. Badehuizen, *Nature*, **140**, 281 (1937).
552. Meyer, K. H., and L. Misch, *Helv. Chim. Acta*, **20**, 232 (1937).
553. Mikawa, H., *J. Chem. Soc. Japan, Ind. Chem. Sect.*, **54**, 651 (1951).
554. Mikawa, H., *et al.*, *Bull Chem. Soc., Japan*, **29**, 245 (1956).
555. Mikawa, H., and H. Okada, *J. Chem. Soc. Japan, Ind. Chem. Sect.*, **54**, 239 (1951).
556. Miles, F. D., *Cellulose Nitrate*, Oliver & Boyd, London 1955.
557. Miles, F. D., and M. Milbourn, *J. Phys. Chem.*, **34**, 2598 (1930).
558. Milks, J. E., and C. B. Purves, *J. Am. Chem. Soc.*, **78**, 3738 (1956).
559. Millet, M. A., *et al.*, *Ind. Eng. Chem.*, **46**, 1493 (1954).
559a. Mills, A. R., and T. E. Timell, *Can. J. Chem.*, **41**, 1389 (1963).
560. Minor, F. W., *et al.*, *J. Am. Chem. Soc.*, **76**, 5052 (1954).
561. Mitchell, R. L., *Ind. Eng. Chem.*, **38**, 843 (1946).
562. Mitchell, R. L., *Ind. Eng. Chem.*, **45**, 2526 (1953).
563. Mitchell, R. L., *Tappi*, **39**, 571 (1956).
564. Mitchell, R. L., and G. J. Ritter, *J. Forest Products Research Soc.*, **3**, 66 (1953).
565. Mithel, B. B., *et al.*, *Tappi*, **40**, 1 (1957).
566. Moelwyn-Hughes, E. A., *Kinetics of Reactions in Solution*, 2nd Ed., Oxford 1947.
567. Monier-Williams, G. W., *J. Chem. Soc.*, **119**, 803 (1921).
568. Montroll, E. W., *J. Am. Chem. Soc.*, **63**, 1215 (1941).
569. Montroll, E. W., and R. Simha, *J. Chem. Phys.*, **8**, 721 (1940).
570. Morehead, F. F., cited in ref. 634.
571. Mosimann, H., and T. Swedberg, *Kolloid-Z.*, **100**, 99 (1942).
572. Murray, G. E., and C. B. Purves, *J. Am. Chem. Soc.*, **62**, 3194 (1940).
573. Mutton, D. B., *Pulp Paper Mag. Can.*, **59**, No. 10, 260 (1958).
574. Nakano, J., *et al.*, *Tappi*, **44**, 30 (1961).
575. Neale, S. M., *J. Soc. Chem. Ind.*, **55**, 602 (1936); *Trans. Faraday Soc.*, **33**, 81 (1937).
575a. Neale, S. M., *J. Textile Inst.*, **20**, T 373 (1929); **21**, T 225 (1930); **22**, T 230, T 349 (1931).
575b. Nelson, R., *Tappi*, **43**, 313 (1960).
576. Nelson, R., and C. Schuerch, *J. Polymer Sci.*, **22**, 435 (1956); *Tappi*, **40**, 419 (1957).

247

577. Nevell, T. P., *J. Textile Inst.*, **39**, T 118 (1948).
578. Nevell, T. P., *J. Textile Inst.*, **42**, T 91, T 130 (1951).
579. Newbauer, L. G., and C. B. Purves, *Can. J. Chem.*, **35**, 388 (1957).
580. Newcombe, A. G., and S. G. Reid, *Nature*, **172**, 455 (1953).
581. Newman, S., *et al.*, *J. Polymer Sci.*, **10**, 463 (1953).
582. Nickerson, R. F., *Advan. Carbohydrate Chem.*, **5**, 103 (1950).
583. Nickerson, R. F., *Textile Research J.*, **21**, 195 (1951).
584. Nickerson, R. F., *et al.*, *Ind. Eng. Chem.*, **34**, 85, 1480 (1942); **37**, 1115 (1945); **38**, 299 (1946); **39**, 1507 (1947).
585. Nishida, K., *et al.*, *J. Japan. Tech. Assoc. Pulp Paper Ind.*, **10**, 667 (1956); **15**, 268 (1961).
586. Nishikawa, S., and K. Ono, *Phys. Math. Soc. Japan* (*Tokyo*) 1913.
587. Nord, F. F., *et al.*, *J. Am. Chem. Soc.*, **72**, 977, 3835 (1950); **73**, 690, 4619 (1951); **75**, 305 (1953); *Experientia*, **15**, 245 (1959); *Holzforschung*, **15**, 1 (1961).
588. Nord, F. F., and W. J. Schubert, *Tappi*, **40**, 285 (1957); *Holzforschung*, **5**, 1 (1951); **15**, 1 (1961).
589. Norman, A. G., and S. G. Shrikhande, *Biochem. J.*, **29**, 2259 (1935).
590. Norman, N., *Acta Cryst.*, **7**, 462 (1954).
591. Nylinder, P., and E. Hägglund, *Medd. Statens Skogsforskningsinst.*, **44**, No. 11, Stockholm 1954.
592. O'Dwyer, M. H., *Biochem. J.*, **17**, 501 (1923); **28**, 2116 (1934); **30**, 254 (1937); **33**, 149, 173 (1939); **34**, 149 (1940).
593. Öhrn, O., and I. Croon, *Svensk Papperstid.*, **63**, 601 (1960).
594. Okawa, T., and T. Fukutome, *J. Soc. Textile Cellulose Ind., Japan*, **9**, 397 (1953).
595. Olleman, E. D., *et al.*, *J. Colloid Sci.*, **3**, 185 (1948).
596. O'Meara, D., and G. N. Richards, *J. Chem. Soc.*, **1958**, 1204.
597. Ost, H., *Angew. Chem.*, **32**, 66 (1919).
598. Ost, H., *Angew. Chem.*, **39**, 1117 (1926).
599. Pacsu, E., *et al.*, *Fortschr. Chem. Org. Naturstoffe*, **5**, 129 (1948); *Textile Research J.*, **16**, 490, 564 (1946); **18**, 387 (1948).
600. Parker, E. A., *et al.*, *J. Am. Chem. Soc.*, **60**, 2980 (1938).
601. Pattersson, R. F., and H. Hibbert, *J. Am. Chem. Soc.*, **65**, 1862, 1869 (1943).
602. Pauly, H., *et al.*, *Ber.*, **67**, 1193 (1934).
603. Payen, A., *Troisième Mémoire sur les Developments des Vegetaux*, Extrait des Memoirs de l'Academie Royale des Sciences. Tome VIII des savants étrangers, Imprincérie Royale, Paris 1842.
604. Pearl, I. A., *J. Am. Chem. Soc.*, **64**, 1429 (1942); **76**, 2224 (1954); *Tappi*, **39**, 171 (1956).
605. Pearl, I. A., *et al.*, *Tappi*, **40**, 374 (1957); **41**, 255 (1958); **42**, 61 (1959); **43**, 611 (1960).
606. Pearl, I. A., *et al.*, *Tappi*, **40**, 45 (1957); **43**, 961 (1960).
607. Pearl, I. A., and L. R. Busche, *Tappi*, **43**, 970 (1960).
608. Pedersen, F. C., *et al.*, *J. Am. Chem. Soc.*, **62**, 2361 (1940).
609. Pedersen, N., *Papier–Ztg.*, **15**, 422, 787 (1890).
610. Pelipetz, M. G., Diss., Columbia Univ. (1937).
611. Peniston, Q. P., *et al.*, *J. Am. Chem. Soc.*, **62**, 2284 (1940).
612. Pennington, D., and D. M. Ritter, *J. Am. Chem. Soc.*, **69**, 665 (1947).
613. Pepper, J. M., *et al.*, *J. Am. Chem. Soc.*, **73**, 3316 (1951).
614. Perilä, O., *Paperi Puu*, **40**, No. 4 A, 159 (1958).

614a. Perilä, O., *J. Polymer Sci.*, **51**, 19 (1961).
615. Perilä, O., and A. Toivonen, *Paperi Puu*, **40**, No. 4 A, 207 (1958); *Ann. Acad. Sci. Fennical*, Serie A II, Chemica No. 76, Åbo 1957.
615a. Perilä, O., and P. Manner, *Paperi Puu*, **38**, 499 (1956).
616. Perronoud, H., *Kolloid-Z.*, **95**, 213 (1941).
617. Peterson, F. C., and C. C. Spencer, *J. Am. Chem. Soc.*, **49**, 2822 (1927).
618. Petitpas, T., *et al.*, *Compt. Rend.*, **243**, 47 (1956), **244**, 346 (1957).
619. Pew, J. C., *Tappi*, **40**, 553 (1957).
620. Pew, J. C., *J. Am. Chem. Soc.*, **77**, 2831 (1955).
621. Pew, J. C., *Tappi*, **32**, 39 (1949).
622. Philipp, B., *Faserforsch. Textiltech.*, **8**, 21 (1957).
623. Philipp, B., *Faserforsch. Textiltech.*, **6**, 180 (1955).
624. Philipp, H. J., and C. F. Björk, *J. Polymer Sci.*, **6**, 549 (1951).
625. Phillips, M., and M. J. Goss, *J. Agr. Research*, **51**, 301 (1935).
626. Pigman, W., *The Carbohydrates*, Academic Press, New York 1957, pp. 767, 773, 775.
626a. Pinder, A. R., *The Chemistry of the Terpenes*, Chapman & Hall, London 1960.
627. Polcin, J., *Chem. Zvesti.*, **10**, 450 (1956); **12**, 60 (1958).
628. Polglase, W. J., in M. L. Wolfrom and R. S. Tipson, eds. *Advances in Carbohydrate Chemistry*, **10**, 281 (1955), Academic Press, New York 1955.
629. Polyani, M., *Z. Physik*, **7**, 149 (1921); **9**, 123 (1922); *Naturwiss.*, **9**, 288 (1921); **16**, 263 (1928).
630. Purves, C. B., *et al.*, *Paper Trade J.*, **116**, No. 14, 26 (1943); **123**, No. 18, 35 (1946); cf. L. E. Wise and E. C. Jahn, eds., *Wood Chemistry*, Reinhold, New York 1952, p. 172.
631. Purves, C. B., *et al.*, *Paper Trade J.*, **115**, No. 7, 41 (1942); **121**, No. 9, 35 (1945).
632. Purves, C. B., cited in L. E. Wise and E. C. Jahn, eds., *Wood Chemistry*, Reinhold, New York 1952, p. 1051.
633. Purves, C. B., *et al.*, *Can. J. Chem.*, **33**, 82 (1955).
634. Rånby, B. G., in F. Bolam, ed., *Fundamentals of Papermaking Fibres*, Tech. Sect. Brit. Paper Board Makers' Assoc., Kenley (England) 1958, pp. 55–58.
635. Rånby, B. G., *Fine Structure and Reactions of Native Cellulose*, Diss., Uppsala (Sweden) 1952; *Svensk Papperstid.*, **55**, 115 (1952).
636. Rånby, B. G., *Discussions Faraday Soc.*, **11**, 210 (1951).
637. Rånby, B. G., *Acta Chem. Scand.*, **6**, 101, 116, 128 (1952); *Arkiv Kemi*, **4**, 241, 249 (1952).
638. Rånby, B. G., *Svensk Papperstid.*, **55**, 115 (1952); *Tappi*, **36**, No. 6, 8 A (1953).
639. Rånby, B. G., and K. Rosengren-Forsblad, Paper presented at the 136th A.C.S. Meeting, Atlantic City (N.J.) 1959.
640. Rånby, B. G., and H. F. Mark, *Svensk Papperstid.*, **58**, 374 (1955).
641. Rånby, B. G., and S. A. Rydholm, in C. E. Schildknecht, ed., *Polymer Processes*, Interscience, New York 1956, p. 351.
642. Rånby, B. G., *et al.*, *Ric. Sci.*, **25**, 208 (1955); *Svensk Papperstid.*, **62**, 230 (1959).
643. Rånby, B. G., and E. Ribi, *Experientia*, **6**, 12 (1950).
644. Rånby, B. G., and R. W. Noe, *J. Polymer Sci.*, **51**, 337 (1961).
645. Rapson, W. H., and G. K. Morbey, *Tappi*, **42**, 125 (1959).
646. Rassow, B., and A. Zschenderlein, *Angew. Chem.*, **34**, 204 (1921).

647. Reese, E. T., *J. Bacteriol.*, **59**, 485 (1950); *J. Gen. Physiol.*, **33**, 601 (1950).
648. Reid, J. D., and L. W. Mazzeno, *Ind. Eng. Chem.*, **41**, 2828, 2831 (1949).
649. Rentz, A., *Papier*, **10**, 192 (1956).
650. Ribi, E., *Exp. Cell Res.*, **5**, 161 (1953).
651. Richards, G. N., *J. Am. Chem. Soc.*, **80**, 4888 (1958).
652. Richards, G. N., and H. H. Sephton, *J. Chem. Soc.*, **1957**, 4492.
653. Richter, G. A., *Ind. Eng. Chem.*, **33**, 75, 532 (1941).
654. Richtzenhain, H., *Ber.*, **72**, 2152 (1939).
655. Richtzenhain, H., *Ber.*, **75**, 269 (1942).
656. Richtzenhain, H., *Acta Chem. Scand.*, **4**, 206, 589 (1950); *Ber.*, **83**, 488 (1950); *Svensk Papperstid.*, **53**, 644 (1950).
657. Richtzenhain, H., and B. Alfredsson, *Acta Chem. Scand.*, **7**, 1177 (1953); **8**, 1519 (1954); **10**, 719 (1956).
658. Richtzenhain, H., *et al.*, *Svensk Papperstid.*, **57**, 473 (1954).
659. Richtzenhain, H., *et al.*, *Svensk Papperstid.*, **57**, 363, 538 (1954).
660. Ridge, B. P., *et al.*, *J. Textile Inst.*, **16**, T 13 (1925); **18**, T 133 (1927); **21**, T 85 (1930); **23**, T 33, T 59 (1941).
661. Ritchie, P. F., and C. B. Purves, *Pulp Paper Mag. Can.*, **48**, No. 12, 74 (1947).
662. Ritter, G. J., and E. F. Kurth, *Ind. Eng. Chem.*, **25**, 1250 (1933).
663. Ritter, G. J., and L. C. Fleck, *Ind. Eng. Chem.*, **14**, 1050 (1922); **15**, 1055 (1923); **18**, 608 (1926).
664. Roberts, I., and H. C. Urey, *J. Am. Chem. Soc.*, **60**, 2391 (1938).
665. Rollinson, R. R., and L. E. Wise, *Tappi*, **35**, No. 11, 139 A (1952).
666. Roschier, R. H., *et al.*, *Paperi Puu*, **35**, 1, 181 (1953); **36**, 27 (1954).
666a. Rosenberger, N. A., *Bumazha. Prom.*, **32**, No. 10, 4 (1957); *Zeilstoff u. Papier*, **6**, 361 (1957).
667. Roseveare, W. E., *Ind. Eng. Chem.*, **44**, 168 (1952).
668. Roudier, A., *Compt. Rend.*, **1958**, 1505.
669. Rowen, J. W., *et al.*, *J. Res. Nat. Bur. Std.*, **39**, 133 (1947); **44**, 313 (1950); **46**, 38 (1951).
670. Rutherford, H. A., *et al.*, *J. Res. Nat. Bur. Std.*, **29**, 131 (1942).
671. Rydholm, S. A., unpublished.
672. Rydholm, S. A., *Svensk Papperstid.*, **53**, 561 (1950); **55**, 661 (1952).
673. Rydholm, S. A., cited in E. Hägglund, *Chemistry of Wood*, Academic Press, New York 1951, p. 262.
674. Rydholm, S. A., and S. E. Lagergren, *Svensk Papperstid.*, **62**, 103 (1959).
675. Rydholm, S. A., *et al.*, *Svensk Papperstid.*, **63**, 591 (1960), **64**, 386 (1961).
676. Saarnio, J., *et al.*, *Acta Chem. Scand.*, **8**, 825 (1954).
677. Saeman, J. F., and E. E. Harris, *J. Am. Chem. Soc.*, **68**, 2507 (1946).
678. Saito, G., *Cellulosechem.*, **18**, 106 (1940).
679. Sakurada, I., and K. Hutino, *Kolloid-Z.*, **77**, 346 (1936).
680. Sakurada, I., and T. Kitibatake, *J. Soc. Chem. Ind. Japan*, **37 B**, 604 (1934).
681. Sakurada, I., and S. Okamura, *Z. Physik. Chem.*, **A 187**, 289 (1940).
682. Samuelson, O., *Svensk Kem. Tidskr.*, **59**, 105 (1947).
683. Samuelson, O., *Svensk Kem. Tidskr.*, **62**, 211 (1950).
684. Samuelson, O., *Svensk Kem. Tidskr.*, **58**, 285 (1946).
685. Samuelson, O., and C. Ramsel, *Svensk Papperstid.*, **53**, 155 (1950).
686. Samuelson, O., *et al.*, *Svensk Papperstid.*, **51**, 179 (1948).
686a. Samuelson, O., *et al.*, *Svensk Papperstid.*, **64**, 812 (1961).
687. Samuelson, O., and N. Hartler, *Svensk Kem. Tidskr.*, **62**, 197 (1950).

688. Sandermann, W., *Cellulosechem.*, **21**, 30 (1943).
689. Sandermann, W., and N. Stockman, *Ber.*, **91**, 930 (1958).
690. Sandqvist, H., *et al.*, *Svensk Kem. Tidskr.*, **42**, 106 (1930); *IVA* (Stockholm), No. 10, 1932; *Ber.*, **63**, 1935 (1930); **64**, 2167 (1931).
691. Sands, L., and W. T. Gary, *J. Biol. Chem.*, **101**, 573 (1933).
691a. Sarie, S. P., and R. K. Schofield, *Proc. Royal Soc.*, (*London*), **A 185**, 431 (1946).
692. Sarkanen, K. V., *et al.*, *Tappi*, **44**, 465 (1961), **45**, 24, 29 (1962).
693. Sarkanen, K. V., and R. W. Strauss, *Tappi*, **44**, 459 (1961).
694. Sarkanen, K. V., and C. W. Dence, *J. Org. Chem.*, **25**, 715 (1960).
695. Sarkanen, K. V., and C. Schuerch, *Anal. Chem.*, **27**, 1245 (1956).
696. Schenck, H., Diss., Berlin 1936.
697. Scherer, P. C., and R. E. Hussey, *J. Am. Chem. Soc.*, **53**, 2344 (1931).
698. Scherrer, P., in R. Zsigmondy, ed., *Textbook of Colloid Chemistry*, 3rd Ed., Leipzig 1920, p. 40.
699. Schmidt, E., *et al.*, *Cellulosechem.*, **12**, 201 (1931).
700. Schmidt, E., *et al.*, *Ber.*, **54**, 1860 (1921); **55**, 1529 (1922); **58**, 1394 (1925).
701. Schmorak, J., and G. A. Adams, *Tappi*, **40**, 378 (1957).
702. Schopmeyer, C. S., *et al.*, *Plant Physiol.*, **29**, 82 (1954).
703. Schorger, A. W., *Ind. Eng. Chem.*, **9**, 556 (1917).
704. Schorigin, P., and N. N. Makarowa-Semljarskaja, *Ber.*, **69**, 1713 (1936).
705. Schulz, G. V., *Z. Elektrochem.*, **43**, 497 (1937).
706. Schulz, G. V., *et al.*, *J. Polymer Sci.*, **3**, 365 (1948); *Ber.*, **80**, 335 (1947); *J. Prakt. Chem.*, **157**, 238 (1941); *Z. Physik. Chem.*, **B 51**, 127 (1942); **B 52**, 23, 50 (1942).
707. Schulz, G. V., and M. Marx, *Makromol. Chem.*, **14**, 52 (1954); *Papier*, **9**, 13 (1955).
708. Schulze, E., *Ber.*, **22**, 1192 (1889); **24**, 2286 (1891); *Z. Physiol. Chem.*, **16**, 387 (1892); **19**, 38 (1894).
709. Schulze, F., *Chem. Zentr.*, **1857**, 321.
710. Schütz, F., and P. Sarten, *Cellulosechem.*, **21**, 35 (1943); *Holzforschung*, **1**, 2 (1947); *Angew. Chem.*, **60**, 115 (1948).
710a. Schwab, E., *et al.*, *Tappi*, **44**, 251 (1961).
711. Schwabe, K., and L. Hasner, *Cellulosechem.*, **21**, 60 (1942), *Holzforschung*, **1**, 42, 79 (1947).
712. Schwalbe, C. G., and E. Becker, *Angew. Chem.*, **33**, 14 (1920).
713. Schwalbe, C. G., and E. Becker, *Angew. Chem.*, **32**, 229 (1919).
714. Schwarzkopf, O., *Z. Electrochem.*, **38**, 353 (1932).
715. Schwerin, G., *Holzforschung*, **12**, 43 (1958).
716. Seek, W., *Melliand Textilber.*, **13**, 314 (1932).
717. Selleby, L., *Svensk Papperstid.*, **63**, 81 (1960).
718. Sharples, A., *J. Polymer Sci.*, **14**, 95 (1954).
719. Sharples, A., *Trans. Faraday Soc.*, **53**, 1003 (1957); **54**, 913 (1958).
720. Sharples, A., *J. Polymer Sci.*, **13**, 393 (1954).
721. Siegel, S. M., *Physiol. Plantagen.*, **6**, 134 (1953); **7**, 51 (1954); **8**, 20 (1955).
722. Sihtola, H., and E. Kaila, *Paperi Puu*, **36**, 341 (1954).
723. Simha, R., *J. Appl. Phys.*, **12**, 569 (1941).
724. Simonsen, J. L., *The Terpenes*, Cambridge Univ. Press 1947–1957.
725. Sisson, W. A., and W. R. Saner, *J. Phys. Chem.*, **45**, 717 (1941).
726. Sisson, W. A., and W. R. Saner, *J. Phys. Chem.*, **43**, 687 (1939).
727. Skraup, Z. H., and J. König, *Ber.*, **34**, 1115 (1901).

728. Smith, D. C. C., *J. Chem. Soc.*, **1955**, 2347; *Nature*, **176**, 267 (1955).
729. Smith, D. M., and C. B. Purves, *Ind. Eng. Chem.*, **49**, 1394 (1957).
730. Smith, F., *et al.*, *J. Am. Chem. Soc.*, **76**, 6097 (1954); **78**, 1404 (1956).
731. Smith, F., and R. Montgomery, *Chemistry of Plant Gums and Mucilages*, Reinhold, New York 1959.
732. Smith, J. H. C., in J. Franck and W. E. Loomis, eds., *Photosynthesis in Plant*, Iowa State College Press, Ames (U.S.A.) 1949, p. 53.
733. Smith, L. H., ed., *Synthetic Fiber Developments in Germany*, P.B. 7416, Textile Research Inst., New York 1946, p. 1006.
734. Sobue, H., *et al.*, *J. Soc. Textile Cellulose Industry, Japan*, **8**, 79 (1952); **9**, 565 (1953).
735. Sobue, H., *J. Soc. Chem. Ind.* (*Japan*), **43**, B 24 (1940).
736. Sobue, H., *et al.*, *Z. Physik. Chem.*, **B 43**, 309 (1939).
736a. Somsen, R., *Tappi*, **43**, 154, 157 (1960).
737. Sönnerskog, S., *Svensk Papperstid.*, **48**, 413 (1945); Diss., Stockholm 1952.
738. Sperling, L. H., and M. Easterwood, *J. Appl. Polymer Sci.*, **4**, 25 (1960).
739. Sponsler, O. L., *Nature*, **120**, 767 (1927); **125**, 633 (1930); *Protoplasma*, **12**, 241 (1931); *J. Gen. Physiol.*, **9**, 221, 677 (1926).
740. Spurlin, H. M., *J. Am. Chem. Soc.*, **61**, 2222 (1939).
741. Stakheeva-Kaverzneva, E. D., *et al.*, *Bull. Acad. Sci. USSR, Div. Chem. Sci.*, **1945**, No. 6, 603; **1952**, 751, 800, 804; cf. *Tekstil'n. Prom.*, **14**, No. 3, 31 (1954).
742. Stamm, A. J., and W. E. Cohen, *J. Phys. Chem.*, **42**, 921 (1938).
743. Stamm, A. J., and E. E. Harris, *Chemical Processing of Wood*, Chemical Publ. Co., New York 1953, Chapters 9 and 11.
744. Staudinger, H., *Trans. Faraday Soc.*, **29**, 18 (1933); *Papier-Fabr.*, **36**, 373, 381 (1938).
745. Staudinger, H., *et al.*, *Ber.*, **70**, 2502 (1937); *Cellulosechem.*, **18**, 25 (1940).
746. Staudinger, H., and E. Dreher, *Ber.*, **69**, 1734 (1936).
747. Staudinger, H., and E. O. Leupold, *Ber.*, **67 B**, 479 (1934).
748. Steinmann, H. W., and B. B. White, *Tappi*, **37**, 225 (1954).
749. Stewart, C. M., *et al.*, *Holzforschung*, **9**, 109 (1955).
750. Stewart, C. M., and D. H. Foster, *Australian J. Chem.*, **6**, 431 (1953).
751. Stockman, L., and E. Hägglund, *Svensk Papperstid.*, **51**, 269 (1948).
752. Stone, J. E., *Tappi*, **38**, 610 (1955).
753. Stone, J. E., and M. J. Blundell, *Anal. Chem.*, **23**, 771 (1951).
754. Stumpf, P. K., and G. A. Barber, *J. Biol. Chem.*, **227**, 407 (1957).
755. Stumpf, W., and K. Freudenberg, *Angew. Chem.*, **62**, 537 (1950).
756. Sultze, R. F., *Tappi*, **40**, 985 (1957).
757. Svedberg, T., and K. O. Pedersen, *The Ultracentrifuge*, Oxford 1940.
758. Svensson, A. Å., *Arkiv Kemi*, **10**, 239 (1956).
758a. Takehara, S., *J Chem. Soc. Japan, Ind. Chem. Sect.*, **62**, 1034 (1959).
759. Tanner, W. L., *U.S. Pat.* 1,896,725.
760. TAPPI T13m–54 Standard Method.
761. Theander, O., *et al.*, *Acta Chem. Scand.*, **8**, 1870 (1954); **11**, 1557 (1957); **12**, 1507, 1887, 1897 (1958); *Svensk Papperstid.*, **18**, 581 (1958); surveyed in *Svensk Kem. Tidskr.*, **71**, 1 (1959).
762. Thomas, E. B., and H. F. Oxley, *Brit. Pat.* 484,317; *U.S. Pat.* 2,135,128.
763. Tiemann, F., and W. Haarmann, *Ber.*, **7**, 606 (1874); **8**, 509 (1875).
764. Timell, T. E., *Tappi*, **40**, 30, 568 (1957).
765. Timell, T. E., *Tappi*, **40**, 749 (1957).

765a. Timell, T. E., *Wood Hemicelluloses*, N.Y. State Univ., Syracuse, N.Y. 1963.
766. Timell, T. E., *Svensk Papperstid.*, **57**, 777, 844, 913 (1954).
767. Timell, T. E., *Studies on Cellulose Reactions*, Diss., K.T.H., Stockholm 1950.
768. Timell, T. E., *Svensk Kem. Tidskr.*, **61**, 146 (1949).
769. Timell, T. E., *Svensk Kem. Tidskr.*, **61**, 49 (1949).
770. Timell, T. E., *Svensk Papperstid.*, **51**, 254 (1948).
771. Timell, T. E., *Svensk Papperstid.*, **52**, 165 (1949).
772. Timell, T. E., *Svensk Kem. Tidskr.*, **62**, 49, 129 (1950).
773. Timell, T. E., *Svensk Papperstid.*, **56**, 483 (1953).
774. Timell, T. E., *Svensk Papperstid.*, **51**, 537 (1948).
774a. Timell, T. E., *Svensk Papperstid.*, **60**, 836 (1957).
775. Timell, T. E., *Tappi*, **43**, 844 (1960), *Svensk Papperstid.*, **63**, 472 (1960).
776. Timell, T. E., *Tappi*, **44**, 88 (1961), **45**, 734, 799 (1962).
777. Timell, T. E., *et al.*, *Svensk Papperstid.*, **64**, 191 (1961).
778. Timell, T. E., *et al.*, *Pulp Paper Mag. Can.*, **59**, No. 10, 242 (1958).
779. Timell, T. E., *et al.*, *Svensk Papperstid.*, **58**, 851, 889 (1955); **59**, 1 (1956); *Tappi*, **40**, 25 (1957); *Pulp Paper Mag. Can.*, **56**, No. 7, 104 (1955).
780. Timell, T. E., *et al.*, *Textile Research J.*, **25**, 870 (1955); *Tappi*, **40**, 749 (1957); *Ind. Eng. Chem.*, **47**, 2166 (1955).
781. Timell, T. E., and E. C. Jahn, *Svensk Papperstid.*, **54**, 831 (1951).
782. Timell, T. E., and H. M. Spurlin, *Svensk Papperstid.*, **55**, 700 (1952).
783. Timell, T. E., and A. Tyminski, *Tappi*, **40**, 519 (1957).
784. Tollens, B., and J. B., Lindsey, *Ann.*, **267**, 341 (1892).
785. Tomlinson, G. H., and H. Hibbert, *J. Am. Chem. Soc.*, **58**, 348 (1936).
786. Tompa, H., *Polymer Solutions*, Academic Press, New York 1956.
787. Tönnesen, B. A., and Ö. Ellefsen, *Norsk Skogind.*, **14**, 266 (1960).
788. Touey, G. P., *Mod. Plastics*, **29**, 109, 183 (Nov. 1951).
789. Traube, W., *Cellulosechem.*, **11**, 249 (1930).
790. Traube, W., *et al.*, *Ber.*, **B 65**, 603 (1932).
791. Traube, W., *et al.*, *Ber.*, **69**, 1483 (1936).
792. Traynard, P., *et al.*, *Assoc. Tech. Ind. Papétière, Bull.*, **1953**, 45.
793. Traynard, P., and A. Eymery, *Papier, Carton et Cellulose*, **3**, No. 5, 87 (1954); *Holzforschung*, **9**, 172 (1955); **10**, 6, 43 (1956).
794. Trogus, C., *Cellulosechem.*, **15**, 104 (1934); cf. G. L. Wilson (1936), cited in F. D. Miles, *Cellulose Nitrate*, Oliver & Boyd, London 1955, p. 59.
795. Trogus, C., and K. Hess, *Z. Elektrochem.*, **42**, 710 (1936).
796. Trogus, C., and K. Hess, *Z. Physik. Chem.*, **B 14**, 387 (1931).
797. Tsuboi, M., *J. Polymer Sci.*, **25**, 159 (1957).
798. Uber, F. M., and T. H. Goodspeed, *Proc. Nat. Acad. Sci., U.S.*, **21**, 428 (1935).
799. Udenfriend, S., *et al.*, *J. Biol. Chem.*, **208**, 731, 741 (1954).
800. Urban, H., *Cellulosechem.*, **7**, 73 (1926).
801. Van Beckum, W. G., and G. J. Ritter, *Paper Trade J.*, **108**, No. 1, 27 (1939).
802. Vink, H., *Arkiv Kemi*, **13**, 193 (1959).
803. Voss, W., *et al.*, *Angew. Chem.*, **49**, 761 (1936).
804. v. Wacek, A., *et al.*, *Holzforschung*, **7**, 58 (1953); **8**, 65 (1954).
805. v. Wacek, A., *et al.*, *Monatsh. Chem.*, **81**, 266 (1950); **83**, 5 (1952); **84**, 453 (1953).
806. Wadman, W. H., *et al.*, *J. Am. Chem. Soc.*, **76**, 4097 (1954).
807. Wald, W. J., *et al.*, *J. Am. Chem. Soc.*, **69**, 1371 (1947).

808. Walkup, J. H., *et al.*, *Tappi*, **39**, No. 6, 190 A (1956).
809. Waller, R. C., *et al.*, *Ind. Eng. Chem.*, **40**, 138 (1948).
809a. Walters, A. J., and D. M. Shepherd, *Brit. Pat.* 621,188.
810. Ward, K., and M. L. Murray, *Tappi*, **42**, 17 (1959).
811. Wardrop, A. B., *Tappi*, **40**, 225 (1957).
812. Wardrop, A. B., *Nature*, **164**, 366 (1949); *Australian J. Bot.*, **2**, 154 (1954).
813. Wardrop, A. B., and H. E. Dadswell, *Australian Sci.J. Research*, **B1**, 3 (1948), and in F. Bolam, ed., *Fundamentals of Papermaking Fibres*, Tech. Sect. Brit. Paper and Board Makers' Assoc., Kenley (England) 1958, p. 187.
814. Watson, J. K., and D. R. Henderson, *Tappi*, **40**, 686 (1957).
815. Weber, O. H., and E. Huseman, *J. Prakt. Chem.*, **161**, 20 (1942).
816. Wedekind, E., and J. R. Katz, *Ber.*, **62**, 1172 (1929).
817. Whistler, R. L., *et al.*, *J. Am. Chem. Soc.*, **78**, 4704 (1956).
818. Whistler, R. L., *et al.*, Paper presented at the 136th A.C.S. Meeting, Atlantic City, N.J. 1959.
819. White, E. V., *J. Am. Chem. Soc.*, **63**, 2871 (1941); **64**, 302, 1507, 2838 (1942).
820. Wieland, H., *Ber.*, **54**, 1784 (1921).
821. Wilcox, H. E., Thesis, N.Y. State College of Forestry, Syracuse, N.Y. 1940.
822. Willamo, H. H., *Paperi Puu*, **33**, 310 (1951).
823. Willstätter, R., and L. Kalb, *Ber.*, **55**, 2637 (1922).
824. Willstätter, R., and L. Zechmeister, *Ber.*, **46**, 2401 (1913).
825. Wise, L. E., *Ind. Eng. Chem. (Anal. Ed.)*, **17**, 63 (1945); *Paper Trade J.*, **122**, No. 2, 35 (1946).
826. Wise, L. E., and E. C. Jahn, eds., *Wood Chemistry*, Reinhold, New York 1952, p. 1264.
827. Wise, L. E., and E. C. Jahn, eds., *Wood Chemistry*, Reinhold, New York 1952, Vol. 1, Part III.
828. Wise, L. E., and J. K. N. Jones, *J. Chem. Soc.*, **1957**, 669.
829. Wise, L. E., and J. Pickard, *Tappi*, **38**, 618 (1955).
830. Wise, L. E., and E. K. Ratcliff, *Arch. Biochem. Biophys.*, **19**, 292 (1948).
831. Wolfrom, M. L., and A. Thompson, in W. Pigman, ed., *The Carbohydrates*, Academic Press, New York 1957, p. 208.
832. Wultsch, F., and F. Senger, *Tappi*, **38**, 25 (1955).
833. Yllner, S., and B. Enström, *Svensk Papperstid.*, **59**, 229 (1956).
834. Young, A. E., and M. Kin, in J. Alexander, ed., *Colloid Chemistry*, Vol. VI, Reinhold, New York 1946, pp. 926, 934.
835. Yundt, A. P., *Tappi*, **34**, 89 (1951).
836. Yundt, A. P., *Tappi*, **34**, 94 (1951).
837. Zapf, F., *Makromol. Chem.*, **10**, 35 (1953).
838. Zemplen, G., *Ber.*, **59**, 1258 (1926).
839. Zentner, T. G., *Tappi*, **36**, 517 (1953).

PART II

PREPARATION OF UNBLEACHED PULP

5

PREPARATION OF WOOD FOR PULPING

I. Forest Operations, Pulpwood Transport and Measurement

It is not the purpose of this book to describe silviculture and the operations of wood procurement. However, it is necessary to stress their importance for the *size*, overall *economy* and even *quality* of pulp production, and to indicate some of the developments going on, which are likely to influence the pulping industry considerably.

The wood costs constitute 50–75 % of the manufacturing costs of pulp and any major improvement of the economy of the forest and wood procurement operations will have an immediate effect on the overall economy which is greater than that of most improvements in the pulping processes (66, 69). As the available forest lands become increasingly utilized by the growing forest industry, the output of pulpwood per area will be limiting for the size of pulp production. The influence of the forest operations on pulp quality is also considerable, as regards dimensions and wood condition as well as species. Both oversize and undersize logs present special handling problems at the mill, and undersize logs will increase the costs of pulp production especially and influence the cleanliness of the pulp adversely. The condition of the wood is important in several respects. Decay will decrease pulp yield, brightness, cleanliness and strength properties. The management of the forest as well as the manner of storage after tree felling is important in that respect. Storage of pulpwood in the forest is sometimes necessary because of the seasonal character of the forest operations in some districts, and it is also desirable from several other respects. Deresination during the pulping operation is often improved by some storage, either in the forest or in the wood yard. However, the costs of storage are considerable, since the cut logs represent a capital that has ceased to grow and storage involves risk of decay of the pulpwood, especially if the debarking is not carried out in the forest (7, 20). In many places therefore the wood is brought 'green' into the mill, although about three months of storage in the forest is more normal, and sometimes even over a year. Wood storage is particularly important for *sulfite* pulpwood, especially of resinous hardwoods. In contrast, *mechanical* pulping is facilitated when the wood is brought green to the mill.

In most forest-growing districts of the world, indigenous forests dominate, although their composition has usually been influenced by silvicultural methods (47). The areas of virgin forests are rapidly decreasing, and pulpwood is mainly derived from planted or seed-controlled forests. After the felling operations, sufficient *seed-producing trees* are often left standing to ensure regrowth. Where the soil and climatic conditions are less satisfactory, artificial seeding is necessary (3). After felling of stands approved of with respect to seed production, the *seed cones are collected* and ripened in special kilns. Alternatively, special *seed orchards* (14) with grafts from trees, grown in the specific sites of different altitudes and soil conditions, are kept for the seed production. Such a system gives continual supply of seed and makes it possible to select trees of favorable genotype for seed production (13). Another system of reforestation applies special *plant nurseries*, where seedlings are grown to a height suitable for planting in the forests (67). This ensures a superior result but is more expensive and is especially suitable for the plantation type of forestry in areas of rapid growth, although it is receiving increasingly wide acceptance. The big pulp-wood consumers often adopt the system of supplying seedlings not only to their own forests but also to the privately owned forests delivering pulp-wood, to an extent corresponding to the purchased wood. This is in accordance with the policy of keeping the forest operations on a sustained yield basis. In areas where this policy was adopted too late, the intense selection of useful pulpwood species for felling has caused a complete change in the type of forest, e.g. from softwoods to hardwoods in the north-eastern United States and eastern Canada (4). On the other hand, in some regions, intense cultivation of the forests has resulted in planting of pulpwood species of the most valuable type, such as spruce, on soils where other species would grow better, or in the production of too closed stands of uniform species where a mixture of softwoods and hardwoods, for example, might prove to give a higher overall yield. Previously, the forests were grown for timber, with the thinnings constituting a second-grade wood usable as pulpwood. Although timber-producing trees have remained more valuable than trees for pulping, calculated by volume or weight, the increasing demand for pulpwood has created a situation where the forests in many districts should be grown with the sole aim of pro-ducing pulpwood, which means that quantity has priority over quality, as judged by the old standards, whereas the special quality considerations of pulpwood must be duly observed.

The *choice of species* is one of the most important means of influencing both quality and quantity of the pulpwood produced. Especially in areas with subtropical climate, where the forests are run as plantations with crops taken at short rotations, there are considerable possibilities of experimenting to get the optimal results in a reasonably short period of time. In those regions, such as Australia, New Zealand, South Africa, South America, southern North America and the Mediterranean area, exotic species have been introduced, which have very high growth rates after adaptation to the new growing conditions (17, 18, 27), whereas the introduction of exotic species to the forests of temperate zones has given less good results (e.g. 63). These species are predominantly *Pinus* and *Eucalyptus* species, such as *Pinus radiata*, *P. patula*, *P. elliottii*, and *P. taeda*, as well as *Eucalyptus saligna, E. grandis, E. globulus* and *E. camaldulensis.* Annual increments *average* about 5 metric tons/hectar of dry wood for *Pinus* plantations (20 t/ha having been reached in Chile) and 12 t/ha for *Eucalyptus* plantations (over 30 t/ha on rich soils in Brazil) in many districts, as compared to 0.5–2.5 t/ha for spruce, fir and pine (*Picea, Abies* and *Pinus* species) in the temperate zones of the northern hemisphere, in the northern United States, Canada, Scandinavia and Russia. In exceptional cases, such as on the rainy western slopes of the Cascade Mountains at the Pacific coast of North America, about 5 t/ha are realized for Douglas fir and hemlock (*Pseudotsuga* and *Tsuga*), and in the southern United States similar yields are sometimes reached for pine, although the average figures are considerably lower, around 2.5 t/ha. *Populus* hybrids in Italy are reported to give as high increments as 7–13 t/ha a year (8, cf. 28), and cottonwood (*Populus deltoides* v. *monilifera*) has given very interesting results in the southern United States. It is interesting to compare these figures with the annual production of straw, which is about 4.5 t/ha in Germany and Holland. In this case, an additional quantity of 1.5 t/ha of grain is produced, but on the other hand agricultural land constitutes the best soil and receives an annual charge of fertilizers, which have so far not been applied in the forests to any large extent. Bamboo in India and Burma has been reported to grow at a rate of 7–13 t/ha.year in 1–3 year rotations, although on average considerably lower yields are obtained. Experimental stands of American bamboo have been found to grow as fast as 10–50 t/ha year.

In addition to the decreased forest capital cost for such fast-growing wood, the costs of forest management and wood procurement will decrease because of the concentrated areas involved, giving short roads for transport, etc. Another advantage with the fast-growing eucalypt forests is the possibility of *coppice treatment,* i.e. re-growth from the stumps of the old trees, eliminating the need of re-planting after the first rotation. Five crops or more have already been taken with this system although in other cases re-plantation is necessary after three crops. Finally, the crops being constituted of young trees, 7–10 years in the case of eucalyptus and 15–20 years for pine, little heartwood is formed, which considerably improves the ease and uniformity of pulping. Short-rotation crops, being planted in 2×2 or 3×3 m spacings, are not thinned, only *pruned* (removal of lower branches) and finally harvested all at the same age, i.e. *clear cutting.* Comparatively fast-growing forests, such as the pines in the southern United States, are cut at an age of 35–40 years or even less, with two intermediate thinnings, at about 12 and 25 years. Heartwood is being developed from an age of about 20–25 years. In the northernmost forests, rotations are as long or even longer than 80 years for pulpwood, with one or two earlier thinnings, and around 100 or more for timber, with heavy thinnings for pulpwood at 30–40 years. Dimensions down to 3 in or 2 in, or sometimes even lower, top diameter are accepted as pulpwood. The spacing of the plants considerably influences the dimensions of the trees but not the wood density (29). The rate of growth increases with closer

259

spacings, but the diameter of each tree gets smaller. Therefore, close spacing will require more thinnings and the logs more work per wood volume on debarking. A compromise thus has to be made between output and labor required, varying with local conditions.

The *environmental influence* on the quantity and quality of the wood produced has been subjected to many studies with considerably conflicting results (62). The quality of the *soil* is an important factor, and the forest land is classified by a range of *site classes* with widely varying average growth rate. Nitrogen supply is one of the most common limiting factors, but fertilizing has not yet been found to be economical, although serious experimentation is taking place on a large scale. A better site seems to yield a somewhat lower wood density (29, 55). The most decisive environmental factors for the rate of growth and wood quality are *climatical*, day length, temperature, precipitation and winds, cf. Chapter 1. The growth rate, summerwood content and wood density generally decrease with increasing latitude and altitude (54), even within the same species, and the same differences are stressed by the different species of the same genera growing in the north and south. This is of consequence also for the pulp type produced.

Obviously, climatic conditions, altitude, soil, etc., to a large extent determine the species which can be chosen for cultivation, and only those parts of the world where fast-growing species of short rotations thrive, are given an opportunity to change over to other species with reasonably rapid results. There, not only the rate of growth of different species should be observed, but also the quality of the pulpwood so produced. Research on the fundamental relationships between wood properties and pulp properties tries to give the basis for such a choice of species, and likewise for the lines of *genetical development* of the species to suit the demands of the pulping industry (12, 31). At the same time, much research is naturally devoted to the modification of the pulping and pulp-consuming processes to suit the fast-growing species. As a result, hardwood utilization has increased considerably on all continents. However, for most paper purposes, the disadvantage of the shorter hardwood fibers as compared to softwood fibers remains. Likewise, some of the fast-growing softwoods contain an unfavorably high percentage of thick-walled latewood fibers, which results in inferior paper properties. Short rotations give a high percentage of core wood, which also for softwoods tend to give shorter fibers and lower basic density (72). However, genetical variations in these properties have been observed (73), giving the possibilities for further developments since a hereditary tendency to a high growth rate is not necessarily connected with a low wood density (56, 72). The genetical methods employed to influence the tree properties are mainly (*1*) *selection* of parent trees displaying favorable properties for the production of seeds, (*2*) *hybridization*, (*3*) *producing polyploids*, and (*4*) *inducing mutations* (30, 31). The attention is directed to the results of these activities on (*1*) growth rate (46), (*2*) fiber dimensions (34, 70), (*3*) cell wall dimensions (59), and (*4*) chemical composition (12, 70). In order to get quick results, the properties of the wood formed during the first few years are studied, and special investigations are therefore devoted to the relationship between the properties of the wood in successive growth rings (70, 74). Of course, the development of improved species for the temperate regions is also undertaken, although of necessity proceeding at a slower rate (30). It is to be expected that the importance of subtropical and tropical forests for the pulping industry will continue to grow. However, as pointed out in Chapter 1, the dominating area of commercial forest land is in the temperate regions, which will continue to deliver the larger part of the pulpwood. It is the goal of silvicultural and technical development to take the best advantage of all growing conditions.

After *felling*, the trees are cut to log length, possibly after *debarking*. *Chemical debarking* by the introduction of poisonous chemicals, such as ammonium sulfamate or preferably sodium arsenite, to a bark-free girdle of the tree during the period of high cambial activity, has been investigated and is practised to some extent (2, 5, 16, 53, 64). The tree dies within a week and the bark is shed during the subsequent months if the tree is left on root. About 0.2 man-hours per solid m^3 is calculated for the application of the poison and total cost is decidedly less than for mechanical debarking in the forest. The operation involves some hazards for the applicator and the wildlife—which can be overcome—and has not yet been very commonly accepted. Some *finishing operations* and *piling for storage* may be done at the place of felling, and subsequently, the wood is *hauled to truck roads* and *transported to the mill* by *rail, road* or *water transport*. Mechanization of all these operations, applying portable power saws, movable mechanical debarkers and various types of handling and transporting equipment (9, 32, 37, 38, 43), is being introduced in a manner suited to the widely varying geographic, climatic and labor conditions. Horses and mules are still important in many areas, and the manual labor involved often exceeds that of the pulping operations, calculated on the same pulp production basis. The building of roads for transport is an important activity of forest management. Road transport is used increasingly instead of water transport. The latter is at present profitable only in the main streams and lakes (26). Floating the logs with the current down-stream is known as *driving*. The logs are transported to the river banks and skidded into the water. In still waters, the logs are towed by small crafts either in *booms*, constituting an area of floating logs enclosed in a loop of interconnected logs, or in *rafts*, which are compact bundles of logs kept together by chains. If the wood is rough, i.e. with the bark on, water transport often leads to diffusion of bark tannins into the wood, with discoloration and sulfite pulping difficulties as a result. Special pulping methods have been developed to overcome that problem. Furthermore, the sinkage losses are somewhat higher in driving rough wood. Water transport of hardwoods is not possible, except in rafts mixed with softwoods, or after special treatment. Water is taken up by the hardwood vessels so quickly that it will sink even on very short journeys. However, sealing the log ends with specially developed resins has been tried with

261

some success (11). The manual operations involved and the special felling periods that must be chosen in order to get the unbarked logs dry, have prevented a common acceptance of the method, and hardwoods are entirely land-transported.

The costs of land transport for hardwoods are usually higher than those of softwoods, thus limiting the areas from which hardwoods could economically be drawn to a pulp mill. The economical factors, however, vary greatly from country to country, which is exemplified by the fact that pulpwood exports sometimes involve Atlantic transports. The total labor used in the forest operations and transport is about 0.6 man-days/solid m³ unbarked wood in Scandinavia, was 0.4 in the southern United States in 1950 and has since been reduced to only about 0.2 man-days/solid m³ (66). This mechanized operation involves felling and limbing by power chain saw, skidding tree lengths by tractor to a concentration point, where the trees are bucked into 1, 2 or 3m lengths and the logs loaded mechanically on haul trucks for transport directly to the mill or for mechanical transfer to rail cars or barges. Sometimes the logging operations are combined in one large tree-harvesting machine. When stored in the forest, unbarked wood deteriorates seriously, lowering not only the quantity but also the quality (7, 20). Thus, as long as the local economical situation allows, the wood should be debarked at the spot of felling. This is imperative in tropical and sub-tropical areas, whereas in the temperate regions the winter fellings are less critical. When it is too expensive to debark in the forest, the transport to the mill should take place shortly after felling, and the storage, if necessary, carried out at the mill after mill debarking.

An important activity of the forest management is the *combating of fires, insects, rodents and diseases* (15). About 10% of the forest area is destroyed or threatened by fire yearly, and insects and diseases kill twice as much timber as fire. Constant vigilance from a system of fire towers is necessary to spot the fires in time to prevent them from becoming conflagrations. Fire breaks of up to 5% of the area are considered necessary in many districts, sometimes covered by less inflammable species, but as a rule left bare. Airplanes and helicopters are often used for spraying insecticides, as well as for *mapping and surveying. Desiccation* of the soil in swampy districts is another important activity to improve the health and growth of the stands.

An important detail of the forest operations is the *measurement and classification of the pulpwood.* At certain centralized places in the forests, as a rule in connection with the change in the type of transport, the wood is measured by persons authorized by seller and buyer. The manner of measuring varies; the diameter and length of each separate log or the dimensions of piles of logs cut to standard length. The manner of expressing the result will also vary. A *cord* of wood, one of the most common measures, is the quantity in a pile of 4-ft wood 8 ft long and 4 ft high, when the wood is stacked in an orderly manner with all sticks parallel. The space occupied by a cord is thus 128 ft³, but the quantity of solid

262

wood will vary with the dimensions of the bolts, their crookedness, the method of piling and the amount of bark retained. Usually only somewhat more than two-thirds of the volume is occupied by wood, and a cord thus contains around 90 solid ft³, with variations from 5–975 or 58–75% of the total volume. Careful conversion factors must be worked out for every separate case, if wood is bought by the cord. A European counterpart to the cord is the 'loose m³', in special cases the 'stere', which is a pile of $1 \times 1 \times 1$ m wood. Measures of solid wood are the *solid ft³*, used in both America and Europe, the *cunit*, corresponding to 100 solid ft³, the *solid m³*, and the *board foot* (bd. ft) which is the amount of wood in a board 1 ft square and 1 in thick and used predominantly for timber. Local variations in the concepts of, for example, a cord, occur. The shrinkage of wood on drying does not facilitate the problem of getting an accurate measure of the quantity delivered. On arrival at the mill, the wood quantity is further checked by various methods, such as loose-volume estimation, counting of the number of logs, measurement of displaced volume on immersion in water, etc., or even by *weighing*. Repeated inventories of the quantity stored in the wood yard are also made. The weight of the wood in the dry state is naturally the figure of direct interest to the pulp mill. However, direct weighing of the logs is a complication in the wood handling and is of no value unless completed by moisture content determinations. Subsequent weighing of the chips and current moisture determination of the latter is a valuable tool for estimation of processing losses when compared to the output, but gives no exact indication as to the quantity of the wood received, as wood yard and wood room losses are not included, except in the case of direct chipping for storage in chip stacks (cf. below). The measurement of pulpwood therefore remains a problem with no ideal solution presented.

II. Wood Handling at the Pulp Mill (50, 65)

The object of the operations in the *wood yard* and *wood room* is to present to the pulping department the wood received from the forest in the desired form and purity and at a suitable rate. To ensure a steady supply and often also to achieve certain quality effects, the wood is stored in the yard, or under water, for some time. The removal of impurities, mainly mineral particles and bark, is carried out with water sprays and *debarking equipment* of various types. The logs are *slashed* by circular saw blades to suitable length for grinding or *chipping*, and in the latter case also chipped and *classified* in the wood room. The sequence of these operations varies for different cases. In order to decrease deterioration losses, it is frequently customary to debark the logs before storage in the wood yard, if debarking has not already been carried out in the forest. For the same reason, the wood yard should be situated on dry ground, and the logs piled in *regular piles* or *ricks* in a manner which facilitates aeration. Then the logs are bunched into slings when removed from the water or unloaded from the transport vehicles. A more rapid seasoning to a uniform moisture content

263

is also obtained, as compared with the results of random-dropped conical *stack-piles*. Piling is carried out with the aid of large stackers or cable cranes.

Surveys on the experience on the biological deterioration of pulpwood have been given (39a, 61a). Storage of unbarked, *ricked* pine pulpwood in the southern United States caused a density loss of 10% during six summer months and 5% during six winter months (39, 44). Storage of barked pine gave lower losses especially during the first month. The kraft pulp yields were found to decrease accordingly or even more (12), and pulp strength was affected measurably after two months' summer storage or five months' winter storage. About the same effects were found for *stack-piling* unbarked pine (19), and gum and oak showed similar tendencies. The decay continues as long as the moisture content is above the point of fiber saturation, which means a very long time for unbarked logs. One method of preventing decay is to store the pulpwood under water to exclude air. This is often practised by northern countries, where rafted pulpwood is stored in bays and lakes. Only the part of the rafts under water are unaffected. A special technique has been developed for the complete underwater storage in large mill ponds of circular or rectangular shape, where the pulpwood can be stored for more than a year without loss in yield and pulp strength (12). This system, however, involves investment in relatively heavy machinery. Storage under water of unbarked logs also has the disadvantage of causing discoloration and tannin damage to sprucewood, which makes it unsuitable for conventional sulfite cooking. A recent variant of solution to the storage problem is outside storage of *wood chips*, which with pine, spruce, gum and oak under similar conditions as for the unbarked stack-piled roundwood gave similar extent of deterioration (1a, 6a, 58, 61b), i.e. 1–1.5% wood losses per month and some or no reduction in pulp strength. By increasing the height of the stack it has been found possible to reduce the deterioration further, and the system is now gaining in importance, since it is practical, inexpensive and labor-saving. The roundwood is dumped directly upon reception into flumes, conveyed to barking drums and further to a chipper, from which the chips are blown to huge stacks, which are currently formed by a bull-dozer working at the top. The temperature in the center of the stack increases through oxidation reactions but levels off at about 50–60°C from lack of oxygen or oxidizable matter, mainly the unsaturated fatty and resin acids, cf. Chapter 16. This oxidation is an advantage in the production of sulfite pulp, since the pitch troubles decrease (1a), but a disadvantage in kraft pulping, where it causes a serious reduction in tall oil yield (61b). The chips are then conveyed pneumatically into the mill at the desired rate.

Debarking is performed on whole logs or on bolts after slashing. The debarkers are either multi-log or single-log barkers. To the former category belong the *barking drums* and the *stationary friction debarkers*. Barking drums are huge horizontal cylinders with coarse slots to allow bark to pass out. They are usually slightly inclined and rotate slowly to induce the rubbing of the logs against each other or against the drum wall, at which action the bark separates from the wood. The logs are fed in continuously at the upper end and leave at the opposite open end. The drums may be run dry or with water sprays to clean the wood and facilitate the bark removal. The stationary friction debarkers of the *Waterous* or *Ormell* type cause a similar rubbing by continually removing the lowest logs from a pile of parallel logs by means of a moving chain belt conveyor. This type is of special interest in the utilization of small dimension thinnings, which are otherwise difficult to debark at a reasonable cost. Single-log debarkers are more economical for logs of medium and large size, preferably prior to slashing. They are of three types, *hydraulic debarkers*, the *mechanical friction type*, and the *knife debarkers*. The first-mentioned is especially useful for the coarse dimensions of the logs at the American Pacific coast with their thick bark. Jets of water at 1,000 atmospheres hit the logs at a suitable angle, while these are continuously moved to expose the whole cylindrical surface to the jets. At the same time, decayed wood is removed. According to the moving arrangements several variants of the hydraulic debarkers are discriminated, suited to different dimensions of logs, etc. The mechanical friction debarkers of single-log type consist of a feeding arrangement and a rotating device, encircling the log cross section and tearing off the bark by pressing iron bars or chains against the log surface. Such are the *Åström* and *Andersson* debarkers and their modern variants the *Sund* and *Cambio* debarkers. These also appear as movable equipment for use in the forest. Knife debarkers make the cleanest logs but cause the highest wood losses, up to 15–20% on careless operation, and are therefore avoided in modern mills. Mechanical devices for knot-removal, etc., are also omitted today.

When leaving the debarkers, the logs are inspected and returned for renewed treatment if the debarking is considered insufficient. Wood species behave very differently in the debarking department. Softwoods are generally easier to debark than hardwoods. Of the latter, ash and some American gumwoods are especially difficult. Crooked wood, as is frequent with some hardwoods, behaves badly in most types of debarkers and some species should preferably be peeled by hand in the forest while still green, an operation which is facilitated during the sapping period. When the wood is allowed to dry with the bark on, barking can be extremely difficult, whereas a moist storage of unbarked wood facilitates the barking through microbiological action (19a). Bark of frozen wood is often particularly difficult to remove. Although still important for the cleanliness of the pulp, the barking operation has become less critical than before through the modern methods of pulp cleaning and it is often astonishing to see how much bark can be tolerated on the logs going to the chippers without showing up in the final pulp. Unbleached sulfite pulp for transparent papers is the grade which is most sensitive to the barking operation, whereas for bleached grades, especially where chlorine dioxide is used, the bleaching cooperates with screening and pulp cleaning in removing bark specks. In some cases, debarking is entirely omitted, e.g. often in the production of unbleached kraft or neutral sulfite pulp for paper boards or of defibrator pulp for construction board.

The disposal of bark is sometimes a definite problem, especially with species with thick bark, such as Douglas fir, where a 30 cm layer is not unusual. For many species the bark constitutes 10–20% of the total volume. It is usually burned, but where the logs have been handled wet, it is necessary first to compress the bark and sometimes to dry it also. Development work has been devoted to the utilization of bark for other purposes and some products are on the market (42).

The purpose of *chipping* is to reduce the logs to wood fragments of a size which facilitates the penetration of the cooking liquor in the chemical and semichemical processes. Mechanical pulping of chips may also become of importance, whereby the ease of water penetration into the wood may be of significance for the pulping result. Wood chips form a fairly free-flowing bulk material, which is comparatively easy to transport, pneumatically or on belt conveyors, and to store. The wood arrives at the chipper in the form of whole logs or slashed bolts, in diameters up to about 1 m. Larger dimensions have to be sawn, or parted in a *splitter* of special construction. The chips are obtained with a length of 15–25 mm, about the same width, and a thickness of 2–4 mm.

The principal construction of a *chipper* is shown in Figure 5.1 (cf. 50, 65).

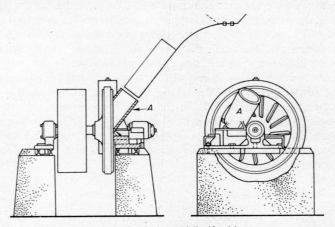

Fig. 5.1. Carthage multiknife chipper

The log is fed via a chute and a spout to a heavy, vertically rotating disk, equipped with radial knives to cut and shear the wood to chips, which then pass through slots behind the knives and are blown through a pipe to the screening department. The spout ends in a bed knife fixed at the stationary housing opposite the knifed side of the disk, to keep the log in position for chipping. By adjusting the knives, the size of the chips can be regulated. There is a variety of chipper types, which will not be described in detail here. Their capacities range from 5–200 t/h. The original chippers had

266

few, generally four, knives. In order to increase the capacity without increasing the speed of rotation, the *Ottersland* (Carthage) and similar chippers were constructed with ten or even more knives. If two knives work simultaneously on the same log, the log is moving more steadily down the spout, and the chip uniformity is improved. However, with normal-dimension pulpwood, this is not generally realized even with multiknife chippers. The *Norman* (Carthage) chipper is especially designed to ensure that each knife pulls the log in at the correct rate to get it in the proper position for the next knife. Therefore, the disk surface is made helicoidal and the bevel of the knives adjusted according to its radial distance from the axis of rotation. In all chippers, the action is so fast, that the log does not move by gravity but is pulled towards the disk by the knives. Therefore, it is not necessary for the logs to be dumped by a more or less vertical feed, since they can also be fed horizontally by a band or roller conveyor. This is the case with the *Hansel* (23a) and the *Söderhamn* chippers and other similar designs. Thus the impact of the falling log against the chipper is eliminated.

In the *screening department*, the chips are fractionated by screens, which are either *inclined stationary*, *rotary*, *gyratory* or *vibratory*. This operation is performed to separate oversize chips and slivers, which would be unsatisfactorily penetrated by cooking liquor and might also cause mechanical trouble, e.g. in continuous digester machinery. Likewise, an undersize or sawdust fraction is removed, which is enriched in bark fragments and resin duct tissues. The oversize fraction is returned to screening via a *chip crusher*, usually a hammer or pin mill, or returned to the chipper, sometimes to a special inlet. It does not therefore represent any wood loss, whereas the sawdust fraction, 1–3% of the wood, is normally sent to the boiler house for burning. With increasing wood prices, many mills have preferred to keep the sawdust in the chip fraction accepted for cooking, although it gives an inferior pulp in lower yield than the main fraction. With improved chipper designs, it has also been found possible to reduce the oversize fraction so that the chip screening department can be omitted. The chips are then conveyed directly to storage in *silos* or *bins*, from which they are charged to the digesters. Chip silos are large constructions in concrete or tiles, storing wood chips for about one shift. Screened chips are introduced at the top and leave by a discharge mechanism at the bottom. The silos are cylindrical or parallelepipedal with steeply sloping bottom walls. It is important that the construction of the silo eliminates arching of the chips, and asymmetrical design is preferred in some constructions. A rotating distributor at the top serves to make an efficient use of the top volume. The discharge consists of a movable screw or a rotating disk. The discharge mechanism and adjoining conveyors are controlled from the digester house for starting and stopping according to consumption. The packing density of the wood chips depends on the basic density of the wood, the chip dimensions, the moisture content and the distributing device. A normal figure is about 0.15 t/m³ o.d. wood with moderate packing. Two examples of the wood

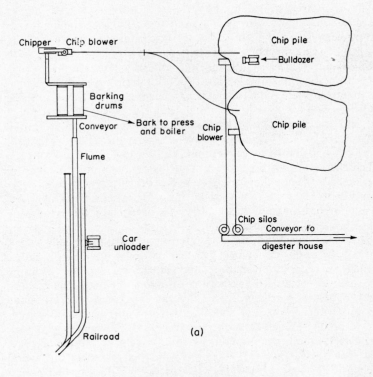

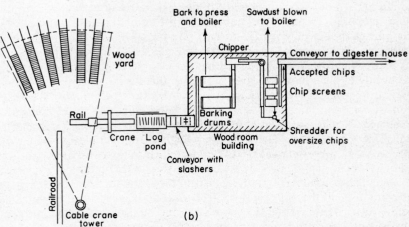

Fig. 5.2. Wood handling. (a) Wood handling system with chip storage (no debarking in the forest). (b) Wood handling system with log storage (peeled or strip barked in the forest)

handling from arrival at the mill to the delivery of screened chips are shown in Figure 5.2.

The degree of perfection of the *chipping operation* not only determines the size uniformity of the chips, but also the quality of the normal-sized chip. This quality noticeably influences the pulp quality, especially in the sulfite process. In order to understand the mechanical damage of the wood on chipping, some details in the chipping operation must be considered. Figure 5.3 shows how the knife acts on the log. After an initial cutting,

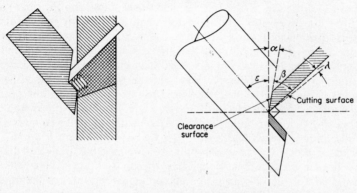

Fig. 5.3. Details of wood chipping. (a) Cross section of log, disk and knife in the moment of chipping (Samson). (b) Cross section showing clearance angle α, sharpness angle β, spout angle ϵ and complementary angle λ to log and cutting surface (Hartler)

the knife blade applies a shearing force in the longitudinal direction of the wood. In the first instance, the wood is compressed behind the cut, but as the blade moves downwards, the forces applied in the deformed region become sufficiently high, and the wood yields along an area perpendicular to the knife, and a chip is formed. Obviously, prior to this moment, the wood has commenced to yield at several planes above the final plane of failure, giving one end of the chip a broomed profile, shown in Figure 5.4.

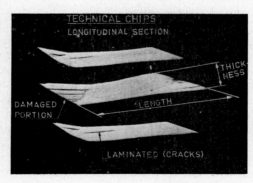

Fig. 5.4. Profile of chips (Hartler)

269

The other end has not been subjected to the shearing forces but is clean-cut. Obviously, the *thickness* of the chips must be related to the shearing forces needed for the wood to yield, and as they should be roughly proportional to the area of failure, the thickness must also be related to the chip *length*. Generally, the thickness is 15–20% of the length (49). The strength of the wood structure must also play an important rôle, and the denser hardwoods often tend to give thicker chips at identical chip length compared with softwoods. Finally, it is obvious, that the steeper the angle for the log, the larger is the shearing force component working in the longitudinal direction of the log. A steep chip angle should thus mean a thin chip. However, this angle is determined not only by the spout angle (which is optimal at around 37°) but also by the log diameter, as long as only one knife at a time cuts at the log. Unless the disk is shaped helicoidally, the log is raised against the disk in the cutting to an extent determined by the log diameter (61). Furthermore, the distance between the knives varies with the distance from the axis of rotation. The geometry of the cutting, and the effects of spout angle, knife sharpness angle and clearance angle, have been studied in detail with reference to chip dimensions and chip damage (24a).

The shear rates involved in chipping are considerable (61). The diameter of the chipper disks is 2–4 m and the speed of rotation 200–500 r.p.m. A normal case of 250 r.p.m. at a distance from the center of 0.8 m gives a knife speed of about 20 m/sec and a shear rate of about 100 m/sec, as the shear force has to move about five times the distance of the knife. The speed of the chip formation is 5,000–10,000 a second, at a thickness of 2–4 mm. Assuming the modulus of shear for wood to be 60 kp/cm², the shear work required for the chipping has been calculated (61) to be about 360,000 kpm/m³ solid wood, or 1 kWh/m³, largely independent of the chip length. This is about 60% of the total energy required for the chipping, the remainder being composed of the cutting action, the friction of wood to spout and disk, the disintegration and transport of the chips in the chipper hood, etc. The considerable noise around a chipper tells a loud story about energy lost in the impact of the logs on the disk, at a frequency corresponding to the passage of one knife through the log. Together with energy losses in transmissions and motors this makes a total energy consumption of about 2.5 kWh/m³ solid wood or 6–7 kWh/t (15, 24, 61). The total energy consumption is related to the chip length, shorter chips requiring more energy (49). Wood moisture has less influence, but wet wood consumes somewhat less energy than dry wood (49). The wear of the knives is considerable, and they should be changed for sharpening every 4 or 8 h. Dull knives exert an increased crushing action on the wood, resulting in increased dust fraction and lower quality of the accepted chips (15). There is a direct correlation between energy consumption and wood density, the former increasing, when based on solid volume, somewhat more than in proportion to increased density. The energy consumption based on the weight of wood thus increased from 3.2 kWh/t at density 0.35 to 4.5 kWh/t at density 0.7 for an experimental chipper (49).

270

A large literature exists on the *influence of chip size and chip damage on the pulping result*. It will be surveyed here, and again from somewhat different aspects in later chapters on chemical pulping. As the main purpose of chipping is to ensure that all wood is penetrated by cooking liquor, the first question is how large chips can be tolerated to fulfil this requirement. The answer is that the type of cooking liquor and the method of impregnation greatly influence the result. In alkaline pulping liquors, where the rate of penetration is about equal in all directions of the wood, the chip *thickness*, being the shortest pathway, will be the critical measure. In neutral and acid pulping liquors, the main penetration will occur longitudinally, and thus chip *length* will be critical. As chip length and thickness are interdependent in the conventional chipping, the chipping problems become fairly similar with all pulping processes. The methods of impregnation have been gradually improved, a combination of steaming and pressure impregnation being among the most efficient (cf. Chapter 6.III). Such methods obviously allow larger chip dimensions than can be tolerated without special precautions for good penetration. Investigations (4, 10, 24, 36, 48, 52) seem to indicate, that with perfect impregnation methods, chips 5–7 mm thick and 45–50 mm long would be the largest tolerable (45). The normal average size, however, is 2–4 mm and 15–25 mm respectively, in order to limit the oversize fraction and to allow for less perfect impregnation methods in practical operation. Failure to effect a satisfactory impregnation in the pulping leads to inferior quality and increased pulp screening rejects.

The second question to be answered is how *small* the chips can be tolerated from operational and qualitative standpoints. As was pointed out earlier, the energy consumption will increase, and hence the capacity of the chipper decrease, on decreasing the chip size, which gives a minimum chip length for a given equipment. The sawdust fraction will likewise increase with a decrease in chip length (49). From a qualitative standpoint the extent of *fiber cutting* and *compression damage* done by the chipping need to be considered. As the relation between resulting fiber length (x), initial fiber length (l) and the chip length (L) is theoretically given by the formula $x = L \cdot l/(L + l)$ (45, 61), as illustrated in Figure 5.5. obviously short-fibered hardwood can be chipped to a shorter chip length than softwoods, before fiber cutting becomes excessive. This is in agreement with the desire to counteract the tendency for hardwood chips to become thicker than softwood chips, and hardwoods are sometimes chipped to 10–15 mm length, where operations allow separate chipping of hardwoods and softwoods.

In practice, the effect of fiber cutting is overshadowed by the compression damage done by the chipping, and it was demonstrated (45) that the decrease in average pulp fiber length with decreasing chip length is steeper than indicated by the theoretical formula. Serious degradation seems to take place in the chip length range of 12–6 mm for mechanical chips (45), whereas the pulp quality remains unaffected in the same chip length interval for hand-cut chips (1, 23). When wood is *compressed*

271

longitudinally, but not so transversally, cracks occur in the wood structure (40, 68). The fiber walls are thereby damaged, the S1 and S2 lamellae separate, and the latter is exposed to chemical attack during subsequent pulping (35). Sulfite pulp fibers from damaged wood swell unrestricted by the S1 influence, which normally causes the well-known ballooning (68). It is likely that the compression damage is not restricted to the separation of S1 from S2 only, but that distortions occur in S2, which cause an increased accessibility of the whole fiber wall at the place of the damage (24a). Springwood suffers somewhat more than summerwood (24a). The effect is still more pronounced at elevated temperatures (6, 35), though

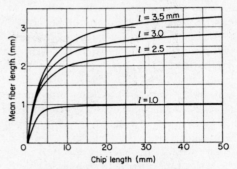

Fig. 5.5. Theoretical relation between the resulting mean fiber length (x), the native fiber length (l), and the chip length (L), according to the formula $x = L \cdot l/(L + l)$ (Samson)

less so than in the 5–50°C interval (24a). Dry wood is less susceptible to damage than is wet wood (24a). The damage results in greatly reduced paper strength properties of especially sulfite pulps but in extreme cases also of kraft pulps (11a), and the compression damage caused by chipping was early found to have that influence (1, 6, 21, 22, 49, 60). Investigations on softwood chips (25, 49, 68) have compared the paper strength of pulps prepared from the clean-cut and broomed halves of the chips respectively and from hand-cut laboratory chips, as well as from wood blocks subjected to direct compression. A strength reduction of 0–3% was found for kraft pulps, 6–12% for bisulfite pulps and 7–9% for acid sulfite pulps when comparing the whole mechanical and laboratory chips, and about twice the difference when comparing the two halves, the better of which was equal in quality to that of laboratory chips. Similar effects have been found for hardwoods (57). The chip damage causes a reduction in the strength of individual sulfite pulp fibers by 20% on average (25), whereas the bonding strength appears unaffected (24a).

These observations have long been a challenge to chipper constructors, and recently a different principle has been applied, which seems to eliminate a considerable part of the damage done in the conventional chippers. In principle, the least *cutting* energy is required if the *plane of cutting* is parallel to the fiber direction and the *direction of cutting* perpen-

272

dicular to the fiber direction (33). However, they have met with considerable difficulty in constructing a cutter of large capacity that will deliver chips of desired dimensions. Some cutter designs are in operation for particle boards, and the *Guillet* cutter was developed to deliver very thin chips for nitric acid pulping according to the *Delbay* process. It seems to be best suited for a particle thickness below 0.5 mm, which on conventional pulping yields an inferior quality (24).

The *Anglo* drum chipper (40), Figure 5.6, consists basically of a rotating drum with grooving tools to cut transverse grooves of a fixed depth into the wood, and trailing lateral blades to slice the wood between the grooves.

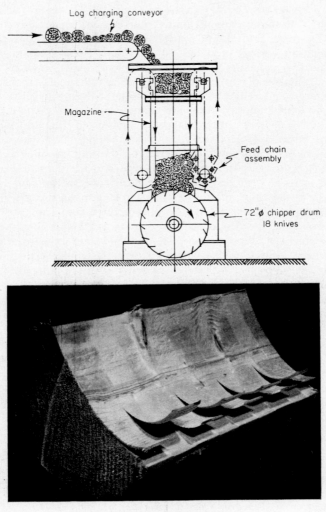

Fig. 5.6. Drum chipper (Logan)

273

Commercial units have 12 or 18 equally-spaced cutting assemblies mounted in the periphery of the drum. Both drum ends are open and permit the chips to escape. The logs are fed from above lengthwise on to the drum surface as in a magazine-type grinder (cf. Chapter 7) with a similar pair of travelling chains on two sides of the magazine. Modifications of the feeding principle, as with grinders, are conceivable. The chip length depends on the spacing of the cutting tools, the thickness on the height of the tools above the drum surface. Knots are sliced in the same manner as the main part of the wood and do not appear after the cooking as is the case with conventional chipping. This represents a saving of about 2–3% of the wood. The uniform chip dimensions allow a uniform penetration and cooking, which in itself means an improvement in quality. However, the greatest advantage lies in the absence of compression damage, which allows the production of stronger sulfite pulp. Experiments and production control figures indicate an improvement of at least 10% on most strength characteristics, and not far from equality with pulps from hand-made chips. A special investigation revealed that a compressive deformation of less than 1.5% can be tolerated to achieve such results. The different principle of chip preparation is also reflected in the low energy consumption, about 2 kWh/t as compared to 6–7 for ordinary chippers, and in the comparatively silent operation. Drawbacks experienced so far are the need of a special feeding device, the need of uniform bolt length, and the chip handling problems. The chips tend to arch in the silos and bins and the digester packing is decreased by about 10%. This may be partly due to the comparatively large width of the chips, often exceeding the length considerably. A mild disintegration subsequent to the chipping may be sufficient to overcome this. In any case, the Anglo chipper represents a major contribution to the development of chippers, especially for the sulfite industry. For kraft pulping, some interest in the chipper may arise from the possibility of increasing the pulp yield without extra troubles in the pulp screening, as the uniformity in thickness will result in low screenings. This goal is achieved also by hammermilling or passing chips through toothed disk refiners (51, 71), but with greater danger for the pulp quality, as excessive wood damage will also be reflected in the kraft pulp quality.

Another principle for avoiding the compression damage, which promises to give a similar improvement in sulfite pulp strength to the drum chipper, is the *Hartler* chipper (24a). This is of conventional design, but with the spout moved upwards on the chipper to give a shear mainly perpendicular to the fiber axis, thereby nearly eliminating compression in the longitudinal direction (24a).

REFERENCES

1. Anderson, C. A., *Pulp Paper Mag. Can.*, **47,** No. 1, 43 (1946); *Paper Mill News*, **67,** No. 40, 16 (1944).
1a. Annergren, G. E., *et al, Svensk Papperstid.*, **67,** 125 (1964).
2. Arend, J. L., *Pulp Paper Mag. Can.*, **53,** No. 7, 159 (1952).

3. Arnborg, T., *Svensk Papperstid*, **61**, 611, (1958).
4. Backman, A., *Paperi Puu*, **28**, 200 (1946).
5. Berklund, B. L., *Tappi*, **40**, No. 3, 180 A (1957).
6. Bildt, O., *Svensk Papperstid*, **41**, 261 (1938).
6a. Bois, P. J., *et al.*, *Tappi*, **45**, 609 (1962).
7. Björkman, E., *Skogen*, **41**, 356 (1954).
8. Brecht, W., *Tappi*, **42**, 664, (1959).
9. Bromley, W. S., *Paper Trade J.*, **131**, No. 18, 18 (1950).
10. Cable, D. A., *et al.*, *Tech. Assoc. Papers*, **10**, 26 (1927).
11. Callin, G., *Svensk Papperstid*, **53**, 51 (1950).
11a. Cowan, W. F., *Tappi*, **42**, 152 (1959).
12. Dadswell, H. E., and A. B. Wardrop, *Pulp Paper*, **33**, No. 4, 117 (1959).
13. Dorman, K. W., *Heredity Variations as the Basis for Selecting Superior Forest Trees*, U.S. Forest Service, Southeast Forest Expt. Station, **15**, 1952.
14. Easley, L. T., *Seed Orchards and Seed Production at Westvaco*, Report 2nd Southern Conf. on Forest Tree Improvement, U.S. Forest Service, Atlanta, Ga., 1953.
15. Edwardes, V. P., *Tappi*, **37**, 300 (1954).
16. Eklund, R., *Paperi Puu*, **34**, 429 (1952).
17. F.A.O., *Chile, Potential Pulp and Paper Exporter*, United Nations, Santiago 1957, p. 69.
18. F.A.O., *Eucalypts for Planting*, F.A.O. Forestry and Forest Products Studies, No. 11, Rome 1955.
19. Ference, G. M., and T. L. Gilles, *Tappi*, **39**, 406 (1956).
19a. Gläser, H., *Papier*, **14**, 710 (1960).
20. Glennie, D. W., and H. Schwartz, *Paper Ind.*, **34**, No. 6, 738 (1952).
21. Green, H., and F. H. Yorston, *Pulp Paper Mag. Can.*, **40**, No. 4, 244 (1939); **41**, No. 2, 123 (1940).
22. Grögaard, L., *Svensk Papperstid*, **49**, 271 (1946).
23. Hägglund, E., *Svensk Papperstid*, **41**, 194 (1938).
23a. Hansel, S., *Papier*, **14**, 56 (1960).
24. Hartler, N., *Svensk Papperstid*, **64**, 101 (1961).
24a. Hartler, N., *Svensk Papperstid.*, **65**, 351, 397, 475 (1962); **66**, 443, 526 (1963).
25. Hartler, N., *et al.*, *Svensk Papperstid.*, **63**, 263, 279 (1960); **66**, 309 (1963).
26. von Heideken, F., I.V.A. (Stockholm), **28**, 36 (1957).
27. Hiley, W. E., *Conifers, South African Methods of Cultivation*, Faber & Faber, London 1959.
28. Hilf, H. H., *Papier*, **4**, 1 (1950).
29. Jayne, B. A., *Tappi*, **41**, 162 (1958).
30. Johnsson, H., *Hereditas*, **31**, 411 (1945); *Z. Forestgenetik*, **2**, 73 (1953); *Svensk Papperstid.*, **58**, 165 (1955).
31. Joransson, P. N., *Tappi*, **42**, 691 (1959).
32. Kilander, K., *Tekn. Tidskr.*, **89**, 541 (1959).
33. Kivimaa, E., *Holz RohWerkstoff*, **10**, 94 (1952).
34. von Koeppen, A., and L. Sitzman, *Australian Pulp Paper Ind.*, *Tech. Assoc. Proc.*, **8**, 264 (1954).
35. Lagergren, S., *et al.*, *Svensk Papperstid.*, **60**, 632, 664 (1957).
36. Laroque, G. L., and O. Maass, *Can. J. Research*, **15 B**, 89 (1937).
37. Leijonhufvud, A. C : son, *Svensk Papperstid.*, **58**, 383 (1955); *Norrlands Skogsvårdsförbunds Tidskr.*, **1958**, 101.
38. Le May, P. V., *Pulp Paper Mag. Can.*, **50**, No. 10, 158 (1949).
39. Lindgren, R. M., *Tappi*, **36**, 260 (1953).

39a. Lindgren, R. M., and W. E. Eslyn, *Tappi*, **44**, 419 (1961).

40. Logan, K. C., *et al.*, *Pulp Paper Mag. Can.*, **61**, No. 11, T 515 (1960); cf. *Paper Trade J.*, **144**, No. 39, 44 (1960); *Pulp Paper Int.*, **13**, 34 (1961).

41. Love, D. V., *Pulp Paper Mag. Can.*, **59**, No. 10, 188 (1958).

42. Marian, J. E., and A. Wissing, *Svensk Papperstid.*, **58**, 745 (1955); **60**, 348 (1957); **62**, 187, 225 (1959).

43. McColl, B. J., *Pulp Paper Mag. Can.*, **51**, No. 5, 128 (1950).

44. McGovern, J. N., *et al.*, *Proc. Forest Products Research Soc.*, **5**, 169 (1951).

45. McGovern, J. N., and G. H. Chidester, *Paper Trade J.*, **98**, No. 18, 41 (1936).

46. Mitchell, H. L., *U.S. Dep. Agr.*, *Forest Prod. Lab. Rep.*, No. 1993 (1954).

47. Mitchell, H. L., *Tappi*, **39**, No. 1, 26 A (1956).

48. Morgan, H., and H. P. Dixson, *Tech. Assoc. Papers*, **21**, 364 (1938).

49. Murto, J. O., *et al.*, *Selluloosanpuun Lastatus I—V* (Chipping of Pulpwood), Rept. from the Central Laboratory, Helsinki, 1951.

50. Nepenin, N. N., *Chemie und Technologie der Zellstoffherstellung*, Germ. Ed., Vol. 1, Akademie-Verlag, Berlin 1960, p. 93 ff.

51. Nolan, W. J., *Tappi*, **40**, 170 (1957).

52. Nolan, W. J., and W. F. Brown, *Tappi*, **35**, 425 (1952).

53. Northeast Pulpwood Research Center, Gorham, N.H., 1951. *The Chemical Killing of Trees to Facilitate Bark Removal.*

54. Nylinder, P., and E. Hägglund, *Medd. Statens Skogsforskningsinst.*, **44**, No. 11, Stockholm 1954.

55. Paul, B. H., *J. Forestry*, **29**, 784 (1931); **37**, 478 (1939); **48**, 175 (1950).

56. Perry, T. O., and W. C. Wu, *Tappi*, **41**, 178 (1958).

57. Pettersson, S. E., and S. A. Rydholm, *Svensk Papperstid.*, **64**, 4 (1961).

58. Rothrock, C. W., *et al.*, *Tappi*, **44**, 65 (1961).

59. Runkel, R. O. H., *Wochbl. Papierfabrik.*, **71**, No. 9, 93 (1940); *Zellstoff Papier*, **21**, 139 (1941); *Holz RohWerkstoff*, **5**, 413 (1942).

60. Rys, L., *et al.*, *Tappi*, **35**, 147 (1952).

61. Samson, T., *Svensk Papperstid.*, **45**, 175 (1942); *Papier*, **4**, 199 (1950).

61a. Shema, B. F., *The Microbiology of Pulpwood*, TAPPI Monograph Ser. 15, New York 1955.

61b. Somsen, R. A., *Tappi*, **45**, 623 (1962).

62. Spur, S. H., and W. Hsiung, *J. Forestry*, **52**, 191 (1954).

63. Stefansson, E., *Svensk Papperstid.*, **58**, 868 (1955).

64. Stegmann, G., *Papier*, **5**, 162 (1951).

65. Stephenson, J. N., ed., *Preparation and Treatment of Wood Pulp*, Vol. 1, McGraw-Hill, London, 1952, p. 163 ff.

66. Stockman, L., *Norsk Skogind.*, **15**, 459 (1961).

67. Stoeckeler, J. H., *Forest Nursery Practice*, *U.S. Dep. Agr.*, *Forest Serv. Agr. Handbook*, No. 110, Washington, D.C., 1957.

68. Stone, J. E., *et al.*, *Pulp Paper Mag. Can.*, **59**, No. 6, 165, No. 7, 191 (1958); **62**, No. 6, 317 (1961); *Tappi*, **42**, 51 (1959).

69. Thiesmeyer, L. R., *Paper Trade J.*, **134**, No. 11, 22 (1952).

70. Watson, A. J., *et al.*, *Australian Pulp Paper Ind.*, *Tech. Assoc. Proc.*, **6**, 243 (1952); **8**, 290 (1954).

71. Wilson, J. W., and H. Worster, *Pulp Paper Mag. Can.*, **61**, No. 11, T 524 (1960).

72. Zobel, B. J., and R. L. McElwee, *Tappi*, **41**, 158 (1958).

73. Zobel, B. J., and P. R. Rhodes, *Forest Sci.*, **3**, 107 (1956).

74. Zobel, B. J., and P. R. Rhodes, *Forest Sci.*, **3**, 281 (1957).

6

GENERAL PRINCIPLES OF PULPING

Chapters 2 and 3 described the construction elements of wood, the *fibers*, and how they form the wood structure. Chapter 4 dealt with the chemical composition of the fibers. The pulp consuming industries are based on the use of either the fibers as such, or their main constituent, *cellulose*. In both cases a *liberation of the fiber* is required prior to further treatment, and this is the primary purpose in the preparation of unbleached pulp. The secondary purpose is to *give the fiber optimal properties* for its ultimate use, to which it may come directly or after further modification in the bleachery.

To achieve these two purposes in the most economical way, a large number of pulping processes have been worked out, each suited to a special end use. In the following chapters these processes will be described in detail. As an introduction, and in order not to lose sight of the general principles of pulping because of the multitude of details, this chapter will stress what the pulping processes have in common and where they differ, and describe the laws that govern them. After a brief historical presentation and classification of the pulping processes, the treatment will start out from the raw materials, describe the strength of the interfiber bonds to be overcome in pulping, and the principles according to which they can be broken. As most pulping processes involve penetration of the wood by liquids this is discussed in a separate section. Turning to chemical and semichemical pulping, the general chemistry of the pulping reactions is treated, and thereafter the structural changes occurring in the wood during these reactions are described. The technical operations involved in pulping are then treated in a general way, followed by a qualitative and economical comparison of the different pulping processes.

I. Historical Development and Classification of Pulping Processes

1. HISTORY

The main demand for pulp comes from the paper industry, and the development of the latter gives the background to the history of pulp. *Papyrus* was the first material used for writing, as early as 3000 B.C. in Egypt. Although of plant origin, it cannot be classified as a paper in the modern sense of the word, i.e. a sheet formed from separate pulp fibers. Papyrus was made from the pith tissues of a sedge, *Cyperus papyrus*, cut in thin slices which were pressed and dried together. Another material for writing, in use before Christ, was *parchment*, or specially treated thin hides.

The first paper originates from China, according to tradition made by *Ts'ai-Loun*, a century before Christ. The raw materials were rags and plant tissues. Only several centuries later did the art of paper-making become known outside China, firstly in Japan, where paper was being made around A.D. 600 from the bast fibers of the mulberry tree. Later on, the knowledge moved westwards, and in the middle of the 8th century the first Arabian paper production started. In Europe, paper was made in Spain from A.D. 1050, in Italy from 1268, in Germany from 1390 and in Scandinavia from 1500. The raw material was generally rags, which were rotted, boiled with potash and beaten before dilution, sheet-formation and drying. Beating was done manually, later on mechanically in *stampworks*, driven by water- or windmills. The *hollander beater* was constructed in Holland shortly before 1700. The sheet formation was done manually until the *paper machine* was constructed in 1799 by *Robert* and improved by the brothers *Fourdrinier*, who installed their first commercial long-wire machine in Frogmore, England, in 1803–04. The first round-wire machine was constructed in 1805 by *Bramah*. These two types of paper machines were made fully continuous in operation in 1815 and 1820 respectively.

The increasing demand for paper through the development of printing was met by this mechanization of the paper industry. However, the problem of raw material supply became accentuated. The rags used for printing and writing paper were not to be colored, which perceptibly limited the source of raw material. This forced the development of bleaching methods. Chlorine had been discovered in 1774 by *Scheele*, its bleaching properties were realized in 1785 by *Berthollet* and its convenient application in the form of potassium, sodium or calcium hypochlorite around 1790. Although colored rags could then be used for paper production, the raw material problem was still serious. In the late 18th century, therefore, efforts were made to produce pulp fibers from wood and straw, in Germany by *Schäffer* and in England by *Koops*. Schäffer tried mechanical and Koops probably mainly chemical methods. However, it was not until 1840 that a wood grinder was constructed in Germany by *Keller*, and developed from 1846 in cooperation with *Voelter* and *Voith*, that really started the *mechanical wood pulping industry*. In 1852 two German mills were in production (Heidenheim and Giersdorf), in 1857 one in Sweden (Önan) and in 1861 a large-scale groundwood mill was erected in Belgium (Poix). In America the first experimental groundwood paper was made around 1840 by Fenerty, and in 1866 production was started in Canada (Valleyfield, Quebec). The mechanical pulping industry then developed with accelerating rate, under continuously improved machinery. In 1869 *Behrend* modified the process by a steam treatment of the wood prior to grinding, resulting in the so-called brown groundwood pulp, and in the 1880's the hot-grinding process was developed in America.

However, paper made with a considerable content of mechanical wood pulp had a low strength, especially when moist, and its yellowing in the sunlight and on storage were great disadvantages. With little knowledge of the chemistry of wood the *chemical wood pulping industry* was developed to remedy these deficiencies. Pulping of straw at atmospheric pressure in solutions of sodium hydroxide and sulfide was already in use in England at the beginning of the 19th century. The process of pulping wood under pressure in sodium hydroxide was patented in England in 1853 by both *Watt* and *Burgess*. The experiments were made on birchwood, and the first commercial mill for *alkaline*, or *soda pulping* was erected in America by Burgess in 1854, working on poplar. Alkaline hardwood pulp was found to be bleachable and had several desirable characteristics which were lacking in mechanical pulps. In 1866 the first European alkaline pulp mill was erected in England and in 1871 the first Swedish one. The method soon called for regeneration of the large quantities of alkali used, through evaporation and combustion of the waste liquors and caustization of the sodium carbonate formed. However, to cover the heavy losses of chemicals, sodium carbonate had to be added, and since that chemical was then made from sodium sulfate by the Leblanc process and was rather expensive, it was reasons of economy that caused *Dahl* in Danzig to modify the soda process in 1879 by direct introduction of sodium sulfate into the recovery system. It was soon found that the pulp quality immediately improved, because of the presence in the cooking liquor of sodium sulfide, which was formed from sulfate by reduction during the combustion. Therefore, most soda-pulp mills were rapidly changing over to the new process, called the *sulfate* or *kraft process*, the features of which were further developed in Sweden by *Müntzing*, who among other things introduced the *diffuser* for black liquor recovery. The technological development of the kraft process concentrated towards the end of the 19th century on heat economy, with the introduction of evaporation batteries, followed by disk evaporators utilizing flue gases. A further perfection of the engineering of the recovery system came with the introduction of the modern combustion furnaces by *Tomlinson* in 1927–33 and the development of the continuous caustization system and lime sludge reburning. The expensive chemicals used in the alkaline processes were an obstacle to the young kraft industry in its competition with the concurrently developing sulfite process, but this impelled the development of the technology of kraft pulping in a way that eventually has given the kraft industry a definite advantage.

In 1866 and 1867 English and U.S. patents were granted to *Tilghman* on the process of treating wood under pressure with solutions of *bisulfites and sulfurous acid*, as a result of experiments at an American soda mill. No commercial process was developed, however, until *Ekman*, chemist at an experimental pulp mill in Sweden (Bergvik), using pressure cooking of wood in water, found that the brown pulp produced could be considerably improved by adding magnesium bisulfite and excess sulfurous acid. In 1874 a small production was started and extended in 1875 to a capacity of 1,000 t/year. At the same time, *Mitscherlich* developed calcium bisulfite cooking in Germany, where the first sulfite mill was built in 1880. Ekman

279

and Mitscherlich used indirect heating, whereas a method developed in Austria by *Ritter* and *Kellner* used direct steam, in a mill operated from 1878. The first *digesters* used were rotary, and much trouble arose from corrosion by the cooking acid. Lead linings were applied in the beginning, and brick linings introduced by *Folin* at the erection of the Billerud mill, Sweden, in 1883.

In the meantime, the *bleaching processes* were gradually changing. Bleaching of rags was originally carried out in cylindrical conventional washing engines. The bleaching of wood pulp required different machinery, and *bleaching hollanders* were introduced, with the beating devices changed to the form of paddle mixers. The Bellmer bleacher was introduced in 1895 and the Wolf bleacher in 1921, allowing consistencies of 7 % and 15–25 % respectively. Bleaching remained a one-stage process until around 1920, when it was found that two-stage hypochlorite bleaching reduced the cost of chemicals. Although it was known, already before 1900, that gaseous chlorine could be used to remove lignin from vegetable materials, it did not become evident until around 1915 that chlorination, followed by alkali treatment, could possibly reduce the costs of bleaching. However, only after the development of the corrosion-resistant steels that started in the 1910's, was a commercial realization of this idea possible. It was preferentially the kraft industry which could benefit from the procedure, since although it was possible to produce fully bleached sulfite pulps with hypochlorite only, kraft pulps required so harsh a hypochlorite bleach to attain a decent brightness, that most of their strength properties were lost. Around 1930 companies in Sweden (Stora Kopparbergs Bergslags AB) and America (Brown Co) were putting fully bleached kraft pulps on the market, as a result of multistage bleaching using chlorination, alkali extraction and hypochlorite bleaching. The development of multistage bleaching further motivated the development of continuous operation in *bleaching towers*, which occurred during the 1930's. The progress in bleaching during the last two decades has been characterized by the perfection of bleaching and washing equipment and the introduction of new bleaching agents for very high pulp brightness, namely peroxides and chlorine dioxide. Lignin-preservative bleaching with dithionite and peroxide is also a recent development, which has followed with the more recent developments of semichemical and mechanical pulping.

Up to 1900, the purpose of pulp production was exclusively to furnish the paper industry with raw materials. In 1892, however, *Cross* and *Bevan* discovered the xanthation of cellulose and realized the possibility of producing a regenerated cellulose fiber. The *viscose process* was developed, and in 1903 a Norwegian sulfite mill (Böhnsdalen) began to deliver bleached sulfite pulp for textile purposes to England. In 1912 several other pulp mills started to deliver rayon pulps, among them one in America (Bangor, Maine). The viscose industry expanded rapidly, 200,000 t being produced in 1930 and 2,000,000 t two decades later. During this time not only the viscose industry developed, but also the production of cellulose esters and ethers, which had started on cotton and cotton linters, gradually changed over to wood pulp. However, the dominating consumer of '*dissolving pulp*' is still the viscose industry. Until the middle of the 1930's, bleached sulfite pulp alone could be used for these purposes. Bleached kraft pulp showed deficiencies in reactivity and caused too great processing troubles in the conversion. However, some American patents on pretreatments prior to kraft pulping appeared already in 1929, and during World War II the *prehydrolysis–kraft process* was developed in Germany, with the first mill operating in Königsberg. Since the war this process, with various modifications, has been installed in Sweden and America. One of the advantages of this process is its applicability to most wood species, whereas sulfite pulping has been mainly restricted to spruces, firs and a few hardwoods.

Although the development of the dissolving pulp production had been rapid, the main user of pulp is still the paper industry, with a consumption of around 60,000,000 t/year in 1960, including also the products for the packaging industry, with various types of boards. The production of machine-dried *paperboard* in a continuous sheet started before 1900 (Lilla Edet, Sweden, 1893), and its rapid expansion came at the same time as the development of the modern distribution technique, so that paperboard production is now as large as that of paper. The production of *wallboard* and other types of *construction boards* started in England (Sunbury-on-Thames) in 1898 on waste paper, with a semihard grade. *Insulating board* was first made in America (International Falls) from 1914, on groundwood pulp rejects. Hardboard from wood chips by the *Masonite process* was produced in America from 1926 (Laurel, Miss.) and in Sweden from 1929 (Rundvik). The *Asplund process* came into commercial operation in Scandinavia from 1934, and is now the dominating method for hardboard production, which is now more than 3,000,000 t/year.

The tremendous expansion of the pulping industries as well as that of other wood consuming industries has caused a yearly consumption of wood as large as that of petroleum products or cereals, and considerably larger than steel consumption. Therefore, the raw material question has once more become critical, and the development of the pulping processes during the last three decades has been characterized by the efforts to meet the raw material problems. Thereby the kraft industry has proved to be less sensitive to the quality of the wood, as regards both species and the amount of impurities. Increasing quantities of hardwoods, saw-mill waste and forest thinnings are now being utilized by the kraft industry. The modifications required in the sulfite process to allow a broadening of its raw material base include the use of soluble bases, which has necessitated the development of regeneration systems also for the sulfite cooking chemicals. In both the kraft and sulfite industry there is also a strong tendency to decrease the wood consumption per ton of pulp to a minimum for each grade of pulp, which has led to the development of the *high yield kraft* and *high yield sulfite* process. However, the increased use of hardwoods has chiefly been made possible by the application of a number of new processes, commonly called *semichemical pulping processes*, in

281

which the high yield kraft and sulfite processes may also be included. This development was started around 1925 but required an improvement of existing machinery for fiberizing to allow a real industrial expansion, which has mainly taken place since World War II, predominantly in America. The most important semichemical processes are the *cold caustic* and the *neutral sulfite process*. The latter has also been modified to be suitable as a treatment prior to *grinding* of hardwoods, and has been called the *chemigroundwood process*. The raw material base for groundwood pulping has recently been further developed by certain additions to the grinder water to allow the use of resinous woods. Yet another remedy for the raw material problems has been the increased utilization of cereal straw and other annual plants for pulping, partly by new methods such as the *mechano-chemical pulping process*. Also the kraft or other alkaline processes are being used for straw pulping, as is the *Pomilio–Celdecor process*, already developed by the 1920's.

The combined effect of these efforts as well as those of forest management is that further expansion of the production has been and will be possible without endangering the raw-material supply. In many countries, the 1960's therefore appear to be characterized by a hunt for markets rather than for raw materials.

2. CLASSIFICATION

In principle, there are two ways of fiberizing, *mechanical* and *chemical pulping*. In the latter, substances of the middle lamella are chemically dissolved to an extent that makes fiberizing possible without mechanical treatment in more elaborate machinery. Usually the blowing of a digester or the jets of the dilution water in the blow pits is sufficient to effect fiberizing, and in the case of dumped sulfite cooks of somewhat higher lignin content a simple wooden construction, an *opener*, suffices to liberate the fibers. The chief drawback of the chemical pulping methods is of course the comparatively high wood consumption, with yields ranging approximately from 35 to 55% of the wood. Mechanical pulping gives nearly quantitative yield but causes rupture of the fiber walls on fiberizing and gives pulps which contain substances of little value for many purposes. For some uses, however, chemical pulps are unnecessarily high-grade and expensive, whereas mechanical pulps may not fulfil the quality requirements. Therefore, some dissolution of substances is required, but it is found unnecessary to cook as far as the '*point of fiber liberation*', which for most wood species and pulping processes occurs at around 55–60% yield. At higher yields special equipment for mechanical fiberizing is necessary, and processes which involve both chemical and elaborate mechanical treatment have been called *semichemical pulping*. This term is now generally accepted, although *chemimechanical* or *chemechanical pulping* were perhaps more adequate descriptions of the treatments involved. A wide variety of processes are included in this category, some of which come rather close to chemical pulping and others to mechanical.

Obviously, the borderline between mechanical and semichemical pulping depends on the definition of physical and chemical softening of the interfiber bonds, and that between semichemical and chemical pulping depends on what is understood by 'elaborate mechanical machinery' for fiber separation. For instance, in the Mason and Asplund processes no doubt chemical reactions take place, but it is doubtful whether they have any influence on the interfiber bonds. On the other hand, both processes apply high temperatures in order to obtain a thermal softening effect on the lignin of the middle lamella. They are therefore classified as mechanical pulping methods. Steamed groundwood pulp uses special equipment for heating the bolts prior to grinding. During this treatment chemical changes occur, which influence the quality of the pulp. Whether they are also important for the softening of the interfiber bonds prior to grinding, or if this is a purely thermal and physical effect is doubtful, but the equipment and operations used are so closely related to the chemigroundwood process, that steamed groundwood pulping is also classified as a semichemical process here, in contrast to the conventional mechanical hot-grinding process.

The difference between a semichemical (high yield) sulfite pulp and a chemical strong sulfite pulp for greaseproof is also diffuse. However, the former uses a modern type of disk refiner, whereas in the latter process a simple opener is sufficient. The semichemical (high yield) kraft pulps also pass through disk refiners, whereas chemical kraft pulps are defibrated during the blowing of the cook. However, the screenings of a chemical kraft cook are often passed through a refiner, and in increasing the pulp yield in a modern kraft mill considerable quantities of screenings are tolerated. As long as the whole stock is not passed through the refiners, the process is considered as chemical.

Another principle for subdivision of the pulping processes depends on the form, bolts or chips, in which the wood is pulped. Further, the chemical pulping processes can be divided into one-stage and multi-stage processes, in the latter of which two or more distinct stages of different chemical treatment occur. Table 6.1 indicates the classification which will be followed in this book.

II. Nature and Strength of the Interfiber Bonds

One of the major objectives of all pulping processes is to liberate the fibers of the wood. Surprisingly little has been published on the nature of the interfiber bonds, and most of these studies have concerned problems of wood technology rather than of pulping technology.

The fibers in the wood are usually joined in a fairly cohesive structure (cf. Chapters 2 and 3). Intercellular spaces occur in reaction wood only, except for a few species such as *Juniperus* spp., where they may occur in normal wood. Because of the special way in which a tree trunk grows, the fibers are formed in fairly regular radial rows but the tangential order within each annual growth ring is less regular, as seen in a transverse

Table 6.1. Classification of pulping processes

Category	Pulping process	Chemical treatment	Mechanical treatment	Pulp yield, % un- bleached
Mechanical				
Bolts	Groundwood, cold	None	Grinder	93–98
	hot	,,	,,	93–98
Chips	Bauerite, Sprout–Waldron	None or bleach	Refiner	93–98
,,	Isogrand	,, ,, ,,	Defibrator	93–98
,,	Asplund	Steam	Defibrator	92–95
,,	Mason	,,	Steam expansion	80–90
Semichemical				
Bolts	Groundwood, steamed	Steam	Grinder	80–90
,,	Decker	Acid sulfite	,,	—
,,	Fish	Kraft	,,	—
,,	Chemigroundwood	Neutral sulfite	,,	80–90
Chips	Water hydrolysis	Steam	Refiner	70–95
,,	High yield sulfite	Acid sulfite	,,	60–90
,,	High yield bisulfite	Bisulfite	,,	60–90
,,	High yield kraft	Kraft*	,,	55–70
,,	Neutral sulfite, NSSC	Neutral sulfite	,,	65–90
,,	Cold caustic	Alkali	,,	80–90
Straw	Mechanochemical	Alkali or kraft*	Hydrapulper	50–75
Chemical				
One-stage	Acid sulfite (Sulfite)	Acid sulfite	Opener or none	40–60
,,	Bisulfite	Bisulfite	Opener or none	45–60
,,	Kraft (Sulfate)	Kraft*	None	40–55
,,	Soda	Alkali	,,	40–55
,,	Nitric acid (Delbay, etc.)	Nitric acid	,,	40–60
,,	Organo-solvent (dioxane, alcohols)	Acid in solvent	,,	40–60
,,	Hydrotropic	Hydrotropic solvents	,,	40–60
Multistage	Neutralsulfite–acid sulfite	Neutral and acid sulfite	,, (opener)	50–65
,,	Bisulfite–acid sulfite	Bisulfite and acid sulfite	,, ,,	40–60
,,	Neutral sulfite–bisulfite	Neutral and bisulfite	,, ,,	50–65
,,	Bisulfite–carbonate	Bisulfite and carbonate	,, ,,	40–50
,,	Acid sulfite–carbonate	Acid sulfite and carbonate	,,	30–45
,,	Acid sulfite–kraft	Acid sulfite and kraft*	,,	30–45
,,	Prehydrolysis–kraft	Acid or water and kraft	,,	30–45
,,	Carbonate–kraft	Green liquor and kraft	,,	40–55
Multistage (straw)	Celdecor (Pomilio)	Alkali and chlorine	,,	35–45

*Sodium hydroxide and sulfide.

section, Figure 2.2. A separation of the wood fibers after physical or chemical softening of the interfiber bonds therefore often starts along radial planes.

As cambial cells divide, a cell plate is formed as a wall common to two adjacent fibers, whose protoplasts eventually develop their own thin primary walls. After the cessation of surface growth the transition lamella, the secondary wall and the tertiary wall are formed. The thickness of the middle lamella in mature cells is $1-2\,\mu$ (9, 91) and that of the primary and the tertiary wall somewhat below $0.1\,\mu$ (9). The middle lamella contains mostly lignin, about 70% in spruce (12, 91, cf. 9) and probably still more in birch (91), together with carbohydrates, mainly hemicellulose with an amorphous structure; the primary wall is somewhat less lignified and contains cellulose microfibrils oriented in all directions and probably with an interwoven structure. The secondary wall, S2, between the transition lamella, S1 (113), and the tertiary wall, S3, forms the main part of the cell wall with a thickness of $1.5-8\,\mu$, thinner in springwood and thicker in summerwood fibers. The main part of the cell wall is carbohydrate with cellulose in microfibrils, which have a helical structure, and relatively little lignin. In the transition lamella this helical arrangement is rather flat and forms a crossed network at an angle of approximately 60° to the fiber direction, while the secondary wall has a helical structure with an angle that is almost parallel to the fiber direction. The inner layer of the fiber wall, the tertiary wall, borders the lumen and is fairly thin. Finally, the cell cavity, the lumen, occupies a space of $20-40\,\mu$ in diameter. The fiber structure was illustrated schematically in Figure 3.2.

Liberation of the fibers obviously requires a separation along the middle lamella or between the middle lamella and the primary wall of one of the fibers. However, as the secondary wall forms the major part of the fiber wall, the primary wall being very thin and the transition lamella relatively thin, a failure between the primary wall and the transition lamella, or between the transition lamella and the main part of the secondary wall does not lead to complete destruction of the fiber wall. As the lignin is mainly concentrated in the middle lamella and the carbohydrate in the inner parts of the fiber wall (91), the position of the failure will be dependent on the relative strength of the lignin and the carbohydrate material. Studies on the mechanical strength of wood under various conditions will give average values for the strength of wood but will tell little about where the failure occurs, and must therefore be accompanied by a microscopical investigation.

Microscopical examination after mechanical strength tests on untreated wood (50) showed that *failure seldom occurs in the middle lamella* in tensile and compression strength tests. Failure takes place instead *either across the fiber walls or between the transition lamella and the main part of the secondary wall*. Similar results have been obtained in other studies (170). Further evidence that failure in tensile strength tests on untreated wood at room temperature is to a large extent across the fiber walls, comes from the tensile strength of wood, which when recalculated to kp/cm² of cell wall is of the same order of magnitude as the corresponding tensile strength determined on single fibers (93, 109). On delignification of wood it is to be expected that the middle lamella, where the bulk of the lignin is located, will be weakened, and that failure will occur to an increasing extent in this layer. This is especially so in strength tests on moist wood, whereas dry delignified wood shows strengths the same as or higher than those of untreated dry wood (84). Obviously, in this case new cohesive forces through hydrogen bonding are formed between the fibers, which now consist entirely of carbohydrates. The failures in mechanical strength tests on these delignified, dried wood samples probably occur not only between the fibers but also between the layers which form weaker areas in untreated wood, i.e. between the transition lamella and the main part of the secondary wall. Failures across the fiber wall are also probable. The wet strength of these delignified samples is very small, around 10% of the wet untreated wood. Strength values for wood will therefore indicate either the strength of the individual fiber, the strength of the bond between different layers in the fiber wall, or the strength of the bonds between the fiber walls (the interfiber bonds), depending on the pretreatment and test conditions. Microscopical examination will show which type of failure predominates.

There are three principal ways of weakening interfiber bonds: by *temperature increase*, by *swelling agents*, and by *delignification*. The *temperature dependence of the mechanical strength* of wood has been investigated in different ways. The moduli of rupture and elasticity of pine are reduced to 70% over the temperature interval of 20–100°C (87). In a series of investigations (68) the compressibility of different types of veneers have been studied, and the changes followed microscopically. In another study on the most suitable conditions for compressed wood manufacture (144), a considerable decrease in water absorption of the product on increasing the temperature of compression from 160–175°C was found. This is valid for compression of relatively dry wood, whereas wood which is wetter shows a much less marked temperature dependence. Other properties such as swelling and residual elasticity show a corresponding temperature dependence. In studies on the *Defibrator* process, a striking decrease in the energy consumption for defibration of both softwoods and hardwoods within the temperature interval of 150–175°C was found (5). The curves given are, however, only semi-quantitative. In an investigation on the shear strength of birch wood a decrease in strength of more than 80% was found within the temperature interval of 25–190°C, the main part of the strength decrease occurring between 60–120°C (155). This study was carried out on moist wood; a corresponding investigation on dry wood showed that the decrease in strength in the absence of water was considerably less and occurred within a somewhat higher temperature range. An investigation on the tensile strength of spruce and birch wood, as well as of neutral sulfite cooked birch (89) showed a considerable decrease in tensile strength as the temperature was raised from room temperature to about 80°C, thereafter a somewhat slower decrease and then once again more rapidly in the region of 140–190°C, Figure 6.1. The neutral sulfite digested birch gave a similar S curve, although because of its partial delignification the tensile strength even at room temperature was only about 10% of that of the original untreated wood. In absolute measure the tensile strength of the neutral sulfite digested wood decreases fairly little, but relatively it goes down by around 60% over a temperature increase from 20–170°C. Refining neutral sulfite digested wood at higher temperatures should therefore give an energy saving. Obviously refining under pressure would also give an advantage to refining at below 100°C. However, chemical reactions might decrease the resulting pulp quality at high-temperature refining.

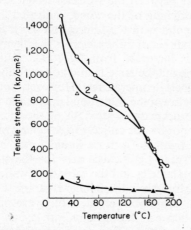

Fig. 6.1. The effect of temperature on the tensile strength of (1) water-swollen sprucewood, (2) birchwood and (3) neutral sulfite-cooked birchwood, 75% yield (Lagergren)

The decrease in the mechanical strength of wood when the temperature is raised has been explained in several different ways. The decrease within the temperature interval of 150–180°C has been connected with the softening range of lignin, which occurs in the range of 165–175°C (17, 98). The presence of water could conceivably depress and broaden the softening interval of lignin. It is also conceivable, that the decrease in strength as the temperature increases is partly due to an increased accessibility of the carbohydrates to water. Such an interpretation of the temperature effect does not, however, neglect the effect of the softening of lignin. That these factors must be taken into consideration is shown for instance by the fact that hydration of hydroxyl groups normally occurs to a larger extent at lower temperature than at high temperature. A decrease in the strength of hydrogen bonds with increased temperature might also contribute to the softening of wood. Another factor, especially at high temperatures, is probably the hydrolysis of carbohydrates.

The S form of the curves seems to indicate two different phenomena affecting the tensile strength. However, it must be kept in mind that the tensile strength, as was pointed out earlier, is a measure of the average strength of the wood, and does not give any information on where failure occurred or whether the failures are of the same type under different test conditions. Microscopical examination of the test pieces after testing (89) indicated that the failures at low temperatures occur partly across the fiber wall, and partly between the transition lamella and the main layer of the secondary wall. At increased temperatures there are in general the same areas of failure with, however, fewer failures across the fiber wall and an increasing number between the transition lamella and the secondary wall. The gradual softening of the wood, indicated by the curves, therefore seems to correspond with the impression given by the micrographs. The decrease in the number of failures across the fiber wall is most striking as the temperature is increased from 20–80°C. Failures in the middle lamella or between the middle lamella and adjacent fiber layers occur also, especially at the highest temperatures. However, this type occurs more rarely than failures between the transition lamella and the main part of the secondary wall. The decrease in strength of the interfiber bonds in the 160–180°C range cannot be due entirely to softening of the middle lamella by the transition of lignin to a more liquid form, but softening of the lignin has probably some significance also for the strength of the bond between the transition lamella and the secondary wall. The importance of lignin for the tensile strength in these inner layers of the fiber wall might be largely due to its hydrophobic effect, which prevents the water from weakening the force between the carbohydrate layers.

The possibility of irreversible changes, which may occur at high temperatures, cannot be neglected in temperature dependence of the strength of wood. A hydrolysis reaction might be suspected as contributing to weakening of the interfiber bonds in the temperature range 150–190°C. Normal temperature for prehydrolysis cooks in water is 160–180°C. However, prehydrolysis cooks are carried out for relatively long times, 0.5–1 h, at maximum temperature, while the strength tests involve treatment for about 1 minute at maximum temperature with a very rapid heating period. The *Defibrator* process gives a yield of about 95% and involves treatment of the wood at about 180°C for 1 minute. The high yield of that process indicates that dissolution by hydrolysis is not important under similar conditions. On the other hand, hydrolytic reactions in the fiber boundary layers may decrease the strength even when there is no dissolution of material. Reversibility tests (89, 155) indicated that especially in the case of birch, irreversible changes occur above 170°C. These may be of both physical and chemical nature. The strength decrease on heating up to around 170°C is, however, largely reversible.

The gradual softening of the wood at increased temperature might also have some consequences in the chemical pulping processes. The penetration of the cooking chemicals into the layers to be delignified might be facilitated by an increase in temperature. The impregnation period, which is considered essential for sulfite cooks, may be connected with this softening of the wood by water at elevated temperature. Further softening of the wood will take place during the impregnation period, both by dissolution of material and since reactions with the lignin will make it more hydrophilic.

Another way of weakening the interfiber bonds without dissolution of the lignin is by *swelling agents*. The modulus of rupture for a series of different wood species on treatment with acids and alkalis has been studied (120). While treatment with acids in most cases does not produce any large decrease in strength, swelling in an alkaline medium, especially sodium hydroxide, gives a very considerable decrease in strength, which is related to the alkali concentration. For instance, the modulus of rupture for hardwood decreases by 70–80% on treatment with 10% sodium hydroxide solution, whereas the corresponding reduction for softwood is 50–60%. The decrease in the interfiber bonds by swelling in alkali is probably connected with the rupture of hydrogen bonds between carbohydrates. Such bonds are broken, although to a lesser extent, by water, as shown by the dependence of strength on the moisture content of the wood (172). Treatment with cold alkali solution probably also softens the lignin and increases the accessibility of the carbohydrate hydrogen bonds to hydroxide ions. Figure 6.2 illustrates the dependence of tensile strength

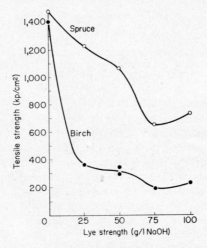

Fig. 6.2. The effect of cold caustic swelling on the tensile strength of spruce and birch (Lagergren)

of spruce and birch wood on alkali concentration (89). It is obvious that *hardwood is decidedly more sensitive to swelling agents than is softwood,* which may be explained by the different distribution of lignin in the fiber walls. Because of the higher concentration of lignin in the middle lamella of hardwoods the remaining strength carrying layers will be more sensitive to chemicals which swell carbohydrates. Microscopical examination (89) showed that in these strength tests the failure occurs mainly between the transition lamella and the secondary wall. There was a minimum tensile strength at about 75 g/l NaOH. The alkali concentrations used in the cold caustic process are usually 50–75 g/l, higher for softwood than for hardwood (42). Only hardwood cold caustic pulps are produced commercially.

The third way of weakening the interfiber bonds is by *delignification* with different types of cooking liquors, which is exemplified in Figure 6.3 for the tensile strength of spruce and birch wood after partial delignification in kraft, acid or neutral sulfite pulping (89). The tensile strength has been

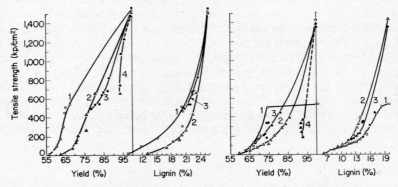

Fig. 6.3. The effect of delignification on the tensile strength at room temperature of spruce (left) and birch. Pulping processes: (1) kraft, (2) sulfite, (3) neutral sulfite and (4) cold caustic (Lagergren)

plotted against cooking yield as well as lignin content, and the tensile strength of spruce for a given yield is highest for kraft cooked wood, whereas sulfite and neutral sulfite cooked wood have lower tensile strengths of about the same order. It is also clear that weakening the interfiber bonds by the cold soda method decreases the tensile strength with a minimum yield loss. Similar results were obtained with birch, but the tensile strength for neutral sulfite cooked wood was higher than that of sulfite, and the curve for the kraft process showed a characteristic discontinuity, which depends on the greater sensitivity of birch towards swelling agents. The values for the kraft curve at around 100% yield show the tensile strength directly after the addition of white liquor and agree with the strength values for the cold soda method at a corresponding alkali concentration.

All curves with the exception of those for the cold caustic method, which does not dissolve large amounts of material, bend towards the point of fiber liberation at about 60% yield. Microscopical examination shows that at the highest yields, failure occurs to a large extent between the

290

transition lamella and the secondary wall, while after further delignification failure occurs to an increasing extent in the middle lamella or between the middle lamella and the fiber walls. This is shown especially by the curve for birch kraft, where after the first large decrease in strength on swelling the failure is mainly between the transition lamella and the secondary wall, and after a further decrease in strength by delignification to yields below 75%, failure occurs in the middle lamella to a much larger extent. The failure in partially delignified wood occurring mainly along the radial planes of the trunk, which has been shown by microscopical studies, cannot be observed to the same extent in undelignified samples. This may be due to somewhat preferential delignification in the radial planes where fiber pits are frequent.

The corresponding curves for the tensile strength plotted against the lignin content are shown in the same figures. In general, there is a very close connection between the lignin content and the tensile strength of the wood. However, comparisons between the different curves should be made with caution. The Klason lignin determination on sulfite pulps gives results which are too low (99) because of the water solubility of the lignosulfonic acids remaining in the pulp. The curves for sulfite cooked wood should therefore be displaced towards somewhat higher lignin contents. This will not affect the conclusions in the case of spruce, where the tensile strength of a kraft cook, which is considerably higher than that of a sulfite cook of a corresponding lignin content, indicates a more selective attack on the middle lamella in the sulfite process. In the case of birchwood, the results are somewhat indecisive because of the uncertainty in the lignin determination for sulfite pulps, but it is obvious that the difference between the various processes is much smaller than for spruce, which may be due to the different distribution of lignin in the wood of the two species.

The point of fiber liberation indicates the state where the wood becomes defibrable without elaborate mechanical machinery. Varying with wood species and pulping methods it occurs for spruce at a pulp yield of around 60% and a lignin content of approximately 10% of the pulp or 20–25% of the original lignin. Keeping in mind that at least half and probably two-thirds or more of the wood lignin is concentrated in the middle lamella or the primary wall, it is obvious that most of this lignin, and at the same time some of the lignin in the secondary wall, has to be removed before the fibers become easily separable. The course of reaction has been followed in the microscope by lignin-staining methods (e.g. 26) as well as by microphotographs in ultraviolet light (91), Figure 6.4, and is considered to begin in the middle lamella for sulfite pulping (91) but probably in the interior of the fiber for alkaline pulping (170a). Fiber liberation is achieved when most lignin in the middle lamella has been removed and the fibers only cling together along those edges which in transverse section constitute the corners of the cells. The edges, Figure 6.5, can be seen on the separated fibers as dark, lignin-rich ribbons, cf. Figure 3.7. The final principal distribution pattern of residual lignin of sulfite and kraft pulps is shown in

Figure 6.6. On the removal of the lignin, the fibers lose their original stiff structure and, depending on the type of fiber and the carbohydrate-swelling ability of the pulping liquor, either collapse to flat structures with only slitlike lumen (sulfite and springwood kraft), or swell to round structures with only a faint central lumen canal (summerwood kraft), cf. Figures 6.19–6.20. In the case of the semichemical pulps such changes are few.

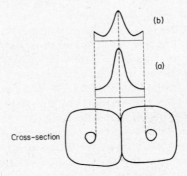

Fig. 6.4. Lignin distribution (a) across the fibers in wood and (b) after partial delignification by sulfite cooking (Lange)

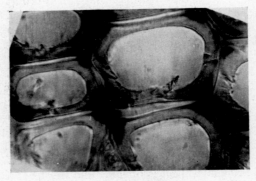

Fig. 6.5. Sulfite pulp near the point of fiber liberation. Residual lignin along the edges of the fibers still maintains the wood structure (Bucher)

The point of fiber liberation can be said to be the borderline between semichemical and chemical pulping. Apart from strength measurements, as exemplified in Figure 6.3, other methods to estimate the interfiber bonding strength have been developed, such as the *cohesive rating* method (174), which measures the amount of screenings obtained from the pulp after fiberizing the soft chips according to a standard method. The ultimate evaluation of the strength of the interfiber bonds of soft chips for semichemical pulping is the energy consumption at their

292

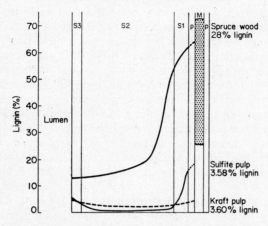

Fig. 6.6. Principal distribution of lignin across the fiber wall of sprucewood, unbleached sulfite and unbleached kraft pulp (Jayme–V. Köppen)

fiberizing. A rough correlation exists between tensile strength values and energy consumption (89), as shown in Figure 6.7. The microscopical studies reveal, however, that the tensile strength or the energy consumption cannot be taken separately as a measure of the fiber damage which must be caused by defibration. It appears for instance to be preferable to

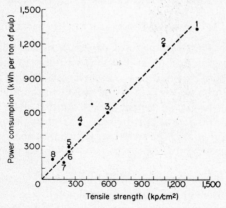

Fig. 6.7. Tensile strength compared with power consumption for some mechanical and semichemical pulps (Lagergren). (1) Mechanical refined pulp. (2) Groundwood. (3) Chemigroundwood. (4) Cold caustic. (5) Semichemical hardwood kraft. (6) Semichemical hardwood neutral sulfite. (7) Thermomechanical (Asplund) softwood pulp. (8) Semichemical softwood sulfite.

decrease the strength of the wood by delignification rather than by swelling or temperature increase if a completely undamaged fiber wall is required. Cleavage between the transition lamella and the main layer of the secondary wall may in some cases have an unfavorable effect on the strength of the fibers. It also seems probable that mechanical defibration of wood softened by temperature increase or by swelling will expose the main layer of the secondary wall to damage by subsequent chemical treatment. The desirability of homogenization of the wood by defibration before chemical delignification has been repeatedly discussed (e.g. 75, 154). The unsatisfactory results of experiments hitherto made to produce chemical pulp from such defibrated wood may be attributed to this exposure of the main layer of the secondary wall to chemical attack. The decrease in pulp quality, especially for sulfite pulp, which is found when the wood has been exposed to greater mechanical stresses before or during the cook, may also be related to this tendency to failure between the transition lamella and the secondary wall. However, in cases where the fiber properties required are different from those of normal paper pulp, the methods of weakening the interfiber bonds, leading to failure between the transition lamella and the secondary wall, may have a definite importance. Thus the cold caustic process is of increasing interest for certain grades of board and speciality papers (42, 46) and the Asplund (7) and Mason (18) processes for the production of fibers for construction boards have been definitely successful for several years.

III. Penetration of Wood by Gases, Liquids and Solutes

1. PURPOSE AND DEFINITIONS

Chemical reactions with wood are of necessity of the phase border type. To ensure uniform reaction, it is vital that all fibers in the wood get their proper share of chemicals and heat. Deficiencies in this respect show up as a higher percentage of screenings and shives in the final pulp, in severe cases colored dark-brown, a higher lignin content at a given yield, less good bleachability and end-use properties. The problem of distributing the chemicals uniformly within the wood structure in a reasonably short time is of the utmost importance for the quality of semichemical and chemical pulps.

In addition to the penetration of pulping chemicals through the wood structure at the initial impregnation period, there are also other changes needed, such as the outward diffusion of entrapped air and gases formed during the process, as well as of organic matter dissolved; and, further, the inward diffusion of chemicals throughout the cook, as the cooking liquor changes its composition through the reactions or by extra chemical charges.

One way to facilitate the distribution is to *decrease the size of the wood pieces* to be penetrated. This is done most radically by fiberizing the wood prior to chemical treatment. As was pointed out in the previous section, fiberizing of untreated wood at lower temperature consumes considerable amounts of energy, and causes rupture of the cell walls. At higher temperature power consumption and mechanical fiber damage decrease, but chemical changes in the wood components render the fibers less reactive to pulping chemicals. Further, mechanical action seems to make the wood more sensitive to subsequent chemical damage, especially in the acid pulping processes. It has been found, that not only fiberizing (75, 139), but also chipping (4, 55, 56), especially when carried out with dull knives, higher temperature (15, 59) or to smaller chip size (111), cause sulfite pulp of lower paper strength and large amounts of short fiber fragments due to hydrolytic attack, cf. Chapter 5. Alkaline processes are less sensitive, but here fiberizing or a reduction of chip length will also cause reduced strength properties. This is true, although to a less extent, for alkaline pulping of chips, reduced to match sizes with bruised ends by hammer-milling or disk refiner treatment (123). Production of very thin chips, 0.2–1 mm thick, has been suggested (35), but large-scale operation has not been realized. The drum chipper, cf. Chapter 5.II, may be a contribution in the same direction, although with good thickness uniformity rather than extremely thin chips as the aim.

Therefore, in most pulp mills, pulping is carried out on chips 15–25 mm long and wide, and 2–5 mm thick. In the very special case of chemigroundwood pulping even bolt size is used, which will obviously accentuate the penetration problem still more.

The penetration phenomena have been classified in various ways (106, 149, 157). Here, both mass penetration and diffusion will be included in the concept of penetration, which is of two types: *forced penetration*, including *gas* and *liquid flow* by an externally applied pressure differential, and *natural penetration*, consisting of *capillary rise* and of *gas, liquid* and *solute diffusion*.

2. PENETRATION IN RELATION TO WOOD STRUCTURE

The structure of wood is a complicated system of capillaries, which is different in softwoods and hardwoods, sapwood and heartwood, springwood and summerwood, normal wood and reaction wood, and different according to species (cf. Chapter 2). Normal pulpwood consists of 50–75 % of void spaces, filled up with water or air. These spaces consist, apart from greater mechanical cracks in the structure, mainly of the lumina of the cells, including the vessels, as well as some resin ducts and other intercellular spaces. Calculated on the weight of wet wood, the chips contain about 25 % moisture at the point of fiber saturation and about 67 % when completely filled up with liquor. They then contain 2 t of water per t of dry wood.

In *softwoods* most cells consist of tracheids, and the penetration occurs through their lumina and the capillaries connecting them. In the *heartwood of softwoods* these interconnecting capillaries are often closed by lignification or resinification.

The penetration of *hardwoods* occurs to a large extent through the

295

lumina of the vessel elements, which are connected to large vertical strands with few or no intercepting walls. To some extent penetration also occurs through the lumina of hardwood libriform cells which, however, can be reached only by diffusion, cf. below. In the *heartwood of certain hardwoods* tylose membranes of parenchymatic origin often enter the vessels through capillaries in the cell walls, and by filling up the vessels with bladder-like structures effectively check penetration.

Springwood with its wider lumina and thinner and more perforated cell walls is more easily penetrated than *summerwood*. *Reaction wood* and *wood knots* are denser and more difficult to penetrate than normal wood, and the knots to a very large extent appear as hard, non-fiberized structures in the pulp after a chemical cook.

The various *wood species* can be classified qualitatively according to their heartwood penetrability into four main groups, as exemplified for a number of American wood species (73). A semi-quantitative method (157), based on a large number of penetrability tests by an air-flow method, gives average values for the *penetration factor* of a number of wood species, sapwood and heartwood, Table 6.2. The penetration factor is defined as the fourth power of the radius of a glass capillary, which will

Table 6.2. Penetrability of various pulpwood species (157)

Species	Penetration factor $\times 10^{10}$	
	Sapwood	Heartwood
Picea engelmannii, Engelmann spruce	5	3
P. mariana, black spruce	—	2
Pinus contorta, lodgepole pine	300	—
P. echinata, shortleaf pine	120	5
P. elliottii, slash pine	6,000	10
P. monticola, white pine	100	10
P. palustris, longleaf pine	4,000	2
Pseudotsuga taxifolia, Douglas fir	70	5
Acer negundo, box elder	1,300	400
A. rubrum, maple	400	120
Betula papyrifera, white birch	1,300	450
Caryax spp., hickory	4,000	400
Fagus grandifolia, American beech	1,000	0.5
Fraxinus nigra, American ash	80	—
Liquidambar styraciflua, sweet gum	1,200	850
Platanus occidentalis, sycamore	4,000	4,000
Populus deltoides, cottonwood	4,000	500
P. tacamahaca, balm of Gilead	800	300
P. tremula, European aspen	5,000	4
P. tremula, European aspen triploid	1,000	2,000
P. tremuloides, American aspen	2,500	1
Quercus alba, white oak	0.7	—
Q. coccinea, scarlet oak	1,000	400
Q. falcata, red oak	4,000	5
Q. stellata, post oak	67	5
Ulmus americana, elm	400	70

permit the same rate of air-flow as one cm² of the wood in question. These factors are determined as air-flow through dry wood and swelling of wood in water may change the relative penetrabilities somewhat, but it is evident that some species are very easily penetrated in both sapwood and heartwood, others have an easily penetrated sapwood and a more impermeable heartwood, whereas some species are difficult or almost impossible to penetrate in all parts of the trunk. Penetration of softwoods is generally slower than in hardwoods, but there is no connection between penetrability and biological relationship. For instance, whereas red oak is easily penetrated, white oak is almost impermeable. Aspen heartwood is difficult to penetrate due to tylose formation in the vessels, but a triploid of the same species, without tyloses, is easily penetrated.

The great penetrability of some softwoods, e.g. slash pine sapwood, is explained by exceptionally large capillaries interconnecting the tracheid lumina. It is of interest to examine the dimensions of the capillaries involved in the penetration of wood. A tracheid fiber is approximately 3 mm or 3,000 μ long and around 30 μ wide. The diameter of its lumen is about 25 μ. The springwood tracheid cell walls are perforated on the radial sides with bordered pits, 50–300 per tracheid and around 20 μ in diameter. Summerwood tracheids have fewer pits, about 25, on both radial and tangential sides (72). The intercepts in the cell walls at the pits are funnel-like and clad with offshoots of the tertiary wall (23), which meet the primary wall and form the pit membranes together with the middle lamella and the corresponding cell walls of the adjacent cell. The pit membrane is lens-shaped, with a thicker lignified central part, the torus, encircled by a thinner zone, probably consisting of a network of fibrils, radiating from the torus, with a perforation normally 0.08–2 μ wide (96, 148). Sometimes, as in the case of slash pine sapwood, the pores are up to 22 μ wide (148), which greatly increases permeability. Also there are transient cell wall capillaries present in a tremendous number in comparison to pit pores. However, it is estimated that they account for only 0.01–0.02% of the total liquid flow from one lumen to the next (148), the main flow occurring through the pit membranes. This is probably not true for liquids with a high swelling power, such as alkaline pulping liquors.

When this capillary system is penetrated by liquid flow, the pressure drop, or resistance to flow, is inversely proportional to the fourth power of the capillary radius (147) and is hence mainly, to 99.99%, concentrated to the pores of the pit membranes. The condition of the latter is therefore important. Especially in heartwood, resin may clog the pores, and it has been shown (142), that extraction of wood with resin solvents appreciably increases permeability. It is also obvious, that the rate of flow will be much higher in longitudinal than in transverse directions, there being approximately 100 times more pit membranes per cm to pass in the latter case, as the ratio of fiber length to diameter is around 100. Longitudinal penetration has also been found to be 50–200 times more rapid than transverse flow (27, 77a, 160, 160a). The above considerations are valid for *softwoods*. *Hardwood* pit membranes contain no pores whatsoever (95), and porosity studies of hardwoods in transverse direction show practically no pene-trability (157, 158). These important observations make it likely that all penetration by flow in hardwoods occurs through the vessels, whereas the libriform fibers are closed cells, to which the pulping chemicals can reach only by diffusion. As diffusion is a slow process in comparison to liquid flow, and can only operate at short distance during the cooking times allowed, it is therefore vital for the uniformity of hardwood cooking, that the vessels allow liquid flow. Those species having pronounced tylose formation in the heartwood are thus less suitable for those pulping pro-cesses where a uniform penetration is important to the quality.

The penetrability of wood is enormously influenced by its state of moisture. With completely empty, gas-filled cavities, resistance to gas flow is at a minimum, and with completely soaked wood, the same is valid for liquid flow. The intermediate state of the capillary system, when it is occupied by interchanging gas and liquid pockets, is very resistant to forced penetration of both gas and liquid, pressures above 20 atmospheres being needed to cause flow.

3. PENETRATION OF AIR-FREE WOOD

Liquid flow in completely soaked wood blocks has been investigated for a wide range of wood species, different fiber directions, temperatures and pressures (27, 77a, 105, 141). It approximately follows the Poiseulle equation

$$\frac{V}{t} = k \cdot \frac{n \cdot r^4 \cdot \triangle p}{l \cdot \eta}$$

where the volume V flows through n capillaries of the radius r and length l at the time t if a pressure differential $\triangle p$ is maintained and the viscosity of the liquor is η. An increase in liquid temperature causes an increase in flow rate proportional to the decrease in liquid viscosity in the lower temperature range, but at temperatures of interest in pulping the increase in flow rate is higher than to be expected from the drop in viscosity. This has been attributed to changes at the pit pores at higher temperature, such as dispersion of resins in the pores. Boiling of wood in water for 12 h has the same effect on permeability as extraction with resin solvents (142). An increase in pressure differential will also increase liquid flow rate more than proportionally, which is attributed to a widening of the pit pores under the increased stress on the membranes.

Diffusion of solutes in completely soaked wood has been studied in various ways (29, 30, 103, 104, 148, 156). Alkalis, which greatly swell the wood structure, were found to diffuse with almost equal rate in all directions, whereas neutral salts and acids diffuse more rapidly in longitudinal than in transverse directions. According to some investigations the relative diffusion ratio in neutral solution is 3 (104), according to others 9 (30) or 10–12 (148) and according to theoretical calculations 10–15 (148). The diffusion rate is in longitudinal direction about half of that in water, and in transverse direction 3–6% of that in water (30, 148). The total cross-sectional area of all the capillaries controls the diffusion, and therefore the *effective cross-sectional area* is around 50% of the geometrical one in the longitudinal direction, and much less in the radial (10%) and tangential directions (6.5%). Figure 6.8 shows the change with pH in the effective cross-sectional area of aspen (156). It is seen that longitudinal diffusion is

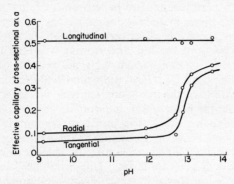

Fig. 6.8. Effect of pH on the effective capillary
cross-sectional area of aspen (Stone)

not changed, whereas there is a considerable increase in the rate of diffusion in the transverse directions in the pH range of 12.8–13.5, although not quite to the level of longitudinal diffusion rate. Hence, the diffusion of chemicals in strongly alkaline pulping liquors, such as in the kraft and soda cooks, is much more rapid than that of chemicals in acid or weakly alkaline pulping liquors of the various types of sulfite cooks. It is interesting to note that the critical pH interval is not around the pK_a value of the phenolic hydroxyls of lignin, about pK_a 10.8, but closer to the pK_a values of the carbohydrate hydroxyl groups, pK_a 13–14. Diffusion through wood is increased by the pretreatment operations (103), indicating that these change the pit membrane structures, where about 90% of the resistance to transverse diffusion is located. It must be kept in mind, that chips ordinarily have a length of 5–10 times the thickness, and consequently diffusion during a cook is to a considerable part transverse as the diffusion paths in this direction are so much shorter. Chip thickness has also been shown to be more important than length as regards the uniformity of akaline cooking (58).

Gas diffusion through soaked wood is of importance both at the earlier stages of the cook, when entrapped air escapes from the wood (126), and in the later phases of cooks with gas relief, which is normal for most discontinuous pulping processes. However, little data are available on the subject. The gas diffusion constant, D, relative to that at 0°C and 760 mm Hg, D_o, will approximately change with temperature and pressure according to the equation (149):

$$D = D_o(T/273)^{1.75} . 760/p$$

4. PENETRATION OF AIR-FILLED WOOD

Penetration in completely soaked wood may be of interest in connection with the main and later phase of the cook. However, most attention has been focused on the preliminary phase, the *impregnation period*, in which liquor charge is generally preceded by different treatments to remove the air of the chips, to permit complete penetration. Pulpwood is generally in a state of a three-phase system, wood substance, water and air, which is most difficult to penetrate. Even green, freshly felled wood contains air in the interior parts of the log, and storage will tend to decrease the water content further, to equilibrium with the relative humidity of the atmosphere, cf. Chapter 2.III. 'Dry' pulpwood will contain around 10% moisture, and ordinarily the moisture content of stored pulpwood is around 15–25%. At the *point of fiber saturation*, wood in equilibrium with air of 100% relative humidity, the moisture content is around 30%, counted on dry-wood basis or around 25% on wet wood. The cavities are then still completely filled with air. At higher moisture content droplets are formed in the capillaries. This is the case with logs which have been transported or stored in water. Such 'wet' pulpwood ordinarily holds 40–50% water (wet-wood basis). Completely soaked wood, with all capillaries filled with water, has a water content, depending on original wood density, of approximately 60–70%.

In the study of *natural liquid penetration of air-filled wood*, it has been found (149) that liquid uptake is around 100 times more rapid at 90°C than at 10°C. This is more than to be expected if capillary rise were the rate dominating process. *Capillary rise* is determined by the following law (102):

$$h^2 = r \cdot \sigma \cdot t/2\,\eta$$

where h is the rise after t seconds in a capillary with the radius r, by a liquid with the surface tension σ and the viscosity η. Obviously surface tension is the driving force in capillary rise, and addition of surface active agents, which lower σ, do not enhance penetration (112, 150). (It should be noted, that forced penetration of hardwoods, where capillary rise is less important, is improved by wetting agents (173).) However, the numerical value of σ/η at an increase of 10–90°C is only about doubled, showing that another mechanism must limit the penetration rate. The ratio of the vapor pressures at the two temperatures is about 60, and with a correction for the change in the gas diffusion constant with temperature it has been made probable that *water vapor diffusion* is the rate determining process in the penetration of dry wood (149). Water vapor from the liquid menisci of the pit pores diffuses into the air-filled cavity of the adjacent cell, condenses and allows further penetration to proceed by capillary rise until the next stop at a new pit membrane, where surface tension no longer constitutes a driving force for penetration into the next lumen until vapor diffusion and condensation have created a new meniscus there. The capillary rise proceeds rather fast, and comparison between water uptake by wood in contact with respectively, liquid water and saturated steam, shows that capillary rise must account for around 90% of the water uptake on liquid penetration (149).

The study described above dealt with water uptake by dry, air-filled wood blocks, carried to fairly low degrees of penetration. It was also shown, that when penetration is allowed to occur from both sides of the blocks, the back-pressure of entrapped air, which becomes compressed by capillary forces from both sides, soon checks the penetration.

Another study on the penetration of dry wood (175) which was carried to more complete penetration, applied pre-gassing of wood chips with inert gases at various pressures, and revealed two distinct stages of penetration, one fast mass penetration, due to forced flow and capillary rise, and a slow secondary penetration. The latter was attributed to outward diffusion of the internal gas, since the rates correlated with the molecular velocities of the gases used, and not with their solubilities in water.

It is thus probable, that the penetration of air-filled wood involves both mass penetration by *forced flow* or *capillary rise*, and penetration under *gas diffusion outwards* by air and *inwards* by water vapor. Hereby gas diffusion is the rate-limiting factor, although mass penetration accounts for the main part of the penetration.

As the summerwood lumina have a considerably smaller diameter than those of the springwood, the capillary force is around ten times greater there (72). Consequently, on the penetration of air-filled chips, the air is pushed from the summerwood into the springwood and is compressed there (72). Consequently, outward gas diffusion takes place from the springwood structure.

It is therefore most vital to *remove the air of the chips* as completely as possible in order to achieve complete penetration. Much work has been devoted to the development of suitable pretreatments. One of the simplest would be to *soak the chips in water* for a long period prior to charging into the digester. The drawbacks are that a fairly long time is needed, and hence large volumes, to achieve complete soaking, further, that soaking in water does not introduce chemicals which have then to diffuse into the water-filled chips, and finally, that much water is unnecessarily introduced into the process, affecting the concentration of the waste liquor and therefore the economy of heat and chemicals recovery.

These drawbacks are overcome by removal of the air through *evacuation*. Experiments have shown (118, 140, 149, 173) that evacuation greatly increases the penetration velocity. This is due not only to the elimination of the back-pressure of entrapped air, mentioned above, but also to the introduction of a pressure differential, which causes *forced liquid flow*, and to an increase in *water vapor diffusion* with the factor $760/p$, where p is the absolute pressure, in mm Hg, of the air in the wood after evacuation (102). Evacuation is the most efficient technique for air removal, but to achieve penetration approaching completion, it is necessary to use fairly low pressures, preferably below 40 mm Hg (106). This is impractical in

301

ordinary digester operation, especially as many digesters are not con-structed to withstand vacuum. Furthermore, evacuation is only effective in removing gas when the chips are completely dry. Air entrapped in wet chips of normal technical type resists evacuation treatment to a large extent (3, 40, 60, 173). This is due to the phenomenon that the surface tension of the interphases in the capillary system counteracts the pressure gradient formed on evacuation (118, 160a).

Another method of air removal is *replacement with another gas*, which should be soluble in the penetrating liquor. To rely on gas diffusion for this operation would be too time-consuming, and *combination of pressure variations with gas diffusion* are suggested. Evacuation to moderate vacuum, followed by introduction of sulfur dioxide (19, 106, 118) to atmospheric pressure will cause a dilution of the residual air in the cavities, and repeated cycles of moderate evacuation and sulfur dioxide introduction will remove the air as effectively as high vacuum treatment, and will require less elaborate equipment. On a subsequent liquor charge, the sulfur dioxide of the cavities will dissolve and cause the liquor to fill up the chips. Similar in action to sulfur dioxide is ammonia gas (19, 22, 54, 64, 125, 149). It is also evident, that instead of *evacuation* to e.g. 1/5 atm., followed by introduction of the soluble gas to atmospheric pressure, an *increase in pressure* by the gas to 5 atm., followed by pressure relief to atmospheric pressure, could be used with the same result. Both treatments would result in an air removal of 80% in one cycle and a total of 96 and 99.2% respectively in two and three cycles. The pressure alternative is more easily suited to existing digester house equipment. However, none of the methods mentioned above are in practical use, mainly because there are simpler methods which are as effective.

The most generally adopted of these methods is *steaming*, already suggested by *Mitscherlich*. Steaming is often started at the chip charging of the digester, when a steam chip packing device is used according to Svensson (161). This method not only secures an effective packing of the chips but also serves to expel the air of the digester and to heat the chips. After chip charging, additional steam is introduced at atmospheric or some-times higher pressure, and left on for half an hour or more. The complete function and effect of steaming is still not entirely clear, but the following concept is probable. By steaming the temperature of the digester is brought up to and slightly above 100°C. This will cause a thermal expansion of the air in the chips and a removal of around 25% of it. Further, the increased vapor pressure of water will aid in expelling the air from the chips. By the increased temperature, gas diffusion will proceed quicker, both out-ward diffusion of air and inward diffusion of water vapor. Finally, the treatment seems to affect the pit membrane pores, thereby facilitating both liquid flow (126) and diffusion (103) through the wood structure. Steaming at higher temperature is of benefit for penetration, but a practical limit is set at around 120°C (72), as a higher temperature leads to both carbohydrate hydrolysis and lignin condensation, both highly undesirable reactions in most pulping processes, and especially in sulfite pulping. In the latter case, a high steaming temperature is also dangerous at the charge of the cooking acid, because during the charge, the chips above the rising liquor level are rapidly taking up sulfur dioxide, which increases the risk of undesirable reactions highly. In general practice, only 100–105°C is maintained, and super-heated steam is avoided for the process.

A variation of the steaming procedure, which also applies the technique of pressure variations described above has been called the *Va-purge process* (65, 106, 163). Steam pressure, 0.7–3.5 kp/cm², is applied and then rapidly released, and the cycle, called a *purge*, is repeated once or twice. This is considered to increase the rate and completion of air removal in comparison with ordinary steaming. A study in the course of penetration after steaming or steam purging (175, cf. 126) has disclosed the following. The variables of importance in penetration preceded by steaming are *steaming temperature* and *pressure, steaming time, cooking liquor temperature* and *cooking liquor pressure*. An increase in steam pressure, especially up to 1.5 kp/cm² improves the result, but still more important is the duration of steaming. Figure 6.9 will illustrate this. The significance of the temperature and pressure of the liquor introduced is evident from Figure 6.10.

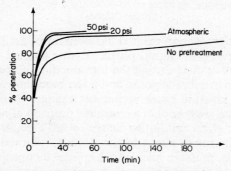

Fig. 6.9. Effect of steaming time and steam pressure on the degree of penetration after 10 min. in water at 90°C and 2 kp/cm². Spruce (Woods)

It is also seen, that there is a very rapid mass penetration, accounting for approximately half the penetration, followed by a slower penetration, which is very slow with no pretreatment, more rapid after steaming at atmospheric pressure and rather fast after prolonged steaming at higher pressure and subsequent introduction of hot liquor under high pressure. Atmospheric steaming should be carried out for at least half an hour to give substantially complete penetration, whereas steaming time at higher pressure could be reduced to 10 minutes. It should be noted that steaming time here means effective time, whereas steaming time in a discontinuous digester includes heating time to steam temperature, which is usually a considerable fraction of the total time. It was also found that steam purging will improve the result or decrease the steaming time somewhat.

303

Microscopical investigation indicated changes in the middle lamella of the purged or steamed wood. Steam purging has been found to consume rather less steam than ordinary steaming for the same air-removing effect (138).

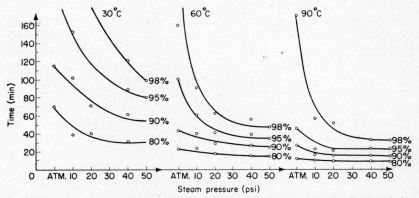

Fig. 6.10. Effect of steaming pressure (steaming for 10 min.) on the time needed for 80–98% penetration by water of 30–90°C and 2 kp/cm² hydraulic pressure. Spruce (Woods)

Recently, an impregnation method has been introduced, which employs pressure variations in the liquid phase. It was pointed out above, that hydraulic pressure applied during the introduction of the cooking liquor tends to widen the membrane pores, and it has been shown, that variations in the hydraulic pressure cause permanent changes in the permeability. The *Vilamo method* (169) applies a hydraulic pressure of about 4.5 kp/cm² immediately after chips and liquor charge to full digester. The increase in pressure should be rapid, about 10–15 seconds, followed by a still more rapid, 5–6 seconds, pressure release to 2 kp/cm² by opening the top valve of the digester. After six or seven such pressure chocks with one-minute intervals, pressure is maintained, and penetration is complete. It is easily understood, that this method is one of the simplest ways to achieve improved penetration but there are as yet little data available regarding the efficiency of the method. However, it has been shown in extensive experiments (3, 11), that the *hydraulic pressure* even without variations is, together with steaming, the most important factor for improving the penetration. Figure 6.11 (11), demonstrates this for three pressure levels, four steaming periods and six penetration periods, in the impregnation of spruce chips with sulfite cooking acid. Increased temperature of the cooking acid improved the rate of penetration up to a point where its pressure approached that of the impregnation pressure. A higher chip moisture content gave easier penetration. The optimal effective steaming period was found to be 5–10 minutes. These effects were also shown to be reflected in the screenings obtained on a subsequent acid sulfite cook with extremely rapid heating to temperature.

It was pointed out in the introduction to this section, that proper penetration is necessary to achieve a uniform pulp quality and avoid burnt chip centres, screening losses, etc. The means of achieving good penetration were originally developed to avoid troubles in the conventional methods, of which the sulfite process has always been the most sensitive. However, as the pretreatment methods have been perfected, newer features have been added to the processes. One is considerably *reduced cooking times*, as pretreatments make the special impregnation period at lower temperature less necessary. However, it must be remembered, that shortened cooking times will put increased claims not only on the heat exchangers and the digester strainers, but also on the even distribution of the heated liquor into the digester, as a uniform heat distribution is as important for the pulp quality as a uniform distribution of chemicals. Reduced cooking period is especially important in the continuous cooking, as it will decrease the size of the expensive digester equipment needed. Continuous cooking offers the best conditions for such developments, since the uniform heat distribution is realized, a high hydraulic pressure can be maintained and an efficient steaming performed.

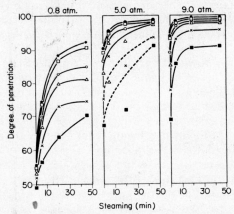

Fig. 6.11. Degree of penetration vs. time of steaming for spruce chips treated at 75°C with an acid containing 5% total SO_2 and applying a pressure of 0.8, 5 and 9 atm. (0.8 atm. corresponding to the vapor pressure of the acid). Penetration after 2 min ■, 5 min ×, 10 min △, 15 min ○, 30 min □, 45 min ● (Aurell)

Another possibility, not yet practically realized to any considerable extent, is 'vapor phase cooking', in which the excess liquor is withdrawn after the impregnation, whereafter the soaked chips with their chemicals are heated with live steam, greatly reducing the amount of heat needed, increasing the solids content of the waste liquor, and rendering quick cooks possible. A prerequisite for this type of cooking is that all the chemicals needed can be introduced at the impregnation. Therefore, cooking liquors on soluble bases have to be used.

305

IV. Chemical Pulping Reactions

The chemical reactivity of the wood components has been described in Chapter 4. Before entering into details about the chemistry of each pulping process, a survey of the nature of the reactions used in pulping is motivated, together with a discussion of their thermodynamics and kinetics.

1. NATURE OF PULPING REACTIONS

The common purpose of all chemical pulping processes is to achieve fiber liberation by *delignification*, and they can be classified according to their different ways of achieving this. The *reactions with the carbohydrates*, which occur at the same time, can from this point of view be considered as side reactions, although it must be emphasized, that dissolution of certain amounts and chemical modification of the remainder determine the quality of both dissolving and paper pulps, and are therefore controlled accordingly. In the same way the *dissolution of the extraneous components* of wood is important for the pulp quality. Finally, purely *inorganic side reactions* occur, which are of importance not only for the regeneration of the pulping chemicals, but indirectly for the reactions with the wood during the cook.

Of importance in *alkaline delignification* is the *alkaline hydrolysis of the phenolic ether bonds*, whereby lignin is rendered soluble in alkali. The rôle of mercaptation (*sulfidation*) by hydrosulfide in the kraft process is not entirely understood, but it may be both accelerating the cleavage of phenolic ether bonds and causing direct cleavage of alkyl ether bonds, as well as protecting alkali-sensitive groups from a condensation which could retard the delignification. In a similar way, *sulfonation* of benzyl alcohol and alkyl ether groups in the *sulfite process* renders the lignin water-soluble, whereafter the cleavage of the alkyl ether bonds, which keep the initially formed lignosulfonates bound to the wood, occurs by *sulfitolysis* or *acid hydrolysis*. At the same time sulfonation of the reactive groups prevents their partaking in condensation reactions. *Neutral sulfite pulping*, which involves less delignification, utilizes sulfonation of certain groups in the lignin to hydrophilic sulfonates, the dissolution of which is effected by unknown reactions, which may involve both sulfitolysis and hydrolysis. Finally, *nitration* and *chlorination* of lignin, used in some minor pulping processes, together with some *oxidation*, cause changes at the aromatic nuclei of lignin, which lead to decomposition of the lignin macromolecules to smaller fragments, soluble in water or alkali.

In all delignification, one side reaction of lignin is most undesirable, its *self-condensation*, which occurs in both acid and alkaline medium, rendering the lignin less soluble and dark in color. Improper cooking conditions may lead to excessive condensation, especially in acid pulping processes, and cause a high percentage of rejects and a bad pulp quality. *Acid condensation with other phenolic compounds*, such as pine heartwood constituents or tannins originating from the bark, seriously limits the raw material base of the conventional acid sulfite process. Even normal chemical pulping cannot entirely avoid lignin condensation, and the lignin remaining in the pulp after cooking is more or less condensed. The bleaching reactions, however, cause such degradation of these lignin molecules, that they can be dissolved.

Although in most pulp uses lignin is an undesirable or at best inert component of the pulp, no preparation of unbleached pulp aims at complete delignification. To some extent this is because the weight of the lignin in the pulp is paid for, but above all because of the unavoidable *reactions with the carbohydrates* during the delignification. These reactions become particularly serious towards the end of the cook, when the rate of delignification is slow, because of the small amounts of lignin remaining and their high degree of condensation and inaccessibility. To some extent the lignin may also protect the carbohydrates against the pulping chemicals during the earlier parts of the cook although it has been shown that cautiously prepared holocellulose, subsequently cooked by the sulfite process together with wood, gives the same paper strength as does the wood (65a). Anyway, when pulps with a high content of hemicellulose are desired, considerable amounts of lignin are left in the pulp. For unbleached pulps the upper limits are set by the brightness and brightness stability required, as well as the extent to which lignin can be allowed to impair the beating and strength properties of the pulp. In the case of bleached pulps the cost of bleaching agents is the limiting factor. The extreme example is offered by the bleached semichemical pulps, which after cooking still contain 10–15% of lignin.

The *alkaline degradation* of carbohydrates starts at the aldehydic end groups and proceeds along the chains in a sort of *peeling reaction under conversion of the sugar monomers to saccharinic and other hydroxy acids*. In addition to this reaction, which already occurs fairly rapidly at temperatures around 100°C and therefore to a certain extent precedes the delignification, at higher temperature there occurs a direct *alkaline hydrolysis* of the glycosidic bonds, which also affects the more crystalline parts of the carbohydrates. This reaction not only leads to new losses of yield by peeling reactions starting at the freshly formed aldehydic groups, but also to a shortening of the cellulose chains and a deterioration of the strength properties of the pulp. Another reaction, involving an intramolecular rearrangement, causes a *stabilization of the carbohydrate molecules under formation of a carboxyl end group*. This reaction proceeds at different rates for different types of carbohydrates, probably decreasing in the order xylan, glucan, mannan, causing the carbohydrate composition of the kraft pulps to deviate widely from that of the wood. Xylan is initially stabilized to peeling at all monomers substituted in the 2-position with glucuronic acid which, however, is also subjected to alkaline hydrolysis, thereby exposing the xylan chain to additional peeling. Several other reactions of the carbohydrates in alkaline medium occur, such as the *deacetylation* of the xylan, which seems to facilitate the adsorption of xylan molecules to the interfibrillar surfaces. Addition of polysulfide or borohydride to the kraft cook gives a reaction at the aldehydic end groups of the carbohydrates, increasing their resistance to alkali.

The main *carbohydrate reaction in acid medium* is a *hydrolysis of the glycosidic bonds*, which causes a depolymerization and dissolution of the more accessible carbohydrates, especially the hemicelluloses, and towards the end of the cook some cellulose also. The dissolved carbohydrates rapidly depolymerize to monomeric sugars and aldobiouronic acids. Hydrolysis also causes formation of methanol from the carbohydrate-bound methoxyl groups. Apart from hydrolysis, other carbohydrate reactions also occur in the sulfite process, such as the formation of *aldonic* and *sugar sulfonic acids* by the action of the bisulfite ion in substitution and oxidation reactions. These occur partly with carbohydrates in solution and thus affect the yield of by-products more than the yield and quality of the pulp, but especially in cooks with higher bisulfite ion concentration there is a possibility that the undissolved carbohydrates, even cellulose, have been oxidized to some extent. In neutral sulfite pulping, hydrolysis is suppressed by proper adjustment of pH. The actual nature and course of the carbohydrate reactions on neutral sulfite pulping is not known, although sulfitolysis and hydrolysis are the most probable reactions as well as deacetylation. However, some of the carbohydrates pass into solution in a fairly high-molecular form and precipitate from the neutral sulfite waste liquors on cooling.

The reaction resulting in the stabilization of some hemicelluloses during the kraft cook leads to pulps with good paper properties but inferior reactivity as dissolving pulps. Therefore, an acid hydrolysis prior to kraft pulping is used to degrade and partly dissolve some alkali-resistant hemicelluloses when dissolving grades are required.

The *selectivity* of the pulping chemicals with respect to delignification determines the yield of the pulping process and to some extent the pulp properties. In the sulfite process, sulfonation and acid hydrolysis contribute to delignification, and acid hydrolysis to the carbohydrate degradation and dissolution. In the kraft process, mercaptation (sulfidation) and alkaline hydrolysis contribute to delignification, and alkaline peeling and hydrolysis to the carbohydrate degradation. The delignification proceeds more rapidly in the sulfite cook than in the kraft cook, and lower temperatures can therefore be used in the former, which is fortunate because the hydrolysis of the glycosidic bonds of the carbohydrates occurs much more rapidly in acidic than in alkaline medium. Alkaline peeling reactions, on the other hand, require lower temperature than the alkaline delignification, and they unavoidably decrease the carbohydrate yield, to a degree which depends on both chemical and physical changes in their structure. Accessibility phenomena improve the selectivity of lignin removal, partly because in the early stages of the cook the morphological structure protects the carbohydrates while being attacked by the pulping chemicals, especially in the sulfite cook, and partly because some of the hemicelluloses are capable of rearrangements to a more ordered and less accessible structure during the cook. The net result of all these phenomena is that softwood pulp yields at a certain degree of delignification are about 3–5% of the wood higher for the sulfite than for the kraft process, whereas hardwood pulp yields are fairly similar. Special reaction conditions can improve the selectivity to give 4–7% higher softwood kraft and sulfite pulp yields and similar improvement in hardwood kraft pulp yields.

The *dissolution of extractives* is more easily achieved in alkaline pulping, since the main part of them is acidic. However, the extractives are also dispersed to a considerable extent in sulfite pulping. The chemical reactions between these components and the pulping liquors have been little studied, although *isomerization* and *polymerization* and possibly *sulfonation* may occur. Their dissolution during pulping is important not only because of the risk of pitch troubles in the subsequent processing and uses, but also because they suppress delignification and carbohydrate reactions in those parts of the wood covered by resinous material.

2. THERMODYNAMICS AND KINETICS OF PULPING REACTIONS

The rate of pulping is governed mainly by the rate of delignification. Of the delignification reactions mentioned above, chlorination is most rapid and occurs at a technically acceptable rate also at room temperature. Nitration is somewhat slower, but can be performed at temperatures below 100°C without overlong reaction times. However, the remaining reactions, which involve the least expensive chemicals and are accordingly the most important, unfortunately require elevated temperatures and pressures to proceed sufficiently rapidly. This causes an expensive heat consumption, expensive pressure vessel constructions, and difficulties in the construction of continuously operating machinery because of the problem of feeding chips against a reaction zone of elevated pressure.

The kinetics of soda, kraft and sulfite processes have been studied by several workers, who have determined the rate of delignification at various stages of the cook, at various maximum temperatures and cooking liquor compositions. From comparisons between the delignification rate with wood meal and chips on pulping with both sulfite (124, 137, 176) and alkali (107) cooking liquors, it is evident that diffusion inwards or outwards cannot be the rate determining factor, since the velocity is almost independent of the size of the wood particles. Furthermore, the considerable temperature dependence of delignification rate confirms that chemical reactions, and not diffusion, must be rate determining. Reaction order, energy of activation, and collision frequency constants have been calculated from the experimental data. No constant rate of reaction has been found in spite of all efforts to keep reaction conditions unchanged. The reaction velocity is found to decrease towards the end of the cook. In general, the results best agree with an assumed *reaction order* of one, although it has been shown in the case of sulfite pulping (52) that the order varies from 2 to 0, being at minimum after the removal of about 75% of the lignin. Not unnaturally, it has been found, that the kinetical data are better fitted to at least two different first-order reactions of different rates, occurring simultaneously or consecutively (47). The *energy of activation* can be calculated with a fair degree of accuracy, and for alkaline pulping is 30,000–38,000 cal./mole, the lower value being calculated from a pulping series (61) with 31 % sulfidity, typical for a kraft cook, and the higher from a pulping series with 0 % sulfidity, or a soda cook. Another investigation on soda pulping gave an energy of activation figure of 32,000 cal./mole (107). A more recent investigation on kraft pulping (88) gave 24,000 cal./mole. In sulfite pulping, the energy of activation has been found (52, 80) to be 16,000 cal./mole in the beginning of the cook up to around 40 % delignification and then to increase to 22,500 at nearly complete delignification. At the same time the energy of activation for the dissolution of the carbohydrate components is fairly constant at around 19,000 (80), 20,200 (107) or 21,000 (52) cal./mole, in a reaction of zero order. This means, that the temperature dependence of the delignification reaction in the sulfite process is somewhat greater than that of carbohydrate removal, which ought to mean that an increase in temperature should favor delignification and result in higher yields of carbohydrates. However, for various reasons, the sulfite cooks to higher yields, such as greaseproof pulp grade, are preferentially carried out at low temperature. Some results indicate, however, that rapid sulfite pulping at increased maximum temperatures will give a higher yield of dissolving grade pulps. The higher energy of activation in the alkaline delignification indicates a greater temperature dependence than in the sulfite process. On average, reaction velocity will increase almost threefold on an increase in maximum temperature of 10°C in a soda cook, 2.5 times in kraft pulping and double in sulfite pulping. For neutral sulfite pulping, it has been found necessary to fit the kinetical data to two assumed reaction courses with different velocity constants and activation energies, 35,000 and 25,000 cal./mole (47).

Table 6.3. Reaction velocities (in h^{-1}) for different pulping processes, assuming first order reactions

Pulping process Reference Liquor ratio	Soda (61) technical			Kraft (61) technical			Sulfite (80) technical	Sulfite (32) excess liquor	
Residual lignin, % of wood	2.5	5.0	7.5	2.5	5.0	7.5	2.5	2.5	5.0
Temperature, °C, 100									0.10
110							0.10		
120							0.20		
130							0.40	0.60	0.90
150			0.06	0.20	0.21	0.23			
160		0.20	0.20	0.46	0.55	0.65			
170	0.41	0.53	0.54	1.0	1.2	1.6			

Table 6.3 gives a very rough comparison of *reaction velocities* of the three pulping processes at different temperatures and degrees of deligni-

310

fication. The velocity constants have been calculated from various data on the approximate assumption of a first-order reaction. Thus the 'constants' indicate only the order of magnitude of the reaction velocities, which also vary with liquor composition (cf. (107) on alkaline and (176) on sulfite pulping). However, it is evident from the table, that sulfite delignification is more rapid and requires less high temperatures than the alkaline processes, of which the kraft process is more than twice as rapid as the soda process. Therefore, the kraft process utilizes temperatures around 170°C, whereas sulfite paper pulps are generally cooked at about 130–140°C. Hardwoods require less high temperatures than do softwoods, but mainly because of their lower lignin content and not so much because of faster reactions during the main reaction period (176). However, at the higher degrees of delignification, the lower accessibility of the residual softwood lignin, and possibly its higher degree of condensation, will lead to a greatly reduced rate of pulping. This is especially evident in soda pulping.

It has become increasingly evident, that kinetic investigations of the pulping processes only give information on the overall rate of pulping and are of little value in the understanding of pulping reactions. This is because of the heterogeneity of the system involved, which does not allow an application of homogeneous reaction kinetics. The accessibility of the various wood constituents in the native state is different, and each of the components has an accessibility spectrum. The reactivity of the components, already varying in the native state, changes during the pulping, partly because of chemical changes in the molecules, and partly because of changes occurring in the accessibility. The condensation of part of the lignin is one example, another is the transition of glucomannan to a more well-ordered structure during various types of sulfite cooking, which retards its dissolution. Glucuronoxylan degradation in the alkaline processes is limited because of partly chemical and partly physical rearrangements. The purely organo-chemical approach has therefore generally yielded more information regarding the actual pulping reactions than the kinetic investigations. The details of the pulping reactions will be treated separately for each process in Chapter 9.

V. Structural Changes of Wood on Chemical Treatment

After penetration of the wood by the pulping liquor, chemical reactions cause structural changes which eventually lead to liberation of the individual fibers. These changes have been followed under the microscope for the main pulping processes applying various techniques, such as polarized or ultraviolet light, different staining methods, and microtome cutting. This section will deal with some of the results, showing similarities and deviations among the pulping processes from a fiber morphological point of view. The structural elements of untreated wood and their detailed architecture were described in Chapters 2 and 3.

The mass distribution within two adjoining cell walls and their middle

311

lamella is given in Figure 6.12 (92). It is estimated that the middle lamella is somewhat more porous, 75–85% of the packing density of the cell wall, which is at maximum somewhere in the outer parts of the secondary wall. This is due to lignin incrustation, since the relative amounts of carbohydrates have been shown to be approximately constant throughout the cell wall (10), Figure 3.23. However, of the carbohydrates, cellulose is concentrated in the innermost part of the main secondary wall (S2), which may consist of about 80% cellulose, whereas the outer parts may contain around 70% hemicellulose, Figure 6.13. The composition of the primary and tertiary walls is somewhat uncertain, but they are likely to contain fairly large amounts of well-ordered material although xylan dominates in the tertiary wall. The lignin is concentrated in the middle lamella, which consists of 70–85% lignin (12, 91), and the outer parts of

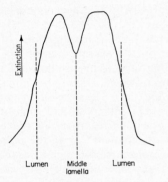

Fig. 6.12. Mass distribution within two adjoining cell walls and their middle lamella, as measured by x-ray absorption (Lange)

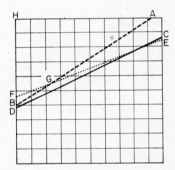

Fig. 6.13. 'Absolute' average material distribution curves for spruce holocellulose, (AB) purified by hot alkali, (EF) cold alkali, and (CD) acid hydrolysis followed by cold alkali (Lange)

the cell wall, although some lignin is incrusting throughout the fiber. About half to two-thirds of softwood lignin is located in the middle lamella and the outer part of the cell wall, in a way shown in Figure 3.22 (91). Figure 6.14 summarizes these facts schematically.

In all chemical pulping the first purpose is to remove the fiber-bonding material of the middle lamella. The other desired effects vary with pulp grade. In the pulps to be bleached especially, the lignin in the cell walls should be removed as completely as possible, and in the case of the dissolving pulps the main part of the hemicellulose should also be removed and the remaining cellulose modified. At the same time as the desired effects other structural changes occur which are undesirable, such as the partial dissolution of hemicellulose and the weakening of the fiber walls in the production of paper pulp grades and the formation of fiber fragments in dissolving pulp cooks. Therefore, although the main change

312

in wood structure to be followed is the *delignification*, the changes of the carbohydrate parts are also of the greatest interest.

The most striking feature in the structural changes of wood on sulfite pulping is that they probably start and proceed mainly from the middle lamella, although the pulping liquor penetrates the structure through the lumina. This must be due to the higher physical density and/or the chemical resistance of the inner, tertiary wall (114) as well as the porosity of the middle lamella structure (92). Anyway, it has been shown (91), Figure 6.4, that on sulfite pulping, the lignin content of the middle lamella decreases more rapidly than that of the cell walls. In the case of alkaline pulping, the selective delignification of the middle lamella has been said to be still more pronounced (16), as is demonstrated by the fact that while the lignin residues after saccharification of the carbohydrates in a kraft

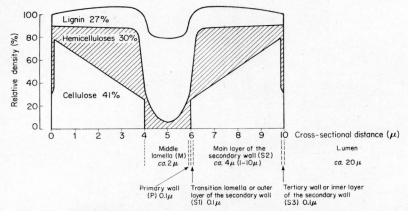

Fig. 6.14. Relative density, thickness and composition of the cell walls and middle lamella of softwoods. Schematically after (10, 91, 92)

pulp are completely structureless, those of a sulfite pulp of the same lignin content still preserve something of the sheathing structure of the middle lamella or outer cell walls (76), Figure 6.15. It has been observed, that the sulfite cooking acid predominantly causes the *radial* middle lamellae to swell, whereas the tangential planes are initially left unchanged (24). It appears that in alkaline pulping the penetration by the pulping liquor through the cell wall starts from the luminae and ends at the middle lamellae, in contrast to the observation on sulfite pulping (170a).

The sulfite pulping liquor is likely to start delignification at the bordered pits and proceed along the middle lamellae, Figure 6.16 (91, cf. however, 25). As pulping proceeds, the connections between the fibers loosen, Figure 6.17 (26), firstly along radial planes, and eventually the fibers stick together only along those edges where several cells meet, Figure 6.18, where delignification is still incomplete. Finally, after removal of most of the lignin, the fibers lose their rigidity and collapse, Figure 6.19, to flat ribbons, or swell in alkaline liquors to round structures with a very narrow

313

lumen canal, Figure 6.20. Already at an earlier stage, the cambial (primary) wall, which is fairly resistant to chemical action, is seen to lose its immediate connection with the secondary wall (16, 24, 26), the outer portions of which shrink on losing lignin and hemicellulose substance. Being very thin, and probably also brittle by chemical attack, the loose cambial wall of

Kraft

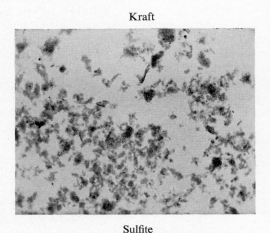

Sulfite

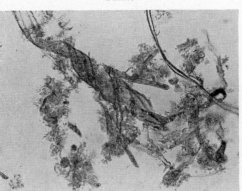

Fig. 6.15. Lignin structures in kraft and sulfite pulps after saccharification of the carbohydrates (Jayme–v. Köppen)

Fig. 6.16. Probable penetration path of sulfite cooking acid (Lange)

314

sulfite pulps easily breaks off at even slight mechanical treatment and is difficult to discriminate from other cell wall fragments (26). However, electron micrographs have shown the presence of primary wall fragments even in commercial bleached sulfite pulps of dissolving grades (162). The cambial wall of kraft pulps may be somewhat less destroyed (16, 51).

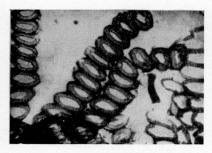

Fig. 6.17. Partial fiber separation along radial planes upon partial delignification by sulfite cooking. Ultraviolet light photomicrograph (Lange)

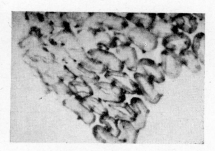

Fig. 6.18. Delignification by sulfite cooking to about the point of fiber liberation. Fibers held together along edges by the residual lignin. Ultraviolet light photomicrograph (Lange)

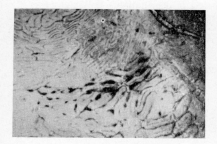

Fig. 6.19. Complete fiber separation and collapse of lumina after delignification by sulfite cooking. Ultraviolet light photomicrograph (Lange)

Fig. 6.20. Cross section of spruce after delignification and swelling in alkaline pulping liquor (Bucher)

In analogy, the tertiary wall, which in the beginning of the cook probably acts as a barrier towards the cooking liquor or at least as a diffusion hindrance for dissolved macromolecules, disappears during the sulfite cook more or less completely, whereas the kraft pulps contain well preserved tertiary walls (26, 114). The dissolution of matter from the main part of the fiber, the secondary wall, occurs in both acid and alkaline processes predominantly in the outer parts and less towards lumen, as shown by determinations on the relative distribution of carbohydrates in the cell walls of sulfite and kraft pulp fibers, as well as in the walls of holocellulose, treated with hot acid or alkali, Figures 6.21–24 (10). However, this is not due to a one-way direct penetration, as has been shown by similar treatment of thin transverse holocellulose sections where

315

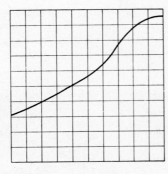

Fig. 6.21. 'Absolute' average material distribution in sulfite rayon pulp fibers. Lumen to the right (Lange)

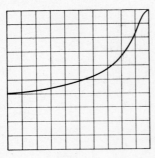

Fig. 6.22. 'Absolute' average material distribution in pine kraft pulp fibers. Lumen to the right (Lange)

the interior of the fiber was macroscopically as accessible as the outer portion (10). The minimal dissolution in the inner part of the cell walls has to be explained by a higher degree of lateral order of crystallinity of the carbohydrates in the inner parts of the cell wall and a lesser molecular

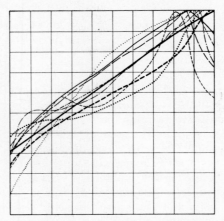

Fig. 6.23. Average material distribution for hot alkali-treated spruce holocellulose. Lumen to the right (Lange)

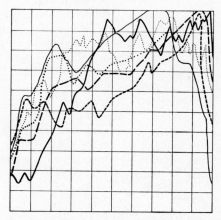

Fig. 6.24. Relative material distribution of
spruce holocellulose after 1 h of Nickerson
hydrolysis. Lumen to the right (Lange)

accessibility to pulping agents. The dissolution of hemicelluloses from the
main secondary wall may be especially pronounced in the region bordering
the transition lamella, which may be seen to loosen from the main part
of the fiber wall. This happens in swelling experiments and even on
swelling in water under light mechanical action, and on beating. Highly
refined dissolving pulps, especially prehydrolysis–kraft pulps, seem to have
lost most of the transition lamellae (79).

As xylan is more resistant to alkali than to acid, a prehydrolysis at low
pH prior to the kraft cook effects a solubilization of the tertiary wall
(25, 114), and the combined acid and alkaline treatment finally leaves a
pulp fiber, where the inner parts have also been dissolved to a considerable
extent, Figure 6.25 (10).

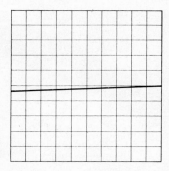

Fig. 6.25. 'Absolute' average
material distribution in pine
prehydrolysis–kraft pulp fibers.
Lumen to the right (Lange)

When comparing the relative carbohydrate distribution curves for sulfite and kraft pulps, Figures 6.21–22, it must also be kept in mind that the nature of the carbohydrates in the two pulps, as to DP and chemical composition, differs more than the distribution curves of matter. The sulfite cooking acid leads to a heavier depolymerization of the hemicelluloses, whereas the cellulose in mild paper pulp cooks is only partly degraded, partly left relatively undegraded. Consequently, the chain length distribution of a sulfite paper pulp is more heterogeneous than that of a kraft pulp, and the low-molecular material is concentrated in the outer parts of the cell walls, Figure 6.26 (76). This partly explains the much greater tendency to swelling and hydration of a sulfite pulp compared to kraft pulps.

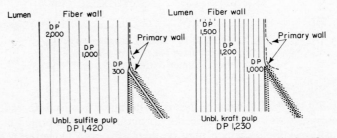

Fig. 6.26. Principal DP distribution across the fiber wall of sulfite and kraft pulp carbohydrates (Jayme–v. Köppen)

The hydrolytic effect of the sulfite cooking acid on the carbohydrates is assumed to be diminished by protection from the lignin or the native wood structure (e.g. 75). The real nature of this protection is somewhat obscure, be it hydrophobicity or mechanical compactness (cf. p. 320), but

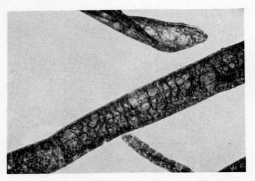

Fig. 6.27. Cracks appearing on the surface of sulfite pulps (Bucher)

it has been repeatedly demonstrated that where the wood has been mechanically damaged, cracks appear in the walls of the fibers after sulfite pulping, Figure 6.27, and in extreme cases rupture to fiber fragments,

318

Figure 6.28 (15). Fiber length distribution curves for kraft pulps in comparison to sulfite pulps of various degrees of cooking, Figure 6.29, show that whereas sulfite pulps of high lignin content have approximately the same fiber lengths, prolonged sulfite cooking causes fragmentation. However, the cracks in the fiber walls cause fragmentation of the more lignin-rich sulfite pulps on beating or on the subsequent paper testing to a higher extent than for kraft pulps, which is believed to be one

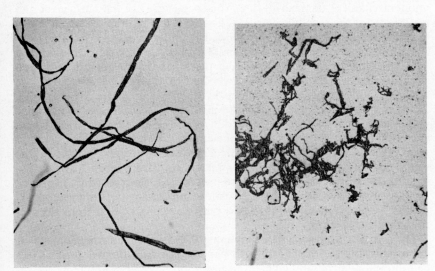

Fig. 6.28. Undamaged and damaged fraction of sulfite rayon pulp from spruce

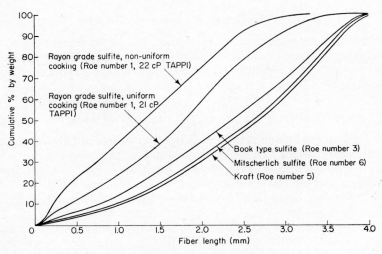

Fig. 6.29. Fiber length (integral weight) distribution of chemical spruce pulps (Rydholm)

319

cause of the lower tear strength of the former pulps (83). The fragmentation due to hydrolytic attack can also be observed in the submicroscopic region, in the micell formation noticeable in the electron microscope before and after swelling the hydrolyzed pulp in alkali (121) and shows up in the analysis of the pulp as an increased solubility in 10% NaOH and a heterogeneous chain length distribution.

One of the more probable regions, exposed to chemical degradation upon mechanical damage of the wood structure, is the surface of the main layer of the secondary wall (S2), since it has been demonstrated (89) that mechanical failure in wood which has undergone little or no delignification preferentially occurs between that layer and the transition lamella (S1), cf. Chapter 6.II. Also native disturbances in the tracheid wall structure, such as in compression wood or at the ray cell crossings, are likely to add to the points where hydrolytic damage may occur (49). Another possibility for the localization of exposed carbohydrate regions upon mechanical damage of the wood is along so-called *slip planes*. These have been found to develop across the entire cell wall and to have a looser microfibrillar texture (170a, 171a). That the hydrolytic attack in the sulfite cooking of damaged wood is related to disturbances in the carbohydrate superstructure rather than to the cracked lignin structure is proved by the previously-mentioned experiment on sulfite cooking cautiously prepared holocellulose. This gave a pulp as strong as that from the surrounding wood chips (65a).

Thus, in the heterogeneous reactions of pulping, many phenomena of importance for the quality of both paper pulps and dissolving pulps can be followed as structural changes in the wood, and microscopic investigations are a valuable complement to the purely chemical studies.

VI. Technical Aspects of Pulping

In this section, some general information will be presented on the equipment and operation technique used for wood pulping. The treatment cannot be made very detailed and for a more complete treatment of pulping machinery, reference is made to (151).

1. EQUIPMENT FOR MECHANICAL TREATMENT AND ITS OPERATION

The pulping technique varies widely with the type of pulping process. The equipment used for mechanical treatment is either *grinders* or *disk refiners*, the former operating on bolts, the latter on chips. Modern types of grinders and all refiners operate continuously. They are generally built for operation below 100°C, but two types of refiners are operated at elevated pressure.

Both grinders and refiners may be combined with a chemical treatment of the wood, in the semichemical pulping. Pulping of straw may be carried out with the aid of high-speed propellers such as the *hydrapulper*, as in the mechanochemical process. In two very special types of mech-

320

anical pulping, the *Mason* process for wood and the *Celotex* process for bagasse, fiberizing is achieved by rapid steam expansion.

A. Grinders (77, 85)

The application of grinders to the wood pulping industry dates back to 1840, when *Fenerty* in America and *Keller* in Europe defibrated wood to pulp by pressing it against a revolving grindstone in the presence of water to cool the stone, which became heated by the friction. The same principle is still the basis of the groundwood pulp industry, although the design of equipment has been developed and perfected to increase production and quality. The early grinders were driven by water wheels, the stones were natural sandstones, and jackscrews were used to maintain pressure. Eventually the *hydraulic grinders* were developed, where a piston in a pocket forced the bolts against the stone with hydraulic pressure, regulated by a throttling valve. *Pocket grinders* are shown in Figure 6.30. The cooling water in the *pit* is surrounding the lower part of the vertical stone, and the water level is regulated with the *dam*. More recently, pitless grinding has been introduced. With the development of the electrical industry it became an advantage to drive the stones electrically, and mills situated at waterfalls installed *generators* for their own power consumption. The speed of the stone and the power input were more easily regulated in the motor-driven grinders. To facilitate feeding of the grinder, the *magazine hydraulic grinders*, belonging to the two-pocket type, were developed, Figure 6.31. Since the pistons in the hydraulic grinders necessarily have to operate intermittently to allow new bolts to enter the pressure zone, various types of *continuous grinders* have been developed. One is the *chain grinder*, Figure 6.32, where the bolts are moved downwards by chains, the spike points or lugs of which are forcing the bolts against the stone. The movement of the chains regulates the pressure. Another type of continuous grinder is the *ring grinder*, such as the *Roberts grinder*, Figure 6.33, which radically deviates from the former type of grinders. Pressure is generated by the slowly-moving ring around the stone. The grinder is surrounded by a housing to which the bolts are charged through a side door. The hydraulic grinders have also been developed to work continuously, with a special mechanism to keep up the pressure when the piston is withdrawn to let in more bolts, the *Kamyr* type.

A development of great importance for the grinder capacity was the construction of *artificial stones* around 1920, which made safe operation at high speed possible. An increase in both stone size and peripheral speed took place, which led to units producing up to 70 t/d pulp, equipped with motors of up to 5,000 hp, as compared to 5–10 t/d and 500–1,000 hp in the early electric-driven grinders. The stones are usually segmented to allow heat expansion. They are of two types, *ceramic* stones with abrasive grits of silicium carbide or aluminium oxide, sintered together, and *cemented* stones with grits of quartz, bound in cement. The grits are of specified size, according to the grade of groundwood pulp desired. For newsprint grades, 50–60 mesh grits are preferred.

321

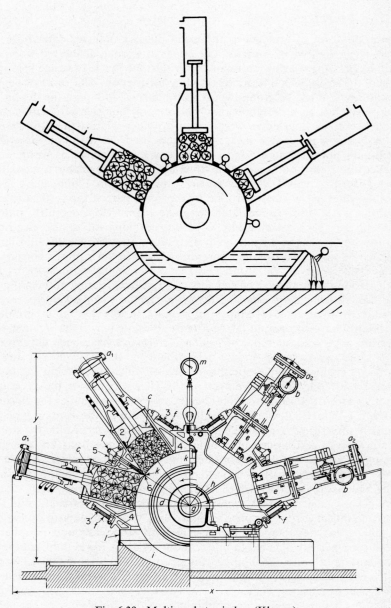

Fig. 6.30. Multi-pocket grinders (Klemm)

The stone surface is *burred* to a certain pattern of grooves before the stone is engaged in production. Likewise, during grinding, as the abrasive grits at the surface are worn off, the stone gets *duller* and has to be sharpened. This is done by a *burr*, or cylindrical steel shell of usually spiral or needle pattern. The burr is pressed against the revolving stone with micrometric precision and creates a pattern on the stone. It is not the type of pattern as such but the depth of the grooves, often expressed as the *sharpness* of the stone, as well as the grit size, which is most important for the pulping result. The layer of abrasives for ceramic stones is 65 mm thick and for cemented stones 150–175 mm. However, because of the higher wear resistance of the ceramic stones, their lifetime is more than twice that of cemented stones.

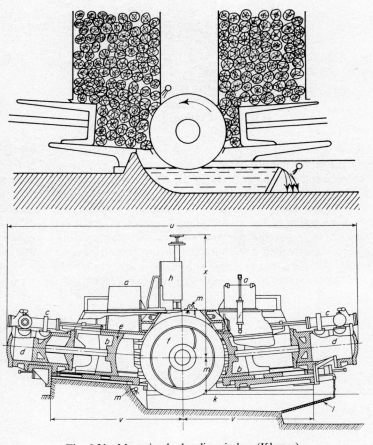

Fig. 6.31. Magazine hydraulic grinders (Klemm)

Another aid in keeping the stone sharp is the rotating *steel brush*, which keeps the stone surface clean from adhering pulp. The grinder is also

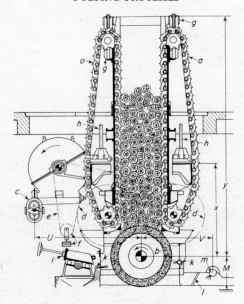

Fig. 6.32. Chain grinder (Klemm)

equipped with water showers to wash the stone clean from pulp and to supply the water needed for cooling. Sometimes the pit dam is removed and the cooling effected entirely by the showers, but usually a considerable part of the stone is immersed in the pit water. The amount of cooling water determines the stock consistency leaving the grinder, and this and the extent of recycling of the white water determines the temperature, which is an important factor for the productivity and pulp quality. *Temperature* is therefore controlled automatically in modern grinders. In the case of hydraulic grinders, the *pressure* is automatically controlled by a valve in the hydraulic system and created by centrifugal high pressure pumps. In

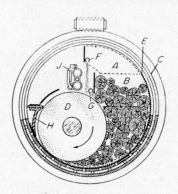

Fig. 6.33. Ring grinder (Johnson)

Table 6.4. Comparative grinding data (4′ basis) for presently used grinder types (20a)

Top-level groupings: columns 1–6 = **Intermittent grinders with pit** (Hydraulic); columns 7–13 = **Continuous grinders with pit**; columns 14–15 = **Pitless**.

Grinder type	Multi-pocket magazine Stand.	Super	Great Northern Super	Stand.	Stand.*	Super	North American Chain 29	53	58	Voith Chain III	V	VI	Ring	Intermitt. Great Northern Chain	Contin. Voith Chain
General data															
Production, t/d 90%	25	21	31	34	44	54	22	22	27	22	38	67	36	54	45
Travelling rate, mm/sec	0.50	0.46	0.52	0.56	0.75	—	0.89	0.56	0.73	0.65	0.92	1.46	0.70	0.89	1.29
C.S. Freeness (regulator), ml	160	92	91	82	84	92	95	94	110	110	110	123	72	—	105
Total power used, hp	1,110	1,680	2,400	2,520	2,860	3,370	1,550	1,610	1,910	1,490	2,410	3,840	2,610	3,750	2,990
No load power, hp	—	130	260	220	260	75	70	170	200	230	350	310	240	200	—
Speed, r.p.m.	240	230	250	250	260	270	220	240	240	250	240	230	340	270	340
Grinding zone, Length (proj.), m	1.52	1.45	1.82	1.82	1.81	2.03	0.74	1.31	1.47	1.00	1.20	1.35	1.43	1.80	1.00
Area (proj.), m²	1.86	1.76	2.23	2.23	2.20	2.49	0.90	1.60	1.80	1.22	1.46	1.65	1.76	2.20	1.22
Spec. production, t/d.m² gr. zone	13.3	12.2	14.0	15.1	16.2	22.0	24.5	14.0	15.2	18.4	26.0	41.0	20.5	24.3	37.0
Spec. load, hp/m² gr. zone	600	950	1,080	1,130	1,300	1,360	1,720	1,010	1,070	1,230	1,650	2,330	1,490	1,700	2,450
Spec. power input, kWh/t	940	1,380	1,360	1,320	1,140	1,100	1,250	1,260	1,240	1,180	1,120	1,000	1,280	1,220	1,170
Grinding conditions (average)															
Peripheral stone speed, m/sec	18	19	21	21	22	24	18	21	22	20	22	21	24	23	25
Spec. grinding pressure (p), kp/cm²	2.6	3.8	3.7	3.3	3.9	3.2	—	—	—	—	—	—	—	4.7	—
$100 \times p \times \mu$	24.8	38.9	38.2	41.2	44.6	43.5	69.7	35.5	37.0	47.9	57.4	83.3	46.3	55.8	69.0
Friction coefficient (μ)	0.094	0.103	0.103	0.127	0.115	0.134	—	—	—	—	—	—	—	0.117	—
Pit consistency, %	2.5	2.6	2.8	2.9	2.2	4.0	2.9	3.2	2.9	2.0	2.0	1.9	2.0	1.5	—
Pit temperature, °C	68	83	81	82	86	80	75	82	73	77	82	76	73	82	—

* Hemlock, other data refer to spruce

the case of the chain or ring grinders, pressure is controlled electrically by the speed of the feeding device.

Table 6.4 gives a schematic comparison of some of the modern grinder types (20a). As the production data have been obtained on different wood species, they are not quite comparable.

B. Refiners and refining

The fiberizing of chips can be achieved in various types of equipment. In the early days of semichemical pulping, in the 1920's, the *rod mill* was considered to be the most efficient machine for fiberizing (51). The chips were fed into a rotating drum at one end, the defibration was achieved by the crushing action of a number of steel rods, and the fibers were collected at the opposite end of the drum. As fiberizing could be performed at high consistency, the energy consumption was fairly low in the rod mill, but its size was large in comparison to its limited capacity, and the pulp obtained fairly coarse.

The *attrition mills* or *disk refiners* were developed later to increasing

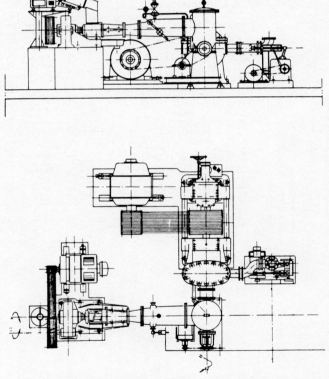

Fig. 6.34a. Top and side view of the Asplund Defibrator with accessories for the production of thermomechanical pulp. Classical (K) design (Defibrator AB)

326

precision and are now used almost exclusively for chip fiberizing. Their development was a prerequisite for the considerable increase in the production of wallboard and semichemical pulp fibers during the last three decades.

The refiners can be divided into four different groups (166):

(1) Non-precise single disk refiners,
(2) High precision single disk refiners,
(3) Semi-precise double disk refiners,
(4) High precision double disk refiners.

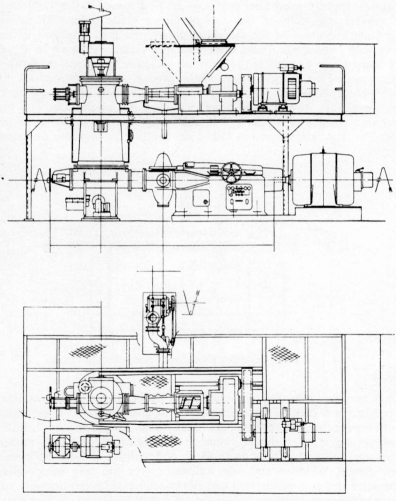

Fig. 6.34b. Top and side view of the Asplund Defibrator with accessories for the production of thermomechanical pulp. Recent (L-VP) design (Defibrator AB)

327

A refiner belonging to the first category, one of the earliest types developed and still used in improved design, is the *Asplund Defibrator*, Figure 6.34, which is operated under pressure in order to utilize the softening of the interfiber bonds occurring at temperatures above 170°C. The speed of rotation of the moving disk is 500–600 r.p.m. The disk diameter is 800 mm, and hence the peripheral speed around 25 m/s. The Defibrator process is treated in Chapter 7.II.

Other non-precise refiners, operating at atmospheric pressure, have higher speed of rotation, 1,800 r.p.m., and larger disks, 36 in., giving a peripheral speed of around 85 m/s. However, modern pulping technique requires more complete fiberizing than can be achieved in the simpler type of refiners, especially in the case of higher grade pulps. To achieve complete liberation of the individual fibers, the high precision refiners have been developed. These work with disk clearances down to around 0.1 mm and are constructed to allow an accuracy of adjustment down to 0.02 mm or even less. This necessitates precise constructions which take into account not only the *contortions* by the high centrifugal forces developed, but also thermal changes during the operation. The high precision refiners of single and double disk type are shown in Figures 6.35–36. The latter type has two disks rotating in opposite directions,

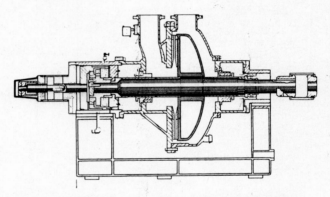

Fig. 6.35. Bauer single disk pressurized ('pump-through') refiner

which permits higher relative velocities of defibration with less rotational speed for each disk. They are supposed to give somewhat lower energy consumption per ton of pulp (42). Sutherland, Sprout–Waldron, Raffinator are single disk refiners, Bauer and Jones are double disk refiners. They are delivered in sizes up to 48 in. and with up to 2,000 hp motors. One Sprout–Waldron and one Raffinator type are also equipped for operation under pressure, and one Bauer refiner of 'pump-through' type has a pressurized inlet.

All refiners are very sensitive to tramp iron, which has to be removed magnetically prior to the defibration of the chips. Even at normal operation the disks are worn and therefore contain interchangeable plates, which can be resharpened in special auxiliary equipment.

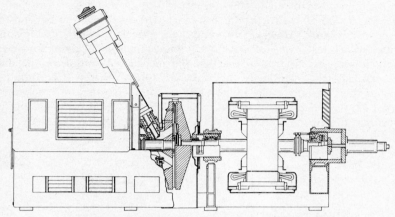

Fig. 6.36. Bauer double disk refiner with open outlet

The conditions of refining should be regulated to the desired level and kept constant. The more important variables are:

(1) Speed of rotation,
(2) Disk inter-distance,
(3) Load,
(4) Temperature,
(5) Consistency.

The speed of rotation is generally determined by the type of refiner. The disk inter-distance is adjusted to give the desired properties of the pulp, and is closely related to the consumption of energy. The load of the refiner should be constant to avoid stresses to the equipment. The energy consumption per ton of pulp also varies with the load of the refiner (1), as does pulp quality. Therefore, various types of feeding arrangements are in use, mainly conveyor belts and screws with provisions to return a certain excess feed. The temperature should be kept constant to avoid thermal changes in disk distances, etc., and generally at the highest possible level, to minimize energy consumption. The consistency also influences the energy consumption, a higher consistency causing less waste energy in the form of heated water (1). However, consistency has to consider the refiner action desired. Three purposes are listed below (166):

(1) *Fiberizing*, requiring high speed, 900–1,800 r.p.m., and high consistency, 8–15%.
(2) *Dispersing*, requiring high speed, but lower consistency, 3–4%.
(3) *Quality development*, requiring lower speed, 450–900 r.p.m., and medium consistency.

Fiberizing is the main purpose of the disk refiners, dispersing is required

329

in the case of resinous pulps or in the de-inking of waste papers and causes dispersion of non-desirable water-insolubles. Quality development is normally performed in special equipment, *beaters* or more or less *conical refiners*. Those are paper production machinery and therefore beyond the scope of this book. However, in some cases, especially where little beating is needed, as in the case of mechanical and semichemical pulps for newsprint, it may be suitable to increase the mechanical action of the disk refiners and hence eliminate the need for special beaters. The quality development of high yield sulfite (119) as well as softwood mechanical pulp (42) has been investigated, and relations found between energy consumption, freeness and strength characteristics, Figures 6.37–38.

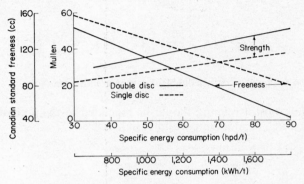

Fig. 6.37. Quality development on refining of mechanical refiner pulp (Eberhardt)

Fiberizing is obtained after a single pass through a disk refiner, working at suitable conditions. However, it is now realized, that in order to achieve complete fiber liberation without decreasing the freeness of the pulp too much, two refiner stages are to be preferred. In some cases only coarse defibration is then desired in the first stage, whereby a non-precise refiner may be adequate but usually a high precision refiner is required. One interesting refiner construction, *Jones Double-D Refiner*, allows two refiner stages in one unit, as the refiner consists of one rotary disk and two stationary ones. This refiner is predominantly used for quality development. Another interesting refiner variant is the *Chemifiner* (Black–Clawson) for high consistency refining (30–35%). The chips are fed into the center of two disks rotating at the same speed and in the *same* direction, but with disk centers offset to give the speed difference.

The energy needed for fiberizing widely varies according to the strength of the interfiber bonds of the soft chips. In Table 6.5 is listed the energy consumption for various types of pulp, together with data derived from Figures 6.1–3 on the strength of the interfiber bonds of spruce and birch after a corresponding softening of the chips.

330

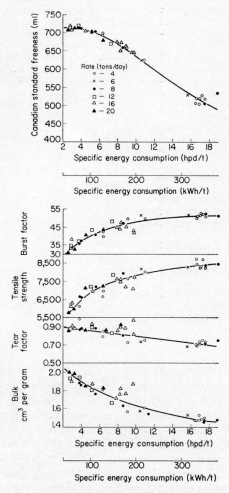

Fig. 6.38. Quality development on refining of semichemical acid sulfite pulp (de Montmorency)

2. EQUIPMENT AND OPERATIONS FOR CHEMICAL TREATMENT

A. *Discontinuous cooking*

Chemical treatment of wood in the chemical and semichemical pulping processes is carried out in *digesters*, which are pressure vessels of various shapes and types, *spherical* or *cylindrical*, *vertical* or *horizontal*, *rotary* or *stationary*, Figures 6.39–40. Stationary, cylindrical digesters are by far the most common type. Because of the difficulty of feeding the chips into a vessel under pressure, most digesters are operated *discontinuously*, with

331

Table 6.5. Energy consumption and strength of interfiber bonds at mechanical and semichemical chip refining

Ref.	Type of pulp	Pulp yield, %	Temperature of refining °C	Energy consumption kWh ptp	Bonding strength kp/cm²
(5, 6, 7)	Defibrator, spruce	95	180	200	200
(42, 70)	Mechanical, spruce	97	25–100	1,600–1,100	1,500–900
(42)	Mechanical, aspen	97	25	1,200	1,400
(42)	Semichemical cold caustic, birch–maple	90	25	500	200
(90, 119)	Semichemical acid sulfite, spruce	70	80	380	140
(119)	Semichemical acid sulfite, spruce	65	80	180	40
(164)	Semichemical kraft, softwood	70		330	650
(164)	Semichemical kraft, hardwood	70		300	240
(166)	Semichemical neutral sulfite, birch	70–75	80	250	220
(166)	Semichemical neutral sulfite, birch	85–90	80	400	600
(110)	Semichemical water hydrolysis, aspen	85	25	300	900
(166)	Groundwood screenings, spruce	97		800	
(85)	*Grinding* spruce	97	25–100	1,500–1,000	1,500–900
(67)	*Grinding* chemigroundwood, hardwood	85		600	600

chip filling, followed by *cooking liquor charging, pretreatment operations, heating to maximum temperature, keeping the digester at this temperature* until a desired degree of cooking is achieved, *relieving the pressure* and *emptying the digester*. Sometimes the waste liquor may be drawn off first and the *pulp washed* in the digester before emptying. All these operations together are called a *complete cooking cycle* or simply 'a *cook*'. Some pulping processes involve two or even three cooking *stages*, or different chemical treatments, separated by a change in the cooking liquor composition and often at the same time a change in temperature and pressure.

(*a*) *Chip filling*. A discontinuous digester is filled with chips from a chip bin above the digester or from a conveyor transporting the chips from silos to the floor above the digester tops. Often the chips pass some sort of weightometer to determine the exact weight of moist chips charged, and a moisture content meter. Alternatively, the whole digester content can be weighed by means of strain gauges (167a). Especially in the kraft cook it is important that the proper amount of chemicals per ton of wood (ptw) be charged. The digester is completely filled up with chips. Quite often, especially in the American kraft industry, the chips are charged without special packing, whereas Canadian and Scandinavian practice employs chip packing by air or preferentially by steam, which is blown into the digester neck through nozzles which give a whirling movement to the chips and results in a uniform, horizontal packing of the chips. Chip

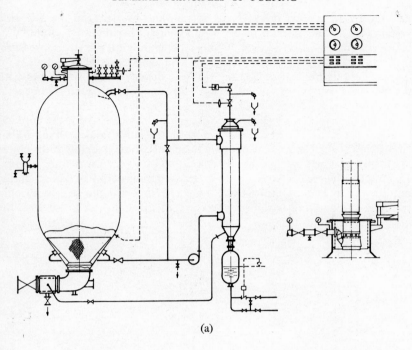

(a)

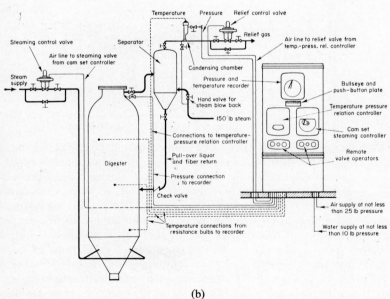

(b)

Fig. 6.39. Cylindrical digesters for (a) indirect and (b) direct heating (Ekstrom and Foxboro)

333

packing by air is used in the *Fresk* system and by steam in the *Svensson* system (161). The amount of dry wood charged per digester volume unit is thereby increased by around 30–45 %, depending on the steam pressure, from about 0.13–0.15 to 0.17–0.20 t/m³ for softwoods with a density of 0.45. These figures naturally vary with the density of the wood and with the moisture content of the chips, wet and heavy chips packing somewhat more compactly.

(*b*) *Liquor charging.* When no chip packing device is used, the cooking liquor can be charged at the same time as the chips, and cooking liquor circulation started as soon as possible to achieve some packing of the chips. With this system, chip and liquor charge takes a very short time, around 15 minutes, whereas steam packing and separate cooking liquor charge require up to half an hour extra time. To increase the degree of chip packing, the cooking liquor can be charged through special nozzles, the

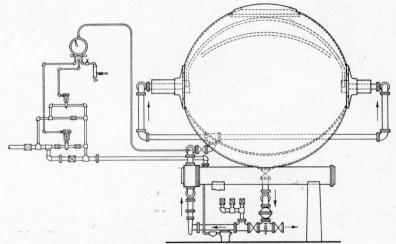

Fig. 6.40. Spherical digester for indirect heating (Stephenson)

Tarkkonen system (165). In the case of sulfite cooking, the acid charge has to be made separately, because the chip charging goes at atmospheric pressure, whereas modern sulfite cooking acid is kept fairly hot and under pressure.

The cooking liquor charge must ensure that all the chips charged are brought in contact with the cooking chemicals. As the chips are normally filled up to the neck of the digester, cooking liquor should also be charged to complete filling of the digester, i.e. all void spaces inside and outside the chips. This results in an approximate liquor : wood ratio of 4.5 : 1 (m³ : t), depending on the degree of chip packing, wood density, the extent of entrapped air in the chips, etc. However, as the cooking proceeds, the chips pack closer and further shrinkage occurs due to dissolution of wood substances. Therefore, during the main part of the cook the above-mentioned liquor : wood ratios are unnecessarily high and would therefore cause an unduly high steam consumption for heating to maximum temperature, and an unnecessarily high dilution of the waste liquor. In sulfite pulping, where good impregnation is most important, a complete filling of the digester is beneficial for the penetration due to the hydraulic pressure obtainable. To achieve lower liquor : wood ratios in spite of this, *side relief* is carried out. This means the bleeding off of a quantity of cooking liquor corresponding to the closer chip packing, at an early stage of the cook, usually at around 110°C, when no appreciable dissolution has taken place and the liquor can still be returned for re-use. Side relief of up to 30% is possible, decreasing the liquor : wood ratio to around 4 : 1 or somewhat lower in calcium-based sulfite cooking and 3.5 : 1–3.0 : 1 with sodium base, provided the strainer for the liquor circulation is placed in the lower half of the digester. When direct steam heating of completely filled digesters is used, side relief is necessary to make space for the condensate.

Also in kraft cooking impregnation is enhanced by complete filling of the digester with cooking liquor, as suggested for instance in the Va-purge process. However, quite often considerably less liquor is charged, normal liquor : wood ratios being 3.0 : 1–3.5 : 1. Still lower ratios are not allowable because of the danger of non-uniform cooks. As the concentration of active alkali in the white liquor is such that with normal chemical charges the ratio of white liquor : wood is around 1.5 : 1, obviously additional quantities of liquor have to be charged, especially if the wood used is dry. These are drawn from black liquor from previous cooks to keep up the final concentration of solids in the liquor sent to the recovery system. The charges of white and black liquors are adjusted according to current determinations of the weight and moisture content of the chips charged, to keep both the liquor : wood and chemicals : wood ratios constant. According to the same principle some mills adjust the concentration and volume of sulfite cooking acid charged, and fill up with water, but this is more unusual, as the sulfite cook is less sensitive to variations in the ratio of chemicals: wood. In sulfite mills with recovery systems, where waste liquor concentration should be kept at a maximum, some recycling of waste liquor has been tried and is also practised in some magnesium-based mills. However, because of increased side reactions in the sulfite cook, this is not possible to the same extent as in the kraft cook.

One drawback with the system of charging chips and cooking liquor at the same time is that no *pretreatment to facilitate penetration* can be made. These methods have been dealt with already in Chapter 6.III. Chip packing with steam and no additional steaming adds only the liquor charging period, *ca.* 10 minutes, to the cooking cycle. *Steaming* takes at least an additional 30 minutes to be complete, and an efficient series of steam purges almost the same time. The *Vilamo* process (169), involving hydraulic pressure variations of the cooking liquor, needs no treatment of the chips prior to liquor charging, and could thus be applied regardless of the charging method used. To maintain hydraulic pressure without variations by means of the cooking liquor pump for a certain period or throughout the cook is practised in many cases. The closing of the digester

335

lid also adds to the time of the cooking cycle, but is often done very rapidly by remote-controlled automatic lids built into the modern digesters.

(c) *Heating*. After proper charging and penetration operations, heating of the digester is commenced. Heating is always done with steam, *directly* or *indirectly* applied. In the former case, the steam should be added at the bottom cone of the digester or in a special, internal liquor circulation system. Direct heating is still practised to a great extent in the kraft industry and has the advantage of allowing rapid temperature increase. Its main disadvantages are dilution of the cooking liquor by the condensate, causing decreased heat economy in the chemicals recovery system, and the risks of non-uniform heating. Indirect heating is used increasingly in all chemical pulping processes and involves the circulation of the cooking liquors through external, usually tubular, *heat exchangers* with the aid of *circulation pumps*, which draw off cooking liquor through *strainers* in the digester walls and deliver the heated liquor at appropriate inlets. Different systems employ strainers in the top, middle, or bottom of the digester and inlets at opposite places, Figures 6.39, cf. Figure 10.11. Some of the most common systems are *NAF-Schauffelberger*, *Brobeck*, and *Morterud*. The distribution of the heated cooking liquor within the digester is most important for the uniformity of the pulp obtained. Especially in larger digesters, insufficient distribution arrangements may cause differences in temperature of up to 5 or even 10°C, and considering the large temperature dependence of all pulping processes (cf. Chapter 6.IV), this inevitably leads to deficiencies in pulp quality. Temperature gradients eventually disappear owing to heat conduction as well as liquor convection, but only gradually, and this is one of two main reasons why there should be a reasonably slow heating to maximum temperature. The other purpose is to allow time for the penetration of the chips by the cooking acid, if not complete after the charging. Deficiencies in this respect will on too rapid a heating lead to a non-uniformity of pulping within the individual chips, as grave as the non-uniformity of pulping within the digester in the case of a deficient heat distribution.

To achieve an even temperature in the digester not only the distribution of heated cooking liquor through the return inlets of the digester is important, but also the absolute flow rate of the circulated liquor. Too slow circulation will result in a noticeable temperature gradient in the digester from the inlets to the strainers. Too rapid circulation may result in clogging of the strainers at the moment the wood in the digester approaches the point of fiber liberation. Generally, provision is made for circulation of the entire liquor volume within a period of 10 minutes during the main period of heating. Towards the end of the heating period, the reactions often have proceeded so far that the chips approach the point of fiber liberation. This results in an increase in the resistance to liquor flow at the strainers and a decreased rate of circulation, and the circulation pump is often stopped when maximum temperature is reached. The uniformity of the heating circulation has been studied by radioactive tracers introduced into the flow line (28).

336

The choice of *cooking curve* and *maximum temperature* is to some degree a matter of local considerations, such as the production capacity required, the capacity of the boiler house, the dimensions of the heating surface of the calorisators, the number of digesters, the maximum pressure allowable, the design of the chemical make-up system, the place of the bottle-neck of the mill, as well as the pulp grade manufactured and the quality required.

However, some general rules can be stated. Heating time to maximum temperature is generally considerably longer than the time at maximum temperature. The main reasons for this are the necessity of good penetration and a uniform heat distribution within the digester. Small-scale experiments have shown, that if the air has been properly expelled from the chips by a suitable technique, thus ensuring rapid penetration, there is no serious objection to bringing a sulfite cook directly to maximum temperature, and similar experiments on kraft cooking have shown that a very rapid heating is not detrimental to the pulp quality. Generally, however, a heating time of 3–7 h is used for the sulfite process, and for the less sensitive kraft and neutral sulfite processes a good deal shorter, in European practice around 2.5 h and in American often less than 2 h. To achieve very rapid heating, direct steam is used, or the cooking liquor is preheated, as in the case of *hydrothermal injection cooking*, where hardwood chips directly after charging are brought in contact with an excess of white liquor preheated to maximum temperature in a separate pressure vessel. Then heating time is reduced to 15 minutes. Normally, most cooking liquors are introduced at a temperature around 70°C, at which most chemical reactions proceed so slowly that penetration can take place before non-uniform delignification occurs.

To speed up heating additionally, *vapor phase cooking* has been suggested (135) and practised. This involves impregnation of the wood with a cooking liquor of higher than normal concentration, followed by removal of most or all liquid outside the chips, and rapid heating with direct steam. Such a technique is principally possible only when the chips after withdrawal of the free cooking liquor still contain sufficient chemicals for the cook. This may necessitate special evaporation of the white liquor used in kraft pulping and the use of soluble bases in the case of sulfite pulping. The amounts of chemicals introduced into the chips on impregnation with calcium-base cooking acid are sufficient for high yield sulfite vapor phase cooking. Vapor phase cooking allows not only rapid heating but considerable heat savings too, as less water has to be brought to maximum temperature.

(*d*) *Completion of the cook. Time at maximum temperature* is either fixed, or adjusted by different methods of end-point determination. In kraft pulping, where the amount of chemicals charged per weight of wood determines the degree of delignification, provided ample time and temperature is allowed for, time at maximum temperature is usually fixed to 1, 1.5 or 2 h. *Maximum temperature* for the kraft cook is around 170–180°C, usually somewhat lower in Europe than in America. Similar

337

conditions are normal in neutral sulfite pulping. In sulfite pulping the time–temperature conditions are more critical than the amounts of chemicals charged, and therefore end-point determinations are generally needed to decide the time at maximum temperature of the individual cooks. The temperature should be chosen to allow an average time of at least 1 h, as end-point variations may otherwise lead to difficulties in keeping a constant pulp quality. Usually time at maximum temperature is kept around 1–2 h for dissolving pulps and softer grades of paper pulps, at temperatures of 140–150°C and 130–140°C respectively, whereas paper pulps with higher hemicellulose content, as greaseproof and glassine pulps, are cooked at 115–125°C utilizing a longer time, up to 8 h, at maximum temperature. The latter type is often called *Mitscherlich* cooks. Since the *end-point determinations* are used mainly in sulfite pulping, they will be treated in Chapter 9.1.

During the cook *pressure variations* occur. Kraft and neutral sulfite cooks start at atmospheric pressure, provided that the cooking liquor is not specially preheated, whereas sulfite cooking acid of the same temperature, 60–70°C is under considerable pressure, 2–3 kp/cm², owing to the content of dissolved sulfur dioxide. On increasing the temperature, the pressure increases, until *top gas relief* is started at or slightly below the maximum pressure allowable by the digester construction. Maximum pressure is in the case of kraft or neutral sulfite pulping somewhat higher than the steam vapor pressure at maximum temperature, or 7–9 kp/cm². The gases relieved in kraft and neutral sulfite pulping are volatile organic compounds and carbon dioxide, together with some steam, whereas in addition, and mainly, sulfur dioxide is gassed off during the sulfite cook. The pressure is thus of importance for the cooking liquor composition and therefore the rate of cooking. A high pressure maintains a high sulfur dioxide concentration and results in a rapid sulfite cook. A high pressure in the neutral sulfite cook, buffered with sodium bicarbonate, leads to somewhat higher acidity and inferior cooking result than when the carbon dioxide formed is allowed to escape. The gases of the kraft cook pass through a cooler to yield hot water and turpentine, and those of the sulfite cook, after cooling and cymene separation, pass to the acid system to be absorbed for re-use.

After completion of the cook the digester is gas-relieved to a lower pressure and either *blown* or *dumped* to the *blow tank, blow pit* or *leach caster*. In some cases, especially in Scandinavia, the liquor is withdrawn and washing liquor introduced before dumping the digester. The blow-down period is carefully controlled in the sulfite process, because the reactions continue during this period, although at a decreased rate.

The blow-down period may be very short, or extended to 1–2 h. To blow the digester is a question of minutes, but to empty a digester by liquor withdrawal, washing and dumping takes several hours.

The whole *cooking cycle*, 'from cover to cover', thus varies, according to process, equipment and practice, from about one hour to one day or even more. An American kraft cooking cycle is 2.5–4 h, a Scandinavian

4–6 h. A sulfite rayon or soft paper pulp cook takes around 8–10 h from cover to cover, a sulfite greaseproof pulp cooking cycle 20–24 h. The different phases of a kraft and a sulfite cook are well illustrated by the temperature and pressure curves recorded by *instruments*, which are becoming general in the digester house, Figures 6.41–43. As a rule the heating is automatically regulated by means of a program controller-recorder instrument.

(*e*) *Digester materials and digester corrosion.* The construction of the pulping digesters has always been complicated by corrosion phenomena. These are most severe in the case of sulfite pulping and required attention from the early days of the industry. *Lead linings* were used initially but proved unsatisfactory because of creeping tendencies, etc. They were substituted by *ceramic brick linings*, which are still dominating. Their main advantages are low cost and good chemical resistance, with a lining life of about 10 years. Continual inspection and repairs are, however, necessary, and down-time for repairs is considerable since the linings cool slowly and will not endure forced cooling. About 15% of the digester

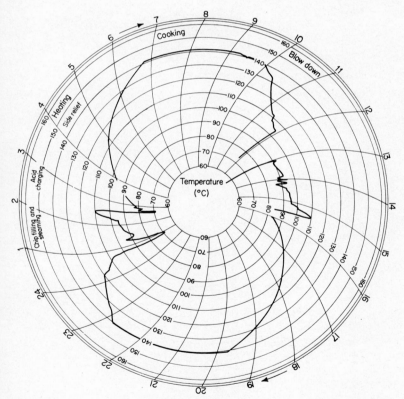

Fig. 6.41. Temperature diagram of two sulfite rayon pulp cooks

339

volume is further occupied by the lining, which also tends to accumulate dirt and scale on its rough surface. This occasionally impairs the cleanliness of the pulp. Two disadvantages have been accentuated in more recent years (78). The old, relatively small riveted digesters were sufficiently stiffened by the butt straps to allow some out-of-roundness. Larger and welded digesters made of high tensile steel become more easily distorted under pressure when out-of-roundness exists, leading to failures in the brick lining. Furthermore, the introduction of soluble bases caused the dissolution of gypsum, which had filled out minor cracks in the lining, and necessitated a more careful application of the bricks in furfuralformaldehyde resin cement and a heavier lining. *Carbon brick linings* are being increasingly used instead, partly because of these drawbacks of the ceramic linings, and are successfully applied also with soluble bases. However, some disadvantages, such as the space required, remain, and have initiated experiments with acid-resistant steel, which had long been used in strainers and pipes. An *all-stainless digester* vessel becomes too expensive because of the heavy shell needed for a large pressure

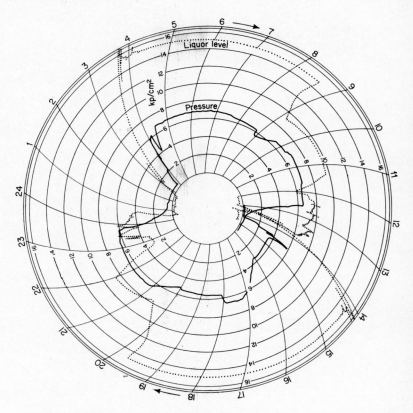

Fig. 6.42.   Pressure and liquor level diagrams of two sulfite rayon pulp cooks

340

vessel. *Compounded* or *clad steel* is the logical material, having a few millimeters of stainless steel material bonded to a carbon steel shell to take up the mechanical stresses. With a polished surface this material is satisfactorily resistant for normal sulfite cooking operation, also with soluble bases and high pressures. Deposited material or pores and cracks will lead to decomposition of entrapped cooking acid and also sulfuric acid corrosion of compound steel (166a). It is less susceptible to thermal shocks than all-stainless digesters and less sensitive to stress corrosion caused by chloride, which occasionally enters the system, e g. with sea-driven wood. Disadvantages are still considerable costs and the skill necessary for repairs when needed. A variant to clad steel is the loose digester lining of stainless steel, called the *Holgersson* or *Kopparfors* lining, which is only point-wise attached to the carbon-steel shell (31, 69, 115). This requires considerably more maintenance but is less costly, since it can be installed in an existing digester. Another variant is *stainless steel weld metal overlay*, used for both sulfite and kraft digesters (37b). A very well-controlled welding is required to prevent corrosion.

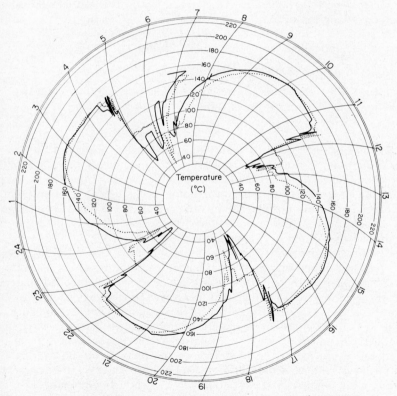

Fig. 6.43.   Temperature diagrams of four kraft paper pulp cooks

Steel corrosion can appear in various forms. One is *intergranular* corrosion, where traces of chromium carbides in austenitic steels inhibit the formation of the passive protective oxide film on the steel surface. The areas adjacent to the carbides become depleted of chromium and corrosion occurs. The small particles isolated by the carbides erode and leave a sandy feeling to the surface exposing new areas to corrosion. *Pitting* often occurs where scaling prevents the formation of the protective oxide layer. A related type of corrosion is caused by salt solutions of variable concentration. The combined effects of *erosion* and corrosion, and of *stress* and corrosion are well known. Both can appear in digesters.

Kraft digesters are also subjected to corrosion, which has tended to increase in recent years (94, 131). To some extent this is caused by the fact that the protective scaling always formed on these mild steel digesters from impurities in the cooking liquor, contains less alumina and silica from the refractories of the modern recovery furnaces than formerly, thus decreasing the protective function of the scale (13). Serious reduction in the corrosion resistance occurs in the presence of silicon in the steel (45, 74, 130), whereas nickel, chromium and copper contents less than 1% were found to have little influence. The important observation that thiosulfate in the cooking liquor considerably accelerates corrosion (153), led to the realization (57, 132, 152) that *polysulfide*, in equilibrium with sulfite, thiosulfate and sulfide according to the reaction:

$$Na_2S_2O_3 + Na_2S \rightleftharpoons Na_2SO_3 + Na_2S_2$$

will drastically reduce the protecting cathodic polarization of the steel by reacting with electrons to form sulfide:

$$S_2^{2-} + 2\,e = 2\,S^{2-}$$

The corrosion of steel in white liquor appears to consist of an anodic dissolution of ferrous ions, which are precipitated in the solution as ferrous sulfide, while an equivalent amount of polysulfide ions reacts with the excess electrons on the corroding steel surface. Yet, polysulfide in high concentration rather inhibits the corrosion (38, 66, 153), probably by anodic polarization (passivation). The effect of polysulfides closely resembles that of oxygen at similar conditions.

The digester corrosion is virtually absent above 120°C, possibly because of the decomposition of polysulfides at higher temperatures (153). The rate of corrosion should therefore be measured in terms of corroded material depth per 1,000 cooks rather than per year. Normal figures are 0.3–0.6 mm/1,000 cooks (less than 1 mm/year) (131), but may amount to figures as high as 1–3 mm/1,000 cooks or up to 7 mm/year (34, 71, 127). With high digester corrosion, the state of oxidation of the liquor coming from the melt dissolvers has to be observed, or the method of substituting the sulfur losses with elemental sulfur instead of with salt cake, since elemental sulfur addition gives rise to polysulfides. Although the change-over to carbon-brick linings (167) or to stainless materials such as Hastelloy F (143) represents solutions to the kraft digester corrosion problems, mild steel digesters are still the general practice. Only in the case of the more expensive and larger continuous digesters is clad steel now preferred.

The presence of sodium chloride, sulfate and carbonate was found to increase digester corrosion in kraft cooks containing less than 1 g/l sodium sulfite, but to be of little consequence at higher concentrations of sulfite (82b). Sulfate and carbonate are always present in quantities depending on the efficiency of reduction and causticizing in the recovery cycle, and chloride may be introduced with the wood, mill water or waste liquor from the chlorine dioxide generation and sometimes build up to 10–20% of the sodium salts of the recovery cycle.

The corrosivity of *neutral sulfite* cooking liquor was considered to be negligible in the early years of that industry, and the digesters were often constructed of mild steel. However, it was soon realized, that stainless steel was required in many constructions, especially where the combined effects of corrosion and erosion occurred (143a). Rotary digesters had the least problems because of the absence of a constant vapor phase region, whereas stationary and especially continuous digesters had considerable trouble. Old sulfite digesters with ceramic linings had less problems. It was found that steel corrosion by neutral sulfite cooking liquor is negligible at pH above 10 but appreciable at lower pH, increasing in proportion to the formation of bisulfite ions (82a). Another cause of corrosion is the formation of thiosulfate, which forms an equilibrium with bisulfite and finely divided sulfur and leads to cathodic depolarization.

B. *Continuous cooking*

Most industrial processes are initially operated discontinuously because of the generally simpler equipment needed. However, as the production develops to a large industrial scale, the advantages of continuous operation are realized. Sometimes, the step from *handicraft* to industry is marked by a change-over from discontinuous to continuous systems, as in the case of paper-making, with the first continuous paper machines operating already at the beginning of the 19th century. Pulping, however, presented certain problems which prevented some of the operations being made continuous. Grinding became semi-continuous with the introduction of multi-pocket grinders and fully continuous with the various types of ring and chain grinders. Barking, chipping and screening have been continuous for a long time, and washing became continuous with the introduction of the filter and press washing systems, cf. Chapter 10. Therefore, the operations on both sides of the cooking are now continuous, and efforts have long been made to convert cooking to continuous operation. The main difficulty has been the feeding of chips into the digester and discharging of pulp or soft chips from the digester under pressure.

The classical design of a continuous pulping process is the *Asplund* or *Defibrator* process, Figure 6.44, cf. Chapter 7 (8). There all the essential elements of continuous cooking are included, i.e. constant and continuous chip feeding by means of a vibrator from the chip bin to the pressure feeder, which charges the chips against the reaction pressure, further

Fig. 6.44. Defibrator assembly with vertical preheater only, for the production of thermomechanical pulp

constant and continuous steam feeding to the reactor, continuous fiberizing and continuous discharge of the pulp from the reactor. However, the retention time of the pressure zone is about 1 minute, during which time only insignificant chemical reactions take place, the whole process being a

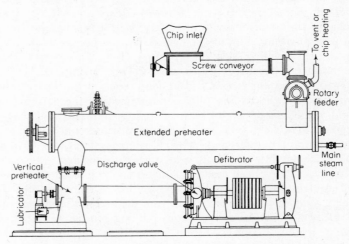

Fig. 6.45. Defibrator assembly with extended preheater (reaction screw), for the production of hydrolyzed pulp and other coarse grades of semichemical pulp

344

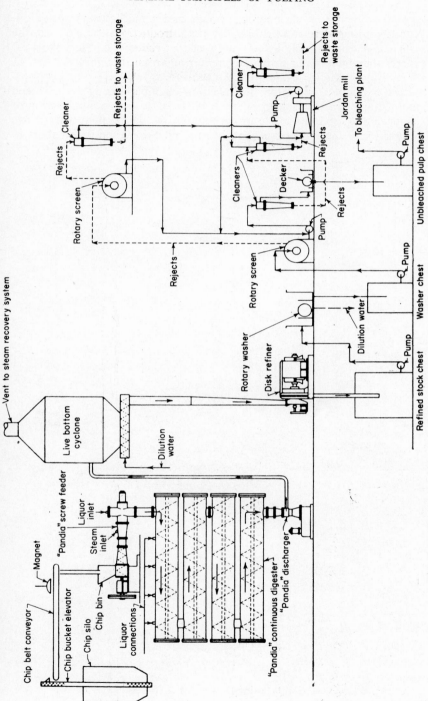

Fig. 6.46. Pandia continuous digester for the production of semichemical pulp (Goodwin)

thermal softening of the interfiber bonds and a mechanical defibration. With a prolonged retention time and the introduction of chemicals, the system is a true continuous cooking system. The simplest semichemical process thereby is water hydrolysis, requiring around 5 minutes at 180°C, which is about the same operating temperature as for the Asplund process. To get 5 minutes' retention, the reaction chamber has to be extended with a simple reaction screw, Figure 6.45 (101). A simple introduction of chemicals, e.g. sodium sulfite or carbonate, into this system will change the quality of the pulp somewhat, but the retention time is too short to

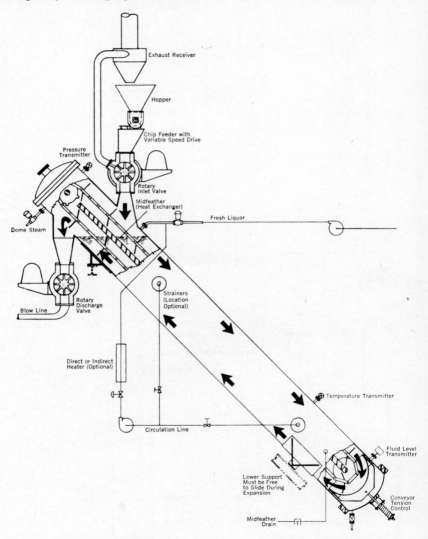

Fig. 6.47. The Bauer Messing-Durkee (M & D) continuous digester

346

allow considerable chemical reaction. Therefore, to achieve true semi-chemical pulps of the neutral sulfite, high yield sulfite or high yield kraft type, cf. Chapter 8, it is necessary to extend the system with a series of 3–8 reaction screws, around 6 m long and 0.6 m in diameter, as in the *Chemipulper* (*Pandia*) (14, 36, 41, 53, 66a, 81, 82, 97, 122, 130), Figure 6.46, or the *Asplund* (*Defibrator*) semichemical pulping systems (101, 108, 116). The reaction screws carry the chips from feeder to discharger during some 10–30 minutes, which, although the system requires somewhat higher temperatures (approaching 200°C) than commonly used in discontinuous pulping, still gives a semichemical pulp of acceptable quality. As the reaction screws tend to plug if liquor is introduced, the cooking in these

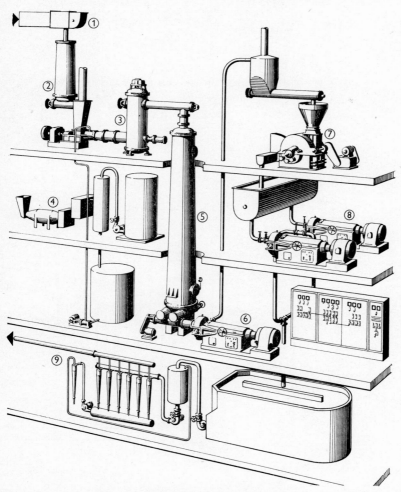

Fig. 6.48. The improved Asplund Defibrator continuous digester system for semichemical pulping

347

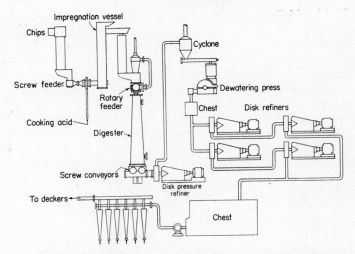

Fig. 6.49. The Storabrite–Asplund continuous digester system
(Evans)

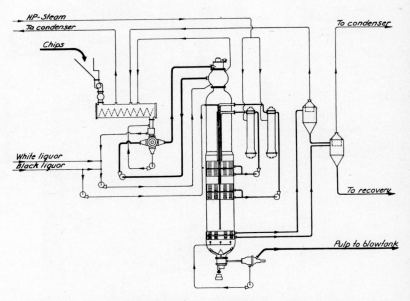

Fig. 6.50. The standard Kamyr kraft and bisulfite continuous digester system
(Richter)

348

systems is in the vapor phase. This, together with the limited retention time and hence short time to maximum temperature, emphasizes the importance of good impregnation. The latter is achieved by a special treatment prior to the digester as in the case of the *Bauer–Grenco* digester (53a) and the *Storabrite* system (86), or by the compressing and relieving action of the feeder. A multi-screw digester, enclosed by one pressure shell, is the *Sprout–Waldron* digester (63a, 134).

Another type of continuous digester, the *Messing–Durkee* system (53a, 100, 117, 168), allows liquid phase cooking. In this unit, Figure 6.47, the

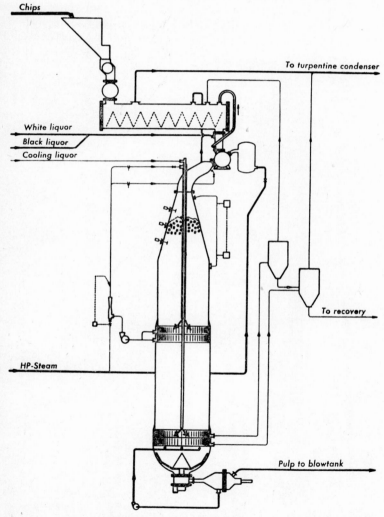

Fig. 6.51. The Kamyr steam phase–liquor phase kraft continuous digester (Richter)

349

reaction chamber consists of an inclined 1.5 m. diameter bent pipe, around 15 m in length and equipped with a parting inner longitudinal wall. A transport chain drags the chips from inlet to outlet through a liquid or vapor phase, and the retention time is about 1 h. Because of its simple design and low maintenance costs, this vessel is also used for the pressureless operations of the cold caustic process.

The type of continuous digester which allows the greatest variations of the process, both as regards cooking phase, retention time and introduction of chemicals, is the vertical type, as in the improved *Asplund Defibrator* and *Storabrite* (86) systems, Figures 6.48–49, the *Escher–Wyss* (20) and particularly the *Kamyr* (12a, 48, 63, 74a, 128, 129, 146) system, Figures 6.50–51. Here both semichemical and chemical pulping is possible. The chips are carried by gravity from inlet to outlet, and in the case of liquid

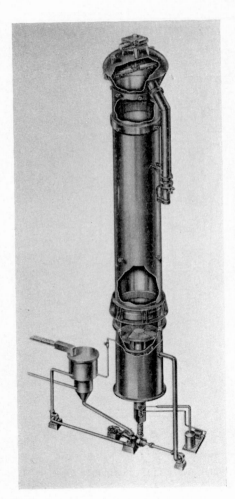

Fig. 6.52. The Impco kraft and neutral sulfite continuous digester system (Carlsmith)

phase cooking there are also strainers, pipe lines and pumps for liquor circulation. The *Impco* digester, Figure 6.52, is a vertical *upflow* digester, where the chips are moved upwards by means of a chip lifter in the bottom (33). A special *Kamyr* design for *two-stage cooking* makes use of one upflow and one downflow digester, interconnected under the same pressure (136), but a redesigned downflow digester could also be used for this purpose. The one-stage Kamyr digester is the dominating construction used for chemical and high-grade semichemical pulping, with an installed digester capacity of about 6,000,000 t/year, mainly of kraft pulp. The maximum output of the largest units, with a digester volume of 900 m³, now approaches 900 t/d of kraft pulp.

There is also a horizontal type of digester, the *de la Roza* system, (39), operating on bagasse. It consists of a huge steam-jacketed rotating cylinder, where the material is slowly moving from inlet to the slightly lower outlet end.

Table 6.6. makes a compilation of the existing types of continuous digesters. It could also include the *hydrapulper*, which is used in the mechano-chemical pulping of straw, and which can also be operated continuously.

Another special type of digester, the *Bauer Rapid Cycle Digester* (43, 53a), Figure 6.53, is strictly speaking a batch digester, but it deviates from the conventional type because of its small size, 3–9 m³, and rapid cooking cycles, 10–25 minutes. It is therefore used in a way which is intermediate between batchwise and continuous cooking, and the supply of pulp to

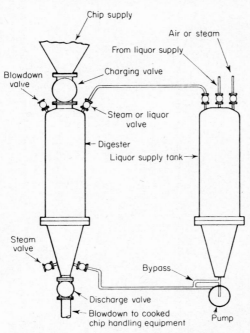

Fig. 6.53. The Bauer Rapid Cycle digester

Table 6.6. Continuous digester types

Name	Digester	Feeder	Cook
Asplund-Defibrator			
Original	Preheater chamber	Plunger or screw	High temperature mechanical, vapor phase
Semichemical	One- or multiscrew	Screw	Semichemical, vapor phase
Semichemical	Vertical downflow	Pocket	Semichemical, vapor phase. Furfural hydrolysis
Bauer			
Bauer–Grenco	One-screw	Pocket	Semichemical, vapor phase
Bauer Rapid-Cycle	Mini-batch vertical	—	Semichemical, vapor phase or submerged
Messing–Durkee (M–D)	Inclined downflow and upflow (chain conveyors)	Pocket	Semichemical, partly submerged
Black–Clawson			
Pandia (B–K)	Multiscrew	Screw	Semichemical, vapor phase. Chemical kraft from sawdust
Celdecor			
Pomilio	Vertical downflow	Screw	Semichemical straw pulp, low-pressure cook
Escher–Wyss	Vertical downflow	Pocket	Semichemical, partly submerged
Impco	Vertical upflow	Skewjector	Semichemical, chemical, submerged
Kamyr			
Conventional	Vertical downflow	Balanced pocket, wet	Chemical, semichemical, submerged
Instant heating	Vertical downflow	Balanced pocket, dry	Chemical, semichemical, mainly submerged
Two-stage	Vertical upflow and downflow	Balanced pocket, wet	Chemical, submerged
de la Roza	Horizontal, slightly inclined (rotating)	Screw	Chemical bagasse pulp, vapor phase
Sprout–Waldron	Multiscrew	Pocket	Semichemical, partly submerged

blow tanks will be less uneven than when normal size digesters are used. Still, the feeding and discharging of the digester has none of the difficulties encountered in continuous operations. It is mainly used for semichemical pulping in the highest yield range.

Chip feeding against the digester pressure is made by *plungers, screws* or *pocket feeders.* In the first two cases, the chips are compressed while meeting the steam of the digester, so as to form a wet plug sufficiently tight to take up the digester pressure. During this compression and subsequent pressure relief, the cooking liquor is introduced and impregnation takes place. This is an advantage in comparison with the pocket feeder. A big drawback, however, is the danger of 'blow-backs', should the chip plug soften by an occasional stop in the chip supply. Another disadvantage is the damage to the fibers, caused by the compression, and which may cause an inferior pulp quality, especially with chemical grades. However, newer types of screw feeders work with fairly low compression ratios, 1.4 : 1 (41), which is said to minimize the damage done. In the case of unbleached semichemical pulps (e.g. 53), as well as with chemical kraft pulp from sawdust (97) and with straw pulp (36), satisfactory results have been obtained with such feeders, within the demand limits of such pulp types and raw materials. The *Impco Skewjector* contains two screws designed to sluice the chips into the digester without compression damage (33). Sawdust and straw can also be fed into the digester with thick stock pumps designed for pulp transport.

The pocket feeders are of two types, 'dry' and 'wet'. In the dry type, or star feeder, the impregnated chips fall down into pockets, situated in a revolving device, and leave the pocket by gravity when it passes the digester inlet. In the wet, or Kamyr, type, the chips fall down into a pocket of a conical revolving device, together with cooking liquor, and after the cone has rotated 90°, the pocket becomes connected with a liquor circulation which pumps the chips into the digester. The latter design has the advantage of being balanced, i.e. to avoid one-sided load on the feeder from the digester pressure. This decreases wear but necessitates some complicating extra arrangements. The dry feeder is unbalanced, and hence friction causes excessive wear between the feeder and its housing. New construction materials seem to have improved the performance of the dry feeders and prolonged their lifetime (100).

Before *discharging* of semichemical pulps the soft chips have to be partially fiberized, which is consequently done under pressure. Either a defibrator, i.e. a coarse refiner of the disk type, or a simple impeller disintegrator can be used. In the case of chemical liquid phase cooking, the cooking liquor has a tendency to escape from the digester more rapidly than the pulp. Before the discharger, therefore, a strainer is placed, allowing concentration of the pulp suspension to the consistency desired. Alternatively, sufficient amounts of liquor can be pumped from the low-pressure side into the digester bottom.

The dischargers are either of the *alternating valves* type with adjustable time of the sluicing cycle, or the *blow valve* type with adjustable discharge

353

orifice. The former caused in the Kamyr digester, which is operated under hydraulic pressure, frequent periodical pressure variations through the entire digester, which led to some trouble in the maintenance of instruments and machinery and has therefore been substituted with the simpler blow valve, generally completed with an adjustable ball valve in the blow line.

The impregnation of the chips with cooking liquor is accomplished in different ways. Where plunger or screw feeders are used, the chemicals are introduced after the compression of the chips, which gives a fairly homogeneous distribution of chemicals. When a wet pocket feeder is used, the air of the chips is expelled by steaming in a separate transport screw prior to feeding. In combination with the hydraulic pressure of the digester, usually *ca.* 10 kp/cm^2, this gives a satisfactory impregnation. For a dry pocket feeder and a subsequent vapor phase cooking, a system of evacuation and impregnation screws, before the feeding and the digesting, has been designed, the Bauer–Grenco system. In the case of commercial, semi-wet chips, steaming is probably to be preferred to evacuation, but this is also possible in the Bauer–Grenco system.

The cold caustic pulping process does not require any pressure reactor but, instead, special arrangements for impregnation, either made by spraying and squeezing in a roll mill applying horn angle pressing (21), or by immersion in lye in a live-bottom retention chamber, preceding a Rapid Cycle or Messing–Durkee Digester, or by squeezing in roll presses (37a) or screw presses, such as the French press, the Fiber–Press and the Pressafiner (46). The extra mechanical treatment required for complete fiberizing is done in disk refiners. At least one installation of the cold caustic process has preferred to use a Kamyr digester in spite of the low process temperature, in order to secure a perfect pressure impregnation.

The pulping conditions are to some extent modified in continuous cooking. The continuous cooking does not cause any principal change to the reactions, which occur in the same sequence of time as in the batch process, although the material is moving instead of stationary. However, due to certain constructional features of the digesters, the conditions deviate from the normal. For instance, in the case of the screw reactors, the cook is performed in the vapor phase, which is unusual in normal practice of discontinuous cooking, as is the immediate heating of the chips to maximum temperature. The shorter cooking times and higher maximum temperatures in this type of digester have also been mentioned. In the Kamyr digester conditions are more similar to batchwise processing, with normal cooking temperature, heating time and time at maximum temperature, liquid phase cook and normal chemicals charge.

The principal advantage of continuous cooking, in addition to simplified large-scale operation, is the greater possibilities for process and quality control. An extensive instrumentation is therefore needed (37), completed by rapid and frequent analysis of product quality. Complete automation with computer control is also becoming realized here (19a). This increased control together with the instantaneous interruption of the reactions at

354

the point of discharge, in contrast to the comparatively long blow down and blow period of the batch cook, facilitates the keeping of a uniform pulp quality. The elimination of the times for filling and emptying the digester results in higher productivity per unit of digester volume. The vertical digester constructions thereby take advantage of the higher degree of chip packing in the lower zones of reaction, in contrast to the vertical batch digesters, which towards the end 'of the cook are only about half-filled. Radioactive tracing experiments have verified the increase of packing towards the bottom, although to a less extent than expected because of the friction from the digester walls exerted on the moving chip pillar (48, 63). Further, the load of the cooking liquor and steam production is far more even, and the feed to the washing and screening departments also occurs more evenly. Less labor is required, since manual operations are minimized. Counter-current cooking and washing in the digester are other possible advantages (145).

Continuous cooking, automatically controlled, should give especially favorable results in processes, where a more complicated sequence of changes has to be performed, as in the case of multistage cooking.

VII. Qualitative and Economical Aspects of Pulping

The pulping processes, as surveyed in section I of this chapter, cover the *yield range* from 98 to about 30% of the wood substance. Obviously, the chemical composition and physical properties of these pulps must vary considerably. Even at the same yield, pulps from *different processes* differ considerably in these respects. Similarly, in choosing the *raw material*, the fiber length can be varied from over 5 mm to less than 1 mm and the fiber wall thickness from 10 to 1μ, which also greatly influences the pulp properties. The varying properties must be compared to the equally varying *manufacturing costs* to give the complete aspects on the possible end uses for these pulps. Although chemical composition and fiber dimensions tell a good deal about the properties to be expected, it is necessary to make a variety of tests, simulating the end use, to get a better understanding of the suitability of the pulp. Still, the final answer has to be obtained only in the large scale use of the pulp, since the nature of the essential service properties is in general complicated and incompletely defined. The cost aspect is often a deciding one, since improvements in the pulp-consuming process might overcome a former deficiency in the cheaper pulp. As the wood cost is the dominating part of the manufacturing costs, a cheaper pulp generally means a pulp from a cheaper raw material, or a pulp in a higher yield. The processing costs also often—but not always—decrease when increasing the yield. Thus, the *economical aspects* tend to favor the use of pulps in higher yield— closer to the point of fiber liberation in the case of chemical pulps, or semichemical or mechanical pulps instead of chemical—and/or made from pine instead of spruce, from hardwoods and grasses instead of softwoods. Softwoods in general cost at least 20% and often 50% more than

355

hardwoods, on a weight basis. The *qualitative aspects* are, as they should be, generally opposite to the economical ones, until some technical improvement is made.

As will be demonstrated in Chapter 22, 80% of the pulp production is still based on *softwoods*, 15% on *hardwoods* and 5% on *grasses*. *Mechanical* and *semichemical* pulps constitute about one-third of the total production, one-third is *unbleached chemical* and nearly one-third *bleached chemical* pulp. Bleached sulfite and bleached kraft are about equally important, whereas unbleached kraft has almost twice the production of unbleached sulfite. Of the end uses, *paper and paperboard* consume over 90 %, whereas *dissolving pulps* constitute only about 5% of the production. Paper takes two-thirds and board one-third of the world production of paper pulps. In North America, the board fraction now approaches 50%. Of paper, some of the main categories are *newsprint, book, fine, coarse* and *tissue*, of board *container board* (two-thirds *liner* and one-third *corrugating*), *boxboard* (two-thirds *folding* and one-third *food board*) and *building board*.

It is necessary to have this end use background to discuss the qualitative and economical aspects of pulps. *Dissolving pulps* are always bleached and substantially free of lignin, hemicelluloses, resin and ashes, and thus approach the chemical concept of cellulose. Some grades also require the removal of short-chain cellulose. The qualitative aspects thus dominate for dissolving pulp, and they are the most expensive grades to manufacture. The highest grades are cord, acetate and nitrate pulps, whereas normal grade viscose rayon pulp tolerates some hemicelluloses. The yield range is 30–50% depending on the grade, the raw material and the process, and normally the yields are about 40%. Sulfite and prehydrolysis–kraft processes are used. The main chance of decreasing manufacturing costs is thus to use cheaper wood, and hardwoods, mainly gum, birch, beech and eucalypt, are increasingly used for dissolving pulps, especially as fiber length is less critical than for most paper pulps.

For *papers* of all grades, the mechanical as well as optical properties of the fiber are important, but obviously to a widely varying degree. For tissue, fine papers, book and newsprint papers, pulps are used which do not give maximum strength but emphasize softness or compressibility, opacity and surface smoothness, some properties of which are included in the concept of printability. Still, the tensile and the tear strength of a newsprint paper should not go below a certain level to perform well in the fast printing presses, and similar tests hold for the other grades. Some long-fibered material, i.e. chemical softwood pulps, are usually incorporated, 15–25% for newsprint and 25–50% for magazine papers, but the main component is short-fibered. The brightness and brightness stability demand will determine whether the short-fibered material should be bleached chemical hardwood pulps, or unbleached (or brightened) mechanical or semichemical pulps.

In fine papers and some better book paper grades, the furnish is predominantly bleached chemical pulps, with about equal quantities of softwood and hardwood pulps. An increased proportion of hardwood pulp is the expected development, especially as the low surface strength of a hardwood paper can be improved by sizing in the paper machine. The question of which pulping process should be used is undecided. Both sulfite and kraft pulps are used, as well as bleached neutral sulfite semichemical. Brightness and opacity are important, as well as good formation, i.e. uniform optical properties. Hardwood pulps and fairly hemicellulose-poor softwood sulfite pulps have the best opacity and formation properties. The yield of bleached softwood pulps is normally in the 45–50% range, with the kraft and soft sulfite pulps on the lower side and the more hemicellulose-rich sulfite pulps at about 50% and sometimes above. Hardwood sulfite pulps are in the same range and hardwood kraft is obtained bleached at or above 50% yield.

The main portion of the book and all newsprint papers contain large quantities of mechanical pulp, of which only an insignificant portion is bleached. Although unbleached pulps are used, the brightness demand is important, although at a lower level, 55–60% GE, than for fine papers. Therefore, spruces and firs have been the preferred raw material for groundwood pulping because of their bright wood, whereas pines and hardwoods were considered to give too dark a pulp—apart from other deficiencies. The poplar hybrids developed in Italy have been selected to deliver the brightest possible wood, and for pine groundwood young trees with little colored heartwood are used. To maintain the strength necessary to run the fast newsprint paper machines and printing presses, chemical softwood pulp has to be added, usually to about 20%. In order not to decrease the brightness below that of the groundwood pulp, semibleached kraft but unbleached sulfite are used. As opacity, compressibility and ink absorption properties are superior for groundwood pulp, the chemical pulp fraction should be kept at a minimum, not only for economical reasons. One trend is therefore to decrease the chemical pulp proportion by improving the paper machine construction, or by improving the strength of the mechanical pulp. One way of doing the latter is the process of coarse grinding with subsequent refining, another the multistage refining of wood chips. The strong softwood pulp in newsprint furnishes has been made less expensive by increasing the yield to the semichemical region, 60–70% instead of the normal 50–55%. This is only possible with sulfite pulp, and by changing to soluble base and the bisulfite process further improvements in yield are possible. Another trend towards cheaper pulp for newsprint is the increased incorporation of hardwood pulps. Mechanical pulps for newsprint are made from poplar in Italy and from eucalypts in Australia. Chemigroundwood, neutral sulfite or cold caustic pulps from hardwoods are sometimes incorporated to replace some of the chemical and some of the mechanical softwood pulp. They normally require some brightening treatment to match the brightness demand. However, an increasing proportion of the printing papers are being clay coated, which again puts other aspects on pulp quality.

The quality demands for coarse papers and paper board put more emphasis on the mechanical properties. A special category of packaging papers are the greaseproof and glassine grades, where the barrier properties and transparency are important. To achieve this, a pulp with much hemicelluloses is required, i.e. for unbleached grades softwood sulfite pulps in 52–58% yield or even higher, and for bleached grades the same type of softwood pulp or neutral sulfite semichemical hardwood pulp in 70–75% unbleached and 55–60% bleached yield. Only in exceptional cases is kraft pulp used for this purpose. For the other types of coarse papers and boards, softwood kraft pulp, mainly unbleached, is the preferred material because of its superior strength. Where brightness is essential, bleached kraft is used, and in an intermediate category, semibleached kraft and unbleached sulfite compete. Bleached sulfite is also used for coarse papers and boards to a considerable extent, but is likely to lose ground unless modifications in the cooking methods, such as the bisulfite process, can improve the strength considerably. This is especially necessary since the introduction of chlorine dioxide, which makes it possible to obtain kraft pulp of the highest brightness without strength losses. Hardwoods have, because of their short fibers, greater difficulties in invading these markets, with some exceptions in the paper board field, where they are used in quantities up to about 50% to improve surface smoothness. Hardwood pulps are generally incorporated in strong papers to only 10–20%. However, developments in the paper machines, such as those leading to more extensible papers, may again place entirely new requirements on the pulp quality needed for strong papers and permit the use of more hardwoods and softwood sulfite pulps.

The yield range used for softwood pulps of the coarse paper category is 45–50% for kraft and 50–55% for sulfite, or fairly close to the point of fiber liberation, and in the region of maximal strength. In some cases the brightness, in other cases the strength cause a reluctance to observe the economical demand of increasing the yield. Although unbleached kraft paper has a brightness of only 20–30% GE, there is still an aspect of brightness to consider, in a way as essential as that of the 85–90% GE range of bleached pulps. There is a straight-line correlation between yield and brightness for unbleached kraft, which can be influenced by cooking conditions and brightening after-treatments only to a fairly limited extent. To overcome such difficulties, the liner board machines have a secondary headbox, where a brighter surface layer is applied, from a pulp of lower yield, or a hardwood kraft pulp, which is usually somewhat brighter. The bottom layer, usually 75–85% of the board, can then be made from a cheaper pulp in the high yield chemical, or even semichemical kraft range. As the strength properties also decrease with an increase in yield, this is permissible predominantly in the higher basis weight boards. These can also contain an increased proportion of hardwood kraft pulp. In those cases, it is also a question of which mechanical properties should be emphasized. Stiffness is a quality which does not always go parallel to the conventional strength qualities measured, such as tensile, burst and tear strength, in changing the pulp type, and stiffness is an essential quality for paper board. For multiwall container board, the corrugating medium paper has stiffness as the one dominating mechanical function. Unbleached neutral sulfite semichemical pulp from hardwoods in yields of 75–85% seems to be ideal for this purpose, and is gradually taking over the market from groundwood- and straw pulp-containing papers. Other grades of paper board, such as some boxboard made on multiwire machines, incorporate large quantities of groundwood pulp in the inner layers, whereas the outer layers are often bleached sulfite from a mixture of softwood and hardwood pulps. Solid bleached boxboard for food and similar packaging purposes is to a large extent made from semibleached

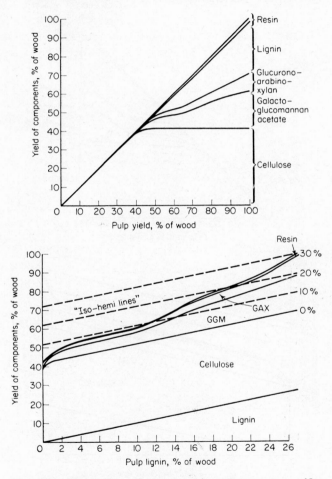

Fig. 6.54. Dissolution of sprucewood components on sulfite pulping. Yield of components as a function of pulp yield or pulp lignin yield. Broken lines indicate constant hemicellulose yield ('iso-hemi lines'), as suggested by Löschbrandt. GAX = glucuronoarabinoxylan, GGM = galactoglucomannan acetate

359

or bleached kraft, containing sometimes appreciable quantities of hardwood. Finally, defibrated wood pulp has been developed and is used mainly for building board.

Figures 6.54–57 illustrate how the chemical composition, the mechanical properties and the brightness of unbleached spruce pulps vary with the yield and the process. The dissolution of wood components during the cook is different for different pulping processes, which is reflected in the pulp composition. For instance, the sulfite process is said to be more selectively delignifying than the kraft process, because more hemicelluloses remain at a certain yield. Whereas this is of *economical* importance,

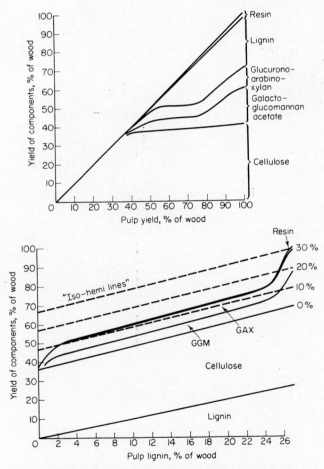

Fig. 6.55. Dissolution of sprucewood components on kraft pulping. Yield of components as a function of pulp yield or pulp lignin yield. GAX = glucuronoarabinoxylan, GGM = galacto-glucomannan acetate

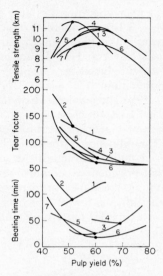

Fig. 6.56. Paper properties of spruce pulps at varying yield and process (Rydholm). (1) Kraft, (2) Prehydrolysis–kraft, (3) Bisulfite, (4) Bisulfite–carbonate (semichemical), (5) Bisulfite–carbonate (chemical), (6) Acid sulfite, (7) Acid sulfite–carbonate

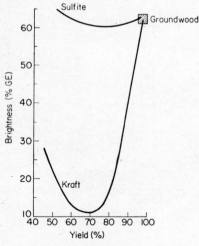

Fig. 6.57. Brightness of unbleached spruce pulps

361

inasmuch as the point of fiber liberation lies at a higher yield for sulfite pulps than for kraft pulps, it is not possible to put a *qualitative* meaning in such terms as X/Y, where X is lignin and Y carbohydrates remaining in the pulp, since the quality of X and Y vary for every process and every yield level. Therefore, it is preferred here to plot $X+Y$ against X or X and Y against $X+Y$ rather than X/Y against $X+Y$, as is done in the so-called *Ross* diagram (159). The maximal *strength* of the pulps generally appears in the chemical pulp region close to the point of fiber liberation, and it is seen to decrease at higher yields more pronouncedly for kraft than for sulfite pulps. The influence of the raw material and the process on the paper properties of pulps with about the same yield is shown by Table 6.7. It appears that the chemical composition of these pulps gives, as such, little indication on the paper properties, neither do the fiber dimensions alone nor the information of which process was used alone. Taken together, they give a complex pattern of contributions to the actual pulp type.

Some additional considerations of an economical nature for the various pulp types are given in Chapter 22.IV.

Table 6.7. Fiber dimensions, hemicelluloses and paper properties of unbleached chemical pulps, made from different wood species by different processes

Wood species	Picea abies	Betula verru- cosa	Eucalyp- tus saligna	Pinus silves- tris	Pseudo- tsuga taxifolia	Betula verru- cosa	Eucalyp- tus saligna
Pulping process	Sulfite	Sulfite	Sulfite	Kraft	Kraft	Kraft	Kraft
Pulp yield, %	52	53	54	47	47	53	54
Fiber dimensions of wood							
Length, mm	3.5	1.1	1.0	3.0	3.4	1.1	1.0
Width, μ	27	20	13	28	37	20	13
Wall thickness, μ	2.4	1.8	1.4	3.2	4.0	1.8	1.4
Fiber length of pulp, mm	2.6	1.0	1.0	2.6	2.6	1.0	1.0
Hemicellulose content, %							
Glucomannan	12	4	4	8	12	<1	<1
Glucuronoxylan	5	17	7	13	7	27	15
Paper properties on Valley beating to							
25°SR Beating time, min	10	7	11	51	55	16	10
Tensile strength, km	8.3	5.7	3.7	9.0	7.6	7.0	6.2
Burst strength	73	45	20	88	77	60	52
Tear strength	90	78	50	121	250	88	114
45°SR Beating time, min	19	17	27	75	74	25	24
Tensile strength, km	9.0	7.5	5.0	9.7	8.2	8.6	10.0
Burst strength	74	59	28	95	83	74	90
Tear strength	83	64	45	108	200	73	108

REFERENCES

1. Aflenzer, F. A., *Tappi*, **37**, 90 (1954).
2. Allgulander, O., *et al.*, *Svensk Papperstid.*, **57**, 542 (1954).
3. Alm, A., and L. Stockman, *Svensk Papperstid.*, **61**, 10 (1958).
4. Anderson, C. A., *Pulp Paper Mag. Can.*, **47**, No. 1, 43 (1946).
5. Asplund, A., *Tekn.*, *Tidskr.*, **69**, K: 81 (1939).
6. Asplund, A., *Wochbl. Papierfabrik.*, **71**, 590, 607 (1940).
7. Asplund, A., *Svensk Papperstid.*, **56**, 550 (1953); **59**, 441 (1956).
8. Asplund, A., *Brit. Pat.* 393,159 (1933); *U.S. Pat.* 2,008,892 (1935); 2,145,851 (1939).
9. Asunmaa, S., *Svensk Papperstid.*, **58**, 308 (1955).
10. Asunmaa, S., and P. W. Lange, *Svensk Papperstid.*, **57**, 501 (1954).
11. Aurell, R., *et al.*, *Svensk Papperstid.*, **61**, 937 (1958).
12. Bailey, A. J., *Ind. Eng. Chem.*, *Anal. Ed.*, **8**, 52 (1936).
12a. Baldwin, N., *Tappi*, **45**, No. 7, 220A (1962).
12b. Behr, E. A., *et al.*, *J. Phys. Chem.*, **57**, 476 (1953).
13. Benedicks, C., and P. Sederholm, *Svensk Papperstid.*, **36**, 402 (1933).
14. Beveridge, J. B., and R. D. Kehoe, *U.S. Pat.* 2,323,194 (1944); 2,422,522 (1947).
15. Bildt, O., *Svensk Papperstid.*, **41**, 148, 261 (1938).
16. Bixler, A. L. M., *Paper Trade J.*, **107**, No. 15, 29 (1938).
17. Björkman, A., and B. Person, *Svensk Papperstid.*, **60**, 285 (1957).
18. Boehm, R. M., *Paper Trade J.*, **118**, No. 13, 35 (1944).
19. Borchers, E., and Ö. Bryde, *Papier-Fabr.*, **32**, 500 (1934).
19a. Boozer, R. F., and E. C. Fox, *Paper Trade J.*, **146**, No. 24, 42 (1962).
20. Brecht, W., *et al.*, *Wochbl. Papierfabrik.*, **88**, 451 (1960).
20a. Brecht, W., and F. Luhde, *Tappi*, **45**, 413 (1962).
21. Brown, K. J., and W. H. Monsson, *Paper Trade J.*, **140**, No. 25, 60 (1956).
22. Bryde, Ö., *Norsk Skogind.*, **3**, 169 (1949).
23. Bucher, H., *Die Tertiärlamelle von Holzfasern und ihre Erscheinungsformen bei Coniferen*, Habegger, Derendingen (Switzerland) 1953.
24. Bucher, H., *Chimia*, **13**, 397 (1959).
25. Bucher, H., *Papier*, **14**, 542 (1960).
26. Bucher, H., and L. P. Widerkehr-Scherb, *Morphologie und Struktur von Holzfasern*, Derendingen (Switzerland) 1947.
27. Buckman, S. J., *et al.*, *J. Phys. Chem.*, **39**, 103 (1935).
28. Burchhardt, Ö., *et al.*, *Svensk Papperstid.*, **62**, 345 (1959).
29. Burr, H. K., and A. J. Stamm, *J. Phys. Colloid Chem.*, **51**, 240 (1947).
30. Cady, L. C., and J. W. Williams, *J. Phys. Chem.*, **39**, 87 (1935).
31. Cape, G., and A. M. Bain, *Tappi*, **44**, 689 (1961).
32. Cannon, J. J. R., Thesis, McGill Univ., Montreal 1939.
33. Carlsmith, L. A., *et al.*, *U.S. Pat.* 2,878,116 (1959); *Pulp Paper* **33**, No. 10, 77 (1959); *Tappi*, **43**, 1013 (1960).
33a. Christensen, G. N., *Australian J. Appl. Sci.*, **2**, No. 4, 430 (1951).
34. Christiansen, C. B., and J. B. Lathrop, *Pulp Paper Mag. Can.*, **55**, No. 12, 113 (1954).
35. Clark, J. d'A., *U.S. Pat.* 2,735,762 (1956).
36. Clark, T. F., *et al.*, *Tappi*, **43**, 934 (1960).
37. Cole, E. J., and M. Todd, *Paper Trade J.*, **140**, No. 48, 44 (1956).

37a. Colombo, P., *Atip Bull.*, No. 4, 133 (1960).
37b. Crooks, K. L., and G. E. Linnert, *Tappi*, **44**, 544 (1961).
38. Delagrange, L. A., *Tappi*, **38**, 347 (1955).
39. De la Roza, J. J., *Pulp Paper Mag. Can.*, **38**, No. 4, 296 (1937); *U.S. Pat.* 2,159,258 (1939).
40. Dorland, R. M., *et al.*, *Pulp Paper Mag. Can.*, **58**, No. 6, 135 (1957).
41. Durant, L. G., *Paper Trade J.*, **138**, No. 43, 40 (1954).
42. Eberhardt, L., *Paper Trade J.*, **139**, No. 37, 26 (1955); **140**, No. 8, 30 (1956); *Tappi*, **39**, No. 7, 126A (1956).
43. Eberhardt, L., *Tappi*, **38**, No. 4, 233 (1955).
44. Eberhardt, L., *Paper Ind.*, **37**, 934 (1956).
45. von Essen, C. G., *Svensk Papperstid.*, **52**, 549 (1949).
46. Evans, J. C. W., *Paper Trade J.*, **140**, No. 46, 24 (1956).
47. Findley, M. E., and W. J. Nolan, *Tappi*, **39**, 758 (1956).
48. Fineman, O., *Svensk Papperstid.*, **60**, 425 (1957).
49. Forgacs, O. L., *Tappi*, **44**, 112 (1961).
50. Garland, H., *Ann. Missouri Botan. Garden*, **26**, 1 (1939).
51. Gocke, W. A., *Paper Trade J.*, **86**, No. 23, 79 (1928).
52. Goldfinger, G., *Paper Trade J.*, **112**, No. 24, 29 (1941).
53. Goodwin, R. G., *Tappi*, **39**, No. 7, 187A (1956).
53a. Goodwin, R. G. *Tappi*, **45**, No. 7, 216A (1962).
54. Grace, N. H., and O. Maass, *J. Phys. Chem.*, **36**, 3046 (1932).
55. Green, H., and F. H. Yorston, *Pulp Paper Mag. Can.*, **40**, No. 4, 244 (1939); **41**, No. 2, 123 (1940).
56. Grondal, N., *Pacific Pulp Paper Ind.*, **13**, No. 7, 12 (1939).
57. Haegland, B., and B. Roald, *Norsk Skogind.*, **9**, 351 (1955).
58. Hägglund, E., *Svensk Papperstid.*, **39**, 95 (1936), **41**, 95 (1938).
59. Hägglund, E., *Svensk Papperstid.*, **41**, 194 (1938).
60. Hägglund, E., *et al.*, *Svensk Papperstid.*, **43**, 99 (1940).
61. Hägglund, E., and R. Hedlund, *Papierfabr.*, **30**, 49, 61 (1932).
62. Häggroth, S., *et al.*, *Svensk Papperstid.*, **56**, 660 (1953).
63. Hamilton, R. P., *Tappi*, **44**, 647 (1961).
63a. Hannan, P. J., *Paper Trade J.*, **146**, No. 25, 41 (1962).
64. Harnist, G., *Ger. Pat.* 469,372 (1920).
65. Hart, J. S., *Tappi*, **37**, 331 (1954).
65a. Hartler, N., *Svensk Papperstid.*, **66**, 443 (1963).
66. Hassler, J. W., *Tappi*, **38**, 265 (1955).
66a. Herbert, W. *Tappi*, **45**, No. 7, 207A (1962).
67. Heuer, J. H., *Pulp Paper Mag. Can.*, **56**, No. 12, 170 (1955).
68. Higgins, H. G., *et al.*, *J. Council Sci. Ind. Research*, **19**, 455 (1946); **20**, 361 (1947); *J. Appl. Sci.*, **4**, 84 (1953).
69. Holgersson, S. P. *et al.*, *U.S. Pat.* 2,694,632 (1954).
70. Holzer, W. F., *et al.*, *Tappi*, **45**, 208 (1962).
71. Hopper, E. W., *Tappi*, **36**, 345 (1953).
72. Howard, E. J., *Pulp Paper Mag. Can.*, **52**, No. 8, 91 (1951).
73. Hunt, G. M., and G. A. Garrett, *Wood Preservation*, McGraw-Hill, New York 1938.
74. Huseby, R. A., and M. A. Scheil, *Tappi*, **34**, 202 (1951).
74a. Jansson, L. B., *Tappi*, **46**, 296 (1963).
75. Jayme, G., and L. Grögaard, *Cellulosechem.*, **18**, 34 (1940); *Papierfabr.*, **38**, 93, 101, 113 (1940).

76. Jayme, G., and A. v. Köppen, *Papier*, **4**, 455 (1950).
77. Johnson, E. H., ed., *Mechanical Pulping Manual*, TAPPI Monograph Series No. 21, New York 1960.
77a. Johnston, H. W., and O. Maass, *Can. J. Research*, **3**, 140 (1930).
78. Jopp, J. M., *Pulp Paper Mag. Can.*, **58**, No. 9, 148 (1957).
79. Jurbergs, K. A., *Tappi*, **43**, 554, 561, 865 (1960).
80. Kaufmann, Z., *Uber die chemischen Vorgänge beim Aufschluss vom Holz nach dem Sulfitprozess*, Diss. E.T.H., Zurich, Switzerland 1951.
81. Kehoe, R. D., *Tech. Assoc. Papers*, **25**, 536 (1942).
82. Kehoe, R. D., et al., *U.S. Pat.* 2,616,802 (1952).
82a. Kesler, R. B., *Tappi*, **41**, 102 (1958).
82b. Kesler, R. B., and J. F. Bakken, *Tappi*, **41**, 97 (1958).
83. Kilpper, W., *Papier*, **3**, 342, 386 (1949).
84. Klauditz, W., *Holzforschung*, **6**, 70 (1952).
85. Klemm, K. H. *Modern Methods of Mechanical Pulp Manufacture*, Lockwood, New York 1957.
86. von Koeppen, A., *Paper Trade J.*, **145**, No. 16, 24 (1961).
87. Kollman, F., *Medd. Svenska Träforskningsinst.*, Stockholm, No. 22, 1951.
88. Kulkarni, G. R., and W. J. Nolan, *Paper Ind.*, **37**, No. 2, 142 (1955).
89. Lagergren, S., et al., *Svensk Papperstid.*, **60**, 632, 664 (1957).
90. Lambert, J. E., *Paper Trade J.*, **144**, No. 43, 36 (1960).
91. Lange, P. W., *Svensk Papperstid.*, **47**, 262 (1944); **48**, 241 (1945); **50**, No. 11 B, 130 (1947); **57**, 525 (1954).
92. Lange, P. W., et al., *Svensk Papperstid.*, **57**, 533 (1954); *Norsk Skogind.*, **11**, 425 (1957).
93. Leopold, B., and D. C. McIntosh, *Tappi*, **44**, 235 (1961).
94. Lientz, J. R., et al., *Tappi*, **38**, 373 (1955).
95. Liese, W., *Holz RohWerkstoff*, **15**, 449 (1957).
96. Liese, W., and I. Johann, *Naturwissenschaften*, **41**, 579 (1954).
97. Linkhart, R., and T. Tudder, *Tappi*, **43**, No. 4, 175A (1960).
98. Ljungbo, S., *Medd. Wallboardind. Centrallaboratorium, Stockholm*, No. 11 B (1953).
99. Lorås, V., and F. Löschbrandt, *Norsk Skogind.*, **11**, 402 (1956).
100. Loving, J. M., *Paper Ind.*, **37**, 933 (1956); *Tappi*, **39**, No. 8, 155A (1956).
101. Lowgren, K. A. U., et al., *U.S. Pat.* 2,396,587 (1946); cf. *Paper Trade J.* **136**, No. 8, 175 (1953); *Tappi*, **45**, No. 7, 210A (1962).
102. Lucas, R., *Kolloid-Z.*, **23**, 15 (1918).
103. Luner, P., *Pulp Paper Mag. Can.*, **57**, No. 3, 216 (1956).
104. Lusby, G. R., and O. Maass, *Can. J. Research*, **10**, 180 (1934).
105. Maass, O., et al., *Can. J. Research*, **10**, 24 (1934).
106. Maass, O., *Pulp Paper Mag. Can.*, **54**, No. 8, 98 (1953).
107. Maass, O., et al., *Can. J. Research*, **16 B**, 242 (1938); **17 B**, 121 (1939); **19 B**, 1 (1941).
108. Magruder, R. S., *Tappi*, **41**, No. 12, 58 A (1958).
109. Mark, H., in L. E. Wise and E. C. Jahn, eds., *Wood Chemistry*, 2nd. Ed., Reinhold, New York 1952, p. 137.
110. McGovern, J. N., et al., *Tappi*, **32**, 440 (1949).
111. McGovern, J. N., and G. H. Chidester, *Paper Trade J.*, **98**, No. 18, 41 (1934).
112. McGovern, J. N., and G. H. Chidester, *Paper Trade J.*, **111**, No. 24, 35 (1940); *Tech. Assoc. Papers*, **24**, 579 (1941).

113. Meier, H., *Holz RohWerkstoff*, **13**, 323 (1955).
114. Meier, H., and S. Yllner, *Svensk Papperstid.*, **59**, 395 (1956).
115. Menges, R. A., *et al.*, *Tappi*, **44**, No. 11, 181A (1961).
116. Messing, H. S., *U.S. Pat.* 2,623,820 (1952).
117. Messing, H. S., and C. L. Durkee, *U.S. Pat.* 2,425,335 (1947).
118. de Montigny, R., and O. Maass, *Forest Serv. Bull.* **87**, 1935.
119. de Montmorency, W. H., *et al.*, *Pulp Paper Mag. Can.*, **57**, No. 4, 128 (1956).
120. Mörath, E., cited in F. Kollman, *Technologie des Holzes*, Springer, Berlin 1936, pp. 269–280.
121. Morehead, F. F., cited in F. Bolam, ed., *Fundamentals of Papermaking Fibres*, Tech. Sect. Brit. Paper Board Makers' Assoc., Kenley (England) 1958, p. 64.
122. Nickerson, A. W., *Tech. Assoc. Papers*, **24**, 461 (1941); *Paper Trade J.*, **112**, No. 20, 45 (1941).
123. Nolan, W. J., *et al.*, *Tappi*, **34**, 529 (1951).
124. Nolan, W. J., *Tappi*, **44**, 484 (1961).
125. Oddo, B., *Gazz. Chim. Ital.*, **49 II**, 127 (1919).
126. Paranyi, N. I., and W. Rabinovitch, *Pulp Paper Mag. Can.*, **56**, No. 3, 163 (1955).
127. Peoples, R. S., and L. Ericsson, *Tappi*, **35**, 403 (1952).
128. Richter, J. C. F. C., *U.S. Pat.* 2,474,862 (1949).
129. Richter, J., *Svensk Papperstid.*, **61**, 741 (1958).
130. Ritter, G. A., *Pulp Paper Mag. Can.*, **46**, No. 7, 528 (1945).
131. Roald, B., *Norsk Skogind.*, **7**, 382 (1953).
132. Roald, B., *Norsk Skogind.*, **10**, 285 (1956).
133. Roald, B., *Norsk Skogind.*, **11**, 446 (1957).
134. Rogers, C. N., *Paper Trade J.*, **142**, No. 6, 37 (1958).
135. Ross, J. H., *Pulp Paper Mag. Can.*, **54**, No. 8, 103 (1953).
136. Rydholm, S. A., *et al.*, to be published.
137. Rydholm, S. A., and S. Lagergren, *Svensk Papperstid.*, **62**, 103 (1959).
138. Sadler, H., and O. Trantina, *Papier*, **9**, 317 (1955).
139. Samuelson, O., and A. Wennerblom, *Svensk Papperstid.*, **56**, 745 (1953).
140. Saunderson, H. H., and O. Maass, *Can. J. Research*, **10**, 24 (1934).
141. Saunderson, H. H., *et al.*, *Can. J. Research*, **8**, 415 (1933).
142. Scarth, G. W., and J. D. Spear, *Trans. Roy. Soc. Can.*, **23**, Sect. 5, 281 (1929).
143. Scheil, M. A., *Tappi*, **36**, 241 (1953).
143a. Scholz, E. K., and F. A. Park, *Tappi*, **43**, No. 7, 228A (1960).
144. Seborg, R. M., *et al.*, *U.S. Dep. Agr.*, *Forest Serv. Bull.* No. 1580, 1948.
145. Sloman, A. R., *Pulp Paper Int.*, **3**, No. 6, 18 (1961).
146. Smith, D., and A. C. McCorry, *Tappi*, **41**, No. 6, 247A (1958).
147. Stamm, A. J., *J. Agr. Research*, **38**, 23 (1929).
148. Stamm, A. J., *U.S. Dep. Agr.*, *Tech. Bull.*, **929** (1946); *J. Phys. Chem.*, **36**, 312 (1932).
149. Stamm, A. J., *Pulp Paper Mag. Can.*, **54**, No. 2, 54 (1953).
150. Stamm, A. J., and W. H. Petering, *Ind. Eng. Chem.*, **32**, 809 (1940).
151. Stephenson, J. N., ed., *Preparation and Treatment of Wood Pulp*, Vol. 1, McGraw-Hill, London 1952.
152. Stockman, L., *Svensk Papperstid.*, **63**, 425 (1960).
153. Stockman, L., and L. Ruus, *Svensk Papperstid.*, **57**, 831 (1954).
154. Stone, J. E., *Tappi*, **38**, 449 (1955).
155. Stone, J. E., *Tappi*, **38**, 452 (1955).

156. Stone, J. E., *Tappi*, **40**, 539 (1957).
157. Stone, J. E., *Pulp Paper Mag. Can.*, **57**, No. 7, 139 (1956).
158. Stone, J. E., and H. V. Green, *Pulp Paper Mag. Can.*, **59**, No. 10, 223 (1958).
159. Strapp, R. K., *Tappi*, **39**, 249 (1956).
160. Sutherland, J. H., *Pulp Paper Mag. Can.*, **32**, 163 (1932).
160a. Sutherland, J. H., *et al.*, *Can. J. Research*, **10**, 36 (1934).
161. Svensson, S., *Swed. Pat.* 86,978 (1935); *U.S. Pat.* 2,029,086 (1936).
162. Svensson, A. Å., *Arkiv Kemi*, **10**, 248 (1956).
163. Symposium on the Va-Purge Process in Chemical Pulping, *Pulp Paper Mag. Can.*, **54**, No. 8, 98–134 (1953).
164. Tank-Nielsen, T., *Norsk Skogind.*, **10**, 268 (1956).
165. Tarkkonen, O., *U.S. Pat.* 2,614,923 (1952).
166. Textor, C. K., *Paper Trade J.*, **135**, No. 20, 281 (1952); *Tappi*, **34**, No. 8, 92A (1951).
166a. Thoresen, G., and B. Roald, *Norsk Skogind.*, **15**, 371 (1961).
167. Tucker, E. F., and L. C. Werking, *Paper Ind.*, **28**, No. 1, 60 (1946).
167a. Ullman, U., *Svensk Papperstid.*, **60**, 584 (1957).
168. Van Derveer, P. D., *Paper Trade J.*, **144**, No. 36, 36 (1960).
169. Vilamo, E., *et al.*, *Svensk Papperstid.*, **58**, 452 (1955); *Paperi Puu*, **36**, 401 (1954); **37**, 216 (1955).
170. Wardrop, A. B., *Australian J. Sci. Research*, **B4**, 391 (1951).
170a. Wardrop, A. B., *Svensk Papperstid.*, **66**, 231 (1963).
171. Wardrop, A. B., and H. E. Dadswell, *Holzforschung*, **11**, 33 (1957).
171a. Wardrop, A. B., and H. E. Dadswell, *Counc. Sci. Ind. Research Bull.*, **221**, (1947).
172. Wilson, T. R. C., *U.S. Dep. Agr., Tech. Bull.*, 282 (1932).
173. Wirpsa, V. J., and C. E. Libby, *Tappi*, **33**, 225 (1950).
174. Woods, J. M., and J. S. Hart, *Pulp Paper Mag. Can.*, **56**, No. 3, 171 (1955).
175. Woods, N. I., *Pulp Paper Mag. Can.*, **57**, No. 5, 142 (1956).
176. Yorston, F. H., *Studies in Sulphite Pulping*, Dominion Forest Service Bull. 97, Ottawa 1942.
177. Yorston, F. H., *Pulp Paper Research Inst. Can., Lab. Rept.* No. 23, 1943, cited by S. W. McKibbins, *Tappi*, **43**, 805 (1960).

7

MECHANICAL PULPING
(27, 30)

I. Mechanical Pulping of Bolts—the Groundwood Process

1. GENERAL DESCRIPTION OF PROCESS

The historical development of the groundwood process has been briefly described in Chapter 6.I. Around 15 M t groundwood pulp are now produced yearly, roughly corresponding to one-fourth of the entire pulp production. The main use for groundwood pulp is in the production of *newsprint* paper together with 15–25% chemical pulp, but an increasing quantity is consumed for book paper grades, such as '*book printing*', '*catalogue*', '*coating*', '*magazine*' and '*rotogravure*', in admixture with 30–70% chemical pulp. Important quantities are also consumed in the manufacture of *boards, tissue, some wrapping paper* and *wallpaper*. (27).

Figure 7.1 illustrates the production of groundwood pulp schematically. The wood, taken from storage in yard or pond (16), is well barked and cut to bolts in lengths corresponding to the size of the grinding stones, 3, 4 or 5 feet. The preferred wood species are spruces and firs, but more resinous wood, such as pines, can now be used. Hardwoods, mainly poplar, are used to some extent, but should preferably be pre-cooked with chemicals. The latter type of process is dealt with in Chapter 8.I. Wet wood is preferred to dry (11, 39).

The bolts are transported to the *grinders* by conveyors or water flumes. The grinder constructions are described in Chapter 6.VI. In principle, the grinder consists of a rapidly rotating stone cylinder, against which the bolts are pressed with their longitudinal direction perpendicular to the direction of rotation. The grinding is performed in the presence of water, partly to cool the zone of friction, where considerable quantities of heat are developed, and partly to plasticize the wood substance. The pulp suspension formed in the grinding zone is collected in the grinder *pit* below the stone, from where it flows in open flumes at a consistency of around 2%. The combined flows from all grinders after dilution pass through *coarse* or *bull* screens for the removal of 1–5% *slivers* or *splinters*, which are either returned for re-grinding or passed for special treatment in *refiners*. A recent development, representing a transition stage between mechanical pulping by grinders and by refiners is called *coarse grinding*, by which process bolts are ground on very coarse stones at high loads, and a much higher proportion of the pulp sent through the screening rejects refiners. This is a convenient way of increasing the grinder room capacity without losing quality (21, 37). The accepted pulp from the coarse screens is re-screened on *centrifugal screens*, the reject of which is sent for secondary screening, possibly together with the pulp from the splinters refiners. The accepted groundwood pulp is passed through *centrifugal cleaners* and then thickened on a decker to around 5–7 % consistency and pumped to the paper mill or pulp *wet lap machine*. The accept of the secondary screening should be returned to the primary centrifugal screens. Further details on groundwood pulp screening are given in Chapter 10.III. The white water of the thickeners is returned for dilution in the coarse and fine screening, as well as to the showers of the grinders. The amount of shower water and its temperature greatly influence the grinding result. A resulting pit temperature below 50°C will be used in '*cold grinding*', whereas '*hot grinding*' applies temperatures of 70–95°C.

The operation of the grinders is the principal factor of groundwood

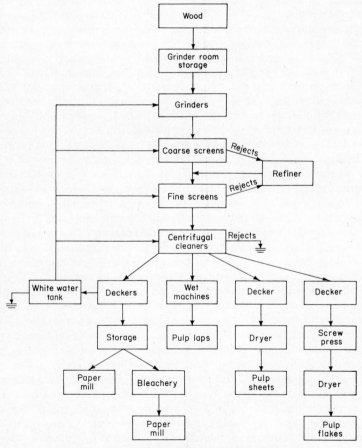

Fig. 7.1. Groundwood mill flow diagram (Johnson)

pulping and determines the capacity, economy and quality of the production.

The production *capacity* is determined by the number and size of the grinders, as well as by several grinder operation factors to be described later. Grinders of up to 90 t/d capacity are in operation, equipped with 6,000 hp motors. In order to maintain an even pulp quality of the ever-changing quality from each grinder, the number of grinders in the mill should be at least 6 or 8. The *manufacturing costs* of groundwood pulp depend mainly on the consumption of wood, energy and abrasives, of which the latter two are considerably influenced by the grinder operation. The wood consumption is low compared to that of other pulping processes, around 0.9–1 cord or 2.2–2.5 solid m³ ptp (per t of pulp), as the pulp yield is 95–98%. Energy consumption is around 1,000–1,500 kWh ptp, and stone consumption in the order of 0.01–0.1 kg ptp.

The pulp *quality* is measured in various ways. As the bulk of the groundwood pulp production is consumed by high-speed newsprint paper machines, the *drainage characteristics* and the *wet web strength* are two of the most important pulp properties. The freeness is low, around 100 ml. Canadian Standard Freeness or 65°SR for newsprint grades and about 60 ml C.S. for other printing paper grades ('catalogue') and some board grades, due to the fairly high proportion of fine fiber fragments formed. Therefore, groundwood pulp is not beaten further prior to paper-making. Also the properties of dried laboratory hand-sheets are tested, such as *tensile, burst* and *tear*, as well as *folding strength, porosity* and *bulk*. One of the most outstanding qualities of this type of pulp is the *absorptivity* and *resiliency* imparted to the paper, giving it excellent printing properties. The bulk is therefore high, corresponding to a sheet density of 0.3–0.5 g/cm³ as compared to 0.6–0.9 for papers of chemical pulps. The strength properties are poor, tensile strength of hand-sheets being 2–3 km as compared to 6–12 km of hand-sheets of chemical pulps after beating to a corresponding freeness. *Brightness* is fair, for groundwood pulp of the best wood species reaching 65% GE or even higher. This is sufficient for most uses, but special purposes, such as coated magazine paper, require higher brightness, and an increasing quantity of groundwood pulp is bleached, by reducing or oxidizing agents, up to or above 70% GE. Groundwood pulp from darker wood or wood containing tannins, such as hemlock, is about 55% GE and has to be brightened even to reach normal brightness level. *Brightness stability* to heat and light is poor, due to the high lignin content, and one of the chief disadvantages of paper from groundwood pulp is in fact its deterioration on storage. Groundwood pulp bleaching is further dealt with in Chapter 13.

The grinding action of the stone will be considered in detail in the following section. The stone is *drilled* to a certain pattern of small cavities or grooves on the stone surface, thereby exposing the grits of the stone. This gives the initial mechanical action on the wood, tearing out its fibers in a more or less damaged form. A newly drilled stone is said to be *sharp*, if too sharp it has to be *dulled*, which should be avoided as unnecessary consumption of abrasive. As the production proceeds, wear on the stone surface causes the stone to get duller, decreasing the rate of production and changing the pulp quality. Finally, the stone has to be sharpened, which happens after a period of a day or a week, depending on stone quality or other production conditions. The sharpening of the stone is still an art and has to be done with care by one or more experienced supervisors. To maintain an even average quality of the pulp, the sharpening of the stones of the different grinders should be performed at different moments, maintaining the same approximate proportions of sharp, dull, and intermediate stones. Other means of influencing the grinding result are by increasing the *load* or *grinding pressure* within a period between two sharpenings, and by adjusting the pit temperature. As a guide for these adjustments, the supervisor has his visual observation of the pulp leaving the grinder, the indications of the electrical instruments installed, as well as the current results of the control department. Adjustments have to be made rapidly, as the pulp of integrated mills will arrive at the paper machine within half an hour.

For visual control of the fibers, the *blue glass*, or better *projectors* are used. The proportions of *splinters, fiber fraction* and *fines* are estimated as well as their qualitative appearance. The fiber fraction, normally more than half the material, should consist of long, flexible, and partly fibrillated fibers, with little damaged, brittle and stiff fragments. The fines should be of the slimy appearance of fibrillated substance rather than wood meal. These qualities are further indicated by the figures for freeness and wet web strength provided by the control department. Other tests are usually too slow to be of any immediate value for adjustments.

Instruments may indicate the load of the grinder, and in some cases the rate of wood consumption also. Combination of these two figures gives information about the state of the grinder. A comparison of the temperatures of the pit and shower water, together with a determination of the pit consistency, may give approximately the same information.

2. MECHANISM OF GRINDING

The mechanism of grinding is still a matter of speculation, mainly because of the difficulty of direct studies of the zone of grinding. Before presenting some of the theories, a few experimental facts should be stressed.

(1) Considerable energy is consumed during grinding.
(2) Considerable heat is evolved.
(3) The less cooling, the less energy is consumed, until 'burning' of the stone appears.
(4) A hydraulic pressure is built up in the pulp suspension between wood and stone.
(5) The surface of the stone changes during grinding towards a more polished state, the grit of the running direction being predominantly affected.

371

(6) The character of the pulp produced changes from much cut, stiff fibers and wood meal to a pulp containing predominantly bruised and fibrillated long fibers with an increasing content of fibrillar fines.

Figure 7.2 shows the specific energy consumption per ton of pulp, as well as the heat evolved, at sharp, normal, and dull states of the stone, at various loads and rates of production (30). Approximately 1,000–1,200 kWh ptp is consumed, more with a dull stone than with a sharp one. At the same time, heat corresponding to around 80% of the energy input is evolved, after deduction of power transfer losses possibly leaving

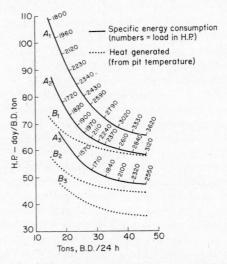

Fig. 7.2. Heat generation and specific energy consumption for different stone surface conditions and loads. 1 hpd/short t = 20 kWh/metr. t. Curve family A–specific energy consumption, curve family B–generated heat (according to grinder pit temperature); (1) with dull stones, (2) with normal stones, (3) with sharp stones (Klemm)

around 150 kWh ptp used for fiberizing and further mechanical deformation of the fibers. Possibly still more heat is evolved, which escapes the determination, and it has in fact been calculated (15, 54) that only about 1 kWh ptp should be needed to increase the wood surface to that of groundwood pulp. On the other hand, this value is probably much too low, as it does not account for the energy needed for deformation in the interior of the fibers (6), which does not show up as increased surface area. In a comparison with the process of peeling with adhesive tape, an energy consumption of about 300 kWh ptp has been calculated (32). Determination of the effective surface energy at the tensile and cleavage fracture of spruce

372

(5a) gave values of the order of 1.10^5 erg/cm² apparent surface area. The latter was shown by electron micrographs not to deviate radically from the real surface area exposed by the fracture. Since the surface free energy of wood can be estimated to be only about 600 erg/cm² (15), it is likely that only a minor part of the fracture energy is converted into free surface energy, and that plastic deformation of the wood structure will require the major part of the energy, which will then dissipate as heat, 'hysteresis loss'. Undoubtedly, most of the energy input is converted into heat, and much thought has been given to the temperatures created in the zone of grinding, with the wellknown softening phenomena of wood on heating in mind. Figure 7.3 shows the calculated temperature of the grinding zone

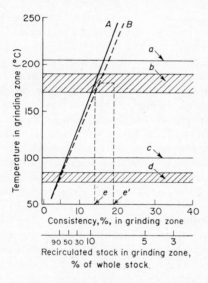

Fig. 7.3. Temperature and consistency in the grinding zone. (*A*) dilution with stock and water from the grinder pit, (*B*) dilution with shower water only, (*a*) temperature of burning of wood, (*b*) field of lignin plasticization, (*c*) boiling point of water, (*d*) temperature in grinder pit, (*e*) theoretical consistency in grinding zone, (*e′*) measured consistency in grinding zone (Klemm)

at various assumed values of the consistency in the zone of grinding (29), at a pit temperature corresponding to hot grinding. The temperature range of lignin plasticization at above 170°C is indicated, as well as the temperature of 'burning' at above 200°C. Obviously, the resulting temperature of the grinding zone will depend on the pulp consistency at that point, i.e. the amount of cooling water present. Although it has been stated that this consistency may amount to 19%, corresponding to temperatures well above 170°C (29), other findings, such as measurements of the stone temperature beneath the stone surface (15, 31) or of the temperature of the pulp in the grinding zone (50), indicate that the temperature on normal operation is below 100°C and not appreciably above the pit temperature and that the consistency in the grinding zone, in a 0.1 mm pulp film, is 2–4% only (50). More recent measurements have revealed that although the pulp film in the grinding zone is only about 100°C, there is an inner zone in the wood at 160–180°C, where the softening of the lignin occurs (35). If the temperature of this inner zone is allowed to rise too much, 'burning' or 'charring' of the wood occurs underneath a wood surface of normal color (6a). As will be shown below, the pressure of the water in the zone of grinding is far below the vapor pressures to be expected at lignin plasticization temperatures. In spite of that, the beneficial influence of a high pit temperature, and consequently high grinding temperature, has been repeatedly demonstrated (e.g. 2, 10, 17, 45, 46), since hot grinding was pioneered in North America in 1888, and it is also conceivable that temperature may rise locally to 170°C or above. As demonstrated in Chapter 6, Figure 6.1, the strength properties of wood decrease fairly continuously over the whole temperature interval and even at temperatures much below 170°C an increase in temperature should thus be of considerable advantage. The phenomenon of burning, which with conventional grinder constructions will put an upper limit to high temperature operation, is generally attributed to developing dry spots on the stone surface through evaporation, with a consequent change in friction conditions and resulting clogging and heat destruction of pulp. At such conditions, considerably higher temperatures below the stone surface have been measured (31).

Figure 7.4 shows the hydraulic pressure developed between stone and wood on grinding at different pit temperatures and grinding pressures (49). Obviously, there is a maximum reached somewhere under the bolt, the developing of pressure being slower than the drop near the further end side of the bolt, as seen in the direction of rotation. It is also observed that even the pressure maximum is considerably lower than the specific grinding pressure applied, indicating solids-to-solids contact in the systems of wood–stone or wood–pulp–stone. These contact points are likely to cause the main fiberizing by tearing out fibers or fiber fragments from the wood, whereas the high shear rates in the liquid film are likely to be responsible for the main re-grinding of the primary fibers (49).

The course of groundwood pulping has been subdivided into several phases (13, 29), mainly *primary* and *secondary* processes. The primary process consists of physical pretreatment of the wood and the initial fiberizing, whereas the secondary process, often called *re-grinding*, involves a further fiberizing of the fibre bundles resulting from the primary process, and fibrillation and fragmentation of the individual fibers. The re-grinding includes the fibrillation of just fiberized material, as well as of fiber adhering to the stone surface when it leaves the pit for renewed contact with the wood. The latter amount is generally somewhat less than the former (29). The ratio of primary to secondary processes decreases as the stone gets duller, as seen by the decrease in freeness and increase in the content of fines of the 'fibrilplasma' type. At the same time there is an increase in strength properties. Finally, the freeness becomes too low for economical operation of the paper machine, and the stone has to be sharpened. Immediately after sharpening, the grinding will produce an inferior quality of pulp, with low strength and low freeness.

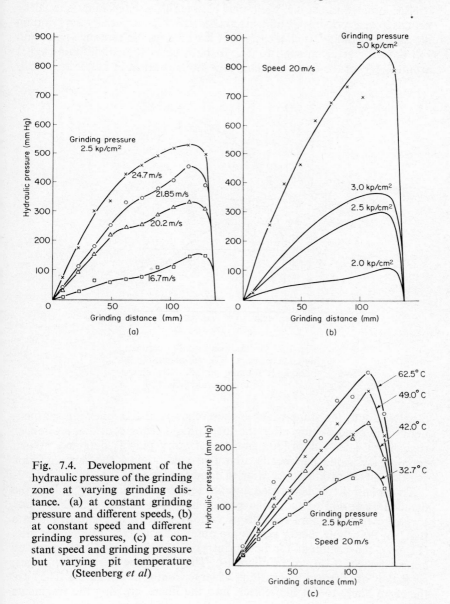

Fig. 7.4. Development of the hydraulic pressure of the grinding zone at varying grinding distance. (a) at constant grinding pressure and different speeds, (b) at constant speed and different grinding pressures, (c) at constant speed and grinding pressure but varying pit temperature (Steenberg *et al*)

375

This pulp contains more stiff and cut fibers and wood meal fines. During a certain *period of self-conditioning*, there is a favorable increase in both strength and freeness, followed by the *main production period* and the *slow-down period*, during which the above-mentioned increase in secondary processes occurs, slowly at first, and then more rapidly, Figure 7.5 (29). Because of the inferior quality of the pulp produced during the self-conditioning of the stone, the cycles between two sharpenings should be kept as long as possible by adjusting other variables, especially the grinding pressure. Normally, such a cycle is at least 5 days for ceramic stones and 1–2 days for artificial sandstones. In both cases the conditioning takes around 15% of the cycle. When a new stone is taken in use, a burr drills

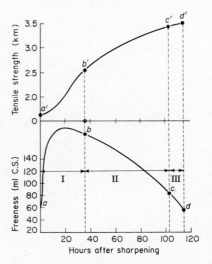

Fig. 7.5. Groundwood quality between two sharpenings. (I) self-conditioning period, (II) main period, (III) slow-down period (Klemm)

a pattern onto the stone which is then renewed at the following sharpenings. The conditioning after the first drilling takes considerably longer time, from 1 to 4 days (30), until satisfactory pulp is obtained. When running the stone backwards after the conditioning, the same inferior pulp quality is produced as prior to conditioning (15).

To explain these phenomena and the actual mechanism of grinding, the detailed condition of the stone surface has been considered. The stone surface consists of abrasive grits of various sizes. Investigations indicate that, on the whole, better results are obtained with relatively coarse grits (17, 29), the optimum for newsprint grades being around 60 mesh or approximately 0.25 mm in diameter. The grits have fairly sharp edges, since they are formed by crushing of larger lumps of abrasives. They are therefore likely to cut like chisels into the fibers, creating the fragments and meal fines at the beginning of the conditioning. After a certain period, their action has changed, probably not by wear of the material itself but by breaking off of edges and breaking out of whole grits (15). Those edges and grits pointing forwards should be more vulnerable to this action whereas others may remain to give cutting if the rotation is reversed. This hypothesis explains the observations made on sharp stones but says nothing about the grinding mechanism during the main production period.

By drilling a pattern into the stone surface, there is no continuous layer of grains, but rather, grooves about 1.5 mm wide, interrupted by high spots of about the same width. The average depth of the grooves is around 0.3–0.6 mm (29). The grinding pressure will cause the wood surface to be sunk down into the grooves. As the stone moves rapidly, at a peripheral speed of around 20 m/s, it is obvious that the wood surface is submitted to repeated compression and expansion, as the grooves and high spots pass by. This is especially so when the stone has been conditioned and the cutting grits removed. The cutting and compressing actions of the stone are schematically illustrated in Figure 7.6a (15). In

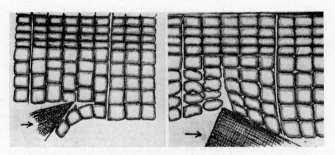

Fig. 7.6a. Schematic illustrations of the concepts of the cutting action of a sharp stone and the compressing action of a conditioned stone respectively (Campbell)

the latter case the fibers are more or less rubbed off from the wood. Possibly the first compression–expansion cycle will not result in the loosening of the fiber but, instead, there will be a failure of fatigue, as the pressure variations at a certain point have a frequency of around 6,000 per second (15). It can be calculated that about 200 grooves and considerably more grits have passed by before a fiber is rubbed off. Obviously, by repeated compression and expansion permanent deformation, crushing and fibrillation, may occur, but a good deal of the work is converted into heat, leading to softening of the fiber walls and facilitating the defibration. On softening, the fibers in the wood lose some of their elasticity, which will tend to decrease not only the work needed for fiberizing but also the heat evolved. This in turn results in a lower temperature, more resistance and more heat evolution. Therefore, the mechanism ought to be in a way self-regulating (30), forming equilibrium

377

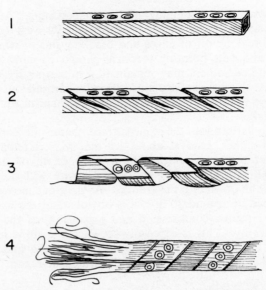

Fig. 7.6b. Schematic drawing of the breakdown of a fiber (1) into ribbons (3) by means of the propagation of cracks (2) running along the S_2 helix. After unravelling, further breakdown of the ribbon into finer ribbons and fibrils occurs (4). The diagonal lines in sketch (4) represent the cell wall corners of the parent fiber (Forgacs)

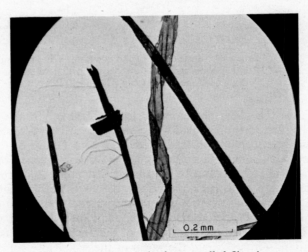

Fig. 7.6c. An almost completely unravelled fiber in a west coast refiner pulp. Note the highly lignified cell wall corners of the parent fiber which appear as dark lines running diagonally across the ribbon. The ribbon itself consisted of the entire cell wall, not just the S_2 layer (Forgacs)

378

conditions, which are only little disturbed by a slight change in, for instance, the water temperature.

Ideally, the entire direct contact between stone and wood occurs at 'conditioned grits' of approximately spherical shape, about 0.2 mm in diameter, interspaced at a distance of 0.6 mm, and making indentations in the wood about 25μ deep (about one fiber width). That these repeated deformations constitute the important mechanism of grinding rather than cutting was demonstrated by producing excellent groundwood pulp from a steel wheel, the periphery of which contained cylindrical protuberances (with a crown radius of 0.1 mm) at right angles to the movement of rotation (6a). The repeated compression–relaxation of the wood structure not only brings about fiberizing but will also lead to radical changes in the fiber wall structure. In contrast to the beating of chemical pulps, which normally leads to destruction of the primary and outer secondary walls, allowing the main secondary wall to swell and fibrillate, grinding or refining of wood leads to rupture of the whole fiber wall along the spiral planes of the S_2 structure (20a), apart from fragmentation by cutting. In extreme cases the fibers wind up along the spiral fracture planes to form ribbons of good flexibility and bonding ability, Figures 7.6b–d.

The time needed for a grit to move along the entire zone of grinding is around 0.05–0.06 seconds in most of the modern grinders. In the same time the downward movement of the wood pile to the stone is in the

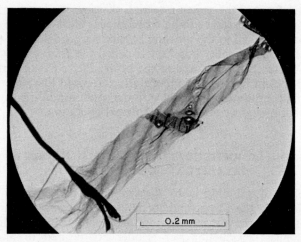

Fig. 7.6d. A ribbon of cell wall produced by unravelling (west coast refiner pulp). Most of the compound middle lamella and S_1 have been sloughed off, although a small fragment of the compound middle lamella is still left adhering in the middle of the field. Note the diagonal striations which were the corners of the parent cell. The lower end of the ribbon has been frayed into the fibrillar components of S_2 (Forgacs)

379

order of 25–50 μ at normal loads (29). As that corresponds approximately to the diameter of the tracheid fibers, it is considered to be a suitable rate of grinding. The ratio of wood advance towards the stone to the average fiber diameter has been called the *'initial grinding factor'* (29) and should be around 1. The depth of the grooves seems to influence the secondary process to some extent, and the *'secondary grinding factor'* (29) has been defined as the rate of pulp production to the rate of passing volume of the grooves. An increase in this factor by, for example, a decrease in that volume (the stone getting duller) will cause a slower pulp of better strength properties.

The *specific grinding pressure*, normally 2–5 kp/cm², is calculated by the load, divided by the geometrical area of contact between wood and stone. As a considerable part of this area does probably not involve true contact, the actual pressure of grits to wood is higher. However, the film of water and pulp probably serve to distribute the grinding pressure more evenly, at least to some extent.

As the main part of the energy consumed in grinding is converted into heat, grinding has often been treated as a problem of friction. Friction occurs between two solid surfaces in contact at rest or at various speeds. The softer material thereby fills out void spaces at the surface of the harder one, to an extent corresponding to the pressure applied perpendicular to the zone of contact. On a relative movement, the protruding parts of the harder material will cause either an elastic compression of those parts of the softer subject filling up the grooves in front of them, or a plastic flow of the softer material, thereby causing scratches in it. In both cases, the resistance to be overcome is called the force of friction, which is proportional to the pressure applied perpendicular to the friction zone. The proportionality constant is called the *friction coefficient*, and is related to number and shape of the protruding parts of surfaces. The friction coefficient between grinding stone and wood therefore varies with the grinding conditions, especially with the condition of the stone surface, but is probably slightly above 0.2 at normal operation.

3. GRINDING CONDITIONS AND THEIR INFLUENCE ON PRODUCTION CAPACITY AND PULP PROPERTIES

The purpose of grinding is to *fiberize the wood* with a minimum of damage done to the fibers, and to *develop the quality* required for the end use. Thereby the lowest consumption of energy and grinding material and the highest production per grinder are desired to minimize the production costs. The following variables are of importance:

(1) *Wood*, species, shape of bolts, moisture content.
(2) *Stone*, type of abrasive, size of grit, type of pattern, depth of grooves, extent of wear.
(3) *Grinder*, type of grinder, specific grinding pressure, which is interrelated to the load and the rate of wood advance, length of

380

grinding zone, width of stone, the latter two variables together constituting the grinding area, tangential speed of stone, pit temperature, pit consistency, shower water temperature, depth of immersion of stone in pit.

Normal practice is shown in Table 6.4 of the previous chapter (12).

A. Specific energy consumption

The energy needed to produce a ton of pulp is called specific energy consumption, usually expressed in kWh ptp or hp-days ptp. It is determined by the interfiber bonding strength, the efficiency of energy transfer from the motor to the grinder and from the stone to the wood. However, apart from the energy of fiberizing, more energy is consumed in the secondary processes of fragmentation and fibrillation, which are also called quality development or beating. Specific energy consumption therefore varies widely with the conditions, and figures given in the literature are seldom quite comparable. An average figure for newsprint grade from softwood is around 1,200 kWh ptp, of which 6% are lost in the energy transfer between motor and grinder, 80% transferred to heat and 14% presumably used up in fiberizing and quality development (29). Of these figures, the second and the third are fairly uncertain, as discussed in the previous section.

As pointed out in Chapter 6.II, the interfiber bonding strength depends, apart from wood species, on temperature, degree of swelling, or chemical dissolution of wood substance. The processes involving chemical treatments prior to grinding are dealt with in Chapter 8.I. Swelling of the wood by water considerably reduces the energy consumption, and the wood is often thoroughly soaked in water prior to grinding. Green wood consumes less energy than stored wood, but storage is often necessary because of seasonal forest operations.

The decrease of interfiber bonding strength with a temperature increase is utilized in all grinding, as the energy consumed is converted to heat to so large an extent. As pointed out previously, the actual temperature of the grinding zone is difficult to measure accurately, but may in the moment of fiberizing amount to the softening range of lignin, which is also reached by direct steam addition in some mechanical pulping processes on chips, cf. Chapter 7.II. In any case, the temperature of grinding must be related to the measurable temperature of the grinder pit water. As the pit is open to atmosphere, this temperature must not exceed 100°C and is in 'cold grinding' below 50°C and approaches 100°C in 'hot grinding'. The heat evolved on grinding is removed by cooling water, which is supplied to the stone showers and to the pit, in which part of the grinding stone is submerged. The resulting pit temperature depends on the heat evolved ptp, the amount of cooling water supplied ptp and its temperature. The amount of cooling water is indicated by the *consistency* of the pulp slurry leaving the grinder, a high consistency meaning a small amount of cooling water and consequently a relatively high pit temperature. Consistencies below 1.5% are considered low and

3–4% high. Although a high consistency at constant temperature of the cooling water will increase the grinding temperature and hence exert a favorable influence on the energy consumption, a high consistency as such is not desirable, as it leads to more re-grinding of pulp through inefficient removal of pulp from the stone. The most favorable results are therefore obtained by low-consistency high-temperature grinding. This requires an increase in the *cooling water temperature*, determined by the extent of recirculation of white water and the amount of fresh water added. Therefore, the consistency of the pulp leaving the thickener after screening becomes an important variable and should be kept high (29). For this reason, thickeners are sometimes substituted by filters. The temperature of the water added to the grinder could then be kept as high as 65°C or more, which results in pit temperatures approaching 100°C.

The higher the pit temperature, the greater the risk of getting dry stone surface and *'burning'* of adhering pulp. This results in a rapid decrease in the grinding effect and a need for brushing and sharpening of the stone, leading to a larger consumption of grinding material. Rapid changes in stone temperature cause danger of cracks in the stone (31). However, with hot grinding it has been possible to remove the pit dam and effect the cooling by spouting large quantities of water of around 65°C and 3.5 kp/cm² pressure directly onto the stone surface (1, 38), the *Risör* high-load grinding. In that way a more efficient cooling is said to be achieved, making it possible to increase the load of the grinder very considerably. Grinder load is often expressed in hp/m² projected grinding area. Normal loads are about 800–900 hp/m², and an increase to 2,300 hp/m² has been found possible to achieve by the *Risör* technique. Re-grinding is decreased and the intervals of sharpening increase up to 500 h, during which up to 2,000 t are produced.

Generally speaking, an increase in pit temperature of 10°C will reduce the total energy consumption by some 10%. The influence of wood species is of the same order of magnitude, poplar drawing around 10% less and pine about 20% more energy than spruce. In comparison it could be said that chemical pretreatment, as in the chemigroundwood process, will reduce the energy requirement by some 50%. The importance of the extent of quality development on the energy consumption could be judged from the fact that a freeness decrease over the normal interval of 200–100 ml. C.S. will cause an increase in specific energy consumption by some 30%. These effects are tabulated in Table 7.1, with the reservation that local conditions might influence the absolute levels of the figures. The energy consumption should thus be related to a certain freeness level because of the importance of the secondary processes for the amount of energy consumed. However, the freeness of the pulp is no clear-cut measure of these processes, since the freeness of pulp produced by an unconditioned stone is low in spite of a fairly low energy consumption. In the same way other grinding conditions might affect the correlation. North American magazine grinders have been found to consume more energy than chain grinders to reach the same freeness level (30) etc.

382

Table 7.1. Specific energy consumption, approximate figures

Wood species	Freeness, ml. C.S.	Pit temperature, °C	Chemical pretreatment	Specific energy consumption, kWh ptp
Spruce	200	70	—	1,050
	150	70	—	1,200
	100	70	—	1,400
	150	80	—	1,100
Pine	150	70	—	1,500
Poplar	150	70	—	1,100
	150	70	Chemigroundwood	600

B. Grinder production and power consumption

The production per grinder and the quality of the pulp are closely related to the condition of the stone surface. Too sharp a stone will produce a coarse pulp with a lot of screenings and wood meal. A very dull stone, with a smooth surface, on the other hand, will yield too much fibrillated material and give a very low production. An optimum is therefore indicated. As a sharp stone eventually gets dull during grinding, burring is necessary. Burring is the operation responsible for most of the stone material consumption and should be limited to a minimum. On the other hand, too great a range of stone sharpness corresponds to too wide variations in pulp quality, and a certain frequency of burring is necessary. Steel brushes, applied on the stone surface leaving the pit after cooling, serve to prevent clogging of organic matter which would decrease the friction. These brushes eliminate some burring and thus prolong the life of the stone. As pointed out previously, the shower water flow and pressure are most important variables to keep the stone clean and to avoid re-grinding (34, 38).

The pattern of the burr has been varied a great deal, spiral patterns being among those more frequently used. However, most patterns left on the stone after burring are nowadays considered to give the same result, the predominant factor being the depth of the grooves and the grit size of the stone.

In treating the grinding as a problem of friction, the grinder capacity can be calculated in the following way. The *area of the grinding zone*, A, in cm², and the *specific grinding pressure*, p, in kp/cm², give together with the *friction coefficient*, μ, the force of friction, F, in kp:

$$F = \mu.p.A$$

Assuming the *peripheral speed* to be u m/s, the *power consumption* of the grinder, W, in kW, must be

$$W = \text{const.}F.u$$

where the constant is a conversion factor from kpm/s to kW, around 0.01. If the *specific energy consumption* of the wood at the grinding

383

conditions applied is E kWh ptp, the production, P, in t/h, of the grinder must be

$$P = W/E \approx 0.01.\mu.p.A.u/E$$

Thus grinder production is increased by higher peripheral speed, friction coefficient, specific grinding pressure, grinding area, as well as by decreased specific energy consumption. How the latter is influenced by wood species, temperature, degree of swelling and chemical treatment, as well as by the freeness desired, was dealt with previously.

However, it must be observed, that the above conclusions are only valid if the variables mentioned are independent. Obviously, if one of them decreases as a consequence of an increase in some other factor, the effect on grinder output will be undecided. Of the five variables of the formula, the latter four could be considered as independent. However, the friction coefficient is affected by a change of most of the others, which makes the practical value of the above formula somewhat dubious. Before choosing another approach, the remaining variables of the formula will be considered. Only seldom is the specific grinding pressure directly measurable, and the values obtained on commercial grinders may be somewhat exaggerated, due to possible binding in the grinder pockets. However, using wood blocks cut to defined dimensions, it can be determined in pocket grinders. It is normally 2–5 kp/cm² but can be increased to 10 kp/cm² or even more. The limiting factor is not the strength of the stone and probably not the crushing resistance of the wood against the stone at high pressures, but the failure of the wood structure at certain critical points, where the pressure of the spike points, lugs or pistons is applied. That pressure will amount to several times that of the grinding zone. The maximal grinding pressure is thus dependent on the grinder construction. The same is true for the grinding area, which is increased by making broader stones and by increasing the effective grinding area in contact with the wood. Stones are now made with a width of up to 1.75 m and with about the same diameter. Modern grinders have stone in contact with the wood of up to 40% of the cylindrical stone surface. The peripheral speed is normally 15–25 m/s, but 40 m/s is possible with modern stones, and 80–100 m/s conceivable in the future (1). The main limiting factor is the mechanical strength of the stone, but other factors are also important. The cooling of the stone must be made more efficient at high speeds, as cooling time between the grinding moments decreases. Further, the centrifugal forces affect the water film on the stone surface and tend to remove it. At constant peripheral speed, the centrifugal forces decrease with increasing stone radius, and large stones are therefore preferred. There is also another reason for choosing stones of large diameter when working at high speed. It has been suggested, that there is an optimal 'initial grinding period' of around 0.05–0.06 seconds, i.e. the time for a grit to pass the entire length of the grinding zone. A high peripheral speed would therefore require a fairly long zone and hence a large stone diameter. The explanation of the optimal time could be that optimal temperature conditions are maintained in the zone of grinding (30), any-way, modern commercial grinders are run at these conditions. Somewhat controversial data on the benefits of increased peripheral speeds have been forwarded (9, 18, 22, 28, 47). With the increase in stone size, speed, and pressure, modern grinders produce up to 90 t/d and must be equipped with motors of up to 6,000 hp.

The change in friction coefficient with the other grinding variables has been the subject of numerous investigations (e.g. 13, 14, 17, 47, 48, 53). The main influence comes from stone sharpness and specific grinding pressure, as exemplified by Figure 7.7. The coefficient of friction will decrease at sharp stones and increase at dull stones with an increase in grinding pressure. It is around 0.3 for sharp stones, 0.1 for a very dull one and slightly above 0.2 at normal operation, decreasing during a pro-duction period. Not unnaturally, peripheral speed and the length of the

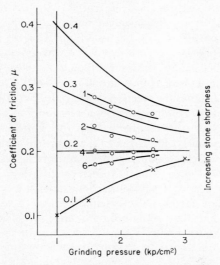

Fig. 7.7. Coefficient of friction vs. grind-ing pressure for different surface con-ditions (Steenberg et al)

grinding zone will also influence the friction coefficient. Obviously, it could, therefore, not be used to describe the state of the stone surface, for which another concept, stone *sharpness*, *S*, has been suggested (48). The stone sharpness is not easily measured in absolute terms, but is defined by the equation:

$$P = \text{const.}S.(W/u)^{\alpha}.u^{\beta}$$

where as before P represents grinder production, W the power input, u the peripheral speed of the stone, and α and β are exponents with values of around 2.0 and 1.0 respectively. Thus, the equation is simplified,

385

omitting the constant of proportionality, to the expression $S = P.u/W^2$. With this expression, changes in stone sharpness can be calculated for any individual grinder from the three known factors of production, peripheral speed, and power load. Attempts have also been made to describe the stone sharpness on studying gypsum images of the stone surface or by specially designed profilometers (26).

C. Quality and grinding variables

The influence of grinding variables on groundwood pulp quality is closely connected with the proportion of primary to secondary processes achieved, and with the type of mechanical action, cutting or crushing, exerted by the stone. This can be followed by fiber fractionation of the pulp, combined with a qualitative evaluation of the fiber fractions. The laboratory classifiers apply screens of around 25, 50, 100 and 200 mesh. The 'longs', remaining on the coarsest screen, are fibers with the least damage, and represent 10–30% of the total pulp. This fraction is important for the strength properties, especially tear and wet web strength, and is larger for conditioned stones than immediately after burring. The 'fines' fraction, passing the finest screen, amounts to 30–45% of the pulp. This fraction largely determines the freeness of the pulp, but will also contribute to the strength properties, especially burst and tensile strength. Thereby, the 'flour' type of fines is less valuable than the 'fibrilplasma' fines (11a). As pointed out previously, the former type is produced by sharp, unconditioned stones and decreases during the conditioning, which results in an increase in freeness, Figure 7.5. On further grinding, the fibrilplasma fines increase, together with the slender long fiber fraction (11b), contributing to strength but causing a decrease in freeness. The quality changes of a sharpening cycle and the contemporary change in the content of fines is further demonstrated in Figure 7.8, which also includes curves obtained on mixing a fiber fraction with various proportions of fines of the two types (29).

The grit size will affect the pulp quality. As seen in Figure 7.9a, coarse and medium grits will give considerably higher strength than fine grit stones, when compared at equal pulp freeness (29). Suitable grit size for newsprint grades is 50–60 mesh. The figure also reflects the changes in strength properties with freeness, as does Figure 7.9b. The type is of little significance (17), whether silicon carbide (Crystolon, Carborundum), aluminium oxide (Alundum, Aloxite), or sand.

The pit temperature will affect pulp quality in the following manner. Freeness increases with temperature, at constant grinding pressure. Compared at equivalent freeness, the strength properties and long fiber fraction increase on increasing pit temperature, Figure 7.10, although a temperature optimum is indicated for dry or decayed wood (30).

The effect of grinding pressure or the rate of advance of the wood is predominantly an increase in pulp freeness. Both temperature and pressure

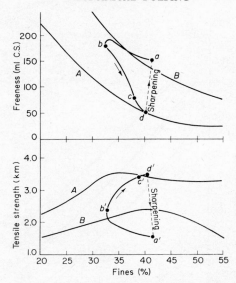

Fig. 7.8. Properties and composition of groundwood during one sharpening cycle. (A) principal curve for groundwood containing favorable ('fibrilplasma') type of fines, (B) principal curve for groundwood containing unfavorable ('flour') type of fines, (abcd) and (a'b'c'd') are actual results during one sharpening cycle (Klemm)

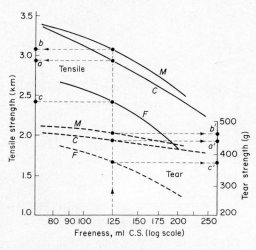

Fig. 7.9a. Groundwood pulp strength vs. freeness when using different stone grit sizes. (C) coarse grits, (M) medium grits, (F) fine grits (Klemm)

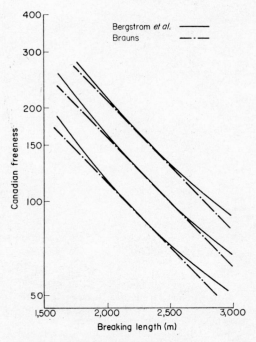

Fig. 7.9b. Paper strength as a function of freeness with groundwood pulp, 'Paterson diagrams' (Brauns)

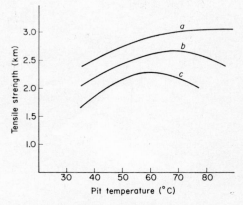

Fig. 7.10. Groundwood pulp strength vs. pit temperature for wood in different conditions. (a) wet wood, (b) dry wood, (c) old wood, badly decayed (Klemm)

388

increases are utilized to compensate for the decrease in freeness and production caused by the decreasing sharpness of the stone.

The influence of the grinding variables on the pulp quality has been investigated (48) using the general equation

$$Q_i = \text{const.}S^{a_i}.(W/u)^{b_i}.u^{c_i}$$

where Q_i denotes any quality measure. The exponents a_i, b_i and c_i have been experimentally determined for freeness, wet web strength, breaking length and air resistance and are given in Table 7.2, which also includes the standard deviations obtained for the exponents, showing statistical significance for all effects but the influence of speed on breaking length. The investigation covered the peripheral speed range of 17–24 m/s.

Table 7.2. Influence of grinding variables on pulp quality (48)

	S, stone sharpness		W, power input		u, peripheral speed	
	a_i	σ_i	b_i	σ_i	c_i	σ_i
Canadian Standard Freeness	+2.8	0.2	+1.5	0.2	+1.1	0.3
Wet web strength	−1.4	0.2	−1.0	0.2	−1.1	0.3
Breaking length	−1.3	0.4	−1.5	0.4	−0.5	0.6
Air resistance	−1.1	0.1	−1.1	0.1	−0.3	0.1

From these expressions for Q_i and the corresponding expression for the production,

$$P = \text{const.}S.W^2/u$$

some deductions can be made regarding the influence of the grinding variables. For instance, at a *constant power input* and *constant speed*, the production decreases as the stone gets duller, in direct proportion to the sharpness. At the same time, freeness decreases according to the relation

$$\text{Freeness} = \text{const.}S^{2.8} = P^{2.8}$$

When production has decreased by 5%, freeness has dropped by 15%.

To keep the important characteristic of *pulp freeness constant* at a *constant peripheral speed*, obviously requires that

$$S^{2.8}.W^{1.5} = \text{const., or } W = \text{const.}/S^{1.9}$$

which means that the power input has to be increased considerably as the stone gets duller. If the sharpness during a cycle is allowed to decrease by 20%, the power input should increase by around 40%. At the same time the specific energy consumption, E or W/P, changes slightly, according to the equations

$$E = W/P = \text{const.}/S.W = \text{const.}S^{0.9}$$

For *constant speed*,

$$\text{Wet web strength} = \text{const.}S^{-1.4}.W^{-1.0}$$

which changes into const.$S^{0.5}$ if the power input is steadily increased to keep freeness constant. This shows that wet web strength will decrease by some 10% during a cycle with a sharpness decrease of 20%, in spite of the fact that constant freeness is maintained. The results quoted above were obtained from an experimental grinder. The principal correlation between freeness and breaking length was found to be the same for a large number of industrial grinders (8). When plotted in a semilogarithmic diagram (42), breaking length is found to be a linear function of log freeness, increasing about 0.7 km for a reduction of the freeness by 50%, Figure 7.9b.

D. Pulp yield

Apart from the excellent printing characteristics of paper rich in groundwood pulp, its chief advantage is that it is the *lowest-priced* pulp in the market. The main contributing factors to this are the absence of chemicals costs and the almost quantitative yield from wood, the yield losses being only 2–5%. As wood is predominantly bought on a volume basis, the wood density is an important factor. Table 7.3 shows the approximate wood consumption for groundwood pulp from various wood species (30, 43).

Table 7.3. Wood consumption for one metric ton of groundwood pulp from various wood species

Wood species	Spruce	Fir	Pine	Poplar
Basic density, t/m³, o.d. weight on wet volume	0.42	0.40	0.48	0.37
Piling density, solid m³/stere (piled m³)	0.72	0.72	0.68	0.72
Assumed pulp yield, %	98	98	95	96
Theoretical wood consumption:				
Solid m³ ptp	2.4	2.5	2.2	2.8
Stere ptp	3.4	3.5	3.2	3.9
Cord ptp	0.95	0.97	0.89	1.08
Practical wood consumption:				
Stere ptp	3.4–3.5	3.5–3.6	3.2–3.3	3.9–4.1

E. Quality of pulpwood and groundwood pulp

Pulpwood quality demands are of the utmost technical and economical significance. Since the groundwood production involves little or no chemical treatment, the physical characteristics of the wood will be strongly reflected in the pulp. One of the immediate demands is, therefore, that the wood should be fairly *bright*. Most hardwoods, as well as softwoods with dark heartwood, are thus ruled out. Some wood species of western North America, such as western hemlock, can be used only when bleached with dithionite (hydrosulfite). Similarly, the wood used should be *clean* and *well-barked* and substantially free from discoloring *decay*. From a technical stand-point, *light* wood is preferred to heavy wood, since it gives a stronger groundwood pulp, but when bought by volume, such wood obviously gives a more expensive pulp than does a heavy wood at equal price. *Compression* wood lowers the quality in contrast to *tension* wood. Of the utmost importance is the *moisture content* of the pulpwood, since drying gives a hornified structure which tends to increase the cutting action of the stone. Freshly cut wood is thus preferred, and storage of the wood in, or even under, water is practised. Because of the grinder construction, the log *dimensions* are critical. The logs are cut to bolts of standard length, and very large as well as small diameters are unsuitable. Saw-mill waste cannot be utilized in grinding. Since a certain strength of the wet web as well as of the paper is required, long-fibered *softwoods* are preferred to *hardwoods*.

Those pulpwood demands have caused a selection of wood species and grades for grinding, which has become reflected in the wood prices. More than 80% of the wood species used are softwoods. *Spruces, firs* and *hemlocks* are the main raw materials, whereas *Douglas fir* and *pines* of old growth give too dark a pulp for most purposes. Young southern pines with little heartwood can be utilized, especially since methods of pitch control have been developed. These involve the addition of alum and sodium hydroxide during grinding and additional alum at the paper machine. Pine groundwood is now made in southern United States, South Africa, New Zealand and southern Europe (cf. Chapter 8.I). Some hardwood species can be used, mainly of low to medium density. In northern United States and in Canada, some *aspen* is ground without chemical pretreatment—although often with a subsequent bleach—and in Europe, especially Italy, a fast-growing *poplar* hybrid has been specially developed for the purpose, which gives an excellent pulp brightness. Some *eucalypt* groundwood is made in Australia and *salai* (Boswelia) groundwood in India. The hardwoods give lower overall strength properties, and the low wet web strength necessitates slower paper machine speeds and higher content of chemical pulp in the furnish, unless the hardwoods are given a chemical pretreatment, cf. Chapter 8.

The better wood grades give a groundwood pulp of 60–65% GE in brightness and the acceptable ones 50–60% GE. Dithionite bleaching will improve the brightness about 5% GE, peroxide bleaching 5–20% GE, according to charge, cf. Chapter 13. For most purposes, 60–65% GE is adequate, but bleached grades gain in importance. Opacity of normal handsheets is over 95%. Tensile strength varies from 1 to over 3 km, the tear factor from 20 to 50 or even more, the lower figures being representative for somewhat dense hardwoods and the higher figures for good softwood mechanical pulp. In contrast to chemical pulps, groundwood pulps increase in both tensile and tear strength as well as in opacity upon a freeness reduction. Groundwood for newsprint is generally produced at a freeness around 100 ml C.S., whereas catalogue and other book groundwood grades are given a lower, about 60 ml C.S., and groundwood for molded products, etc. a considerably higher freeness.

II. Mechanical Pulping of Chips

1. LOW TEMPERATURE DISK REFINING

Mechanical pulping in grinders was the first technological approach to the problem of separating wood fibers mechanically. Although modern grinders show many advanced details of construction, their main principle of tearing the fibers out of a log pressed against a grinding stone is primitive and has several drawbacks. One of the main objections is the difficulty of separating the fibers without damage to the fiber walls, especially in the case of hardwoods with their high content of vessel elements with thin walls. Groundwood pulp therefore gives low-strength papers, and requires long-fibered softwoods.

To achieve acceptable mechanical pulp also from lower-priced hardwood and from softwood saw-mill waste, methods have recently been developed which start from chips and use disk refiners of various types. The action of a disk refiner differs from that of a grinder and the pulp produced consists of less damaged fibers than that of groundwood. However, it is beneficial for both pulp quality and energy consumption to soften the wood before fiberizing, and this can be done in several ways. Some methods use swelling in alkali or dissolution of considerable amounts of wood substances, and are therefore classed among the semichemical pulping processes, Chapter 8. Others use thermal softening together with swelling in water as the chief means of softening the interfiber bonds, and will be treated in this section. Recalling the temperature dependence of the interfiber bonds in aqueous medium, Figure 6.1, it is evident that a considerable effect can thereby be achieved by heating to 90–100°C, as also utilized in hot grinding, and additional weakening of the interfiber bonds when temperature is brought up above the softening interval of lignin at 150–70°C. The former methods are called low temperature defibration and can be carried out at atmospheric pressure.

The *Isogrand* process operates on European beech at temperatures around 100°C and with an Asplund defibrator, to give a mechanical pulp, which is further treated with alkali for resin removal, chlorinated at an increased pH and bleached with hypochlorite to yield a fairly bright pulp, which must be characterized as bleached mechanical (3, 20b).

The fiberizing of softwood chips as a real competitor to the groundwood process is a recent development (20, 23, 30, 40, 52). This has been promoted by the two largest American producers of precision refiners, *Bauer Bros.* and *Sprout–Waldron*. Figure 7.11 shows a principal flow sheet. Softwood chips are fed from soaking pits to a hopper and further via screw conveyors to two or three refiner stages. The pulp so produced is screened and vortex cleaned. To ensure water penetration, some installations use screw presses (Pressafiner or Anderson Fiber Press) to squeeze the chips prior to refining, but for purely mechanical pulping the press is not considered necessary. In such cases the soaking bin can also be omitted or substituted by a steaming vessel. Especially when using saw-mill waste it has proved to be an advantage to rinse the chips in water together with a surfactant. This treatment removes sand and other particles, which would otherwise wear on the refiner plates. A magnet to trap tramp iron is also useful.

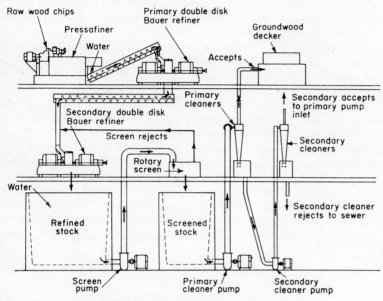

Fig. 7.11. Mechanical pulp from chips (Eberhardt)

Initially, the energy consumption for chip refining exceeded that of grinding considerably (20, 41), and the main incentive to proceed with the development work lay in the possibility of using cheaper wood, i.e. saw-mill waste and logs of dimensions less suited to grinding. This is especially valuable for the industry located on the North American west coast, and there the process has been further developed. It was found that a high consistency improved the power economy, and the pulp now leaves the refiner at more than 15% consistency and about 100°C. Still higher consistency results in steam blow-backs in the refiner. Improved results have also been obtained by increasing disk size and speed of rotation. Double disk refiners having 48 in. disks rotating at 1,200 r.p.m. each and equipped with two 2,000 hp motors, have been stated to do the best work, and this means that refiner units now in use have capacities as large as all but the largest grinders. Single stage refining does not allow operation at a higher consistency than 8% because of the heat evolved, but two-stage refining allows about twice that value in the first stage, where only 30–50% of the total energy demand should be applied (23). In both cases, a final freeness control by a 'pump-through' single disk refiner is necessary, but that refining should be kept at a minimum, since its action is more freeness-reducing than strength-developing.

393

With that development, energy consumption has been reduced to a value only slightly above that of grinding, or about 1,400 kWh ptp, as compared to 1,200–1,300 kWh ptp, and it is believed that further development is possible (19, 23). The quality of mechanical refiner pulp is generally considered superior to that of groundwood because of higher strength, and larger content of long fibers. Also in this respect, further improvement is anticipated by finding optimal refiner conditions, the most suitable plate pattern etc. A drawback as yet is the formation of short wood fragments, or *chops*, which makes it necessary to remove about 2% by vortex cleaning. The plate wear gives a cost of about $1 ptp, and necessitates a change after a production of almost 1,000 t, or similar to the better results of grinding. The mechanical refiner pulp has so far been used for newsprint production only in trial runs or in admixture with groundwood. The trial runs with this 'supergroundwood' as sole newsprint furnish were very successful and a rapid development in this direction is expected (39a). Other uses are molded products, tissue papers and board.

The refiner pulp characteristics given so far (20a, 23, 39a), Table 7.4, indicate great possibilities as well as a lack of knowledge about the fundamentals of the process and its variables, and therefore widely varying results. Such knowledge is, however, now being accumulated. A technique involving successive removal of the plate pattern (6b) has demonstrated

Table 7.4. Mechanical refiner pulp, power consumption and quality as compared to groundwood

Wood species	Western hemlock (23)					Spruce (39a)		Spruce-fir (20a)	
Scale	Pilot plant		Large		Ground-wood	Pilot plant (av.)	Ground-wood	Pilot plant (av.)	Ground-wood
Stages	1	2	1	2					
Spec. energy consumption, kWh ptp	1,400	1,400	1,700	1,500	1,300	2,000	1,300	—	—
Percentage power in stage 1	100	50	100	95	—	—	—	—	—
Freeness, ml C.S.	100	100	100	100	100	140	106	95	90
Tensile strength, km	2.9	3.4	2.9	2.7	2.4	3.5	3.2	3.7	3.5
Burst factor	12	14	12	11	10	17	14	20	17
Tear factor	60	70	50	35	40	80	48	65	42
Wet web strength, units	—	—	—	—	—	90	68	220	160
Fractions, % Plus 20 mesh	10	11	3	2	11	24*	14*	27*	16*
35	21	21	18	15	15	23	17	19	19
65	17	20	24	22	16	14	20	13	18
150	11	13	15	20	18	10	17	7	9
Minus 150	41	35	40	41	40	29	32	34	38

* The fractionations of the spruce and spruce-fir pulps employed the following mesh numbers instead: 28, 48, 100 and 200

strated the state of chip disintegration at various points in the refiner. Dynamic considerations as well as practical evidence indicate that after an initial disintegration the chip fragments assume an approximately cylindrical shape and roll between the disk plates, radially orientated, until the repeated compressions–relaxations, caused by the bars and grooves, lead to collapse of the wood structure and pulping. Less fiber cutting and development of a long fiber fraction with a larger specific surface (20a) appear to be the causes of the improvements in wet web and paper strength as compared with groundwood.

Chip refining obviously offers possibilities of *chemical pretreatment* to a much larger extent than does grinding, especially when using softwoods. Various types of chemical treatments have also been tried, from simple addition of sulfite or bisulfite in the refiner, to more pronounced precooks using Rapid-Cycle or continuous digesters, preferably with the same chemicals. Thus, a somewhat brighter pulp may be obtained, as well as stronger pulps with somewhat lowered opacity and yield and considerably reduced energy consumption (19). Thereby, the border-line between mechanical and semichemical pulping is passed and further comments should be saved for the next chapter. Whereas such pulps offer new perspectives for several types of papers, strictly mechanical refiner pulps are also of utmost interest because of their higher strength, or higher freeness, as compared to groundwood, the possibility of utilizing wood waste, and the greater possibilities of quality control. Even sawdust can be used as a raw material for certain grades of mechanical pulp (51).

In order to reduce energy consumption without chemicals, thermal softening of the interfiber bonds can be utilized. High-temperature disk refining is used in the *Asplund process* and high-temperature steam expansion in the *Mason process*, which are dealt with in the following section. However, in contrast to the low-temperature refining process, they do not yield pulps suitable for newsprint and do not represent an alternative to groundwood pulping.

2. HIGH TEMPERATURE DISK DEFIBRATION—THE ASPLUND PROCESS

A new pulping process was developed in the early 1930's, which used mechanical forces for fiberizing chips that had been softened with the aid of water and high temperature (4, 5, 33). The process was named after its inventor, *Asplund*, or after the fiberizer, *Defibrator*, a single disk semiprecision refiner, admitting operation under pressure. The first Defibrator was installed in Sweden in 1934 and in America in 1937. In 1955 more than 100 mills with a capacity of 3,000,000 t were making Defibrator pulp for wallboard and roofing and flooring felt. An increasing quantity of semichemical pulp is also being refined in Defibrators.

A flow sheet of the Asplund thermo-mechanical pulping process for hardboard is shown in Figure 7.12. The raw material, roundwood or saw-mill waste, is chipped in the conventional way, cf. Chapter 5, and the chips are fed from a bin continuously to the Defibrator units. Tramp iron is removed magnetically. The chip feed is regulated by a vibrator. The chips are compressed in a plunger or screw feeder through a narrow pipe, where they form a compact plug, blocking the escape of steam from the preheater. The steam, which is introduced into the preheater immediately after the pipe, helps in forming the plug. With chips from green

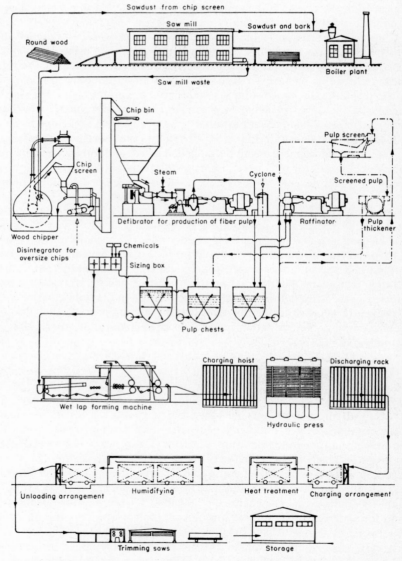

Fig. 7.12. Production of thermomechanical pulp for hardboard according to the Asplund method (Defibrator Bulletin)

or floated wood, with a moisture content around 50%, steam condensate and chip moisture are sufficient to give the preferred water: wood ratio of 1.3–1.9. If the wood is drier, some water has to be added with the steam. Steam of 7–13 kp/cm^2 is used, giving a temperature of 170–190°C after 30–60 seconds, whereafter the softened chips are immediately defibrated in less than one second in the 40 mm wide grinding zone of the disks, of which one rotates with a speed of 500–600 r.p.m. Plate interdistance is about 0.3 mm. During this short time at high temperature very little hydrolysis occurs, and the yields obtained from softwoods are around 93–97%. The pulp is blown to a cyclone through a reciprocating outlet mechanism and is received by a pulp chest, from which it is pumped either to screening and thickening or to additional refining or beating. After sizing and wet lap forming, the laps are compressed under heating to around 200°C for 10 minutes to form the wallboard, which is subsequently heat-treated at 150–165°C for several hours to complete the physical changes needed for low water absorptivity and swelling properties. Defibration requires only 150–200 kWh ptp as against 1,000–1,500 kWh ptp for ground-wood. Steam consumption is around 0.5 t ptp.

In contrast to groundwood pulp, Defibrator pulp consists of fibers with comparatively undamaged walls. Its color is yellower than that of ground-wood pulp, but considerably brighter than brown groundwood pulp or kraft pulp. The wellknown brown color of wallboard is not developed until the pressing and heat treatment operations. Being a pulp of high lignin content, Defibrator pulp is only suited to lignin-brightening bleach-ing methods (25). The tensile strength of the individual fibers is close to that of wood. However, the paper-bonding properties are poor, probably due to the high lignin content and its hydrophobic properties as well as to the coarse structure of the pulp. Fibrillation to a greater degree may, however, be developed during the high temperature fiberizing by special methods, indicating potentialities of paper-making from this pulp. High-precision disk refiners for high temperature and pressure are being developed which may be able to realize these possibilities.

The easy water-drainage of Defibrator pulps is an advantage in the wet lapping of the wallboard and the consequently bulky sheet formed is valu-able in the asphalt saturation of the roofing and flooring felts.

The ambition of the Defibrator method of developing a field of wood waste utilization has only been partly realized. A wallboard, competitive in quality, should be made from barked softwood of good quality. How-ever, where surface appearance is of less importance, greater amounts of bark can be tolerated. Then the use of forest thinnings of small dimen-sions, as well as all kinds of saw-mill waste are suitable sources of raw material. Hardwoods and vegetable fiber materials are also used for Defibrator pulp production. Because of the dispersion of parenchyma cells, abundant in annual plants, yields from the latter are only 60–70%.

All sorts of modifications of the Defibrator process have been suggested, cf. Chapter 6.VI. By employing reaction screws or other suitable pre-treatment chambers, chemical reactions during 10–120 minutes or longer have been made possible. These processes, however, are semichemical pulping methods. Chemical treatment subsequent to fiberizing has also been suggested as a means to uniform and rapid chemical pulping (24). However, as discussed in Chapter 6.V, the damage of the wood structure causes excessive chemical degradation on cooking, making this development less promising.

3. HIGH TEMPERATURE EXPLOSIVE DEFIBRATION—THE MASON PROCESS

Although other processes have also employed the principle of high temperature defibration by steam expansion, it is tied to the name of *Mason*, who in 1926 patented a process and apparatus for production of wood fibers by steam heating to high temperatures, followed by a rapid pressure release (7, 36). The first mill was erected in Laurel, Miss., in 1926. As this process utilizes higher temperatures than that of Asplund, a higher loss in pulp yield occurs through hydrolysis, and it is open to question whether the Mason process should be assigned to mechanical or semi-chemical pulping. It is fairly certain that both thermal and chemical softening of the interfiber bonds occur, and the reason why the process is treated under the heading of mechanical pulping in this book is that the thermal softening is considered to be the essential part of the process, and that the reason for employing temperatures far above the softening temperature range of lignin, 150–170°C, is not predominantly to achieve a certain degree of hydrolysis but to obtain the energy needed for defibration. The latter is performed through rapid steam expansion from fairly high steam pressures.

Wood chips are fed into small digesters originally of around 0.1 t of wood capacity, the so-called *Masonite guns*. The charging valve is closed, high pressure steam is introduced and the temperature is rapidly brought up to around 200°C, where it is maintained for approximately 15 seconds. Then the softened chips are further heated to 280–285°C and the temperature kept at this level for 4–5 seconds. The content of the digester is then blown to the atmosphere in an explosion with an estimated velocity of 1,200 m/sec. Thereby defibration takes place, and the steam is separated from the fibers in a cyclone. The total cooking cycle takes only somewhat more than a minute, and operation is fully automated. This is important, as a change of 0.5 seconds at maximum temperature will change the quality of the end product noticeably. The steam consumption is likely to be in the order of 1 t ptp and the steam used in excess of that of the Asplund process corresponds to approximately the amount of energy introduced into the Asplund process by the disk refiner.

After defibration, the pulp is worked up in a way similar to that of the Asplund process, with further refining, screening, wet lapping and pressing into hardboard sheets at 200°C. As a matter of fact, some of these operations were developed by Mason.

Pulp yield is 80–90%, and some dissolution therefore has taken place.

In addition to deacetylation, which also occurs in the Asplund process, hydrolysis of glycosidic bonds takes place, especially in the hemicellulose part of the wood. Workers on the process also stress the importance of the cleavage of lignin–carbohydrate and intra-lignin bonds (7), to yield the lignin in an 'activated state', as evidenced by the increasing portion of organosoluble lignin upon increasingly harsh conditions in the process. The significance of these reactions, however, does not seem to have been clearly demonstrated from a purely lignin chemical point of view.

Mason fiber is applied for similar purposes as Asplund fiber. Both softwoods and hardwoods are used as raw material. However, as they require different time–temperature conditions, softwoods and hardwoods should be pulped separately and the fibers subsequently mixed. A similar process, the *Celotex* process, utilizes bagasse as the raw material (44).

REFERENCES

1. Ancker, C., Papers presented at Papirind. Tekn. Forenings Teknikeruke, Oslo, 1950, cf. ref. 38.
2. Andrews, H., *Pulp Paper Mag. Can.*, **41**, No. 2, 87 (1940).
3. Anon., *Tappi*, **39**, No. 9, 162A (1956).
4. Asplund, A., *Brit. Pat.* 393,159 (1933); *U.S. Pat.* 2,008,892 (1935); 2,145,851 (1939); *Tekn. Tidskr.*, **69**, K:89 (1939); *Wochbl. Papierfabrik.*, **71**, 590, 607 (1940); *Svensk Papperstid.*, **56**, 550 (1953); **59**, 441 (1956); **61**, 701 (1958).
5. Asplund, G., *Svensk Papperstid.*, **55**, 505 (1952).
5a. Atack, D., *et al.*, *Tappi*, **44**, 555 (1961).
6. Atack, D., and W. D. May, *Pulp Paper Mag. Can.*, **58**, No. 3, 265 (1958).
6a. Atack, D., and W. D. May, *Tappi*, **45**, 145 (1962).
6b. Atack, D., and W. D. May, *Pulp Paper Mag. Can.*, **64**, No. C, T 75 (1963).
7. Boehm, R. M., *Paper Trade J.*, **118**, No. 13, 35 (1944); cf. *Ind. Eng. Chem.*, **22**, 493 (1930).
8. Brauns, O., *Svensk Papperstid.*, **64**, 662 (1961).
9. Brecht, W., *Papierfabr.*, **33**, 113, 121, 129 (1935).
10. Brecht, W., *et al.*, *Papierfabr.*, **38**, 53, 61 (1940).
11. Brecht, W., *et al.*, *Papierfabr.*, **36**, 421 (1938); *Papier*, **8**, 462 (1954).
11a. Brecht, W., and M. Holl, *Papier fabr.*, **37**, 74 (1939).
11b. Brecht, W., and K. H. Klemm, *Pulp Paper Mag. Can.*, **54**, No. 1, 72 (1953).
12. Brecht, W., and F. Luhde, *Tappi*, **45**, 413 (1962).
13. Brecht, W., and W. Müller, *Papierfabr.*, **36**, 198 (1938).
14. Cameron, E. P., *Forest Prod. Lab. Can.*, Quarterly Review No. 18, 17 (1934).
15. Campbell, W. B., *Pulp Paper Mag. Can.*, **35**, 218 (1934), **52**, No. 3, 217 (1951).
16. Chesley, K. G., *et al.*, *Tappi*, **39**, 129, 609 (1956).
17. Collicut, S. A., *Pulp Paper Mag. Can.*, **52**, No. 3, 159 (1951).
18. Collicut, S. A., and J. A. Cochrane, *Pulp Paper Mag. Can.*, **53**, No. 3, 215 (1952).
19. Dorland, R. M., *et al.*, *Tappi*, **45**, 257 (1962).
20. Eberhardt, L., *Paper Trade J.*, **139**, No. 37, 26 (1955); **140**, No. 8, 30 (1956).
20a. Forgacs, O. L., *Pulp Paper Mag. Can.*, **64**, No. C, T 89 (1963).
20b. Grand, L., *Papier, carton et cellulose*, **5**, No. 2, 130, 134 (1956.)
21. Hoholik, F. S., *Pulp Paper Mag. Can.*, **59**, No. 10, 141 (1958).

22. Holland, W. W., *Pulp Paper Mag. Can.*, **50**, No. 4, 79 (1949).
23. Holzer, W. F., *et al.*, *Tappi*, **45**, 208 (1962).
24. Jayme, G., and L. Grögaard, *Cellulosechem.*, **18**, 34 (1940); *Papierfabr.*, **38**, 149 (1940).
25. Jayme, G., and R. Wettstein, *Papierfabr.*, **36**, 519 (1938).
26. Johansson, O. S., and T. Pettersson, *Svensk Papperstid.*, **55**, 497 (1952).
27. Johnson, E. H., ed., *Mechanical Pulping Manual*, TAPPI Monograph Series No. 21, New York 1960.
28. Jones, J. B., and W. W. Holland, *Pulp Paper Mag. Can.*, **43**, No. 3, 141 (1942).
29. Klemm, K. H., *Pulp Paper Mag. Can.*, **56**, No. 12, 178 (1955).
30. Klemm, K. H., *Neuzeitlich Holzschlifferzeugung*, Sändig Verlag, Wiesbaden 1957, and the American Ed., *Modern Methods of Mechanical Pulp Manufacture*, Lockwood, New York 1959.
31. Kraft, M. S., and H. Kalbfleisch, *Pulp Paper Mag. Can.*, **56**, No. 12, 156 (1955).
32. Lamb, G. E. R., *Tappi*, **43**, 939 (1960); **45**, 364 (1962).
33. Lowgren, U., *Paper Trade J.*, **113**, No. 11, 29 (1941); **127**, No. 12, 41 (1948); *Paper Ind.*, **22**, No. 12, 1241 (1941); *Papier*, **45**, 17 (1942); *Pulp Paper Ind.*, **21**, No. 1, 42 (1947).
34. Luhde, F., *Pulp Paper Mag. Can.*, **60**, No. 10, T 300 (1959).
35. Luhde, F., *Pulp Paper Mag. Can.*, **61**, No. 11, T 544 (1960).
36. Mason, W. H., *U.S. Pat.* 1,578,609 (1926); 1,586,159 (1926); 1,655,618 (1928); 1,663,503 (1928); 1,663,504 (1928); *Paper Trade J.*, **83**, No. 8, 53 (1926); **84**, No. 8, 131 (1927).
37. de Montmorency, W. H., *Pulp Paper Mag. Can.*, **59**, No. 3, C 203 (1958).
38. de Montmorency, W. H., *Pulp Paper Mag. Can.*, **61**, No. 8, T 402 (1960).
39. Morris, W. S., *Pulp Paper Mag. Can.*, **44**, No. 7, 501 (1944).
39a. Neill, M. T., and L. R. Beath, *Svensk Papperstid.*, **66**, 508 (1963); *Pulp Paper Mag. Can.*, **64**, No. C, 127, No. 7, T 299 (1963).
40. Otis, B., *Paper Trade J.*, **141**, No. 7, 36 (1957).
41. Ottar, H., *Norsk Skogind.*, **11**, 219 (1957).
42. Paterson, H. A., *Pulp Paper Mag. Can.*, **37**, No. 2, 79 (1936).
43. Perry, H. J., *et al.*, *Manufacture of Mechanical Pulp*, in J. N. Stephenson, ed., *Preparation and Treatment of Wood Pulp*, Vol. 1, McGraw-Hill, London 1952, p. 182.
44. Rivise, C. W., *Paper Trade J.*, **95**, No. 22, 25 (1932); **97**, No. 19, 39 (1933).
45. Sätre, K., *Svensk Papperstid.*, **42**, 321 (1939); *Zellstoff Papier*, **19**, 517 (1939).
46. Schafer, E. R., and J. C. Pew, *Paper Trade J.*, **101**, No. 13, 71 (1935); *Tech. Assoc. Papers*, **19**, 401 (1936).
47. Schafer, E. R., and J. C. Pew, *Tech. Assoc. Papers*, **23**, 579, 623 (1940).
48. Steenberg, B., *et al.*, *Svensk Papperstid.*, **60**, 409 (1957).
49. Steenberg, B., *et. al.*, *Norsk Skogind.*, **11**, 235 (1957); *Pulp Paper Mag. Can.*, **58**, No. 10, 172 (1957).
50. Steenberg, B., and A. Nordstrand, *Tappi*, **45**, 333 (1962).
51. Stewart, D. L., *Pulp Paper Mag. Can.*, **59**, No. 7, 125 (1958).
52. Textor, C. K., Bauer Bros. Progress Report, Springfield, Ohio, July 1957.
53. Thickens, J. H., *U.S. Dep. Agr.*, *Forest Serv. Bull.*, 127, Washington D. C. 1912.
54. Van den Akker, J. A., in F. Bolam, ed., *Fundamentals of Papermaking Fibres*, Tech. Sect. Brit. Paper and Board Makers' Assoc. Kenley (England) 1958, p. 182.

8

SEMICHEMICAL PULPING

INTRODUCTION

'With an ever decreasing supply of wood comes a constantly changing economic condition which may alter the relations governing the pulp industry so far that some of these (non-conventional) processes and the modified products growing out of them may find profitable application. Particularly is there a need for some process which will produce a pulp capable of supplementing and substituting for groundwood in both quality and cost. Such a product must be made from mill waste, logging waste or those species of wood which grow and reproduce rapidly and which are not in urgent demand for other uses. It is to be hoped that the need is sufficiently impressive to incite many minds to come to grips with the problem.' (154)

These words, written in 1925 in a review of the few efforts towards semichemical pulping up to that date, forebode the exact condition for an important development (160, 195). It could have been added, that the changes in the methods of ware distribution and the consequent growing need of cheap fiber materials in the packaging industry would be one of the greatest incitements to solve these production problems.

The definition of semichemical pulping was given in Chapter 6.I, as a process involving an *essential chemical treatment followed by a treatment in advanced mechanical fiberizing equipment.* This definition thus includes such processes as high yield sulfite and high yield kraft pulping, whereas sulfite cooking of greaseproof pulp, which only requires a simple opener of wooden construction to complete fiber liberation, is assigned to chemical pulping. Likewise cold caustic pulping, requiring no pressure equipment but still involving an essential chemical treatment prior to mechanical fiberizing, is considered a semichemical process, as are the simple water hydrolysis processes, whereas the Asplund and Mason processes, which mainly utilize steam treatment to achieve a thermal softening of the interfiber bonds, although some hydrolysis cannot be avoided, are assigned to the mechanical pulping processes and have thus already been treated in Chapter 7.

The principles underlying the semichemical processes are partly dealt with in Chapter 6.II on the strength of the interfiber bonds. Three ways were indicated to decrease this strength and make mechanical fiberizing possible without excessive damage to the fibers, namely *thermal softening, chemical swelling* and *chemical dissolution* of wood substance. The thermal softening principle is assigned to the mechanical pulping methods and the two others to semichemical pulping, as they involve an essentially chemical treatment.

The equipment used in semichemical pulping was described briefly in Chapter 6.VI, showing the trends towards repeated disk refining following the chemical treatment, which is increasingly performed continuously. It has also been mentioned that the semichemical, like the mechanical, processes start out from wood in either bolt or chip form, and that subdivision will be followed here.

I. Semichemical Pulping of Bolts

1. GENERAL CONSIDERATIONS

Almost since the invention of the groundwood process, attempts have been made to modify it by additions of chemicals during grinding or by pre-treatment of the bolts to achieve various effects, above all lower energy consumption, less fiber damage and improved pulp quality, as well as utilization of wood species less suitable for the conventional process. Only a few of the many suggestions have led to commercial application, and these are of far less importance than the conventional groundwood process. Because of the ever increasing demand for pulpwood for grinding, and the diversification in the uses of groundwood pulp, these processes are of a certain interest for the future. With the development of precision refiners, however, semichemical pulping of chips has become the most rational solution, since the fiberizing can be done as satisfactorily and the pre-impregnation of wood with chemicals is more easily achieved than in the case of bolts.

2. PROCESSES INVOLVING ADDITION OF CHEMICALS DURING GRINDING

By addition of chemicals to the grinder showers it is possible to achieve certain effects (27). The chemical action in the grinding zone is accelerated by the heat evolved. Still, these processes are essentially mechanical, although representing a transitional stage to semichemical. Reducing agents improve the brightness (16, 85, 194), alkali and other chemicals are recommended to eliminate resin troubles (167, 168) and to improve pulp strength (39, 60).

The *Powell–River* process (46) employs addition of a concentrated (18%) sodium sulfite solution to the grinder showers, in an amount of about 8 kg ptp Na_2SO_3. Brightness is improved by 2.5% and energy consumption reduced by some 8%. No decrease in pulp yield has been noted. To ensure that all the chemicals used arrive at the zone of grinding, impregnation of the bolts with sodium sulfite during the under-water pond storage employed in the southern states of the U.S.A. has been suggested (104). A considerable improvement in strength properties and brightness is thereby possible.

A still more important process of this category has been developed to facilitate the grinding of pine (74, 83, 147). Because of the high resin content, about 3%, pine is not suitable for conventional groundwood production. Troubles arise if only a fraction of this resin is sticky. The sticky particles clog together, deposit on the stone surface, disturb grinding operation and cause further specks in the final paper. In modern, fast-running paper machines, the presence of sticky pitch at, e.g. the press rolls, makes it impossible to maintain the speed of the machine.

In order to convert the resin to a non-tacky form, sodium hydroxide or carbonate and aluminium sulfate are added to the grinder water in proportions to give a pH of 5.5–6.5, and more aluminium sulfate to the paper machine water system, resulting in a pH of slightly above 4.0 on the machine. Chemical consumption is around 6 kg ptp NaOH or 8 kg ptp Na_2CO_3 and around 20 kg ptp $Al_2(SO_4)_3$. Half the alum is added to the grinder system. The alum additions are generally kept constant and the alkali addition to the grinder system is controlled with impulse from the pH of the headbox. This process is operated in several southern integrated mills for newsprint production.

Another interesting suggestion to decrease the tackiness of the resin is to add cationic surface active agents in small amounts, around 1 kg ptp (108).

3. PROCESSES INVOLVING PRETREATMENT OF BOLTS

As early as 1868 Mayh and von Behrend used superatmospheric steaming of wood as a means to soften the interfiber bonds prior to grinding. The wood gave a groundwood pulp with considerably less fiber damage. The dark brown color developed during steaming was the great disadvantage, which gave the product the name *brown groundwood pulp* and limited its potential application to coarse papers and boards. The process is still operated in several mills (104). Either *boiling* or *steaming* are used, i.e. water treatment in liquid or vapor phase. The bolts are loaded on special wheeled cord racks, which are rolled into horizontal digesters of 50–60 m^3 volume, Figure 8.1. After closing the digester, water or steam is introduced and the temperature maintained at around 150°C (5 kp/cm²) for about 6–12 h. The acetyl groups of wood are split off, decreasing the pH of the water and causing some hydrolysis of the carbohydrates, as well

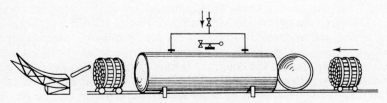

Fig. 8.1. Brown (steamed) groundwood, working principle (Klemm)

as lignin condensation which gives the brown color. The pulp yield is thus reduced to 80–85% of the wood. Both pine and spruce can be used. The influence of the two main variables, temperature (115–160°C for 4 h) and time (0–14 h at 150°C) has been investigated (25). At around 150°C the strongest pulps are produced, requiring most grinding energy. A pulp of higher freeness, lower strength and energy consumption is obtained at higher or lower temperature. Generally, energy consumption in comparison with ordinary groundwood pulp is reduced by 20–30%. The strength is improved considerably. The brightness is about the same as for kraft pulp, or 15–30% GE. Since the development of other pulping processes for board pulp, especially the neutral sulfite semichemical process, brown groundwood pulp is decreasing in importance.

In order to improve the color of the pulp, several processes for pretreatment with chemicals at high temperature have been investigated. Thereby all existing pulping liquors and several other chemicals have been suggested, as surveyed in several articles (25, 26, 114). Some patents (10, 53, 61, 132, 148) suggested mild cooks in sulfite cooking acid, or in bisulfite or sulfite with (61, 192) or without (12, 165, 166) subsequent acidification. Other methods included cooking of bolts in alkaline liquors, such as lime (201), white liquor (143), black liquor (102) or sodium hydroxide solution (62, 79, 183, 200). Bicarbonate-buffered sulfite cooks were investigated for softwoods (118) and later on for hardwoods (88, 114). All these methods encountered the difficulty of impregnating the bolts, which was particularly great because they concentrated on the conventional raw material, softwood. Several of the processes have been in commercial use for some time, whereby steaming, evacuation and pressure treatments, as well as incuts in the logs, were all tried to facilitate the impregnation. However, it was not until research was directed to hardwoods that a commercially successful process could be worked out, because of the greater ease of pulping liquor penetration and the lower wood costs which compensated for the yield losses caused by the chemical treatment. The finally successful process was worked out by New York State University, College of Forestry, and called the *chemigroundwood* process (54, 84, 104, 114, 115). In this process, penetration of the wood by the cooking liquor is achieved by evacuation followed by pressure impregnation. In its first, semi-commercial application the bolts were piled on wheeled cord racks, which were rolled on tracks into a horizontal digester in the same manner as in brown groundwood pulp production. For the first large-scale operation, Great Northern Paper Co., Millinocket, Maine, vertical digesters were chosen, 18 m high and 3 m in diameter, into which the bolts of mixed hardwoods are dumped, Figure 8.2. The digesters are then closed and evacuated to 60 mm Hg for 30 minutes, whereupon the cooking liquor is introduced and a hydraulic pressure of 10.5 kp/cm^2 maintained throughout the cook. Even this form of treatment often gives unsatisfactory penetration (177, 196) in the case of excessive tylose formation in the heartwood of some species (cf. Chapters 2 and 6). The cooking liquor introduced contains sodium sulfite buffered with sodium carbonate–bicarbonate of a pH around 9.5, as in the case of neutral sulfite semichemical pulping of chips, cf. Chapter 8.II, and cooking conditions are chosen to give 85–90% yields of hardwood chemiground-wood pulp. Approximate conditions are: 135–150°C, 5–6 h, 125 g/1 Na_2CO_3, of which 85% has been converted to Na_2SO_3. 50–60 kg ptw chemicals are consumed and the residual liquor is pumped to a storage tank for chemical make-up. The bolts are dumped into a pool and hauled to the grinding room. Grinding requires around 600 kWh ptp or only half the energy consumption of untreated wood. At the same time, grinder capacity is doubled. Pulp quality is greatly improved by the pretreatment, and pulp strength of chemigroundwood from hardwoods exceeds that of spruce groundwood considerably, whereas opacity is lower. The pulp is used for a wide variety of grades, such as newsprint, book, tissue and towelling paper. The furnish ordinarily used for newsprint contains 80% softwood groundwood and 20% sulfite pulp. Instead 60% softwood groundwood, 30% hardwood chemigroundwood, and 10% sulfite pulp can be used. Thus the chemigroundwood has been substituted for part of the groundwood and part of the sulfite pulp. A chemiground-wood pulp mill, employing horizontal digesters, has started production in France (140). A similar process, the *ALB Semicell*, has been developed in Austria for neutral sulfite cooking of *softwoods* prior to grinding (164).

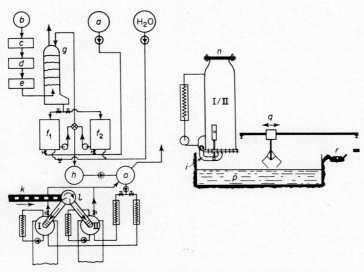

Fig. 8.2. Liquor preparation and cooking of wood for chemiground-wood production. (I), (II) wood digesters, (*a*) storage and saturating tank for soda ash, (*b*) silo for sulfur, (*c*) sulfer melter, (*d*) molten sulfur storage, (*e*) sulfur burner, (*f*) sulfiting tanks, (*g*) absorption tower, (*h*) cooking liquor storage tank, (*i*) steel door for bottom seal of digester, (*k*) log feed conveyer, (*l*) turntable, (*m*) feed chute, (*n*) top cover, (*o*) cooking liquor accumulator, (*p*) dump pond, (*q*) grapple crane, (*r*) conveyer belt for logs to grinder room (Klemm)

405

An investigation on the quality of chemigroundwood pulp from birch (94) showed that the wet web strength of spruce groundwood could be appreciably increased when mixing it with 30–40% chemigroundwood pulp but not sufficiently to replace all chemical pulp in newsprint furnishes. A comparison of chemigroundwood pulp from birch and pine with groundwood from spruce (95) showed that power consumption for chemigroundwood pulping is only slightly lower than for spruce grinding, when comparing pulps of equal freeness. However, the strength properties are developed more rapidly in the case of the pretreated wood, and therefore the chemigroundwood pulps only require half the energy needed for spruce grinding when comparing on equal strength basis. The brightness of chemigroundwood pulps is lower than that of spruce groundwood pulp.

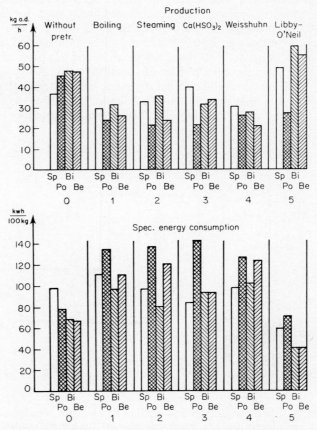

Fig. 8.3. Influence of pretreatment on grinder production and specific energy consumption. (Sp) spruce, (Po) poplar, (Bi) birch, (Be) beech, (1) boiling: 5 h, 120°C, water, (2) steaming: 25 h, 152°C, steam, (3) Ca(HSO₃)₂: 3 h, 110°C, acid sulfite, (4) Weisshuhn: 3 h, 143°C, bisulfite, (5) Libby–O'Neil: 6 h, 160°C, neutral sulfite (Brecht)

Birch chemigroundwood pulp is equivalent to birch neutral sulfite semi-chemical pulp from chips when used for corrugating medium board, whereas pine gives too brittle fibers for this purpose.

An interesting comparison (24a, 26, 27) of the various types of semi-chemical pulps from bolts is given in Figures 8.3–8, in reference to ordinary groundwood pulp. In one series of experiments *spruce* was used. Some of the processes involved cooking at fairly low temperatures 110–120°C, whereas others employed temperatures around 150°C. Alkaline, neutral and acid solutions were used. Obviously, the low-temperature cooking did not change the yield, specific energy consumption or brightness appreciably, but it decreased the fiber damage on grinding somewhat and improved the strength properties a little. The use of sulfite cooking acid gave the best results. The high-temperature cooking caused greater changes, especially those corresponding to the *Schwalbe* treatment with sulfite cooking acid and the *chemigroundwood* process. The substance losses are higher, as well as the decrease in brightness, but the specific energy consumption is reduced, as is the fiber damage, leading to an improvement in strength properties. Experiments on *pine* gave identical results, although the strength properties were lower throughout. The most interesting results are, however, obtained with the various *hardwoods*. They show that without pretreatment, the fiber damage on grinding hardwoods is excessive, causing very low paper strength. Of the various pretreatments, the chemigroundwood process is outstanding, causing the

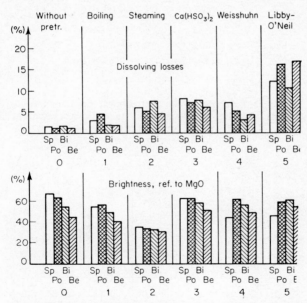

Fig. 8.4. Influence of pretreatment on groundwood pulp yield and brightness. Process numbers as in Figure 8.3 (Brecht)

407

least fiber damage, least energy consumption and giving fairly bright pulps of high strength. Poplar is rather better than birch, and both are much superior to beech. The yield losses are considerable, around 15%, but owing to the higher density of most hardwoods as compared to spruce, the wood consumption, calculated on volume basis, is less than for spruce groundwood pulp. An exception is poplar, which has a fairly low density.

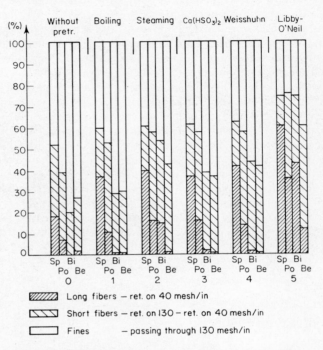

Fig. 8.5. Influence of the pretreatment on the morphological categories of groundwood pulp. Process numbers as in Figure 8.3 (Brecht)

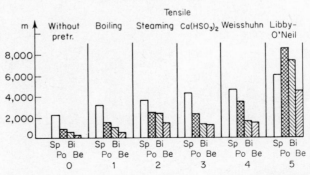

Fig. 8.6. Influence of the pretreatment on the tensile strength of groundwood pulp. Process numbers as in Figure 8.3 (Brecht)

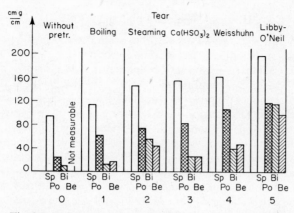

Fig. 8.7. Influence of the pretreatment on the tear strength of groundwood pulp. Process numbers as in Figure 8.3 (Brecht)

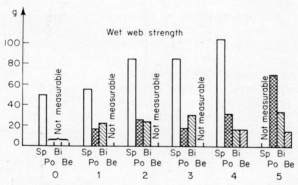

Fig. 8.8. Influence of the pretreatment on the wet web strength of groundwood pulp. Process numbers as in Figure 8.3 (Brecht)

Table 8.1 gives the approximate wood consumption of chemigroundwood pulp from various wood species in comparison with ordinary groundwood pulp.

Table 8.1. Wood density and consumption for groundwood and chemigroundwood pulps from various wood species (cf. 26)

Species	Spruce	Fir	Pine	Poplar	Birch	Maple
Basic density, t o.d. wood/m³ green wood	0.42	0.40	0.48	0.37	0.53	0.53
Wood consumption, solid m³ ptp:						
Groundwood	2.5	2.6	2.2	2.9	—	—
Chemigroundwood	—	—	2.5	3.1	2.2	2.2

409

II. Semichemical Pulping of Chips

As impregnation was found to be one of the main problems in semi-chemical pulping of bolts, interest soon concentrated on the treatment of chips. At the same time as the development of the mainly mechanical processes of Mason and Asplund in the 1920's and early 1930's, there was a line of semichemical pulping development work, carried out to a certain extent in Germany (158) but more extensively at the U.S. Forest Products Laboratory, Madison, Wisconsin, as well as in the American pulp industry. The industrial development was retarded, however, until the efforts of the pulping machinery industry had resulted in the construction of ample fiberizing equipment, especially the high precision refiners, cf. Chapter 6.VI. Thus, although the chemical knowledge of the three main semi-chemical processes was available in 1930 and the industrial application had started, it was not until 1945 that the production of semichemical pulps attained more significant quantities, and the main industrial develop-ment has occurred during the last two decades. As in the case of semi-chemical pulping of bolts, it was realized that special advantages, both technical and economical, could be obtained with hardwoods, and today the dominating raw material for semichemical pulps is hardwood, although especially in high yield sulfite and high yield kraft pulping softwoods are used. Another raw material well suited to semichemical pulping is straw. The main use for semichemical *hardwood neutral sulfite* pulps is *corru-gating medium boards*, although some is used as a *newsprint* furnish component and bleached neutral sulfite pulps are used in *printing* and *greaseproof* papers. Semichemical *softwood kraft* pulp is becoming increasingly used in the bottom layer of *liner board*, and semichemical *softwood sulfite* pulp in newsprint. Semichemical *hardwood cold caustic* pulp is used as a component of *boards, newsprint, magazine* and *tissue* papers.

1. WATER HYDROLYSIS

One of the simplest chemical treatments is, as in the case of bolt pulping, water hydrolysis by steaming or boiling. Already by 1869 this method was mentioned in a patent (73), and the inventor was performing mill scale experiments in Bergvik, Sweden, at the time when Ekman came to introduce his sulfite process there (173).

It is difficult to judge where physical action of water ends and chemical hydrolysis becomes of importance for the ease of fiberizing. Water definitely has a softening effect on the interfiber bonds already at room temperature, as proved by mechanical strength determinations on moist and dry wood (103). This must be due to the splitting of hydrogen bonds and subsequent swelling, predominantly in the carbohydrate regions. Hydrolysis occurs at elevated temperature at the acetyl groups of the hemicelluloses, at the glycosidic bonds of all carbohydrates, especially the easily accessible parts, at the lignin–carbohydrate bonds, which are probably also of glycosidic nature, and finally at intra-lignin bonds, mainly benzyl alkyl ether bonds. These reactions are accompanied by an increase in acidity due to the organic acids formed, as well as by a dissolution of carbohydrates and lignin (6). At the same time, condensation reactions of the lignin occur, which tend to darken the products.

Wood hydrolysis has been studied from different angles, and the discussion here will be confined to hydrolysis in connection with semichemical pulping. Some processes aim at coarse pulps for *insulating* and *construction boards* and *saturating felt*. Inasmuch as defibration is made at high temperature, thermal softening has been considered the main purpose of the processes, which were therefore treated in Chapter 7. In other cases defibration in coarse fiber production for the same purposes is made at lower temperature after a regular hydrolysis cook (1, 2, 182). Studies on aspen water hydrolysis prior to complete fiberizing (6, 82, 128) showed that excessive decomposition takes place at temperatures above 192–198°C even at heating times as short as 2–4 minutes. Reaction velocity seems to become about 3 times faster at an increase of 10°C. The hydrolysis goes fairly rapidly down to yields around 75% and then considerably

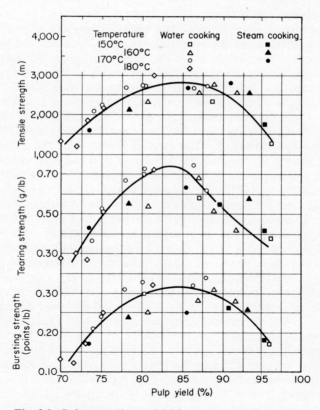

Fig. 8.9. Pulp strength vs. yield for aspen, water-cooked or steamed at 150–180°C (McGovern *et al*)

411

slower. The proportion of lignin to carbohydrates remains approximately constant in the residues. Maximum pulp strength is reached at yields around 80–85%, corresponding to 3–6 minutes at 180°C or 10–20 minutes at 170°C, or 30–60 minutes at 160°C. Almost identical results are obtained with vapor and liquid phase hydrolysis. During the cook pH drops from 7 to 4 or slightly below. Figure 8.9 shows the strength characteristics of aspen hydrolysis semichemical pulps at various pulp yields. Tests on corrugating boards showed that a fair quality can be obtained. Energy consumption on fiberizing was around 300 kWh ptp, a relatively low figure. However, as far as is known, no commercial use is yet made of the process for corrugating board, except the early production of pulp from tannin-extracted chestnut chips, where the extraction stage automatically involved a water hydrolysis of some wood components. This product has been largely succeeded by hardwood neutral sulfite pulps, which give improved crush resistance to the board.

2. COLD CAUSTIC PROCESS

A. General considerations

Pulping with sodium hydroxide has been investigated at various temperatures. At elevated temperature and pressure a real delignification takes place, and the method employing those conditions, the soda process, is treated among the chemical pulping processes in Chapter 9. At lower temperatures, the delignification as well as the dissolution of carbohydrates is of less importance for the weakening of the interfiber bonds, whereas swelling is more important. At 100°C, dissolution is still considerable, and pulp yields in the order of 80% are obtained after 8 h from both hardwoods and softwoods. The ease of fiberizing of these chips varies with the species, as for instance, treatment in a rod mill required 2–3 h for beech and maple and 6–7 h for pine and spruce, to achieve substantially complete defibration (157). The *Marsoni* process (122) for *straw* is reported to work at room temperature and very long retention periods, and is thus a cold caustic process, although fairly complete fiber liberation is already achieved by the chemical treatment. Several processes work for straw with sodium hydroxide at 100°C, but here the dissolution of organic substances, even lignin, is also of greater importance. Such straw pulping is either to be considered as high yield kraft or as the special process of mechano-chemical pulping (cf. Subsection 5). However, treatment in cold alkali lye at concentrations of 7–18 g/l NaOH followed by mechanical fiberizing gives cold caustic straw pulps in 75–85% yields, suitable for corrugating board (63).

When swelling *hardwoods* in cold alkali lye, the middle lamella increases in thickness by only 4% and the fiber section area by 8%, whereas the lumen area decreases by as much as 25% (190). The swelling is considerably restrained by the lignified regions of the transition lamella, the primary wall and the middle lamella, and considerable stresses develop within the fiber wall, which on subsequent mechanical action cause failure between the transition lamella and the main secondary wall (109, 190). Part of the outer layers will remain attached to the adjacent fibers, and part will be torn off and appear in the fines fraction. The comparatively little lignified main secondary wall is consequently exposed, and relieved of the restraint of the outer layers it swells considerably. In the case of *softwoods*, the lignification of the main fiber wall is more intense, cf. Chapter 3, and therefore its swelling in alkali much more restricted (109, 190), cf. Chapter 6.II. Penetration of the lye is less easy, and more energy is needed for fiberizing. The cold caustic process is therefore almost exclusively applied to hardwoods (35). The first commercial installation was at Gould Paper Co., Lyons Falls, N.Y., in 1956 (66). Several production units are now in operation in areas with low-cost hardwoods, such as eastern United States, Italy, Japan, and Australia (13, 34, 48, 172).

Obviously, the first aim of this pulping process must be a thorough *impregnation* of the chips. The swelling reaction is almost instantaneous once penetration is complete. However, ordinarily there is no perforation of the libriform fibers, and the alkali has to diffuse from the vessels into the fibers. Surfactants may improve the impregnation (55), as does higher temperature, hydraulic pressure, and a longer retention time (29, 38). However, mechanical action is desirable to enhance the penetration. By *compressing* the chips prior to and after soaking in alkali, not only the absorption of lye by the vessels is facilitated, but probably the diffusion paths are made shorter. Finally, it is possible that the complete removal of the compound middle lamella and the transition lamella in the *refining* stage will be facilitated by such crushing action.

Because the fiber wall still contains some lignin, the fibers will be comparatively stiff, and adhering fragments of the highly lignified outer layers likewise decrease the possibilities of intimate interfiber carbohydrate contact. Therefore, the papers made from cold caustic pulps will be fairly weak, and hitherto their use has been limited to plain and crepe sanitary papers, corrugating medium board and newsprint paper. Some of these applications require a fairly bright, unbleached pulp, and the caustic treatment will always cause a discoloration of the wood. It is desirable to adjust the pulping conditions to give a maximal brightness, and as a rule a bleaching is added.

B. Description of process

The problem of impregnation has been solved in different ways. The chips could be *disintegrated* to matchstick size by a shredder. A live-bottom bin in which a lye level is maintained then provides a retention time of over one hour, Figure 8.10 (13). A continuous *roll mill* with spraying of the lye and horn angle pressing (30) has been devised. Another system uses pressure soaking in a Rapid-Cycle or Messing–Durkee digester followed by pressing in a *screw press* prior to refining (59, 66). A further system applies *three consecutive roll presses*, with intermediate and subsequent soaking chambers followed by a severe screw pressing prior to refining (48). This makes a fully continuous system, schematically

413

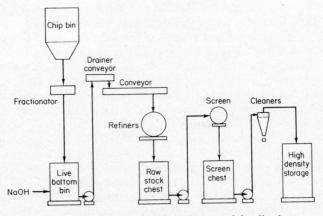

Fig. 8.10. Cold caustic process flow sheet, applying live bottom bin soaking (Bodenheimer *et al*)

indicated in Figure 8.11 (48). The transport of the chips between the pressing and refining stages is carried out by band or screw conveyors, or by pumping in excess lye. The press rolls operate with linear pressures of 250–400 kp/cm and with nips 3.5, 2.5, and 1.5 mm wide, in order to reduce the unpenetrated chip core accordingly. The total retention time in contact with the lye is only 10–15 minutes. To facilitate diffusion, the temperature is generally somewhat elevated, adjusted according to species

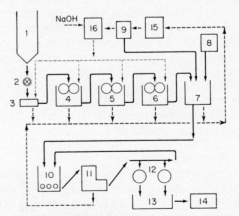

Fig. 8.11. Cold caustic process flow sheet, applying impregnation roll presses. (1) chip bin, (2) feeder, (3) conveyor, (4, 5, 6) roll presses, (7) soaking tank, (8) screen rejects, (9) liquor filter, (10) recirculation bin, (11) Anderson press, (12) S–W refiners, (13) stock chest, (14) washing, (15) recirc. liquor tank, (16) soaking liquor tank (Colombo *et al*)

414

and retention time, 30–50°C being common. Cooling of the lye is sometimes necessary. The lye concentration is 25–50 g/1 NaOH, and 0.5 g/l surface active agent is often added.

The purpose of the final press, in addition to improving the lye impregnation, is to remove excess alkali by giving a final consistency of 55–60%. Refining is then carried out in one or two stages at about 10–15% consistency after dilution with water, whereupon the pulp is washed, screened and cleaned and finally pumped to the paper mill. Recycling of the drain lye, press lye and wash lye to decrease the alkali consumption has been investigated (11), whereby pulp brightness is the limiting factor. The waste liquor from the washers may be added to the recovery system of an adjacent kraft mill to cover the sodium losses of the latter. The use of white liquor from a nearby kraft mill is an economical alternative to purchased lye, but may tend to decrease the brightness of the pulp.

The total power consumption is considerable, about 750 kWh ptp, of which 500–700 is consumed in the refining to a freeness of 400–200 ml C.S. and about 100 in the final pressing operation. High consistency refining may save 200–300 kWh ptp (76). The pulp yield is 80–85%, the losses being about equally divided chemically and mechanically. The chemical reactions consume about 50–70 kg ptp NaOH and generally at least a further 50 kg ptp NaOH are lost mechanically. Bleach liquor, peroxide, dithionite or hypochlorite, could be added in or after the refiners, which in the former case serve as mixers and heat source (107).

C. Reactions, and influence of reaction conditions on pulp yield and quality

A considerable number of wood species have been investigated with the cold caustic process, such as aspen (32, 33, 86), poplar (38, 48, 142), cottonwood (29, 32), birch (32, 48, 188), beech (48, 159, 188), oaks (29, 32, 107a, 188), sweetgum (29, 32), eucalypts (14, 145, 190, 191) and other hardwoods, as well as some softwoods and straw (35). Softwoods respond poorly to the treatment and require a high fiberizing energy, whereas most hardwoods are easily pulped, consuming 400–600 kWh ptp, at pulp yields of 87–94%. Pulp strength is as high as or often considerably higher than for spruce groundwood pulp, and corrugating medium boards made from the pulps may come up to the standard of commercial neutral sulfite pulp boards in crushing resistance, tensile and bursting strength though not in tear resistance (32, 33, 142). Likewise newsprint, magazine and book coating base papers from cold caustic aspen pulp were found to be adequate in burst and tensile strength but low in tear and opacity. The deficit in tear can be compensated by mixing with pine kraft pulp and addition of groundwood will increase opacity. In actual practice, the cold caustic pulps are therefore preferably mixed with groundwood and chemical pulps in proportions suited to the desired qualities, and cannot be regarded as a substitute for either category. Birch gives the best paper properties, followed by aspen and poplar, eucalypts and willow; oaks are less good and beech gives rather unsatisfactory results. All species

415

develop a yellowish color, which is most pronounced with poplar, and the brightness values vary from 35–55% GE, depending on species and pulping conditions. The ease of bleaching varies with the species, and is particularly good with eucalypts but not so good for birch. 65–70% GE can be obtained in one or two stages of hypochlorite and a consumption of 100–150 kg ptp act. Cl (active chlorine). The same effect is reached with 10–20 kg ptp H_2O_2.

After an investigation of the influence of temperature, time and alkali concentration (31) it was concluded that for most hardwoods nothing is to be gained by working at the highest temperatures (90°C). The dissolved

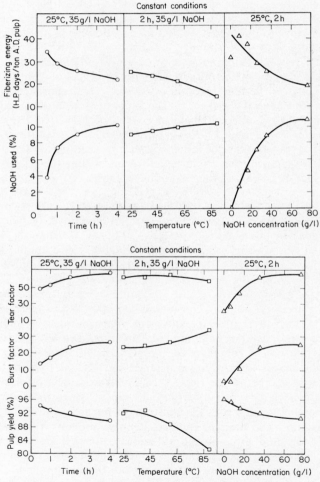

Fig. 8.12. Influence of the cold caustic process variables on fiberizing energy, chemicals consumption, yield and pulp strength. Oak mixture (Brown)

416

matter was found to be mainly hemicelluloses. Another study of the reaction variables (38) came to the conclusion that as compared to lower temperature operation, 90°C gives lower yield and brightness, higher alkali consumption, higher sheet density and strength and lower opacity. Prolonging the reaction time or increasing the lye concentration has a similar effect to increasing the temperature. A minimum of 25 and a maximum of 50 g/l NaOH is therefore recommended (29, 33), the lower concentrations being used for papers where opacity and brightness are important and the higher ones for strength. Figure 8.12 illustrates the effects of time, temperature and lye concentration in cold caustic pulping of oaks (29). Further investigations (33) showed the importance of complete impregnation, and reaction times could be decreased by employing suitable impregnation methods, e.g. by repeated compression and soaking, from the normal 1–10 h down to one minute in a continuous operation.

It is thus conceivable that in the cold caustic process the physical reactions of lye penetration and fiber swelling are desirable and should be facilitated by mechanical means, whereas the chemical reactions, such as the dissolution of carbohydrates and lignin, as well as the discoloration of lignin and resin in the pulp, should be avoided, which means that temperature should be as low and time as short as the swelling reaction will allow. At normal conditions 5–10% of the lignin and as much of the carbohydrates is dissolved, the optimal yield being 90–93%, or corrected for mechanical losses of fragments from the middle lamella during the refining, about 85%. There is a close correlation between yield and alkali consumption, and 50–100 kg ptp NaOH are normally consumed in chemical reactions, primarily in the neutralization of acetic acid formed from the acetyl groups in the xylan and of the uronic acid groups, but also to some extent in the 'peeling' degradation of hemicelluloses to saccharinic and other hydroxy acids, which occurs at elevated temperature and is an important reaction in the kraft and soda cooks.

An interesting parallel to the cold caustic process is the treatment of poplar groundwood with caustic lye, which changes the pulp properties towards higher strength and lower opacity and brightness (144).

3. SEMICHEMICAL SULFITE, KRAFT AND SODA PULPING

Chemical treatment according to conventional chemical pulping methods could be limited to give yields above the point of fiber liberation. The chemical reactions are thus essentially the same as during the earlier part of a chemical cook, and will therefore be treated in detail in Chapter 9. Here the special aspects of high yield pulping according to these methods, the reaction conditions, the technical performance and the properties and uses of these pulps will only be described briefly.

The point of fiber liberation is somewhat undecided and varies with wood species and pulping process, but occurs at around 55–60% yield. In practice it is impossible to carry out chemical pulping at a yield level

417

too close to the critical value, because variations between cooks or within a cook would easily give high screening rejects due to insufficient defibration. With the conventional equipment of chemical pulping, softwood pulp yields above 55% for sulfite and above 50% for kraft are therefore rare. With increasing wood prices there has, however, been a development towards still higher yields, and the first stage towards semichemical pulping is to provide refiners to take care of the high screenings, which after refining are returned to the screening room. Such a process could still not be called semichemical, but *high yield chemical*. However, at still higher yields the whole stock has to be passed through refiners, i.e. true *semichemical* pulping. There has been some confusion as to which terms should be applied to these processes, the term high yield sulfite and high yield kraft being applied sometimes to chemical and sometimes to semichemical processes. In this book, those commercial processes referred to as semichemical sulfite and kraft give pulps in yields around 60–80%, in special cases above 90%, have to pass refiners and are thus true semichemical pulps.

To obtain *acid sulfite pulps* in high yield, reaction conditions should be chosen to give somewhat slower reactions than in chemical pulping, if batch operation is maintained, which is still largely the case. Slower reaction is achieved by lower temperature or higher combined SO_2 (lower acidity). Ordinary cooking conditions are 120–130°C maximum temperature and 6.0/1.3% SO_2 (total/combined) for a total cooking time of 6 h (51, 81, 89). However, great deviations from these conditions may be necessary for different wood species, pulping techniques etc. With soluble bases the content of combined SO_2 is often increased and total SO_2 decreased to approach the composition of pure *bisulfite* solution with no excess of sulfurous acid (77, 78, 99, 101). Maximum temperature must then be increased to around 155°C. This type of cook gives better strength properties and will therefore allow 5–10% higher yields, but causes increased chemical costs. The point of fiber liberation is then also moved towards higher yields, pulps at 65% yield having been classified as chemical ones (17). Because semichemical sulfite pulp is used where low cost is essential, in newsprint and wrapping paper, ordinary cooking acid composition and calcium base has been preferred so far. It has also been shown that vapor phase sulfite cooking to high yields is possible on calcium base (179). Perfect impregnation prior to cooking is essential for the process, even without the vapor phase technique (141).

After the cook, the soft chips should be blown from the digester, whereby special arrangements may be needed to blow clean (171). From the blow pits the chips are taken to an equalizing chest preceding a drainer conveyor leading to the disk refiners (133). A modern system is to blow the soft chips to blow tanks, from which they are pumped to the refiners, screening rejects being added before they reach the pumps to facilitate pumping and prevent blocking (52). To make the fiber separation complete, the pulp may be passed from the refiners to *curlators* after mixing with some groundwood pulp. The curlator was developed to rub and curl

418

the fiber bundles at fairly high consistency, giving fiber liberation without bruising the fibers. It is especially well suited to semichemical sulfite pulp (170, 171). With improved refiner technique, curlators have lost importance. A machine of different design but similar action is the *frottator*. The pulp then goes to screening and is mixed with groundwood pulp in suitable proportions. Vortex cleaning is an important addition to the screening of semichemical pulp. Figure 8.13 (110) shows some flow sheets of semichemical acid sulfite pulping, indicating a trend towards the equipment arrangements illustrated below for semichemical kraft pulping.

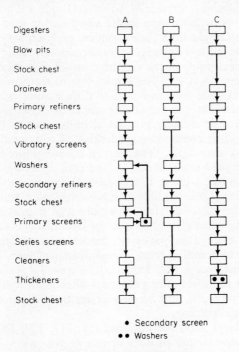

Fig. 8.13. Trends in process flow sheets (progressing from A to C) for semichemical acid sulfite pulping (Lambert)

Fiberizing of pulps in the lower yield range is achieved with only one pass through a disk refiner, but in the higher yield range, two passes or one pass and one curlation is necessary. The energy required to fiberize a sulfite pulp of 67–70% yield is about 150 kWh ptp (133), which is lower than for most semichemical pulps. For quality development approximately the same amount is required in addition. Mill experience indicates about 350 kWh ptp for 65% and 400 kWh ptp for 70% yield (110).

Semichemical sulfite pulps are used mainly as a mixture with groundwood pulp for newsprint. It is claimed that it is possible to use the same blends as with ordinary chemical sulfite pulp. *Softwood* is used almost

419

exclusively, in America spruce, firs and hemlock, giving Roe numbers of 25–30 at 65–70% yield, in Europe spruce, giving Roe numbers of 16–20 at the corresponding yields. Chips screenings are also a possible raw material (93). Paper strength properties throughout are lower for semichemical sulfite pulps than for the chemical grades, maximal strength being obtained at about 50–55% yield (76a, 125, 160a). However, this is not felt much in the newsprint mill at machine speeds running as high as even 650 m/min., and not even with 75% yield pulp (175). Semichemical *bisulfite* pulps in yields of 70–75% are likely to gain in importance in a number of applications, especially when methods of brightening have been developed. Now, both acid sulfite and bisulfite semichemical pulps are somewhat less bright than their chemical counterparts. In still higher yields, 80–95%, bisulfite pulps may in some cases substitute for both mechanical and chemical pulps in the manufacture of, for example, magazine coated base papers (56, 186). The border-line to mechanical refiner pulp (cf. Chapter 7.II) then becomes rather diffuse, and when bisulfite is just added to the refiner, the pulp could rather be described as brightened mechanical pulp. For a really precooked pulp, such as that of Blandin Paper Co., strength is increased considerably as compared to mechanical pulp, but opacity decreased. The energy consumption is only slightly reduced, and the yield is about 93%. The cooking is done continuously for 15 min. at 140°C, with a nearly neutral liquor containing sodium sulfite and bisulfite (186). Similar to mechanical pulp and in contrast to semichemical pulps of lower yield, this pulp type improves in opacity as well as in strength when refined to a lower freeness. This fact, as well as the pronounced change in paper properties at a certain yield range, 85–95%, has led to a special term, *chemimechanical pulp*, being used for these ultrahigh yield pulps (42, 56, 151a). *Hardwood* semichemical pulps have been found to have better properties after neutral sulfite than after acid sulfite cooking (130), and *hardwoods* are therefore not used for acid sulfite semichemical pulping.

Semichemical kraft pulps are obtained (50, 112, 120, 180, 198, 199) by modifying the conventional process in one of two ways: decreasing the charge of chemicals or decreasing cooking time and temperature. The former is usually applied, with only about half the normal quantity of white liquor charged. However, this alkali is consumed very rapidly, and if normal cooking conditions are maintained, pH will drop to neutrality or even below, especially in hardwood pulping. This will cause discoloration of the pulp and may even lead to sacrifice of some strength. Therefore, cooking time and temperature are generally reduced in the same way to keep pH above 9. A white liquor charge of 150 kg ptw (active alkali as NaOH per t wood) is sufficient (117) for really high yields, but as much as 170 kg ptw is used for liner board pulp for somewhat lower yields, Roe number 13. However, where dark color is no drawback, it is not necessary to maintain pH, and one kraft mill (181, cf. 193), using unbarked birch, even utilized the pH drop to increase the yield to 100–110%. This was achieved by pulping in black liquor from chemical kraft cooks. At the drop in pH caused by the liberation of acetic acid from the birchwood, lignin from the black liquor precipitated on the birch chips and followed the birch pulp to the board mill.

Usually, however, the semichemical kraft pulps are obtained in 55–70% yield, corresponding to Roe numbers 17–31 for American softwoods (24, 100, cf. 116, 117, 161), 12–25 for Scandinavian softwoods and 2–17 for hardwoods (lignin contents 14–25%, 10–20% and 2–14% respectively). The point of fiber liberation is for hardwoods somewhat higher than 55%. As in the case of sulfite pulps, the semichemical kraft pulps are much lower in paper strength properties than the corresponding chemical pulps, optimal yield for strength in the kraft process being below 50%. Another serious disadvantage is the darker color and less beating response of the semichemical kraft pulps as compared with the chemical kraft. The brightness drops about 1% GE for every per cent increase in yield. Of the hardwoods, oaks are considered especially suitable for semichemical kraft pulping (24, 161), as other pulping processes give unsatisfactory results with that wood, whereas the neutral sulfite process is often preferred for gumwood. Semichemical kraft pulps are used for coarse papers and boards. For corrugating medium board, however, several semichemical kraft mills have recently been converted into neutral sulfite mills, as the neutral sulfite pulps give a stiffer board, in spite of the fact that some of the conventionally determined strength properties are often better for the kraft pulps (18, 41). The main use of semichemical kraft is now as the bottom layer of liner board, with a brighter top layer of chemical kraft applied in the secondary headbox (4a).

Flow sheets for discontinuous and continuous semichemical kraft pulping are presented in Figures 8.14–15. In the former, rotating or stationary digesters are used and fiberizing is done between the blow tank and the washers. The knotters are omitted. A breaker trap followed by two stages of pump-through refiners are used in a closed system to avoid foaming. In the continuous pulping systems, countercurrent washing can be done in the lower part of the digester, thus simplifying the subsequent equipment.

Bleaching of semichemical kraft pulps has been tried (18, 117), but

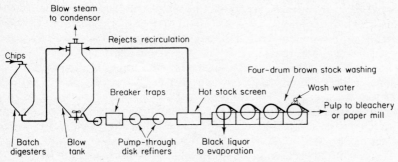

Fig. 8.14. Semichemical kraft pulping, batch system

chlorine demand is very high and several chlorinations and alkali extractions are necessary, which makes this type of pulp economically less attractive, although its strength properties are excellent. In contrast with the sulfite process the carbohydrate yield is not very much improved in semichemical kraft pulping as compared to chemical, and the yield of bleached pulp is therefore fairly low, up to 50 % for a Roe number of about 20 (117).

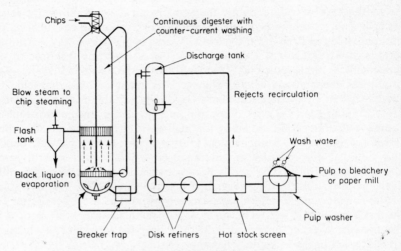

Fig. 8.15. Semichemical kraft pulping, continuous system

4. NEUTRAL SULFITE SEMICHEMICAL PULPING

A. General considerations

Pulping in neutral or alkaline sulfite solutions was already suggested in 1880 (49) and then repeatedly investigated and covered by patents (e.g. 6, 19, 20, 46, 57, 151, 153, 163), as surveyed in 1925 by Rue (153). The principal feature was the use of fairly strong solutions of sodium sulfite, to which small amounts of other chemicals were added, such as sodium hydroxide, carbonate, bicarbonate, thiosulfate, sulfide, or bisulfite (19, 46). Fairly high temperature, 170–190°C, had to be used to achieve fiber liberation within reasonable time, and excessive temperatures could easily lead to serious degradation (151). Although various methods of regeneration of the cooking chemicals were suggested, cf. Chapter 11, none met with technical success, and the fairly high cost of chemicals together with the fact that drastic cooking conditions had to be used to obtain pulp, prevented a more common industrial application of the process, although it was tried for some time under the name of the *Drewsen*, or the *Keebra* processes (19, 46).

It was realized eventually that the method was more suited to hardwoods than to softwoods, because of the lower lignin content of the former and also probably because of the more extensive localization of the hardwood lignin to the middle lamella. Furthermore, hardwoods were not utilized for pulping and were available at a much lower price than softwoods. This compensated to a certain extent the higher cost of cooking chemicals. The slow rate of delignification of the process also suggested semichemical rather than chemical pulping, and this would increase the yield and hence further decrease the cost of manufacture. As also reviewed by Rue (154), the idea of semichemical pulping was long known, but until 1925 had not met with any commercial success. At that time, however, a semichemical pulp plant using the neutral sulfite process was started by the Southern Extract Company, Knoxville, Tennessee, on extracted chestnut chips, a waste from the tanning agents industry. The process had been worked out by the U.S. Forest Products Laboratory, Madison, Wisconsin (155, 156), and consisted of

'(1) a pressure impregnation of the chips with the cooking liquor,
(2) a mild digestion of chips with chemicals which are practically neutral and which are capable of maintaining neutrality during the liberation from the wood of considerable quantities of organic acids, followed by
(3) a mechanical reduction of the softened chips to pulp.' (156)

The mechanical part of the pulping was initially carried out in rod mills, but it was not until the development of the modern high-precision refiners (cf. Chapter 6.VI) that considerable expansion took place in neutral sulfite pulping, which today is the dominating process in semichemical pulping, with a production of more than 2,000,000 t/year.

The pulp yield is 65–85%, and the hardwood pulps contain 10–15% lignin as compared to 0–5% lignin in conventional chemical pulps. Because of the neutral cooking conditions a large quantity of hemicelluloses are preserved. This imparts stiffness to the products made of the pulp. That is one of the most important properties of corrugating board, for which the pulp, from the very beginning until today, has been predominantly used. The high lignin content and the fairly low conventional strength properties are of less consequence for this use. The high hemicellulose content also suggests the use for greaseproof and glassine paper, but the residual lignin checks the swelling of the pulp on beating, and has to be removed by bleaching, usually a conventional chlorine–alkali–hypochlorite treatment (cf. Chapter 12.IV and 17.V). Bleached neutral sulfite semichemical pulps from hardwoods are as strong as bleached sulfite softwood pulps when used in dense papers. However, because of the high lignin content of the unbleached pulp, the cost of bleaching chemicals is considerable. With a bleached pulp yield of up to 60%, this is made up for by decreased wood costs in comparison to bleached softwood sulfite, and an increasing quantity of bleached semichemical pulp is produced for various grades of fine paper. Then it is sometimes preferred to carry the delignification in the cooking somewhat further, accepting a slightly higher loss of carbohydrates. This is achieved by prolonging the cook, or allowing the pH to drop during the cook from the sulfite to the bisulfite level, cf. below.

To avoid the severe yield losses of full bleaching, one-stage brightening of the unbleached pulp with hypochlorite or peroxide is also practised. Brightness is thus increased from about 50% GE to the brightness level of unbleached sulfite and groundwood pulps. However, in this case most of the lignin is not removed from the pulp, and continues to exert a hindering influence on the swelling of the pulp on beating. For certain softer grades of paper, this type of pulp has certain possibilities.

Unbleached or brightened neutral sulfite pulp has also been used to replace softwood sulfite pulp in newsprint (174), but has to compete with the recently advanced semichemical acid sulfite or bisulfite softwood pulps, which may be cheaper where softwoods are still available, and with the cold caustic hardwood pulps, which require somewhat lower installation costs. The neutral sulfite process, however, is more flexible than the cold caustic process with respect to pulp yield and properties, and for a newsprint or magazine paper mill it is possible to substitute more or less of the chemical pulp or the groundwood component by choosing the yield level of the neutral sulfite pulp produced. Neutral sulfite pulping, properly conducted, always gives a brighter pulp than does the cold caustic process.

B. Description of process (3, 4, 58, 64, 65, 70, 75, 105, 121, 134, 162, 174)
The main features of the original process, i.e. the impregnation of hardwood chips with a cooking liquor of sodium sulfite and carbonate or bicarbonate, followed by cooking at fairly high temperature, and eventually by mechanical defibration, have been preserved, but the operations have been perfected to suit modern large-scale production. The youngest of the three main cooking processes, neutral sulfite pulping, was the first to adopt continuous cooking. This was due partly to the difficulty of blowing a stationary digester clean of the soft but undefibered chips. To some extent that called for digesters permitting easy dumping, and spherical rotary digesters had a momentary renaissance. However, an increasing quantity of neutral sulfite semichemical pulping is now made continuously, with continuous impregnation, cooking and defiberation, thus eliminating much handling of soft chips outside the digester. Only the fact that a considerable number of old mills with stationary digesters have been converted to neutral sulfite pulping, accounts for the high percentage of discontinuously cooked pulp. To drain the cooked chips, these mills use leach casters, i.e. bins with perforated bottom or 'live bottom' with screw or chain conveyors to the refiners.

The continuous digesters are of the Pandia, Defibrator, Kamyr or Impco types (cf. Chapter 6.VI). Figure 8.16 shows a flow sheet of continuous semichemical pulping of unbleached neutral sulfite pulp. After chipping and screening, the chips enter a screw feeder, where they are impregnated with cooking liquor, prepared by gassing up a sodium carbonate solution with a suitable amount of sulfur dioxide. The con-

424

centration of the cooking liquor is in the case of screw digesters fairly high, so that the impregnated chips can be cooked in the vapor phase. In the Kamyr and Impco systems a liquid phase cook is performed after steaming and impregnation, applying a rather weaker cooking liquor. Maximum temperature is adjusted according to the retention time in the digester, and the quality desired. In the screw digesters, cooking time is short, 10–20 minutes, and maximum temperature around 200°C, whereas the vertical digesters allow 1–3 h at maximum temperature, which is kept at about 160–175°C. The latter alternative is considered to be best suited to the production of bleached grades.

After cooking, the chips are broken up by an impeller or a defibrator under full digester pressure and the coarse pulp is then discharged to a blow tank, from which the refiners are fed. Refining is done as close to 100°C as possible in order to decrease energy consumption (100–300 kWh ptp) and to improve pulp quality. However, refining at still higher temperature has proved detrimental to pulp quality, particularly for bleached grades (91). Prior to refining, the pulp is compressed by a disk or screw press and then diluted with wash liquor from the washing system to a consistency of about 15%. After washing on filters or on screw presses, the refined stock goes to high density storage. Unbleached pulp for corrugating board may be used directly after beating, provided the wood was reasonably well barked. Otherwise, and especially in the case of bleached grades, the pulp has to be screened and cleaned. Screening should remove larger impurities and coarse fiber bundles, the latter being returned to the refiners. Prior to or after bleaching, small specks and chops should be removed in vortex cleaners. The screening is discussed further in Chapter 10 and the bleaching in Chapter 17.

The waste cooking liquor presents a definite problem, since it is low in organic and high in inorganic chemical content. Its evaporation and

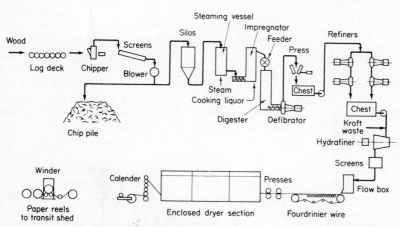

Fig. 8.16. Neutral sulfite pulping flow sheet for the production of corrugating medium paper boards from hardwoods

burning is therefore difficult and uneconomical. Combined with a kraft mill, the neutral sulfite mill could deliver its waste liquor to the conventional reclaiming system, and be credited for some of the chemicals, and in combination with sulfite mills some joint regeneration is also possible. Alone, a neutral sulfite mill could increase the solids content of the spent liquor by recirculation, at some sacrifice in unbleached pulp brightness. It could also rely on wet combustion. These problems are discussed further in Chapter 11.

C. Reactions, and influence of reaction conditions on pulp yield and quality

As the reactions occurring during the neutral sulfite cook are principally similar to those in chemical sulfite pulping and its more recent variations, they will be dealt with more fully in Chapter 9.I. In the same way, the detailed composition of the cooking liquor will be discussed there. However, some principal features of the process reactions should be mentioned here, together with a discussion on how the reaction conditions affect pulp yield and quality.

Neutral sulfite pulping aims at a selective delignification with as much of the hemicelluloses preserved as possible. Extreme acidity and alkalinity, which affect the hemicellulose, are therefore avoided. However, this means that delignification is also retarded, although to a lesser degree than the dissolution of hemicellulose, especially for hardwoods. Further, when about half of the lignin has been dissolved and the delignification tends to slow down and become less selective, cooking is interrupted and pulping completed by mechanical means. However, one category of compounds, included in the hemicellulose concept, is always dissolved during the cook, i.e. the organic acids, originating from the acetyl groups of the xylan. Also some of the easily hydrolyzed hemicellulose sugars enter into solution where to some extent they are further degraded to organic acids, in addition to the uronic acid groups of the native wood xylan.

Therefore, considerable quantities of organic acids form during the cook and tend to decrease the pH of the cooking liquor to a level where the acid-sensitive hemicelluloses are more rapidly dissolved. To prevent that the cook must be *buffered* towards the acid side. This should not be done with excessive amounts of alkali in the form of hydroxide, since that would give an initial pH too high to prevent alkaline dissolution of carbohydrates. The buffer should therefore act towards the alkaline side as well. This is done most efficiently and cheaply by a bicarbonate–carbonate buffer, which forms when a sodium carbonate solution is treated with sulfur dioxide to a certain limit. How far this conversion of the carbonate solution to sulfite should be carried has been much discussed, but it is now generally agreed that around 75–85% of the carbonate should be converted to sulfite. Another type of buffer is that of ammonia in a solution of ammonium sulfite, prepared by gassing up ammonia with sulfur dioxide to around 70%. In both cases pH during the cook is kept around 9–7, provided the carbon dioxide of the sodium

426

based cook is allowed to escape. Limited amounts of sodium hydroxide buffer, which are immediately consumed in the deacetylation reaction, can be tolerated without degradative effect on the hemicelluloses.

The conditions disclosed in the first publication on the subject (156) have been changed very little. The chemical charge was 142 kg ptw sulfite and 24 kg ptw bicarbonate, both calculated as Na_2CO_2, and the cook performed at 155–160°C for 4 h, giving a pulp after rod milling in 75% yield. Power consumption was about 200 kWh ptp. Birch gave the strongest pulps, followed in order by aspen, maple and black oak. The ratio mentioned of 6 : 1 for sulfite to bicarbonate, was lowered in other examples. An investigation on the effect of various proportions (21) indicated that the rate of reaction was somewhat increased on decreasing the ratio, and the consumption of chemicals somewhat decreased. A ratio of 3 : 1 seemed to give the brightest pulps. A study of various buffers (97) indicated more rapid reaction on increasing alkalinity. The brightest pulps were obtained with no addition of buffer in cooks with sodium sulfite in quantities sufficient to keep the final pH above 7. Decreasing the sulfite: carbonate ratio was found to decrease cooking time, preserve strength and decrease pulp brightness (44). A study, using the ratio 4 : 1, investigated the temperature dependence of the delignification rate and found that an increase in reaction rate more than doubled on a rise in temperature of 10°C (22). More extensive investigations on the kinetics of the neutral sulfite process have been carried out more recently, with similar results (69). It was found that the reaction rates do not follow any particular single order but could be fitted to two different first-order reactions occurring simultaneously or consecutively. A maximum temperature of 170°C required 1–2 h to give 70–75% pulp yield at a charge of 160 kg ptw Na_2CO_3, of which 75% have been converted to sulfite (ratio 3 : 1). These figures should correspond to modern practice for discontinuous neutral sulfite semichemical pulping, with modifications for wood species and local conditions. Temperatures much higher than 170°C are considered (68, 151) to lead to excessive carbohydrate degradation and lignin condensation and thus to inferior pulps. It has been demonstrated (189) that this is mainly caused by incomplete penetration of the wood, since cooks on thin veneers of aspen sapwood could be carried out in the temperature range of 175–210°C without appreciable differences in chemical composition and quality of the pulps of equal yield. The time required for 70% yield then varied between 30 and 1 min.

The liquor : wood ratio in the cook, which determines the chemical concentrations, has been found to be of little practical importance within the range 5 : 1–2 : 1, provided the distribution of chemicals and heat is satisfactory (98). The limits mentioned are approached in practice by discontinuous liquid phase and continuous vapor phase cooking respectively. The problem of penetration is thereby solved by pre-steaming, pre-soaking (92) or compressing the chips, and the result of these operations is very important for the pulp quality, as burn chip centres occur easily on cooking badly impregnated chips (178).

In well-buffered neutral sulfite cooks in the most common yield range of 85–70%, 50–75% of the lignin and 30–45% of the hemicelluloses pass into solution (80, 97, 126, 131). Investigations on the lignin dissolved in an aspen neutral sulfite cook indicated that the first part of the lignin to enter solution mostly contains guaiacyl units, whereas further dissolution increases the content of syringyl-containing lignin (123, 176). This may be distinctive of aspenwood. The lignin is sulfonated to an increasing degree during the cook, corresponding to about 0.3 S/monomer towards the end of a normal semichemical cook (123). Most of the aspenwood lignin was found to be removable by prolonged cooking to chemical pulps. Sulfonation appears to start in the middle lamella and dissolution of the lignin occurs by diffusion from the inner parts of the cell wall towards the middle lamella. No principal differences were found in the delignification in neutral sulfite and bisulfite liquors other than in the rate, which is much higher for bisulfite pulping.

The hemicelluloses of an aspen neutral sulfite cook to 75% yield (111) were found to be dissolved to a third, of which 25% could be recovered in a reasonably undegraded form and the remainder did not in any case appear as mono-, di- or trisaccharides in the spent liquor. The hemicelluloses remaining in the pulp were shown to be almost undegraded, though more accessible to alkaline dissolution than in the wood. Further investigations on the neutral sulfite cooking of aspen to 95–75% yield (149) showed that some low-DP carbohydrates, probably pectic matter, are removed in the beginning of the cook, and subsequently hemicelluloses and lignin are dissolved at approximately the same rate, Figure 8.17. At the 75% yield level, 9–10%, wood basis, of both hemicelluloses and lignin had been removed, not counting acetyl groups, which together with

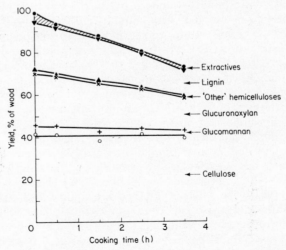

Fig. 8.17. Dissolution of hardwood components during the neutral sulfite cook (Quick)

extractives removed account for the remaining dissolved matter. The DP of the pulp hemicelluloses remained at about the same level, DP 200, as in the wood. The cellulose is likely to remain unaffected by the cook. Only half (111) or a third (149) of the dissolved hemicellulose could be accounted for by analysis of the liquor. A partial explanation might be the formation of sugarsulfonic acids, which has been shown to occur on neutral sulfite cooking of xylose (197). Another investigation on hemicellulose DP indicated that the xylan of a neutral sulfite birch pulp is slightly degraded as compared to native xylan or kraft pulp xylan, but much less degraded than acid sulfite pulp xylan (138). The results illustrate the mild action of the neutral sulfite cook on the hemicelluloses, which accounts for the favorable stiffness imparted to the corrugating board by the unbleached neutral sulfite pulps and the easy beatability and high density and strength of the greaseproof and glassine papers made from the bleached grades. The xylan content of both unbleached and bleached hardwood neutral sulfite pulps is about 20–25%, and the deacetylation of the xylan is almost complete (137). The recovery of acetic acid from the waste liquor as a by-product has been investigated but found to have doubtful economic justification (15).

Because of the ability of lignin to become sulfonated by an alkaline sulfite–bisulfite liquor even in the presence of thiosulfate (cf. Chapter 4.IV), and because the stability of the liquor is unaffected by thiosulfate in alkaline medium, the neutral sulfite cook can be carried out in the presence of large quantities of thiosulfate. The yields, chemical composition, strength characteristics and ease of bleaching are unaffected, but the unbleached pulp brightness is decreased (124). The same effects are obtained by recirculation of waste liquor for re-use after adjustment of its chemicals content. With fresh sodium-based cooking liquor, a pulp brightness of about 50% GE is obtained from typical hardwood raw-materials, which is considerably brighter than for the cold caustic process. Ammonium-based cooks give much darker pulps, but yields and ease of bleaching are approximately the same (95a, 136).

The raw material has a considerable importance for pulp quality. Bark impurities decrease the strength properties (96), although more bark can be tolerated in the unbleached board grades than in most other pulps. The influence of wood species could be judged from a comparison at the same yield, Table 8.2 (185). Most hardwood species are being utilized, such as mixed oak-gum stands of the south-eastern United States (47), birch–beech–maple and aspen stands of the north-eastern and central United States (90, 187), red alder in the western United States (106, 150), oak mixed with other hardwoods in England (72), birch in Sweden (36, 43, 71, 195a) and Finland (169), poplar in Italy (2a), beech and oak in Japan (75), etc. Neutral sulfite pulps from eucalypts give very interesting paper characteristics (135). Softwoods are more resistant to this type of pulping (23). They yield unbleached pulps which are generally stronger than those of hardwoods, but weaker than conventional chemical pulps, whereas the hardwood pulps made with this process are frequently stronger than

Table 8.2. Influence of wood species on the quality of neutral sulfite pulps (185)

Wood type	Species	Density	Lignin content	Pulp strength	Pulp lignin content
Hardwood	Oaks	High	High	Low	High
	Poplars	Low	Low	Medium	Low
	Birches	Medium	Medium	High	Medium
Softwood	Firs	Low	High	Poor	High

chemical hardwood pulps (41). The strength properties of the neutral sulfite pulps increase for decreasing yields to a flat maximum at around 55–60% yield (37, 41, 131). In comparison with kraft semichemical pulps, they give higher strength at yields above 65% (119, 127). Therefore, kraft semichemical pulp mills have often changed over to neutral sulfite pulping in cases where hardwoods are the raw material and where the spent liquor does not present any difficulties. One investigation (40) compared chemical kraft and semichemical neutral sulfite pulps from oak and found the latter to be weaker in the unbleached state but stronger in the bleached state than the corresponding kraft pulps. The neutral sulfite pulps were in this case of a rather low yield. Another investigation (146), comparing acid sulfite, neutral sulfite and kraft pulps of birch, found that the unbleached and bleached kraft pulps had the best strength characteristics, and that the neutral sulfite pulps resembled the acid sulfite pulps prepared from undamaged, hand-made chips. A similar comparison has been made for kraft and neutral sulfite pulps from maple and birch (119a).

It should be noted that the principal use of neutral sulfite hardwood pulps is corrugating medium board, where the conventionally determined strength factors are of little importance, but a high stiffness and crush resistance are desired instead. These pulps impart a stiffness to the board exceeding that of softwood pulps made with the chemical kraft process, as well as with kraft or neutral sulfite semichemical processes (41). In the case of the more short-fibered hardwoods, it may be preferable to mix in softwoods to a minor extent before or after pulping in order to increase the runnability of the furnish on the board machine (150). Neutral sulfite pulp from Douglas fir sawdust, which is inferior to that of alder chips, can be used in mixture with the alder pulp (160b). For liner boards, hardwoods can be used only to a limited extent, about 25%, and hardwood kraft is then preferred to neutral sulfite because of the higher burst strength (67).

In the production of neutral sulfite pulp for newsprint and magazine paper, it is vital that the wood chips are well penetrated by cooking liquor in order to secure maximum brightness (36). Freshly cut birch then gave an unbleached pulp brightness of up to 75% GE, and 60% GE was obtained for stored wood. This applies for a yield level of 80–85%, which is the most suitable for newsprint. Extremely mild neutral sulfite cooks, giving pulp yields of 85–95% from both hardwoods and softwoods, are also of interest for newsprint (42). They have been called *chemimechanical* pulps as distinct from semichemical pulps, cf. Subsection II.3, although as stated in Chapter 6.I, it is preferred here to consider the terms as synonymous. Opacity increases and strength decreases with an increase in pulp yield, thereby suggesting that the pulps should substitute more of the groundwood and less of the chemical pulp the higher the yield. Table 8.3 illustrates the paper properties of these pulps.

Table 8.3. Properties of pulps in the mechanical–semichemical yield region (42, 160a)

Wood species	Pulping process	Yield, %	Freeness, ml C.S.	°SR	Breaking length, km	Tear factor	Sheet density, g/cm³	Brightness, % GE	Opacity, %	Spec. scatt. coeff.
Poplar	Neutral sulfite	90.0	340	45	1.8	20	0.35	56		550
		86.5	340	45	4.0	40	0.45	58		450
		79.0	340	45	8.5	45	0.70	57		200
		77.5	340	45	8.6	55	0.72	55		180
	Cold caustic	83.0	340	45	6.4	55	0.60	45		350
	Groundwood	95	220	56	1.0	30	0.30	64	97	620
Aspen	Neutral sulfite	92	180		3.0	33	0.46	51	94	
		88	180		4.3	52	0.61	49	88	
	Cold caustic	92	335		3.6	60	0.61	54		
		88	250		6.4	63	0.62	—	75	
	Groundwood	97	70		3.1	44	0.40	59	94	
		97	60		2.4	33	0.38	60		
Mixed hardwoods (maple–oak–birch)	Neutral sulfite	92	180		1.5	26	0.34	38	98	
		87	180		3.4	55	0.46	41	95	
	Cold caustic	92	180		3.0	42	0.44	44	—	
		90	180		4.4	53	0.57	42	—	
Balsam fir	Neutral sulfite	95	320		2.9	85	0.43	53	83	
		92	260		5.3	94	0.47	50	87	
		91	325		4.6	92	0.44	51	85	
	Bisulfite	90	380		4.2	113	0.34	46	88	
	Cold caustic	—	245		3.1	49	0.44	47	86	
	Groundwood	97	113		3.1	51	0.40	56	ca. 95	
Western hemlock	Neutral sulfite	93	260		4.1	101	0.37	47	91	
		87	310		5.5	95	0.49	42	83	
	Acid sulfite	46	450		7.3	93	0.73	42	67	
	Groundwood	97	100		2.6	54	0.43	54	95	

Although the buffered neutral sulfite process is now fairly well established, research has more recently been directed towards more acidic cooks, in the pH range of 4–7, which are still far from conventional acid sulfite cooks. They are classified as mixed *bisulfite–sulfite* cooks and can be made both chemical and semichemical. An advantage to neutral sulfite pulping would be the decreased consumption of cooking chemicals. However, although some results indicate unchanged yields and strength at a certain degree of delignification (87), others show that strength is decreased and opacity at the same time increased (37, 184), as would be expected on losing hemicellulose. The *Magnefite* (magnesium-based

431

bisulfite) semichemical pulping process thus gave lower stiffness than did sodium-based neutral sulfite pulping (184). Opacity of the bleached grades is, however, of value for fine papers, which apart from greaseproof paper and glassine is the principal grade for bleached neutral sulfite pulp from hardwoods. The semichemical bisulfite cook is of more interest for softwoods and was discussed in Subsection II.3. Neutral sulfite cooking of softwoods is seldom practised because of the low delignification velocity, but it is used as a precook before a bisulfite or acid sulfite cook in order to deacetylate the softwood glucomannan and thereby obtain a higher pulp yield (cf. Chapter 9).

5. MECHANO-CHEMICAL PULPING

The pulping of annual plants, such as cereal straw and bagasse, is to a large extent carried out according to conventional chemical processes, kraft, soda, or neutral sulfite pulping, cf. Chapter 9.IV. In an attempt to increase the over-all economy of straw pulping and decrease the investment needed, the mechano-chemical process was worked out (5, 7, 8, 9, 152). This process deviates from conventional semichemical pulping in that it applies chemical and mechanical action simultaneously and not as a two-stage treatment. This is made possible by the softer structure of straw as compared to wood, and by the use of *hydrapulpers*, which are impeller vessels designed for reslushing pulp in paper mills. Figure 8.18 shows a flow sheet of the process. The straw is chopped in a cutter and delivered to the hydrapulpers. In the case of bagasse a pretreatment for de-pithing in a special apparatus is sometimes desirable. In the hydrapulpers the straw is charged together with pulping liquor at a consistency of about 10% and in an amount permitting good vortex formation at the impellers. Temperature is maintained at 100°C for 1 h, as compared to the 5 h at 140°C considered necessary for similar results on pressure digestion without mechanical action. This latter statement, however, has only limited validity, as the pulping rate of straw can be very much influenced by the alkali charge.

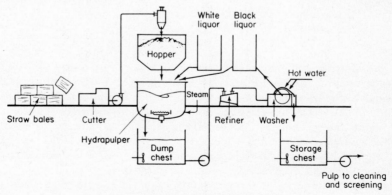

Fig. 8.18. Mechanochemical pulping of straw

Several pulping liquors have been tried, at various conditions. Sulfite liquors give too slow action, kraft white liquor and sodium hydroxide solutions give almost identical results. An alkali charge of 60–120 kg of active alkali per t straw has been applied, for different yields. The more alkali charged, the more rapid is the reaction. Temperatures around 75, 85 and 95°C were tried, and at the highest temperature 55% delignification was achieved after 5 minutes and 70% after 60 minutes. At the same time 30–35% of the pentosans were dissolved with 85–90% of the ash content of the straw. Yields of 65–70% are obtained, but higher or lower yields might also be desirable for special purposes.

The pulped charges are dumped to a chest, pumped through a refiner to a wash filter from where part of the black liquor is recirculated for new use. The washed pulp is screened and may be bleached prior to the paper-making operations. The pulps in the higher yield range are used un-bleached in corrugating board and liner in admixture with other pulp. The bleached grades of lower yield may be used as a substitute for unbleached softwood sulfite pulp in newsprint, or in mixture with bleached sulfite for book and bond papers.

The reasons for the rapid delignification in this process may to some extent be the slightly different type of lignin in straw as compared with wood lignin, but also probably its greater accessibility to the pulping liquor with the aid of the mechanical action.

REFERENCES

1. Anon., *The Story of Fir-Tex*, Fir-Tex Insulating Board Co., St. Helens, Oregon, 1941.
2. Anon., *Pulp Paper*, **22**, No. 1, 38 (1948).
2a. Anon., *Pulp Paper*, **29**, No. 3, 86 (1955).
3. Anon., *Paper Ind.*, **31**, No. 7, 818 (1949).
4. Anon., *Pulp Paper*, **24**, No. 4, 44 (1950).
4a. Anon., *Pulp Paper*, **35**, No. 13, 39 (1961).
5. Aronovsky, S. I., *Tappi*, **36**, No. 4, 167A (1953).
6. Aronovsky, S. I., and R. A. Gortner, *Ind. Eng. Chem.*, **22**, 264, 941 (1930); **25**, 305, 1260, 1349 (1933).
7. Aronovsky, S. I., and E. C. Lathrop, *Tappi*, **32**, 145 (1949).
8. Aronovsky, S. I., and G. H. Nelson, *Tappi*, **34**, 216 (1951).
9. Atchison, J. E., *Paper Trade J.*, **138**, No. 33, 22 (1954).
10. Bache-Wiig, C., *U.S. Pat.* 913,679 (1909); 1,084,244 (1914); 1,169,597 (1916).
11. Baird, P. K., *et al.*, *Tappi*, **40**, 314 (1957).
12. Bandelin, C. E., cited in ref. 154.
13. Beaujean, J., and V. B. Bodenheimer, *Tappi*, **45**, No. 3, 190A (1962).
14. Bhat, R. V., *et al.*, *Indian Pulp Paper*, **11**, 281 (1956); **12**, 374 (1957); *Indian Forest Bull.*, No. 211, 1956.
15. Biggs, W. A., *et al.*, *Tappi*, **44**, 385 (1961).
16. Björnstad, P. L., *Swed. Pat.* 117,070 (1946).
17. Bölviken, A., and H. W. Giertz, *Norsk Skogind.*, **10**, 344 (1956); **12**, 235 (1958).

18. Bouchayer, H., *Papeterie*, **70**, No. 6, 162 (1948).
19. Bradley, L., and E. P. McKeefe, *Can. Pat.* 219,557 (1922); 246,477 (1925); 248,096 (1925); 268,181 (1926); 279,696 (1928); 281,105 (1928); 281,285 (1928); *Paper Trade J.*, **88**, No. 8, 131 (1929).
20. Braun, C. A., *U.S. Pat.* 1,387,441 (1921); *Ger. Pat.* 388,998 (1920).
21. Bray, M. W., and P. R. Eastwood, *Paper Trade J.*, **90**, No. 25, 57 (1930).
22. Bray, M. W., and P. R. Eastwood, *Paper Trade J.*, **93**, No. 17, 38 (1931).
23. Bray, M. W., and J. S. Martin, *Southern Pulp Paper Mfr.*, **5**, No. 1, 7 (1942).
24. Bray, M. W., and J. S. Martin, *Paper Trade J.*, **113**, No. 25, 35 (1941); **120**, No. 3, 45 (1945).
24a. Brecht, W., *Pulp Paper Mag. Can.*, **59**, No. 10, 275 (1958).
25. Brecht, W., and W. Kilpper, *Papier*, **4**, 240, 462 (1950).
26. Brecht, W., and S. Pulst, *Papier*, **9**, 551 (1955).
27. Brecht, W., and H. Weiss, *Papier*, **11**, 82 (1957).
28. Brown, K. J., cited in *Paper Trade J.*, **140**, No. 25, 60 (1956).
29. Brown, K. J., *Tappi*, **42**, 158 (1959).
30. Brown, K. J., and R. D. Hilton, *Paper Trade J.*, **140**, No. 21, 42 (1956).
31. Brown, K. J., and J. N. McGovern, *Tappi*, **33**, 364 (1950).
32. Brown, K. J., and J. N. McGovern, *Paper Ind.*, **35**, No. 1, 66 (1953).
33. Brown, K. J., and W. H. Monsson, *Tappi*, **39**, 592 (1956).
34. Bugg, E. J., *Paper Trade J.*, **142**, No. 51, 26 (1958).
35. Byrne, J. R., and M. H. Voelker, *Tappi*, **43**, No. 5, 261A (1960).
36. Cederquist, K. N., *et al.*, *Svensk Papperstid.*, **62**, 652 (1959).
37. Ceragioli, G., *et al.*, *Tappi*, **40**, 8 (1957).
38. Ceragioli, G., *Cellulosa Carta (Rome)*, **10**, No. 1, 5 (1959).
39. Chambers-Allison, R., *U.S. Pat.* 1,813,988 (1931).
40. Chesley, K. G., *Tappi*, **42**, 130 (1959).
41. Chidester, G. H., *Paper Trade J.*, **129**, No. 20, 84 (1949).
42. Chidester, G. H., *et al.*, *Tappi*, **43**, 876 (1960).
43. Christenson, T., and H. Jonson, *Svensk Papperstid.*, **61**, 366 (1958).
44. Christiansen, C. B., *Tappi*, **43**, 586 (1960).
45. Clark, J. d'A., *Paper Trade J.*, **83**, No. 22, 43 (1926).
46. Cochrane, J. A., *Pulp Paper Mag. Can.*, **57**, No. 3, 201 (1956).
47. Collins, R. E., *Paper Trade J.*, **141**, No. 33, 36 (1957).
48. Colombo, P., *et al.*, *Atip Bull.* No. 3, 60 (1956); No. 4, 133 (1960); *Tappi*, **40**, No. 9, 205A (1957); *Atip Bull.*, **14**, No. 4, 133 (1960).
49. Cross, C. F., *Brit. Pat.* 4,984 (1880).
50. Curran, C. E., and M. W. Bray, *Ind. Eng. Chem.*, **22**, 830 (1930).
51. Curran, C. E., *et al.*, *Paper Trade J.*, **90**, No. 14, 65 (1930).
52. De Carufel, G., *Pulp Paper Mag. Can.*, **60**, No. 9, T 272 (1959).
53. Decker, N. N., *U.S. Pat.* 1,915,410 (1933).
54. Dentremont, A. E., *Paper Trade J.*, **139**, No. 8, 32 (1955).
55. Diehm, R. A., *et al.*, *Tappi*, **43**, 364 (1960).
56. Dorland, R. M., *et. al.*, *Tappi*, **45**, 257 (1962).
57. Drewsen, V., *U.S. Pat.* 730,439 (1903); 1,229,422 (1917); 1,511,664 (1924); 1,831,206 (1932); *Paper Trade J.*, **83**, No. 24, 41 (1926).
58. Durant, L. G., *Paper Trade J.*, **138**, No. 43, 40 (1954).
59. Eberhardt, L., *Tappi*, **39**, No. 7, 126A (1956).
60. Elsner, J. G., *Ger. Pat.* 211,047 (1908).
61. Enge, L., *Ger. Pat.* 296,949 (1915); 353,105 (1919).
62. Enge, L., *Ger. Pat.* 296,973 (1915).

63. Ernst. A. J., *et al.*, *Tappi*, **43,** 34 (1960).
64. Evans, J. C. W., *Pulp Paper Mag. Can.*, **50,** No. 9, 65 (1949).
65. Evans, J. C. W., *Paper Trade J.*, **136,** No. 18, 14 (1953).
66. Evans, J. C. W., *Paper Trade J.*, **140,** No. 46, 24 (1956).
67. Fahey, D. J., and V. C. Setterholm, *Tappi*, **43,** 643 (1960).
68. Field, J. L., *Tappi*, **36,** No. 8, 140A (1953).
69. Findley, M. E., and W. J. Nolan, *Tappi*, **39,** 758 (1956).
70. Flinn, E. S., *Paper Trade J.*, **138,** No. 43, 30 (1954).
71. Flodén, I., *Svensk Pappserstid.*, **61,** 365 (1958).
72. Frankel, T., and E. M. Whitcomb, *Paper Trade J.*, **142,** No. 47, 27 (1958).
73. Fry, G., *Fr. Pat.* 88; 120 (1869).
74. Giese, E., *Zellstoff Papier*, **4,** 268 (1955).
75. Goodwin, R. G., *Tappi*, **39,** No. 7, 187A (1956).
76. Gremler, E. R., and J. N. McGovern, *Tappi*, **43,** No. 8, 200A (1950).
76a. Hägglund, S. E., *Svensk Papperstid.*, **57,** 465 (1954).
77. Hart, J. S., *et al.*, *Pulp Paper Mag. Can.*, **55,** No. 10, 114 (1954).
78. Hart, J. S., and J. M. Woods, *Pulp Paper Mag. Can.*, **56,** No. 9, 95 (1955).
79. Henckel, N. N., *Austr. Pat.* 34,816 (1912).
80. Herbst, J. H. E., and H. B. Marshall, *Pulp Paper Mag. Can.*, **52,** No. 13, 106 (1951).
81. Heritage, C. C., *et al.*, *Paper Trade J.*, **87,** No. 17, 129 (1928).
82. Heritage, C. C., and T. C. Duvall, *Southern Pulp Paper Mfr.*, **11,** No. 9, 50 (1948).
83. Herty, C. H., 1930–1938.
84. Heuer, J. H., *Pulp Paper Mag. Can.*, **56,** No. 12, 170 (1955).
85. Hirschkind, W., *U.S. Pat.* 2,071,304 (1937); 2,071,307 (1937).
86. Hosaka, H., *et al.*, *J. Japan. Forestry Soc.*, Spec. Issue, Trans. 63rd Meeting, **1954,** 345.
87. Husband, R. M., *Tappi*, **36,** 529 (1953); **38,** 577 (1955); **40,** 412, 452 (1957).
88. Hyttinen, A., and E. R. Schafer, *Tappi*, **32,** 69 (1949); *Pulp Paper Mag. Can.*, **56,** No. 12, 140 (1955).
89. Ichikawa, S., *J. Japan. Tech. Assoc. Pulp Paper Ind.*, **2,** No. 2, 7 (1948).
90. Jackson, D. T., *et al.*, *Pulp Paper Mag. Can.*, **60,** No. 6, T 182 (1959); cf. *Pulp Paper* **30,** No. 5, 88 (1956).
91. Jansson, L., *et al.*, *Pulp Paper Mag. Can.*, **59,** No. 10, 217 (1958); *Tappi*, **42,** 649 (1959).
92. Jayme, G., *et al.*, *Papier*, **14,** 186 (1960).
93. Jenness, L. C., and G. L. Nyström, *Paper Trade J.*, **126,** No. 24, 53 (1948).
94. Jensen, W., *et al.*, *Paperi Puu*, **39,** No. 4A, 165 (1957).
95. Jensen, W., *et al.*, *Paperi Puu*, **39,** 405, 457 (1957).
95a. Jones, R. M., and T. E. Detcher, *Tappi*, **34,** No. 8, 88A (1951).
96. Keller, E. L., *Tappi*, **33,** 556 (1950).
97. Keller, E. L., and J. N. McGovern, *Tappi*, **32,** 400 (1949).
98. Keller, E. L., and J. N. McGovern, *Tappi*, **38,** 568 (1955).
99. Kerr, W. D., and S. A. Harding *Pulp Paper Mag. Can.*, **56,** No. 9, 102 (1955); *Tappi*, **39,** 308 (1956).
100. Kerr, W. D., and J. S. Hart, *Tappi*, **42,** 254 (1959).
101. Kerr, W. D., and J. S. Hart, *Tappi*, **40,** 681 (1957).
102. Kittelsen, T. and E., *Ger. Pat.* 324,053 (1919).
103. Klauditz, W., *Holzforschung*, **6,** 70 (1952).

104. Klemm, K. H., *Neuzeitliche Holzschlifferzeugung*, Sändig Verlag, Wiesbaden 1957, p. 255.
105. Knechtges, R. G., *Paper Trade J.*, **138**, No. 10, 14, No. 43, 32 (1954).
106. Knight, R. G., *Paper Trade J.*, **141**, No. 52, 22 (1957).
107. von Koeppen, A., *Paper Trade J.*, **145**, No. 16, 24, No. 17, 28 (1961).
107a. Cabella, S., *Tappi*, **46**, No. 4, 196A (1963).
108. Kopparfors AB., *Brit. Pat.* 769,849 (1957).
109. Lagergren, S., *et al.*, *Svensk Papperstid.*, **60**, 632, 664 (1957).
110. Lambert, J. E., *Paper Trade J.*, **144**, No. 43, 36 (1960).
111. Lea, D. C., *Tappi*, **37**, 393 (1954).
112. Leavitt, E. M., *Tappi*, **35**, No. 6, 48A (1952).
113. Legg, G. W., and J. S. Hart, *Tappi*, **43**, 470 (1960).
114. Libby, C. E., and F. W. O'Neil, *Tappi*, **33**, 161 (1950).
115. Libby, C. E., and F. W. O'Neil, *U.S. Pat.* 2,713,540 (1955).
116. Limerick, J. McK., *et al.*, *Pulp Paper Mag. Can.*, **52**, No. 3, 175 (1951).
117. Limerick, J. McK., *Tappi*, **36**, 294 (1953); *Paper Trade J.*, **140**, No. 4, 20 (1956).
118. Lougheed, E. H., *Pulp Paper Mag. Can.*, **46**, No. 3, 165 (1945).
119. MacLaurin, D. J., and J. R. Peckham, *Tappi*, **36**, 557 (1953).
119a. MacLaurin, D. J., *et al.*, *Tappi*, **36**, 553 (1953).
120. MacLaurin, D. J., and J. F. Whalen, *Tappi*, **37**, 143 (1954).
121. Magruder, R. S., *Tappi*, **41**, No. 12, 58A (1958).
122. Marsoni, S., *Brit. Pat.* 553,423 (1941).
123. Marth, D. E., *Tappi*, **42**, 301 (1959).
124. May, M. N., and J. R. Peckham, *Tappi*, **40**, 914 (1957).
125. McGovern, J. N., Paper presented before TAPPI, Feb. 23 (1950).
126. McGovern, J. N., *Tappi*, **33**, 486 (1950).
127. McGovern, J. N., *et. al.*, *Fibre Containers*, **33**, No. 1035 (1948); *Tappi*, **32**, 179 (1949).
128. McGovern, J. N., *et al.*, *Tappi*, **32**, 440 (1949).
129. McGovern, J. N., *et al.*, *U.S. Dep. Agr.*, *Forest Prod. Lab.*, R 1738 (1949).
130. McGovern, J. N., and G. H. Chidester, *U.S. Dep. Agr.*, *Forest Prod. Lab.*, R 1292 (1942).
131. McGovern, J. N., and E. L. Keller, *Pulp Paper Mag. Can.*, **49**, No. 9, 93 (1948).
132. Mitscherlich, A. M., *Brit. Pat.* 2,939 (1874).
133. de Montmorency, W. H., *et al.*, *Pulp Paper Mag. Can.*, **57**, No. 4, 128 (1956).
134. Murtfeldt, L., *Pulp Paper*, **24**, No. 9, 38 (1950).
135. Nolan, W. J., *Tappi*, **41**, 41 (1958).
136. Ogiwara, Y., *J. Japan. Tech. Assoc. Pulp Paper Ind.*, **7**, No. 5, 2 (1953); *J. Soc. Textile Cellulose Ind.*, *Japan*, **13**, 209 (1957).
137. Öhrn, O. E., and I. Croon, *Svensk Papperstid.*, **63**, 601 (1960).
138. Öhrn, O. E., and B. Enström, *Svensk Papperstid.*, **63**, 817 (1960).
139. Olson, K. E., and W. W. Marteny, *Paper Trade J.*, **133**, No. 10, 118 (1951).
140. Ottar, H., *Norsk Skogind.*, **11**, 215 (1957).
141. Pamén, L., *Svensk Papperstid.*, **63**, 550 (1960).
142. Pancirolli, F., and G. Ceragioli, *Ind. Carta, Milan*, **13**, No. 2, 13 (1959).
143. Parrett, A. E., *Pulp Paper Mag. Can.*, **34**, 515 (1933).
144. Parsons, S. R., in E. H. Johnson ed., *Mechanical Pulping Manual*, TAPPI Monograph Series No. 21, New York 1960.

145. Pearson, A. J., *et al.*, *Appita*, **12**, No. 3, 57, 73 (1958); *Paper Trade J.*, **142**, No. 51, 16, 18 (1958).
146. Pettersson, S. E., and S. A. Rydholm, *Svensk Papperstid.*, **64**, 4 (1961).
147. Porphyre, J. A., *Papeterie*, **78**, 251 (1956).
148. Possaner von Ehrenthal, B., *Ger. Pat.* 708,592 (1939).
149. Quick, R. H., *Tappi*, **39**, 357 (1956).
150. Quick, R. H., *Tappi*, **40**, No. 1, 135A (1957).
151. Rawling, F. G., and J. A. Staidl, *Paper Trade J.*, **81**, No. 8, 49 (1925).
151a. Richardson, C. A., *Tappi*, **45**, No. 12, 139A (1962).
152. Root, E. M., *Paper Mill News*, **72**, No. 13, 58 (1949).
153. Rue, J. D., *Paper Trade J.*, **81**, No. 16, 54 (1925).
154. Rue, J. D., *Paper Trade J.*, **81**, No. 16, 57 (1925), T.S. 157.
155. Rue, J. D., *et al.*, *U.S. Pat.* 1,859,845–1,859,848 (1932).
156. Rue, J. D., *et al.*, *Paper Trade J.*, **83**, T.S. 106 (1926).
157. Runkel, R. O. H., *Ger. Pat.* 518,985, cf. ref. 158.
158. Runkel, R. O. H., *Papier*, **5**, 329 (1951).
159. Runkel, R. O. H., *et al.*, *Holzforschung*, **7**, 9 (1953).
160. Runkel, R. O. H., and K. F. Pratt, *Halbzellstoffe; Rohstoffechemie und Verfahrenstechnik–Wirtschaftliche Bedeutung*. Güntter Staib Verlag, Biberach (Germany) 1958.
160a. Rydholm, S. A., *Papier*, **14**, 535 (1960) and unpublished.
160b. Samuels, R. M., *Tappi*, **45**, No. 10, 160A (1962).
161. Sapp, J. E., *Paper Trade J.*, **130**, No 26, 22 (1950).
162. Sapp, J. E., *Tappi*, **35**, No. 6, 40A (1952).
163. Schacht, W., *Papier-Ztg.*, **26**, No. 84, 3143 (1901); *Ger. Pat.* 122,171 (1900).
164. Schuler, K., *Papier-Ztg.*, **64**, No. 6, 5, No. 7, 5 (1958).
165. Schulte, H., cited in ref. 154.
166. Schwalbe, C. G., *Ger. Pat.* 203,230 (1907).
167. Schwalbe, K., *Swed. Pat.* 93,169 (1938).
168. Schwartz, R., and T. Henning, *Ger. Pat.* 707,894 (1941).
169. Sihtola, H., *Svensk Papperstid.*, **55**, 807 (1952); **61**, 364 (1958); *Paperi Puu*, **34**, 409 (1952).
170. Silver, F. P. *Pulp Paper Mag. Can.*, **50**, No. 3, 195 (1949).
171. Silver, F. P., and L. R. Beath, *Pulp Paper Mag. Can.*, **54**, No, 3, 215 (1953); *Tappi*, **36**, 305 (1953).
172. Snyder, K. L. and R. A. Premo, *Tappi*, **40**, 901 (1957).
173. Spaak, G., *Svensk Papperstid.*, **56**, 509 (1953).
174. Stephenson, J. N., *Pulp Paper Mag. Can.*, **54**, No. 10, 104 (1953).
175. Stewart, D. L., and H. F. Crotogine, *Pulp Paper Mag. Can.*, **60**, No. 9, T 284 (1959).
176. Stone, J. E., *Tappi*, **38**, 610 (1955).
177. Stone, J. E., *Pulp Paper Mag. Can.*, **57**, No. 7, 139 (1956).
178. Stone, J. E., and H. V. Green, *Tappi*, **42**, 700 (1959).
179. Strapp, R. K., and J. M. Woods, *Pulp Paper Mag. Can.*, **57**, No. 5, 124 (1956).
180. Sutherland, D. M., *Paper Trade J.*, **124**, No. 15, 49, No. 22, 62 (1947); *Paper Mill News*, **72**, No. 21, 48 (1949).
181. Tank-Nielsen, T., *Norsk Skogind.*, **10**, 268 (1956).
182. Textor, C. K., *Wood Fiber Production with Revolving Disk Mills*, Forest Products Research Soc., Chicago 1948.
183. Thickens, J. A., *U.S. Pat.* 1,138,907 (1915).
184. Trout, P., *Tappi*, **45**, No. 1, 190A (1962).

185. U.S. Forest Products Laboratory, *Fibre Containers*, **34,** No. 11, 66 (1949).
186. Van Derveer, P. D., *Paper Trade J.*, **144,** No. 36, 36 (1960).
187. Van Derveer, P. D., *Paper Trade J.*, **141,** No. 44, 34 (1957).
188. Vilars, J., *Chim. Ind. (Paris)*, **72,** No. 1, 67 (1954).
189. Walters, W. Z., and M. N. May, *Tappi*, **43,** 881 (1960).
190. Wardrop, A. B., and H. E. Dadswell, *J. Inst. Wood Sci.*, **1958,** No. 2 (Nov.) 8.
191. Watson, A. J., *et al.*, *Appita*, **11,** No. 6, 145 (1958).
192. Weisshuhn, C., *Papierfabrik.*, **25,** 60 (1927); *Ger. Pat.* 280,283 (1930).
193. Wells, S. D., *U.S. Pat.* 1,714,459 (1929).
194. Werle, F. A., *Ger. Pat.* 227,064 (1910).
195. West, C. J., *et al.*, *Semichemical Processes*, Bibliographic Series No. 175, Appleton, Wisc. 1950 and 1955.
195a. Whitcomb, E. M., *et al.*, *Paper Trade J.*, **142,** No. 52, 24 (1958).
196. Wultsch, F., *Wochenbl. Papierfabrik.*, **84,** 946 (1956).
197. Yllner, S., *Acta Chem. Scand.*, **10,** 1251 (1956).
198. Yundt, A. P., cited in *Pulp Paper*, **26,** No. 4, 53 (1952).
199. Yundt, A. P., *Tappi,* **35,** No. 6, 46A (1952).
200. Zacharias, A., *Ger. Pat.* 280,476 (1914).
201. Zimmermann, B., *Ger. Pat.* 376,910 (1922).

9

CHEMICAL PULPING

I. Sulfite Process

1. GENERAL CONSIDERATIONS

The sulfite process, its main features already formed by the 1880's, is still, together with the kraft process, the main method of chemical pulp production, although it has lately lost much ground to the kraft and neutral sulfite methods. In the early years the sulfite method had the advantage of yielding the brightest unbleached chemical pulp, and the most easy-bleaching one, and was therefore used for all grades where light color was of importance. When in about 1930 it was learned how to bleach kraft pulp without any serious loss in strength, the kraft pulps began to gain ground in certain fields because of better paper strength properties. In the special field of dissolving pulps the sulfite process ruled alone until about 1940, when the prehydrolysis process made it possible to introduce kraft pulp even for viscose rayon purposes, whereas acetate pulp had to be made by the sulfite process. Finally, the sulfite process was for a long time the only method of producing mildly cooked pulps, rich in hemicelluloses, for unbleached and bleached greaseproof and glassine papers, but since 1950 neutral sulfite pulps of bleached grades have been used increasingly in this field and even some bleached kraft pulp has been applied.

Two main factors have made the sulfite industry less capable of competition, namely its *sensitivity to the wood raw material*, and the *difficulty of recovering the cooking chemicals and utilizing its waste products*, which correspond to half the wood substance. The sulfite process still uses mainly softwood, and only softwood free from certain extractives of phenolic character. In Europe, therefore, mainly spruce and in America, spruces, firs and hemlocks are used, whereas pine, Douglas fir and larch, especially their heartwood, are not sufficiently pulpable by the conventional sulfite process. Hardwood may be used but their extractives often cause difficulties. Finally, even spruce may be unsuitable as a raw material if its surface layer has become impregnated by tannins from the bark. Such damage arises when unbarked logs are water-driven, which is necessary in certain parts of the world, or occurs when unbarked wood of small dimensions is soaked in water for a certain time in order to facilitate subsequent barking.

The kraft industry, on the other hand, accepts without difficulty hardwood as well as softwood of any grade and species, even pine and tannin-

439

damaged spruce, as well as wood of small dimensions and saw-mill waste. It is also far less sensitive to bark impurities in the chips. The neutral sulfite process preferentially operates on hardwoods. The result is that sulfite pulpwood generally sells for 10–30% more than kraft pulpwood, which has considerable economical importance. The situation is accentuated by the fact that the groundwood pulp industry has been limited to the same source of raw material as the sulfite industry.

The problem of utilizing the organic by-products and recovering the cooking chemicals of the sulfite process is examined in Chapter 11. One of the difficulties involved depends on the sulfate formation in side reactions during the cook, which leads to gypsum scale formation on evaporation of the waste liquor. Therefore only fairly recently has evaporation and burning of calcium-based sulfite waste liquor met with industrial success, more than half a century after the corresponding operations were introduced to the kraft industry. Furthermore, on burning, mainly calcium sulfate is formed from the cooking chemicals, which practically prevents a regeneration of the latter. In many cases the sulfite waste liquors have become a direct burden on the process economy, as their disposal into the rivers or seas has often been prohibited by law, which has led to expensive measures for their elimination.

The sulfite industry has in several ways tried to remedy the drawbacks of the process and develop its advantages. By certain modifications, especially the change from calcium to ammonium or sodium base, as well as from one-stage to multistage cooking, the cooking of hardwoods, pine heartwood and tannin-damaged spruce has become possible. Evaporation and burning of the waste liquors is facilitated by the use of a base having a soluble sulfate, as is the regeneration of chemicals by using bases other than calcium. The utilization of the organic compounds of the waste liquors by other means than burning has also been successful in some cases. Finally, it has been possible to raise the pulp yield for certain grades, in the so-called high yield or semichemical sulfite pulping. These lines of development have just begun, and their full possibilities have not yet been entirely realized and investigated. Some of the modifications of the sulfite process are so thorough-going that in contrast to the mere change of bases they lead to processes which cannot really bear the same name as the old sulfite process. The *neutral sulfite process* is an example of this. Similarly, cooking in liquors of mainly bisulfite without any excess of base or of sulfur dioxide, is a process which deserves a name of its own and has been called the *bisulfite process*. The nomenclature is not very precise at this point, since the conventional sulfite process has sometimes been called the bisulfite process as contrasted to the neutral or monosulfite process. However, the term should be reserved for the process utilizing bisulfite solutions of pH 3–6, and the conventional process be called *sulfite*, or when necessary *acid sulfite process*. The border-lines between the acid sulfite, bisulfite and neutral sulfite processes as to type of reactions are not very sharp, and a large number of investigations cover conditions belonging to more than one of these processes. Therefore they will all be treated in this chapter as regards chemical reactions, whereas other aspects of neutral sulfite pulping have been treated in Chapter 8 on semichemical pulping, and the same is valid for semichemical acid sulfite and bisulfite pulping.

2. DESCRIPTION OF PROCESS

The development of the sulfite cooking technique has involved several important improvements, some of which are listed below:

(a) Introduction of the *hot acid system* with complete reclamation of all digester reliefs, to improve heat economy, decrease sulfur consumption, increase acid strength (content of total SO_2) and prevent calcium sulfite precipitation in the digester.

(b) Introduction of *internal cooking liquor circulation*, to eliminate local overheating at the live steam inlets.

(c) Introduction of *external forced circulation* through heat exchangers, avoiding the dilution of the cooking liquor with steam condensate.

(d) Perfection of the *chip filling* by steam or air packing, thereby not only increasing digester output but also preventing channelling of the circulating cooking liquor.

(e) Perfection of the *impregnation technique*, especially the use of pre-steaming and pressure impregnation by the cooking acid.

(f) Perfection of the *process control by instrumentation*, such as recorders and controllers of temperature, pressure, liquor level, rate of circulation, weight of digester content, etc.

(g) Introduction of *soluble bases, multistage cooking* and *continuous cooking*, to improve productivity and quality.

A great aid in the development of the sulfite process has been the increased availability and improved quality of acid-resistant steel. A grade considered suitable in the digester department contains 17.5% Cr, 10.5% Ni, 1.5% Mo and less than 0.06% C. Sometimes the nickel and molybdenum content is increased by 1%. Whole digesters are now made in compound steel, although the majority are still ceramic or carbon brick lined (cf. Chapter 6.VI).

Figure 9.1 gives a flow sheet for a sulfite pulp mill. Local practice shows great variations. The equipment and operations were described in general terms in Chapter 6.VI, and some specific details on the sulfite process will be given here with two examples of modern cooking practice.

A sulfite *digester cycle for rayon pulp* is illustrated by the temperature, pressure and liquor level diagrams of Figure 9.2. After filling spruce chips, 38 t dry weight containing 16 t moisture, into the 200 m³ digester from a belt conveyor coming from the chip silo, which takes about 30 minutes using steam packing, steam is introduced for another 30 minutes, until the charge is brought to 100°C throughout and steam appears from the digester air outlets. Around 6 t of low-pressure live steam are consumed in filling and steaming. Cooking acid, 146 m³, containing 6%

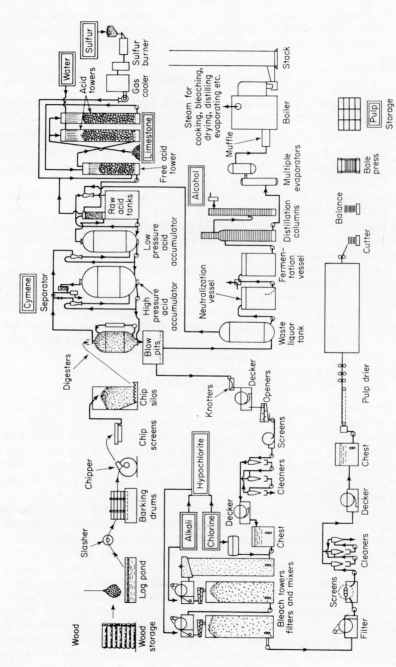

Fig. 9.1. Sulfite pulp mill

total SO_2 and 0.9% (about 37 kg ptw) combined SO_2, is charged by a medium-pressure, high-capacity pump in 20 minutes, the circulation is started and the indirect heating begun. The pressure, which at completed liquor charging has a peak, created by the hydraulic pressure of the pump at full digester and the subsequent release when the pump line is shut off and the top relief valve opened, rapidly increases during the heating until maximum pressure, 6 kp/cm², is reached and the top pressure control valve opens. The *top gas relief* goes to the 3 kp/cm² tank for pressure acid. At 100–110°C, *side relief* of 25 m³ cooking liquor to the 1 kp/cm² pressure acid tank is performed, causing a slight, incidental pressure drop. The liquor-to-wood ratio is thereby reduced from 4.4: 1 to 3.8: 1. Maximum

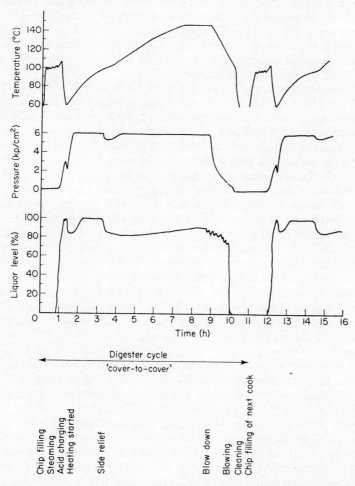

Fig. 9.2. Acid sulfite cooking of rayon pulp; temperature, pressure and liquor level diagrams indicating the various operations

temperature, 148°C, is reached 4–6 h after the start of the heating, and the steam is automatically shut off. The cook proceeds at maximum temperature until end-point determinations, made colorimetrically, after 90 minutes show that it is time for the blow down. The gas relief to the 1 kp/cm² tank is opened and the pressure drops to 2 kp/cm² in 30 minutes. The relief is then transferred to the ejector tank for cold cooking acid, passing a gas cooler on the way, and proceeds for another 45 minutes. The condensate from the gas cooler contains, apart from dissolved sulfur dioxide, *p*-cymene, volatile aldehydes and organic acids, and is removed from the system. When 0.5 kp/cm² is reached, the cook is blown for 30 minutes to the blow pit, where the waste liquor is drawn off by percolation with weak waste liquor and finally wash water, and sent to the alcohol plant for neutralization and fermentation. The unbleached pulp is obtained in 43% yield and, consequently, 16.5 t or 83 kg/m³ digester volume of unbleached pulp, dry weight, is produced in one cook. The digester is cleaned from pulp by water jets and vented prior to next chip charging. The total cooking cycle takes 9–12 h 'from cover to cover'.

A corresponding *cooking cycle for greaseproof pulp* is shown by Figure 9.3. Chip filling, steaming and acid charging follow the same pattern as the rayon pulp cook. The cooking acid composition is rather different, as the content of combined SO_2 is increased to 1.25% (50 kg ptw) in order to guarantee conditions which preserve a large fraction of the hemicelluloses in the pulp. For the same reason, the temperature increase is made slowly and the maximum temperature kept as low as 122°C. Side relief is performed in the same manner, but the top gases are already relieved at 5 kp/cm², which is quite sufficient at this low temperature. The end point of this slow cook is determined by sampling the pulp at a suitable stage and subsequent rapid chlorine number analysis. From the result of that determination the moment of blow down is calculated. The gas is relieved in the same manner as in the rayon pulp cook, but the pressure is permitted to drop to that of the atmosphere. Then the waste liquor is drained from the digester and a preliminary washing with weak waste liquor and hot water is carried out in the digester before the pulp, in a yield of 53%, is dumped to a leach caster for further washing. The total cooking cycle in this case is considerably longer, with approximately 20 h 'from cover to cover'.

The two types of cook described represent two extremes in European practice, and intermediate types of pulp require intermediate conditions of cooking acid composition, time and temperature. Strong paper pulps are cooked at about 130–135°C, softer grades at 140–145°C. American practice generally employs shorter heating periods, somewhat shorter times at maximum temperature, often leaves out pre-steaming and as a rule blows the cooks. The time from cover to cover is therefore decreased to 8–10 h, which is still considerably more than required for a kraft cook. There is a trend towards increasing the total SO_2 content to 10%, which in conjunction with increased digester pressures up to 10 kp/cm², will increase the rate of delignification. The introduction of magnesium, ammonium and sodium

444

bases has not caused any considerable change in one-stage cooking practice, apart from rather shorter cooking cycles and special precautions with the digester linings. The regeneration of cooking chemicals made possible with magnesium- and sodium-based liquors should facilitate a more deliberate use of cooking chemicals, and an increase in the content of combined SO_2 has in special cases a favorable effect on pulp quality. It also introduces the possibility of deviations from the conventional acid sulfite cook, such as the bisulfite and two-stage sulfite processes. The practice of two-stage cooking is dealt with in a separate section of this chapter, and a common practice of bisulfite cooking has hardly developed yet. Bisulfite cooking should deviate from the conventional practice mainly in shorter periods of heating and higher cooking temperature, 150–160°C, and in the composition of the cooking liquor, which contains about 4%

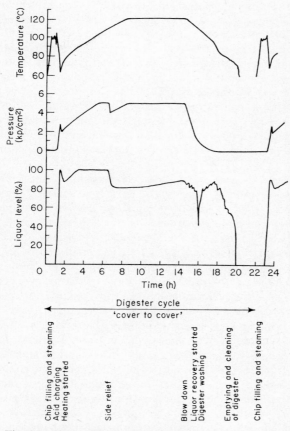

Fig. 9.3. Acid sulfite cooking of pulp for greaseproof and glassine paper, 'Mitscherlich type cook'; temperature, pressure and liquor level diagrams indicating the various operations

445

total and 2% combined SO_2 at pH 4. The practice of semichemical acid sulfite and neutral sulfite cooking has been dealt with in Chapter 8.

Two of the most important operations in sulfite cooking practice are the *impregnation of the chips* and the *end-point determination of the cook*. The former, which was treated in Chapter 6.III, is met by various types of pretreatments, predominantly steaming and hydraulic pressure application, as well as by an ample heating period. The second problem, which to a great extent has remained an art, requiring a certain skill from the operators, will be dealt with here in some detail.

There is an important reason why end-point determination of a sulfite cook is necessary, in contrast to kraft cooking, where the charge of cooking chemicals and the maximum temperature largely determine the time required for a certain degree of delignification. In the kraft cook, the active chemicals are largely consumed in the reactions, and the liquor remaining towards the end of the cook is comparatively inactive. In contrast, although the reactions of the sulfite cook likewise largely consume the cooking chemicals, they maintain or increase the acidity of the cooking liquor, which determines the rate of the carbohydrate hydrolysis and also influences the rate of lignin removal. Therefore, some of the reactions of importance for pulp quality do not slow down but even accelerate towards the end of the cook. The precision required for the correct period of cooking is therefore far greater for the sulfite than for the kraft process. Although there are sulfite mills, especially among those cooking lignin-rich pulps, which operate with a predetermined length of cook, general practice favors some sort of end-point determination used in every cook.

There are two main types of such determinations, based on analysis of *wood residue* or *cooking liquor*. The former category suffers from two disadvantages. First, it is not possible to remove a sample from the digester which is quite representative for the entire cook, and local irregular deviations from the average degree of cooking in the neighbourhood of the sampling device may cause some error. Secondly, most pulp analyses of any accuracy will require a minimum of 20–30 minutes including the time of sampling and sample preparation. Therefore, this category of end-point determination can only be used for relatively slow cooks, and only one or two checks per cook can be made. The usual test is a chlorine or permanganate number determination, carried out on the screened and dried pulp sample. In order to facilitate judgement of when it is time for the final test, a quick colorimetrical method is used by some mills. That method is based on the fact that lignin-rich pulps, dipped in a concentrated hypochlorite solution, rapidly develop a reddish-brown color. Wet balls of pulp samples are dipped into a standard solution and compared to others of known lignin content. The method is generally not accurate enough to be used as the sole test for the end point.

Even if analysis of pulp samples is too slow to be used as end-point determinations in the faster sulfite cooks, it is used indirectly for the purpose, since analysis of an average sample of the blown cook is taken as a control of the end-point determination used and leads to correction of the end-point test level for the next cook. Then both objections to the pulp analysis category of tests disappear, since there is ample time for the analysis, and the sample can be taken in a more representative way. The dominating tests of this type are chlorine or permanganate number for most paper pulps, and pulp viscosity for soft paper pulps and dissolving pulps.

The other category of tests, cooking liquor analysis, suffers from being an indirect method, measuring the reaction medium of the cook towards the end instead of its actual result. Slight variations in the cooking conditions, such as in the liquor-to-wood ratio, in the composition of the cooking acid charged, or in the maximum pressure or temperature, may affect the relationship between the pulp quality and the properties in the cooking liquor towards the end of the cook. In fact, this always happens, and a current correction in the end-point level of the liquor test, based on subsequent pulp analysis of the finished cook is a prerequisite for all cooking liquor end-point tests. The advantages of these tests are otherwise obvious: the samples, preferably taken in the liquor circulation, represent the entire digester content, and the analysis can be carried out rapidly and accurately, sometimes automatically also, and can be recorded on instruments.

The cooking liquor tests, as well as the pulp tests, suggested for end-point determination are listed in Table 9.1. Most are still in use.

Table 9.1. Methods used for end-point determination of sulfite cooks

Sample	Method	Ref.
Pulp	Chlorine number	628
	Permanganate number	630, 761
	Hypochlorite-developed color	475
	Viscosity	759
Liquor	Iodometric titration of total SO_2 and available combined SO_2	576
	Mitscherlich test	583
	Refractive index	421, 461
	Viscosity	421, 506
	Ultraviolet light absorbence at 280 or 205 mμ	443, 579
	Color	380, 653
	pH	378
	Conductivity	11a, 421

Some of these liquor tests measure the concentration of the material dissolved. As indicated in Figure 9.4 that is the case for the *refractive index* and *ultraviolet light absorbence* measurements. The former indicates the dissolution of both carbohydrates and lignin, and their relative contributions to the refractive index have been studied (421). The ultraviolet light absorbence is mainly proportional to the lignin concentration of the liquor and disregards the carbohydrate dissolution. However,

447

during the last period of a rayon pulp cook, condensation reactions of the lignin cause changes in its absorption spectrum, especially at 280 mμ and higher wavelengths (380). Therefore, 280 mμ absorbence is not an ideal measure of the lignin concentration of the cooking liquor, whereas 205 mμ has been found strictly proportional to the latter (443). *Liquor viscosity*, which is a measure of dissolved organic matter, mainly lignin, is also probably affected by condensation reactions and, furthermore, has been found to require careful removal of solid impurities, which may clog the capillaries of the viscosimeters (421).

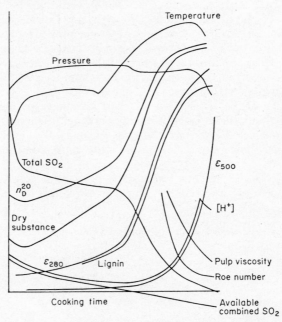

Fig. 9.4. Analytical methods for the end-point determination of a sulfite (rayon pulp) cook. n_D^{20} refractive index, E_{280} absorbency at 280 mμ, E_{500} absorbency at 500 mμ, H$^+$ acidity at cooking temperature. 'Lignin' determined as methoxyl content of the waste liquor dry substance (Rydholm)

All methods measuring the concentration of dissolved matter during the sulfite cook suffer from the disadvantage that the values obtained change considerably at an intermediate stage of the cook but more slowly towards the end of normal cooks. They are therefore better suited for end-point determination of high-yield semichemical and chemical cooks, and less so for cooks for soft paper pulps and rayon pulps, where the delignification is almost complete and a certain degree of hydrolytic degradation is the chief quality criterion. Small changes in the liquor-to-wood ratio will always cause serious errors in this type of end-point determination.

448

Other liquor tests measure changes in the concentrations of the inorganic components of the cooking liquor, mainly the acidity and the bisulfite ion concentration. Iodometric titration of *total SO₂* gives little information of the end-point, since its concentration will depend not only on chemical reactions but also on the top gas relief, i.e. variations in maximum temperature at constant maximum pressure. Determination of *available combined SO₂* (576) would, if correctly performed, give valuable information on the consumption of chemicals during the cook, on the hydrogen and bisulfite concentrations prevailing, and, therefore, on the end point of the cook (653, 654). However, as will be discussed further in a subsequent section of this chapter, it is not easy to determine available combined SO_2 with great accuracy, since some bisulfite ions are consumed in α-hydroxysulfonate formation occurring on the cooling of the liquor samples, and also because some fairly weak organic acids disturb the correct iodometric–alkalimetric titration. It is still a useful indication and frequently applied for strong paper pulp cooks, including bisulfite cooks. A rough idea of the available combined SO_2 of calcium-based cooks can also be obtained by the *Mitscherlich* test, where a liquor sample is drawn from the digester without cooling and received in an excess of ammonium hydroxide (583). The volume of settled precipitate, consisting of calcium sulfite, will be proportional to the amount of SO_2 remaining after degassing of the hot liquor sample and thus to the content of bisulfite ions (583).

pH measurement of the cooking liquor is also difficult. pH of cooled liquor samples differs greatly with that at cooking temperature, and until recently there was no suitable equipment for direct pH measurement in the digester. However, some installations for high-temperature pH measurement have been made recently (378). One persistent disadvantage is the comparatively short life-time of the glass electrode at high temperature. *Conductivity* measurements are rather more suited to high-temperature and pressure installations (421), and a method for end-point determination has been worked out (11a) and is in use. As the changes in conductivity are mainly caused by acidity changes, both methods indicate similar phenomena. These curves, as well as the one for *cooking liquor color* are in contrast to those of the other end-point tests, very steep towards the end of the cook and thus less sensitive to changes in the liquor-to-wood ratio. As they develop only when the combined SO_2 is nearly consumed, the application of these methods is less suited to the production of the less delignified grades of paper pulp and preferably applied on rayon pulp cooks.

As the color determination of the cooking liquor is the most important method for end-point determination of rayon and soft paper pulp cooks up to a chlorine number of about 3, its theoretical background should be scrutinized here. Figure 9.5 shows the absorbence in ultraviolet and visible light of the cooking liquor at various stages of a rayon pulp cook (380). It is seen that the absorbence at 280 mμ and shorter ultraviolet waves increases predominantly at an intermediate phase of the cook, whereas the absorbence in the visible region is low until the very last period, when it becomes pronounced, especially in the blue range of the spectrum. The liquor color turns from light yellow to reddish-brown and finally to black-brown. A spectrum of a simple slope without characteristic peaks develops. The color of the cooking liquor was early ascribed to lignin condensation products (276), and although polycondensates of carbohydrate origin have also been suggested (669), it has been thoroughly demonstrated (299) that the color is attached to the lignin fraction of the liquor, and that lignin preparations but not holocellulose, turn brown on acid sulfite cooking. However, the exact configuration causing the color has not been found, although the most likely assumption is that a condensation of carbonyl groups of lignin will cause chromophors (276), cf. Chapter 4.IV. According to that theory, the carbonyls are protected by bisulfite as α-hydroxysulfonate groups during the main part of the cook, but as the bisulfite ion concentration decreases to low values on prolonged cooking, these groups decompose under re-formation of carbonyls, which condense with the benzene rings of adjacent lignin monomers and give rise to color. The velocity of condensation ought to be proportional to the acidity prevailing, and also dependent on the cooking temperature.

Thus the development of liquor color is probably a complicated function of reactions leading to the consumption of bisulfite ions and development of acidity. However, in one respect it should be rather better suited to end-point determinations, as it measures the result of a temperature- and

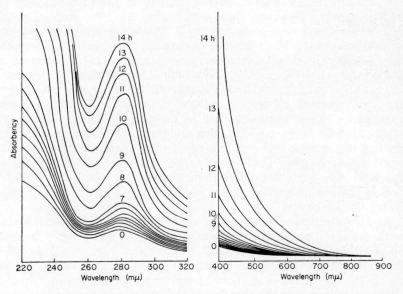

Fig. 9.5. Absorbency in ultraviolet and visible light of sulfite (rayon pulp) cooking liquor at various stages of the cook. Numbers indicate cooking time

pH-dependent reaction, as is the hydrolytic degradation of carbohydrates. As its practical applicability is also fairly simple, its wide use is understandable. However, although the relation between liquor color and final pulp viscosity shown in Figure 9.6 is fairly good, there are several sources of errors included which require a current calibration of the end-point color level with the pulp viscosity result achieved. One of them would be variations in the charge of combined SO_2 ptw, which will cause some change in the relation of hydrolytic degradation and carbonyl liberation and condensation, and hence with liquor color. Another source of error would be variations in the blow-down conditions, as the end-point test is

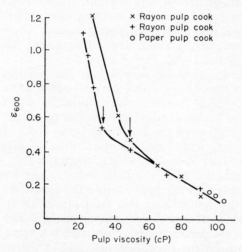

Fig. 9.6. Absorbency in visible light vs. pulp viscosity during the final phase of sulfite cooks. Arrows indicate point of blow-down (Rydholm)

made at maximum temperature and its result is the final pulp quality *after* the blow-down period.

Various bases will give various liquor colors at a given degree of cooking. Sodium and calcium bases give fairly similar color, but ammonium base cooks develop a much darker color, probably because of a specific condensation reaction between the carbonyl groups and the ammonium ion or ammonia. Furthermore, various wood species give rise to different liquor colors, birch causing darker liquors of a more reddish shade than spruce. Pine cooking liquor is rather darker than that of spruce, and turbid from resin.

The practical performance of the cooking liquor test varies widely. The simple way is comparison with test tubes containing standard liquor colors, but these often tend to darken. More advanced are various types of colorimeters, some equipped for continuous liquor flow. These are well suited to automatic control of the cook.

3. REACTIONS OF THE SULFITE PROCESS

A. *Introduction*

The sulfite process depends upon one of the most important reactions of lignin, its *sulfonation* (cf. Chapter 4.IV). In spite of this it is incorrect to treat the chemistry of the sulfite process mainly as applied lignin chemistry. The reactions taking place during the sulfite cook are a complicated system of intercourse between inorganic compounds, between them and lignin, carbohydrates and extractives of the wood, as well as between the organic components exclusively. The reactions occur partly in the cooking liquor, partly in the boundary regions between wood and liquor, and are thus of both homogeneous and heterogeneous nature. The morphological and physical structure of the wood plays an important rôle in the latter case (cf. Chapters 2, 3 and 6.V).

What is required in the sulfite process is a *dissolution of lignin, hemicellulose and extractives* to an extent corresponding to the pulp grade desired. In certain cases, semichemical acid sulfite and neutral sulfite pulping, cf. Chapter 8, this dissolution is limited to only 20–40% of the wood, and the liberation of the fibers has to be completed by strong mechanical treatment. However, the dissolution is generally carried beyond the point of fiber liberation, which occurs at a pulp yield of about 60%. At this point the middle lamella between the fibers is mainly dissolved, but the cell walls still hold considerable quantities of lignin and hemicellulose. Pulps approaching this yield are called *strong*, whereas pulps with low lignin and hemicellulose content are *soft*. This classification is old and refers to the paper strength properties, but nowadays there are no rigid limits between the two categories, and in the same way pulp strength and softness need not necessarily be contrasted. A classification in *bleachable* and *easy-bleaching* pulps is now also out of date as all sulfite pulps are bleachable and bleached grades are made from the most varying types of unbleached pulps. A classification according to yield or chemical composition is more rational. Statement of the lignin content is used frequently, generally, however, not in per cent lignin, because a quantitative lignin analysis is difficult, time-consuming and for most sulfite pulps not very accurate. Instead, the consumption of chlorine or an oxidant by the pulp under standardized conditions is stated, which is an indirect measure of the lignin content. Among the multitude of methods (cf. Chapter 20.I) the Roe chlorine number and the permanganate number according to TAPPI or CCA standards are, as well as the Kappa permanganate number, the most commonly accepted. Figure 9.7 gives an approximate relation of Roe number or permanganate number to pulp yield as well as the older methods of classification.

Another important reaction besides the dissolution of lignin and hemicellulose occurs, and is desired in the special sulfite cooking of dissolving pulps, namely a controlled, *hydrolytic degradation of the cellulose* remaining in the pulp. This degradation can be followed by analysis of pulp viscosity, which gives an expression of the average molecular length of the cellulose chains. Usually the viscosity is expressed in cP TAPPI, referring to an accepted standard method, cf. Chapter 20.I. Figure 9.8 gives an approximate relation of pulp yield to pulp viscosity in the range of dissolving pulps. This is a better way of comparing yields of dissolving pulp grades, since lignin content varies very little in this range and is also of minor importance for bleaching costs and quality for these types of pulp.

In addition to the desired reactions of dissolution of lignin and carbohydrates, and the controlled degradation of the cellulose in the pulp, various side reactions also occur. *Lignin undergoes intracondensation* to larger molecular complexes which are less easy to dissolve. A similar reaction occurs between lignin and certain phenolic extractives of the wood. The *polysaccharides dissolved degrade to various sugars*, to a large extent monosaccharides. The sugars as well as other carbonyl compounds in the cooking liquor form labile compounds with bisulfite ions, known as

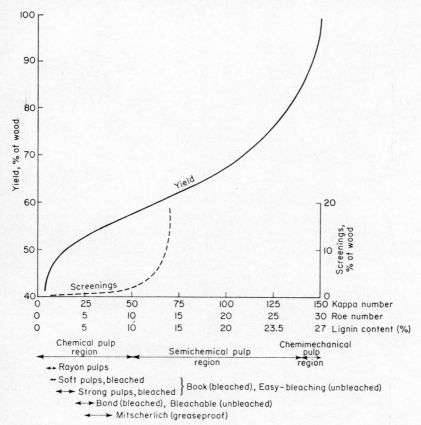

Fig. 9.7. Yield and screenings of acid sulfite (and bisulfite) pulps vs. Kappa number, Roe number and approximate lignin content. Classification of pulp grades. Spruce

α-hydroxysulfonates. They also degrade to *aldonic acids* or *stable sulfonates* in little known reactions, in which the α-hydroxysulfonates may play an important rôle as intermediates. In these reactions *thiosulfate is also formed from bisulfite ions.* Thiosulfate accelerates the *decomposition of the bisulfite ions* leading to increasing quantities of sulfate and thiosulfate. Most of the side reactions affect the acidity and bisulfite ion concentration of the cooking liquor and as those are of great importance for the main reactions of the sulfite cook, the side reactions must not be neglected.

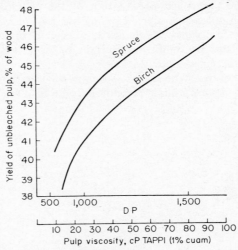

Fig. 9.8. Yield of unbleached sulfite rayon pulp
vs. TAPPI viscosity and DP

The reactions during the sulfite cook thus consist of:

(1) *physico-chemical impregnation courses* to ensure uniform distribution of chemicals before the main pulping reactions proceed with appreciable velocity. This problem has been treated in Chapter 6. III;
(2) *sulfonation and condensation reactions of lignin* preceding and contemporary with its dissolution;
(3) *dissolution reactions of both lignin and carbohydrates,* probably including both sulfitolysis and hydrolysis;
(4) *degradation of carbohydrates* in both the pulp and the cooking liquor, including mainly hydrolysis but also oxidation by bisulfite;
(5) *side reactions of the inorganic ions* of the cooking liquor with the organic matter dissolved in the liquor as well as interaction of purely inorganic nature.

Chemically, the reactions of the sulfite cook can be subdivided into *sulfonation, condensation, hydrolysis* and *redox reactions.* Sulfonation mainly occurs with lignin, but as a side reaction with carbohydrates also. Condensation mainly concerns lignin and certain extractives, but is not

454

completely excluded for some carbohydrates and their degradation products. Hydrolysis occurs in lignin as well as hemicellulose and cellulose. Redox reactions occur in the inorganic decomposition reactions, but also with carbohydrates and may also be the cause of some color reactions of lignin. The extent of these reactions depends on time and temperature. Hydrolysis and condensation further depend on the *acidity* of the reaction medium, which is the cooking liquor or the solid wood phase. The detailed mechanisms of sulfonation and redox reactions are not quite established, but they are likely to depend on *acidity* and *bisulfite ion concentration*. In order to understand the course of reactions during the sulfite cook it is therefore important to know the concentration of hydrogen and bisulfite ions in the cooking liquor and the changes of these concentrations during the cook.

B. Composition of the cooking liquor during the sulfite cook (653, 654)

The preparation of the cooking acid will be described in Chapter 11. The cooking acid consists of a solution of bisulfite in water, containing an excess of dissolved sulfur dioxide, obtained by reacting a carbonate or hydroxide with sulfur dioxide and water:

$$M_2CO_3 + 2\ SO_2 + H_2O = 2\ MHSO_3 + CO_2$$
$$MOH + SO_2 \qquad\quad = MHSO_3$$
$$H_2O + SO_2 \qquad\quad = H_2SO_3$$

where M is usually Ca/2 but sometimes Mg/2, Na or NH_4.

Bisulfite may be considered to consist of water, sulfur dioxide and a basic oxide, such as Na_2O or CaO, and the latter is often mentioned as the *base* of the cooking acid, e.g. lime base. In a broader sense it is also often said that the cooking acid *is based on* calcium, magnesium, sodium or ammonium.

The composition of the cooking acid is of old described by the contents of *total* and *combined* SO_2. The former concept corresponds to the iodine-reducing components of the cooking acid, i.e. the total content of SO_2 taken up by the acid (dissolved by the water in a more or less hydrated form, as well as sulfurous acid and bisulfite ions). Combined SO_2 generally corresponds to the '*base content*' of the acid and is defined as the amount of SO_2 bound as neutral sulfite (Na_2SO_3, $CaSO_3$, etc.). Sometimes the concepts of *free* and *loose* SO_2 are also used. However, they are derived from the other two (by subtraction from total SO_2 of combined SO_2 and twice the combined SO_2 respectively) and are therefore superfluous.

The concepts of total and combined SO_2 define the composition of the cooking acid sufficiently (strictly speaking temperature is also needed for an exact definition, as will be seen below). However, they give no direct expression of the actual chemical composition in molecules and ions, and the following section will be devoted to showing the relation between the analytical terms and the actual chemical concentrations.

Pure cooking acid contains H_2O, SO_2, $SO_2.nH_2O$, H_2SO_3, HSO_3^-, $S_2O_5^{2-}$ and M^+ (Na^+, NH_4^+, Ca^{2+} or Mg^{2+}). Impurities of both inorganic and organic character are present in the acid charged into the digester, such as S, Se, $HS_2O_3^-$, $S_2O_3^{2-}$, $SSeO_3^{2-}$, Fe^{2+}, HSO_4^- and SO_4^{2-}, as well as minor amounts of volatile acids and aldehydes, sugars and lignosulfonates introduced from the top and side reliefs of preceding cooks.

The concentrations of hydrogen and bisulfite ions are related through the dissociation equilibrium of sulfurous acid. The systems H_2O–SO_2 and H_2O–SO_2–M_2O have been objects of many investigations. Vapor pressure, solubility, density, electrical conductivity at various temperatures have been measured (57, 421), as well as heat effects (637) and absorption spectra (173, 485). Several investigations on the dissociation of sulfurous acid at room temperature have been performed (e.g. 426, 491, 717, 763). From the collected data the dissociation constants of sulfurous acid at temperatures from 0–90°C have been calculated (57), and these calculations have later been corrected for interionic effects (411). These values have been extrapolated to the temperature range of sulfite cooking (421, 653, 654). Later, direct measurement on aqueous SO_2 solutions at temperatures up to 150°C have been performed (378), making it possible to calculate the dissociation constants, which agree with the extrapolation of the uncorrected values from (57), as well as with calculations from conductivity measurements at high temperature (421, 654). Table 9.2 gives these approximate dissociation constants (654).

Table 9.2. Temperature dependence of the apparent ionization constant of sulfurous acid (57, 654, cf. 378, 421)

Temperature, °C	K_a	pK_a
25	0.0172	1.8
70	0.0046	2.3
100	0.0024	2.6
110	0.0016	2.8
120	0.0011	3.0
130	0.0008	3.1
140	0.0005	3.3
150	0.0003	3.5

Evidently, the dissociation constant of sulfurous acid decreases rapidly with temperature. The constant is defined by the equation

$$k = \frac{[H^+] \cdot [HSO_3^-]}{[H_2SO_3] + [SO_2]} = \frac{[H^+] \cdot [HSO_3^-]}{[\text{total } SO_2] - [HSO_3^-]}$$

Because of the analytical difficulty of discriminating between sulfurous acid and dissolved sulfur dioxide, the sum of both is taken to the denominator. Sulfurous acid is in equilibrium with two systems, as described by the equations for dehydration and electrolytic dissociation:

$$SO_2 + H_2O \rightleftharpoons H_2SO_3 \rightleftharpoons H^+ + HSO_3^-$$

A considerable part of the sulfur dioxide in an aqueous solution is not hydrated to sulfurous acid. On increasing temperature the equilibria are shifted towards dehydration. Assuming that the true dissociation constant, as defined by the equation

$$k = \frac{[H^+] \cdot [HSO_3^-]}{[H_2SO_3]}$$

does not change with temperature, it has been calculated (115) from the change of the apparent dissociation constant with temperature, that the SO_2 fraction hydrated to sulfurous acid at 90°C is only 8% of that at 0°C (the corresponding figure at 130°C would be about 2%). But even at 0°C the considerable vapor pressure of a sulfur dioxide solution indicates that appreciable amounts of SO_2 exist in a form other than H_2SO_3 (115). Therefore, the real dissociation constant of H_2SO_3 is fairly high, probably even at high temperature, and the concentration of sulfurous acid, especially at cooking temperature, is very small. The spectrophotometric investigations (173, 485), especially in infrared (217), have led to similar conclusions.

Recent investigations of the Raman spectra of sulfite, bisulfite and sulfurous acid solutions as well as of alkyl sulfites and sulfonates (717) have led to the conclusion that the bisulfite ion is mainly in the HSO_3^- form, i.e. with H–S bonding and very little H–O bonding. Contradictory results from investigation of the Faraday effect are explained by the finding that a large part of the bisulfite ions are dehydrated to the pyrosulfite form:

$$2\, HSO_3^- \rightleftharpoons S_2O_5^{2-} + H_2O$$

Increasing concentration of salts, i.e. decrease in water content, results in a shift in the equilibrium towards pyrosulfite formation. Likewise, addition of SO_2 to a bisulfite solution, which takes water in demand for hydration, will lead to more pyrosulfite ion formation. No quantitative data on pyrosulfite concentration are available so far. However, as no change in acidity occurs on the pyrosulfite formation from the bisulfite ions, these new concepts need not affect the foregoing discussion on the dissociation constants in any other respect than that both bisulfite and pyrosulfite ions are included in the value of $[HSO_3^-]$ in the numerator, in the same way as the hydrated and unhydrated forms of SO_2 are taken into the denominator. As both bisulfite and pyrosulfite ions are likely to react with lignin, or are at least rapidly converted into the other form, the new concepts need not interfere with previous conclusions regarding the sulfonation reaction.

With the knowledge of the apparent dissociation constant of sulfurous acid and the content of total and combined SO_2, the acidity and bisulfite ion concentration of a cooking acid at any temperature, e.g. that immediately after acid charging to the digester, can be computed according to the equations

$$\begin{cases} k & = \dfrac{[H^+] \cdot [HSO_3^-]}{[\text{total } SO_2] - [HSO_3^-]} \\ [M^+] & = 2 \cdot [\text{combined } SO_2] \\ [M^+] + [H^+] & = [HSO_3^-] \end{cases}$$

457

Then the hydrogen and bisulfite ion concentrations change during the cook because of two reasons. The *increase in temperature* lowers the apparent dissociation constant of sulfurous acid and also causes a relief of sulfur dioxide gas. This tends to *decrease* acidity and bisulfite ion concentration. *The reactions during the cook* tend to *increase* acidity and *decrease* bisulfite ion concentration.

In discussing the acidity during the sulfite cook, the formation of lignosulfonic, α-hydroxysulfonic, 'sugarsulfonic', sulfuric, aldonic, formic, acetic and carbonic acids during the cook is usually treated in general terms, without considering the state of dissociation more closely. In a stricter sense it is necessary to distinguish between *acids* formed, which are more or less undissociated under the conditions of the sulfite cook, and *anions* formed, corresponding to completely dissociated acids. The various sulfonic acids and sulfuric acid belong to the latter category, whereas aldonic, formic, acetic and carbonic acids are probably dissociated to a very limited extent in the *acid sulfite* cook, and therefore do not affect the acidity. Bisulfate ion is one of the few acids formed which may have a changing degree of dissociation during the cook, but its concentration is usually so low, that these changes will not affect the acidity appreciably. In the *bisulfite* cook, the carboxylic acids are partially ionized and hence responsible for some consumption of 'base', and in the *neutral sulfite* cook they are completely ionized.

The strong acids formed during the cook do not, however, increase the hydrogen ion concentration to an extent corresponding to their concentration, although they are completely dissociated. Generally, this has been explained by the *buffering* action of the cooking acid (209, 273b, 421). The 'base' or the 'combined SO_2' in the cooking acid is said to neutralize the acids formed. Speaking in stricter terms, that should mean that bisulfite ions in the cooking liquor buffer the system by conversion into undissociated sulfurous acid (or unhydrated sulfur dioxide), according to the equations

$RSO_3H \rightarrow RSO_3^- + H^+$ (dissociation of strong acids formed)
$HSO_3^- + H^+ \rightarrow H_2SO_3 \rightarrow (SO_2 + H_2O)$ (buffering action of bisulfite ion)
$RSO_3H + HSO_3^- \rightarrow RSO_3^- + H_2SO_3$ (net reaction)

However, the strong acids formed in the sulfite cook all seem to originate from reactions in which the bisulfite ion, and *not* sulfurous acid, takes a part, e.g.

$HSO_3^- + \text{lignin–OH} \rightarrow \text{lignin–}SO_3^- + H_2O$ (formation of ligno-sulfonate)
$HSO_3^- + R\text{–}CHO \rightarrow R\text{–}CH(OH)SO_3^-$ (formation of α-hydroxy-sulfonate)
$4\,HSO_3^- \rightarrow 2\,HSO_4^- + S_2O_3^{2-} + H_2O$ (formation of bisulfate)

or generally

$HSO_3^- \rightarrow RSO_3^-$ instead of $H_2SO_3 \rightarrow RSO_3H$

458

This is especially obvious in the bisulfite cook. Therefore, it might be said that there is no formation of strong acids during the sulfite cook, only a formation of their corresponding anions. The rôle of the bisulfite ions with this concept will be a direct participation in the reactions and *not* a buffering action. The cause of the rapid rise in acidity towards the end of certain cooks therefore will not be that the *buffering* bisulfite ions are exhausted, allowing the strong acids formed to increase the acidity, but that the *reacting* bisulfite ions are becoming low in concentration, which causes a formation of new ions from sulfurous acid (sulfur dioxide) according to the dissociation equilibrium

$$(H_2O + SO_2) \rightarrow H_2SO_3 \rightarrow H^+ + HSO_3^-$$

which increases the acidity.

The 'combined SO_2' is defined as the part of the sulfur dioxide in the cooking acid which corresponds to the 'base' content and could be formulated as M_2SO_3. The old term 'available combined SO_2' during the cook, correctly determined (653), corresponds to the initial 'combined SO_2' less the strong acid anions formed, i.e.

$$2 \,.\, [\text{combined } SO_2] = [M^+]$$
$$2 \,.\, [\text{available combined } SO_2] = [M^+] - [A^-]$$

Now, there is a relation between this concept, the total SO_2, the apparent dissociation constant of sulfurous acid, and the hydrogen and bisulfite ion concentrations (654), because

$$\frac{[H^+] \,.\, [HSO_3^-]}{[\text{total } SO_2] - [HSO_3]} = k$$

$$[M^+] + [H^+] = [HSO_3^-] + [A^-]$$

from which the following expressions can be derived

$$[H^+] = \frac{[A^-] - [M^+] - k}{2} + \sqrt{\frac{([M^+] - [A^-] - k)^2}{4} + k \,.\, [\text{total } SO_2]}$$

$$[HSO_3^-] = \frac{[M^+] - [A^-] - k}{2} + \sqrt{\frac{([M^+] - [A^-] - k)^2}{4} + k \,.\, [\text{total } SO_2]}$$

These relations are illustrated graphically in Figure 9.9, where the hydrogen and bisulfite ion concentrations are represented on the Y-axis, and on the X-axis twice the available combined SO_2, i.e. $[M^+] - [A^-]$, on a decreasing scale, commencing at 0.30 g ions/l, which corresponds to 0.96% combined SO_2 in the cooking acid, a fairly normal value. The available combined SO_2 then decreases to zero and becomes negative. On the same scale the strong acid anions formed, $[A^-]$, may be represented on the X-axis, rising from zero to 0.30 g ions/l, at zero available combined SO_2. As the formation of strong acid anions during the cook proceeds with roughly uniform rate, the X-axis may also be taken roughly to represent cooking time.

There is one family of curves for acidity and another for bisulfite ion concentration, the former increasing and the latter decreasing with decreasing available combined SO_2. Each curve relates hydrogen or bisulfite ion concentration to available combined SO_2 at a constant concentration of total SO_2 and an unchanged ionization constant k, i.e. constant temperature. However, during the cook total SO_2 decreases

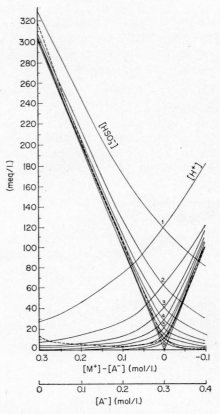

Fig. 9.9. The relations of hydrogen and bisulfite ion concentrations to combined SO_2 (or to strong acid anions formed) at constant levels of total SO_2 and temperature (Rydholm)

Curve 1 5.12% SO_2, k = 0.020 (20°C)
  2 5.12%   0.005 (70°C)
  3 5.12%   0.002 (105°C)
  4 5.12%   0.001 (125°C)
  5 2.56%   0.001 (125°C)
  6 2.56%   0.0005 (140°C)
  7 1.28%   0.0005 (140°C)
  8 0.64%   0.0005 (140°C)
  9   0

dotted curves: technical sulfite cook conditions

460

because of gas losses and reaction, and k decreases because the temperature rises. Therefore, to get a correct representation of the changes in hydrogen and bisulfite ion concentrations during the cook, it is necessary to connect those points on the various curves which correspond to the temperature and total SO_2 content of the liquor at a certain content of available combined SO_2. In this way, curves of the type indicated with dotted lines in the figure are obtained. Different types of cooks, e.g. with varying maximum temperature, varying initial total and combined SO_2 content, varying amounts of strong acid anions formed, and varying maximum digester pressure, will of course yield different curves for hydrogen and bisulfite ion concentration. Thus a cook low in initial combined SO_2 and/or with a relatively high maximum temperature reaches the point of zero concentration of available combined SO_2 sooner. At this point, the bisulfite ion concentration is low and acidity tends to rise sharply. Cooks high in initial combined SO_2 and/or with low maximum temperature may never reach this point, and thus maintain a fairly low acidity. The former type of cook, especially at higher temperatures, usually causes appreciable degradation of the cellulose (653) whereas the latter usually does not. It is, however, evident from the above, that there is no definite relation between final acidity of the cooking liquor and final viscosity of the pulp. The generally used method of determining the end point of a rayon pulp cook, i.e. measuring the color of the cooking liquor as it develops, is likely to depend on lignin condensation reactions (273b), which like the degradation of the cellulose should be proportional to both acidity, temperature and time. Even if this method has its drawbacks, it is as yet the best known for its purpose. On the other hand, the conditions during the cellulose degradation, e.g. the acidity level, may of course influence the quality of the pulp.

The bisulfite ion concentration decreases during the cook for three main reasons: (i) the loss in total SO_2 in gas relief, etc., (ii) the rise in temperature, accompanied by a lower concentration (or degree of dissociation) of sulfurous acid, and (iii) the formation of strong acid anions (decreases in available combined SO_2). From the curves in Figure 9.9 it is evident that the first two reasons are less important than the last. Thus it is mainly the direct consumption of bisulfite ions in the formation of sulfonates and bisulfite (formerly called the buffering action of the bisulfite ions on the strong acids formed) which causes the decrease in bisulfite ion concentration. The level of the latter is thus almost entirely a function of the available combined SO_2 during the cook, i.e. dependent on the initial base content and the amount of strong acid anions formed.

Several investigations have been devoted to pulping with sulfur dioxide solutions containing none or only small amounts of combined SO_2. From the above results it is evident that such solutions will only contain small amounts of the sulfonating agent, the bisulfite ions, especially at high temperature where the concentration (or dissociation) of sulfurous acid is low. It is therefore natural that pulping with such solutions is only possible at lower temperature (159, 188, 298, 332, 586, 622) and with a very high total SO_2 content (332, 421, 622). It is thus not only the fact that the acidity soon becomes fairly high when cooking at ordinary temperatures with liquors low in combined SO_2, as is usually stressed, which prevents the pulping, but also that such solutions lack sufficient amounts of sulfonating agent. Both these circumstances tend to yield a ratio of lignin sulfonation to lignin condensation unfavorable for pulping. If the velocity of lignin sulfonation is assumed to be proportional to the product $[H^+] . [HSO_3^-]$ and that of lignin condensation to acidity alone, the comparative ratio of sulfonation rate to condensation rate could be expressed as

$$\frac{k_1 . [H^+] . [HSO_3^-]}{k_2 . [H^+]}$$

where k_1 and k_2 are reaction rate constants. If it is assumed that the temperature dependence of the two reactions is the same, this ratio varies during the cook in the same way as the bisulfite ion concentration. This is in agreement with the above-mentioned facts, that a cook, low in initial base content tends to give a residue containing much condensed lignin, and also indicates that condensation reactions in normal cooks become more dominant towards the end of the cook.

One apparent exception to the rule that cooks low in initial combined SO_2 lead to condensation has been investigated. It was found possible (211, 560, 609) to pulp wood at $130°C$ in sulfur dioxide solutions containing no combined SO_2 according to analysis, in the presence of 4–5% sodium sulfate. The correct conclusion was drawn that the added sulfate combines with free sulfur dioxide to form bisulfite and bisulfate. Here is an example of a *buffered* sulfite cook. The (second) dissociation constant of sulfuric acid decreases appreciably with increasing temperature (567), and its value at $130°C$ has been calculated (776) to be about 0.0004. This would mean that about 90% of the sulfate added in the sodium sulfate buffered cook is converted to bisulfate, and a corresponding amount of bisulfite formed. The system could in this case be described by the equations (654):

$$\frac{[H^+] . [HSO_3^-]}{[total\ SO_2] - [HSO_3^-]} = K_1$$

$$[Na^+] + [H^+] = [HSO_3^-] + [HSO_4^-] + 2 [SO_4^{2-}] + [A^-]$$

$$1/2 . [Na^+] = [HSO_4^-] + [SO_4^{2-}] = C$$

$$\frac{[H^+] . [SO_4^{2-}]}{[HSO_4^-]} = K_2$$

where K_1 and K_2 are the dissociation constants at cooking temperature of sulfurous acid and bisulfate ion, and C is the molar concentration of sodium sulfate added. Stoichiometrically, 4–5% Na_2SO_4 corresponds to 0.9–1.1% combined SO_2, and 90% conversion therefore to 0.8–1.0% combined SO_2, which are normal values for acid sulfite pulping.

As shown in Figure 9.9, the hydrogen ion concentration increases and the bisulfite ion concentration decreases with decreasing available combined SO_2 at constant temperature and total SO_2 content. As both ions influence the rate of lignin sulfonation (cf. 819), it is of interest to plot similar curves for their product, Figure 9.10. At constant total SO_2 content and constant temperature there is a slight increase in the product with decreasing available combined SO_2, but under the conditions of a normal sulfite cook the product decreases steadily as indicated by the dotted line. It is interesting to note that whereas the changes in $[HSO_3^-]$ were caused mainly by the reactions during the cook, the changes in $[H^+] \cdot [HSO_3^-]$ are principally caused by the changes in temperature and total SO_2 content (the latter of which decreases partly by reaction but mainly by gas relief). The importance of high maximum pressure and a high initial total SO_2 content for a rapid reaction is thus evident.

Of course the decrease in 'sulfonating power' of the liquor during the

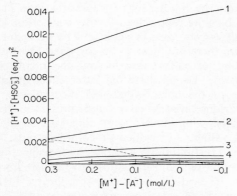

Fig. 9.10. The relation of the product of hydrogen and bisulfite ion concentrations to combined SO_2, at constant levels of total SO_2 and temperature. Indication of curves as in Figure 9.9 (Rydholm)

cook does not mean that sulfonation is most rapid in the beginning of the cook, because the temperature dependence of sulfonation and the varying nature of the sulfonatable groups of lignin must also be taken into account.

The experimental confirmation of these expected changes in hydrogen and bisulfite ion concentration has been achieved in several ways. Until recently (378), electrodes for pH-determination capable of enduring the high temperatures and pressures of the cook have not been available. Therefore other methods of estimating the acidity have been tried. The rate of starch hydrolysis in cooking liquor samples was compared with that in sulfuric acid of varying concentration (297). pH determinations on cooled cooking liquor samples, which are often made, tell very little about the acidity at digester temperature. This is due not only to the increased ionization of sulfurous acid at lower temperature, but also to the formation of considerable quantities of α-hydroxysulfonate (653, 654). The latter are formed according to the general formula on the next page:

463

$$R_2CO + HSO_3^- \rightleftharpoons R_2C(OH)SO_3^-$$

and this equilibrium is determined by the equation

$$\frac{[R_2C(OH)SO_3^-]}{[R_2CO] \cdot [HSO_3^-]} = k$$

where k is the formation constant of the α-hydroxysulfonate. Consequently, the concentration of α-hydroxysulfonates should increase on cooling the liquor samples, as the bisulfite ion concentration increases on cooling. This should already be the case at unchanged equilibrium constant k. Furthermore, it is likely and has also been shown (749) that k is higher at low temperature. Both these circumstances cause an increase in α-hydroxysulfonate concentration when the cooled liquor samples are withdrawn from the digester for pH determination. The corresponding consumption of bisulfite ions causes further ionization of sulfurous acid and, consequently, an increase in acidity. The pH values determined at room temperature therefore have to be corrected for both the change in ionization constant of sulfurous acid and the increased formation of α-hydroxysulfonates. To calculate the latter effect quantitatively is not possible because of the complicated and incompletely known systems involved. The various carbonyl compounds present in the cooking liquor have widely different abilities for combining with bisulfite, which shows up in different k values. Formaldehyde combines most strongly, methyl glyoxal, trioses and furfural fairly strongly, whereas pentoses, hexoses and the carbonyl groups of lignosulfonates have much lower and likewise varying k values. The calculation is also complicated by the fact that the *rate* of formation of the α-hydroxysulfonates is little known, especially at high temperature. As the components of the reaction change perpetually in concentration during the cook, it is not certain that complete equilibrium is established in every moment. The various carbonyl compounds are formed at different stages during the cook, and the bisulfite ion concentration changes with the other reactions of the cook.

It has therefore been found necessary to determine directly the concentration of α-hydroxysulfonates during the cook (653). Model experiments with mannose and formaldehyde have shown that whereas the latter combines very quickly with bisulfite, the reaction between bisulfite and mannose is fairly slow and easily measurable by repeated titrations. The combination of bisulfite and formaldehyde was further shown to be complete both at room temperature and 90°C, whereas mannose combination is incomplete at room temperature and much more so at elevated temperature. Therefore it was found possible by a rapid cooling of the cooking liquor samples and repeated titrations of loosely combined SO_2 to estimate the concentration of α-hydroxysulfonates in the digester by extrapolation to the moment of sampling. With this estimation, and with the knowledge of the change in sulfurous acid ionization with temperature, it was possible to apply corrections to the pH determinations of the cooled cooking liquor samples and arrive at the acidity at cooking temperature.

The acidity curves obtained agree well with what could be expected from the foregoing discussion in connection with Figure 9.9, and show a decrease in acidity in the initial stage of the cooking, due to the rise in temperature, followed by a flat minimum and then a rapid increase in acidity towards the end of the cook, as shown in Figure 9.11. Cooks, rich in combined

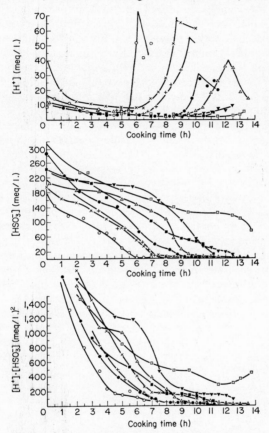

Fig. 9.11. The hydrogen and bisulfite ion concentrations and their product in some technical sulfite cooks, as functions of cooking time (Rydholm)

Key	Type of pulp	Base	Max. pressure kg/cm²	Max. temp. °C	Time to relief h min	Cooking acid			Final pulp	
						Total SO₂ %	Com-bined SO₂ %	Comb. SO₂ kg/t wood	Roe no.	Visc. cP TAPPI
×	Soft	NH₃	5.0	131	8 40	6.2	0.74	30	1.1	53
○	Rayon	CaO	6.9	146	6 15	7.8	0.99	40	1.2	21
+	Rayon	CaO	5.0	150	9 45	6.1	0.94	39	0.9	22
●	Rayon	CaO	5.0	150	10 05	7.5	1.08	46	0.9	25
△	Rayon	CaO	5.0	145	12 00	6.7	0.90	38	1.1	17
▼	Medium	CaO	5.0	135	11 30	6.1	0.97	41	1.6	70
■	Strong	CaO	5.0	135	9 40	5.6	1.01	45	2.5	93
□	Greasepr.	CaO	4.7	122	13 00	6.1	1.22	54	5.3	100

SO_2 and with low maximum temperature, never reach the final stage of the sharp increase in acidity. All but the softest paper pulps are cooked in that way. The rayon pulp cooks to medium and low viscosity on the other hand all have a more or less pronounced final acidity peak. The increased rate of reaction in cooks of a higher than normal pressure is also reflected in the sharpness of the acidity peak. Cooks with a low initial combined SO_2 reach the point of increase in acidity sooner, and when maintained at a certain pulp viscosity level they reach a higher final acidity than a cook with a higher initial combined SO_2. Even the acidity level in the earlier part of the cook is somewhat higher with a low initial combined SO_2. The acidity minimum for most cooks is about 0.002–0.003 g ions/1, corresponding to a pH of 2.5–2.7. The acidity maxima in the rayon pulp cooks are in the range 0.030–0.060 g ions/1, corresponding to pH 1.2–1.5. The course of acidity changes found in technical sulfite cooks with this technique is in good agreement with direct pH measurements in a laboratory digester carried out with a special electrode set up, Figure 9.12 (378). The final decrease in acidity shown by the curves occurs during the blow-down period, and is caused by the decomposition of α-hydroxysulfonates to bisulfite ions and carbonyl compounds. The bisulfite ions combine with hydrogen ions to sulfurous acid, which is in turn decomposed during the relief. In rayon pulp cooks, most of the sulfur dioxide relieved during the blow-down period originates from α-hydroxysulfonates.

Figure 9.11 shows the bisulfite ion concentration during the same cooks, and the product of hydrogen and bisulfite ion concentration. As was pointed out before, the bisulfite curves mainly show the same course as the 'available combined SO_2' during the cook.

The foregoing discussion dealt with the composition of the cooking

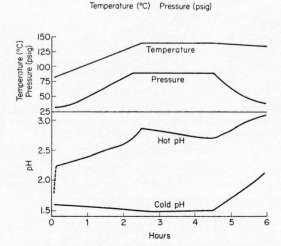

Fig. 9.12. pH of cooking liquor at temperature and at cooled liquor samples. Acid sulfite paper pulp cook
(Ingruber)

466

liquor in normal *acid sulfite pulping*. There are certain variations in the initial composition of the cooking acid charged, as regards both total and combined SO₂. The unsuccessful trials of *cooking in pure sulfurous acid solutions* when employing normal time–temperature schedules have already been mentioned. The lower limit of combined SO₂ is not quite definite as it also depends on the content of total SO₂, Figure 9.13 (421), but practically a chemical sulfite cook will need a minimum of around 30 kg ptw of combined SO₂, which at a normal liquor : wood ratio of 4 : 1 corresponds to about 0.75% combined SO₂ in the cooking acid. Rayon pulp cooking acid usually contains less combined SO₂ than acid for paper

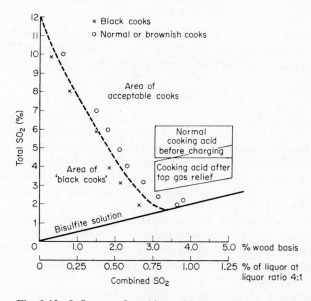

Fig. 9.13. Influence of cooking acid composition on lignin condensation in acid sulfite cooking of spruce at 130°C (Kaufmann)

pulp cooking, where no development of acidity in the final stages is desired. The cooking of pulps rich in hemicellulose for greaseproof paper requires as high a content of combined SO₂ as possible. Two factors limit the combined SO₂ content, one of technical and one of economical nature. Where no recovery of chemicals is provided for, the combined SO₂ of the cooking acid charged determines the cost of cooking chemicals, the consumption of sulfur and of the 'base' being largely equivalent to twice the combined SO₂.

The technical limitation appears in calcium-based cooking acid and is connected with the insolubility of calcium sulfite. Calcium-based cooking acids high in combined SO₂ precipitate calcium sulfite when heated at a temperature, which depends on the composition of the cooking acid (57).

The higher the content of total SO_2 or the lower the combined SO_2, the higher the precipitating temperature. For ordinary cooking temperatures and pressures (which determine the total SO_2 content), the practical limit is around 1.3% combined SO_2 (57). The phenomenon of calcium sulfite precipitation, which in the old days caused frequent 'liming up' of the digesters, is explained in the following way. The increase in temperature causes less ionization of the sulfurous acid and a reduction in bisulfite and hydrogen ion concentration. The reduction in acidity is proportionally much greater than the reduction in bisulfite ions. The changes cause a shift of the equilibrium

$$HSO_3^- \rightleftharpoons H^+ + SO_3^{2-}$$

towards the right, i.e. towards formation of sulfite ions. The higher the initial content of combined SO_2 the greater the reduction in acidity and the more the sulfite ions formed. Finally, the solubility product of calcium sulfite

$$L = [Ca^{2+}] \cdot [SO_3^{2-}]$$

is reached and precipitation occurs. Assuming the solubility product for calcium sulfite to be about $10^{-5.3}$ at elevated temperature (714) and the pK_a of the bisulfite ion to be 6.4 (714), it can be calculated that a cooking acid with 1.3% combined SO_2 will precipitate calcium sulfite at a pH of 2.0–2.5, or at about 100°C. However, some rapid sulfonation reactions occur during the heating with wood and normally consume sufficient combined SO_2 to prevent scaling.

This limitation does not apply to the so-called *soluble bases*, sodium and ammonium, where the corresponding sulfites are soluble. Magnesium base is an intermediate and allows bisulfite but not neutral sulfite pulping. The appearance of solid $MgSO_3.6H_2O$ at room temperature occurs at pH 5 for high concentrations and at pH 6 for low ones (429a). These bases likewise make partial or complete chemical recovery quite possible, which removes at least some of the economical objections to increasing the combined SO_2 content of the liquor. This bursts the borders of conventional acid sulfite cooking and allows the variations of *bisulfite* and *neutral sulfite cooking*.

Variations in the amount of *total* SO_2 in the cooking acid are also frequent and depend to a considerable extent on the efficiency of the absorption and recycling systems for SO_2 in the mill, cf. Chapter 11. A high content of total SO_2 in an early stage of the cook is considered beneficial for the impregnation, as full digester pressure is rapidly developed. Any great importance for the chemical reactions during the cook is not achieved, unless digester pressure is increased, as the excess SO_2 otherwise passes rapidly through the gas relief lines. In actual mill practice, 5% initial total SO_2 is considered to be on the low side, 6% fairly normal and up to 10% is used in special cases. However, after dilution with wood moisture and steaming condensate, as well as after gas relief up to the temperature where reactions begin to occur, the total SO_2

content of the cooking liquor is down to 4% or below, which is ample enough to prevent the liming up of the digester (at normal content of combined SO_2) and quite sufficient for the reactions.

A suitable figure for bisulfite cooking is also 4% total SO_2. In a true bisulfite cook, i.e. in a pure bisulfite solution, the content of combined SO_2 is, by definition, half the total SO_2, for instance 2% at 4% total SO_2. In mixed bisulfite–monosulfite cooks, the combined SO_2 is more than half the total SO_2, and in a pure monosulfite cook it is, by definition, equal to total SO_2. Figure 9.14 illustrates the different ionic concentrations in varying types of cooking liquors, in a *Bjerrum* diagram showing pH against ionic concentrations on a logarithmical scale, and in Figure 9.15

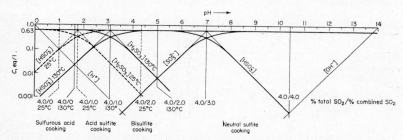

Fig. 9.14. Bjerrum diagram showing pH and ion concentrations of various types of sulfite cooking liquors, assuming pK_a of sulfurous acid to be 1.75 at room temperature and 3.1 at 130°C, and pK_a of the bisulfite ion to be 7.0

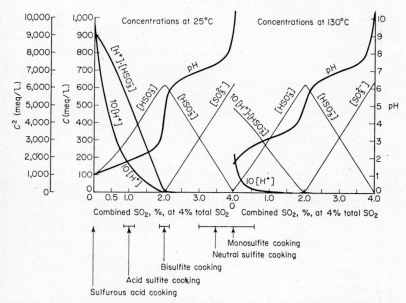

Fig. 9.15. Ion concentrations and pH of sulfite cooking liquors of varying type at room and elevated temperature. Constant SO_2 content (40 g/l, '4%') and base content varying from 0 to 40 g/l ('4%') combined SO_2

469

these concentrations are given as a function of liquor composition and temperature. The results are summarized in Table 9.3. The cooking liquor compositions chosen, 4.0/0.0, 4.0/1.0, 4.0/2.0, 4.0/3.0 and 4.0/4.0% total/ combined SO_2, correspond to *sulfurous acid, acid sulfite, bisulfite, bisulfite-monosulfite* and *monosulfite* pulping. The first three liquors change on heating because of the changes in the ionization of sulfurous acid, whereas the latter two remain unaffected. The change in ionization of the bisulfite ion with temperature is not known and is assumed to be nil, although it might decrease with a temperature increase if analogous to the bisulfate ion (567). The conditions at room and cooking temperature have been calculated.

Table 9.3. Ionic concentrations of sulfite cooking liquors of varying composition and temperature

Analytical composition % total SO_2	Concentrations, mol/l							
	$[H^+]$ at		$[HSO_3^-]$ at		$[H^+].[HSO_3^-].10^6$ at		pH at	
% comb. SO_2	25°C	130°C	25°C	130°C	25°C	130°C	25°C	130°C
4.00/0.00	95.10^{-3}	22.10^{-3}	45.10^{-3}	22.10^{-3}	9,100	485	1.02	1.65
4.00/0.25	60.10^{-3}	$5.2.10^{-3}$	139.10^{-3}	83.10^{-3}	8,400	435	1.22	2.28
4.00/0.50	38.10^{-3}	$2.4.10^{-3}$	195.10^{-3}	159.10^{-3}	7,400	380	1.42	2.62
4.00/0.75	24.10^{-3}	$1.3.10^{-3}$	258.10^{-3}	236.10^{-3}	6,300	310	1.62	2.89
4.00/1.00	16.10^{-3}	$0.8.10^{-3}$	328.10^{-3}	313.10^{-3}	5,100	250	1.80	3.10
4.00/2.00	50.10^{-6}	9.10^{-6}	623.10^{-3}	613.10^{-3}	30	6	4.35	5.05
4.00/3.00	100.10^{-9}	100.10^{-9}	313.10^{-3}	313.10^{-3}	0.03	0.03	7.00	7.00
4.00/4.00	$0.04.10^{-9}$	$0.04.10^{-9}$	$0.3.10^{-3}$	$0.3.10^{-3}$	0.00	0.00	10.40	10.40

In pure sulfurous acid, hydrogen and bisulfite ion concentration are alike, giving a pH of 1.0 at room temperature and 1.7 at cooking temperature. In acid sulfite cooking acid of the composition 4.0/1.0% SO_2, the sulfurous acid has reached the 'point of half neutralization', where $[H_2SO_3] = [HSO_3^-]$. This results in a pH equal to the pK_a of the acid, or 1.8 at room temperature and 3.1 at cooking temperature. It should be remarked here that pH during an acid sulfite cook seldom reaches 3.1, because appreciable reaction has taken place before maximum temperature is attained. This results in the previously mentioned pH maximum of around 2.8 in an acid sulfite cook. During the cook most of the combined SO_2 is consumed, and the waste liquor before gassing down corresponds principally to a cooking acid of the composition 2.0/0.0% SO_2, with a pH of around 1.7 at 130°C and 1.0 at room temperature. As pointed out previously in the detailed discussion of the acid sulfite cook, the final composition varies with the type of cook, rayon pulp cooks ending up with a negative combined SO_2 content and lower pH and paper pulp cooks often with a residual combined SO_2 and therefore higher pH than those just mentioned.

The bisulfite cooking acid corresponds to a complete neutralization of the sulfurous acid to bisulfite ions and therefore has a pH corresponding to the average of the pK_a's of sulfurous acid and bisulfite ions, or 4.3 at room temperature and 5.0 at cooking conditions. This is in agreement with experimental evidence, Figure 9.16 (374). In this liquor the concentrations of sulfurous acid and of sulfite ions are alike. Two circumstances of principal interest deviate from acid sulfite conditions, both of consequence for the pH changes during the bisulfite cook. One is that consumption of bisulfite ions in the reactions does not cause any pH changes, in contrast to acid sulfite cooking, where a consumption in bisulfite ions leads to increased ionization of sulfurous acid and hence an increase in acidity. The other important deviation from acid sulfite cooking is that the formation of acetic, formic, uronic and aldonic acids is likely to cause a decrease in pH. The ionization constants of those acids at elevated temperature are not known (indications are that the ionization constant of acetic acid

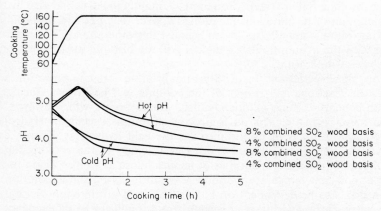

Fig. 9.16. pH of cooking liquor at temperature and at cooled liquor samples. Bisulfite cooking of birch (Husband)

decreases from $10^{-4.7}$ to $10^{-5.0}$ at a temperature increase from 25 to 162°C (374)), but if not considerably decreased, the acids are at least partly ionized in the cooking liquor, in contrast to the acid sulfite cook. The decrease in pH during the bisulfite cook is, however, fairly small, to around 3.5 in the waste liquor at room temperature or 4.0–4.5 at cooking temperature. The combined SO_2 content has then decreased to approximately 0.5%.

The cooking liquor of 4.0/3.0% SO_2 for mixed bisulfite–monosulfite cooks, such as practised in the so-called chemimechanical (ultra high yield semichemical) pulping, corresponds to a state where the point of half neutralization of the bisulfite ions is reached and their concentration equals that of the sulfite ions. pH then equals the pK_a of bisulfite ions, or about 7.0. In the literature values from 7.2 (763) and 7.0 (717) to 6.4 (714) are found. This represents the lower limit of the pH range of the so-called neutral sulfite cooks, whereas the upper pH limit is represented by the pure

monosulfite cook. This, with an initial liquor composition of 4.0/4.0 %
SO_2, corresponds to a state where bisulfite ion concentration corresponds
to that of hydroxyl ion concentration, resulting in a pH of 10.4. Typical
of these liquors, on the alkaline side of the bisulfite solution, is that consumption of bisulfite ions leads to a *decrease* in acidity, in contrast to those
on the acid side, where bisulfite consumption leads to an *increase* in acidity.
This is because sulfite ion concentration dominates over sulfurous acid
concentration and a shift of the equilibria to make up for the bisulfite ion
consumption results in a consumption of hydrogen ions:

$$H^+ + SO_3^{2-} \rightleftharpoons HSO_3^-$$

Further, in the cooking liquors on the alkaline side the weak organic
acids formed during the cook are completely ionized and hence cause considerable decrease in pH. This decrease is of course counteracted by the
sulfite–bisulfite buffer system around pH 7, mainly pH 8–6, and also by the
consumption of bisulfite ions mentioned above. The pH of a monosulfite
cooking liquor is not affected by an increase in temperature (374), in agreement with the assumption that the pK_a of the bisulfite ion changes only
little with temperature.

How these variations in acidity and bisulfite ion concentration will
affect the reactions and results of the cooking will be further elucidated
in subsequent sections of this chapter. Some points will, however, be
made here, with the facts on ionic concentrations specified. Hydrogen
ion concentration is of importance for the acid hydrolysis of both carbohydrates and lignin. Hence a decreased acidity of the cooking liquor
should leave increasing quantities of hemicellulose as well as lignin in the
pulp at constant temperature and time conditions. As the dissolution of
lignin seems to be dependent on both acidity and bisulfite ion concentration, whereas the hydrolysis of carbohydrates ought to be independent of
the latter, an increase in bisulfite ion concentration should result in a
pulp with less (hydrolytically) degraded carbohydrates at constant degree
of delignification. Finally, as lignin condensation velocity ought to be
proportional to acidity and independent of bisulfite ion concentration,
whereas sulfonation rate is proportional to both hydrogen and bisulfite ion
concentrations, the ratio of sulfonation : condensation ought to be proportional to the bisulfite ion concentration. At very small concentrations
of bisulfite ions, this should lead to dominance of condensation and a
retarded delignification, although the product $[H^+] . [HSO_3^-]$ is then at a
maximum, which would otherwise mean a maximal rate of delignification.

Summing up, an increase in combined SO_2 content of the cooking
liquor leads to an increase in bisulfite ion concentration to a maximum
and thereafter a decrease under increasing sulfite ion formation, further, a
decrease in acidity and a decrease in the product of hydrogen and bisulfite
ion concentrations. These changes ought to cause a decreased rate of
delignification, apart from a sharp increase to a maximum on an increase
in combined SO_2 content from zero to around 0.75 % or on the low side
of commercial acid sulfite pulping, further, a decreased condensation of

472

lignin and a decreased hydrolytic degradation of the carbohydrate components in pulps of the same lignin content.

These conclusions also point to the different grades of pulps to which the various processes are suited. *Sulfurous acid cooking* leads to excessive condensation unless extreme SO_2 concentrations and low temperature are maintained and is not an industrial pulping process, *acid sulfite pulping* yields chemical pulps, well delignified but also with somewhat degraded carbohydrates, *bisulfite pulping* has to be performed at higher temperatures than acid sulfite pulping in order to achieve the same degree of delignification but is still suited to chemical pulping and results in pulps of higher paper strength because of less hydrolytic degradation, whereas *neutral sulfite pulping* has to be performed at still higher temperature and is yet more suited to semichemical pulping to fairly high yields of pulps rich in lignin but also rich in undegraded carbohydrates, even in the case of the more easily accessible hemicelluloses.

In preparation of cooking liquors on the alkaline side of bisulfite solution fairly large amounts of chemicals are needed. Whereas in the five examples of cooking liquors chosen, the sulfur content is the same, the content of sodium compounds increases in proportion to the combined SO_2. Further, in acid sulfite cooking liquor, initially 4.0/1.0% SO_2 after charging, the consumption of chemicals in reactions corresponds to the combined SO_2, calculated as bisulfite, thus leaving a spent liquor of around 2.0/0.0% SO_2 where most of the SO_2 is easily recoverable through gas relief, thus saving half the initially charged sulfur. However, in bisulfite and neutral sulfite cooking liquors all total SO_2 charged is combined in the form of bisulfite or sulfite and therefore not recoverable by gas relief. This is why neutral sulfite pulping liquors are prepared to contain not only sulfite and bisulfite, but also other and cheaper chemicals with similar buffering action. As was pointed out earlier, the rôle of the sulfite–bisulfite system of neutral sulfite cooking liquors is not only to react with lignin but also to neutralize the weak organic acids formed, and this can be done more cheaply. Thus, sodium-based neutral sulfite cooks could be performed with sodium sulfite in an amount corresponding to or slightly more than the sulfonation needed, plus an excess of sodium hydroxide, carbonate or bicarbonate to neutralize the organic acids formed. Ammonium-based neutral sulfite cooks could be carried out in a mixture of ammonium sulfite and excess ammonia for neutralization. Figures 9.17–19 illustrate, in the form of *Bjerrum* diagrams, these buffer systems. To preserve the more easily soluble hemicelluloses, pH during the cook should be kept above 7. To avoid, on the other hand, alkaline degradation of the hemicelluloses, pH must not be too high in the earlier phases of the cook. In the case of the pure sulfite cooking liquor of composition 4.0/4.0% SO_2, or 79 g/l Na_2SO_3 solution, the buffering against low pH is done by the sulfite–bisulfite system remaining towards the end of the cook. However, this buffer system is not too well suited to keep pH above 7 since only about 50% of the buffer capacity is utilized at that pH, and consequently fairly high excess of chemicals is needed. pH in the

473

beginning of the cook is also rather high, or about 10. If some sulfite is exchanged against sodium hydroxide, less chemicals are needed totally, as the hydroxide is utilized completely in the organic acid neutralization. However, pH in the beginning will be still higher than in the case of pure sulfite solution, or 12–13, and too high for a good cooking result unless it is rapidly decreased by the initial deacetylation. Sodium carbonate is better in this respect, and gives an initial pH theoretically of 11.5, and in practice about 10.5. Still better is sodium bicarbonate, which causes an initial pH of only 8.7 but yields a pH of 7.0 after the cook, provided the carbon dioxide formed during it is carefully relieved. Bicarbonate is the usual buffer, since the cooking liquor is normally made by introducing

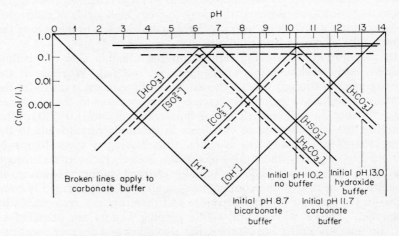

Fig. 9.17. Sodium-base neutral sulfite cooking liquors, bicarbonate, carbonate, hydroxide or no buffer

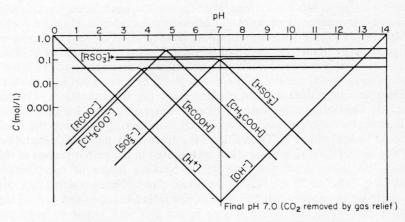

Fig. 9.18. Sodium-base neutral sulfite waste liquor, assuming complete CO_2 relief. RSO_3^- lignosulfonate, RCOOH uronic and aldonic acids

474

sulfur dioxide in soda ash. A cook in a pure sodium sulfite solution with the same amount of sodium compounds (and consequently higher sulfur content) starts at pH 10.2 and ends at pH 6.0. In the case of ammonia-buffered ammonium sulfite cooks, corresponding amounts of chemicals as in the bicarbonate-buffered cook should give a pH of about 9 at the start and 7 towards the end. Therefore, ammonia-buffering and bicarbonate-buffering are about equivalent. Irrespective of the type of buffer, however, as long as the buffer quantity is properly chosen, the deacetylation of the hardwoods rapidly decreases the pH to a level, 8–9, which is of little danger to the carbohydrates, and therefore the availability and price of the chemicals determine the choice of the buffer chemical. Figure 9.20 (657) illustrates the pH history of a neutral sulfite cook.

The figures given above are derived from practical neutral sulfite cooking of European birch at 170°C (in the case of ammonium sulfite 165°C) for 2 h to a yield of 70–75%. The pH's directly measured correspond closely to those taken from the *Bjerrum* diagrams with the assumption of 0.3 mol/l acids to be neutralized during the cook. Birch contains about 4.7% acetyl and 4% glucuronic acid monomers. At a liquor : wood ratio of 4 : 1 this means 0.27 + 0.06 mol/l acids. The total sulfite consumption during the cook is around 0.18 mol/l, corresponding to a degree of sulfonation of 0.7 S per phenylpropane unit if all sulfur were consumed in lignin sulfonation. However, under these conditions only half that degree of sulfonation is likely to occur. The remainder is consumed in side reactions under formation of sugar sulfonates, aldonic acids, sulfate and thiosulfate. Of all the sulfur-consuming reactions, most use up bisulfite under formation of neutral sulfonates (of lignin and sugars) and consequently lead to hydroxyl ion formation, as the bisulfite ion is an acid during these conditions. Another, probably not very important,

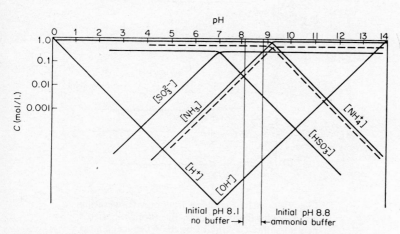

Fig. 9.19. Ammonium-base neutral sulfite cooking liquor, ammonia or no buffer

category of reactions leads to some acid formation, although less than that corresponding to the bisulfite consumption:

$$4\ HSO_3^- \longrightarrow 2\ SO_4^{2-} + S_2O_3^{2-} + H_2O + 2\ H^+$$

This also causes, although to a minor extent, a decrease in acidity. Finally, some reactions lead to formation of as much acids as the bisulfite ions consumed:

$$2\ HSO_3^- + 2\ RCHO \longrightarrow 2\ RCOOH + S_2O_3^{2-} + H_2O$$

Aldonic acid formation will thus probably cause no change in acidity and has therefore not been included in the above-mentioned 0.3 mol/l acids formed during the cook, although it is likely to be considerable, or around 0.08 mol/l (5% of the wood).

Therefore, 0.10 of 0.18 mol/l sulfite consumed are assumed to take a part in reactions leading to a decrease in acidity and can be subtracted from the 0.3 mol/l acids formed. The residual 0.2 mol/l have to be neutralized by the various buffering systems, of which the sulfite remaining after the cook is one. To facilitate computing, the whole amount of carbon dioxide of the carbonate–bicarbonate systems has been assumed to be removed by gas relief during the cook. Then 0.2 mol/l acids correspond to about 40 kg ptw Na_2CO_3, the normally applied quantity in excess of about 120 kg ptw Na_2CO_3 which are converted to sulfite. The ionization constant of carbonic acid at high temperature is not known, but decreases probably in a similar way to that of sulfurous acid, from a pK_a of 6.3 at room temperature to a value of 8–9. This makes it possible to relieve carbon dioxide from the digester already at the pH conditions of a neutral sulfite cook. This circumstance likewise makes the importance of carbon

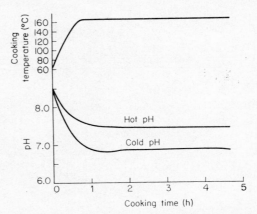

Fig. 9.20. pH of cooking liquor at temperature and at cooled liquor samples. Bicarbonate-buffered neutral sulfite cooking of birch. Chemical charge 30% Na_2CO_3, wood basis, of which 5/6 converted to sulfite and 1/6 to bicarbonate (Husband)

476

dioxide relief somewhat dubious, since its contribution to the acidity at cooking temperature is likely to be small. However, trial cooks without gas relief, to simulate the conditions of liquid phase continuous cooking with no gas room (cf. Chapter 6), showed somewhat lower yields at the same lignin content than pulps cooked with appropriate gas relief, indicating a definite increase in acidity.

C. Acidity of the solid phase during the cook

The previous discussion has been confined to the composition of the cooking liquor at digester temperature. Still more complicated is the elucidation of the acidity within the chips during the cook. As considerable quantities of lignin are sulfonated in the solid phase without immediate dissolution, an ion exchanger system is formed, obeying the *Donnan* law. A mathematical treatment of the system is difficult because of the difficulty in determining the activity coefficients to the solid phase. The wood achieves a maximal sulfur content of 1 %, which is kept fairly constant for some time during the intermediate part of the cook. Calculating with a density of the fiber phase of 1.0, the concentration of the lignosulfonate groups equals about 0.3 N (308), in agreement with measurements of partition factors of various ions (183) which indicate an ion concentration in the solid phase of 0.2–0.4 N. The pH of the solid phase in the absence of cations other than hydrogen ions is therefore very low; even if the surrounding solution is pure neutral water, pH has been estimated (183) to be as low as 0.8. Therefore it is also possible to dissolve the solid lignosulfonic acid by a hot water treatment (281, 460).

In the presence of other cations the acidity of the solid phase is greatly diminished, and it was found early that calcium ions were taken up by the wood during the acid sulfite cook (540). The affinity for the solid phase is in every case of ion exchange studied increasing in the order (795):

$$H^+ < Na^+ < NH_4^+ < Mg^{2+} < Ca^{2+} < Ba^{2+} < Al^{3+}$$

The acidity of the solid phase should therefore be lowest in the presence of aluminium ions in the cooking liquor and highest in the presence of sodium ions. This may have some significance for the yield and paper strength of mild sulfite cooks to the advantage of calcium or magnesium base as compared with sodium or ammonium base, and may also partly explain the somewhat greater velocity of delignification of the latter cooks. Studies (633, 660) on the rate of delignification of presulfonated wood, saturated with the series of cations mentioned above prior to a final pulping stage of SO_2–water gave a slight decrease in the rate of delignification in those cooks containing cations of the highest affinity to the solid phase as shown in Table 9.7, Section D. The differences found between the delignification velocity of cooks containing mono- and divalent cations roughly correspond to those found in the technical cooks based on these cations.

Provided comparison is made between cooks on the same base, the acidity of the solid phase is always related to that of the cooking liquor. Furthermore, the *Donnan* effects of the sulfite cook gradually disappear as

477

delignification proceeds. Towards the end of the cook, when the carbohydrates are most sensitive to hydrolytic damage, the importance of the *Donnan* effects is less and practically nil in the stage of viscosity regulation of a rayon pulp cook. The significance of the composition of the cooking liquor outside the fiber phase is therefore always considerable.

D. Lignin reactions during the sulfite cook

The mechanism of delignification during the sulfite cook and the factors governing the rate of cooking have been of interest since the start of the sulfite industry. A long period of practical experience and research has taught us the influence of certain factors, such as temperature, pressure and the analytical composition of the cooking liquor, on the rate of cooking and pulp quality. The detailed mechanism of delignification, however, in spite of numerous investigations is not understood completely. The reasons are the complicated and incompletely known systems involved, the structure of wood, the molecular structure of lignin and the molecular composition of the cooking acid. Considerable progress has been made in these fields since the basic theories on the mechanism of delignification were first advanced, and these theories should therefore be compared to the more recent results. The discussion will be mainly confined to reactions of the *technical* sulfite cook and its modern variations.

In an early investigation it was found (539) that the rate of delignification is proportional to a function

$$[\text{total SO}_2] - 2 \, . \, [\text{combined SO}_2]$$

or the so-called *excess sulfur dioxide* of the cooking liquor.

Extensive investigations by Canadian workers (110) indicated that the rate of delignification is proportional to the function

$$[\text{total SO}_2] - [\text{combined SO}_2]$$

or the so-called *free sulfur dioxide* in calcium-based cooks, whereas later studies on magnesium and sodium base (111, 118), covering a wider interval of combined SO_2, gave deviating results. Vapor pressure determinations (57) on cooking liquors of varying composition seemed to indicate (819) that the rate of delignification is proportional to the vapor pressure. As the latter should be proportional not to free SO_2 but to excess SO_2, there is a contradiction in the experimental results of the Canadian workers (110, 111). On the whole, the Canadian results on calcium, magnesium and sodium base sulfite cooking indicate a relation between the rate of delignification and excess SO_2 in the cooking acid, which corresponds approximately to the sum of H_2SO_3 and unhydrated SO_2 at cooking temperature. In this sum the unhydrated SO_2 dominates, and as this is also proportional to the vapor pressure of the cooking acid and to the product of $[H^+] \, . \, [HSO_3^-]$, there is an agreement in the published results (57, 110, 111, 118, 539).

In concurrence with these kinetic investigations on the mechanism of delignification, the problem was treated rather differently by the Swedish school (277). It was found that in the earlier stages of a normal sulfite cook increasing amounts of sulfonate groups are combined with the wood, and that these groups can be dissolved as a low-sulfonated lignin on a subsequent treatment in acids without sulfur dioxide. The rate of this delignification was shown to be proportional to the acidity and dependent on the presence of other cations (277), which is to be expected with any hydrolysis from a solid phase exhibiting *Donnan* effects. Therefore, the theory was advanced (273a, 277) that the delignification in the sulfite cook is a two-stage mechanism, consisting of a sulfonation of the lignin in the solid phase, followed by a hydrolysis of the 'solid' lignosulfonic acid, which may subsequently be further sulfonated in solution. The hydrolysis was considered to be the slower and rate-determining reaction (cf. 736).

The Canadian school opposed this theory, having found that the rate of delignification is proportional not only to the acidity, as would be the case with a rate-determining hydrolysis, but also depends in some way on the bisulfite ion concentration. One explanation (110) accepted the two-stage theory but suggested that the sulfonation of the lignin is the rate-governing reaction and not the hydrolysis of the solid lignosulfonate. The other side, maintaining the view of a two-stage mechanism with a rate-governing hydrolysis (273a), pointed out that a higher degree of sulfonation of the solid phase should accelerate the hydrolysis. A later investigation (308) indicated that the rate of delignification is determined by the hydrolysis when the acidity of the cooking liquor is low, whereas at higher acidity and lower content of sulfur dioxide, the sulfonation may be the rate-determining reaction.

Quite often it is stated that the rate of *diffusion*, either of chemicals to the reaction zone, or of lignosulfonates from the solid phase into solution, would influence the rate of delignification. No doubt the penetration of the cooking liquor into the chips is very important for the ultimate result, but once the capillary system of the wood has become thoroughly penetrated the paths of diffusion are very short. The strong temperature dependence of the rate of delignification (150, 819) as well as the comparatively small differences found in the rate for well penetrated chips and for wood meal, present further evidence of the comparatively insignificant influence of the rate of diffusion on the overall course of reaction. Finally, it has been found (563) that although the rates of delignification of spruce and maple are almost identical under comparable reaction conditions, the average size of the lignosulfonate molecules dissolved is much lower in the case of maple, and their rate of diffusion considerably higher. These facts constitute the most direct indication that the diffusion of lignosulfonate from the zone of reaction is not the rate-determining component of the delignification mechanism in *normal* acid sulfite cooks. Obviously, in cooks where excessive initial condensation of the lignin occurs, the lignosulfonate molecules may become so large that delignification is retarded by exceptionally slow diffusion.

As will be shown below, the delignification during the sulfite cook follows soon after sulfonation, and the latter is a heterogeneous, topochemical reaction. In spite of the fact that the rate of delignification is highly temperature dependent, it is therefore still likely that the diffusion of chemicals to the lignin of the fiber wall is checked, even granted the full penetration of the capillary system. Thus, in a way the extremely slow diffusion of cooking chemicals into those parts of the fiber wall where the lignin is unsulfonated and hydrophobic will retard the delignification. However, the sulfonation of the lignin in the outer parts of the fiber wall will expose further regions to the sulfonating chemicals, and the rate of diffusion in the hydrophilic regions will not be rate-determining for the overall reaction.

Two main features in the investigation technique used deserve comment, since they deviate from the normal conditions of the technical acid sulfite cook. Many workers (206, 273a, 303, 482, 489) extended the pH range of the cooking liquors to neutral and alkaline media. The results from these investigations are of the greatest value for the comprehension of not only the neutral sulfite cook and the bisulfite cook but also of the technical *acid* sulfite cook, though only if all differences between the neutral and acid sulfite cooks are considered. For instance, the observation that only part of the sulfonatable groups can be sulfonated in neutral medium and that the main part of the lignin does not enter into solution if not subsequently treated with acids, is not quite sufficient for the conclusion that the groups which are initially sulfonated in acid medium are those sulfonatable in neutral medium (cf. 490), although it is quite probable; nor is it quite certain that the 'solid' sulfonates formed are then hydrolytically dissolved in the later stages of the acid cook.

Many of the investigations have been carried out with wood meal instead of chips to eliminate penetration and diffusion difficulties, and a large excess of cooking liquor has been used to maintain constant chemical concentrations. Conclusions drawn from such experiments transferred to the technical sulfite cook have to consider the possibility of a greater heterogeneity in the latter, and also to observe that the low liquor-to-wood ratio in the technical sulfite cook causes changes in the liquor composition during the entire cook. As shown in Section 3B, these changes are considerable for the two dominating reagents of the sulfite cook, the hydrogen and bisulfite ions.

It could be advocated that this difficulty of using large excess of cooking liquor is overcome if the experiments cover such a broad range of liquor compositions as corresponds to the changes of cooking liquor composition during the technical sulfite cook. However, even in such a case there is a difference. The wood residue in the technical sulfite cook at a chosen moment, and with a surrounding cooking liquor of a certain composition, has not had the same pre-history as a wood residue of the same lignin content, cooked in a large excess of a liquor of that composition. This ought to influence the degree of sulfonation and condensation of the remaining lignin and hence also the rate of the following delignification. As a matter of fact, similar reasons may have caused some of the anomalies in the results of the Canadian school.

In the kinetic investigations, determinations of yield and residual lignin were mainly used. The work leading to the theory of the two-stage mechanism used sulfur and methoxyl analysis as well, to determine not only the amount of dissolved and residual lignin but its degree of sulfonation too. Two more recent investigations (308, 660) on the rate-determining reaction have defined the hydrolysis reaction as the amount of methoxyl dissolved during the cook at a certain stage, and the sulfonation reaction as the same amount of methoxyl *plus* the amount dissolvable on a subsequent hydrolytical treatment of the wood residue in mineral acid. There are certain objections to this technique (308), but it is a direct and practical method.

Studies of the sulfonatable groups of lignin have had great importance for the knowledge of the structure of lignin, cf. Chapter 4.IV. Modern concepts of the structure of lignin likewise offer new aspects on the mechanism of delignification in the sulfite cook, and should therefore be briefly summarized.

Softwood lignin is considered to be constituted of phenylpropane monomers, each containing one methoxyl, and one phenol or phenolic ether group. Most monomers also have an alcohol, alkyl ether or carbonyl group on the α-carbon of the side chain. These monomers are linked by non-hydrolyzable bonds to larger units, containing 4–6 monomers (490) or more. These 'lignin units' seem in turn to be linked either to each other or to carbohydrates by hydrolyzable benzyl alkyl ether bonds forming larger aggregates containing on average about 50 monomers.

The functional groups at the α-carbon atom are responsible for several of the most important lignin reactions, such as sulfonation or condensation. The degree of sulfonation is measured by S/OCH_3, which largely corresponds to the amount of sulfonate groups per phenylpropane monomer. When treating wood with neutral sulfite solutions generally only an average degree of sulfonation of around 0.3 S/OCH_3 is reached (282), and the groups so reacted have been called A groups. The remainder can be sulfonated in acid medium and have been called B groups. If wood, sulfonated in neutral medium, is hydrolyzed, the dissolved low-sulfonated lignin can be further sulfonated in acid or neutral medium to at least 0.7 S/OCH_3 and in some cases up to 1.0 about S/OCH_3 (1, 482). The B groups, which thus correspond to 0.4 or perhaps even 0.7 S/OCH_3, are therefore rendered more reactive through hydrolysis, after which they are called B' groups. Although the molecular configuration corresponding to the different sulfonatable groups of lignin is not completely elucidated (for example are the γ hydroxyls possibly responsible for part of the sulfonate groups?), model experiments make is probable that the A groups are benzyl alcohol or alkyl ether groups in monomers activated by a free phenolic hydroxyl, whereas the B groups are unactivated benzyl alkyl ether groups, which after hydrolysis are converted to benzyl alcohol or carbonyl (B') groups. Figure 4.39 (490) illustrates the rate of dissolution of wood lignin at different pH of the sulfite cooking liquor, and Figure 4.40 (490) the degree of sulfonation obtained of the lignin in the wood residue.

481

It may be remarked that the above conclusions are based on comparisons between the reactivity of model compounds and the reactivity of the lignin *in situ*, and that complete accessibility of the latter has been assumed. To some extent, however, the observations might also be explained with varying accessibility of the wood lignin. As a matter of fact, neutral or weakly acid sulfite pulping of mildly isolated lignin yields water-soluble products of a sulfonation degree considerably higher than 0.3 S/OCH_3, viz. 0.5–0.6 S/OCH_3 (75), and the fraction dissolving on treating wood meal at 135°C for 15 h with bisulfite–sulfite solutions at pH 5.3 has a similar degree of sulfonation (482). This fraction constitutes about 30% of the wood lignin.

The sulfonation reactivity of a benzyl alcohol or ether group is increased by higher acidity and by the substitution of the aromatic ring, especially in the *p* position, with phenol or phenolic ether groups, as is the case with

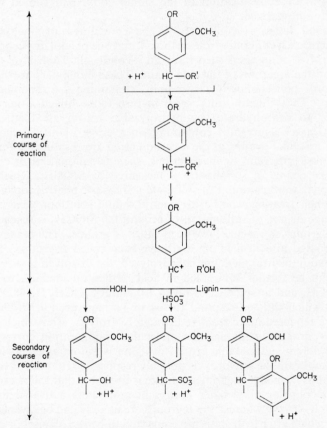

Fig. 9.21. Mechanism of lignin sulfonation etc., assuming proton activation. (1) hydrolysis (R′ alkyl) or status quo (R′ H), (2) sulfitolysis (R′ alkyl) or sulfonation (R′ H), (3) condensation (Rydholm–Lagergren)

482

lignin and most lignin model substances. This indicates that the reaction is a nucleophilic aliphatic substitution, probably bimolecular, S_N2 (377, cf. 490), of the type illustrated in Figure 9.21 (660). In a similar way hydrolysis, alcoholysis and condensation reactions are likely to occur. The consequence for the mechanism of delignification should be, that not only hydrolysis but also sulfonation can break the bonds attaching the lignin in the wood, taking into account *sulfitolysis* as well as *hydrolysis* (660). The primary reaction in both cases would be a proton addition to the benzyl ether oxygen. What the final substituent at the subsequent splitting of the carbon–oxygen bond will be depends on the relative reactivities and concentrations of bisulfite ions and water, as well as adjacent condensable phenylpropane monomers. The rate of dissolution of the lignin should then be proportional to the acidity in the case of hydrolysis and to both acidity and bisulfite ion concentration in the case of sulfitolysis.

Therefore, the results of the Canadian school, showing the rate of delignification as being proportional to $[H^+] . [HSO_3^-]$, need not necessarily be explained by the assumption of a rate-determining sulfonation preceding a rapid hydrolysis, but also by the idea that the sulfonation of the lignin to a solid lignosulfonate is continued by sulfitolysis. Figure 9.22

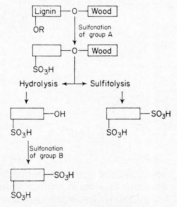

Fig. 9.22. Mechanism of delignification according to two concepts: sulfonation followed either by sulfitolysis or by hydrolysis with subsequent further sulfonation in solution (Rydholm–Lagergren)

(660) illustrates the two concepts. It is probable that both hydrolysis and sulfitolysis take place, and in the technical sulfite cook, where the chemical composition of the cooking liquor changes, the relative proportions between sulfitolysis and hydrolysis should change continually, and in the same way as the bisulfite ion concentration changes (819), as

$$\frac{\text{sulfitolysis}}{\text{hydrolysis}} = \frac{k' . [H^+] . [HSO_3^-]}{k'' . [H^+]} = \frac{k'}{k''} . [HSO_3^-].$$

483

This means that hydrolysis should be accentuated towards the end of the cook, cf. Figure 9.11, although, as nothing is known of k' and k'', sulfitolysis may still be the dominating delignification reaction (660).

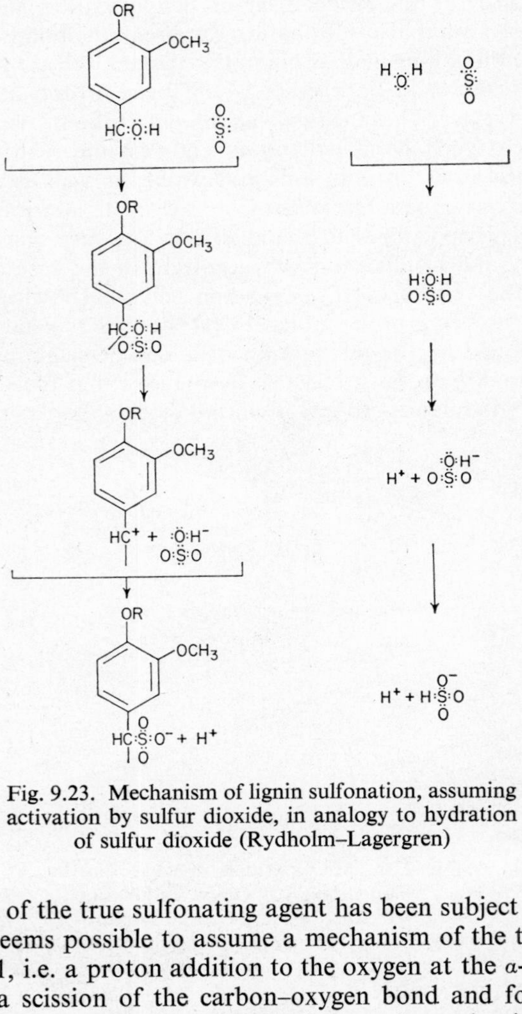

Fig. 9.23. Mechanism of lignin sulfonation, assuming activation by sulfur dioxide, in analogy to hydration of sulfur dioxide (Rydholm–Lagergren)

The nature of the true sulfonating agent has been subject to discussion. Although it seems possible to assume a mechanism of the type suggested in Figure 9.21, i.e. a proton addition to the oxygen at the α-carbon atom, followed by a scission of the carbon–oxygen bond and formation of a sulfonic acid by addition of a bisulfite ion to the carbonium ion, there are other possibilities. Russian workers suggested (188), after finding that the rate of sulfonation is proportional to the SO_2 dissolved in excess of the bisulfite ions, that the dissolved SO_2 rather than the bisulfite ion should be the sulfonating agent (cf. 549). The experimental result, however, is in agreement with those of the Canadian school, that the rate of delignification is proportional to the vapor pressure of SO_2 (at constant temperature) and to the 'excess SO_2' (see above) and all these

484

results could be interpreted in favor of both theories, since there is a proportionality between 'excess SO_2' and the product $[H^+] . [HSO_3^-]$. There is, however, one indication that dissolved SO_2 could be the active

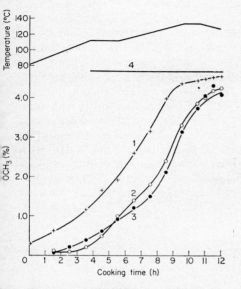

Fig. 9.24. Sulfonation and delignification of a one-stage calcium base acid sulfite cook, spruce. 1) dissolved plus hydrolytically dissolvable methoxyl ('sulfonation curve'), values based on methoxyl content of wood residues after hydrolysis, (2) dissolved methoxyl ('delignification curve'), values based on methoxyl content of wood residues before hydrolysis, (3) dissolved methoxyl, values based on non-volatile methoxyl of cooking liquor samples, (4) total methoxyl of original wood (Rydholm–Lagergren)

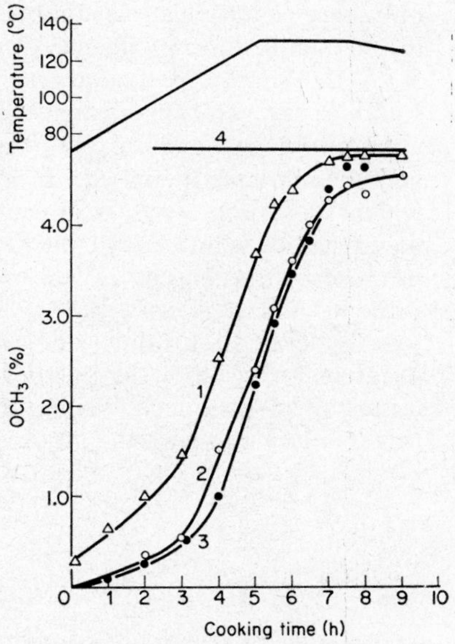

Fig. 9.25. Sulfonation and delignification of a one-stage ammonium base acid sulfite cook, spruce. Key to numbers, see Figure 9.24. (Rydholm–Lagergren)

sulfonating agent. On increasing the temperature, the ionization of H_2SO_3 is decreased, and hence likewise the product of $[H^+] . [HSO_3^-]$. The decrease is about 35% for every 10°C. If the sulfonation reaction should proceed only by the mechanism originally suggested, and thus its rate be proportional to $[H^+] . [HSO_3^-]$, its temperature dependence would be unusually low. As that is not the case (150, 819), it seems likely that dissolved SO_2, or the metabisulfite ion, could also act as sulfonating agents. The reaction mechanism would then be as indicated by Figure 9.23 (660). The acceptor of electrons from the α-carbon oxygen is not in this case a proton but the sulfur atom of SO_2, in analogy with the hydration of SO_2 to sulfurous acid. Thereby a bisulfite ion is formed together with the carbonium ion, and the sulfonation then occurs. It must, however, be emphasized, that there is no clear-cut experimental evidence in favor

485

of one or the other mechanism of reaction, and that the question is of fairly little consequence for the main discussion on the sulfite pulping reactions.

Until recently, the technical sulfite cook was fairly well defined. The only base economically available, calcium, allowed only minor deviations in the composition of the cooking acid, and the cook was decidedly acid. With the increased availability of chemicals and the development of suitable regeneration systems, the use of soluble bases, magnesium, ammonium and sodium, has become possible, and the varieties of the sulfite cook have increased. Even disregarding the neutral sulfite process, which in several ways is an entirely different process, there are many new types of sulfite cooks, such as the bisulfite cook, working with solutions consisting mainly of sodium bisulfite with little or no sulfurous acid present, and various types of multistage cooks, beginning neutral or weakly acidic or alkaline, and ending as normal acid sulfite cooks. It is of interest to see how the change of base or the composition of the cooking liquor affects the mechanism of delignification. Figures 9.24–29 exemplify this (660) by showing the amount of methoxyl dissolved during the cook

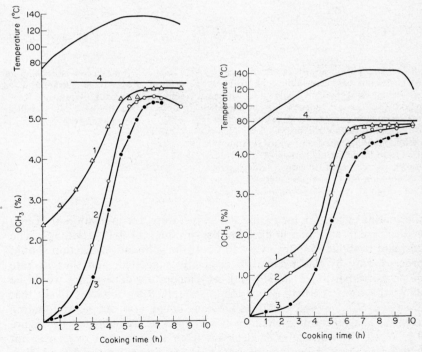

Fig. 9.26. Sulfonation and delignification of a one-stage ammonium base acid sulfite cook, birch. Key to numbers, see Figure 9.24 (Rydholm–Lagergren)

Fig. 9.27. Sulfonation and delignification of a one-stage sodium base acid sulfite cook, spruce. Key to numbers, see Figure 9.24 (Rydholm–Lagergren)

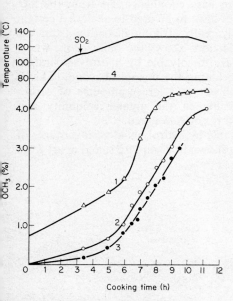

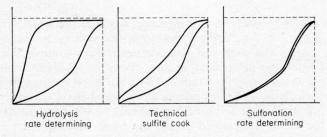

Fig. 9.28. Sulfonation and delignification of a two-stage sodium base neutral acid sulfite cook, spruce. Key to numbers, see Figure 9.24 (Rydholm–Lagergren)

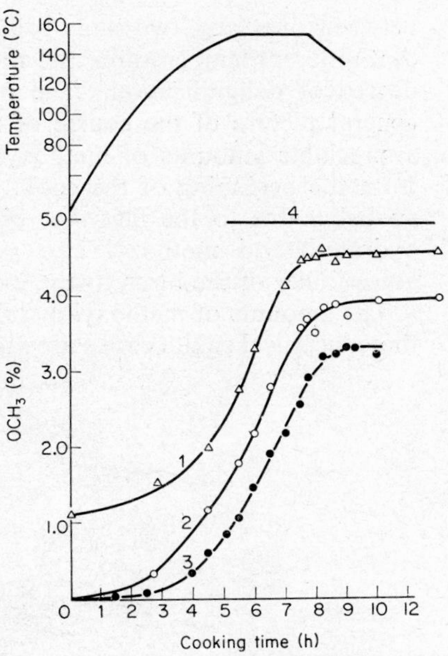

Fig. 9.29. Sulfonation and delignification of a one-stage sodium bisulfite cook, spruce. Key to numbers, see figure 9.24 (Rydholm–Lagergren)

for various technical sulfite cooks and the additional amount dissolvable with subsequent hydrolysis in mineral acid. Figure 9.30 shows similar curves for two extreme hypothetical cases, illustrating rate-determining hydrolysis and rate-determining sulfonation respectively. Obviously, the actual course of reactions is somewhere between these extremes. Further, there is no principal difference between the cooks on calcium, ammonium and sodium base, nor between acid sulfite and bisulfite cooking nor

Fig. 9.30. Sulfonation and delignification curves, principal course of a technical sulfite cook, as well as of two hypothetical cases, assuming hydrolysis or sulfonation as the rate-determining reaction (Rydholm–Lagergren)

487

between one- and two-stage sodium base cooking, apart from the fact that different temperatures and times have to be used to achieve a certain degree of delignification. The only really striking deviation from the general picture of the course of reactions shows the birch cook, where appreciable amounts of methoxyl are dissolvable by hydrolysis straight from the beginning of the cook, including the uncooked wood. This is probably due to the fact that birch contains larger amounts of carbohydrate-bound methoxyl and possibly to the greater solubility and accessibility of the birch lignin, even if not sulfonated.

The amounts of methoxyl dissolvable by hydrolysis at various stages of these technical sulfite cooks are also shown in Figure 9.31, and apart from

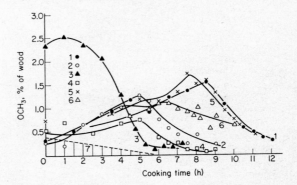

Fig. 9.31. Amounts of methoxyl, hydrolytically dissolvable at various stages of sulfite cooks of different type.

(1) one-stage calcium base acid sulfite cook, spruce,
(2) one-stage ammonium base acid sulfite cook, spruce,
(3) one-stage ammonium base acid sulfite cook, birch,
(4) one-stage sodium base acid sulfite cook, spruce,
(5) two-stage sodium neutral acid sulfite cook, spruce,
(6) one-stage sodium bisulfite cook, spruce,
(7) approximate amount of residual carbohydrate methoxyl (Rydholm–Lagergren)

the birch cook all curves start from about 0.5% of the wood, or a little more than carbohydrate-bound methoxyl, increase to a maximum of 1.0–1.5% during the cook and then decrease again towards the end of the cook, when the delignification approaches completion. Figure 9.32 shows the amounts of sulfur combined with the wood residues before and after the hydrolysis, all values calculated on wood basis. A maximum of 0.7–0.9% S is reached, followed by a straight-lined decrease to almost zero, as the lignin is dissolved during the cook. Subsequent hydrolysis of the wood residues causes an appreciable reduction in these values. In Figure 9.33 the corresponding degrees of sulfonation are shown. There is an increase in S/OCH_3 during all but the last stages of the entire cook. The maximal degree of sulfonation of the lignin in the wood residues is around

488

0.3 S/OCH₃. The lignin remaining after hydrolysis contains far less sulfur, 0.05–0.15 S/OCH₃, and the lignin dissolved during the hydrolysis can therefore be calculated to have a degree of sulfonation of 0.3–0.5 S/OCH₃. It is therefore obvious that the lignin in the wood residue during the cook is not uniformly sulfonated, but to an extent varying with its accessibility. Laboratory cookings have indicated the same heterogeneity (208, 275),

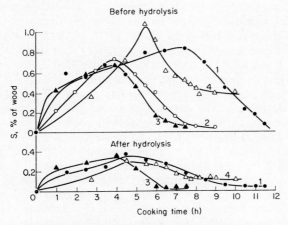

Fig. 9.32. Amounts of sulfur in the solid phase at various stages of sulfite cooks of different type, before and after standard hydrolysis.
(1) one-stage calcium base acid sulfite cook, spruce,
(2) one-stage ammonium base sulfite cook, spruce,
(3) one-stage sodium base acid sulfite cook, spruce,
(4) one-stage sodium bisulfite cook, spruce (Rydholm–Lagergren)

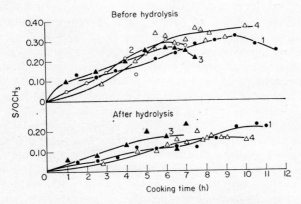

Fig. 9.33. Degree of sulfonation of lignin in the solid phase at various stages of sulfite cooks of different type, before and after standard hydrolysis. Key to numbers, see Figure 9.32 (Rydholm–Lagergren)

489

although cooking in weakly acidic sulfite solution with larger chemicals-to-wood ratios than used technically will give a rather more uniform sulfonation of the lignin (308, 660).

To achieve sufficient hydrophility the lignin must be sulfonated to a certain minimal degree of sulfonation, around 0.3 S/OCH_3. Then additional linkages must be broken by hydrolysis or sulfitolysis to effect dissolution. If sulfitolysis is the dominating reaction, the lignosulfonate fractions dissolved during the cook all have a degree of sulfonation exceeding 0.3 S/OCH_3. Unfortunately, little is known about the degree of sulfonation of the lignin dissolved during the sulfite cook, as the investigations have been concentrated on the waste liquors (207). The minimal degree of sulfonation found is about 0.45 S/OCH_3 in the high-molecular fraction, whereas reasonably pure low-molecular fractions contain 0.6–0.7 S/OCH_3. That not all sulfonatable groups in the lignin are sulfonated during the sulfite cook depends on the condensation reactions, which compete with sulfonation for the reactive groups. In bisulfite cooks, the lignin remaining in the wood residue has been found to reach an average of 0.3 S/OCH_3 (208, 308), from which the fraction dissolvable by hydrolysis had a degree of sulfonation of 0.37 and the residual portion contained 0.2 S/OCH_3 (208).

Thus, at least no experimental evidence forwarded contradicts the assumption that a continuously increasing sulfonation may be the main cause of the delignification, although it is quite probable that the two-stage mechanism of sulfonation succeeded by hydrolysis is responsible for part of the delignification, especially towards the end of the cook.

The fairly limited amounts of hydrolyzable lignin found in the wood residues during the technical cooks underline that hydrolysis cannot be the rate-determining reaction. In fact, if hydrolysis were very much slower than sulfonation, sulfitolysis would take over the dissolution. The hydrolyzable lignin portions after 50% delignification vary from 17–33%, the higher figures being obtained in the slower cooks. However, even on acid cooking at 100°C, the picture of the delignification following soon after sulfonation remains unchanged, and therefore the extreme two-stage mechanism concept is not valid.

The reaction mechanism of sulfonation and delignification has been further illustrated by an experimental technique involving presulfonation by acid sulfite cooking at fairly low temperature (421, 622, 633) or bisulfite cooking at somewhat higher temperature (660), followed by washing in water and subsequent cooking in SO_2–water. In contrast to treatment with other mineral acids, SO_2–water effects nearly complete delignification, in spite of a very limited presulfonation. That the pulping efficiency was not due to any remaining bisulfite was ensured by subjecting the presulfonated wood to acid washing for ion exchange and further ion exchange to mono-, di- or trivalent cations prior to cooking in SO_2–water (633, 660). Some of the results are shown in Table 9.4. Obviously, although the presulfonation was limited enough to prevent pulping by mineral acid hydrolysis, the SO_2–water cook leads to pulp of normal quality. That type of cook must therefore involve continued sulfonation, together with

Table 9.4. Presulfonation of sprucewood by acid sulfite or bisulfite cooking, followed by hydrolysis in sulfuric, phosphoric or sulfurous acid (660)

Pretreatment. Heating for 2 h to and 2 h at maximum temperature in a sodium-based liquor. Liquor ratio 4:1, either in *acid sulfite* liquor, 6% total and 1% combined SO_2 at 100°C, or in *bisulfite* liquor, 4% total and 2% combined SO_2 at 140°C. Washing in distilled water overnight at 20°C and then 5 times 1 h at 100°C.

Hydrolysis. Liquor ratio 10:1. *sulfuric acid,* 1 N, 48 h, 100°C, or *phosphoric acid* pH 1.9, 12 h, 115°C, or *sulfurous acid* 5% SO_2, 2 h heating, 4 h at 115°C.

Cooking liquor		Yield, % of original wood	Roe no.	OCH_3, % of pulp	S, % of pulp	Lignin, % of pulp	S/OCH_3 in pulp
Pretreatment	Hydrolysis						
Acid sulfite	None	78.2	26.1	4.41	0.47	25.7	0.10
	H_2SO_4	69.2	29.1	4.99	0.43	30.6	0.08
	H_3PO_4	70.3	27.6	4.57	0.33	28.3	0.07
	H_2SO_3	58.3	16.8	2.29	0.40	14.6	0.17
Bisulfite	None	81.9	(23.4)	4.47	0.61	23.2	0.13
	H_2SO_4	70.8	31.4	5.01	0.58	32.5	0.11
	H_3PO_4	63.6	23.4	4.25	0.34	23.3	0.08
	H_2SO_3	49.1	4.1	1.16	0.18	3.6	0.15

sulfitolysis and hydrolysis. The differences noted have been interpreted as being caused by different *solubilities* of the various metal lignosulfonates (633). However, all are quite water-soluble. Another interpretation regards the different *viscosities* of the lignosulfonate solutions, as exemplified by the values of Table 9.5 (683) for solutions of 20% concentration. Because of these differences in viscosity, the rate of diffusion will be different, as found by diffusometric determinations, Table 9.5 (683). Obviously, diffusion is retarded for the more highly viscous lignosulfonate solutions, and this is likely to be of some importance for the rate of delignification. However, as pointed out previously as well as below, the latter seems to be governed by a chemical reaction rather than by diffusion, and another circumstance than the viscosity variations is likely to be the main cause of the differences experienced. The velocity of both sulfonation and hydrolysis must depend on the acidity of the reaction zone, i.e.

Table 9.5. Relative viscosity of a 20% lignosulfonate solution with various metal counter ions and diffusion measurements on these solutions (683)

Cation	Rel. viscosity	Distribution of dry substance, %, in layer			
		I	II	III	IV
Na^+	1.95	41.8	31.1	17.4	9.7
NH_4^+	1.97	41.7	31.5	18.0	8.8
K^+	1.92	42.0	30.2	17.6	10.2
Ca^{+2}	2.58	50.0	31.0	12.8	6.2
Zn^{+2}	2.52	50.4	30.7	13.0	5.9
Fe^{+2}	2.55	50.3	30.0	13.1	6.6
Ba^{+2}	2.50	50.7	30.5	12.8	6.0
Al^{+3}	3.55	55.2	29.0	10.9	4.9

the solid–liquid interphase boundary, which is a function not only of the acidity of the cooking liquor, but also of the *Donnan* equilibria prevailing. The effects of different cations observed could therefore be explained by shifts in the *Donnan* equilibria. The more metal ions attached to the solid phase, the less is the acidity there, and the slower the delignification. Divalent ions therefore cause rather slower delignifications of the wood than monovalent cations. With only hydrogen ions in the solid phase, lignin condensation retards the dissulution. The ion exchange effects are further demonstrated in Table 9.6 (660) for similar cooks, where additions of neutral calcium chloride to the SO_2–water is shown to retard the delignification further, although the acidity of the surrounding cooking liquor is left virtually unchanged. It is obvious that this experimental evidence could not be explained in terms of varying viscosity of the lignosulfonate to be dissolved but rather by the above-mentioned *Donnan* effects.

It was also shown, Table 9.7 (660), that cooking in SO_2–water of pre-sulfonated wood containing calcium or sodium ions at the sulfonate groups, gave completely different distributions of the cations during the cook. In the case of calcium, the solid phase remained virtually saturated with calcium, whereas most of the sodium was found in the solution.

Table 9.6. Presulfonation of sprucewood by bisulfite cooking, followed by exchange to various cations and subsequent SO_2–water cook, without or in the presence of a neutral salt (660)

Pretreatment.
1. Sodium bisulfite, liquor ratio 4:1, 4% total and 2% combined SO_2, pH 4, 2 h to and 2 h at 140°C.
2. Washing in distilled water overnight, 20°C, and then 5 times 1 h at 100°C.
3. Soaking in 5% HCl, 48 h, 20°C, for exchange to hydrogen ions.
4. Washing in distilled water overnight.
5. Soaking in 0.8 N chloride solution for exchange to H^+, Na^+, NH_4^+, Mg^{+2}, Ca^{+2}, Ba^{+2}, Al^{+3}.
6. Washing in distilled water overnight, 20°C, and then 5 times 1 h at 100°C.

SO_2–water cook. 5% SO_2, liquor ratio 10:1, 2 h to and 4 h at 115°C, with 0.0, 0.1, 0.3 and 1.0 N CaCl$_2$.

CaCl$_2$ content	Cation	SO_2, %, in waste liquor	Yield, % of orig. wood	Roe no.	OCH$_3$, % of pulp	S, % of pulp	Lignin, % of pulp	S/OCH$_3$ in pulp
0.0 N	H^+	2.5	60.9	16.9	2.59	0.74	15.6	0.28
	Na^+	3.4	52.3	5.1	0.84	0.16	4.7	0.18
	NH_4^+	3.2	51.6	5.0	1.00	0.15	4.5	0.14
	Mg^{+2}	3.4	55.5	8.0	1.22	0.25	6.5	0.20
	Ca^{+2}	3.4	55.5	8.3	1.56	0.25	7.8	0.16
	Ba^{+2}	3.4	53.7	8.1	1.27	0.34	7.5	0.26
	Al^{+3}	3.4	60.7	16.2	2.89	0.42	15.4	0.14
0.1 N	Ca^{+2}	—	61.8	15.1	2.55	0.64	15.0	0.24
0.3 N	Ca^{+2}	—	64.4	18.3	3.02	0.67	18.2	0.22
1.0 N	Ca^{+2}	—	64.2	22.2	3.61	1.21	21.9	0.29

Table 9.7. Distribution of cations on the solid and liquid phases during the SO₂-water cook subsequent to the presulfonation cook. Spruce (660)

Pretreatment.
1. Sodium bisulfite, liquor ratio 4:1, 4% total and 2% combined SO₂, pH 4, initially; and 2.6% total and 1.3% combined SO₂, pH 3,4, finally, after 2 h to and 2 h at 140°C.
2. Washing in distilled water overnight, 20°C, and then 5 times 1 h at 100°C.
3. Hydrogen ion exchange in 5% HCl, 20°C, 48 h.
4. Washing in distilled water overnight, 20°C.
5. Metal ion exchange in 0.8 N sodium or calcium chloride, 20°C, 48 h.
6. Washing in distilled water overnight, 20°C, and then 5 times 1 h at 100°C.

SO₂-water cook. 5% SO₂, liquor ratio 10:1, 2 h to and 0, 1, 2 and 4 h at 115°C, with 0.0 or 1.0 N chloride.

Chloride content originally	Cation	Cooking time, h	SO_2, % in waste liquor	Yield, % of orig. wood	Roe no.	OCH_3, % of pulp	S, % of pulp	Lignin, % of pulp	Cation content liquor g/l	Cation content pulp %	Cation content eq/t of orig. wood in liquor	Cation content in pulp	Anion content eq/t of orig. wood, in pulp
—	Na^+	0 + 0	—	77.6	26.7	3.53	0.54*	21.5	0.000	0.185	0	(65)	132
0.0 N		2 + 0	3.5	70.3	15.0	3.06	0.43	20.2	0.238	0.0327	82	10	95
		2 + 1	3.4	54.1	8.1	1.27	0.23	6.4	0.263	0.0085	92	2	39
		2 + 2	3.3	53.4	6.9	1.02	0.24	5.2	0.255	0.0071	90	1.7	40
		2 + 4	3.2	50.8	2.7	0.61	0.10	3.2	0.263	0.0087	91	1.9	16
1.0 N		2 + 4	3.6	59.8	11.5	1.99	0.53	12.2	18.4	0.120	—	31	99
—	Ca^{+2}	0 + 0	—	80.2	26.7	3.80	0.61*	22.5	0.000	0.420	0	168	153
0.0 N		2 + 0	3.5	70.8	21.0	3.33	0.60	21.1	0.181	0.405	72	143	133
		2 + 1	3.5	60.8	14.5	2.54	0.57	15.2	0.213	0.325	85	99	108
		2 + 2	3.2	55.5	12.2	1.59	0.31	9.2	0.238	0.210	95	58	54
		2 + 4	3.2	51.6	8.1	1.28	0.25	7.8	0.264	0.160	106	41	40
1.0 N		2 + 4	3.4	63.4	14.4	2.51	0.64	15.5	13.7	0.475	—	150	127

* S/OCH₃, in both cases 0.15.

493

Applying *Donnan*'s law for the systems and neglecting the activity co-efficients, the following equation for the acidity of the solid phase was derived (660):

$$[H^+]_i = (n[M^{+n}]_o + [H^+]_o) \cdot \left(\frac{[M^{+n}]_o}{[M^{+n}]_i}\right)^{1/n} - n[M^{+n}]_i + [RSO_3^-]_i$$

where i and o denote inner and outer phases, $[M^{+n}]$ molarity of the metal cation and $[RSO_3^-]_i$ the concentration of the sulfonate groups in the solid phase. The latter has been estimated (183, 308) to be of the order of 0.2 N. In comparison, the first term was low in the above experiments and will be of significance only when the second term in size approaches that of the third, i.e. where the solid phase is approximately saturated with metal ions, as with calcium. For the experiments, the acidity of the solid phase was calculated to have been about 0.18 N in the case of sodium and 0.007 N in the case of calcium. Even the use of activity coefficients would not change the fact that a considerable acidity prevails in the presence of sodium and a much lower one with calcium. Therefore, it is at first sight astonishing that the difference in the rate of pulping was not found to be greater. However, it also indicates that at such cooking conditions hydrolysis is not the rate-governing reaction of the delignification. In sulfur dioxide solutions containing no combined SO_2, the rate of delignification should be rather independent of variations in the acidity, since the product of $[H^+] \cdot [HSO_3^-]$ will then remain essentially constant. In the case of ordinary sulfite cooks with their higher electrolyte content, the differences between the acidity of the solid phase for cooks of different bases are likely to be smaller, and the difference in the rate of delignification between calcium- and sodium-based cooks is not great (e.g. 747).

The dissolution of lignosulfonate in acid sulfite cooking (563) as well as in bisulfite solutions of increasing acidity (220) has been followed by determination of average molecular weight and molecular weight distribution of the dialyzed fractions by means of diffusion coefficient measurements. In the acid cook, lignosulfonates of increasing molecular weight were dissolved as the cook proceeded, as shown in Figure 9.34. The average molecular weight of the initial softwood lignin fractions was 2,000–4,000, whereafter lignosulfonate molecules of up to 100,000 in weight passed into solution, increasing the average molecular weight of the lignin dissolved to around 10,000 at 74–90% delignification, in agreement with other investigations (237a). On prolonged delignification a decrease in the average molecular weight was observed, followed in some cases by a new increase. The results were interpreted as the effects of contemporary hydrolysis, condensation and diffusion. The smaller fragments formed by hydrolysis of the solid lignosulfonates diffuse into the liquid phase with the highest velocity and are followed by larger molecules. Condensation counteracts the hydrolytic fragmentation of the molecules. In the case of hardwood lignin, considerably smaller lignosulfonate molecules were dissolved, with a relatively constant molecular weight of 1,000–2,000 throughout the cook, probably partly the effect of the lesser condensation tendency of hardwood lignin. In spite of that, the rate of delignification was found to be virtually the same, cf. Figure 9.35 (563), for softwood and hardwood, which indicates strongly that diffusion is not governing the rate of delignification.

That the small lignin molecules dissolved in the initial phase of a sulfite cook are not entirely formed by hydrolytic degradation of larger molecules is shown by the results of the step-wise delignification by increasingly acidic sulfite cooking liquors. About a third of the softwood lignin is thus dissolved already by a cooking liquor of pH 5 (1) and was shown to be of comparatively low molecular weight (220), whereas the fractions subsequently dissolved in more acidic liquors are of larger molecular size. Further hydrolytic treatment of all fractions in hydrochloric acid or sulfite cooking acid considerably reduced their average molecular size.

The degree of sulfonation of the fractions dissolved increases during the incremental delignification of wood in liquors of increasing acidity (220, 234), from around 0.3 S/OCH$_3$ to 0.6–0.8 or even higher.

The main lignin reaction, which retards or prevents delignification by sulfite cooking acid, is *condensation*. As pointed out in Chapter 4.IV, acid condensation of lignin involves the benzyl alcohol, and possibly alkyl ether and carbonyl groups, especially in those monomers containing a free phenolic group. The reactive center of the co-condensing molecule, which may be a phenolic compound belonging to the group of 'extractives' or another lignin molecule, is a certain atom of a benzene ring, as was illustrated in Figure 9.21. In the aromatic part of the lignin molecules, the 5- and 6-positions in monomers with a free phenolic group are especially reactive, as indicated by oxidative degradation studies of lignosulfonates as compared to untreated wood lignin (624). Thereby a carbon–carbon bond is formed, which is stable to hydrolysis and thus constitutes

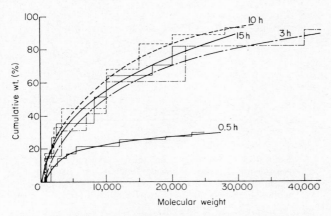

Fig. 9.34. Estimated distribution in molecular weights of dissolved hemlock lignin sulfonates after various times of treatment (Nokihara)

495

an enlargement of the lignin molecule. At the same time a sulfonatable group is blocked and delignification therefore made still more difficult. As in the case of sulfonation, the reaction mechanism is likely to involve an initial proton activation, and the extent of condensation therefore depends very much on the acidity of the solid–liquid interphase. Similar to the ratio of sulfonation-to-hydrolysis, the ratio of sulfonation-to-condensation might be said to depend on the bisulfite ion concentration prevailing, as

$$\frac{\text{sulfonation}}{\text{condensation}} = \frac{k' . [\text{H}^+] . [\text{HSO}_3^-]}{k'' . [\text{H}^+]} = k . [\text{HSO}_3^-]$$

A high bisulfite ion concentration thus ensures a limited condensation. As the cook proceeds, the bisulfite ion concentration will drop and condensation become more dominant. However, if the initial bisulfite charge was sufficient, sulfonation has already protected the most reactive benzyl alcohol and carbonyl groups and ensured sufficient hydrophility for the dis-

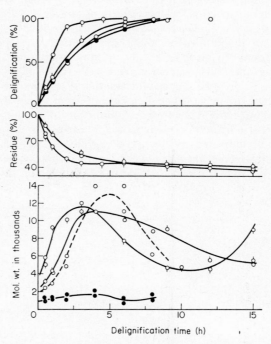

Fig. 9.35. Percentage delignification and wood residue and average molecular weights of dissolved lignin sulfonates after various times of delignification with sodium bisulfite–sulfurous acid solutions.

○, spruce, 3.1% 'free' SO_2;
◔, hemlock, 4.0% 'free' SO_2;
♀, hemlock, 8.0% 'free' SO_2;
●, maple, 3.1% 'free' SO_2 (Nokihara)

solution of the lignin. Those left unsulfonated and the new benzyl alcohol groups formed by hydrolysis may undergo condensation, but that will occur mainly in solution and will not normally lead to lignin molecules so large that they reprecipitate onto the pulp. In normal acid sulfite cooks, only fairly small amounts of lignin, corresponding to about 1% of the original lignin in the wood, presumably the least accessible part, will remain in the pulp condensed to such a degree that it will not dissolve upon prolonged cooking. It will give a minimum chlorine number of 0.5–1.0 in the rayon pulps and has to be removed by chlorination and oxidation in the bleaching.

If conditions are chosen which do not favor an initial sulfonation, condensation will occur to such an extent that delignification is rendered impossible, and a *burnt* or *black* cook will have occurred. This phenomenon caused serious financial losses in the early days of the sulfite industry but is seldom experienced nowadays if proper control of the variables, especially the cooking acid composition and the time–temperature schedule, is maintained. However, several important consequences follow from this tendency to condensation of unsulfonated lignin, such as:

(1) sensitivity of the sulfite process to preheating of the wood;
(2) necessity of good impregnation prior to sulfite pulping;
(3) difficulties encountered in the pulping of certain wood species.

In order to investigate the effect of condensation of lignin on the ease of delignification in the sulfite cook, several types of pretreatments prior to sulfite pulping have been carried out, as well as interruption of the cook at a certain stage for a special treatment before continuing the cook. Buffer solutions covering a wide range of pH's from strongly acid to alkaline solutions have been used (109, 149), containing various types of anions and cations (113), at various temperatures for various times (147).

Figure 9.36 (149) shows the influence of the pH of the buffer solution on pulp yield and lignin content, when the pretreatment is extended to 6 h at 130°C, followed by an acid sulfite cook for 3 h at 140°C. Minimum damage is caused at pH 4–5 as was also found in other investigations (108, 618), in agreement with the condensation tendency of phenol–aldehyde systems (414). Pretreatment at pH 7 (435) or in unbuffered water (148) had been earlier found to retard delignification. The influence of the temperature of the pretreatment was tested at three different pH levels (147), and in most cases a slower delignification in the subsequent sulfite cook was experienced. Insignificant retardation was found at pH 5 at 100–110°C, whereas higher temperature also caused damage at pH 5. In that series of investigations, the pretreatment carried on for 6 h. The effect of the time of the pretreatment at two different temperatures and pH levels was shown to be most important during the first hours (147).

If the pretreatment has not been excessive, the delignification is retarded, but not completely checked. As shown in Figure 9.37 (148), the delignification is slower during the first few hours and then assumes the same velocity as in cooking untreated wood.

497

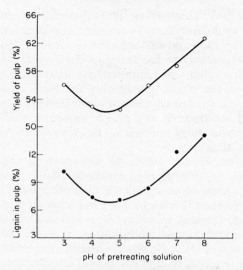

Fig. 9.36. Yield and lignin content of pulps from wood preheated in buffer solutions (Corey–Maass)

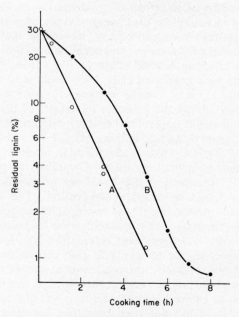

Fig. 9.37. Rate of delignification of untreated and of preheated spruce chips. (A) untreated, (B) preheated in water for six hours at 130°C (Corey–Maass)

The nature of the pretreatment effect is not entirely clear, as both chemical and physical factors may play a rôle. Chemical condensation will enlarge the molecules and decrease the amount of groups available for sulfonation. The increased retardation at pH's lower than 4 has most likely chemical causes, as also directly demonstrated by the increased yields of benzene polycarboxylic acids upon oxidation (108). Likewise an alkaline condensation would be responsible for part of the considerable retardation at comparatively high pH's. In a study (257) of the formation of 2,4-dinitroguaiacol (DNG) by nitration of spruce and birch wood with nitric acid in ether at room temperature, chemical evidence of lignin condensation was sought, since experiments with model compounds had shown that only configurations of the type

OH
|
/_OCH$_3$
| |
\\ /
|
C

would yield DNG. Pretreatment of the wood at 150°C for 6 h in buffer solutions varying from pH 0.4–12.0 was found to have the influence on the DNG yield shown in Figure 9.38 (257). Thus, the chemical effect is

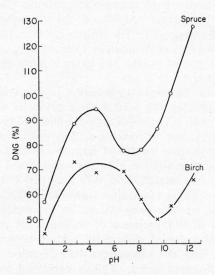

Fig. 9.38. The amount of dinitro-guaiacol (DNG) formed by nitration of spruce and birch wood, which have been cooked at various pH values, calculated as a percentage of DNG given by un-cooked wood (Gustafsson–Soila)

greatest at low pH and has a minimum around pH 4–5. The increase in the DNG yield in the alkaline range is likely to depend on secondary effects. It is remarkable that the DNG yield on pretreatment at pH 4–5 is so little affected, since the treatment virtually prevents delignification by the sulfite process (cf. 149). However, it has been pointed out (148) that physical changes of the submicroscopic particles of the protolignin on heating in aqueous solutions might be considerable. Agglomeration might decrease their surface and thus diminish the zone of reaction of the subsequent sulfite cook. Such agglomeration is noted, for example, on heating milled wood lignin powder in water (75). On heating sprucewood in buffer solutions of pH 6.7 and 4.7 at 150°C for 6 h, followed by a sulfite cook, it was found that delignification was retarded and the average degree of sulfonation decreased but that the degree of sulfonation of the hydro-lytically dissolvable lignin was not changed (275). The effect was consequently considered to be physical rather than chemical. However, condensation, especially of such groups (mainly carbonyls) which do not form stable sulfonates, would also explain the experimental evidence.

The effect of various anions in the precooks could possibly be explained as physical effects of swelling and agglomeration (113), since the retardation of the delignification in the subsequent sulfite cook increases with the swelling power of the anion according to the lyotropic order. The effect of various cations does not, however, agree with the lyotropic order, multivalent ions of the precook retarding delignification to a somewhat greater extent than monovalent cations. Specific anomalies are exhibited by thiocyanate anion and the ammonium cation, both retarding delignification greatly. The former has been found to react with lignin in the same manner as bisulfite or hydrosulfide, and thus competes for the sulfonatable groups (634). The latter is likely to react specifically with the lignin carbonyls.

A decided effect of chemical condensation is observed in the treatment of *presulfonated* wood in hot acid buffers prior to a finishing sulfite cook (290, 344). Figure 9.39 (344) shows the effect of cooking wood after 0, 2 and 5 h presulfonation in cooking acid at 100°C, in phosphoric acid buffers of pH 2 for varying lengths of time at 120°C. One of the buffers was 0.5 n with regard to sodium ions, the other was a pure acid buffer. Presulfonation was very limited, 0.00, 0.13 and 0.20 S/OCH$_3$ respectively. Whereas the buffer cooking of unsulfonated wood retarded the subsequent delignification in a manner proportional to the heating period in the buffer, irrespective of the presence of sodium ions in the buffer, the presulfonated wood behaved differently. After cooking in the buffer containing sodium ions, the subsequent delignification was retarded less than for the unsulfonated wood. This is explained by the assumption that some of the most reactive groups in lignin had been protected for condensation by the presulfonation. However, this effect is more than balanced in the case of the buffer cooks in pure phosphoric acid by the increased acidity of the solid phase of the sulfonated wood, which develops in the absence of sodium ions, and an extensive condensation occurs.

The degree of sulfonation of the residual, condensed lignin was around 0.4–0.5 S/OCH₃, as compared to 0.3 S/OCH₃ in the uncondensed or less condensed lignin remaining in the pulp of the normal sulfite cook. The degree of sulfonation of the lignosulfonates dissolved during the sulfite cook being 0.4–0.7 S/OCH₃, the above figures show that condensation has not prevented the lignin being sulfonated to an extent which ordinarily gives sufficient hydrophility, but that the increase in the molecular size prevents the dissolution. Similar high degrees of sulfonation have been found in the residual lignin of pulps from cooks subjected to an acid precook (819).

All the above results stress the importance of achieving good impregnation of the wood chips at temperatures below 110°C, especially when it is kept in mind that the impregnation by the cooking liquor is preceded by gaseous SO₂. This creates an acidic medium, that may be accentuated by sulfonation of some of the most reactive groups of the lignin to solid lignosulfonic acids having not counter ions but hydrogen ions. Therefore longer digester cycles than for kraft pulping are generally necessary, although the heating time can be shortened by appropriate forced impregnation methods (cf. Chapter 6.III). Impregnation at 70–80°C was found superior to that at 100–110°C which is the usual practice (237b).

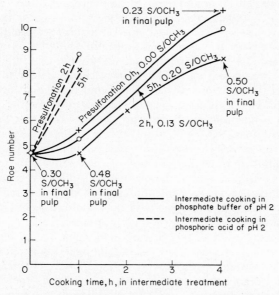

Fig. 9.39. Effects of acid condensation, with and without the presence of sulfonate or sulfonic acid groups, on the delignification of spruce by sulfite cooking acid. Presulfonation 0–5h, 100°C, 4.6% total SO₂, 1.25% combined SO₂; intermediate condensation treatment 0.4h, 120°C, pH 2 in phosphoric acid or phosphate buffer; final cooking 12h, 128°C, 4.6% total SO₂, 1.25% combined SO₂ (Hedlund)

It is also evident that acid prehydrolysis as well as alkaline cooking stages prior to sulfite pulping do not meet with success (622), at least in the case of softwoods (cf. (478) on beechwood prehydrolysis–sulfite pulping), and that steaming of the wood chips must not be carried out for very long times nor at temperatures much above 100°C, although such conditions would enhance the subsequent penetration of the cooking liquor (cf. Chapter 6.III). Finally, special precautions are needed when cooking pines, Douglas fir, tannin-damaged spruce etc., to prevent condensation of the lignin with certain extractives. They will be dealt with specially in a subsequent section.

Condensation reactions in the cooking liquor eventually cause a dark-brown color, which facilitates the determination of the end points of cooks for soft paper pulp and rayon pulp grades. It is not quite clear whether that reaction is caused by the same type of condensation which has been dealt with above, although lignin condensation always seems to be accompanied by the development of a brownish color. As pointed out in Chapter 4.IV, the color reaction is likely to indicate condensation of carbonyl groups of lignin. These are probably protected during the main part of the cook through the formation of α-hydroxysulfonates with bisulfite ions, but as the latter gradually disappear towards the end of the cook, condensation and color formation occur.

A very important lignin reaction during the sulfite cook is that occurring with thiosulfate. As will be discussed in a subsequent section, thiosulfate is formed from bisulfite by several reactions during the cook. Thiosulfate acts as a catalyst in the decomposition of bisulfite to more thiosulfate, whereby the decomposition tends to accelerate, unless thiosulfate is removed from the reaction. It has been found that lignin under normal acid sulfite cooking conditions will remove a considerable quantity of thiosulfate in a reaction which does not lead to sulfonate groups. The terms *organic excess sulfur* (602) and *loosely combined thiosulfate* (694) were coined to describe the sulfur unaccounted for by conventional analyses of sulfur and sulfonate groups. Experiments with lignin models (246) as well as with wood and radioactive thiosulfate (694) have revealed the mechanism. The guaiacyl alcohol groups of lignin react not only with bisulfite to sulfonate but also with thiosulfate to guaiacyl thiosulfate groups, which can react with additional monomers under formation of a lignin sulfide and bisulfate ions, Figure 9.40. The first reaction product corresponds to the concept of loosely combined thiosulfate, and both are included in the term organic excess sulfur. Towards the end of a rayon pulp cook, the lignosulfonate may contain 0.10–0.15 such groups per monomer. The reaction competes with sulfonation, and once sulfonated, the guaiacyl alcohol groups cannot react with thiosulfate. Weakly acidic or neutral medium favors the sulfonation reaction, which is one of the causes of the greater decomposition tendency of the bisulfite and especially neutral sulfite–bisulfite cook as compared with the normal acid sulfite cook, since the thiosulfate formed is not continually removed in lignin reactions.

502

E. Carbohydrate reactions of the sulfite cook

The carbohydrates of the sulfite cook are subjected to several changes, the most important reaction of which is *acid hydrolysis of the glycosidic bonds*. This hydrolysis causes a depolymerization which results in the dissolution of the more accessible and low-molecular part, mainly hemicellulose, and a degradation also of the remaining carbohydrate elements of the fiber, resulting in a weaker paper pulp. The portion dissolved in the cooking liquor undergoes further depolymerization to monomeric sugars, which are partly destroyed under formation of aldonic acids and sugar sulfonates. Some sugars are also dehydrated under formation of heterocyclic compounds such as furfural.

The extent of carbohydrate decomposition is largely controlled by three factors, *time, temperature,* and *acidity,* whereas delignification is also dependent on the bisulfite ion concentration. The ratio of delignification to carbohydrate hydrolysis during the cook, according to the following equation:

$$\frac{\text{delignification}}{\text{carbohydrate hydrolysis}} = \frac{k' \cdot [\text{H}^+] \cdot [\text{HSO}_3^-]}{k'' \cdot [\text{H}^+]} = \frac{k'}{k''} \cdot [\text{HSO}_3^-]$$

should therefore vary largely with the bisulfite ion concentration, which decreases during the cook, cf. Subsection I.3B of this chapter. Consequently, delignification during the sulfite cook proceeds at the same time as and partly somewhat in advance of the carbohydrate removal, whereas delignification in the kraft cook occurs simultaneously or somewhat lagging behind the dissolution of carbohydrates. The temperature dependence of the carbohydrate removal velocity is somewhat larger than that of the delignification rate, the energies of activation having been calculated to be 19–21,000 and 17–19,000 cal./mole respectively (245, 421). This means that pulps rich in hemicellulose, such as greaseproof pulps,

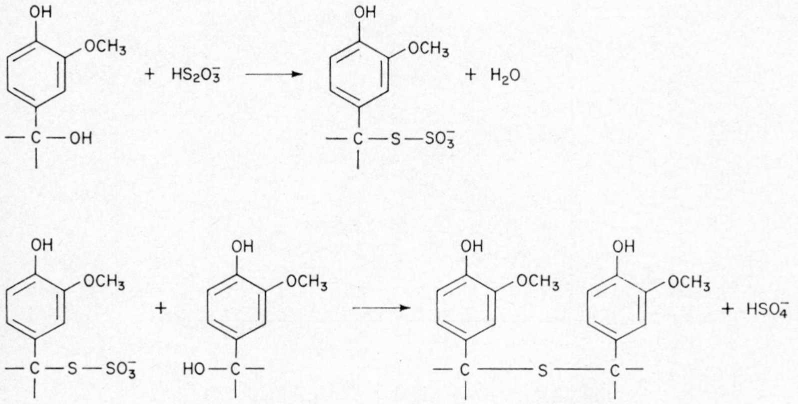

Fig. 9.40. Thiosulfate-consuming reaction of lignin

503

should be prepared at fairly low temperature, whereas softer grades of paper pulps, as well as rayon grades, are preferentially manufactured at higher temperature.

The hydrolysis of the various carbohydrates (cf. Chapter 4.II) naturally depends on the acidity of the zone of reaction. On increasing the pH of the cooking liquor, and thereby the bisulfite ion concentration, more favorable conditions for the preservation of acid-sensitive carbohydrates are secured. However, this will slow down the delignification velocity and necessitate longer cooking times or higher maximum temperatures. Therefore, only insignificantly higher yields at a certain degree of delignification are secured on increasing the combined SO_2 charge from the normal level, although the yields do decrease by decreasing the charge to unusually low levels, which leads to excessive acidity towards the end of the cook, cf. Subsection I.3B. This is true for ordinary sulfite pulps, Figure 9.41 (176, 300, 819), but especially noticeable in the high-yield pulp range. Due to the resistance to removal of softwood lignin in neutral sulfite pulping, this process is used mainly for hardwoods, where considerable delignification could be achieved at well preserved hemicellulose content. However, as was pointed out in Chapter 8.II, buffering of the neutral sulfite cook to a final pH of 6–7 is necessary to avoid considerable hydrolytic dissolution of xylan.

The various carbohydrates of the pulp hydrolyze at different rates. This depends on differences in both reactivity and accessibility. A rough idea of the changes in carbohydrate composition on pulping to different yields is given by Figure 9.42 for spruce and birch, and in Figure 6.55a the

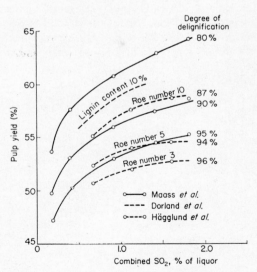

Fig. 9.41. Pulp yield vs. combined SO_2 at various degrees of delignification. Acid sulfite cooking of softwoods

corresponding curves for the removal of the different components are shown (18). Obviously arabinose is hydrolyzed and dissolved at a very early stage of the sulfite cook, in contrast to kraft pulping. Later, xylan and glucomannan dissolve, and xylan especially is much more efficiently removed in acid sulfite pulping than in the kraft cook. Glucomannan is somewhat more resistant to acid hydrolysis than is xylan (526a). Comparatively little cellulose is degraded to an extent which causes dissolution, until the pulp yield decreases below 50%.

The comparative ease of delignification in the sulfite process makes the latter well suited to produce pulps rich in hemicelluloses, and special grades for greaseproof and glassine paper are preferably made by the sulfite processes rather than alkaline pulping. Acid sulfite pulping is then better suited to softwoods and neutral sulfite pulping to hardwoods. On the other hand, the comparative ease of hemicellulose removal on prolonged sulfite cooking, using slightly higher temperature and acidity also makes it possible to produce sulfite pulps of high cellulose purity, suitable for opaque papers and dissolving purposes. The sulfite process is therefore more versatile and has a broader register of pulp grades than the one-stage kraft process, because of its potential in regulating the hemicellulose content of the pulps at will by means of hydrolytic degradation.

However, a very important disadvantage of the process is the fact that in regulating this hemicellulose content, the properties of the carbohydrates remaining in the pulp are impaired. The main reaction causing those changes is also acid hydrolysis. The degree of polymerization is decreased, firstly of the more easily accessible part of the carbohydrates in the outer layers of the fibers, thereby causing a decrease in the paper bonding strength, and later in the body of the fibers also, including the main part of the cellulose. That will cause a reduction in the strength of the individual

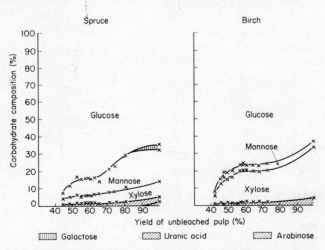

Fig. 9.42. Carbohydrate composition of sulfite pulps at various yields (Annergren–Rydholm)

505

fibers, as shown by the decrease in tearing strength of the paper prepared, and in the viscosity and alphacellulose content of the pulp. These effects show up at different stages of the sulfite cook. The paper bonding elements begin to be affected at an early stage, which is obvious from the fact that tensile and bursting strengths are always lower than in the kraft pulps. The DP of birch xylan has already decreased to half its original figure at pulp yields of 70 % of the wood (570). More serious decrease in the fiber wall (tearing) strength occurs on cooking to pulp yields below 48 % (spruce). At the same time the dissolution of glucose becomes more noticeable. At still lower yields the attack on the fiber is aggravated, causing increasing formation of fiber fragments. Even a moderate mechanical action on the fibers at that stage of cooking might cause more severe fragmentation. As the fiber fragments are more soluble in alkali than the whole fibers, especially at 10 % NaOH concentration, there is a corresponding decrease in alphacellulose content. The drop in pulp viscosity caused by the hydrolysis reaction during the sulfite cook is already noticeable at pulp yields above 50 %, and is often taken as a measure of the degree of cooking. The viscosity figures give a value of the weighted average of the DP of the carbohydrates. However, a closer study, involving fractionation of the carbohydrates, reveals a polymolecularity, which is partly due to the native composition of wood, but depends to a large extent on the heterogeneous attack of acid hydrolysis upon the carbohydrates. Thus, some long-chain cellulose material of low accessibility is always preserved even in pulps of comparatively low viscosity, which naturally means that there is also a large fraction of short-chain material of lower DP than that corresponding to the viscosity figure. This tendency to less uniform chain-length distribution of the low-viscosity sulfite rayon pulps will cause some deficiencies in the properties of certain rayons, especially those of the high-tenacity type, as compared to prehydrolysis–kraft pulps, and has led to the production of sulfite rayon pulps of higher viscosity, leaving the degradation necessary to the aging of the alkalicellulose, where a more uniform chain-length distribution is achieved. Figure 9.43 surveys the various symptoms of carbohydrate degradation during the sulfite cooking to various pulp yield levels.

The *changes in fiber length distribution* on sulfite cooking to various yields are shown in Figure 6.32. As pointed out above, the chemical action is not the only cause of fiber fragmentation, but fairly mild mechanical treatment will also tend to increase the damage, such as blowing the cook instead of dumping it, or too rapid a pressure release during the blow-down period. The curves of Figure 6.32 are therefore only indicative of the changes in fiber length distribution, and local variations in the pulp handling in the later stages of the digester cycle may cause appreciable deviations. However, it is the combined chemical and mechanical action which causes the damage, and it is therefore always more serious in the low-yield range. The hydrolytic attack is likely to be especially serious at those regions of the fiber wall where so-called slip planes have been formed or where the resistant transition lamella (S1) has been loosened from its contact with the secondary wall (S2). That is normally the case when the wood has been subjected to mechanical damage prior to cooking (71, 269), and crushing in the longitudinal direction of the fibers has been found to be much more dangerous than in transversal direction (746). Chipping will cause 'acid-susceptible wood' at that end of the chips which is bruised by the chipper knife when being broken away from the log (14, 251, 335). Dull knives are likely to increase the mechanical damage and enhance the hydrolytic attack on the fiber walls during the sulfite cook. A similar effect, which is also likely to be caused by the just-mentioned morphological disturbances (466), is the failure to get sulfite pulps of any paper strength when the wood is converted to coarse mechanical (Asplund or groundwood) pulp prior to cooking (268, 391). The pulp obtained consists to a large extent of fiber fragments. Defibration at any stage of the sulfite cook will also lead to hydrolytic damage, as judged from alphacellulose analysis of the pulp obtained, in comparison with sulfite pulp from normal cooks (675).

The compression damage of the wood chips not only leads to some fiber fragmentation on sulfite cooking, but also to a general weakening of the strength of those fibers which appear superficially to be undamaged. At an axial compression of 10%, a decrease in average fiber strength of about 20% was measured, whereby the majority of the fibers were found to be weaker than the weakest fibers of undamaged wood after the same sulfite cook (330a). In contrast, the bonding strength of sulfite pulp fibers from damaged and undamaged wood is identical (330c), which underlines the local character of this hydrolytic damage.

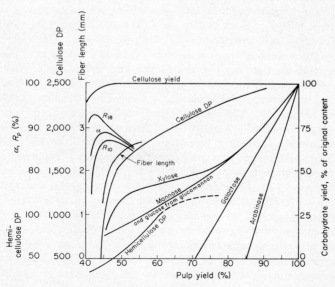

Fig. 9.43. Carbohydrate degradation phenomena during sulfite cooking of spruce

The cause of the excessive hydrolytic degradation experienced in the sulfite cook in the regions of mechanical wood damage is probably the native structure being less accessible to the hydrogen ions where M, P and S1 restrict the fiber swelling. As soon as swelling of S2 can take place the degradation assumes a rate nearly corresponding to that of a homogeneous system at the prevailing temperature and acidity. The theory of a protecting, hydrophobic shell of lignin, cracking at the point of mechanical damage (253a), has had to be abandoned as an explanation for the local carbohydrate damage, since it has been demonstrated that morphologically undisturbed holocellulose can be cooked together with wood by the sulfite process, thereby yielding as strong a paper pulp as did the surrounding wood (330b).

The dissolution of carbohydrates from the fiber wall during the sulfite cook has been studied by microscopical methods (41), and shown to occur predominantly in the outer parts of the fiber wall, in agreement with the concept of localization of the main part of the hemicelluloses. The xylan-rich tertiary wall, S3, is also subjected to degradation in the sulfite cook. Figure 6.24 illustrated the carbohydrate distribution of a sulfite pulp fiber.

The fragmentation of the fibers indicates far-reaching *changes also in the submicroscopic structure* of the fiber. Studies on the hydrolysis of cellulose (598, 599, 754) have revealed that the cellulose microfibrils degrade into fragments, so-called *micelles*, of varying length and mainly of the same width as the microfibrils. Normally, a comparatively harsh hydrolytic treatment is necessary to form micelles from cellulose, but such is likely to occur locally at the mechanically damaged parts of the wood.

The *changes in average molecular weight* and in *molecular weight distribution* of the carbohydrates during the sulfite cook have been studied for both softwoods and hardwoods (99, 100, 404, 415). The changes are caused by heterogeneous hydrolysis and occur at a rate and in a manner which depend on the cooking conditions and the wood species. In a homogeneous system, the rate of hydrolysis of the glucosidic bonds has been found to vary with their place in the cellulose molecule (233), as shown in Table 4.19. The end monomers of the polysaccharide chains are therefore dissolved by hydrolysis rather faster than the scission of glycosidic bonds elsewhere in the chain. Still, the latter is the main cause of the chain shortening. The presence of electronegative groups, such as carbonyls or carboxyls somewhere along the chain, tends to increase the rate of hydrolysis of the adjacent glycosidic bond, and a reductive (but not oxidative) treatment tends to decrease the rate of hydrolysis (505), a phenomenon suggested to explain the somewhat slower hydrolysis of cotton as compared with wood cellulose in homogeneous solution. On the other hand, the presence of electronegative groups in a monomer will stabilize the glycosidic bond of the same monomer (606), which explains the persistence during the sulfite cook of the glucuronic groups attached to the xylan.

The reaction mechanism in all cases is assumed to involve the addition

508

of a proton to the acetal oxygen, heterolysis to form a carbonium ion, which subsequently reacts with water to give a new aldehydic end group and a proton (104). The heterolysis is rate-determining. Furanosidic bonds are known to be cleaved much faster than pyranosidic bonds, which accounts for the rapid dissolution of arabinose in the sulfite cook. The relative rates of acid hydrolysis of the methylglycopyranosides were given in Table 4.18, which indicates that the galactosidic and xylosidic bonds are cleaved about five times and mannosidic three times as fast as the glucosidic bonds (813), in good general agreement with the pulping experience. However, in pulping, the cellulose is proportionally more resistant to dissolution as compared to the hemicelluloses than those figures for chemical reactivity imply, and data on the heterogeneous hydrolysis of wood (256), recalculated with regard to the present knowledge of the chemical composition of hemicelluloses, show that glucomannan and xylan dissolve at a rate 15–30 times as fast as cellulose. In fact, hardly any cellulose is dissolved until the very last stages of the sulfite cook. Therefore, the chemical differences are greatly overshadowed by the *influence of the supermolecular structure.* As was pointed out in Chapter 4.II, not only different parts of the hemicelluloses, but also of the cellulose, are quite differently accessible to acid hydrolysis. The different degree of accessibility will cause the hemicelluloses to dissolve faster than the cellulose, part of the hemicelluloses to remain fairly resistant, and a small fraction of the cellulose to hydrolyze more rapidly than the remainder. The degradation velocity of the resistant carbohydrates is only a few per cent of that in homogeneous solution (415).

Not only is the accessibility of the various polysaccharides in the native wood structure varying, but it is also *changing* during the sulfite cook. Although some degree of lateral order has been indicated for the native hemicelluloses, they can be considered as largely amorphous on account

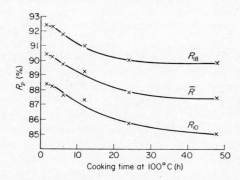

Fig. 9.44. Non-solubility in 18 and 10% NaOH of final rayon grade pulps from acid sulfite cooks of varying impregnation periods at 100°C. The curves have been adapted after the interpolated or extrapolated values at the pulp viscosity of 25 cP TAPPI

of their branches and substituents extending from the straight-chain backbone of the main molecule (cf. Chapter 4.III). On losing these substituents, the linear hemicellulose fragments tend to assume a better ordered structure, either by intercrystallization or by adsorption to the cellulose. Pretreatment of softwoods by sulfite cooking liquor of normal acidity at low temperature, or by slightly alkaline liquor at higher temperature gives an increased carbohydrate yield and a lower alphacellulose content after a subsequent acid sulfite cook to a given viscosity level, Figures 9.44–45 (18). The pretreatment causes an increase in mannose

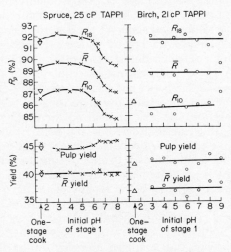

Fig. 9.45. Two-stage sulfite cooking of spruce and birch at varying pH of stage 1 and a standard acid sulfite cook in stage 2. Non-solubility in 18 and 10% NaOH and pulp yield vs. pH of stage 1. Triangles denote one-stage reference cooks (Annergren–Rydholm)

and a decrease in the xylose content of the resulting pulp, Figure 9.46, and a stabilization of glucomannan to acid hydrolysis is thus indicated. The reason has been found to be an initial deacetylation of the glucomannan acetate to leave linear molecules, which then intercrystallize or are adsorbed to the cellulose microfibrils, Figure 9.47. In the conventional one-stage cook, the deacetylation is less selective and the degradation has passed to a rather low-molecular stage before the acetate groups have been removed. Some adsorption is also bound to occur in the conventional sulfite cook, however, and probably both glucomannan and xylan fragments partake. When the glucomannan is selectively stabilized, adsorption takes place at a comparatively early stage and the subsequently liberated linear xylan fragments cannot compete for the limited microfibril surface available, which accounts for the decrease in xylan content experienced. The hydrolysis of the well-ordered glucomannan molecules

510

does not proceed appreciably faster than that of the cellulose (658), and their DP, originally about 100, is 30 after a severe rayon pulp cook to a cellulose DP of 1,000–1,200, irrespective of the quantity remaining, i.e. in pulp from one-stage as well as two-stage cooks. It is probable that effects of heating time and maximum temperature of a normal sulfite cook

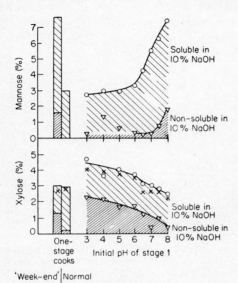

Fig. 9.46. Two-stage sulfite cooking of spruce at varying pH of stage 1 and a standard acid sulfite cook in stage 2. Content of mannose and xylose vs. pH of stage 1. x denotes pentosan analysis (Annergren–Rydholm)

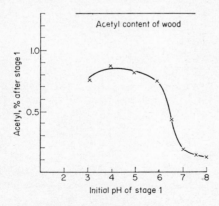

Fig. 9.47. Acetyl content of sprucewood residues after treatment at 125°C for 1.5 hours at varying pH levels (cf. Figure 9.45) (Annergren–Rydholm)

511

on the carbohydrate yield are also caused by a varying degree of gluco-mannan stabilization. The temperature dependence of the hydrolysis of glycosidic bonds seems to be more pronounced than that of deacetylation, and hence more glucomannan stabilization takes place at low temperature. The effect of glucomannan stabilization develops soon after the neutral sulfite precook, already at very high yield, Figure 9.48, and is utilized to increase the yields of paper pulp (658, 778, 790), Figure 9.49. The extent of

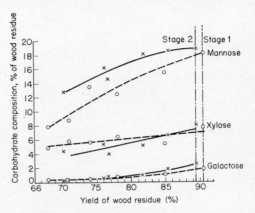

Fig. 9.48. Carbohydrate reactions during the precook at pH 8 (continuous line) or pH 4 (broken line), as well as during the early part of the acidified cook (Annergren–Rydholm)

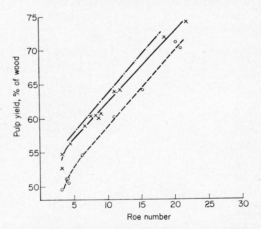

Fig. 9.49. Yield of unbleached pulp on bisulfite and neutral sulfite–bisulfite cooking (Annergren–Rydholm)

– – – one-stage bisulfite cooks,
———— two-stage neutral sulfite–bisulfite cooks,
—.—.—. two-stage neutral sulfite–bisulfite maximal effect pretreatment; pH 8, 125°C, 1.5 h

glucomannan stabilization depends not only on pH, but also on time and temperature of the pretreatment, Figure 9.50, and by increasing the temperature, an improvement in pulp yield can be obtained also at slightly acid conditions such as pH 6.

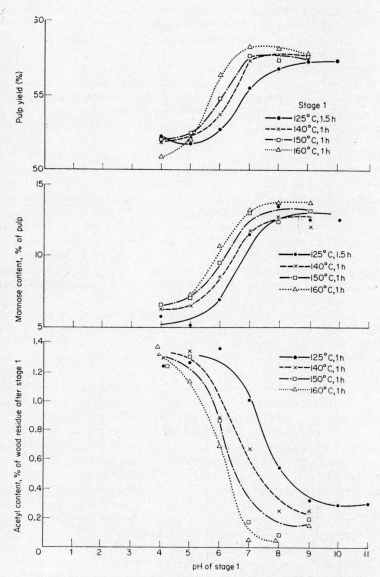

Fig. 9.50. Pulp yield, mannose content and acetyl content of two-stage sulfite pulps, cooked to constant lignin content at varying pH and temperature conditions of stage 1 (Croon *et al*)

Xylan stabilization of a similar type is conceivable in hardwoods, as a pretreatment at 85°C in buffers of pH 9–11 prior to chlorite holocellulose preparation was shown to give a slightly increased yield of hydrolytically resistant xylan, in contrast to buffer solutions of lower pH (73). However, two-stage sulfite cooks of hardwoods at similar conditions as those which give glucomannan stabilization in softwoods do not give increased yields of xylan (18). Obviously, deacetylation takes place but the glucuronic acid substituents of the deacetylated xylan prevent a close association with the cellulose.

Adsorption of hemicellulose fractions onto cellulose has been studied also at room temperature and been found to occur more rapidly for glucomannan than for xylan (550). The effects, which are all in the order of 5% of the cellulose, are likely to involve mainly monolayer adsorption, since the degree of order is likely to decrease sharply on multilayer adsorption of flexible polymers (235). In paper pulps obtained by glucomannan-stabilizing two-stage cooking, the additional glucomannan yield is about 5–7% of the wood, or more than 10% of the cellulose. In this case inter-crystallization of the glucomannan fragments is also probable, whereas the adsorption phenomena are likely to dominate for the glucomannan fraction remaining after the more severe hydrolysis of a rayon pulp cook.

This variety in accessibility to hydrolysis is reflected not only in the selectivity of carbohydrate removal, but also by the heterogeneity in chain length of the material remaining undissolved after a heterogeneous hydrolysis. This is demonstrated by Figures 4.16 and 9.51 (415), where the weight frequency distribution curves for mildly pulped spruce and aspen at various stages of heterogeneous hydrolysis are shown. The spruce pulp develops three distinct frequency maxima which prevail through the entire hydrolysis, whereas the aspen pulp maintains a more uniform distribution during the hydrolysis. In this respect aspen behaves more like cotton pulp. On the other hand, birch sulfite pulp has been found to have similar molecular length distribution to spruce pulps (404). Figure 9.52 (415) shows the corresponding distribution curves for spruce sulfite pulps cooked to varying viscosity. They give the same impression of heterogeneous hydrolysis, showing that the degradation during the sulfite cook essentially resembles that of a heterogeneous mineral acid hydrolysis. In contrast, spruce pulps, dissolved and hydrolyzed in phosphoric acid, give much more uniform molecular weight distribution diagrams (415).

The cause of the distinct heterogeneity of the carbohydrate chain length in softwood sulfite pulps as compared to cotton has been mainly ascribed to a less perfectly ordered structure in the wood, giving rise to greater varia-tions in the degree of accessibility in different parts of the fiber, and especi-ally in its submicroscopic micellar structure. Although these differences have been found to be considerable, the inherent macroscopical and micro-scopical heterogeneity in any wood pulp material also has to be taken into account, such as that caused by imperfect process conditions, and by the heterogeneous wood structure (e.g. springwood–summerwood, etc.).

In studying Figures 9.51–52, it must be remembered that the hydrolytic degradation of paper pulps in the sulfite cook is seldom carried below a (viscosity) weight average DP of 1,200–1,500, and in rayon pulps seldom below 900–1,000. The degradation is especially noticeable at pulp yields below 50%, as pointed out earlier, but some decrease in DP already occurs in the high-yield pulp range above the point of fiber liberation. Figure 9.53 indicates the approximate trend of the decrease in (viscosity) weight

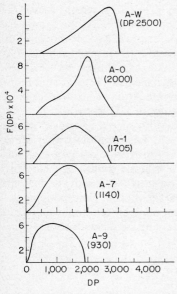

Fig. 9.51. Weight frequency distribution curves for aspen neutral sulfite pulp upon heterogeneous acid hydrolysis (Jörgensen)

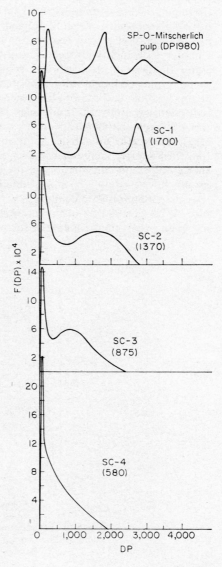

Fig. 9.52. Weight frequency distribution curves of acid sulfite pulps from spruce, cooked to different average DP's (Jörgensen)

515

average DP during the acid sulfite cook (100, 415). Accurate results are difficult to obtain since the DP level depends on the exactitude in the choice of the *Staudinger* constant K_m, and especially because completely soluble nitrates cannot be obtained from softwood pulps above a certain yield level. It should also be kept in mind that the average DP values obtained in any viscosity determination give only a crude idea of the state of degradation of the comparatively heterogeneous material.

As the degradation of the carbohydrates proceeds during the sulfite cook, *carbonyl groups* are introduced, mainly as end groups of the chain fragments. This is demonstrated in Figure 9.54 (672), which shows the hot alkali solubility of sulfite pulps of varying viscosity. At the same time as the formation of end groups, the hot alkali solubility will increase, cf. Chapter 15, which will decrease the yield of hot alkali purified pulps. A small fraction of the carbonyl groups, which are caused by *oxidative* damage, may be located along the chains. Such groups cause scission of the chains in alkali and can be eliminated by chlorite oxidation or borohydride reduction, whereby the molecules become more stable to alkali. Thus these phenomena show up on the determination of pulp viscosity in the alkaline cuoxam or cuoxen solutions. It has been demonstrated (335), that the viscosity increases somewhat upon borohydride reduction of acid sulfite pulps and considerably in the case of bisulfite pulps. The carbonyl groups have probably been introduced by oxidative action of the bisulfite ion, a reaction found to occur also with sugar alcohols at elevated temperature (487a). Oxidation of the terminating monomers to aldonic acid units has been proved experimentally for bisulfite pulp hemicelluloses (210a).

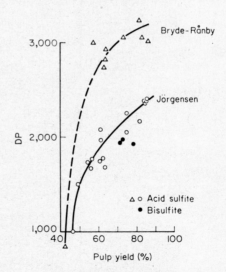

Fig. 9.53. Degradation of cellulose during acid sulfite cooking (Jörgensen and Bryde–Rånby)

The *dissolved carbohydrates* are further *degraded into monosaccharides* during the cook. These are fermentable and form the basis of ethanol and yeast manufacture from the waste liquor. The yield of sugars has therefore been the object of detailed studies. As might be expected, the hydrolysis to monosaccharides is less complete at lower acidity as in the neutral sulfite and the bisulfite cooks, as much as 25% (478a, 596a) and 20% (292, 427) respectively of the sugars dissolved *remain in polysaccharide or oligosaccharide form*, at least in high-yield pulp cooks. In the waste liquors of normal acid sulfite cooks, less of the carbohydrates dissolved remain incompletely hydrolyzed (359, 507, 750, 751, 768), but as much as 15% of the carbohydrate content of a strong paper pulp cook has been found to be in the oligosaccharide form, when fractionating sulfite waste liquor by ion exclusion methods (228, 708, 709). Their DP was low, 2–7 (708), and the components after further fractionation were found to be the following four (228): galactoglucomannan, glucomannan and xylan fragments and 4-*O*-methylglucuronic acid-(1 → 2)-D-xylose. The latter component reflects the wellknown hydrolytic resistance of the aldobiouronic acids and amounted to almost half the oligosaccharide quantity. Table 9.8 (228) shows the detailed chemical composition of the waste liquor of the strong paper pulp cook from spruce. Rather more than half the organic matter originates from the lignin and somewhat less than half is of carbohydrate origin. Of the monosaccharides in the waste liquor, mannose is the dominating one in the case of softwood sulfite cooks. Hardwood cooks give a waste liquor where xylose dominates among the monosaccharides, as shown in Table 9.9 (228, 713). The figures largely reflect the different hemicellulose composition of the different wood species. As is to be expected from the data on the carbohydrate composition of the wood residue shown in Figure 9.42, arabinose first appears in the cooking liquor, followed by galactose, xylose and

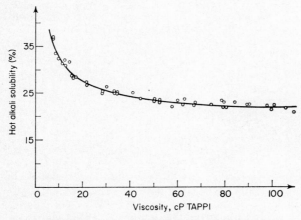

Fig. 9.54. Relation between hot alkali solubility and viscosity for unbleached sulfite pulps from spruce (Samuelson *et al*)

Table 9.8. Chemical composition of the dry substance in the sulfite waste liquor from a strong paper pulp of spruce cook, after removal of inorganic constituents (228)

Fraction group	Description of component	Percentage	
I	Lignosulfonic acids, 'high-molecular'	23.7	
	,, ,, 'low-molecular'	28.6	
	α-Conidendrin (?)	0.4	
	Hydroxymatairesinolsulfonic acid (?)	2.2	
	Carbohydrate sulfonic acids (?)	0.6	
	,, ,, ,,	1.9	
	Substances not investigated	2.6	
			60.0
II	O-(4-O-methyl-α-D-glucosyluronic acid)-(1 → 2)-D-xylose	2.5	
III	Glucuronic acid + small amounts of impurities	1.0	
IV	Four polysaccharides yielding		
	(1) Glucose, mannose, galactose		
	(2) Glucose, mannose		
	(3) Mannose, glucose		
	(4) Xylose		
			3.2
V	D-Glucose	2.6	
	D-Xylose	4.6	
	D-Mannose	11.0	
	D-Galactose	2.6	
	L-Arabinose	0.9	
	Substances not investigated, probably aldonic acids	4.4	
			26.1
VI	Main component acetic acid		5.7
	Total		98.5

Table 9.9. Monosaccharide composition of sulfite waste liquors from various wood species, in per cent of dry substance (228, 713)

Wood species	Spruce	Birch	Aspen
Monosaccharide content, %			
Galactose	2.6	0.6	0.0
Glucose	2.6	1.1	0.5
Mannose	11.0	6.4	3.1
Xylose	4.6	21.1	24.3
Arabinose	0.9	0.0	1.5
Glucuronic acid	1.0	1.6	1.2
Total	22.7	30.8	30.6

mannose, whereas some glucose appears with the mannose but in larger amounts is found only in the later phase of the cook, and especially in soft paper and rayon pulp cooks (359, 507, 751, 768). The side relief cooking liquor consequently contains arabinose as the dominant sugar, in contrast to the waste liquor (713). During the acid sulfite as well as the bisulfite cook, hemicelluloses appear in the cooking liquor in quantities corresponding to about 2–4% of the wood, and can be precipitated from the liquor with ethanol. They appear to consist of galacturanogalactan and galactoglucomannan but rather little xylan, and disappear eventually to form monoses and aldonic acids (210b).

However, it was observed at an early stage, that the yield of reducing sugars in the waste liquor did not correspond to the amount of carbohydrates dissolved, even when carrying the hydrolytic degradation of the latter to completion and in spite of the fact that no reversion occurs (264). Part of the discrepancy, which amounts to 30–60% depending on the cooking conditions, has been found to be an *oxidation of the aldoses to aldonic acids* according to the overall reaction (278, 531):

$$2 \text{ RCHO} + 2 \text{ HSO}_3^- \longrightarrow 2 \text{ RCOOH} + \text{S}_2\text{O}_3^{2-} + \text{H}_2\text{O}$$

The oxidizing agent is thus the bisulfite ions, and consequently a high bisulfite ion concentration and a low acidity will favor sugar destruction. In accordance it has been found that cooking acids of high combined SO_2 give lower yields of sugar, two comparative calcium-based cooks of 1.6 and 0.7% combined SO_2 to 46% pulp yield gave 9.6 and 20.3% sugars, calculated on the wood (291) (a result which may also partly be caused by different amounts of oligosaccharides remaining). A two-stage process (562), involving an initial cook at a comparatively high acidity and low combined SO_2 followed by a withdrawal of most of the sugar-rich liquor and completing the cook with a new charge of cooking acid with the additional amount of combined SO_2 needed, is a logical conclusion of that discovery. However, as far as is known, that process is not in operation. The sulfite pulp mills getting the highest yields of sugars and alcohol are those producing rayon pulps, because of both the larger amounts of carbohydrates dissolved and the comparatively low combined SO_2 content of the cooking acids used by those mills.

All sugars give rise to aldonic acids at sulfite cooking conditions. Of a total concentration of 6.4 g/l aldonic acids in a waste liquor, 0.3 g/l was found to be *gluconic acid*, whereas about 1.5 g/l each of *xylonic, arabonic, mannonic* and *galactonic acids* were present (674). Similar quantities of the same acids were found in the waste liquor from a bisulfite cook (674). A more detailed investigation (671) on the formation of aldonic acids during the sulfite cook, Table 9.10, revealed that all types are formed simultaneously and that the main formation occurs during the later stages of the heating period (pulp yield range 65–45%), and that in the last phase of the cook, when no bisulfite is left, only little aldonic acids are formed.

The decomposition of aldoses to aldonic acids is likely to occur over the *sugar–bisulfite compounds*, which are α-*hydroxysulfonates*, and the corresponding *ketosulfonates* (279):

$$\text{RCHO} + \text{HSO}_3^- \rightleftharpoons \text{RC}\underset{\diagdown \text{OH}}{\overset{\diagup \text{H}}{-}}\text{SO}_3^-$$

$$2 \ \underset{\underset{\displaystyle OH}{|}}{\overset{\overset{\displaystyle H}{|}}{RC}}\!-\!SO_3^- + 2 \ HSO_3^- \longrightarrow 2 \ \underset{}{\overset{\overset{\displaystyle O}{\|}}{RC}}\!-\!SO_3^- + S_2O_3^{2-} + 3 \ H_2O$$

$$\overset{\overset{\displaystyle O}{\|}}{RC}\!-\!SO_3^- + H_2O \longrightarrow RCOOH + HSO_3^-,\ \text{giving the net reaction of}$$
$$2 \ RCHO + 2 \ HSO_3^- \longrightarrow 2 \ RCOOH + S_2O_3^{2-} + H_2O$$

The α-hydroxysulfonates are unstable and in equilibrium with the aldoses and bisulfite ions in a manner characteristic for each sugar (750). The equilibrium is forced towards decomposition of the α-hydroxysulfonates at an increase in temperature, and although the sugars are responsible for a large proportion of the 'loosely combined SO_2' of cooled liquor samples, the amount of sugar α-hydroxysulfonates at cooking temperature is likely to be small. Before fermentation of the sugars of the waste liquor, the α-hydroxysulfonates are decomposed to yield sugars. Inasmuch as they are oxidized to ketosulfonates during the cook, an irreversible destruction of the corresponding sugar occurs. Not all this destruction results in the formation of aldonic acids, rearrangements to *stable sugar-sulfonates* also take place. These contain sulfonate groups as well as carboxyl groups (3, 210, 279, 345, 670, 691a), but their structure is not quite elucidated. Model experiments with cooking acid and glucose, mannose and xylose indicated that only xylose forms a sulfonate (722), and a *sulfocarboxylic acid* from xylose was identified in the reaction mixture of neutral sulfite and xylose, α, δ-dihydroxy-γ-sulfovaleric acid (816). Arabinose likewise forms a similar sulfonate (146).

Some decomposition of hexoses by dehydration and hydrolysis of carbon–carbon bonds also occurs during the cook, as *trioses* have been indicated and *methyl glyoxal* found in the waste liquors (4). Dehydration of xylose is also indicated by the presence of *furfural* (4). Glucose is likely to yield *hydroxymethyl furfural*, which in turn decomposed into *levulinic acid* and *formic acid* (722). The formation of *formaldehyde* may also be explained by dehydration–hydrolysis reactions of aldoses, but is also of lignin origin (232). Dehydration reactions are favored by low pH, oxidation reactions by higher pH (722). All these carbonyl compounds are capable of forming α-hydroxysulfonates with bisulfite ions, and their ability to bind bisulfite even at high temperature is much higher than that of hexoses and pentoses (653). Although not formed in great amounts, Table 9.11 (4), these compounds play some rôle in the cook by consuming bisulfite ions, corresponding to about 0.1–0.2% combined SO_2 (4, 657). Their α-hydroxysulfonates are also likely to be oxidized in a similar manner as those of the aldoses, forming carboxylic acids as *formic acid* (from formaldehyde–bisulfite), which in turn can be further oxidized to *carbonic acid* (739).

As will be discussed further in a subsequent section, the thiosulfate ions formed in the reactions of bisulfite with the carbohydrates is detrimental to the stability of the cooking acid.

520

Table 9.10. Carbohydrate monomer distribution at various stages of a spruce sulfite cook, carried beyond the stage of normal rayon pulp cooking practice (671)

Cooking time h	temp. °C	Yield, % of wood	Sugar composition of pulp, %					Sugars in liquor, g/l		Sugar composition of liquor hydrolysate, %					Aldonic acids in liquor, g/l				
			Galactose	Glucose	Mannose	Arabinose	Xylose	before hydrolysis	after hydrolysis	Galactose	Glucose	Mannose	Arabinose	Xylose	Galactonic and gluconic†	Mannonic	Arabinonic	Xylonic	Total aldonic
0	—	100	3.5	69.8	16.7	1.5	8.6	0	0										
6.3	125	76.8	0.0	82.9	11.1	0.0	5.9	19	32	18	12	39	11	20	0.02	0.06	0.13	0.03	0.24
7.8	134	58.6	0.0	87.3	7.7	0.0	4.9	31	59	17	10	44	7	21	0.69	0.20	0.69	0.68	2.26
9.3*	148	47.2	0.0	92.1	4.1	0.0	3.8	45	69	17	14	43	4	22	2.07	1.35	1.10	1.84	6.36
10.3	148	43.5	0.0	95.0	2.8	0.0	2.3	46	72	10	15	47	5	23	2.41	2.30	1.19	2.09	7.99
11.8	148	39.9	0.0	98.0	1.2	0.0	0.8	52	80	11	21	46	4	19	2.41	2.36	1.21	2.27	8.25

* Maximum temperature just reached   † Galactonic acid entirely dominating

521

Table 9.11. Content of loosely combined SO_2 (α–hydroxysulfonates) and volatile carbonyl compounds in sulfite waste liquors (4)

Waste liquor from cook for	Strong paper pulp	Rayon pulp
Content, mmol/l, of		
Loosely combined SO_2	81	31
Formaldehyde	6	18
Methyl glyoxal	9	7
Furfural	6	6

The *methanol* formed during the sulfite cook is likely to be of carbohydrate origin, as there is no formation of lignin phenolic groups during the cook (6, 46). The quantity of methanol formed is about 4 kg ptw (spruce) or approximately corresponding to the carbohydrate-bound methoxyl groups (4-O-methyl glucuronic acid). The methanol formation proceeds fairly linearly during the whole sulfite cook and similarly for spruce and birch (577). *Acetic acid* is formed from the acetyl groups of the carbohydrates by acid hydrolysis in amounts nearly corresponding to the acetyl groups of the wood species used. Of the volatile organic acids formed during the cook acetic acid is the dominating component, and the formic acid found in the waste liquor constitutes only a few per cent of the total acids (8). Much of the acetic acid is formed during the early stages of the cook. However, both softwood (18) and hardwood acid sulfite pulps (17, 526a, 571) have been found to contain surprising quantities of acetate groups, in contrast to neutral sulfite and kraft pulps. Of the 12 % acetyl of a native birch xylan, 7 % remains in the residual xylan of a severely cooked rayon pulp. Small amounts of a xylobiose monoacetate having an angularly located acetate group were isolated from the waste liquor. The importance of the glucomannan deacetylation at softwoods for the hydrolytic resistance of the glucomannan was stressed previously. The 4-O-methyl glucuronic acid substituents of the xylan are found partly in the waste liquor in the form of xylobiouronic acid, partly as demethylated glucuronic acid, as demonstrated in the previous Table 9.10. However, the pulp xylan contains considerable quantities of glucuronic acid, at least half the original amount (e.g. 526a, 571).

F. Side reactions during the sulfite cook

In addition to the sulfonation, dissolution and condensation of the lignin, and the dissolution and degradation of the carbohydrates by hydrolysis, which constitute the main reactions of the sulfite cook, there also occurs a sequence of reactions which are not without importance to the course and result of the cook. Table 9.12 lists some of these, expressed as the net reactions of more complicated intercourses.

These reactions all have in common a consumption of bisulfite ions, which are converted to more or less stable sulfur compounds. The side reactions therefore lead to a *sulfur consumption* in excess of that necessary for delignification. By the consumption of bisulfite ions and the formation

Table 9.12. Side reactions of the sulfite cook

Formation of	Net reaction
Sulfate	$4\,HSO_3^- \longrightarrow 2\,SO_4^{2-} + HS_2O_3^- + H_2O + H^+$
α-Hydroxysulfonate	$HSO_3^- + RCHO \longrightarrow RCH(OH)SO_3^-$
Sugar sulfonates	$n\,HSO_3^- + RCHO \longrightarrow R'(COOH)SO_3^- + HS_2O_3^-$
Aldonic acids	$2\,HSO_3^- + 2\,RCHO \longrightarrow 2\,RCOOH + S_2O_3^{2-} + H_2O$
Carbonic acid	$2\,HSO_3^- + 2\,HCOOH \longrightarrow 2\,CO_2 + S_2O_3^{2-} + 3\,H_2O$
p-Cymene	$2\,HSO_3^- + 2\,C_{10}H_{16} \longrightarrow 2\,C_{10}H_{14} + S_2O_3^{2-} + 3\,H_2O$

of hydrogen ions the acidity conditions during the cook are influenced, and thereby the main reactions and the pulp quality. The *formation of sulfate ions* has at calcium-based cooks consequences in the form of *gypsum incrustations* in the digesters, the blow pits, pipe lines, alcohol distillation columns and spent liquor evaporation plant. The formation of thiosulfate catalyzes the sulfate formation and therefore accelerates the gypsum formation. The formation of sugar sulfonates and aldonic acids means the *destruction of* considerable quantities of fermentable *sugars*. The side reactions are therefore undesirable, and by research and experience industry has learned to limit them. Yet it may still happen that the side reactions increase and affect the results of the cooking, if some changes are made which deviate in some respect from the general practice. For instance, the side reactions prevent the recirculation of considerable quantities of spent liquor for new acid-making, which would otherwise lead to definite advantages in the alcohol and evaporation plants. The side reactions also complicate the regeneration of the sulfite cooking chemicals to a degree, in that the conversion to the more expensive soluble bases in the sulfite industry has been delayed. Conversion to higher digester pressures may also lead to increased side reactions in certain cases.

The reaction formula first given represents the spontaneous, autocatalytic decomposition of the bisulfite ion and is an entirely inorganic reaction. The other reactions involve the participation of the organic constituents of the cooking liquor, and these reactions will be treated first.

The bisulfite ion is added to carbonyl groups under the formation of *α-hydroxysulfonates* according to the reaction

$$R_2CO + HSO_3^- \rightleftharpoons R_2C(OH)SO_3^-$$

The principal reaction was discovered fairly early (425), and it was found that these sulfonates were unstable towards alkali. The bisulfite ions liberated by alkaline treatment could be determined with a conventional iodine titration after acidification, provided titration was carried out sufficiently rapidly before any recombination to sulfonates took place. The compounds were therefore also classified analytically as 'loosely combined SO_2', and their formation during the sulfite cook was followed by determination on cooled cooking liquor samples (261, 359). However, since the formation of α-hydroxysulfonates is an equilibrium reaction, their concentration in the cooking liquor is dependent on changes in the bisulfite ion concentration on cooling the liquor samples. Further, the equilibrium of α-hydroxysulfonates of monosaccharides has been shown to be heavily dependent on temperature (749). Therefore, the concentration of the α-hydroxysulfonates at cooking temperature is much lower than when determined on the cooled liquor samples and has to be estimated in the way described in Subsection I.3B of this chapter. The development of α-hydroxysulfonates during some sulfite cooks is shown in Figure 9.55

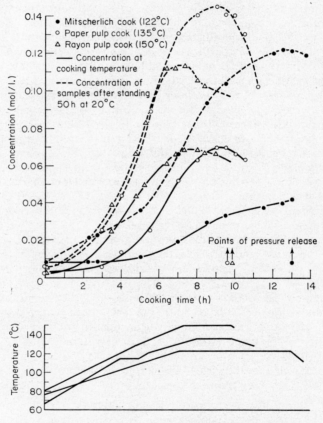

Fig. 9.55. Formation of α–hydroxysulfonates during three technical acid sulfite cooks as well as during subsequent storage of cooking liquor samples (Rydholm)

(653, 654). Generally speaking, their formation occurs at the same time as the dissolution of wood substance, whereupon they finally decompose during the blow-down period to an extent dependent on maximum cooking temperature and residual bisulfite ions. In rayon cooks carried out to

524

low pulp viscosity and at around 5 kp/cm² pressure most of the sulfur dioxide escaping during the blow-down period originates from α-hydroxysulfonates. In paper pulp cooks with considerable residual bisulfite ion content, more undecomposed loosely combined SO_2 remains. In cooks with a low bisulfite ion concentration towards the end of the cooking, there is also a decomposition of α-hydroxysulfonates already prior to the blow-down. The α-hydroxysulfonate content of cold spent liquors from rayon and paper pulp cooks has been studied (4, 749) and found to consist of a variety of compounds. Some of the carbonyl compounds combine more firmly with SO_2, viz. formaldehyde, furfural and methyl glyoxal, all volatile, and some trioses, whereas pentoses and hexoses as well as lignosulfonate carbonyl groups combine more loosely (4). Acetaldehyde is not formed during the sulfite cook but is produced on the fermentation of sugars in the alcohol plant and likewise combines with SO_2. Apart from their importance for the acidity of the cook, dealt with in Subsection I.3B, the α-hydroxysulfonates tend to decrease the alcohol yield on fermentation of the spent liquor sugars (61). Formation of α-hydroxysulfonic acids from volatile aldehydes and sulfur dioxide in the stripping columns of the alcohol plant makes the purification of the ethanol from aldehydes more difficult (677). On the other hand, formation of α-hydroxysulfonic acids from volatile aldehydes is made use of in the Rosenblad evaporation plant for spent liquor, where the surface of the heat exchangers is washed free of gypsum incrustations with the acid condensate of steam from the previous evaporation effects.

The hexoses and pentoses are formed during the cook by hydrolysis of hemicelluloses and cellulose. At cooking conditions they are likely to combine with SO_2 only to a very limited extent. The trioses are formed by the decomposition of hexoses (4), and methyl glyoxal by further rearrangement. Furfural is formed by dehydration of pentoses, and some hydroxymethyl furfural to a less extent from hexoses. Formaldehyde is formed from the hydroxymethyl groups of lignin (232), and the carbonyl-containing formic acid is probably formed by oxidation of formaldehyde by bisulfite ions in the cooking liquor, and may be further oxidized to carbonic acid (739), both reactions similar to the formation of aldonic acids described previously, involving α-hydroxysulfonates as an intermediate stage. Other reducing compounds are also oxidized by the bisulfite ion upon formation of thiosulfate. The difficulty of making sulfite pulp from Douglas fir has been ascribed to the oxidation of dihydroquercetinol (352) and the contemporary thiosulfate formation. p-Cymene is formed by the oxidation of α-pinene by bisulfite (639).

The decomposition reactions of the bisulfite ion have been subjected to a considerable number of investigations and found to be fairly complicated. It was found that the decomposition of the bisulfite ions is autocatalytic and that one of the catalysts involved is thiosulfate, formed during the decomposition (226, 434, 436). The net reaction at and above 100°C is:

$$3 HSO_3^- \rightarrow 2 SO_4^{2-} + H^+ + S + H_2O$$

Table 9.13. Reactions in the autocatalyzed decomposition of bisulfite solutions (776)

Initial reaction	$4\,HSO_3^- \longrightarrow 2\,SO_4^{2-} + HS_2O_3^- + H^+ + H_2O$		Slow
Trithionate formation and hydrolysis	$2\,HSO_3^- + HS_2O_3^- + H^+ \longrightarrow S(OH)_2 + S_3O_6^{2-}$		Slow
	$2\,HSO_3^- + S(OH)_2 \longrightarrow S_3O_6^{2-} + H_2O$		
	$4\,HSO_3^- + HS_2O_8^- + H^+ \longrightarrow 2\,S_3O_6^{2-} + 3\,H_2O$	Net reaction of triformation	Rapid
	$S_3O_6^{2-} + H_2O \longrightarrow SO_4^{2-} + HS_2O_3^- + H^+$	Subsequent hydrolysis	Rapid
	$4\,HSO_3^- \longrightarrow 2\,SO_4^{2-} + HS_2O_3^- + H^+ + H_2O$	Net reaction	Slow
Tetra- and pentathionate formation	$HSO_3^- + 2\,HS_2O_3^- + H^+ \longrightarrow S_4O_6^{2-} + S(OH)_2 + H_2O$		Rapid
	$HSO_3^- + HS_2O_3^- + S(OH)_2 \longrightarrow S_4O_6^{2-} + 2\,H_2O$		Slow
	$2\,HSO_3^- + 3\,HS_2O_3^- + H^+ \longrightarrow 2\,S_4O_6^{2-} + 3\,H_2O$	Net reaction of tetraformation	
	$3\,HS_2O_3^- + H^+ \longrightarrow S_5O_6^{2-} + S(OH)_2 + H_2O$		
	$2\,HS_2O_3^- + S(OH)_2 \longrightarrow S_5O_6^{2-} + 2\,H_2O$		
	$5\,HS_2O_3^- + H^+ \longrightarrow 2\,S_5O_6^{2-} + 3\,H_2O$	Net reaction of pentaformation	Rapid
Polythionate equilibria	$HS_2O_3^- + S_4O_6^{2-} \leftrightarrows HSO_3^- + S_5O_6^{2-}$		Rapid
	$HS_2O_3^- + S_3O_6^{2-} \leftrightarrows HSO_3^- + S_4O_6^{2-}$		Slow

The hydrogen ions formed should act as inhibitors to the decomposition by decomposing the catalyzing thiosulfate ions. However, no free sulfur is formed during a normal sulfite cook, and the decomposition of the bisulfite ions up to the point of sulfur precipitation has been particularly studied (776). Sulfur precipitation only occurs when the product of hydrogen and thiosulfate ion concentrations reaches a certain level. The decomposition prior to that can be expressed by the net reaction:

$$4 \, HSO_3^- \rightarrow 2 \, SO_4^{2-} + HS_2O_3^- + H^+ + H_2O$$

whereby the protons formed could be written as free ions or combined to bisulfate or bithiosulfate. The actual ionization of these two latter ions at cooking temperature is unknown.

The reaction is begun with a spontaneous and very slow decomposition, a disproportionation of probably the same form as the net reaction, in any case under formation of thiosulfate or some related sulfur compound. The thiosulfate formed catalyzes the reaction, probably according to the formulas shown on the opposite page, Table 9.13 (776).

From bisulfite, thiosulfate and hydrogen ions are formed trithionate and the unstable compound $S(OH)_2$ in a rate-determining, pH-dependent reaction, whereafter $S(OH)_2$ rapidly reacts with more bisulfite to trithionate. The trithionate then rapidly decomposes by hydrolysis to sulfate, thiosulfate and hydrogen ions, and the trithionate concentration is always low in the sulfite cook. The net reaction of trithionate formation and hydrolysis is the same as the overall net reaction. However, tetra- and pentathionate are formed in reactions analogous to trithionate formation. These thionates are more stable against hydrolysis to sulfate. The sulfate formation therefore goes mainly over trithionate, whereas other poly-thionate formation is to be considered as side reaction. However, the equilibria between the polythionates leads to a slow decomposition of tetra- and pentathionate over trithionate to sulfate. Figure 9.56 schematically illustrates the reactions. The detailed mechanism of the formation and transformation of polythionates has been further studied with radio-active isotope techniques (95), and found to involve transfer of SO_3 and SSO_3 groups rather than sulfur atoms. It is interesting to note, in Figure 9.50, that in the slow, rate-determining reactions bisulfite, thiosulfate and hydrogen ions take part. In addition to the known catalyzing effect of the thiosulfate ions, a high acidity should also increase the rate of decomposition up to the point of sulfur precipitation, and this has been shown experimentally (336, 776). The stability of a bisulfite cooking liquor is thus greater than that of an acid sulfite cooking liquor (330), although the bisulfite cooks for other reasons are more sensitive to decomposition catalysts than are acid sulfite cooks. The bisulfite ion concentration is also important for the rate of decomposition. Copper and other sulfide precipitating metals inhibit the reaction, cobalt and molybdenum are accelerators. The important accelerating action of selenium was recognized early (226, 284, 434). Selenosulfate is formed, which has principally the same, though considerably greater, catalyzing effect as thiosulfate, and necessitates a careful separation of selenium in the cooking acid preparation.

It is obvious that the inorganic decomposition of the bisulfite ions must be influenced by the other side reactions of the sulfite cook, inasmuch as they influence concentration and acidity. That must mean that the sulfate formation during the sulfite cook does not completely follow the same laws as in a pure cooking acid. For instance, if high acidity will accelerate the decomposition of pure cooking acid, it may be that this is not the case during the cook, if some of the other thiosulfate-*forming* reactions, such as the aldonic acid formation, is checked by a high acidity (or rather a low bisulfite ion concentration). In the same way and this may be as important, thiosulfate-*consuming* reactions which occur during the cook, may be influenced by acidity. That such reactions must occur during the sulfite cook is evident from the following thiosulfate balance, Table 9.14.

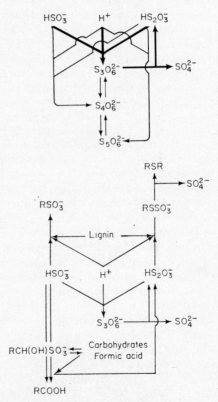

Fig. 9.56. The decomposition of sulfite cooking acid in the absence of organic matter, as well as the interaction of cooking liquor components and the wood components in forming and consuming the decomposition catalyst, thiosulfate

Table 9.14. Thiosulfate formation during the sulfite cook and its causes

Cause	$S_2O_3^{2-}$, g/l.	Sulfur loss, kg ptp
Aldonic and sugar sulfonic acid formation (5% sugar decomposition, wood basis)	4.0	23
Carbonic acid formation (0.3% formic acid, wood basis)	0.9	5
Cymene formation (0.5 kg ptp)	0.02	—
Sulfate formation (2–3 g/l.)	1.5	9
Total thiosulfate formation	6.5	37
Found as thiosulfate	0.5–2	
Found as polythionate (expressed as thiosulfate)	0.5–1.5	
Total thiosulfate found	1 –3.5	5–20

It has been assumed, that some of the organic constituents of the cook, probably lignin, take up thiosulfate or some related sulfur compound (678) and it has also been demonstrated (679) that lignosulfonate, heated in thiosulfate solution, takes up 10–20% more sulfur than the corresponding sulfonate groups. The formation of such organically combined 'excess sulfur' during an extreme rayon pulp cook is demonstrated in Figure 9.57 (602), and the quantity found fairly well accounts for the deficit of Table 9.14, approximately 6 g/l $S_2O_3^{2-}$, which recalculated to excess sulfur equals 1.7 g/l S. The quantity of organic excess sulfur of technical waste liquors was found to be about 1.2–1.9 g/l. As was pointed out in a previous

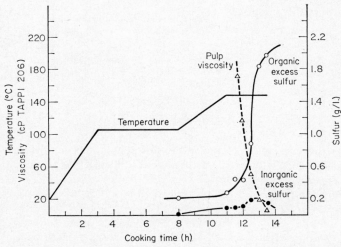

Fig. 9.57. Formation of inorganic (•) and organic (○) excess sulfur as a function of cooking time (hours), on acid sulfite cooking of spruce (Samuelson–Regestad)

529

section on lignin reactions, sulfur is combined with lignin. It should be emphasized, that these thiosulfate-consuming reactions are necessary for the sulfite cook. A pure cooking acid, to which similar amounts of thiosulfate are added, rapidly decomposes in the absence of wood. It is also important to observe that the thiosulfate consumption by the lignin during the initial stages of the cook (80–120°C) is lower in the bisulfite and neutral sulfite cook because of their lower acidity, as shown in Figure 9.58 (694).

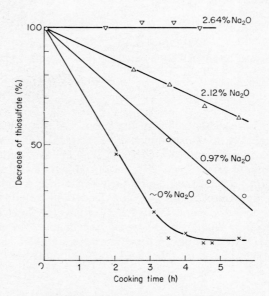

Fig. 9.58. The decrease of the thiosulfate content at the beginning of acid sulfite cooking with thiosulfate-enriched liquor (Schöön)

	Na_2O, %	total SO_2, %	combined SO_2, %
—×—	0.0	5.7, 5.8	0.0
—○—	0.97	5.5	1.0
—△—	2.12	5.5	2.2
—▽—	2.64	5.5	2.75

Although decomposition of the sulfite ion does not occur in the neutral sulfite cook, which is therefore insensitive to thiosulfate (517), the bisulfite cook is extremely sensitive to the presence of thiosulfate. The acid sulfite cook will tolerate up to 2 g/1 thiosulfate initially (563a), and small additions may even have a beneficial effect (331a), Figure 9.59. As shown in Figures 9.60–62 (694), the formation of thiosulfate from the oxidation of sugars to aldonic acids dominates during the main part of the cook, whereas in the final phases the formation via polythionates is more pronounced. Lignin will take up as much thiosulfate sulfur in the bisulfite cook as in the acid sulfite cook, but since its sulfur-binding capacity is limited, and the

530

aldonic acid formation more pronounced in the bisulfite cook, the latter will be more sensitive to external thiosulfate additions, such as from the chemicals recovery plant. Figure 9.56 illustrates the more important reactions between the wood components and the cooking liquor components.

In Subsection I.3B of this chapter it was shown that after consumption of the combined SO_2 charged to the cook, the bisulfite ion concentration is low and acidity tends to rise sharply. The consumption of combined SO_2, that is of bisulfite ions, occurs in the main reaction of sulfonation, as well as in the side reactions. Some side reactions increase and others decrease with an increase of the combined SO_2 charged. Thus most of the organic side reactions are favored by low acidity and a high bisulfite ion content, and sugar destruction and bisulfite consumption are higher in paper pulp cooks of high combined SO_2 than in rayon pulp cooks of low combined SO_2 (291, 301). On the other hand, the inorganic decomposition reaction under sulfate formation is accelerated by hydrogen ions, and cooks low in combined SO_2 (and at high temperature) have the highest sulfate formation (288), Figure 9.63. Obviously the main sulfate formation occurs towards the end of the cook.

In the production of rayon pulp to low viscosity, the increase in acidity

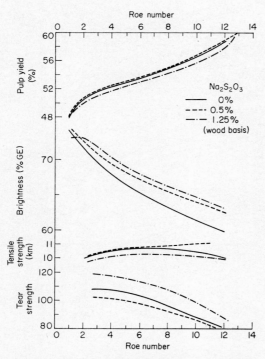

Fig. 9.59. Influence of small additions of thiosulfate on acid sulfite cooking of wood (Hartler *et al*)

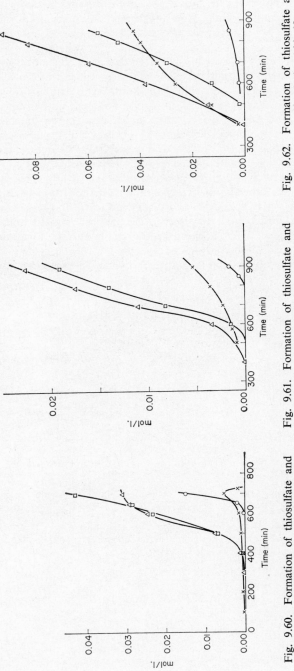

Fig. 9.60. Formation of thiosulfate and organic excess sulfur during an acid sulfite rayon pulp cook (Schöön)

—□— organic excess sulfur
—△— thiosulfate formed *via* aldoses and hydrogen sulfite
—○— thiosulfate formed *via* polythionates and hydrogen
—×— thiosulfate concentration of the cooking liquor

Fig. 9.61. Formation of thiosulfate and organic excess sulfur during an acid sulfite paper pulp cook (Schöön)

—□— organic excess sulfur
—△— thiosulfate formed *via* aldoses and hydrogen sulfite
—○— thiosulfate formed *via* polythionates and hydrogen sulfite
—×— thiosulphate concentration of the cooking liquor

Fig. 9.62. Formation of thiosulfate and organic excess sulfur during a bisulfite cook (Schöön)

—□— organic excess sulfur
—△— thiosulfate formed *via* aldoses and hydrogen sulfite
—○— thiosulfate formed *via* polythionates and hydrogen sulfite
—×— thiosulfate concentration of the cooking liquor

532

towards the end of the cook is wanted. As the sulfonation of lignin only consumes a limited quantity of bisulfite ions, it would be very critical to charge the correct amount of combined SO_2 per weight of wood to the cook in order to get the proper increase in acidity without side reactions. Too much combined SO_2 charged and the increase would never come, causing a serious delay in the hydrolysis reaction down to the viscosity level desired. However, with the side reactions, and especially the formation of sulfate towards the end of the cook, the peak in acidity is always developed, even if the consumption of bisulfite ions for the main reaction, the sulfonation, should be completed before the combined SO_2 were exhausted. In this way, the side reactions also get a positive function in the quality control.

Figure 9.64 (657) exemplifies the formation of sulfate and thiosulfate in two cooks at 5 and 7 kp/cm² pressure, the latter with none too perfect digester circulation. The acidity at cooking temperature was also determined and has been indicated. In the former cook the thiosulfate content increases with the time of cooking and decreases again during the blow-down period to some extent. The sulfate formation cannot be judged completely from the sulfate ion determinations, as in calcium-based cooks gypsum tends to precipitate on the pulp as the wood approaches the point of fiber liberation and develops crystallization centres. But it is evident that the main sulfate formation occurs towards the end of the cook. The corresponding curves for the cook at higher pressure give a more dynamic impression, and the increase in acidity is also considerably sharper. Cooks of this type give rise to difficulties in quality

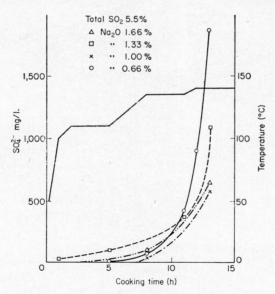

Fig. 9.63. Sulfate formation during sodium acid sulfite cooks of spruce (Hägglund *et al*)

533

control, and the spent liquor may give unwanted gypsum and sulfur precipitations. To some extent, the side reactions towards the end of the cook are accentuated by an unsatisfactory distribution of heat from bad circulation conditions, because liquor from overcooked parts of the digester contains larger quantities of thiosulfate ions which accelerate the side reactions in the undercooked parts. Hardwood cooks seem to lead to rather higher thiosulfate formation than softwood cooks. Ammonium-based cooks give a definitely lower thiosulfate formation than calcium-based ones, possibly because the ammonium ions react with the decomposition catalysts or with the aldehyde groups, which would otherwise cause thiosulfate formation. This effect is responsible for the somewhat lower sulfur consumption of the ammonium-based cooks. Table 9.15 gives the thiosulfate content in the spent liquors of rayon pulp cooks to 25 cP TAPPI (cellulose DP 1,000–1,200).

Attempts to determine the polythionate content gave uncertain values because of the analytical difficulties in determining polythionates when they occur together with the organic substances of the cooking liquor. Later studies (694) have revealed, that the polythionates, mainly tetra-thionate, amount to 10–100 % of the thiosulfate concentrations in ordinary acid sulfite cooks, depending on the cooking conditions. Figures 9.65–66 show the content of thiosulfate, tetrathionate and sulfate during one conventional cook and one cook starting out with thiosulfate in the cooking acid (694). The thiosulfate consumption by the wood lignin is obvious.

A pure bisulfite solution, with or without excess sulfur dioxide, is colorless, although with a certain absorption of ultraviolet light. Ordinary

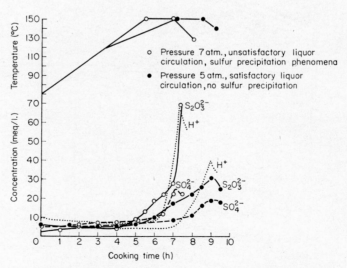

Fig. 9.64. Thiosulfate, sulfate and hydrogen ion concentrations during the rayon pulp sulfite cooks (Rydholm)

Table 9.15. Thiosulfate content in the spent liquor of rayon pulp cooks to 25 cP TAPPI (D.P. 1,000–1,200) (657)

Wood	Combined SO_2 in acid, %	Base type	Max. pressure, kp/cm²	Digester circulation	Thiosulfate content, g/l
Spruce	0.99	Ca	7	Bad	1.70
	1.02	Ca	7	Bad	2.20
	0.93	Ca	7	Fair	0.75
	0.96	Ca	5	Fair	0.85
	0.83	Ca	5	Fair	0.85
	0.90	Ca	5	Good	0.70
	0.92	Ca	5	Good	0.55
	0.80	NH_4	5	Fair	0.25
	1.08	NH_4	5	Fair	0.30
Birch	0.94	Ca	5	Fair	1.55

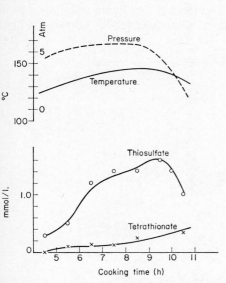

Fig. 9.65. The concentration of thiosulfate and tetrathionate in the cooking liquor during an ordinary calcium acid sulfite cooking. Total SO_2, 5.4%; combined SO_2, 1.05% (Schöön)

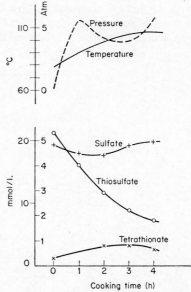

Fig. 9.66. The concentration of thiosulfate, tetrathionate, and sulfate in the cooking liquor during an ordinary sodium acid sulfite cooking with the addition of chemicals from the recovery plant (beginning of the cooking). Total SO_2, 7.2%; combined SO_2, 1.0% (Schöön)

535

cooking acid is slightly yellow, owing to impurities received by top or side relief. During the sulfite cook the cooking liquor gradually changes its color to a more intense yellow, later to orange, and finally to reddish brown in softer paper pulp cooks and to dark brown or black in rayon pulp cooks. This change involves an increase in absorption at all wavelengths of visible light, but especially at shorter wavelengths. In ultraviolet, absorption increases to very high values during the cook, showing the characteristic lignin spectrum (cf. Chapter 4.IV), with peaks at 205 and 280 mμ, whereas the absorption in visible light has no peaks but only an even slope towards low values at high wavelengths.

Figure 9.67 illustrates the changes of cooking liquor absorption in ultraviolet light during a sulfite cook (441). From a similar investigation (657), the absorbency values at 280 and 500 mμ at different times of cooking have been derived and plotted in the previous Figure 9.4 against cooking time, together with methoxyl analysis of the liquor. It is seen, that whereas the absorption at 280 mμ follows the curve for lignin dissolution for all but the last part of the cook, liquor color is intensified during the last period. That the ultraviolet absorbency changes do not represent the dissolution of the lignin towards the end of the rayon pulp cook is due to the formation of other conjugated systems, e.g. furfural and hydroxymethyl furfural, which also absorb ultraviolet light. To a considerable extent it also depends on the fact that lignin on condensation somewhat increases its absorption of ultraviolet (380). Ultraviolet light

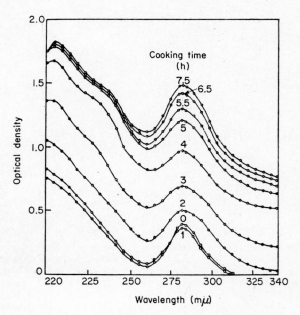

Fig. 9.67. Ultraviolet absorption curves of acid sulfite liquors sampled during the cook (Kleinert *et al*)

absorbency at 280 mμ can therefore not be used with any precision for end-point determination of the cook as a measure of the lignin dissolution, as has been suggested (579). As shown in Figure 9.68 (441), the absorbency at 205 mμ is a more reliable measure of the dissolved lignin towards the end of the cook. It is also evident from Figure 9.4 that absorbency in the visible range is subject to far greater changes in the last cooking phase, and should therefore be more suited for end-point determination, as was pointed out in Section 2 of this chapter.

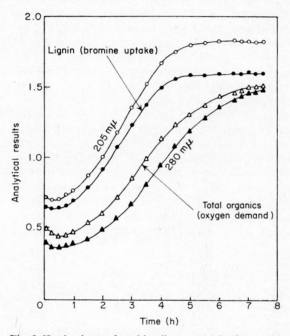

Fig. 9.68. Analyses of cooking liquor samples from acid sulfite cooking, showing the improved lignin determination by measuring the ultraviolet light absorption at 205 mμ as compared to 280 mμ (Kleinert *et al*)

Figure 9.69 shows cooking liquor color determinations for some different types of cook, together with the corresponding curves for the acidity at cooking temperature (653, 654). It is seen that in the paper pulp cooks, liquor color is faint, and the acidity level low. In rayon pulp cooks, the development of liquor color follows the development of the acidity peaks fairly closely. However, there is only a correlation within the cooks, the relative places of the curves change for each cook. The colored compounds are no pH indicators, at least not in the acid pH range. It must be concluded that they indicate the result of acid-catalyzed reactions generally assumed to be condensation reactions. Although it has been suggested that carbohydrate degradation products might contribute to the cooking

537

liquor color (669), substantial proof has been forwarded to show that the main color originates from the lignin (299). Whereas sulfite cooking of holocellulose gives little color, lignosulfonates as well as hydrochloric acid lignin rapidly darken to dark brown. Waste liquors from which the main fraction of lignosulfonates has been precipitated in virtually pure form lose most of their color.

The chromophors of brown lignin preparations are little known (cf. Chapter 4.IV). It was early suggested that they result from condensation of carbonyl groups which in sulfite cooking become exposed towards the end of the cook (276). Carbonyl groups are located at the γ, β and α carbon atoms of the phenyl propane monomers, which on condensation with monomers containing phenolic hydroxyls are likely to yield configurations as shown in Figure 9.70 (380). The first configuration (A) is probably responsible for the yellow-green color developed by the action of concentrated mineral acids on wood at room temperature (5), but owing to the relative scarcity of coniferyl aldehyde groupings, this structure is only likely to be of minor importance in the case of sulfite cooking liquor color. The next configuration (B), which probably dominates, may originate not only from the 0.07 α-carbonyl groups per monomer, but may also arise by oxidation of the structure (C) in Figure 9.70 which is the main configuration to be expected from the inter-condensation of lignin monomers containing benzyl alcohol groups and phenolic hydroxyl groups, respectively. Such an oxidation which is analogous to the oxidation of leuco bases of triphenyl methane dyestuff compounds, could be caused by bisulfite ions, which would be reduced to thiosulfate (380).

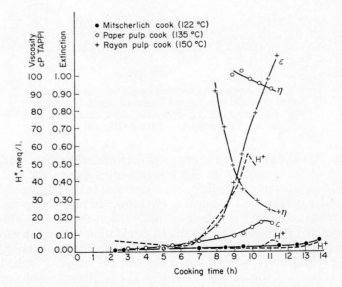

Fig. 9.69. Acidity (H^+), pulp viscosity (η) and liquor absorbency at 600 mμ (ϵ) for three acid sulfite cooks (Rydholm)

On treating the dark cooking liquor with sulfur dioxide or adding more bisulfite, some of the absorption disappears. This may be due to hydrosulfonate formation at the double bond of the coniferyl aldehyde grouping in the former of the chromophoric configurations. By removal of the loosely combined bisulfite, the color darkens again. The fluorescence of lignosulfonates and sulfite pulps undergoes similar changes, but it decreases on removal of the loosely combined SO_2 (276).

Ammonium-based sulfite cooks yield cooking liquors and unbleached pulps of much darker color than those based on metal bisulfites. This is caused by a selective reaction of the ammonium ion with the organic components, probably mainly lignin (380). Amines are known to react in two ways with lignin, partly in a condensation with its carbonyl groups to colored compounds, but also with its benzyl alcohol or ether groups, according to the formulas D–F in Figure 9.70. The latter of these configurations may also, after oxidation, give rise to colored compounds.

At the same time as the darkening of the liquor, viscosity increases, in the case of ammonium-based liquors much more than with other bases. Therefore, it is possible that reactions with ammonium ions create linkages to larger molecular complexes. Such further condensation is a drawback in the evaporation of ammonium-based spent liquor, since the increase in viscosity limits the dry content obtainable from the evaporated liquor.

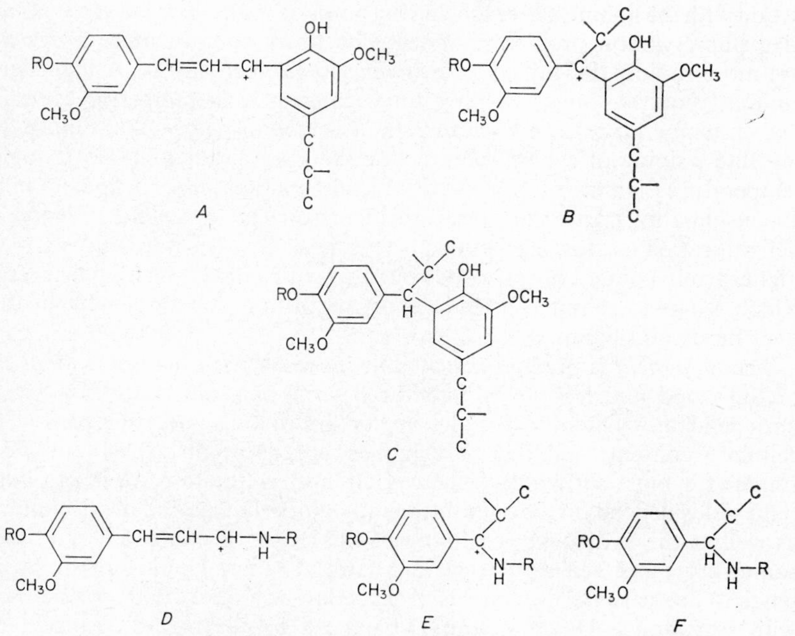

Fig. 9.70. Condensed lignin systems, containing chromophors or potential chromophor configurations

4. INFLUENCE OF REACTION CONDITIONS ON PULP YIELD AND PROPERTIES

A1. *Wood structure and condition*

A variable of dominating influence on the result of all pulping is the nature and condition of the wood raw material. A subsequent section will deal with the special problems in the sulfite pulping of hardwoods and certain resinous softwood species. Only the effects of variations in the conventional sulfite pulpwood will be considered here.

As discussed in Chapter 2, wood has a heterogeneous structure containing structural elements of widely differing size and chemical composition. The various wood species differ considerably in these respects, and considerable variations occur within a species because of heredity factors and growing conditions. These differences are reflected in all pulping processes, and the sulfite process can be said to be perhaps the most sensitive to the properties of the wood raw material. They influence the rate of pulping, the pulp yield and properties.

The *rate of pulping* is influenced by such factors as wood density, fiber wall porosity and the chemical composition of the wood. A dense wood species with only few pores in the fiber walls, such as many *hardwoods*, presents impregnation difficulties. Certain *heartwood* extractives of some species, such as the pines, retard the rate of pulping because of their condensation with the lignin. The tracheid ring pores of the heartwood close up and give impregnation problems. *Springwood* fibers contain more pores and are more rapidly delignified than *summerwood* fibers (102). A high lignin content requires longer pulping time, causing longer digester cycles or higher temperatures for *softwoods* than for *hardwoods*. Acid sulfite and bisulfite pulping of spruce requires for the same grade about 5°C higher temperature than with birch. Neutral sulfite pulping of softwoods requires a considerably greater temperature increase to give a similar degree of delignification as for hardwoods. This is connected not only with the higher lignin content of softwoods but also with a deviating lignin structure which seems to require an acid depolymerization to a larger extent than does hardwood lignin.

The *pulp yield* is predominantly influenced by the *chemical composition* of the wood and less so by structural variations, although they are interdependent. Dissolving pulp yields are mainly determined by the cellulose content, and therefore highest for eucalypt species and fairly similar for most softwoods, whereas birch gives the lowest yields. Paper pulp yields depend on the combined content of cellulose and hemicelluloses, as well as the hydrolytic sensitivity of the latter. Xylan can be said to be somewhat more sensitive to acid hydrolysis than glucomannan, which tends to decrease the pulp yields of the xylan-rich hardwoods as compared with softwoods. However, this is balanced by the higher hemicellulose content and lower lignin content of the hardwoods, giving bleached chemical sulfite pulps in the 45–50% yield range for both categories, as illustrated by Figures 9.71 (657). The pulp yields of *sapwood* and *heart-wood* from spruce are quite similar (283, 287), whereas they differ in the case of pine, because of the lignin condensation encountered in the heartwood. *Summerwood* gives a higher pulp yield because of its higher cellulose content as compared with *springwood* (568), and *compression wood* gives a lower yield than normal wood because of higher lignin content (406, 743, 779). Species and stands containing a higher per-centage of summerwood fibers should thus also give a slightly higher pulp yield. *Fast-growth wood* tends to give a somewhat lower yield than normal-growth wood (267, 273a), which is probably for similar reasons.

The *properties of dissolving pulps* are also more dependent on the

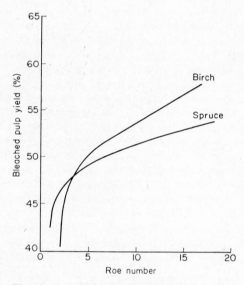

Fig. 9.71. Yield of bleached pulp vs. Roe number upon acid sulfite cooking and subse-quent bleaching of spruce and birch

chemical composition of the wood than on its structural details, although short-fibered hardwood pulps give some deficiencies in the sheet cohesion in sheet steeping and lower capacity in the pressing after slurry steeping. *Paper pulp properties* are influenced by the chemical composition but determined especially by the structural elements of the wood (283, 408). Short *hardwood* pulp fibers improve the sheet formation but give a lower strength, especially tear, than *softwood* pulps. The flexible *springwood* fibers offer considerably more points of interfiber contact than the stiff and springy *summerwood* fibers. Tensile and burst strength are improved by increasing interfiber contact, whereas tear strength generally has the opposite trend because an increasing fixation of the fibers in the paper tends to concentrate the local stresses of the tear test to a few or even one single fiber. Whereas the higher tear strength of softwood pulps as compared with hardwood pulps depends on the fiber length, the extreme tear of some American softwood pulps as compared with European pulps stems from the lower degree of interfiber bonding and thicker fiber walls of the former, which thus have a higher basic density and a higher content of summerwood. These differences also occur with kraft pulps (354), and most effects of the structural variations are only pronounced when comparing different wood species. The variations caused by the growth conditions within one species are less unambiguous (283), and overlapping effects of different variables make an interpretation uncertain. *Rapid-growth* wood tends to give somewhat lower pulp strength than normal wood (273a), but extreme *slow-growth* wood also causes deficient pulp strength (568). More summerwood and higher basic density give the same trends for pulp strength at variation within a species (406, 409) as mentioned earlier for different wood species. *Compression wood* gives lower pulp strength than normal wood (548, 779). *Sapwood* on average contains longer and more thick-walled fibers than *heartwood* and gives pulps with higher tear but lower tensile and burst strength (205, 287).

Decay has expectedly been found to affect the yield and properties of sulfite pulp (50, 76, 353, 456, 646). The effect is very much dependent on the type and degree of decay. A limited attack will cause only a slight, if any, decrease in yield and only somewhat lower brightness, whereas a more extensive decay will affect both yield and strength properties considerably. Storage in the wood yard for one or two years is permissible for peeled wood, whereas storage of unpeeled wood, or any wood under damp conditions, will lead to serious losses. Hardwoods are often more sensitive to decay than softwoods.

The *moisture content* of the wood is considered important in sulfite pulping. Most mill experience indicates that a lower yield and inferior quality is obtained with dry wood. Whether the damage is already done in the chipping or is connected with the inferior chip packing of the digester is a matter of debate. Physical changes in the wood structure on drying may also cause cracks which form points of chemical attack during the pulping. However, the effects are not easily detected in laboratory work, and there are actually results in opposite direction, indicating less damage in chipping dry wood (331). Anyway, the wood is often dampened by water jets or by waterlogging prior to chipping in order to improve the results. In general, the uniformity of the moisture content rather than its absolute level is considered essential. Too dry a wood will resist penetration because it will require some time for swelling, and with very wet wood the transport of chemicals will have to rely on diffusion only. An ideal dry content is therefore about 70% (237b).

The state of disintegration of the wood for sulfite pulping is important for the cooking result. On one hand, the uniform distribution of chemicals and heat is favored by a fairly small chip size, and on the other hand, the yield and pulp properties are affected by an excessive mechanical damage to the wood, as was pointed out in Chapter 5.V and 6.III. As a compromise, the average chip length normally used is around 20 mm and the thickness 2–4 mm. The effect of smaller chip sizes has been debated and contradictory evidence found (273d, 521, 616). Anyway, complete disintegration to fibers leads to an excessive chemical attack in the subsequent sulfite cook (268, 391, 675). Cracks in the wood structure, caused by mechanical treatment, e.g. crushing (71, 746) or chipping of hot wood or chipping with dull knives (14, 251, 269, 331), will lead to a corresponding hydrolytic damage. The chipping aspects were treated in Chapter 5.II. The acid sulfite process is particularly sensitive to chip damage, but bisulfite pulp strength is also reduced considerably by chip damage, whereas kraft pulp strength is almost unaffected. Technical chips thus give acid sulfite and bisulfite pulps with about 10% lower strength data than hand-made chips (331), and the bruised ends of the chips about 20% lower strength. Thereby the springwood pulp appears to be considerably more affected than the pulp from the summerwood (330e). The *Anglo* drum chipper avoids the greater part of that damage and may be of future importance for the sulfite pulping industry (494).

A2. Wood species

(*a*) *Introduction.* Sulfite pulping predominantly uses spruce, fir, and hemlock. The pulping of other wood species, mainly pines and some hardwoods, by the acid sulfite method has for a long time been the subject of research, but to date only a few mills are using these types of wood. The explanation is not entirely clear but in most cases the difficulties are in some way connected with either the *presence of extractives* in the wood, especially in the heartwood, or *penetration barriers* in the wood.

The difficulties caused by the extractives are of two kinds. In some of the resinous hardwoods, the *resin* is not easy to remove, even in the production of bleached pulp grades. In other cases, tannin-containing hardwoods, such as oaks or chestnut, as well as the pines, Douglas fir, and tannin-damaged spruce, some *phenolic compounds* among the extractives tend to co-condense with the lignin and/or reduce bisulfite ions with formation of thiosulfate. The pulping difficulties of that category appear in high screenings, a high residual lignin content in pulps of low or normal yield and viscosity, i.e. in a retarded delignification.

Penetration barriers are found in the heartwood of certain softwood species as well as hardwood species.

(*b*) *Pulping of hardwoods.* Although the differences between springwood and summerwood fibers are not so pronounced as in softwoods, the hardwoods present a less homogeneous fiber material for pulping, cf. Chapter 2, as they contain more cell types, libriform cells, ray cells, vessel elements, etc. Even the most useful of these, the libriform cells, which constitute around 80–90% of the weight of the wood, are considerably shorter than the softwood tracheids, usually 1 mm or less, as compared with 2–5 mm for softwood tracheids. As the fiber length is of considerable importance to the paper strength properties of the pulp, hardwoods have on the whole been considered to constitute an inferior raw material, especially as their procurement and debarking is often more difficult than those of softwoods. However, with the increasing demand for pulpwood, and the increasing supply of hardwoods in the pulpwood-producing areas, methods have been worked out to overcome the deficiencies of the hardwoods and the technical difficulties presented by them, and at the same time some of their advantages have been realized. Thus many hardwoods, such as the *Eucalyptus* and *Populus* species, grow faster than the softwoods and therefore produce a higher acreage yield, cf. Chapter 5. Further, most hardwoods are denser than the softwoods (cf. Chapter 2) and if bought by volume at a price comparable to that of softwoods tend to give a lower cost of wood per ton of pulp. The lower lignin content and higher hemicellulose content of the hardwoods present some technical possibilities, especially in the field of high-yield pulps, and have been realized in the neutral sulfite process, thereby compensating to some extent for the shorter fibers. Finally, the latter have not always been found a disadvantage; in dissolving pulp grades for example they can be accepted, and in fine papers they improve opacity.

Certain hardwoods, of which white oak is one of the most notorious, are difficult to penetrate because of tylose formation in the heartwood, and require long impregnation times (161, 545, 650, 802). If well penetrated, hardwood chips are usually satisfactorily pulped, except those few containing tannins. Attention has also been called to the consequence of the higher density of most hardwoods as compared with softwoods (594). For once this results in a higher weight of solid wood charged to the digester and somewhat smaller volume of cooking acid. The composition of the latter would have to be adjusted accordingly, if it were not for the fact that the lower lignin content of the hardwoods in most cases eliminates the need for an adjustment. Furthermore, the higher density might cause a deficiency of combined SO_2 inside the chips during the cook. Whereas wood of low density, 0.3, such as light aspenwood, can hold about 2.7 m^3 ptw of cooking liquor in the capillaries, and spruce of density 0.4 around 1.9 m^3 ptw, a high-density hardwood, such as birch (0.5) would hold as little as 1.35 m^3 ptw (0.3–0.5 m^3 ptw should be added to all figures for liquor absorbed by the wood substance). Inasmuch as diffusion governs the rate of cooking, the denser wood ought to be more difficult to cook, requiring lower maximum temperature and a longer digester cycle. However, as indicated by the considerable temperature dependence of the rate of pulping, as well as other evidence, chemical reactions rather than diffusion are likely to be rate-determining, and the delignification of maple (563) aspen and birch (250, 819) was found to proceed as fast as that of spruce, Figure 9.35 (563). Because of the lower lignin content of hardwoods, a low lignin content of the pulp is reached sooner, and in comparison to hemlock or spruce, birch pulping should be carried out at 2–5°C lower maximum temperature to preserve the same digester cycle. In the case of some resinous hardwoods, such as birch, it is often found difficult to remove the last few per cent of lignin because the delignification of the resinous ray cells is considerably retarded. Ray cell fractions, isolated and extracted with organic solvents, contain above 10% lignin even in low-lignin dissolving pulps, which means an extra amount of about 1% residual lignin in the total pulp. The libriform fibers, on the other hand, are at least as well delignified as softwood tracheids, pulped at comparable conditions.

Aspen, poplar, beech, birch and maple are used predominantly in Europe and the north-eastern part of North America for acid and neutral sulfite pulping as are eucalypts in southern Europe and South Africa. The most extensive of earlier investigations on the pulping of different hardwood species (802), states the following suitability of hardwood species to acid sulfite pulping, Table 9.16. Those hardwoods found less

Table 9.16. Suitability of American hardwoods to acid sulfite pulping (802)

Diffuse-porous species	Suitability	Ring-porous species	Suitability
Poplars	+	Hackberry	+
Gums	+	Elm	+
Willows	+	Ash	+
Magnolias	+	Hickory	+
Maples	+	Catalpa	−
Sycamore	+	Sassafras	−
Birches	+	Red oak	−
Butternut	+	White oak	−
Basswood	−	Chestnut	−
Red gum	−	Slippery elm	−
Ohio buckeye	−	Black locust	−

suitable either contained unfavorable extractives or were difficult to penetrate, and it has been pointed out (594) that the pulping conditions chosen were comparatively unfavorable. However, it remains true that to date more hardwoods are pulped by other processes, the soda, kraft, and neutral sulfite process, than with the acid sulfite process.

Special studies have been devoted to birch (63, 250, 286, 361, 402, 545, 617, 777, 815), beech (307, 361, 395, 440, 575, 691, 701a, 764, 815), aspen, poplar (250, 387, 427, 428, 545, 716), eucalyptus (59, 124, 390, 665), etc. Some general surveys on the subject of acid sulfite pulping of hardwoods are also found in the literature (594, 650).

Excepting kraft pulp, the main quantity of hardwood pulp is made by the neutral sulfite semichemical process, cf. Chapter 8, where the larger amounts of hemicelluloses in the hardwoods are maximally preserved. The stiffness imparted to the sheet even from unbleached pulps of high lignin content makes hardwood NSSC pulp ideally adapted to corrugating board, which takes the main part of the production. After cautious bleaching, those pulps are well suited to glassine manufacture. For softer grades of papers, acid sulfite pulping (130) or bisulfite pulping (373) is better suited. Sulfite pulping of poplar at widely varying acidity has been described (427), and the results are illustrated in a subsequent section by Figure 9.76.

The quality of the acid sulfite *hardwood paper pulps* differs from that of softwood pulps in several respects. As exemplified in Figure 9.72 (657), the tensile and burst strength values for birch pulps are around 80 and 65% of that of spruce pulps, and tear still lower. Yet birch gives one of the best hardwood sulfite pulps, as indicated by Table 9.17 (657).

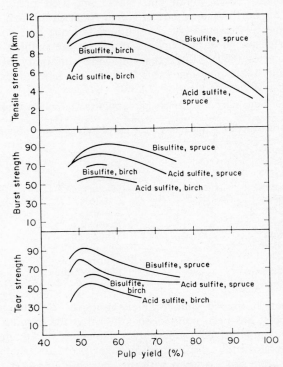

Fig. 9.72. Paper properties of bisulfite and acid sulfite pulps from spruce and birch (Rydholm)

Table 9.17. Composition and paper properties of some acid sulfite pulps from hardwoods as compared to spruce (657)

Species	Pulp yield, % of wood	Roe no.	Cellu-lose	Gluco-mannan	Glucu-rono-xylan	25° SR Beating time, min.	Tensile strength, km	Tear strength	45° SR Beating time, min.	Tensile strength, km	Tear strength
Betula verrucosa, birch	53	4	79	4	17	7	5.7	78	17	7.5	64
Populus × eura-mericana, poplar	54	5	88	4	8	3	4.7	46	12	6.5	43
Eucalyptus saligna, Sydney blue gum	54	5	91	4	5	10	4.0	55	24	5.4	51
Eucalyptus globulus, blue gum	54	4	90	4	6	8	3.9	48	21	5.0	45
Picea abies, spruce	52	4	83	12	5	10	8.3	90	19	9.0	83

The table header "Carbohydrate composition, %" spans the Cellulose, Glucomannan, and Glucuronoxylan columns. The header "Paper properties of unbleached, wet pulp" spans the columns from beating time onward.

The hardwoods give a bulkier sheet, often with a higher opacity and softness, provided sufficient hemicellulose has been removed, in which case
there is only little strength preserved and the pulp is used as a 'filler' pulp in
fine papers to improve formation and printability (410). Birch, aspen,
beech and eucalypt pulps are used in this manner. Aspen yields such
pulps of very low strength (650). The yield of birch paper pulp is generally
higher than that of spruce pulp cooked to a comparable lignin content, as
seen in Figure 9.71 (657). The suitability of hardwoods for acid sulfite
dissolving pulp manufacture, where the shorter fibers should mean less
disadvantage, has been repeatedly investigated, including birch (286, 361,
404, 617, 657), maple (361), beech (361, 764), aspen (716), eucalypts, etc.
The production of short-fibered hardwood acid sulfite pulps for cellophane
and staple fiber has increased recently in Europe, North America and South
Africa, now probably exceeding 0.5 M t yearly, mainly from birch, beech
and eucalypts. Pure hardwood pulps are produced, as well as admixtures
with softwood fibers. As exemplified in Table 9.18 (657), the rayon pulp
yield and purity obtainable from hardwoods are in proportion to the
cellulose content of the respective wood species, of which some contain
more, others less than the softwoods. The main troubles encountered are
in resin removal in the case of birch pulping, and in the viscose plants there
is some trouble in the mercerization presses, especially with beech pulp,
because of the lower strength of mercerized pulp sheets (slurry steeping
preferred), as well as in the filtration of the viscose from some hardwood
pulps.

Table 9.18. Yield and purity of some acid sulfite rayon pulps from hardwoods (657)

Species	Cellulose content of wood, %	Pulp yield, % of wood	Roe no.	Carbohydrate composition, % of pulp			R_{18} %	R_{10} %	$\overline{R}$ %
				Cellulose	Gluco-mannan	Glucu-rono-xylan			
Betula verrucosa, birch	40	43	3	88	4	8	89.5	86.0	87.7
Populus × euramericana, poplar	44	48	2	91	4	5	91.0	87.0	89.0
Eucalyptus saligna, Sydney blue gum	50	50	2	95	2	3	94.5	90.5	92.5
Eucalyptus globulus, blue gum	49	50	2	93	2	5	92.5	88.5	90.5
Picea abies, spruce	42	46	1	93	4	3	91.5	87.5	89.5

R_{18} and R_{10} are alkali resistant fraction in 18 and 10% NaOH. Their average, R,
approximately equals alphacellulose content.

(*c*) *Pulping of softwoods containing phenolic compounds.* A large part
of the softwoods, the pines, larches, and Douglas fir, have for a long time
been considered less suitable for sulfite pulping. Since they are all resinous
woods with colored heartwood they have also been less suited for the

production of mechanical pulp, leaving mainly the kraft process for their utilization in the pulping industry. This has naturally caused the price of such pulpwood to be generally 10–20% lower than that of the softwood species normally used for sulfite and mechanical pulping. Considerable efforts have been devoted to modifying the sulfite process to suit the species mentioned, and they are now used to a limited extent for sulfite pulp production as well as in mechanical pulping.

The comparatively high resin content of these wood species is a definite problem, especially in the production of unbleached grades, but the main trouble is the lignin condensation occurring during the acid cook, which leads to high screenings and a high lignin content of the accepted pulp. The species investigated which give rise to such troubles are listed in Table 9.19.

Table 9.19. Species less suited to acid sulfite pulping because of lignin-condensing extractives

Species	Ref.
Pinus silvestris	285, 309
Pinus banksiana	83, 128
Pinus resinosa	748
Pinus densiflora	11, 258, 340
Pseudotsuga taxifolia	96, 132, 352, 585
Larix leptolepis	533
Picea abies, bark tannin damaged	7, 49, 205, 752, 778
Quercus and *Castanea* spp.	594

It was maintained earlier that the pulping of pines and similar species was merely a penetration problem caused by the abundant presence of resin (431), and cooks applying extremely slow heating were found to improve the results (690). However, wood flour of those species is also less well pulped by the acid sulfite process (206), and chemical reasons must be sought. It is also evident that only the heartwood offers exceptional resistance to pulping (83, 132, 285), whereas the sapwood is as well suited to sulfite pulping as spruce. The wood of young trees, and the saw-mill waste from the sapwood are therefore also used by several mills, even on calcium base (306, 382). The resin content of the sapwood is quite often as high as in the heartwood, e.g. 4–7% against 5–9% in the heartwood (204), and thus the whole resin fraction is not the detrimental factor. It was found fairly early (262) that an ether extraction of the wood did not improve the pulpability, whereas a subsequent acetone extraction removed compounds which caused the troubles. Sapwood of Scots pine contains only 0.2–0.5% of these compounds, as compared with 1.3–1.8% in the heartwood. Half the acetone solubles in pine were found to consist of the phenolic compounds *pinosylvin* and its monomethyl ether (204):

548

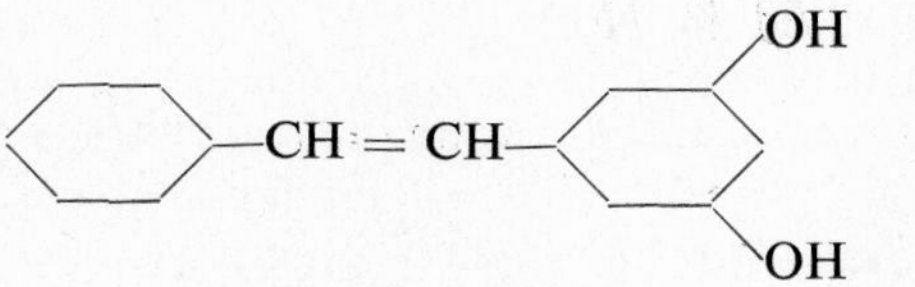

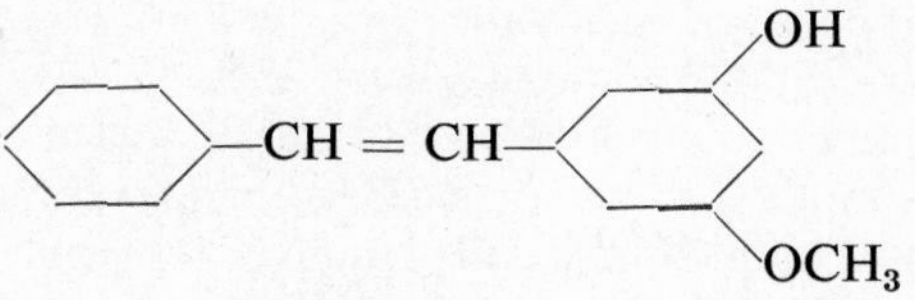

whereas the undesirable compound of Douglas fir was shown to be the flavanone *dihydroquercetinol* also called *taxifolin* (585):

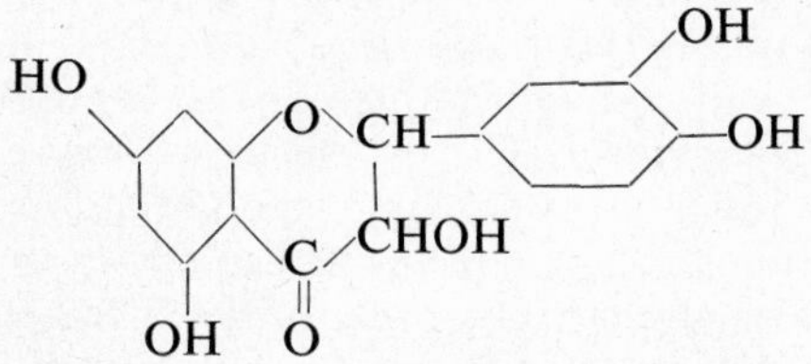

Larch heartwood contains a similar flavanone (533). These compounds, as well as the tannins of bark-damaged spruce, oaks and chestnut, are as reactive as resorcinol and similar phenols in the co-condensation with the wood lignin (206). Furthermore taxifolin, having pyrocatechol groups, tends to reduce bisulfite to thiosulfate, thereby decreasing the stability of the cooking acid (352).

The other resin components are harmless in that respect but cause other troubles. Wood with much resin is not easily penetrated by calcium-based cooking acid, especially in the heartwood, where the bordered pits have closed up. Unbleached sulfite pulp of pine has to be deresinated by alkali extraction prior to screening (140, 730). In the production of bleached pulp, most of the resin is readily removed in the alkali stage, and as it contains proportionally less unsaponifiables than spruce sulfite pulp resin, quite low residual resin contents of the bleached pulp are generally obtained (306).

To prevent condensation of the lignin with the phenolic extractives, the conditions of the sulfite cook must favor sulfonation of the reactive groups of lignin. In principle that is the same method as used to prevent intra-condensation of lignin in a normal acid sulfite cook of spruce, except that the risk of condensation is considerably increased by the presence of the extractives. Low acidity and low temperature will favor sulfonation. Concentrated sodium bisulfite solutions without excess SO_2 were found to be able to pulp pine heartwood (262). Especially suited to the pulping of these wood species should be a two-stage process, with an initial, less acidic, neutral or alkaline stage, as early suggested (248) and much later commercially realized in Norway (309) and Sweden (467, 730, 778). Thereby the most reactive groups of lignin are protected, the carbonyl groups by α-hydroxysulfonate formation and the benzyl alcohol and alkyl ether groups of monomers containing a free phenolic group by sulfonation (cf. Subsection I.3D), thus preventing excessive lignin condensation in the wood, although some condensation with phenols in the liquid phase is likely to occur by the lignosulfonates dissolved (489). However, it is vital that the conditions of the two-stage cook are also chosen cautiously, to allow time for a good penetration and with ample amounts of combined SO_2 in the cooking liquor. In some cases, therefore, the concentration of the cooking liquor applied in the first stage is kept high, and around 70 % of the liquor is drained off after that stage to be used again after refortification in a subsequent cook (311). The digester is then charged with a cooking acid low in combined SO_2 or simply gassed up with sulfur dioxide and heated with live steam to the desired maximum temperature. A pH of 4–5 is preferred during the initial stage, at a temperature of 120–140°C, followed by a conventional acid sulfite cook at a temperature according to the grade desired. However, in some cases ordinary one-stage acid sulfite cooks are also used in cooking pine (382, 738), and then a prerequisite for obtaining acceptably low screenings is the use of a soluble base. Comparatively ample charge of combined SO_2 is also of value in the one-stage acid sulfite cook to reduce lignin condensation. The reason why calcium base is less suitable to one-stage pulping of pine is likely to be the slower penetration of calcium-based cooking acid, possibly by precipitation of calcium sulfite in the capillaries as the advancing front of cooking liquor loses some excess SO_2. It has also been suggested that precipitation of calcium sulfate occurs, caused partly by side reactions induced by the phenols, such as the dihydroquercetinol of Douglas fir (352). However, a method for pine sulfite pulping on calcium base has been suggested, which employs the use of pulp refiners (698). In the two-stage pulping of pine (253) as well as bark-damaged spruce (49), the acid cooking liquor of the second stage could be calcium-based, thereby saving the more expensive sodium base and avoiding the necessity of sodium recovery. The sodium losses could be further reduced by displacement with calcium-based cooking acid of the liquor from the initial stage, with or without subsequent removal of contaminating calcium from the recovered sodium-based liquor by addition of lime or caustic soda to precipitate calcium sulfite (253).

The necessity of presulfonation in the initial stage has been discussed, since it was found at least in one process, maintaining slightly alkaline conditions during the initial stage, that only about 0.06 S/OCH_3 was introduced and that a sodium bicarbonate solution with no SO_2 caused similar improvement in the pulping (778). As the most reactive of the condensable groups may be rapidly converted to sulfonates when sulfur dioxide enters the bicarbonate solution in the chips, the assumed mechanism may still be valid. However, as the pulps obtained with bisulfite or sulfite in the initial stage are brighter, the original procedure is preferred. In working with sodium-based sulfite cooking it has also been found (657), that a high content of combined SO_2 is the essential prerequisite for satisfactory pulping of pine, irrespective of the quantity of total SO_2, i.e. in bisulfite, acid sulfite as well as two-stage pulping. It therefore seems to be important that sufficient base enters into the wood structure to avoid excessive acidity. Then sulfonation precedes condensation even in an acid sulfite cook. Pressure impregnation is therefore also an essential operation in pine sulfite cooking (140).

B. Cooking liquor

B1. Introduction. By varying the cooking liquor composition the rate of pulping as well as pulp yield and quality is greatly influenced, and many investigations have been devoted to the subject of liquor composition. It should be stressed at once that the *chemical charge in relation to the wood* is of the greatest importance, as far as the bisulfite ions are concerned, and therefore the liquor-to-wood ratio should always be observed in investigations dealing with the influence of the cooking liquor composition.

In a previous section the cooking liquor composition and its changes during the cook have been described for both acid sulfite, bisulfite and neutral sulfite pulping, and the relations between the analytical concepts of *total* and *combined SO₂* with the actual ion concentrations of hydrogen and bisulfite ions were described. It was shown that the bisulfite ion concentration equals twice the available combined SO_2 *plus* a small contribution from the ionization of sulfurous acid. The concentration of sulfurous acid approximately corresponds to the *excess SO_2* or total SO_2 *minus* twice the combined SO_2. The contribution of the sulfurous acid ionization to the bisulfite ion concentration is smaller the higher the temperature, as the (apparent) ionization constant acid decreases considerably at a temperature increase. It was also demonstrated how the ionization of sulfurous acid will increase when the bisulfite ion concentration decreases during the cook as the bisulfite ions react to form sulfonates. Thus there is also an increase in acidity, which becomes more important when the bisulfite is virtually consumed and the 'available combined SO_2' therefore approaches and passes the zero level.

Obviously, therefore, the charge of combined SO_2 in relation to wood will determine whether or not that zero level will be reached before the cook is completed, and considering the sharp increase in acidity at that level it is natural to conclude that for pulps rich in hemicellulose, the charge of combined SO_2 should be ample, whereas for soft paper pulps and especially dissolving pulps, where considerable hemicellulose removal and some hydrolytic degradation of cellulose is required, the charge of combined SO_2 can be more restricted. Naturally, the time–temperature variables are also very important in regulating these relations, and a low temperature could to some extent, but not entirely, compensate for a deficiency in combined SO_2 in a paper pulp cook, as could a high temperature in a rayon pulp cook charged with too much combined SO_2.

When choosing the cooking liquor composition, its influence on the

551

rate of delignification must be considered. As was discussed in the previous Subsection I.3D, the rate of lignin removal is largely proportional to the product $[H^+]$. $[HSO_3^-]$ or to $[H_2SO_3]$, or roughly to the excess SO_2, as exemplified in Figure 9.73 (308). This product will decrease rapidly at constant total SO_2 content when the combined SO_2 content, and thus the bisulfite ion concentration, is increased and the acidity decreased, Table 9.3. This decrease in the rate of delignification must be compensated by an increase in temperature to keep the cooking time within reasonable limits. Acid sulfite cooks are generally performed in the temperature range of

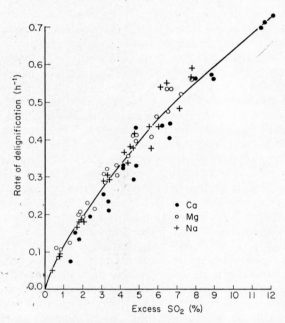

Fig. 9.73. Rate of delignification (expressed as inverse time to 90% delignification) vs. excess SO_2 (total SO_2—2 × combined SO_2 and approximately equal to sulfurous acid concentration). Three types of bases, 130°C (data of Maass *et al*)

120–150°C, bisulfite cooks required 150–160°C and neutral sulfite cooks 150–180°C. However, even these differences in temperature are not sufficient to make up for the decreased rate of cooking of the less acid sulfite cooks, and more lignin has to be left in those pulps, especially from neutral sulfite cooking, where the bisulfite ion concentration is also low.

From previous sections on lignin and carbohydrate reactions of the sulfite cook it is also clear that the ratio of

$$\frac{\text{lignin removal}}{\text{carbohydrate removal}} = \frac{k' \cdot [H^+] \cdot [HSO_3^-]}{k'' \cdot [H^+]} = k \cdot [HSO_3^-]$$

i.e. that the delignification is more selective the higher the bisulfite ion concentration. Naturally, the ratio of lignin to carbohydrate removal is not as strictly proportional to the bisulfite ion concentration as the above schematic relation suggests, partly because none of these heterogeneous reactions can be treated in terms of homogeneous reaction kinetics. In technical cooks, with a limited charge of chemicals, the bisulfite ion concentration will decrease throughout the cook and thus favor carbohydrate removal towards the end of the cook. Furthermore, in increasing the bisulfite ion concentration, and compensating for the decrease in delignification velocity by a higher temperature, the rate constants of the two reactions may change in a manner which favors carbohydrate removal and partly counteracts the benefits of the higher bisulfite content of the cooking liquor.

Another experience from Subsection I.3D was that the ratio of

$$\frac{\text{lignin sulfonation}}{\text{lignin condensation}} = \frac{k' \cdot [\text{H}^+] \cdot [\text{HSO}_3^-]}{k'' \cdot [\text{H}^+]} = k \cdot [\text{HSO}_3^-]$$

i.e. that lignin condensation is favored by low bisulfite ion concentrations. That will explain the tendency to 'burnt' or 'black' cooks or higher screenings and lignin content and darker pulps in cooks low in combined SO_2 and further, the beneficial influence of an increase in total SO_2 in those cooks. Thus a low temperature is also an advantage, partly because of the higher degree of ionization to bisulfite ions of the sulfurous acid, possibly also because of a favorable change in the ratio of the rate constants k' and k''.

B2. Sulfurous acid process. With these basic concepts in mind, it is understandable that *pulping in pure sulfur dioxide solutions* with no base present has been tried with less good results (131, 159, 332, 341, 412, 586, 622, 766, 812), unless high SO_2 concentrations, 5–27%, long cooking times, 4 h–16 months at low temperature, 60–100°C, were chosen. It is essential to achieve an initial sulfonation at mild conditions to avoid lignin condensation, whereas subsequent delignification can be performed at higher temperature. Completely satisfactory sulfite pulps were obtained from spruce in this manner by choosing 22% SO_2, 95°C for 6 h in the first stage and 5% SO_2, 115°C for 2–3 h in the second stage, while maintaining a pressure of 15 kp/cm² (332). It has even been found possible just to charge liquid SO_2 to steamed chips in a quantity corresponding to about 25%, calculated on the chip moisture, keeping the mixture at similar conditions as above and obtaining quite satisfactory pulps with a considerably reduced SO_2 quantity (657).

B3. Acid sulfite cooking with little combined SO_2. A fairly clear picture of the influence of the composition of the cooking acid is given by Figure 9.13 (421), where the border-line between normal and black cooks is drawn as a function of total and combined SO_2 content of the cooking liquor. Naturally, no such sharp border-line exists in reality, and the curve just indicates an intermediate region of brownish, incompletely delignified pulps. Nor does the figure take into account the improvements possible by variations in temperature and time, as well as multistage treatments.

553

Keeping cooking time and the content of total SO_2 constant at normal values of 3–7%, the pulp yield, screenings, lignin content and brightness vary in a manner indicated by Figure 9.74 (657). Pulp brightness is the most sensitive indication of unsatisfactory conditions. It is seen that a content of around 0.75% combined SO_2, corresponding to a charge of

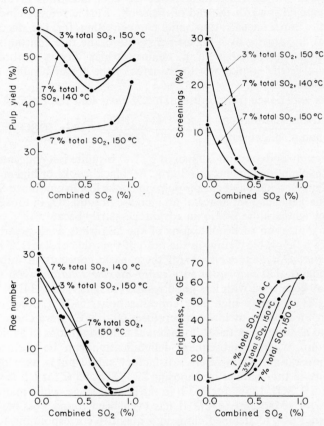

Fig. 9.74. Sulfite cooking with various amounts of combined SO_2. Delignification and lignin condensation phenomena (Rydholm)

30 kg ptw combined SO_2, seems to be the minimum amount of bisulfite required to avoid detrimental lignin condensation in the case of sprucewood at otherwise normal cooking conditions. Assuming 75% of the bisulfite to be converted to lignosulfonate groups, this corresponds to an average degree of sulfonation of around 0.5 S/OCH_3, which is about the minimum observed in technical lignosulfonates. However, it is obviously an oversimplification to say that lower charges of combined SO_2 do not

554

admit proper sulfonation of the lignin because the chemicals are used up before the delignification becomes complete, since sulfurous acid solutions can also act as sulfonating agents, especially at lower temperature. In this connection reference should be made to the experiments described in Subsection I.3D, where wood, subjected to limited presulfonation with normal cooking liquors, was shown to be quite easily delignified in SO_2–water, provided some metal counter ions for the solid lignosulfonates were available in the second stage, and a comparatively low temperature was maintained (184, 421, 468, 633). Similarly, it has been demonstrated (332, 622), that presulfonation with SO_2–water at low temperature also facilitates subsequent delignification with SO_2–water at higher temperatures. Obviously, some of the most reactive and accessible groups of lignin should be protected against condensation prior to SO_2 pulping at higher temperature. However, none of these processes has attracted technical interest, partly because the waste liquors of pure SO_2 pulping are more corrosive and become more viscous on evaporation than ordinary sulfite waste liquors.

One remark should be made here concerning lignin condensation on cooking in acids low in combined SO_2. Excessive condensation prevents proper delignification by the sulfite process and leads to high screenings and lignin content of the pulps. However, the condensation has seldom proceeded so far that delignification by the *kraft* process is impossible. For the first stage in the sulfite–kraft two stage pulping process for high-alpha dissolving pulps, the cooking liquor composition can therefore be chosen with somewhat different norms than in other cases, and as a complete regeneration system for both kraft and sulfite pulping is too elaborate for one mill, the combined SO_2 of such cooks is kept at a minimum (cf. 357).

B4. Sodium sulfate–sulfur dioxide process. A special variant to sulfur dioxide water cooks as well as to sodium base acid sulfite pulping is the cook with *sodium sulfate–sulfur dioxide* solutions. As deduced already in Subsection I.3B of this chapter, this type of cook utilizes the fact that part of the sulfate ions is converted to bisulfate ions by sulfurous acid under formation of bisulfite ions, schematically

$$H_2SO_3 + Na_2SO_4 = NaHSO_3 + NaHSO_4$$

A quantitative mathematical treatment of the ion concentrations involved is not possible until reliable data on the ionization constants at cooking temperature have been gathered (654). It suffices to say here, that only part of the sulfate is converted to bisulfate, but that the equilibria are more favorable at high temperature. Consequently, more sodium salts are necessary for a good result with this type of cook than with ordinary sodium base acid sulfite cooking. However, the use of sodium sulfate together with sulfur dioxide as the only chemical make-up gives certain aspects on the problem of chemicals recovery which has led to some investigations on this type of pulping process (211, 266, 560, 619) as well as to a patent (609). That a formation of bisulfite ions by the above-mentioned reaction is involved, and that it is not only a question of the sodium ions being necessary as counterions to the sulfonate groups formed in the solid phase of the wood, is evident from the fact that sodium salts of strong acids, such as sodium chloride, do not prevent lignin condensation in sulfur dioxide pulping (266, 619). It was also demonstrated (266), that the acidity of a sulfur dioxide solution at cooking temperature will decrease by the addition of sodium sulfate.

A cooking acid containing 20–40 g/l Na_2SO_4 was found to give the most satisfactory results (211, 619). An increase in the SO_2 content of the cooking liquor allowed a decrease in the sodium sulfate concentration (560), 4–5 % SO_2 requiring 30 g/l and 7–8 % SO_2 only 20 g/l Na_2SO_4 for satisfactory pulping (liquor-to-wood ratio 6 : 1). However, on increasing the amount of SO_2 and decreasing the Na_2SO_4 content, the character of the cook was changed from an ordinary acid sulfite cook towards sulfur dioxide cooking. The yield and quality of the pulps obtained were found to be inferior to those of ordinary sulfite pulps (560). By increasing the sodium sulfate concentration to 40–50 g/l and maintaining a high total SO_2 content, 7–9 % (liquor-to-wood ratio 4 : 1), pulps were produced in both the strong, greaseproof and dissolving pulp range which were in every respect equivalent to the ordinary acid sulfite pulp grades (211). Temperatures up to 170°C were used, and the same trend for dissolving pulps towards higher yield and alphacellulose content as experienced with ordinary acid sulfite cooking (cf. below) was noted. Increasing the sodium sulfate content or decreasing maximum temperature gave improved paper properties and pulp yield for paper pulps of Roe number 5.

The sodium sulfate–sulfur dioxide pulping process therefore seems to offer the same possibilities as the conventional acid sulfite process as regards pulping. As the consumption of chemicals is considerable, its technical interest is entirely dependent on the possibilities of chemicals recovery. The most straightforward recovery would be combustion of the waste liquor in a way securing complete oxidation of the melt to sodium sulfate, and at the same time maintaining the gaseous sulfur compounds as sulfur dioxide. Such a process has not been realized technically, and would meet the additional difficulty of absorbing the SO_2 of the flue gases into a non-alkaline liquor. It is also probable that some of the sodium of the melt would be in the form of carbonate, but that is obviously no disadvantage from the stand-point of pulping and would facilitate the absorption of sulfur dioxide. A more complete discussion on the problems of chemicals recovery will be found in Chapter 11.

In some of the regeneration processes for soluble-base chemicals the recovered SO_2 will be contaminated with SO_3, which on the preparation of cooking acid will consume base in the formation of sulfate. The investigations of the sodium sulfate–sulfur dioxide process have shown that this base is not entirely lost but could be considered approximately 50 % active in the acid sulfite process.

B5. Normal acid sulfite process and cooks with much combined SO_2. Normal acid sulfite liquors contain 0.9–1.3 % combined SO_2, corresponding to a chemical charge of 35–60 kg ptw combined SO_2. The cooks for rayon pulps and soft paper pulp grades fall in the lower range, those for paper pulps rich in hemicellulose in the higher. As the consumption of chemicals is approximately proportional to the charge of combined SO_2, still higher concentrations are not used without provisions for chemicals recovery. Soluble base is also a prerequisite for a further increase in combined SO_2. The *bisulfite cook* utilizes a content of 1.5–2.5% combined SO_2, or 60–100 kg ptw. *Neutral sulfite cooks*, which in many respects differ from the other processes mentioned, and could not be strictly compared with them, are charged with about 160 kg ptw, calculated as Na_2CO_3, which recalculated into combined SO_2 means about 100 kg ptw, although only 75 kg ptw of SO_2 are charged altogether, leaving some of the soda as a bicarbonate buffer.

The *influence on the rate of pulping* of varying amounts of total SO_2 when the alkali charge is kept constant and fairly high, is demonstrated in Figure 9.75 (636) for softwoods and in Figure 9.76 (427) for hardwoods.

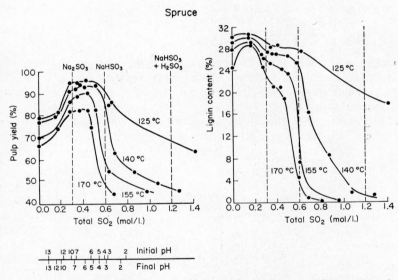

Fig. 9.75. Influence of liquor composition and temperature in sulfite cooking of spruce. Combined SO_2 0.3 mol/l (1.92%), 4 hours (Ross *et al*)

The time of cooking was kept constant at several temperature levels. The two series cover the whole pulping range from alkali cooks to acid sulfite cooks. It is clearly seen that there is a minimum in the rate of pulping at around neutrality, in the 'buffer region' between sodium sulfite and bisulfite, and that the rate of pulping increases towards the acid side, especially in the presence of some excess SO_2. In acid sulfite cooks, the rate of delignification will decrease on increasing the combined SO_2, unless the total SO_2 is at the same time increased to keep the excess SO_2

557

Aspen

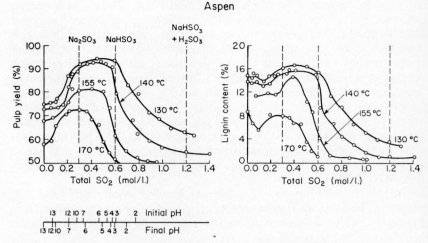

Fig. 9.76. Influence of liquor composition and temperature in sulfite cooking of aspen. Combined SO_2 0.3 mol/l (1.92%), 1 hour (Kerr–Harding)

constant, as demonstrated for sprucewood cooks with normal liquor-to-wood ratio (4 : 1) and 7 kp/cm² maximum pressure in Figure 9.77 (657). The variation in yield and lignin content of the first series of cooks covers the whole range from semichemical bisulfite pulping to acid sulfite pulping of dissolving grades. In the second series, where the initial content of excess SO_2 was kept constant, the differences are much smaller and

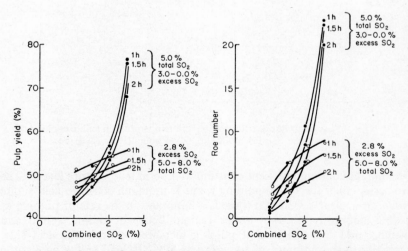

Fig. 9.77. Influence of cooking liquor composition on the rate of sulfite cooking of spruce. Constant total SO_2 or constant excess SO_2 at varying combined SO_2, 1–2 h at 150°C

indicate that the excess SO_2 is also an important variable for the rate of pulping in the technical type of sulfite cook. This was suggested fairly early (131, 265, 539) and the results of the kinetical investigations employing high liquor-to-wood ratios (110, 111, 118) demonstrate it still more conclusively, as shown in Figure 9.73 (308). However, it was also realized (325, 541) that the amount of excess SO_2 remaining in the digester during the cook is largely determined by the combination of temperature and pressure employed, irrespective of the original cooking acid composition, and the effect of the maximum pressure of the digester was investigated (131, 325, 541). Figure 9.78 (819) demonstrates that the rate of delignifica-

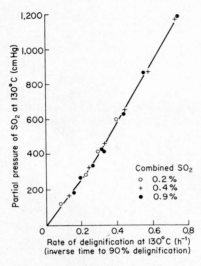

Fig. 9.78. Partial pressure of SO_2 vs.
rate of delignification (Maass *et al*)

tion is almost directly proportional to the partial pressure of SO_2 in the cooking liquor at constant temperature, and in Figure 9.79 (325) the total cooking time at various temperature and pressure levels to obtain a Roe chlorine number of 3.5 is shown as a function of the partial pressure of SO_2. Obviously, the diagram is only indicative of the combinations of conditions necessary, since other wood species and cooking acids than those used in the experiments give deviating results. Hardwoods normally require about 5°C lower temperatures and so do ammonium-based acids. Figure 9.80 (57) shows the vapor pressure of solutions containing various amounts of excess SO_2 at varying temperature, to indicate what cooking acid composition can be fully utilized at a certain temperature–pressure combination. Digester pressures of 5 kp/cm² were standard for a long time, but since the development of the welding technique and construction materials, 7 kp/cm² have become frequent and 10 kp/cm² not unusual. That development has caused cooking times to decrease, or the maximum

559

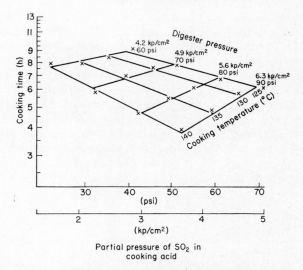

Fig. 9.79. Cooking time required to reach Roe number 3.5 at various cooking temperatures and pressures (Hart–Strapp)

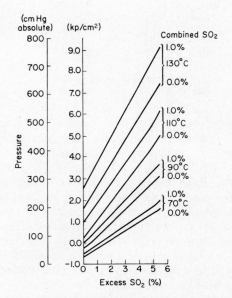

Fig. 9.80. Pressure of sulfite cooking acids of various compositions at various temperatures (Beazley *et al*)

temperatures, since a certain period of time at temperature is desirable for a proper reproducibility of the batch cooks.

In spite of the fact that the digester pressure determines the amount of excess SO_2 by the top gas relief, it is general practice to employ higher initial contents of SO_2 than can be preserved in the digester, and to provide for an elaborate system of reclaiming the top relief gases. That is partly because a high initial SO_2 content is believed to have a beneficial influence on the *rate of impregnation* of the wood chips (518, cf. however 47). A reasonably high content of total SO_2 is also necessary in calcium-based cooks of high combined SO_2 content to prevent precipitation of calcium sulfite at higher temperatures. Figure 9.81 (56) demonstrates the critical conditions for this phenomenon, which caused considerable trouble in the early days of the sulfite industry, known as 'liming-up' of the digesters.

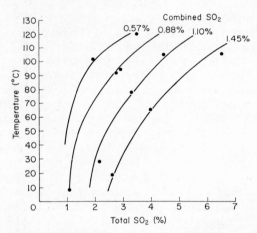

Fig. 9.81. Approximate critical temperature for calcium sulfite precipitation from cooking acids of varying composition (Beazley)

The *concentration* of combined SO_2 means little to the pulping result, as long as the *charge* of combined SO_2 is kept constant. By varying the liquor-to-wood ratio between 6:1 and 3:1 it was demonstrated that the rate of pulping is somewhat decreased at an increase in the concentration; the yield increases a little but the strength properties remain unaffected (294).

The pulp yield and quality is likewise influenced by the cooking liquor composition. The pulp yield at a certain degree of delignification will increase with an increase in the charge of combined SO_2 (110, 111, 118, 176, 300) as clearly demonstrated by Figure 9.41 (110, 300, 819). This holds true for all types of bases and degrees of delignification, and depends on the fact that the rate of carbohydrate removal is proportional to the pH of the cooking liquor, whereas the rate of delignification is affected by the bisulfite ion concentration as well (819). However, the effect is most pronounced at a low range of combined SO_2 charges, where there is a

561

danger of receiving an acidity peak towards the end of the cook. As there is an increase in the hemicellulose content of the pulp when the combined SO_2 content of the cooking liquor is increased, a denser paper with higher tensile and bursting strength and rather lower tear is obtained (273c). At the same time, the unbleached pulp brightness is increased (273c). However, an increase in combined SO_2 necessitates an increase in total SO_2 to keep the time of cooking constant, or else a higher temperature has to be applied, which affects the pulp properties in the adverse direction. The effect of increased rate of reaction on increasing the excess SO_2 could on the other hand be utilized to decrease the temperature level and thus obtain still better yield and strength properties (265, 518, 797). Then it is necessary to have a comparatively high maximum pressure of the digester in order to get the full benefit of the high SO_2 content of the cooking liquor. A change in the digester pressure will not influence the pulp yield and quality at constant degree of delignification, only the rate of pulping (325, cf. 518). It should also be observed that not all strength properties are improved by increasing the excess SO_2 and decreasing the temperature or time, as tear and folding strengths decrease (325, 495, 518, 681), and it is thus rather a change in the character of the pulp. On decreasing the time of cooking and keeping the temperature constant, the effect of an increase in excess SO_2 has been investigated (348) and found to be different for different types of pulp, the yields and strength of soft pulps being improved and those of harder pulps the reverse, although it appears quite possible that the effect should be positive for all pulp grades. The type of wood was also found to influence the result, western hemlock responding positively and white fir negatively to a similar change of excess SO_2 and time (518), a result which probably means that the actual effects fall within the range of experimental error. The main changes in yield and strength properties observed on changing excess SO_2 and temperature simultaneously are therefore probably due to the temperature effect, cf. below.

The *influence of pH on pulp yield and properties* has more recently been examined extensively, largely encouraged by the development of soluble base recovery systems. The acid pH range up to neutrality can be reached by ammonium, sodium and magnesium bases. Ammonium base is the least interesting of the three, since the unbleached pulps obtained are discolored by side reactions and there is no acceptable recovery method available. This does not prevent the use of ammonium base in conventional acid sulfite pulping, cf. below, but increasing the pH in the cooking generally means an increase in the base content, and bisulfite pulping will consume almost twice as much base chemicals as the acid sulfite cook. For sodium and magnesium bases, however, recovery methods are available and the choice of base is mainly determined by the advantages and disadvantages of the recovery methods rather than the pulping aspects, at least in the pH range mentioned. For higher pH's, such as in neutral sulfite pulping, or when an alkaline precook or posttreatment is desired (cf. Section III), sodium base is preferred.

562

Neutral sulfite pulping is with few exceptions a process for hardwoods, whereas bisulfite pulping, with its less slow rate of delignification, can also be used with advantage with softwoods, and most investigations of this process have in fact been carried out with softwoods. After an early study (263), made mainly with lignin–chemical aspects, most investigations in bisulfite pulping have been carried out since 1950 (177, 242, 323, 326, 373, 627, 657, 741, 770, 809). Two commercial variants of bisulfite cooking have been named, the *Arbiso* (177) and the *Magnefite* (627, 770, 809) processes, on sodium and magnesium bases respectively. Both have become realized in several mills. Figures 9.82–84 (741) show the influence

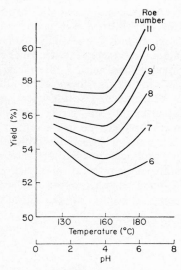

Fig. 9.82. Unscreened yield vs. pH and cooking temperature at different Roe numbers, in the sulfite pulping of spruce (Hall–Stockman)

of pH on the temperature necessary for chemical cooking, as well as on pulp yield and properties. It is seen that in comparison with conventional acid sulfite pulping, the temperature has to be increased from 130°C to about 160°C for bisulfite pulping (pH 4) and to about 180°C for mixed monosulfite–bisulfite pulping (pH 6–6.5). The yield of pulp at a certain degree of delignification is very similar for acid sulfite and bisulfite cooking, whereas cooks at higher pH tend to give increased yields, which is an effect of glucomannan stabilization, cf. Subsection I.3E on carbohydrate reactions and Section III on multistage cooking. It is also observed that bisulfite cooking tends to give lower yields than acid sulfite pulping at the highest degrees of delignification, and it is a common observation that bisulfite cooking is not suited for the production of pulps of low lignin contents, neither soft paper pulps nor dissolving pulps. This is connected with the low hydrolyzing power of the bisulfite cooking liquor, as well as its extreme sensitivity to thiosulfate, which is formed in larger amounts towards the end of the cook and often results in total decomposition of the remaining bisulfite and a dark pulp at unduly prolonged cooks. In the range of strong chemical paper pulps, the bisulfite process gives at least as high brightness as acid sulfite pulping, whereas cooking at pH 6 gives a somewhat darker pulp when cooking to chemical pulp yields. The paper properties of bisulfite pulps are considerably better than those of acid sulfite pulping, the only disadvantage being a somewhat higher beating energy required. Cooks at pH 6 give less good results, probably because of the excessive temperatures needed to arrive at chemical pulps in reasonable times. This also illustrates the unsuitability of the neutral sulfite process for chemical pulps, especially from softwoods. The improved paper strength has encouraged further investigation with two main aspects in mind, competitiveness with kraft pulps in the chemical pulp range and the chance of making semichemical bisulfite pulps with strength properties as good as the best acid sulfite chemical pulps. Figure 9.85 (657, 741) shows that although the tensile strength of bisulfite papers amounts to that of a kraft paper, the tear strength is appreciably lower. The same differences are noted in papers from bleached wet and bleached dried pulps (657), and mill scale trials have shown that bisulfite pulps cannot replace kraft pulps in the production of sack and strong bag papers. The main deficit is the lower stretch properties of the bisulfite paper. The lower production costs, especially of the bleached bisulfite pulp as

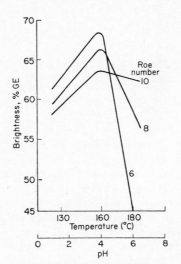

Fig. 9.83. Brightness vs. pH and cooking temperature at different Roe numbers, in the sulfite pulping of spruce (Hall–Stockman)

compared to kraft, is an incitement to further development in the paper machine to compensate for the lower stretch. With unbleached pulps, the semichemical bisulfite pulps are of the greatest interest because of good strength properties even in the 70–80 % yield range, with a pulp brightness which is satisfactory for many purposes. Liner board, magazine paper and newsprint are among the most interesting applications here, as well as the wrapping paper field. Cooks at pH 6 are interesting in this yield range, as well as for the ultra-high yields above 90 %, the *chemimechanical* pulps, cf. Chapter 8.II. Bisulfite pulps from *hardwoods* likewise become stronger than the corresponding acid sulfite pulps, but, especially after bleaching, are inferior to the corresponding neutral sulfite semichemical pulps, since the bisulfite process attacks the xylan considerably. A further complication in the production of chemical bisulfite pulp from hardwoods is that the point of fiber liberation is not far from the point of cooking liquor decomposition. Figure 9.86 shows that although nothing is gained in pulp yields from softwoods, hardwood bisulfite pulps are obtained at a slightly

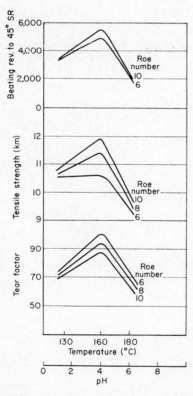

Fig. 9.84. Paper properties vs. pH and cooking temperature at different Roe numbers, in the sulfite pulping of spruce (Hall–Stockman)

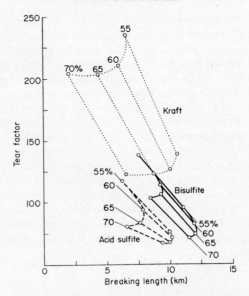

Fig. 9.85. Tear factor versus breaking length for pulps both unbeaten and beaten to 45°SR in a PFI-mill (Hartler *et al*)

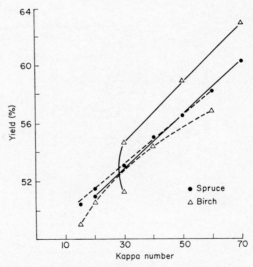

Fig. 9.86. Yield versus kappa number. Liquor–wood ratio 4

——— Bisulfite cooks, sodium base. Combined SO_2 9.6% of the wood; max. temp. 160°C
– – – – Acid bisulfite cooks, calcium base. Combined SO_2 4.8% of the wood; max. temp. 135°C (Hartler *et al*)

higher yield than the corresponding acid sulfite pulps. Figure 9.87 (741) indicates a similar gain in paper strength properties for hardwoods as for softwoods.

The effect of the cooking liquor composition in the bisulfite process has also been studied in some detail. In choosing a constant initial pH of 4.5 the quantity of combined SO_2 was varied in the range 50–100 kg ptw combined SO_2 (741). Lower yields and higher lignin contents were experienced at charges below 80 kg ptw, as well as longer cooking times. Not much is gained in increasing the charge above 80 kg ptw. During

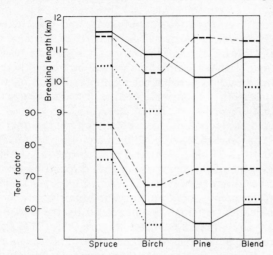

Fig. 9.87. Breaking length and tear factor for pulps of different wood species beaten in a PFI-mill to 45°SR

————— Bisulfite cooks, sodium base 65% yield;
– – – – Bisulfite cooks, 55% yield;
. . . . . Acid bisulfite cooks, calcium base 55% yield (Hartler *et al*)

the bisulfite cook some reactions, especially the formation of acetic acid, tend to decrease the pH. At the same time, some sulfurous acid is formed. With no gas relief, pH will drop from 4.5 to 3.0, whereas a gas relief at 5.5 kp/cm² maintains the original pH. This affects the cooking time considerably, so that in the former case 3.5 h and in the latter 8.5 h are needed at 160°C for equal delignification. Obviously, pH control of the charged liquor and digester pressure control during the cook are essential in the production of bisulfite pulp of even quality. The pulp quality at a certain lignin content, however, is not influenced by these variations, and a detailed investigation showed equivalent results for pH 4.5 and 3.0, disregarding the rate of pulping. Lower or higher pH, however, should be avoided because of decreased pulp quality.

B6. Sulfite pulping with various types of base. To the description of the

567

influence of the cooking liquor composition on the pulp yield and quality also belongs a discussion of the differences obtained with *different bases*. For economical reasons, calcium or mixed calcium–magnesium bases have been dominating the preparation of sulfite cooking acid. However, in recent years interest has increased in other types of base, partly because of stream pollution reasons, partly because methods for the regeneration of the cooking chemicals have been developed, cf. Chapter 11, but to some extent because of the special effects to be obtained in the cooking. Some of these effects are due to the fact that the sulfites of the new bases are water-soluble, in contrast with calcium sulfite. This allows adjustment of the composition of the cooking acid, and those effects have just been discussed, or will be treated in Section III of this chapter on multistage cooking. Only the effect of the various bases on the result of cooking in normally composed acid sulfite liquors will be treated here, although it should be pointed out at once that the main possibilities for the new bases lie in deviations from the normal cooking process, which has been developed through the years for calcium base.

For normal acid sulfite cooking, the use of the different soluble bases, sodium (176, 322, 427, 522, 616, 636, 700, 701), ammonium (54, 60, 79a, 160, 170, 247, 366, 371, 416, 463, 464, 738) and magnesium (51, 52, 69, 370), has been described, generally in comparison with calcium base, and sometimes all bases have been compared (321, 327, 342, 523, 633, 747, 819). Although the results are frequently contradictory, it is fairly safe to say that the rate of delignification is somewhat increased by the use of monovalent bases, especially by ammonium base. Figure 9.88 (747) shows that the differences are not great, but mill experience indicates that to keep the length of the cooking cycle constant, maximum temperature could be

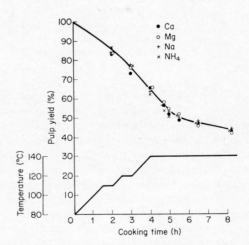

Fig. 9.88. Rate of acid sulfite cooking of softwood at identical conditions but different base types (Strapp *et al*)

decreased by some 5°C by changing from calcium to ammonium base (54). Although this is an advantage it does not pay for the increased cost of cooking chemicals. The possible reduction of cooking time at maximum temperature is generally not a substantial saving either. However, it has also been found that screenings are reduced on changing from calcium to sodium or ammonium base, and that the lignin content at a certain yield or viscosity level is lowered (54, 237b). This indicates a better penetration of the cooking chemicals and a more uniform cook, and has been utilized by decreasing the time of heating to maximum temperature. Therefore, a changeover from calcium to sodium or ammonium base will increase the digester house capacity, which for some mills will be an economical advantage. Another possibility lies in the utilization of a more impenetrable wood raw material, such as jack pine (738).

The reason for the better penetration and higher rate of delignification for soluble bases as compared with calcium base has been much discussed. Often the different rates of diffusion of the different cations have been advanced as the cause of the *differences in penetration ability*, but as seen on Table 9.20 (728), the differences are not great for the various base cations excepting the hydrogen ion. Furthermore, the sodium ion is slower

Table 9.20. Equivalent conductance of some cations, ohms^{-1}

Temperature, °C	75	100	118	156
Ion				
H^+	565	644	722	777
Na^+	116	155	203	249
K^+	159	206	263	317
NH_4^+	159	207	264	319
$1/2\ Ca^{2+}$	142	191	252	312
$1/2\ Ba^+$	149	200	262	322
$1/3\ La^{3+}$	173	235	312	388

than the calcium ion. Therefore it is felt that diffusion of the cations in the liquid phase is not critical for the uniformity of the cook at short heating periods to maximum temperature, but, rather, some phenomenon connected with the solubility of the sulfite. It is suggested (cf. 685), that in the capillary system of wood at the advancing front of cooking acid, losses of excess SO_2 might occur which locally increase the pH sufficiently to cause local and temporary precipitation of calcium sulfite at the elevated temperature. The danger for precipitation would be especially great at the pit membrane perforations. This repeated precipitation and re-dissolution slow down the penetration of calcium-based cooking acid and necessitate longer heating periods. Another cause of the slower penetration may be the formation of calcium salts of wood resin that prevents the dispersion of the latter, which to a considerable extent is located along the paths of penetration. As was pointed out in the section on the influence of wood species on the pulping result, resinous wood is especially difficult

569

to pulp with calcium-based acids, and a change to soluble base has given a considerable improvement, as evidenced by the much lower screenings obtained.

The reason for the *more rapid delignification* in the cooks on soluble base is not entirely clear either. The rate of diffusion of the different cations should in this case be unimportant in comparison with that of the lignosulfonate ions. It is possible that the lignin molecules are rather less condensed because of the more uniform penetration of the cooking acid in the case of the soluble bases, but no experimental evidence has been presented so far to substantiate this. It has also been suggested (633) that the solubility of the various lignosulfonates should vary. However, even calcium and barium lignosulfonates are completely water-soluble. The interesting experimental evidence advanced to substantiate the theory has also been interpreted to mean that the acidity in the solid phase decreases as the affinity of the cation to the solid phase increases (cf. Subsection I.3B of this chapter), according to the *Donnan* law. The effects were illustrated by Tables 9.6–7.

The somewhat higher acidity of the solid phase in the case of mono-valent bases is also likely to develop some difference in the dissolution of carbohydrates and the hydrolysis of the remaining polysaccharides. Some

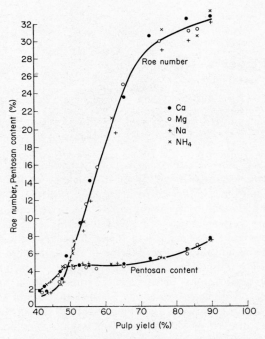

Fig. 9.89. Influence of the base type on the selectivity of delignification in the acid sulfite pulping of Canadian softwood (Strapp *et al*)

effects on pulp yield, strength, viscosity, alphacellulose content and carbohydrate composition might therefore be expected. However, the better penetration of the cooking acids based on monovalent ions may counteract those effects, and on the whole, no statistically significant effects have been reported, although some investigations indicate slightly higher alphacellulose content in the case of monovalent bases (321, 322). Figure 9.89 (747) does not indicate any appreciable differences in the relations of yield, lignin and pentosan content, and Figure 9.90 (747) shows no great differences in the paper properties of pulps from various types of base. A more detailed investigation on the relative merits of sodium and calcium base in acid sulfite chemical pulping revealed that the total yields are about 0.5–1.0% (wood basis) better for sodium base and screened pulp yield is 1.0–1.5% higher (237b).

The brightness of the unbleached pulps is fairly similar for all bases but ammonium, which yields decidedly darker pulps, approximately 1–5% GE lower in brightness (54, 464). The lower brightness of ammonium-

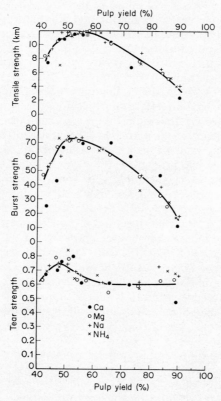

Fig. 9.90. Paper pulp properties vs. pulp yield on acid sulfite pulping of Canadian softwood with various bases (Strapp *et al*)

based pulps is probably due to a selective reaction between the ammonium ion and carbonyl groups of lignin. This reaction also produces a much darker color of the ammonium-based spent liquors, as well as a higher liquor viscosity noticeable on the evaporation of the liquors (cf. Chapter 11). However, there is no difference in the case of bleaching of ammonium-based pulps in comparison with other pulps. The specific effect of the ammonium ion was also mentioned in connection with the finding, that of all pretreatments of comparative pH, temperature and time, those containing ammonium ions have the worst effect in checking subsequent delignification in the sulfite cook. It appears that the reactive groups become rapidly protected by sulfonation when ammonium and bisulfite ions are charged together, and that the carbonyls again become exposed towards the end of the cook.

C. Temperature, time and pressure

The influence of temperature has several aspects, and can be subdivided into the *effect of the rate of heating* and the *effect of the maximum temperature level*. The former will influence the extent of lignin condensation occurring prior to perfect impregnation and the uniformity of the cook in the later stages of the heating period, the latter determines the rates of removal of lignin and carbohydrates.

The rate of heating which could be allowed in an acid sulfite cook depends on the condition of the wood, the type of pretreatment, the composition of cooking acid, etc., factors which all influence the rate of penetration (cf. Chapter 6.III). Furthermore, the uniformity of the heating circulation will determine the rate of heating. The time needed to ensure full penetration of untreated laboratory softwood chips somewhat larger than normal size, is around 3 h at 100°C or 2 h at 120°C for cooking acid of normal strength (518). For normal mill chip size and especially after thorough steaming, that time is considerably reduced. Before the impregnation of the cooking acid is complete, SO_2 gas will have penetrated the chips to some extent, and acid condensation of the lignin occurs (547). As that reaction is rather temperature-dependent, little condensation occurs below a temperature of 110–125°C, varying with the type of wood (369, 518, 538, 755), which has been called the 'critical' temperature (538). As the impregnation is also more rapid the higher the temperature, it is desirable to approach the critical temperature range. If it is exceeded prior to complete impregnation, delignification is retarded resulting in high lignin content of the pulp and high screenings. Quite often therefore, the heating is interrupted or retarded at around 110°C for about an hour.

The rate of heating after the impregnation period was especially important to the uniformity of the cook in those days when heating was done by live steam and the digesters did not possess cooking liquor circulation. Then it was often customary to maintain a very slow heating throughout the cook, never reaching any definite maximum temperature (541). In a way that was the most reliable system to ensure a uniform

572

temperature distribution in the digester, as compared with rapid heating to maximum temperature at some stage of the cook. A rise of 3–7°C per hour was recommended (755). As there was often a maximum temperature level stipulated which should not be exceeded, the temperature curve levelled off there until the end point of the cook was reached. With the introduction of external liquor circulation and indirect heating, the uniformity of the temperature distribution has improved, although it is by no means perfect, and the cook is therefore brought to maximum temperature more rapidly, 10–20°C per hour or even more, and maintained there. It is an advantage to shut off the liquor circulation well before the point of fiber liberation, at which stage blocking of the strainers by pulp fibers will otherwise often occur.

The choice of maximum temperature has to consider productivity and quality demands. As temperature is the chief variable influencing the rate of delignification (541), production demands favor a high maximum temperature, whereas quality demands favor a low maximum temperature when strong paper pulps are desired. That is explained by the temperature coefficient of the rate of carbohydrate removal being somewhat higher than that of the rate of delignification. Figure 9.91 (245, 421) shows the energy of activation for the two reactions at various stages of the cook.

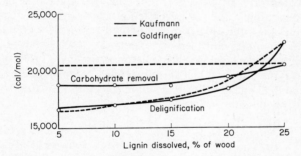

Fig. 9.91. Energy of activation at the dissolution of the wood components by acid sulfite pulping of softwood (Goldfinger and Kaufmann)

As pointed out before, the system of wood and cooking liquor is not suited to kinetic considerations which apply for homogeneous systems, but some conclusions might be derived. Especially the energy of activation of the delignification increases towards the end of the cook, showing the greater difficulty in removing the less accessible and probably more condensed part of the lignin. In the main part of the cook, the temperature dependence of the delignification is smaller than that of the carbohydrate removal, indicating that an increase in temperature will lead to less selective delignification. In accordance, the pulp yields on cooking to a certain residual lignin content of the pulp are higher the lower the maximum temperature, as exemplified by Figure 9.92 (211) for strong paper pulps of chlorine number 5. The same tendency also prevails for the sodium sulfate–sulfurous acid process (211). Therefore, it is general practice to use 120–125°C for hemicellulose-rich greaseproof pulps and 130–135°C for less hard paper pulps of higher opacity. Sometimes, 140°C is claimed to be the highest maximum temperature recommended for paper pulps (538), and only very soft paper pulps are produced at higher temperature. Figure 9.93 (325) gives a comparison of the paper strength properties of pulps cooked at different maximum temperature. As is to be expected, the pulps more rich in hemicellulose form papers with stronger interfiber bonding, and give a higher sheet density, higher tensile and bursting strengths and lower opacity and tear.

Considering the relative rates of hemicellulose and cellulose degradation, the temperature dependence of the former reaction is stronger than the latter, and dissolving pulps are preferably cooked at relatively high temperature. The higher alphacellulose content and alphacellulose yield of the high-temperature cooks at a certain viscosity level show a more complete removal of hemicellulose for a constant extent of cellulose degradation (211, 391, 780). Less good lignin removal at very high temperatures limits the maximum temperature of rayon pulp cooks to about 150–155°C.

Most effects of temperature on softwood sulfite pulp yield and alphacellulose content are likely to be connected with glucomannan stabilization, cf. Subsection I.3E. A lower temperature gives a more selective deacetylation of the glucomannan at a limited degree of degradation. This gives the glucomannan molecules an opportunity to rearrange to a less accessible structure. An increased glucomannan content has been experienced with both rayon (18) and paper pulp cooks (651) of increased yields.

The rate of delignification in acid sulfite cooks is approximately doubled at an increase in temperature of 10°C (112, 150, 541, 819), a normal

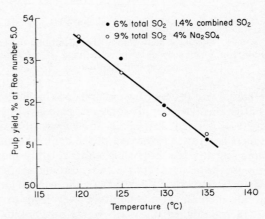

Fig. 9.92. Pulp yield at constant lignin content upon pulping spruce at various maximum temperatures by the acid sulfite or the sodium sulfate–sulfur dioxide process (Eriksson–Stockman)

temperature dependence for chemical reactions which implies that a chemical reaction and not diffusion of the reactants is the rate-determining factor. The time needed to reach the residual lignin content of around 4% in a strong paper pulp, which means a little more than 90% delignification, is somewhat more than an hour at 140°C, 2–3 h at 130°C, 6 h at 120°C and something like a day and night at 100°C. A rayon pulp cook which takes around 2 h at 150°C will require less than one hour at 160°C and only a little more than a quarter of an hour at 170°C. Naturally these reaction periods will also depend on the other reaction variables, such as the composition of the cooking liquor. Cooks with the shortest reaction periods mentioned need high precision in the end-point determination and blow-down operations and require special equipment as e.g. continuous digesters. Figure 9.94 (211) illustrates the approximate time–temperature relations of two extreme pulp grades. However, this is only valid at cooks with no top gas relief. Normally there is a decrease in the SO₂ content, which is larger at higher maximum temperature. The decrease in excess SO₂ during the cook therefore counteracts the increase in delignification velocity caused by the increase in temperature, as is evident from the previous Figure 9.79. As pointed out previously, an increase

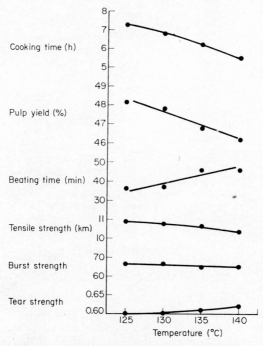

Fig. 9.93. Cooking time, pulp yield and properties on acid sulfite cooking of Canadian softwood to Roe number 3.5 at various maximum temperatures. Average of cooks at 4 pressure levels (Hart–Strapp)

575

in the digester *pressure* will increase the rate of pulping proportionally (325, cf. 518).

The bisulfite (741) and neutral sulfite cooks (88, 175, 781, 794) have a similar rate dependence on the temperature. In a bisulfite cook, 90% delignification is reached in 6 h at 155°C as compared to 120°C for the same time in acid sulfite cooking. Neutral sulfite semichemical cooks never attain more than about 50–60% delignification and use temperatures of 160–180°C or even more. The temperature-limiting factor for all categories of sulfite cooks is the liquor penetration, which at too rapid cooks tends to be insufficient and leads to excessive contents of residual lignin.

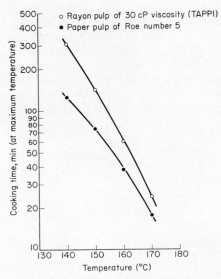

Fig. 9.94. Influence of temperature on the rate of delignification and cellulose degradation in the cooking of paper pulp and rayon pulp respectively (Eriksson–Stockman)

II. Kraft Process

1. GENERAL CONSIDERATIONS

The dominating pulping process today is the kraft process. The main reasons for this are the comparative simplicity and rapidity of the process, its insensitivity to variations in wood condition and its applicability to all wood species, as well as the valuable properties of the pulp produced. Since the introduction in 1879 of sodium sulfate (*kraft* process) instead of carbonate (*soda* process) as the make-up chemical to cover the losses in the recovery cycle of the cooking chemicals cycle, which lead to a considerable improvement in the rate of pulping and the quality of the pulp, the main advances have been made in the technology of the process, especially in the recovery plant. The cooking process itself has essentially remained the same, the reason being partly that the chemistry of the process has not been clearly understood, partly that the process of cooking wood chips with the sodium hydroxide and sulfide of the white liquor from the recovery plant involves such reactions with most of the wood components that come close to the ideal, at least in the production of paper pulps. The hydroxide is capable of opening the alkylaryl ether bonds of lignin, which withstand most other pulping liquors, and the lignin degradation products thus formed are soluble in alkaline medium. The sulfide accelerates the lignin dissolution, partly by reacting with some groups in lignin, which otherwise initiate condensation, and by the same sulfidation reaction the cleavage of the alkylaryl ether bonds is facilitated. Extractives of certain wood species, which in acid medium condense with lignin, dissolve in the alkaline liquor and do no harm to the process. Other extractives, which in sulfite pulping lead to pitch troubles, are likewise dissolved or dispersed in the alkaline liquor. The carbohydrate molecules, which through their aldehydic end groups are sensitive to alkali, to a large extent undergo intramolecular rearrangements which make them alkali-stable. This is one of the most important reasons for the outstanding paper properties of kraft pulps, another being the removal of some less-ordered cellulose and the relatively insignificant degradation of the well-ordered cellulose, even if some occurs in the mechanically damaged parts of the chips. Decayed parts of the wood as well as bark fragments are aggressively attacked by the white liquor and removed to a large extent. One drawback is a relatively large amount of residual, highly condensed lignin, which cannot be removed by extended cooking without degradation of the carbohydrate fraction. This lignin imparts a relatively dark color to the unbleached kraft pulp, which to some extent, though not very seriously, has limited its use for certain grades of wrapping paper. The residual lignin of kraft pulps is more difficult to remove by bleaching than the lignin of sulfite pulps. Therefore it was a considerable gain for the kraft process, when multistage bleaching, commencing with elemental chlorine and further involving alkaline extraction and oxidative bleaching stages, solved the problem of kraft pulp bleaching. A final improvement in that respect has been the introduction of chlorine dioxide as a finishing bleaching agent. Bleaching of kraft pulps is dealt with in Chapter 17.

The stabilization of carbohydrates towards alkali, which is such an advantage in the production of kraft paper pulps, for a long time made it impossible to manufacture kraft dissolving pulps, as the stabilized hemicelluloses, especially the xylan fraction, decreases the reactivity of the pulp towards the viscose and acetate processing chemicals. However, with the introduction of the prehydrolysis treatment prior to kraft pulping, it became possible to produce pulps for dissolving purposes, and such pulps now constitute a large percentage of the entire dissolving pulp production.

Prehydrolysis and similar pretreatments are dealt with in Chapter 9.III. Although several other modifications of the kraft process have been suggested, few or none has had such advantages as to motivate the introduction of any complications of the present system. However, an important trend towards higher pulp yields for some grades has occurred with the introduction of disk refiners, whereby the cook is interrupted already at a stage of incomplete fiber liberation. High yield chemical and semichemical kraft pulps are used increasingly for coarse papers and boards. Those pulps have been discussed in Chapter 8. The recent modifications of the cooking equipment have been dealt with in Chapter 6.IV, and the recovery system will be described in Chapter 11.

2. DESCRIPTION OF PROCESS

The operation of the batchwise kraft cooking is quite similar to that of sulfite cooking described in Chapter 9.I, although some deviations are necessary because of the different cooking chemicals used. Thus chip filling and liquor charging are often performed at the same time, whereby the liquor circulation is used as soon as possible to increase the degree of digester packing. The cooking liquor contains about 200 kg of active alkali (calculated as NaOH) per ton of dry wood, and is made up of *white liquor*, containing the main part of active chemicals and *black liquor*, which is liquor from a previous cook containing organic substance and consumed chemicals, and which is used as a diluent to ensure good liquor circulation without introducing extra water. The liquor : wood ratio is therefore around 3.5 : 1. The sulfidity is kept at around 25–30 %. The terms of active alkali and sulfidity will be defined in a subsequent section.

Because of the more rapid penetration into the wood by the alkaline pulping liquor compared to sulfite cooking acid, the heating to maximum temperature is performed much more rapidly than in the sulfite cook, usually in 1–2.5 h, whereas the retention at temperature is about the same as in the more rapid sulfite cooks, 1–2 h. Maximum temperature is 160–180°C. The gas relief system does not need the same elaborate design as in the sulfite cook as only small quantities of gas are evolved. These contain malodorous organic components, such as mercaptans and sulfides, as well as turpentine and methanol. The relief gases are condensed and the turpentine recovered. The blow steam is included in this recovery system. At the end of the cook, pressure is often decreased 1–2 atmospheres before blowing. Figure 9.95 exemplifies the digester cycle of a batchwise kraft cook.

Nowadays practically all kraft cooks are blown, and various precautions are taken to ensure a clean blow, which is vital for the digester house capacity. Blowing is especially difficult in the case of hardwood kraft cooking, and in mills using both hardwoods and softwoods, black liquor containing softwood resin soaps is often introduced to the hardwood-containing digesters at the end of the cook to facilitate the blow (as well as to eliminate subsequent pitch troubles by dispersing the hardwood extractives). In modern practice the cooks are blown to a large blow tank with a capacity of several cooks. Each generally contains 5–10 t of pulp. In older mills, the cooks are blown to the diffusers via a central blow cyclone. The former system was illustrated in Figure 8.14, and batch digesters were shown in some detail in Figure 6.41.

The problem of kraft digester corrosion has been touched in Chapter 6.VI. Although cast iron digesters dominate, those of compounded stainless steel have gained ground, especially for continuous cooking, which has recently become an established operation for the kraft process. The use of instruments for indication, recording and controlling has also become increasingly common in kraft cooking, especially elaborate instrumentation being required in continuous cooking.

As the operation of a batch cook was described in detail for the sulfite process, Chapter 9.I, and as continuous cooking has first been developed

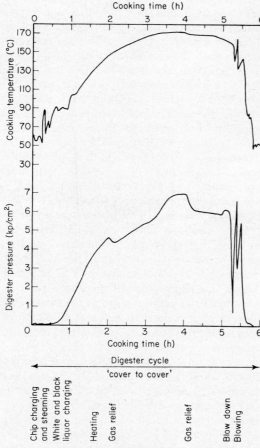

Fig. 9.95. Digester pressure and temperature of a batch pine kraft cook

579

for the kraft process, some details of continuous kraft cooking according to the Kamyr system will be given here (382a, 623, 725). Figure 9.96 schematically illustrates the equipment of a kraft mill with continuous cooking. The digester system was shown in more detail in Figure 6.51, and semichemical kraft systems of the batch and continuous type were illustrated in Figures 8.14–15. The digesters are built for capacities approaching 900 t/d of kraft pulp, with volumes of up to 900 m³. The larger units are normally placed outdoors to save building costs. There are several variants on the system shown. The chips, which should preferably contain only little sawdust (826), are stored in a hopper above the steaming vessel and fed by vibrators to a metering wheel. Here the production capacity of the system is set by adjustment of the speed of rotation. From the metering wheel the chips pass through a low-pressure rotating cell feeder to a steaming vessel, which consists of an enclosed screw conveyor. The steam pressure is automatically controlled and kept at around 0.5 kp/cm² ($110°C$). The retention time is 2–3 minutes only, but it should be observed, that in contrast to steaming of a batch cook, the chips are almost instantaneously heated to steaming temperature. As the steaming is virtually done by blow steam, the steaming vessel likewise provides for a low-cost preheating. At the end of the screw conveyor, the chips drop into the high-pressure rotary feeder, consisting of a conical plug valve of stainless steel, rotating in a housing clad with monel metal. The plug has normally four through pockets, and the chips are packed into them by means of a packing circulation on the low-pressure side, the pump of which receives its liquor through a slotted part of the housing. As the valve slowly revolves the pocket filled with chips and liquor passes from a vertical to a horizontal position and is thus connected on both sides to the high-pressure system. By means of a circulation pump, drawing its liquor from behind a strainer at the digester top, the chips are pumped from the pocket to the top of the digester and drop down to the chip pillar, which is slowly moving downwards during the cook. The chip level is kept somewhat below the screw which rotates at the top to keep the top strainer clean. Therefore as the feeder pocket again reaches vertical position it only contains liquor. The space taken up by the new chips dropping in causes some liquor to pass over to a levelling tank and this liquor has to be pumped back into the digester together with liquor leaking from the high-pressure to the low-pressure side of the feeder. It is done by a high-pressure pump, which sometimes also receives the white liquor needed for the cooking, although this function may be performed by a separate pump. This white liquor is fed to the system at a regulated, constant flow, set in relation to the feed rate of the chips and to the concentration of the white liquor. In order to keep the digester under hydraulic pressure, usually 10–12 kp/cm², the high-pressure pump also receives black liquor from a buffer tank. The pressure impulse from the digester regulates the total feed of the high-pressure pump, and the levelling tank above the pump gives a level impulse to the black liquor feed. The size of the latter depends on the chip moisture and the consistency of the pulp leaving the digester. A higher moisture content

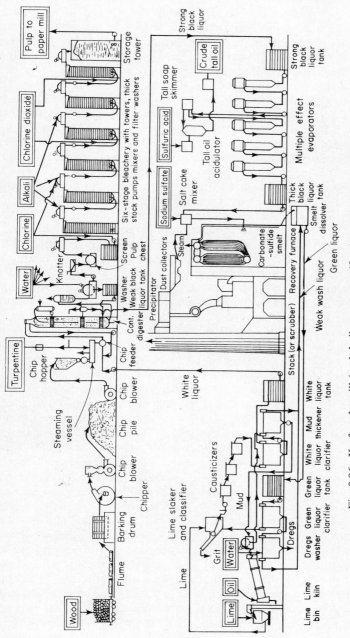

Fig. 9.96. Kraft pulp mill (excl. boiler, water purification and chlorine dioxide generation plants)

reduces the amount of compensating black liquor, as does a higher consistency of the blown pulp. In connection with the cooling and washing systems in the digester bottom (cf. below), the whole flow of pressure-compensating black liquor has been moved to the bottom of the digester.

The degree of packing of the digester has been measured with the aid of radioactive tracers (221, 316) and was found to be on average for the whole digester 0.16–0.20 tons of dry wood per m³ of digester volume, the packing being somewhat higher in the bottom of the digester. The retention time depends on the production and the digester volume and is normally around 2–3 h, of which 1–2 h are at maximum temperature. A variant of the system employs heating at the digester top, thus omitting any impregnation period, whereby a somewhat different feeding system is needed. Heating in the normal system is performed by external circulation, and the heated liquor is reintroduced through a central pipe, ending just above the strainer. The latter is halved and provisions made for automatic periodical changes in the circulation from the upper to the lower half. This ensures that the strainers are kept clean by the moving pillar of chips. The temperature employed varies with the production and is approximately 170–175°C. The hydraulic pressure should be kept some atmospheres above the partial steam pressure to ensure that no steam forms behind the strainers. The chemicals needed are approximately the same as in batch cooking.

The discharge machinery consists of a bottom scraper, a disk strainer and a blow valve. The strainer is connected to a pump, which returns some liquor to the digester. In that way the consistency of the pulp to be blown is adjusted to the desired value, which is automatically controlled. The pulp is blown to a cyclone, may pass a screw press and enters a blow tank, in the bottom of which diluting black liquor is introduced prior to filter washing of the brown stock. The blow steam leaving the cyclone and the blow tank is conveyed to the steaming vessel, the pressure of which determines the blow pressure. Excess blow steam passes to a condenser for heat and turpentine recovery. The system of using the blow steam for the initial steaming is beneficial for the heat economy. The steam consumption is less than 1 t of steam consumed per t of kraft pulp, or considerably less than in batch cooking. Eventually, it became clear, that it is necessary to cool the pulp prior to discharge, in order to avoid quite substantial losses in the strength properties (449, 659). A bottom temperature of 100°C has been shown to leave a pulp with the same, or better, strength characteristics as that of batch cooks (659). The bottom cooling can be performed in several ways, the simplest being to introduce some cold black liquor to the bottom circulation, at some expense of the heat economy. Still more satisfactory systems involve the use of a strainer system in the bottom part of the cylindrical digester shell. The cooling black liquor enters the digester through a central pipe to displace the hot black liquor from the cook, which is withdrawn through the strainer to an expansion tank, from which steam leaves for the chip steaming vessel. In this system there is ordinarily not much use for the disk strainer, as there is little need to maintain a high discharge consistency, and little steam will leave the blow tank. A further improvement of this '*cold blow*' *system* is the *hot counter-current washing system* (382a). The cold blow radial displacement already gives some contribution to the brown stock washing efficiency, and by allowing for vertical displacement of the cooking liquor by the cooling weak black liquor in counter-current upflow to the downwards moving pulp, a considerable part of the washing can be done in the digester. Although there may be some objection to occupying pressure vessel volume for a washing operation, it is felt that a height increase of an outdoor digester is economically justified, especially as one or two brown stock filters are saved thereby. A final development of this line is the straight *counter-current cooking*, which needs an additional strainer, whereby the black liquor is removed in the upper part of the digester, and the white liquor and heat are introduced to the lower half of the digester after the zone of counter-current washing (724). The advantage of counter-current cooking is primarily an improvement in pulp brightness, at least in the case of eucalypt soda cooking.

3. REACTIONS OF THE KRAFT PROCESS

A. Composition of cooking liquor during the cook

White liquor is strongly alkaline, and the sodium hydroxide concentration of the cooking liquor at the beginning of a soda or kraft cook is in the order of 40 g/l, or 1 N, corresponding to pH 14. In the case of the *soda process*, sodium hydroxide is the dominating component, with only minor amounts of sodium carbonate present, varying with the degree of caustization. In the case of kraft cooking small amounts of sodium sulfate are also present, varying with the degree of reduction in the regeneration furnace, and larger amounts of sodium sulfide, which vary mainly with the proportions of sodium to sulfur losses in the regeneration system. An example of the initial composition of the cooking liquor (disregarding the content of organic matter from the black liquor mixed with the white liquor) is given in Table 9.21, assuming a sulfidity (cf.

Table 9.21. Initial composition of cooking liquor in a normal kraft cook (disregarding organic matter from the black liquor charge)

| Compound | Formal composition | | | Actual composition |
	g/l as Na_2O	g/l as NaOH	g/l of compound	g/l of compound
NaOH	27	35	35	38
NaSH	—	—	—	4
Na_2S	12	15	15	9
Na_2CO_3	6	8	11	11
Na_2SO_4	0.1	0.1	0.2	0.2
Na_2SO_3	0.1	0.1	0.2	0.2
$Na_2S_2O_3$	0.2	0.2	0.4	0.4

Sulfidity 30%, effective alkali 42.5 g/l NaOH, active alkali 50 g/l NaOH

below) of 30%, a fairly normal value. The total sulfide content is then 0.2 M. Although the presence of sodium sulfide in the cooking liquor is a result of the *kraft* system of covering the sodium losses of the cooking chemicals with inexpensive sodium sulfate, it was soon found to have a beneficial influence on the rate of pulping and the quality of the pulp produced. The ionization state of the sodium sulfide at different stages of cooking is therefore of great interest. It has also been necessary to develop practical terms of expressing the amounts of hydroxide and sulfide charged to the digester. As there has been some confusion in the terminology this deserves a special comment, but to facilitate the understanding of the various terms it is useful first to have discussed the state of ionization of the sulfide.

Hydrogen sulfide is ionized in two stages according to the formula

$$H_2S \rightleftharpoons H^+ + HS^- \rightleftharpoons 2H^+ + S^{2-}$$

If a metal sulfide is dissolved in water, the corresponding reactions of hydrolysis are

$$S^{2-} + H_2O \rightleftharpoons HS^- + OH^- \text{ and } HS^- + H_2O \rightleftharpoons H_2S + OH^-$$

Hydroxyl ions are thus formed in amounts depending on the ionization constants of hydrogen sulfide and the presence of excess sodium hydroxide. As the acidity of H_2S corresponds to a pK_a of 7.0, and the final pH of a kraft cook is normally 10–12, obviously very little hydrogen sulfide is formed. The acidity of the HS^- ion is not determined with any certainty, values for pK_a between 12.5–14.9 being quoted (472), with a probable value of around 13.5. As the initial alkalinity of the kraft cook is in the order of pH 14, obviously only a fraction of the sulfide could be hydrolyzed to hydrosulfide upon formation of hydroxyl ions, but as alkali is consumed during the cook, and pH decreases, hydrosulfide ions are increasingly formed. This is illustrated by the *Bjerrum* diagram of Figure 9.97.

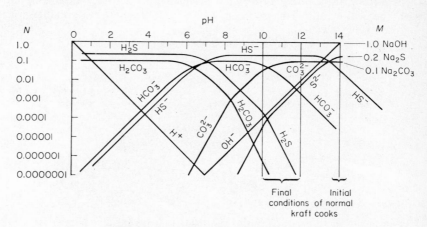

Fig. 9.97. Electrolyte systems of kraft cooking liquors

Because of the uncertainty of the acidity of the hydrosulfide ion and the activity data of such concentrated solutions, it is not possible to calculate the degree of hydrolysis of sulfide to hydrosulfide ion at various stages of the kraft cook. However, as hydrosulfide is likely to be the active chemical with respect to lignin reactions (cf. below) the question is of great interest, and an attempt has been made to determine the degree of hydrolysis experimentally (509). By determining the sulfide ion concentration in solutions of varying concentrations of sodium sulfide and hydroxide, degrees of hydrolysis from 1–93% were measured. Although some reservation must be made for the principal correctness of the method of sulfide ion analysis applied (509, 604), the results warrant observation. The degree of hydrolysis was found to change very little with the temperature and with the concentration of sodium sulfide in the range of 0.15–0.35 M solution, but to be considerably depressed by the addition of sodium hydroxide, as evidenced by Table 9.22 (509).

Table 9.22 (509). Hydrolysis of sodium sulfide, percentage

NaOH molarity		0	0.25	0.50	0.75	1.5
Temperature, °C	Na$_2$S molarity					
25	0.15	93	80	67	57	38
	0.25	92	80		59	41
	0.35	84	72		55	33
110	0.20	89	79	67	52	43
165	0.20	92	85	72	54	47

For two kraft cooks, on the low and high side of the normal sulfidity range, which were followed by analysis of hydroxide and total sulfide, the degree of hydrolysis was estimated with the aid of the data in Table 9.22 and others obtained with the same experimental technique (509). It was found that the hydrosulfide ion concentration in the high-sulfidity cook increases during the cook because of the decrease in alkalinity, in spite of some reduction in the total sulfide concentration caused by the lignin reactions, whereas in the low-sulfidity cook there is a drop in hydrosulfide ion concentration in the beginning of the cook, probably due to lignin reactions, and then possibly a small increase as the alkalinity decreases. The degree of hydrolysis was initially in both cases around 40% and increased towards fairly complete hydrolysis of the sulfide remaining at the end of the cook. The results are exemplified in Figure 9.98. Earlier assumptions on the degree of sulfide hydrolysis have covered the whole range from 0 (80) to 100% (85, 317), and even 200%, i.e. assumed hydrolysis to hydrogen sulfide during the later stages of the cook.

The consumption of sulfide or hydrosulfide sulfur during the kraft cook has been a matter of discussion, and some difficulties arise in the analytical determination. Argentopotentiometrical methods (10, 27, 80, 346), as

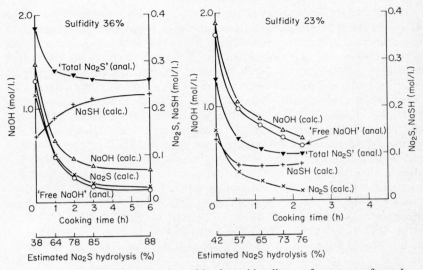

Fig. 9.98. Inorganic composition of kraft cooking liquors from two softwood cooks of different sulfidity. Analytically determined 'total Na₂S' and 'free NaOH' have been recalculated to give actual concentrations of NaOH, Na₂S and NaSH, applying certain constants to estimate the sulfide hydrolysis (Martin)

well as polarometrical ones (27), yield reasonably reliable values for residual sulfide in the black liquor. The problem is further complicated by the fact that air oxygen readily converts hydrosulfide ions into thiosulfate (143, 368, 773) and the presence of other inorganic sulfur compounds, such as polysulfide, sulfite and sulfate. Polythionates are unstable in alkali and probably absent.

Judged from the amount of sulfur, 2–3.5%, organically combined with the kraft lignin, around 5–10 kg ptw S are consumed. For kraft cooks of normal sulfidity (30%), this corresponds to 20–35% of the total amount of sulfide sulfur charged (80, 191, 260). Table 9.23 (191) demonstrates the sulfur consumption during 3 h at various temperatures for kraft cooking liquor (30% sulfidity) and a pure hydrosulfide solution (200% sulfidity). It is seen that the temperature dependence of the sulfur consumption is considerable and that at conditions which yield normal kraft pulps around 10 kg ptw S are consumed, or approximately one-third of the sulfur charged

Table 9.23 (14). Sulfur consumption in kraft and hydrosulfide cooking of spruce for 3 h at various temperatures

Temperature, °C	22	100	130	160
Sulfur consumption, kg ptw				
in kraft cooks (30% sulfidity)	0.1	2.9	3.7	9.6
in hydrosulfide cooks	7.9	12.1	16.4	28.0

at 30% sulfidity. The table also makes it probable that the reactant is the hydrosulfide ion rather than the sulfide ion.

The small discrepancy between the total sulfide consumption and the sulfur found to be combined with the kraft lignin is probably to some extent explained by the low-molecular lignin fractions of high sulfur content, which are non-precipitable by acid. The amounts of sulfur lost in the relief gases are comparatively small (64, 80, 260), in the order of 0.5 kg ptw. Other inorganic sulfur compounds, especially thiosulfate and sulfite, found in the black liquors of kraft cooks, have to a large extent been formed by air oxidation after the cook and during the analysis (368), or were present already in the initial cooking liquor. The relatively small amount of sulfur which is thus found to be organically combined, in comparison with that of hydrosulfide or sulfite cooks, confirms the opinion expressed (190, 368) that the role of the hydrosulfide ion in the kraft cook approaches that of a catalyst, the lignin adding hydrosulfide sulfur and eventually losing it again in the form of hydrosulfide ions, split off by the alkaline treatment.

The consumption of alkali, occurring virtually in parallel with the dissolution of the carbohydrates and to a minor extent the delignification, will cause changes in the pH of the cook, which are important to the final result, not only because they affect the state of ionization of the hydrosulfide ions, but because at decreasing pH there is a reprecipitation of organic components of the cooking liquor, carbohydrates, lignin, and some other colored compounds which affect the final properties of the pulp. Because the consumption of alkali is largely proportional to the dissolution of substances, the pH towards the end of the cook will be dependent on the initial charge of alkali, on cooking to constant yield. As pointed out earlier, normal values of final pH are 10–12, but in certain cases, a high alkalinity is maintained, as in the *hydrothermal injection* and the *counter-current* kraft processes, which are of minor importance. In other cases, especially in high yield kraft pulping, where the alkali charge is often very limited, pH may drop considerably below 10. Likewise, in the two-stage kraft processes employing black liquor in the initial stage, the pH of that liquor after use will also have dropped considerably. In both cases, troubles have been experienced with incrustations in the evaporation plant because of precipitating organic matter.

In calculating the amount of alkali available for the pulping reactions, the concept of *active alkali* includes the sum of sodium hydroxide and sodium sulfide charged, calculated as sodium equivalents and expressed as Na_2O (116, 222, 762) or NaOH (756). The charge is expressed in percentage of wood or in kg ptw, the latter figure being 10 times as great as the former. In this book, following the Swedish standard, the active alkali will be expressed as kg ptw NaOH. In order to convert the figures into Na_2O in percentage of wood, multiply by the factor 0.0775.

Obviously, as the concept of *active alkali* corresponds to NaOH $+$ Na_2S, this implies that the hydrolysis of sulfide proceeds completely to hydrogen sulfide and leaves two moles hydroxide per mole sulfide available for pulping. But for the exceptions mentioned above, the pH during the kraft cook does not drop further than sufficiently to allow a fairly complete hydrolysis to hydrosulfide, liberating only one mole hydroxide per mole sulfide. The actual amount of alkali available for the kraft pulping reactions is therefore closer to the concept of *effective alkali*, which corresponds to $NaOH + 1/2\ Na_2S$, also calculated as sodium equivalents and expressed as Na_2O or $NaOH$. In those cases where the final pH is kept on the high side, there is not even complete hydrolysis of the sulfide to hydrosulfide, but then the amount of unhydrolyzed sulfide could preferably be included in the figure for residual hydroxide, and hence the concept of effective alkali is still valid.

A great number of investigations have been carried out dealing with the influence of the alkali charge on pulp yield and properties. As long as the sulfidity is kept constant it is unimportant if *active* or *effective* alkali is chosen to express the independent variable. But as soon as the sulfidity of the alkali used is varied also, which is very common, the choice of concept becomes important, and as the gain in sodium hydroxide by the second stage hydrolysis of the sulfide is mainly active for normal kraft cooks, it could be considered that the concept of *effective alkali* should be used. This is also often applied. However, for reasons discussed further in Subsection II.3B, the concept of *active alkali* has both theoretical and practical justification. As is evident from Figure 9.97, although the concentration of sodium carbonate in technical cooking liquors may be as high as $0.1\ M$, the hydrolysis of sodium carbonate is almost negligible during the kraft cook, and its contribution to the alkali available for pulping reactions can therefore be normally disregarded.

To define the *amount of sulfide charged* the most rational manner would be to report in percentage of wood or kg ptw Na_2S. However, as in the mill practice the proportion of sodium hydroxide to sulfide is fixed by the regeneration system and the sodium hydroxide always remains the most important pulping chemical charged, the sulfide charge will have to follow any changes in the hydroxide charge. Therefore, it is practical to relate the sulfide charge to the total alkali charge, which gives the concept of *sulfidity*. There has been considerable confusion as to how to define sulfidity (604), but since 1954 the same definition is recommended in most kraft pulp-producing countries (116, 222, 756, 762). Sulfidity should be used to define the fraction, in sodium equivalents, of

$$\frac{Na_2S}{NaOH + Na_2S}$$

expressed in percentage. Obviously, the term, defined as above, takes only the active pulping chemicals into account, whereas an older definition (760) also included sodium carbonate in the total alkali of the denominator,

$$\frac{Na_2S}{NaOH + Na_2S + Na_2CO_3}$$

In that sense the term sulfidity can also be used for uncausticized green

588

liquor, and will be in Chapter 11 on the regeneration of cooking chemicals, but here, in the chapter dealing with the reactions of the kraft cook, sulfidity will only take into account sulfide and hydroxide.

The terms to be used in the following treatment are thus:

Effective alkali charge, in kg ptw NaOH, $= NaOH + 1/2 \ Na_2S$

Active alkali charge, in kg ptw NaOH, $= NaOH + Na_2S$

$$Sulfidity, \text{ in } \%, = 100 \cdot \frac{Na_2S}{NaOH + Na_2S} \text{ (sodium equivalents)}$$

Hitherto the changes in cooking liquor composition dealt with have been restricted to the inorganic components. The content of organic material will vary with the amount of black liquor added prior to the cook. The dissolution of organic material from the wood is illustrated in Figure 9.99 (191) for low-temperature kraft and soda cooks. It is seen that the dissolution of carbohydrates is rapid and already fairly complete after the heating period, whereas the delignification is decidedly slower. Whereas the delignification of the soda cook almost comes to a standstill, the dissolution of lignin in the kraft cook proceeds at a satisfactory rate, which is obviously an effect of the sulfur compounds reacting with lignin. It is also noted that the carbohydrate reactions proceed with the same rate for both cooks, irrespective of the sulfur content. The alkali consumption is obviously in parallel to the carbohydrate reactions. As will be further discussed in the section on carbohydrate reactions, these cause the main alkali consumption, but as much as a quarter of the total alkali is required by lignin reactions. However, this alkali is used up in the neutralization of phenolic groups, which are very weak acids, and consequently will be included in the figures for residual effective alkali unless special precautions are taken in the volumetric determination. One such precaution is addition of barium chloride solution and removal of the lignin as barium phenolate prior to titration of the liquor. The curves for alkali consumption in Figure 9.99 should therefore be taken as representative for the carbohydrate reactions only. A normal cooking temperature of the kraft cook is considerably higher than that of the cook shown in that figure, but a similar set-up of curves is obtained for a normal kraft cook, only at shorter cooking times.

Because of the dissolution of organic substance during the cook, the large amounts of cooking chemicals used, and the practice of charging black liquor to the digester prior to cooking, the total solids content of the black liquor leaving the digester is as high as 15–22%.

B. Lignin reactions

Delignification in alkaline cooking involves *lignin degradation* and subsequent *dissolution through its phenolate groups*. Alkali lignin can be precipitated from the black liquor by mild acidification or by addition of neutral salts of divalent ions, such as barium chloride. However, the protolignin also contains considerable amounts of phenolic groups, about 0.3 per monomer, and mildly isolated lignin, such as milled wood lignin,

589

dissolves directly in fairly weak alkali at room temperature (75). Why is it still necessary to perform an alkaline cook at such high alkalinity and temperature? It could be argued that milled wood lignin might be mechanically degraded, facilitating the dissolution of the molecules, but its molecular weight is still about 10,000 (DP 50–60), which is higher than most lignin preparations except those apparently condensed, and considerably higher than the fragments called alkali lignin, of 1,000–7,000 (249), 1,000–1,500 (190), 1,100 (697), 1,000–1,800 (413) or 900–1,500 (537). These figures correspond to a DP of only 5–10, in spite of the fact that considerable secondary condensation is likely to have occurred during the cook. The only possible explanations for the severe cooking conditions necessary to achieve delignification are therefore the physical structure of wood and lignin, and possibly the existence of lignin–carbohydrate complexes. The ease of delignification of grasses by alkali at 100°C when applying simultaneous mechanical treatment was pointed out in Chapter 8.II. On the whole, the location of the lignin in the fiber wall seems to be important for the ease of pulping, softwoods offering the greatest resistance, hardwoods decidedly less, and grasses the least.

Another important early observation was that the *presence of sulfides* in the alkali improves the rate of delignification and therefore the pulp quality. That the lignin dissolution is accelerated, whereas the rate of carbohydrate removal is comparatively unaffected, has been demonstrated for both softwoods and hardwoods (198, 272, 274, 384). It was observed early (436) that sulfur combines with the lignin, but the exact nature of this reaction and why it improves the rate of delignification has required

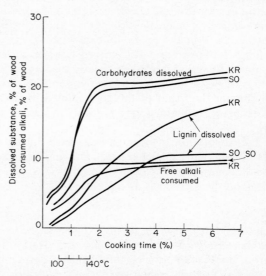

Fig. 9.99. Alkali consumption and dissolution of wood substance in low-temperature (140°C) kraft (KR) and soda (SO) cooks of spruce (Enkvist)

590

considerable research and still remains incompletely understood. Lignin from a kraft cook contains 1–3 % sulfur (15, 413), or 0.1–0.2 S per monomer. The nature of these sulfur groups is not clear, but it has been demonstrated (413) that no *thiol, thiocarbonyl, disulfide, polysulfide* or *dialkylsulfide* but possibly *sulfoxide* or *sulfone* groups are present, although dialkylsulfides (thioethers) have often been suggested as the most probable structure (190) and have also been indicated in other investigations (239). As will be shown, the nature of the sulfur groups remaining in the lignin after the kraft cook is not likely to throw much light on the mechanism of kraft cooking, since that mechanism involves the introduction of such sulfur groups into the lignin molecule, that are not stable to alkali but are subsequently and continually removed under regeneration of sulfide and hydrosulfide ions.

Therefore, studies on the 'sulfidation' of wood and lignin have been performed at pH and temperature conditions which do not correspond to those of a kraft cook (e.g. 192, 193, 194, 198, 199, 302, 824). The so-called *hydrosulfide cooks* are performed at 80–100°C at pH 7–9. Figure 9.100 (193) shows the delignification of sprucewood at 100°C in hydrosulfide solutions of various pH. It is seen that the dissolution is parallel with the hydrosulfide concentration, whereas the hydrogen sulfide does not seem to be an active pulping agent. Hydrosulfide cooks at 100°C, however, dissolve only part of the lignin, up to 30 % softwood lignin (193) and decidedly more hardwood lignin (198). Even higher temperatures do not lead to complete fiber liberation, as much of the middle lamella lignin remains undissolved (193). Some of the lignin was observed to 'melt' during a hydrosulfide cook at higher temperature and to flow into the fiber lumen (193), a phenomenon not experienced in other pulping

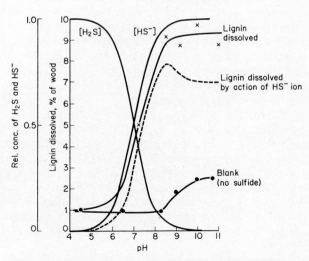

Fig. 9.100. Delignification of softwood by hydrosulfide at varying pH (Enkvist)

591

processes. These changes indicate that the hydrosulfide ions react with the lignin in a manner which causes degradation of the macromolecules, although insufficient to effect complete dissolution. The wood structure does not influence the reactions of the hydrosulfide cook, as judged by experiments with pre-beating and pre-swelling of the wood (193).

Thiolignin from hydrosulfide cooks contains up to 12–18% sulfur, or 0.8–1.2 S per monomer (190, 201). Hydroxymercaptan formation with carbonyl groups of lignin, an earlier suggested mechanism (9), could not possibly explain such amounts. About half the sulfur of such thiolignin was shown (201) to be *disulfide* sulfur (oxidized *mercaptan* groups) and 50–75% is probably located at the α-carbon atoms (239). *Mercaptan* and *sulfide* groups explain some but not all of the remaining sulfur in combination with the lignin. Treatment with alkali lye at room temperature, however, causes partial and at 80°C a more complete change in the thiolignin molecule, accompanied by a loss of water but not of sulfur. Heating with alkali at kraft cooking temperature, however, causes considerable *sulfur removal*, to a sulfur content corresponding to that of kraft lignin (196). The main part of the inorganic sulfur of the white liquor is therefore found in the black liquor as hydrosulfide after the kraft cook (368), but the lignin reactions with the sulfur compounds must still be of deciding importance for the delignification.

Other important reactions of lignin during the kraft cook are *hydrolysis* and *condensation*. Hydrolysis is indicated by the comparatively low molecular weight of the kraft lignin, and by the losses of methoxyl. Softwood kraft lignin contains about 13% methoxyl (413) as against 16% in the protolignin, corresponding to a loss of about 0.2 OCH_3 per monomer. No or few carbonyl, benzyl alcohol or alkyl ether groups remain (200, 532), whereas the phenolic hydroxyls have increased from 0.3 per monomer in the protolignin to almost 1.0 in the dissolved lignin (196) and almost as much in the residual lignin of soda or kraft pulps. In contrast, lignin in wood treated with white liquor or sodium hydroxide at 100°C contains only a little more phenolic hydroxyls than protolignin (187). Likewise, thiolignin, mildly prepared by a hydrosulfide cook at neutral conditions, contains only the same amount of phenolic hydroxyls as the protolignin, but treatment by alkali already at room temperature and more completely at 80°C causes *formation of large quantities of phenolic groups*, indicating *hydrolysis* by alkali.

According to more recent investigations (514a), about 0.16 carboxyl groups per monomer are formed in the lignin on alkali cooking, but the major part of the acid groups of kraft lignin must still be phenolic. The kinetics of the *demethylation* have been studied (684a), and in addition to hydroxyl ions, hydrosulfide and methyl mercaptide ions also cause demethylation (195b), forming methanol, methyl mercaptan and dimethyl sulfide, the latter two being responsible for the foul smell of all kraft pulp mills.

The lignin undergoes *condensation* during the kraft cook. This is evident from analysis of the oxidation products of kraft lignin (108, 624).

As in the case of acid condensation, the 5-position of the benzene ring is the most reactive point of condensation, and the formation of phenolic groups during the cook is likely to increase that reactivity. The condensation reactions are accompanied by a loss of aliphatic hydroxyl and carbonyl groups (200, 532). The vanillin-forming configurations upon nitrobenzene oxidation of lignin likewise disappear during the kraft cook (200), which is also an indication of condensation reactions. On the other hand, it has been observed (192) that 7% of the wood, or 25% of the wood lignin from kraft, soda or hydrosulfide cooking is obtained in a water-soluble form, and this fraction is rather low-molecular. Aceto-guaiacone and propioguaiacone, corresponding to about 1–2% of the wood (39, 192), have been identified among these compounds, and further quantities can be obtained by additional heating of alkali lignin. Soda cooking does not yield these ketones (39), and only small amounts of other water-soluble substances.

A contributing mechanism to lignin condensation during the kraft cook and particularly the soda cook is the dehydration at the α–β carbon atoms of the side chain with formation of a double bond, and the subsequent splitting of the β–γ carbon bond with formation of formaldehyde (238). Formaldehyde is known to readily condense with phenols in alkali, cf. below.

Additional information on the lignin reactions of the kraft cook has been obtained by comparing the *sulfonation* and *sulfidation* reactions, which appear to compete for the same groups in lignin. Presulfonated wood or lignin does not take up more sulfur on neutral hydrosulfide cooking at 100°C (199), but on heating in more alkaline solutions of hydrosulfide at 160°C the lignin will lose the sulfonate groups and sulfidation occurs to an extent of almost 1 S per monomer. On the other hand, hydrosulfide-treated wood (pH 7, 100°C) can be sulfonated to an extent increasing with the acidity of the bisulfite solution. Much of the groups thus sulfonated may be located at monomers containing etherified phenolic hydroxyls and thus not presulfidized. However, this lignin did not dissolve upon sulfonation, possibly because of secondary condensation during the treatments. In contrast, the presulfidized lignin can be dissolved by a two-stage sulfonation, with a neutral stage preceding the acid sulfonation, in which case the sulfur groups are eliminated by simultaneous introduction of sulfonate groups (240). Other reagents, known to react at the α-carbon atom of lignin, such as *dimethyl sulfate, methanolhydrochloric acid* and *phenols*, likewise affect the sulfidation reaction (199).

All these observations on the behavior of wood lignin during the kraft cook have been completed by more recent work on *low-molecular lignin model substances* (39, 194, 199, 201, 202, 238, 239, 338, 488, 534, 535, 536, 824). Of the model compounds, only those containing a *p*-hydroxybenzyl alcohol or alkyl ether configuration react with hydrosulfide, in analogy with the reactivity on sulfonation in neutral sulfite solutions, cf. Chapter 9.1, whereas etherification of the phenolic group renders the compounds practically unreactive. Model compounds containing other

593

functional groups, known to be present in lignin, such as carbonyls, ethylenic double bonds, and alkylaryl ether bonds, did not react with hydrosulfide, either in neutral (194) or alkaline (824) medium at lower temperature. One of the simplest and most studied models is *vanillyl alcohol*, which is readily converted to mercaptan and vanillyl disulfide or sulfide upon treatment with hydrosulfide (201, 534), Figure 9.101. The reaction is believed to involve quinone methide formation (372), I, which reacts with the nucleophilic hydrosulfide ion to the mercaptan (338), II. The mercaptan remains in the solution at pH below 7 (201) until the reaction vessel is opened and oxidation to the disulfide occurs, III. At neutral to alkaline conditions vanillyl sulfide is formed by reaction of the mercaptan with more quinone methide (534), IV. Unreacted vanillyl alcohol also reacts with the quinone methide to give formaldehyde and diguaiacone methane (338), V. The latter reaction illustrates one possible condensation mechanism, and the formaldehyde liberated gives further possibilities for condensation. Consequently, in sulfur-free alkaline cooking of vanillyl alcohol, polymer formation was found to dominate (338). The mercaptan and sulfide formation illustrates the sulfidation reactions, and further studies on the alkaline decomposition of vanillyl sulfide give information on the subsequent reformation of hydrosulfide ions. The sulfide was believed to give thiovanillin, which forms vanillin and hydrosulfide ion upon hydrolysis (536), but vanillin is not a major reaction product (338) so that the hydrolysis must be of another nature.

Similar results have been obtained with more advanced model compounds (39, 202, 238, 239, 824). One model of particular interest because of its lignin-representative structure is *guaiacylglycerol-β-guaiacyl ether*, VI, and the corresponding methylated derivative, *veratrylglycerol-β-guaiacyl ether*, VII, (39, 238, 239). The former was *not* found to be cleaved by alkaline hydrolysis when treated at high temperature in sulfide-free lye, but, instead, to split off water and formaldehyde, whereas the methylated compound gave guaiacyl and veratrylglycerol (238), whereby the cleavage was probably preceded by *epoxide* formation with the neighbouring α-hydroxyl. On the other hand, the guaiacylglycerol-β-guaiacyl ether reacted readily with hydrosulfide and could be further cleaved by alkaline hydrolysis, whereas the methylated derivative could not. Thus the assumed mechanism, VIII, would be the mercaptation of the *p*-hydroxybenzyl alcohol group, displacement of the aroxyl function by a neighbouring group mechanism under formation of an *episulfide*, which subsequently is probably hydrolyzed by alkali to form hydrosulfide ions again. The formation of aceto- and propioguaiacone was also observed from guaiacylglycerol-β-guaiacyl ether under the same conditions as from wood, and intermediate reaction with hydrosulfide is also a prerequisite here (39).

From the collected evidence of wood, lignin and model compound reactions, the *following delignification mechanism* is emerging (cf. 195a). In sulfur-free alkali (soda) cooking, cleavage of the alkylaryl ether bonds occurs at high temperature between monomers lacking free phenolic

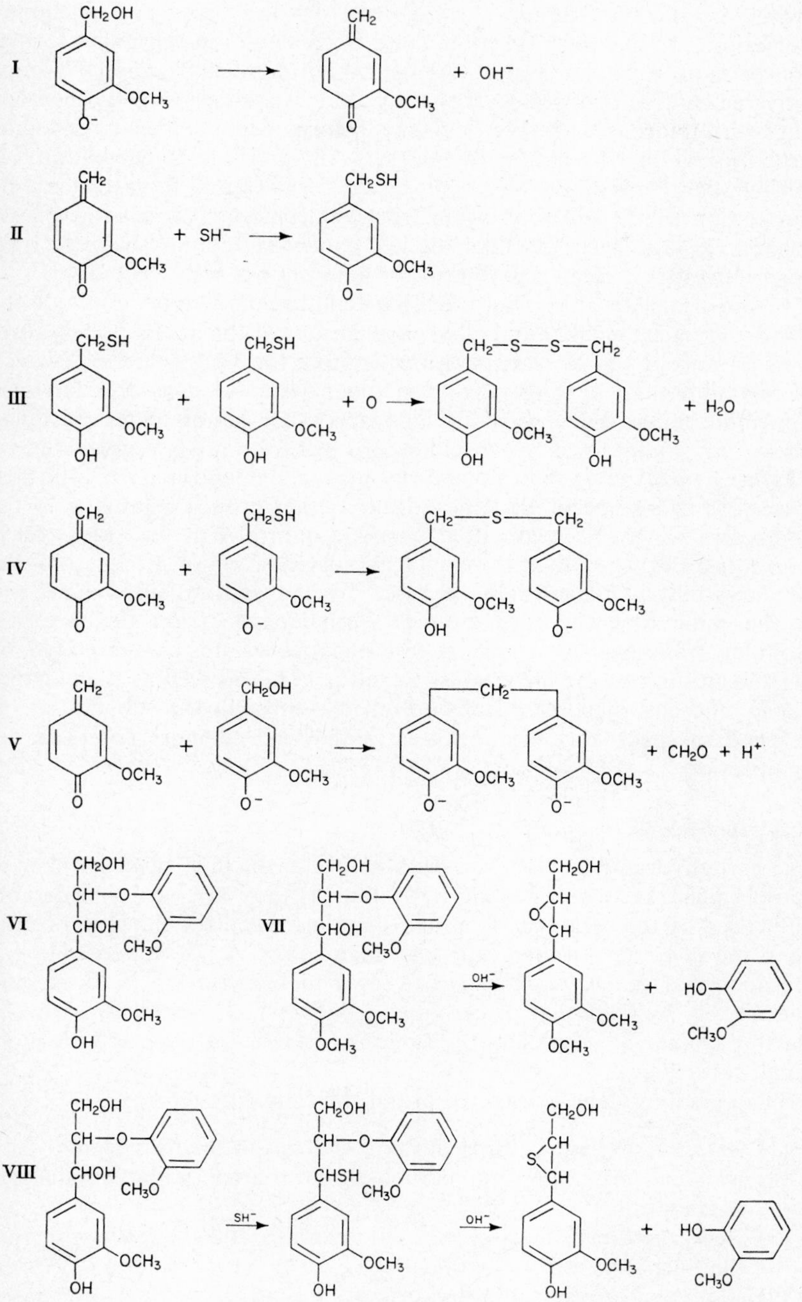

Fig. 9.101. Model compound reactions illustrating the lignin reactions of alkaline cooking and the role of the sulfide in kraft cooking (Enkvist *et al*)

hydroxyls, and the degradation fragments dissolve because of phenolate formation. Some methoxyl groups are likewise eliminated under formation of more phenolic groups. At the same time, benzyl alcohol groups activated by free phenolic groups may condense, either with the benzene rings with unoccupied 5-position, or with formation of dibenzyl methane structures upon elimination of one side chain from the 1-position. A further source of condensation will be the formation of formaldehyde by elimination of the γ-carbon atom from some monomers activated by a phenolic group. The formaldehyde will condense with any benzene ring, predominantly at the 5-position, to form additional methylene links.

In the presence of sulfide and hydrosulfide ions (kraft cooking), the p-hydroxybenzyl alcohol and alkyl ether groups of the lignin already form mercapto groups at low temperatures (during the heating period), which on the additional heating may form dibenzylsulfide structures but also contribute to the cleavage of the alkylaryl ether bonds under episulfide formation. Sulfide and hydrosulfide ions are continually regenerated by alkaline hydrolysis of the thiolignin at higher temperature, and will then react with those benzyl alcohol and alkyl ether groups belonging to the monomers which received a free phenolic hydroxyl in the recent alkylaryl ether cleavage. In this manner, the degradation of the lignin at the alkylaryl ether linkages is accelerated by the sulfur compounds, and at the same time the formation of formaldehyde from the γ-carbon atom of monomers activated by free phenolic groups is eliminated by the substitution at the α-carbon with sulfur. This, as well as the elimination of the activated benzyl alcohol groups through the substitution, is believed to check condensation greatly and lead to more complete delignification.

C. Carbohydrate reactions

The carbohydrate chemistry of the alkaline cooks involves a number of complicated reactions. As far as is known they are not considerably influenced by the presence of sulfur compounds, and should consequently be of the same type in both kraft and soda cooks. A possible exception is the action of the *polysulfide ions*, known to increase the yield of pulp conceivably by oxidation of carbonyl groups, which would otherwise be starting points of degradation reactions, as will be discussed in more detail subsequently.

The reactions to be considered are of the following types:

(1) *Alkaline swelling*, causing physical changes in the fiber wall.
(2) *Alkaline dissolution* of carbohydrate matter without chemical degradation.
(3) *Reprecipitation* of dissolved carbohydrates and their *adsorption* on the fiber structure.
(4) *Alkaline hydrolysis* of acetyl groups.
(5) *Alkaline 'peeling,'* a reaction sequence involving enolization, hydrolysis of β-alkoxycarbonyl bonds and further *degradation* of

the products of hydrolysis, including isomerizations, as well as hydrolysis, to hydroxy acids.

(6) *'Stopping' reactions*, involving dehydration and *fragmentation* or intramolecular *rearrangements* to alkali-stable configurations.

(7) *Alkaline hydrolysis* of β-glycosidic bonds, resulting in *depolymerization* of the chain molecules to shorter fragments, which are exposed to further degradation by alkaline peeling.

Of these, the peeling reaction is responsible for most of the alkali consumption and yield losses.

The initial reaction between alkaline cooking liquors and the wood carbohydrates is a *solvation* of the hydroxyl groups by the hydroxyl ions and water. At the same time the carboxyl groups of the uronic acids are neutralized and the carboxylate groups solvated. The solvation results in considerable *swelling* which is probably mainly intermicellar and restricted by the presence of lignin and the helical structure of highly orientated cellulose in the outer parts of the cell wall. Still, swelling facilitates the penetration of the cooking liquor and the diffusion of chemicals from the liquor outside the wood chips and is therefore of considerable importance for the uniformity of the cook. Swelling to an extent necessary to allow easy penetration and diffusion in all directions only occurs at pH levels above 13 (745). In the kraft cooks, alkalinity is generally in the order of 1 N NaOH initially, corresponding to pH 14. As the acid strength of the hydroxyl groups of carbohydrates corresponds to a pK_a of 13.5–14 (114, 557, 684), swelling is obviously accompanied by partial ionization of these groups.

At the same time as swelling, some carbohydrate molecules which are easily accessible and of low molecular weight are solvated to such an extent that they are disconnected from their adjacent molecules and *physically dissolved* in the lye. This will happen not only in the initial stage of the cook, but whenever a new region is made accessible or previous degradation has made the molecular chains sufficiently short. The phenomenon is particularly marked with hardwoods, where a considerable quantity of xylan appears fairly undegraded in the cooking liquor, to an increasing extent during almost the entire heating period, but disappearing again towards the end of the cook (156a), Table 9.24. The dissolved material is then *further decomposed* to a large extent in solution, or *reprecipitated* onto the fibers when the alkalinity of the liquor has decreased to such an extent that solvation becomes insufficient (157, 818). It is significant that the critical pH range for reprecipitation is about the same as that for swelling, or pH 13–14.

Alkaline hydrolysis of the acetyl groups, resulting in the formation of acetate ions, occurs at an early stage of the cook, probably immediately upon the contact of the white liquor with the wood. As the acetyl groups of the hardwood xylan and softwood glucomonnan form irregularities in the straight chain configuration, their hydrolysis from some dissolved material may be a prerequisite for the reprecipitation of these chains. The

Table 9.24 (156a). Polysaccharides dissolved in the liquor during soda cooking of birch

	Pulp composition							Liquor polysaccharides				Polysaccharide composition					
Cooking temp. °C	time h	Pulp yield %	Lig-nin, %	Cellu-lose, %	Gluco-mannan, %	Glucu-ronoxy-lan, %	Galactan and arabi-nan, %	Polysaccharide content, % of wood	$\overline{DP}_n$	Lig-nin, %	Uronic acid, %	OCH$_3$, %	Gal. %	Glu. %	Man. %	Ara. %	Xyl. %
100	0.55	77.8	22	52	1	24	2	4.5	169	3.7	13.9	2.1	3.5	0.5	0.2	1.3	94.5
120	1.05	76.5	21	54	1	23	1	5.5	180	3.4	13.4	2.1	3.8	0.6	0.5	1.3	93.8
130	1.30	74.3	21	55	1	22	1	5.5	165	4.5	11.9	2.2	3.4	0.5	0.4	1.6	94.2
140	1.40	72.2	20	57	1	22	0	6.5	159	6.5	13.0	2.0	5.0	0.3	0.3	0.8	93.6
150	2.00	67.8	18	59	1	22	0	8.0	155	4.9	8.4	1.8	4.3	0.2	0.1	0.8	94.7
160	2.30	62.3	14	62	1	23	0	7.5	129	7.6	8.5	0.9	3.6	0.1	0.2	1.0	95.1
170	3.05	53.0	4	72	1	24	0	3.5	68	18.2	5.5	1.1	11.6	0.3	0.2	1.5	86.4
170	5.05	50.3	3	73	0	25	0	1.0	36	—	5.9	0.8	17.1	1.0	0.4	2.0	79.6

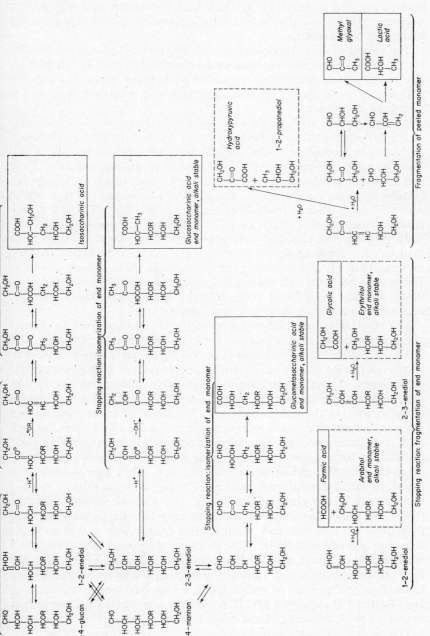

Fig. 9.102. Reactions of 1 : 4-linked hexosans in hot alkali

removal of *glucuronic acid groups* from the xylan is also important in this connection, and as indicated by Table 9.24, the uronic acid content will decrease in the dissolved polysaccharide fraction when the cook approaches maximum temperature.

The course of the *alkaline peeling reaction*, which is also of importance for the hot alkali purification stage in the bleaching of pulp, cf. Chapter 15, has recently been fairly well elucidated (424, reviewed in 423 together with earlier work on the alkaline degradation of carbohydrates), and is visualized as follows.

Alkaline peeling starts as the *enolization of carbonyl groups* of end units in the carbohydrate chains (166), followed by *isomerization to β-alkoxycarbonyl* configurations, which are extremely sensitive to hot alkali and undergo rapid *decomposition* (423, 424), whereby the end unit is split off, and a new, aldehyde-containing end unit is formed, which in its turn can be split off in the same manner. The peeling will proceed to the extent of about 50–65 monomers from every starting point (229, 673), until finally another reaction mechanism, called the *stopping reaction* (499, 500, 501, 625), provides the end unit with a configuration stable to alkali. The tendency for the stopping reaction to occur might be higher in the case of xylan than for glucan, and lower for mannan (625). Those molecules which have been split off during the peeling reaction are further decomposed by alkali to hydroxy acids, whereby *hydrolysis* and *intramolecular rearrangements* are the important reactions.

The enolization and isomerization reactions are illustrated for glucan and mannan as well as for xylan in the following formulae, Figure 9.102–103. The initial isomerizations thus consist of formation of *enediols*, which are further isomerized to β-alkoxycarbonyl and β-hydroxycarbonyl compounds. These are extremely sensitive to alkali and are rapidly dealkoxylated and dehydrated respectively. The former reaction results in the removal of the end monomer, the formation of a new aldehyde end group and leads to a peeling degradation along the chain from the end, until stabilization occurs. The dehydration reaction leads to a configuration which by a special (benzilic acid) isomerization rearranges to an alkali-stable chain, ending in a carboxyl group. This type of reaction is therefore called the stopping reaction. In the example shown, the end monomer is of the *glucometasaccharinic* and *glucosaccharinic acid* type (500, 501), but other stopping reactions may also be possible, e.g. the formation of carbinol end groups with contemporary formation of *formic* or *glycolic acid* (145). That carbinol end groups might exist to a considerable extent in stabilized molecules is indicated by the fact that the sum of aldehyde and carboxyl end groups is always considerably lower than the number of molecules in a cellulose sample treated with hot alkali at 120 (136) or 170°C (229). About one third of the end groups appear to be of the carbinol and other unknown types.

The general mechanism of the action of dilute alkali on different types of polysaccharides is regulated by the point of attachment of the glycoside grouping to the parent aldose (424). Thus, as illustrated in Figure 9.103,

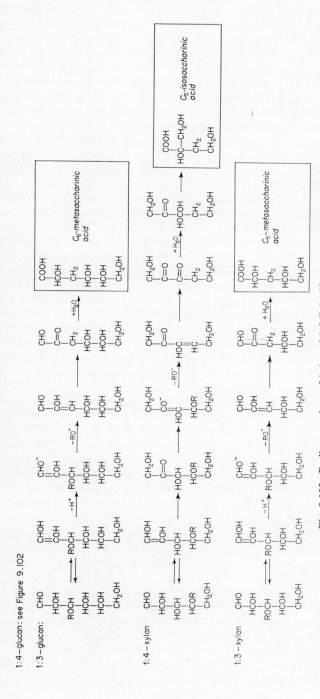

Fig. 9.103. Peeling reactions of 1:4- and 1:3-linked hexosans and pentozans in hot alkali

in the case of 1:3 attachment (e.g. for the arabinose substituents of softwood xylan), the mechanism involves the carbonyl group in 1-position, but for 1:4-linked polysaccharides, which is the predominating mode of linking in the wood polysaccharides, it only operates from a carbonyl group in 2-position after isomerization of the end monomer to a corresponding ketose. In the former case *metasaccharinic acids* are formed, whereas with 1:4-linked carbohydrates the end products are *isosaccharinic acids*. This has been demonstrated for various types of di- and polysaccharides. Apart from C_6-saccharinic acids from hexosans and C_5-saccharinic acids from pentosans, acids of lower molecular weights are also formed in *fragmentation reactions*, as exemplified above for *lactic acid*, which is formed via other C_3-bodies such as dihydroxyacetone and glyceraldehyde (607). Smaller amounts of volatile *methyl glyoxal* (224, 657) is formed at the same time, which gives the characteristic smell to sulfur-free alkali cooks. An alternative formation of 1,2-*propanediol* and *hydroxypyruvic acid* is indicated by the fact that potentiometric titrations show the presence of strong acids of pK_a around 2.4 (657) but has not been definitely proven. Other acids have also been found in alkaline cooking of pure glucan, such as *formic* and *acetic acids* (607). The detailed mechanism of their formation is not quite established, but formic acid is likely to be formed from 1-2-enediols. In such a case, simultaneous formation of alkali-stable polysaccharide chains with terminating alcohol groups is also possible. Carbohydrates containing 1:2-linked end monomers, such as for the glucuronic acid substituents of xylan, do not form β-alkoxycarbonyl configurations and are thus stable to alkaline peeling, until the α-substituents are removed by high-temperature alkaline hydrolysis.

The above-described concept of the mechanism of the action of dilute alkali on polysaccharides was originally derived mainly from model experiments, often at low temperature and with lime-water (423, 424). Some deviations might be expected for the course of a high-temperature kraft cook. Experiments on cotton performed with 0.5 N NaOH at 100, 170 and 220°C indicate decreasing yields of isosaccharinic acid and increasing yields of lactic acid at an increase in temperature (145, 499, 607). However, a fairly constant amount of acids, 1.5 mol/glucose unit dissolved, was found, as is also the case in the hot purification of pulp, cf. Chapter 15. This fact shows that the formation of low-molecular acids with less than 6 carbon atoms must occur to a considerable extent. As most of the acids formed are hydroxyl acids, lactone formation likewise occurs to some extent.

If the mixture of reaction compounds from alkaline cooking of cotton at higher temperature is already complicated, the mixture of products obtained from a kraft cook on wood is still more so. Some attempts have been made to characterize the products of carbohydrate origin found in black liquor. Only as little as 2% of the dissolved polysaccharides can be recovered in the black liquor (664). The remainder is present in the form of saccharinic, lactic and other organic acids and lactones (433, 436). Based on wood, 18% of hydroxy acids and lactones, of which 5% is lactic acid, has been found (259, 515). The presence of C_6-isosaccharinic and C_6-meta-saccharinic (252) acids has been demonstrated, and C_5- as well as C_4-metasaccharinic acids together with much lactic and other low-molecular acids have been indicated chromatographically (252). In view of the dominance of 1:4-linked polysaccharides in wood, the large proportion of metasaccharinic acids found in comparison to isosaccharinic acids is surprising, and indicates a rearrangement of the peeling-off monomers, possibly involving intermediate hydration and dehydration, parallel to the isosaccharinic acid formation mechanism described. The presence of C_5-metasaccharinic acids is also explained by the 'stopping' rearrangement induced by the arabinose substituents in the 3-position on xylose monomer.

As the main alkali consumption of the kraft cook is caused by peeling and similar reactions, this is the place to make a rough calculation on how the consumption of alkali is distributed in the different reactions. Assuming a normal softwood kraft cook giving a pulp yield of 47%, of which 3% is lignin, the dissolved material should consist of roughly 3% resin and ashes, 24% lignin, 24% carbohydrates and 2% acetyl groups. With a sulfidity of 30%, the consumption of active alkali is around 180 and of effective alkali around 150 kg ptw NaOH. The dissolved lignin contains about 0.8 phenolic groups per monomer, requiring approximately 40 kg ptw NaOH for neutralization. The remainder, 110 kg ptw, is consumed partly by the hydrolysis of the acetyl groups, around 15 kg ptw, and partly by the carbohydrate degradation reactions, 95 kg ptw. The latter figure roughly corresponds to 1.6 moles of acids per hexose unit, a probable value, which agrees with what has been found in the hot alkali degradation of cellulose (145). Lignin is thus responsible for only about a quarter of the alkali consumption of the kraft cook.

As pointed out earlier, the tendency to degrade in hot alkali differs for various carbohydrate components (625). To some extent, this can be explained by differences in the manner of linking between the monomeric units, 1:3-attachment being more sensitive to degradation. However, although the arabinose substituents are thus easily removed from the xylan end monomers during the peeling, they induce at the same time a rearrangement of this end monomer to a metasaccharinic acid unit. The substitution of xylan by glucuronic acid groups in the 2-position likewise tends to stabilize against alkaline degradation, since peeling is prevented by 2-substitution. However, model experiments have shown (48a, 156) that the glucuronic acid groups at terminating xylose monomers are readily hydrolysed by alkali at elevated temperature. Therefore, the glucuronic acid substituents are no real protection against peeling. Further, the tendency to dehydrate in the stopping reaction may be different for different types of end monomer. Finally, the degree of accessibility to the cooking liquor may be different for the different types of polysaccharides. A more crystalline configuration, as in the case of cellulose, is likely to be more alkali-resistant. However, in contrast to the sulfite cook, where the cellulose remains in the pulp almost quantitatively until fairly low contents

603

of lignin and hemicellulose have been reached, the cellulose of the kraft cook is dissolved to a considerable extent, about 10%, already at pulps with fairly high lignin contents. The end monomers of cellulose remaining after an alkali cook have been found to consist of glucometasaccharinic acid (12a) as required by the stopping mechanism theory.

The chemical stabilization of polysaccharide end groups towards hot alkali peeling degradation is thus caused partly by native structural features, as in the case of the glucuronic acid groups of xylan, and partly by spontaneous rearrangement and fragmentation reactions occurring during the cook, the stopping reactions. However, some stabilization reactions can be *induced* by pretreatments of the wood or by addition of special chemicals to the kraft cook, which convert the end groups to alkali-stable configurations. The alternatives investigated are *glycosidation* (500, 529), selective *oxidation* with hypohalites (62) or chlorite (40, 529), and *reduction* with tetrahydroborate (40, 530, 625), and all have been shown to stabilize to a somewhat varying degree. The possibility of stabilization by *calcium hydroxide* addition has also been studied (40, 500), since the presence of calcium ions has been found to facilitate the benzilic acid rearrangement of the spontaneous stopping reaction (572). Most of the investigations have been carried out on cellulose or hydrocellulose samples rather than with wood, but *tetrahydroborate reduction* as well as *chlorite oxidation* and *polysulfide oxidation* has led to increased yields in kraft pulping experiments, as will be further discussed in a subsequent section.

One important carbohydrate reaction with alkali remains to be considered, namely the *alkaline hydrolysis of glycosidic bonds*. This reaction is responsible for a shortening of the polysaccharide chains, which is likely to have some bearing on the paper properties of the pulp. It is a fairly old observation that overcooked kraft pulps of low chlorine number have a much lower viscosity than normal kraft pulps. The phenomenon is accentuated when lignin condensation prior to the kraft cook, as takes place on prehydrolysis, necessitates more severe kraft cooking conditions than normal. The comparatively low viscosities of unbleached prehydrolysis–kraft pulps from softwoods is thus caused by alkaline degradation in the kraft cook and not directly by acid hydrolysis in the pre-cook. Further, high-temperature *kiering*, or alkali cooking, of cotton linters has been used for quite some time as a means of regulating the viscosity of the linters pulp (105).

This type of alkaline degradation only becomes noticeable at fairly high temperatures (673), whereas normal hot alkali purification of pulp at 100°C or even 130°C does not cause any decrease in viscosity, but a slight increase due to the removal of low-molecular carbohydrates. It has also been shown (145, 229) that the depolymerization reaction is independent of the presence of small amounts of oxygen and is therefore entirely an alkaline hydrolysis of glycosidic bonds, as also indicated by model experiments with glycosides (487). Mannosides have been shown to be more resistant to alkaline hydrolysis than the corresponding glucosides, galactosides and xylosides (487). The glucuronic acid substituents are also hydrolyzed by the same mechanism (314), but remain unhydrolyzed to a significant extent, 30–40%, in the pulp xylan because of the decreased alkalinity towards the end of the kraft cook (138a, 157, 158, 526a). Another possible reaction of similar type is the alkaline hydrolysis of β-phenylglycosidic bonds (487), assuming such types of bonds in a hypothetical lignin–carbohydrate complex. The cleavage of such bonds leads to the formation of an epoxide, which is quite reactive and could either decompose to the corresponding aldose, or react with an aliphatic hydroxyl group to give a β-glycoside, or form an internal glycoside with an alcohol group in the same monomer. In principle, the same reactions are possible at the alkaline cleavage of the β-glycosidic bond between the polysaccharide monomers, although higher reaction temperature is necessary. Therefore, these reactions may also occur in the kraft cook without an assumed lignin–carbohydrate complex.

The reaction with alcohol groups has special interest as it implies transglycosidations between the carbohydrate components. The existence of carbohydrate cross-linkages, assumed to explain the so-called alkali-resistant pentosans of kraft pulp (526) and possibly their higher strength have thus received a less hypothetical background. As will be demonstrated below, the existence of alkali-resistant pentosans does not require any assumption of transglycosidation reactions, and so far no evidence for transglycosidations in the kraft cook has been presented.

The problems connected with the presence of fairly large amounts of alkali-resistant hemicelluloses, especially xylan, in kraft pulps have attracted considerable attention. The resistance of these carbohydrates towards hot alkali is remarkable enough in view of the rapid initial degradation of polysaccharides in alkali at elevated temperatures, but has been explained by the various stabilization reactions possible. The importance of the latter to the yield and quality of kraft paper pulps is obvious. However, there is also a remarkable resistance of the hemicelluloses, especially some xylan, of kraft pulp to cold alkali extraction. This makes it difficult to prepare dissolving pulps by a straight one-stage kraft process. Bleached kraft pulps are less reactive in the viscose process and yield products with impaired properties from all dissolving processes as much of the resistant hemicelluloses remain in them. This led finally to the prehydrolysis–kraft process (cf. Chapter 9.III) for dissolving pulps in which the non-desirable hemicelluloses are degraded and partially dissolved by acid hydrolysis prior to the kraft cook.

The exact nature of the cold-alkali resistant hemicellulose fractions and their mode of formation has been much discussed. In kraft pulp from hardwoods there is 8–11% xylan, non-dissolvable in 17% NaOH (e.g. 445, 693). However, lye of mercerizing strength lacks the optimal concentration for xylan removal, 6–6.5% NaOH lye being more effective (527, 693). Potassium hydroxide is more efficient in removing xylan (693), and most of the resistant xylan can be obtained by a two-stage extraction with 17% NaOH followed by 24% KOH, whereby less resistant hemicelluloses are removed in the first fraction and fairly pure xylan can be obtained upon acidification of the latter lye. This demonstrates that most of the resistant xylan cannot be chemically combined with the cellulose of the pulp. Another procedure is to extract with 5% KOH followed by 10% NaOH, the former removing more than half the xylan in a fairly pure form, the latter a mixture of galactoglucomannan and glucuronoxylan, leaving a residue of only 1% xylan and 4% glucomannan. It has also been demonstrated repeatedly (504, 693, 818) that the content of cold-alkali-resistant xylan of holocellulose or sulfite pulp prepared from the same wood as the kraft pulp is considerably lower. Something must have happened during the alkaline cook to modify the xylan itself, or the fiber structure. Native hardwood xylan contains about 0.1 uronic acid substituents per xylose unit in the 2-position, and softwood xylan is substituted by 0.2 glucuronic acid in the 2-position and by up to 0.2 arabinose units linked in the 3-position. In addition, the hardwood xylan contains 0.7–0.8 acetate groups per monomer. Hot alkali removes all three types of substituents, but to a varying degree. Deacetylation is complete almost directly, whereas complete removal of arabinose and glucuronic acid requires fairly high temperature. At the same time, DP of the xylan is reduced. Alkaline degradation of both softwood and hardwood xylan in solution has been found to decrease the uronic acid content to zero (313, 314). In agreement hereto, early investigations showed kraft pulps from softwoods to lack uronic acids, and the uronic acid content of hardwood kraft pulp to be low (315, 663). However, later investigations showed the kraft pulp xylan to contain 30–40% of the original glucuronic acid content (157, 158, 570, 584). The reason is probably that when the rate of hydrolysis of the glucuronic acid groups becomes significant in the kraft cook (at 160–170°C), there is normally not much alkali left, and their removal remains therefore incomplete. In some fractions, however, the glucuronic acid content is very low, about 0.02 groups per monomer. Obviously the acetate groups, arabinose and uronic acid units, protruding from the straight 1 : 4-xylopyranose chains, prevent crystallization and their removal during the kraft cook will increase the tendency of xylan to crystallize (376, 818, cf. 820). The configuration of the xylose units allows a close contact of the xylan chains with the cellulose, and it is likely that part of the xylan after the removal of its substituents tends to co-crystallize with or become adsorbed to the cellulose of the pulp. This intimate contact, even if it is a mere adsorption to the surface of the cellulose microfibrils, should make the xylan difficult to remove by cold alkali extraction. It has also been demonstrated (818) that xylan of kraft pulps has a greater resistance than the xylan of holocellulose or sulfite pulps to acid hydrolysis, the classical test on the degree of molecular order of cellulose. Furthermore, if xylan extracted from hardwood holocellulose by cold alkali is heated with cotton linters in water or alkali, xylan is adsorbed by the linters in amounts increasing with the temperature used to a maximum in the temperature range of 150–170°C (818). This xylan is partly fixed to the linters in a cold-alkali resistant form, also showing a certain resistance to hydrolysis. The same or greater effects are obtained on heating sulfite

606

pulp or extracted holocellulose with xylan solutions, or together with white liquor and a hardwood or hardwood holocellulose. As the same effect is achieved in the presence of hardwood as with hardwood holocellulose, the assumption of a transglycosidation by cleavage of lignin–carbohydrate bonds is unnecessary, and as the fixation of the xylan is achieved as well on heating in water as in alkali, transglycosidation upon alkaline cleavage of β-glycosidic bonds between aldose monomers is also less likely to be an important feature. This leaves the alternative of acetyl, uronic acid and arabinose removal as the most probable cause. The extent of xylan adsorption is further dependent on the pH of the cooking liquor, as seen in Figure 9.104 for cotton linters heated at 170°C with alkali of varying

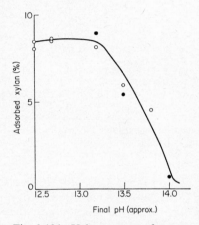

Fig. 9.104. Xylan content of cotton linters after heating for 3 h at 170°C with birch xylan in sodium hydroxide solutions of varying concentration (and final pH) (Yllner–Enström)

strength (818). The critical interval for the xylan solubility is thus pH 13–14. Although it was found that the degree of substitution will influence the adsorption tendency to cellulose during kraft cooking (157, 333), a considerable glucuronic acid content does not prevent such adsorption. In the case of birch the glucuronic acid substitution of the native xylan ranges from about 0.05–0.10, whereas in birch kraft pulps the corresponding substitution spectrum of the xylan was about 0.02–0.05. Probably not all of that xylan could be regarded as adsorbed to the cellulose merely remaining undissolved at its original location in the fiber, but a considerable portion should have been relocated, and no fraction of the xylan was found to be free of glucuronic acid. In the case of pine, all fractions contained about 0.05 glucuronic acid and 0.1 arabinose groups per xylose monomer (158). These effects are illustrated by Table 9.25, where the DP values of the kraft pulp hemicelluloses are also given, which indicate

607

Table 9.25. Fractionated extraction of kraft pulps by hydroxide solutions (157, 158)

Wood fraction	Yield, % of pulp	4-O-Methyl-D-glucuronic acid, % of the xylan	Sugar composition					DP
			Galac-tose, %	Glu-cose, %	Man-nose, %	Arabi-nose, %	Xylose, %	
Birch Pulp (50% of wood)	100	—		71.9	1.6		26.5	
α-residue	71.9	—		96.6	0.7		2.7	
β 5% NaOH	22.3	5.6	1.5	1.3	—		97.2	155
γ 5% NaOH	2.4	6.7	2.8	1.9	2.1		93.3	150
β 10% NaOH	2.5	3.0	1.8	20.6	3.7		73.9	
α 10% NaOH	0.9	5.3	1.7	6.1	4.2		88.0	145
Pine Pulp (42% of wood)	100	6.0	0.5	83.6	6.9	1.0	9.4	
α-residue	84.7	—	0.9	94.8	3.4	—	0.9	
γ DMSO	2.8	7.9	1.4	2.6	0.6	8.1	87.4	84
β + γ 5% KOH	5.1	7.8	3.5	1.8	2.8	9.1	82.9	99
β_I	0.3		0.1	82.6	10.0	0.3	7.0	188
β_II 10% NaOH	0.4		0.5	68.5	23.2	0.3	7.5	
β_GM	0.2		1.4	21.5	69.1	0.3	7.7	80
β_X	0.4	6.7	0.2	11.7	0.1	8.5	79.5	122
γ 10% NaOH	7.8		3.1	13.7	30.9	6.2	46.2	
γ_GM 10% NaOH	1.6		6.4	22.6	66.0	0.1	4.8	70
γ_X 10% NaOH	3.4	6.1	0.4	2.6	3.8	8.6	84.6	90

α, β and γ denote fractions insoluble, soluble but precipitable, and soluble non-precipitable respectively. DMSO denotes dimethylsulfoxide. The indices GM and X denote fractions dominated by glucomannan and xylan respectively.

only moderate degradation (157, 314, 570), in contrast with the sulfite pulp hemicelluloses (570, 584). Demethylation of the 4-O-methyl glucuronic acid units occurs somewhat more rapidly than the removal of the latter, leaving the major part of the glucuronic acid groups unmethylated after the cook (138a, 156a).

The consequence of all these results for the mechanism of xylan stabilization in the kraft cook would be that during the heating period of the kraft cook, when the alkali concentration is comparatively high, there is a partial degradation of the wood xylan by peeling and hydrolysis, resulting in shorter chains comparatively free of acetate groups, arabinose and uronic acid units. Undegraded and degraded xylan are dissolved in the pulping liquor to a considerable extent, but as the cook proceeds the alkali concentration decreases below the critical point and degraded, short-chain xylan precipitates in a more or less crystalline form within the chips to a certain extent on the surface of the cellulose microfibrils. This behavior of the xylan fraction has been demonstrated not only by the precipitation of xylan on xylan-free material during an alkaline cook, but also by experiments on kraft cooking of wood using continuous liquor flow of constant concentration of various levels and determining the rate and extent of removal of lignin and the various carbohydrate fractions (817). The results are illustrated in Figure 9.105 for cooks heated to 170°C in 3 h and kept at 170°C for 2 h. The curves indicate the yield of the various components when using two extreme cooking liquors, approximately corresponding to the initial and final alkalinity of an ordinary kraft cook. Obviously, up to a temperature of 100°C very little dissolution occurs. In the temperature interval of 100–125°C a considerable part of the galactoglucomannan and some xylan, as well as some lignin is dissolved. When 170°C is reached, about half the lignin and one-third of the xylan have been dissolved, and the 2 h at maximum temperature complete the delignification. The extent of lignin, xylan and glucan removal depends greatly on the alkalinity maintained, whereas mannan dissolution is fairly independent of the alkalinity. This dependence is to some extent a consequence of the degradation reaction velocity being influenced by the hydroxyl ion concentration, but in the case of xylan, with its extreme dependence on the alkalinity, a limited solubility at the lower alkali concentrations is indicated also. It should also be observed that the remaining carbohydrate fractions, especially the glucan and mannan fractions, are very stable towards prolonged heating in alkali. The resistant glucomannan of the kraft pulp is also likely to be at least partially adsorbed to the cellulose (8a). The influence of the delignification on carbohydrate removal is also striking, especially when it is kept in mind that the peeling reaction is rapid already at temperatures around 100°C (cf. hot alkali purification of pulps, Chapter 15), provided the alkali has access to the carbohydrates. The compactness of the wood tissue in the lignified, outer parts of the cell wall is therefore sufficient to protect the hemicelluloses, especially the xylan, until the lignin removal will expose them to the alkali. The initial drop in mannan and some galactan and glucan is an obvious exception and is likely to have some morphological explanation.

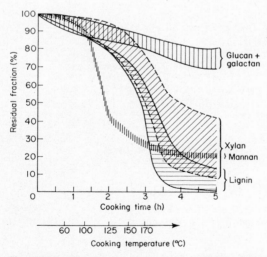

Fig. 9.105. Dissolution of lignin and carbohydrate components during the kraft cooking of pine; upper curves 0 g/l NaOH, 10 g/l Na₂S, lower curves 35 g/l NaOH, 10 g/l Na₂S (Yllner et al)

609

4. INFLUENCE OF REACTION CONDITIONS ON THE RATE OF PULPING, PULP YIELD AND PROPERTIES

The main reaction variables in kraft and soda pulping are the following:

(a) Wood, species and condition.
(b) Temperature.
(c) Time.
(d) Charge of cooking chemicals, hydroxide as well as sulfide.
(e) Concentration of cooking chemicals.

After a short discussion on the first-mentioned variable, the influence of the others on the rate of pulping will be considered, and then their effect on the analytical composition of the pulp and its physical properties will be described.

A. Wood, species and condition

The main quantity of kraft pulp is produced from *softwoods*, mainly pines and Douglas fir, but also spruces, firs and other species. Table 9.26 lists some of the softwood species studied and used for kraft pulping. Among these are several resinous woods, considered less suitable for mechanical and sulfite pulping. It is a great advantage of the kraft

Table 9.26. Softwoods studied in kraft pulping

Wood species		Ref.
Abies alba	European silver fir	389
Abies amabilis	Pacific silver fir	86
Abies lasiocarpa	Alpine fir	808
Araucaria brasiliana	Brazilian pine	161
Larix dahurica	Daur larch	219, 821
Larix decidua	European larch	225, 375
Larix sibirica	Siberian larch	742
Matasequoia glyptostroboides	Japanese redwood	454
Picea abies	Scandinavian spruce	272
Picea engelmanni	Engelmann spruce	808
Picea mariana	Black spruce	82, 324, 429
Pinus banksiana	Jack pine	135, 479a, 480, 801
Pinus contorta, v. *latifolia*	Lodgepole pine	519
Pinus densiflora	Japanese pine	339
Pinus echinata	Shortleaf pine	514
Pinus elliottii	Slash pine	117, 172
Pinus glabra	Spruce pine	450
Pinus palustris	Longleaf pine	84
Pinus pinaster, v. *maritimus*	Maritime pine	66, 125
Pinus silvestris	Scots pine	225, 604
Pinus taeda	Loblolly pine	103, 126
Pseudotsuga taxifolia	Douglas fir	85, 135, 462, 479a, 480, 513, 668 808
Thuja plicata	Western red cedar	90, 134, 354, 808
Tsuga heterophylla	Western hemlock	808, 822

process to be almost independent of the wood raw material, giving hardly any resin troubles and no excessive screenings due to lignin condensation with phenolic constituents of the wood, in contrast to sulfite pulping. Therefore less-prized wood could be utilized, including *saw-mill waste*, which to a large extent originates from wood species less suitable to sulfite pulping. Saw mill waste is a raw material source of immense importance at the Pacific Coast kraft industy of North America. Even sawdust and shavings are being used for special grades (492), the sawdust preferably being made by a coarse feed saw (512). The *yield of pulp* from the various conifer *species* at normal degrees of delignification (chlorine numbers 4–7) varies from 42–44% (western red cedar) to 48–52% (spruce). The variations depend to a great extent on the different lignin and extractives contents of these species. Similar variations in yield are obtained for *sapwood* and *heartwood* (604), for variations within a tree (129) and for variations caused by growth conditions (103). The strength increases and the yield decreases with increasing *age* of the tree, at least for the first thirty years (604a). Brown rotting fungi, and other organisms, cause *decay* which may seriously affect the pulp yield and the paper strength properties of kraft pulps (407, 408).

Most kraft pulps have excellent *strength properties*, but important differences are noted for different wood *species*. Two main types are produced, which with a broad generalization have been classified as Scandinavian and North-American types of kraft pulp. The former is characterized by higher tensile and bursting strength and the latter by a higher tear. These differences arise from the different size and shape of the fibers. The southern and western American pines and Douglas fir have a higher basic density, 0.46–0.56, as compared to the Scandinavian scots pine, 0.38–0.44, and some northern American and Canadian softwoods, such as western red cedar, Engelmann spruce and alpine fir, 0.3–0.4. The light-weight woods contain more springwood, whereas in the heavier wood species summerwood dominates. There is an increasing kraft pulp production in Canada from lightweight softwoods, which give the Scandinavian type of pulp, as exemplified by Table 9.27 (354). There the paper properties of two extreme representatives of the two categories are shown, namely for Douglas fir and western red cedar. The high

Table 9.27. Paper properties of kraft pulps from some typical North-American pulpwoods (354)

Wood species	Beating time, min., 600 ml C.S.	400 ml C.S.	Burst strength, 600 ml C.S.	400 ml C.S.	Tear strength, 600 ml C.S.	400 ml C.S.
Douglas fir	33	47	142	154	2.95	2.65
Loblolly pine	30	42	143	152	2.48	2.20
Western hemlock	33	48	189	200	1.80	1.74
Eastern spruce	33	55	204	214	1.43	1.36
Western red cedar	28	53	223	231	1.57	1.53

percentage of thick-walled summerwood fibers of Douglas fir (354) as well as some southern pines (74, 162) gives a coarser paper with less interfiber bonding, which is the reason for the extreme properties of those pulps. The close interrelation between *wood density, fiber wall thickness* and *paper properties* is also seen in Table 9.28 and Figure 9.106 (19). With increasing

Table 9.28. Properties of wood and kraft pulp from some typical American and European softwoods (19)

Wood species	Abies lasio-carpa Alpine fir	Pinus con-torta v. latifolia Lodge-pole pine	Picea engel-manni Engel-mann spruce	Picea abies Scand. spruce	Pinus silves-tris Scots pine	Pinus pinaster v. mari-timus Maritime pine	Pinus elli-ottii Slash pine	Pseudo-tsuga taxifolia Douglas fir
Basic density, t/m³	0.32	0.34	0.37	0.40	0.41	0.42	0.55	0.49
Fiber length, mm	3.0	3.0	3.0	3.5	2.9	3.1	2.3	3.4
Fiber width, mm	0.029	0.032	0.030	0.027	0.028	0.040	0.036	0.037
Fiber wall thickness, μ	2.0	2.9	2.9	2.4	3.2	3.7	3.8	4.0
Extracted wood composition:								
Lignin %	28	26	27	27	27	27	28	26
Cellulose, %	44	44	44	41	42	42	43	43
Glucomannan acetate, %	16	16	16	19	17	16	16	21
Glucurono-arabino-xylan, %	10	11	11	10	11	11	11	6
Galactan, %	2	3	2	3	3	4	2	4
Pulp yield at Roe no. 6	48	48	50	51	48	47	46	50
Paper properties on beating to 45°SR:								
Beating time, min.	84	78	80	84	74	64	53	74
Tensile strength, km	12.8	12.4	12.2	11.2	10.4	9.8	8.7	8.2
Burst strength	127	128	116	100	92	94	81	75
Tear strength	91	97	108	129	121	138	158	200
Sheet density, g/cm³	0.78	0.73	0.74	0.70	0.72	0.71	0.70	0.69

basic density and fiber wall thickness, beating time decreases to a certain degree, tensile and burst decrease and tear increases. Since the basic density of Scandinavian scots pine increases with decreasing latitude, it has also been found that the tensile strength of the corresponding kraft pulp decreases and tear strength increases accordingly (740a). *Fiber length* in the interval of 2.5–3.5 mm is of less significance for the paper properties. Paper made from summerwood fibers alone is extremely 'hairy' and porous, whereas paper from springwood fibers is very hard and dense (354, 406), and neither give an acceptable paper. The large proportion of summerwood fibres in *compression wood* likewise affects the paper properties of pulp prepared from such wood (163, 587). The kraft pulp yield is also considerably lower because of the high lignin content of compression wood

(163). *Heartwood* is as easily penetrated by the kraft pulping liquor as in the sapwood, but gives 2–3% lower yield because of higher extractives content, and higher tensile and burst but lower tear because of a lower summerwood content than in the sapwood (604). For similar reasons, the *tree top part of the trunk* gives similar deviations from the average i.e. lower yield and tear but higher tensile and burst strength (87, 127).

The influence of the *moisture content* of the wood chips on the pulping result has been found to be insignificant (289, 293, 783, 786). In the special case of absolutely green wood, 'biological' pulps of very high strength can be obtained (389, cf. 783).

The sensitivity of the kraft pulp properties to *mechanical damage* of the softwood prior to pulping is less than in the case of sulfite pulps, but it is still not possible to obtain kraft pulps of acceptable strength from defibered wood (271, 391), or from wood compressed in the axial direction (153, 746), whereas squeezing by roll presses of chips perpendicular to the fiber axis does not cause any damage but improves the uniformity of the pulping (143). The compression damage done by chipping, which is so detrimental to sulfite pulp quality, has little influence on the kraft pulp quality (251, 335), an important advantage. Pulping of small subdivisions of chips, however, gave inferior yield and quality (442), and kraft pulp from *sawdust*, produced in Pandia digesters, is used where formation, rather than strength, is important. Sawing to produce fragments of a larger size than normal sawdust, so-called *saw kerf chips*, is achieved by feeding at an unusually rapid rate per saw tooth and using special blades (20a). Such kerf chips contain longer fibers than sawdust and give kraft

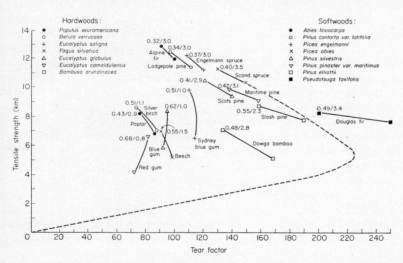

Fig. 9.106. Paper properties of kraft pulps from various wood species. Numbers indicate basic density and average fiber length of the corresponding wood. Broken curve indicates properties of Scandinavian spruce at low degrees of heating, full lines the properties between 25 and 45°SR (Annergren–Rydholm–Vardheim)

613

pulp of rather good strength, yet inferior to that of ordinary chips (681a). Mechanical action during the cook is also detrimental to the final quality as in the sulfite cook so that stationary digesters are preferred to rotary digesters, and even the blowing of a digester after the cook will impair the strength properties. The discharge of a continuous digester of the Kamyr type has been found to lower the pulp quality unless cooling of the discharge part of the digester is provided for (449, 659). The presence of *bark* on the pulpwood is not as detrimental to pulp cleanliness in the kraft as in the sulfite process, since a large part of the bark impurities are dissolved in the cook. This is of particular importance when pulping saw-mill waste. Some investigations have been carried out on the pulping of Douglas fir (462, 668), pine (514) or oaks (97) with large quantities of bark, expecially for board grades, and it is concluded that in combination with vortex cleaning more than 10 but less than 20% bark in the pulpwood can be tolerated. The same conclusion is drawn for bleached grades. However, since the bark yields only little fiber but consumes much alkali, the market value of pulpwood with 10% bark is only about 80% of that of bark-free wood.

The considerable amount of pulpwood available from *hardwood* species has attracted great interest from the kraft pulping industry. Investigations have revealed that most hardwoods are well suited to alkaline pulping, and some of the difficulties encountered, such as penetration problems and pulp resin troubles, are far less pronounced in kraft pulping than in any other process. Therefore, a large quantity of alkaline hardwood pulp is being produced, for paper as well as dissolving purposes. In the latter case, prehydrolysis–kraft pulping is practised, cf. Chapter 9.III.

A soda pulping industry on hardwoods was developed early, whereas softwood soda pulping was found impractical. However, the presence of sulfide has also proved of value also in the case of hardwoods, as repeatedly demonstrated (e.g. 394, 479). The sulfidity could be kept somewhat lower than in the case of softwoods, possibly because of the lower lignin content and the lesser tendency of hardwood lignin to undergo condensation. The alkali consumption is somewhat lower than in the case of softwood pulping, which is astonishing because the hardwoods contain more hemicelluloses and less lignin than the softwoods, and the alkali consumption is caused predominantly by the dissolved carbohydrates. However, hardwoods need shorter time or lower temperature, e.g. 160°C, to be pulped and leave a higher yield at a certain degree of delignification. This is not only due to the milder cooking conditions practised on hardwoods, but also to the higher alkali-resistance of the hardwood hemicelluloses, mainly the xylan. The more exclusive location of the hardwood lignin to the middle lamella causes the point of fiber liberation to be reached at chlorine numbers as low as 5–7 (401), in contrast with about 10 in the case of softwoods, but the yield of hardwood pulp is considerable, 50–55%, even at chlorine numbers as low as 2–4. The wood consumption in comparison with softwoods is further reduced by the higher density of most hardwood species.

614

A great number of hardwood species have been investigated, North-American, European, as well as tropical ones (648), see Table 9.29.

Table 9.29. Hardwoods studied in kraft or soda pulping

Wood species		Ref.
Acer rubrum	Red maple	498
Alnus glutinosa	Black alder	98
Anacardium excelsum	Espave	758
Aspidosperma cruentum	Mylady	758
Avicennia marina	—	451
Betula lutea	Yellow birch	596
Betula papyrifera	Paper birch	479, 596
Betula pubescens	Birch	401, 403
Betula verrucosa	Silver birch	401, 403, 438, 765
Brugueira gymnorrhiza	Brugueira	452
Brugueira parviflora	Brugueira	451
Campostemon schultzii	—	452
Carpinus caroliana	Ironwood	498
Ceiba pentandra	Ceiba	758
Cecropia juranyana	Imbauba	476
Cordia alliodora	Laurel blanco	758
Diplotropis purpurea	Supupira	758
Eucalyptus sp.	Eucalypt	727
Eucalyptus camaldulensis (rostrata)	Murray red gum	484
Eucalyptus deglupta	—	451
Eucalyptus gigantea	Giant gum	92, 775
Eucalyptus globulus	Blue gum	68
Fagus grandifolia	American beech	596
Fagus silvatica	European beech	384, 394
Fagus sp.	Japanese beech	432
Gordonia lasianthus	Loblolly bay	227, 596
Halesia carolina	Wild olive tree	227, 596
Holopyxidium latifolium	Jarana	758
Ilex vomitoria	Yaupon	227, 596
Jacaranda copaia	Copaia	758
Licania buxifolia	Marishiballi	758
Liquidambar styraciflua	Red gum (Sweet gum)	89, 498, 511, 647, 758
Liriodendron tulipifera	Yellow poplar	498
Lucuma dissepala	Abiurana	476
Magnolia virginiana	Bay	498
Nyssa silvatica	Black gum	498
Populus deltoides v. *monilifera*	Cottonwood	596
Populus nigra	European poplar	383, 438
Populus tremula	European aspen	98
Populus tremuloides	American aspen	354, 442, 479
Protium heptaphyllum	Breu branco	476
Qualiea dinizii	Pau mulato	476
Quercus alba	White oak	97, 120, 164, 498, 758
Quercus coccinea	Scarlet oak	227, 596
Quercus falcata	Red oak	498, 758
Quercus laevis	Scrub oak	564, 565
Quercus laurifolia	Laurel oak	227, 596
Quercus marilandia	Blackjack oak	498
Quercus nigra	Water oak	498

Table 9.29. Hardwoods studied in kraft or soda pulping—*continued*

Wood species		Ref.
Quercus pagoda	Swamp Spanish oak	227, 596
Quercus palustris	Pin oak	227, 596
Quercus rubra	Southern red oak	97, 227, 596
Quercus shumardii	Swamp red oak	227, 596
Quercus stellata	Post oak	498
Rhizophora apiculata	Mangrove sp.	452
Simaruba amara	Simaruba	758
Somneratia aceda	—	452
Swarzia bannia	Bannia	758
Tabebuia pentophylla	Roble blanco	758
Terminalia amazonia	Nargusta	758

The paper strength properties of hardwood kraft pulps are generally lower than those of softwood pulps, as exemplified in Table 9.30 (657). The reason is predominantly their shorter fibers. Even for the most long-fibered hardwood pulps, such as birch (401), the tearing strength is only somewhat more than half that of softwood pulp, and for more short-fibered species, such as maple (498), much lower tear values are obtained. Tensile and bursting strength generally compare more favorably with those of softwood pulp, but are not quite up to their standard. When beaten to a comparatively high degree, kraft pulp from *Eucalyptus saligna* especially gives a paper strength approaching that of pine kraft. Some hardwoods, particularly those of very high density, give kraft pulp of less good bonding properties, useful only as 'filler' pulp. The paper formation characteristics of the hardwood pulps are quite good, which is probably the reason why up to 20% birch pulp could be mixed with pine pulp without any decrease in strength properties and why 10% admixture was even found to cause a slight increase (401). The same result was obtained in mixing the wood chips in corresponding proportions prior to pulping. Therefore, it is quite customary for the kraft mills to mix some hardwood into the pulpwood, even in the production of wrapping and sack paper, and considerable quantities in liner and food board. Pure hardwood kraft pulp, especially bleached grades, is also finding increasing use. The stronger types, such as birch kraft, are now very big competitors to softwood sulfite pulp, and the weaker grades, such as beech kraft, represent in admixture with pine kraft an acceptable and inexpensive alternative to spruce sulfite pulp.

Hardwood kraft pulps present a higher resistance than softwood pulps in diffuser washing but are well suited to filter washing. They screen well, and most are easily bleachable.

B. *Rate of pulping*

As was stressed in Chapter 6.V and is evident from the complexity of reactions occurring in the phase borders of wood and a pulping liquor, no pulping process can be treated as having reaction kinetics similar to those

Table 9.30. Properties of wood and kraft pulp from some hardwoods as compared with Scots pine and bamboo (19) (cf. Table 9.28)

Wood species	Eucalyptus saligna Sydney blue gum	Eucalyptus globulus Blue gum	Populus × euramericana Poplar hybrid	Betula verrucosa Silver birch	Castanea vesca Chestnut (extracted)	Fagus silvatica European beech	Pinus silvestris Scots pine	Bambusa arundinacea Dowga bamboo
Basic density, t/m³	0.51	0.63	0.43	0.51	0.38	0.55	0.41	0.48
Fiber length, mm	1.00	1.01	0.92	1.10	1.5	0.96	2.9	2.8
Fiber width, mm	0.013	0.013	0.016	0.020	0.017	0.014	0.028	0.016
Fiber wall thickness, μ	1.4	1.2	1.2	1.9	1.4	3.3	3.2	3.1
Extracted ash-free wood composition:								
Lignin, %	25	21	24	21	28	23	27	27
Cellulose, %	52	49	46	40	44	41	42	47
Glucomannan, %	3	4	7	3	3	3	17	1
Glucuronoxylan acetate, %	19	25	23	35	24	32	11	23
Galactan, etc., %	1	1	0	1	1	1	3	3
Pulp yield, %, at Roe no. 3	54	54	54	54	42	52	48*	46
Pulp pentosan content, %	16	19	18	27	12	24	9	17
Paper properties on beating to 25°SR:								
Beating time, min.	12	12	13	16	7	18	46	14
Tensile strength, km	6.5	5.8	6.8	7.0	3.1	5.2	9.3	5.0
Burst strength	56	43	57	60	11	33	85	41
Tear strength	114	92	87	88	51	98	140	168
Sheet density, g/cm³	0.57	0.58	0.69	0.70	0.58	0.56	0.66	0.48
Paper properties on beating to 45°SR:								
Beating time, min.	24	28	27	25	30	32	74	28
Tensile strength, km	9.8	8.4	8.2	8.6	4.4	6.9	10.4	7.0
Burst strength	89	65	68	74	20	48	92	56
Tear strength	110	95	76	73	67	91	121	134
Sheet density, g/cm³	0.71	0.70	0.79	0.79	0.60	0.66	0.72	0.56

* Roe no. 6

617

of homogeneous reactions in solution. However, in certain periods of the cook, the overall pulping reaction can be approximated to a first-order reaction. An approximate velocity constant for the delignification can be calculated from the equation

$$- dL/dt = k(L - L_d)$$

where k is the velocity constant, L the lignin remaining after t h and L_d the last few per cent of more difficultly removable lignin, which follows a different reaction mechanism (121, 459, 473, 706). Calculations (473) carried out on experimental results of soda cooking (496), as well as similar calculations for kraft cooking with 25 % sulfidity (459), disregarding the last few per cent of residual lignin, which are more difficult to remove (cf. 752a), indicate an energy of activation of about 32,000 cal/mole of soda and 24,000 for kraft pulping. This means that the rate of reaction approximately is doubled for an increase in *maximum temperature* of 10°C in the kraft cook (276, 324, 744, 793). To obtain a normal kraft pulp of a chlorine number of 6, about 1.5 h at 170°C is needed, and therefore 0.75 h at 180°C and 3 h at 160°C would give about the same result, applying identically the other conditions which also influence the rate of pulping. This temperature dependence has been used to deduce a factor called the *H factor* (793) to include both the effects of temperature and time in a single number. An H factor of 1 thus arbitrarily represents the pulping effect of 1 h at 100°C, which with the temperature coefficient assumed means an H factor of 1,000 for 1 h at 171°C. Normal heating periods contribute by 150–300 to the H factor, and 1,500–2,000 are needed for normal kraft pulps, as shown in Figure 9.107 (793), where the residual lignin and pulp yield from the kraft pulping of spruce at various temperatures and times (296) have been plotted against the H factor. The relation holds only for the same wood and chemical charges, but as long as the temperature dependence is unchanged the same curve holds for various temperatures. As the soda process has a somewhat larger temperature dependence than the kraft process, the yield vs. H factor relation is different for different soda cooking temperatures, as long as the H factors of the kraft process are applied, Figure 9.107. The higher rate of pulping in the presence of sulfide is also clearly demonstrated.

The influence of cooking *temperature and time* at zero, medium and high sulfidity is shown by Figure 9.108 (296) in a more conventional manner. It has been pointed out (769) that the time gained by an increase of temperature in batch cooking does not quite correspond to the temperature dependence of the reaction velocity. The time to maximum temperature is appreciable and determined by the equipment and a further increase in temperature also takes additional time. The reduction in total cooking time at an increase from 170 to 180°C is thus only about 25 % instead of 50 %, and the reduction is still less in relation to the entire cooking cycle from cover to cover. However, in continuous cooking, the full benefit of high temperature can be realized, and cooking at 190°C requires only about 15 min and is allowable from a quality standpoint,

618

provided the impregnation is satisfactory (744). This requires pre-steaming and hydraulic pressure cooking. However, so far this possibility is not quite utilized in continuous Kamyr cooking, as temperatures just above 175°C are normal. This may be partly due to the fact that saving digester volume is of relatively little economical consequence.

One of the most dominating variables is naturally the *charge of alkali.* Kinetic studies have often worked with a large excess of chemicals to maintain an approximately constant alkali *concentration* throughout the cook, and then that variable becomes especially important. This is demonstrated in Figure 9.109 (473), where the velocity constants for the delignification of spruce at 160°C, employing various types of *sulfide-free* alkali in varying concentration, are shown. It is evident that the alkali concentration has a definite influence upon the rate of delignification. It is also known that the rate increases in the order LiOH < NaOH < KOH, compared at constant molar concentration (473). This phenomenon, as well as the increased rate of delignification on changing the solvent from water to methanol and ethanol (473), is probably explained by a decreasing

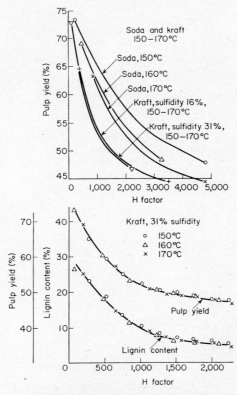

Fig. 9.107. Pulp yield and lignin content vs. H factor in the alkaline pulping of spruce (Vroom)

solvation of the alkali and therefore easier penetration and reaction of the alkali with the wood constituents.

The effect of the *liquor concentration* has also been shown in the case of *kraft* cooking (459, 516, 707), where in the range 0.5–1.5 M solution the rate constants show a linear dependence on the concentration, Figure 9.110 (459). Normally, however, the charge of cooking chemicals is limited to an amount which only slightly exceeds that consumed in the cook, and the concentration will consequently change throughout the

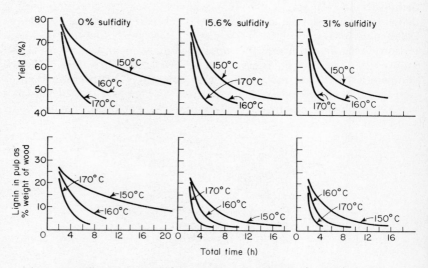

Fig. 9.108. Effect of cooking time, temperature and sulfidity on the rate of kraft cooking of Scandinavian spruce. Heating time 2 h, active alkali charge 242 kg ptw (Hägglund–Hedlund)

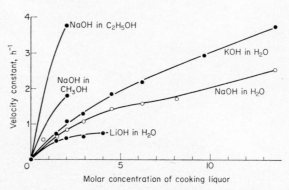

Fig. 9.109. Reaction velocity vs. molar concentration of sodium hydroxide on pulping sprucewood at 160°C (Larocque–Maass)

620

cook. The possibility of affecting the rate of pulping by increasing the concentration is in actual practice thus fairly limited, and although additions of excess cooking chemicals are sometimes used to increase the capacity of the digester house, a temperature increase is a more efficient means. However, it has also been found (e.g. 516) that it is desirable to maintain a high chemical concentration by keeping the *liquor-to-wood ratio* at a minimum. A liquor-to-wood ratio of 3:1 will allow a reduction in the alkali charge by 20% in comparison with a cook with the ratio 6:1, to achieve the same degree of delignification (516), or also a corresponding reduction in time or temperature. Figure 9.111 (707) demonstrates that the effects within the normal variations in the liquor-to-wood ratio are not very great, and that an increase in chemical concentration may result in somewhat decreased yields at constant degree of delignification. In batch cooking it is necessary to maintain a certain minimum volume of cooking liquor to achieve a uniform liquor circulation in the digester, normal liquor-to-wood ratios being around 3.5–4.5:1, and black liquor is used for dilution to avoid extra costs in the evaporation plant. Therefore, an initial concentration of 40–60 g/l. NaOH of active alkali in the cooking liquor is normal. Continuous cooking does not require the same liquor ratios, and modern practice involves only white liquor feed to the digester top. This, together with chip moisture and steaming condensate, would constitute about 2.0–3.0 m³ ptw, depending on the moisture content of the chips.

The beneficial effect of *sulfide* in alkaline cooking for both the rate of pulping and pulp quality has been well known since the start of the kraft pulping industry, but the exact amount of sulfide necessary has been a matter of discussion. The question is of both theoretical and

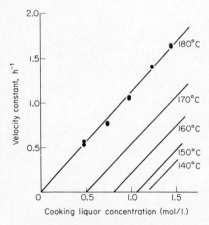

Fig. 9.110. Reaction velocity vs. cooking liquor concentration on the kraft cooking of slash pine at varying temperature (Kulkarni–Nolan)

621

practical interest. Since only half the sodium sulfide molecule could be regarded as alkali effective for pulping, an increased sulfidity at a maintained charge of effective alkali means an increased load on the sodium regeneration system. However, since it has borne out that the charge of effective alkali can be decreased on increasing sulfidity for a certain result of the pulping, that is no serious problem. Furthermore, the costs of causticization are reduced by an increased sulfidity, as the hydrolysis of the sulfide produces hydroxide without lime consumption. But the sulfidity of the cooking liquor is not a variable which can be easily adjusted at will. As will be shown in Chapter 11 on the regeneration of cooking chemicals, the sulfidity of the cooking liquor depends on the relative proportions of sulfur and sodium losses. The sodium losses occur to a large extent in the washing operations after the cook, and the sulfur lost at that time is considerably less than the sulfur introduced with the sodium sulfate to cover these sodium losses. Therefore, the sulfidity of the cooking liquor would be steadily increasing, if the sulfur losses in the evaporation plant and the regeneration furnace were not proportionally higher than the sodium losses there. These sulfur losses increase with the sulfur content of the black liquor. An equilibrium is thus maintained'

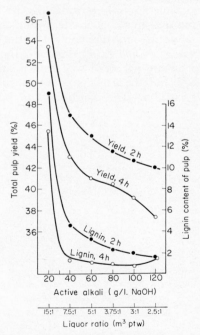

Fig. 9.111. Effect of alkali concentration at constant alkali charge in the kraft cooking of Douglas fir. Effective alkali 263 kg ptw NaOH, 170°C, 2 and 4 h (Schwartz–Bray)

622

which among other things is dependent on the operation of the furnace and the washing efficiency. As the latter has been considerably improved through technical advances, there has lately been a tendency for the sulfidity to drop to a level where the advantages normally experienced with the kraft process in comparison with soda cooking become questionable. This has initiated research on two lines, the addition of elemental sulfur to the digester, to the white liquor or to the regeneration furnace to make up for the low sulfide content (154, 510, 785), and oxidation of the black liquor prior to evaporation and burning in order to reduce the sulfur losses of the regeneration system (553, 787, 825). Both lines have yielded satisfactory results, but the situation has nevertheless renewed the interest in the influence of the sulfidity on the cooking result. Most of the kraft pulp is now likely to be produced at sulfidities of 20–30%, sulfidities lower than 15% being avoided and above 40% seldom experienced (172, 788).

As pointed out in previous sections, the two cooking chemicals, sodium hydroxide and hydrosulfide, should be regarded as independent in function, the former promoting hydrolysis of the phenolic ether bonds of lignin and neutralizing the acids formed by the alkaline degradation of both lignin and carbohydrates, the latter reacting almost exclusively with the lignin, in a way which facilitates the delignification but at the same time results in the decomposition of the sulfidized lignin under reformation of most of the hydrosulfide. Only about 10 kg ptw S of a normal sulfide charge are consumed in the kraft cook (191). Considering these different functions of sodium hydroxide and hydrosulfide, it appears logical to investigate their importance for the kraft cook as effects of two independent variables, and not interdependent through the concept of sulfidity. However, for practical reasons most investigations have varied the hydroxide charge at constant sulfidity of the cooking liquor, or the sulfidity at constant hydroxide charge. In the former case, the hydrosulfide charge is automatically varied at the same time as the hydroxide. In the latter case the hydrosulfide charge is varied proportionally to the sulfidity if the *active alkali* is kept constant, and varied in a rather different manner if the *effective alkali* is kept constant. Cooking in pure hydrosulfide solutions does not give slush pulp because of incomplete delignification (101). Pure sodium sulfide solution, on the other hand, is more efficient as pulping agent, when used in sufficient amounts, because it is hydrolyzed to sodium hydroxide and hydrosulfide prior to and during the cook. However, it is obvious that it will contain a considerable quantity of hydrosulfide in excess of what is needed for the sulfidation of the lignin, and that portion must be considered as fairly inactive during the pulping. Therefore, in experimental pulping series, where the sulfidity was changed at constant *active alkali*, the amount of effective alkali is decreasing with increasing sulfidity. In pure sodium sulfide solution it is only half that in pure hydroxide solution, and a decrease in the rate of pulping is noted at very high sulfidities, as demonstrated in Figure 9.112 (89). However, in those experimental series where the sodium hydroxide available for pulping, i.e. the *effective alkali*, was kept constant, the beneficial influence of the hydrosulfide is experienced almost throughout the sulfidity range, Figure 9.112–113 (85, 89). The advantages at sulfidities higher than 50% for softwoods and 35% for hardwoods seem questionable, and relatively small above 25%. Below that level, the rate of pulping, as judged from

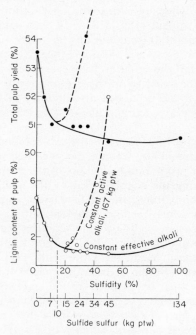

Fig. 9.112. Effect of sulfidity at kraft cooking of sweet gum. Constant effective alkali (167 kg ptw NaOH), 170°C, 1.5 h (Bray–Martin)

the data on both pulp yield and lignin content, is considerably accelerated by the presence of hydrosulfide. The effect is particularly great in the range of 0–10% sulfidity, and indicates a critical amount of hydrosulfide sulfur of around 10 kg ptw S, a figure which coincides with the sulfur consumption found for kraft cooks of normal sulfidity, cf. Subsection II.2A of this chapter. In addition to that minimum quantity, which is obviously consumed in a more irreversible way by the lignin, further amounts of sulfur seem to be of use to accelerate the delignification, possibly by combination with the lignin in the wood and re-liberating from the dissolved lignin. Similar results as those demonstrated in the figures for Douglas fir and sweet gum have been achieved by a number of other investigations on various wood species, such as spruce (296, 318, 324, 457) and scrub oak (638). For beech the critical amount of hydrosulfide sulfur was found to be 7 kg ptw S, at a minimum of 150 kg ptw NaOH effective alkali (394, cf. 384). Curves for varying sulfide charges at constant effective alkali of several different levels on kraft cooking of western red cedar (134), indicated that the importance of the sulfide charge for the rate of pulping is somewhat greater at low hydroxide charges, but that minimum charge of hydrosulfide sulfur remains in the neighbourhood of 10 kg ptw S, as seen in Figure 9.114. However, as also shown in previous figures and further illustrated in Figure 9.115 (479), there is a gain at considerably higher additions of sulfide up to about 15–20 kg ptw S (35–50 kg ptw Na_2S). This gain in pulping rate allows a decrease in the hydroxide charge to reach a constant degree of delignification, and in the sulfidity region of normal kraft pulping this results in constant lignin content of the pulp for varying sulfidity if the charge of *active alkali* is kept constant rather than that of effective alkali (172, 604), as demonstrated in Figure 9.116 (604). That has been utilized for mill control purposes (788), where quite often the active alkali content of the white liquor is determined and used as a basis rather than the content of effective alkali. However, this must not be misinterpreted to have any such theoretical significance as a second stage hydrolysis of the sodium sulfide. There is only one more known reason which might give an increased *theoretical* justification for the concept of active alkali as ruling

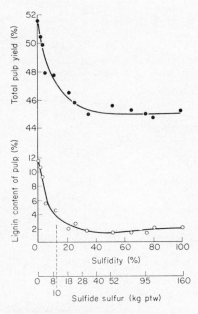

Fig. 9.113. Effect of sulfidity at kraft cooking of Douglas fir. Constant effective alkali (200 kg ptw), 170°C, 1.5 h (Bray *et al*)

625

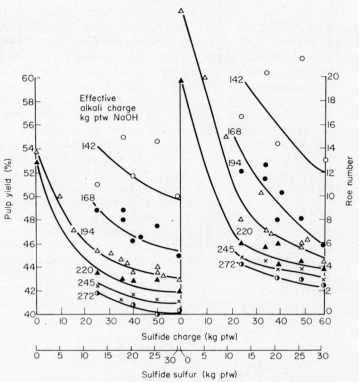

Fig. 9.114. Effect of sulfide charge at varying levels of effective alkali charge, in kraft cooking of western red cedar (Christiansen *et al*)

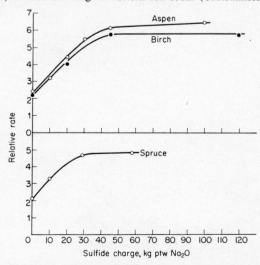

Fig. 9.115. Influence of sulfide charge on the rate of kraft cooking (Hägglund–Hedlund and Legg–Hart)

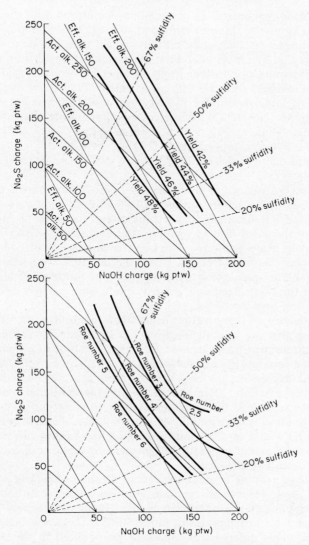

Fig. 9.116. Influence of alkali and sulfide charges on the pulp yield and Roe number on the kraft cooking of pine. Constant sulfidity, active alkali and effective alkali indicated (Regnfors–Stockman)

the rate and results of pulping. As pointed out in the section on lignin reactions, the hydrosulfide ions are likely to react primarily with the benzyl alcohol or alkyl ether groups of lignin. That should mean the formation of one hydroxyl ion for every hydrosulfide ion consumed. In splitting off sulfur from the lignin, that hydroxyl ion will be neutralized

627

again, but the amount of sulfur remaining combined with the lignin, or around 10 kg ptw S, should correspond to a quantity of about 12 kg ptw NaOH formed. At a very low sulfidity, where most sulfide is consumed, that means that one mole of sodium hydroxide is formed from the sulfide on hydrolysis and one further mole on reaction, which would therefore correspond entirely with the concept of active alkali ruling the degree of pulping. At somewhat higher sulfidity, where all sulfide is not consumed, these 12 kg ptw NaOH still mean a considerable supply of alkali available for pulping. Thus, at 20% sulfidity and a charge of *active alkali* of 200 kg ptw NaOH, corresponding to 180 kg ptw NaOH *effective alkali* according to definition, around 192 kg ptw NaOH are in reality *available* for pulping.

Another consequence of the excess of hydrosulfide present during the kraft cook is that black liquor charge to a cook in addition to the white liquor charge will mean an increased sulfidity of the cook. A black liquor charge will therefore help to maintain the hydrosulfide concentration at mills keeping a low sulfidity. The effect is diminished of course by the fact that black liquors of cooks, where the low sulfidity is really critical, will not contain much excess hydrosulfide. The influence of black liquor charge on the rate of pulping is fairly small, both positive and negative effects having been observed (155, 304, 324).

The influence of temperature and alkali concentration at constant sulfidity on the rate of delignification has been fitted to a *mathematical rate expression*, which can be used to predict the time of cooking needed to achieve a certain degree of delignification at a chosen set of conditions (121). The expression has been derived from the previous equation for a first-order reaction, after application of the Arrhenius temperature dependence equation, the equation for the cooking curve, the concept of 'average alkali concentration' of the cook, etc. Experimental data fit the equation within certain limits of cooking conditions, one prerequisite being that the sulfidity should be sufficient to make sodium hydroxide the rate-controlling chemical.

The rate of pulping is much dependent on the *species and condition of the wood used*. Hardwoods contain less lignin than softwoods and the rate of delignification is somewhat higher. Pulps of relatively low lignin content are therefore obtained in shorter time from hardwoods than from softwoods. This difference is especially pronounced in the soda cook, where pulps from hardwoods are obtained after approximately 3 h at 170°C, but no softwood pulp of normal lignin content can be obtained without serious degradation and yield losses. Also in kraft pulping, hardwood pulps are obtained after shorter time or lower temperature and with lower lignin content than softwood pulps. The reason for the higher delignification velocity is probably the greater accessibility of hardwood lignin, which is concentrated to the middle lamella to a larger extent than softwood lignin, cf. Chapter 6.V, but also the lesser tendency of hardwood lignin to undergo condensation, which retards the delignification. The presence of sulfide accelerates the pulping of both softwoods and hardwoods, as mentioned earlier. The variations in accessibility and re-activity appear to influence the rate of pulping for softwoods as well. Each species has its own optimal conditions, with an optimal charge of alkali and sulfide, above which no improvement in the rate of pulping is obtained, but rather a decrease in the yield and quality (479a). At optimal conditions, the rate of pulping is rather similar for the various softwoods (479a).

The rate and uniformity of pulping is further dependent on the moisture content and size of the wood chips and various types of pretreatment for penetration. Although, as was stated in Chapter 6.III, the alkaline pulping liquors are capable of penetrating the wood in all directions and at a rate exceeding that of acid pulping liquors, there are maximal dimensions of the chips, above which the non-uniformity of pulping becomes pronounced. In contrast to neutral and acid cooking, alkaline pulping is not extremely sensitive to penetration effects so long as the initial penetration was sufficient to give a slight alkalinity. Since the consumption of alkali in carbohydrate reactions is rapid already at 100°C, i.e. in the initial stages of the heating period, the alkali introduced by penetration of the cooking liquor is rapidly consumed, and the alkali needed for the main delignification has to be introduced into the completely liquor-penetrated chips, Figure 9.117 (330a). The rate of diffusion in longitudinal direction, which for neutral and acid sulfite cooking liquors is considerably higher than that

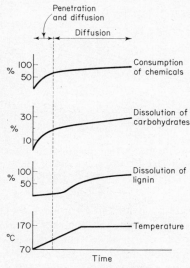

Fig. 9.117. Consumption of chemicals, dissolution of carbohydrates, dissolution of lignin and temperature respectively vs. time during kraft pulping of pine. The graphs indicate the approximate periods in which (a) both penetration and diffusion and (b) only diffusion occur (Hartler)

629

in transversal directions, is also at kraft cooking conditions slightly higher, Figure 6.8 and Figure 9.118 (330a). However, the ratio between diffusion rates is lower than the corresponding geometrical distances of the chips, making chip *thickness* the critical dimension, in contrast to the chip *length* in the neutral and acid pulping processes. During the kraft cook, the rates of diffusion approach each other, Figure 9.119 (330a).

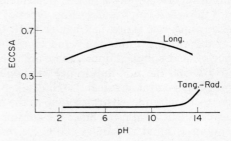

Fig. 9.118. Effective capillary cross-sectional area (ECCSA) vs. pH for the diffusion into wood blocks (O. Hägglund, cited by Hartler)

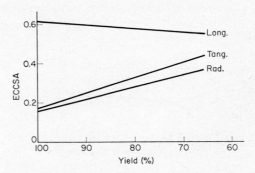

Fig. 9.119. ECCSA vs. pulp yield for blocks of partially digested wood at a pH of 13.2 (C. E. Bäckström, cited by Hartler)

These phenomena are illustrated in Figure 9.120 (459), where the lignin distribution in a 50 mm wood block after a rapid kraft cook is shown. The significance of pre-evacuation is also demonstrated. It is seen that the distance to the center should not in any case exceed 4 mm, and preferably be less. Normal chip thickness is in the order of 2–4 mm, thus with only 1–2 mm to the center. As demonstrated in Figure 9.121 (459), some increase in the lignin remaining after a limited kraft cook of constant conditions is experienced if the chip thickness exceeds 5 mm. The effect is rather more pronounced on air-dry chips than on pre-soaked ones. It is also probable that the rate of heating will influence the result, a shorter heating period requiring a smaller chip size to ensure sufficient uniformity,

630

and it has been demonstrated (566) that shredding of the chips in hammer-mill or rotating disk shredder will reduce the screenings at 48 % yield from 27 to 9 % at very rapid cooks at high temperature and almost no heating period. Such conditions prevail in certain types of continuous digesters whereas in the Kamyr type of continuous digester as well as in most batch digesters, the heating period and the lower maximum temperature allows a more uniform pulping also of ordinary mill size chips. As both shredding and chipping to smaller size will affect pulp quality, it is desirable to choose

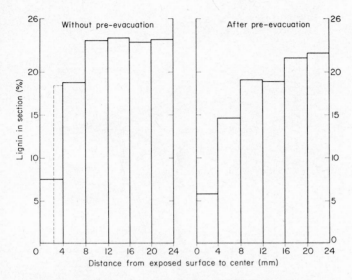

Fig. 9.120. Lignin gradient in cooked blocks of slash pine with and without pre-evacuation (Kulkarni–Nolan)

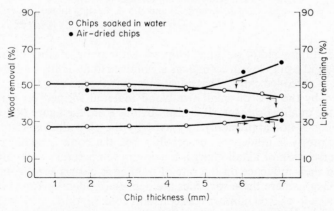

Fig. 9.121. Effect of chip thickness on total wood substance and lignin removal on kraft pulping of slash pine, dried or soaked chips of varying thickness (Kulkarni–Nolan)

631

such conditions as allow the normal chip size. However, some compromise must always be made with the production capacity requirements. Figures 9.122–123 (566) demonstrate the total and screened yield at various stages of a normal batch cook and a cook with instant heating to maximum temperature, using mill size or shredded chips, respectively. There is a sharp

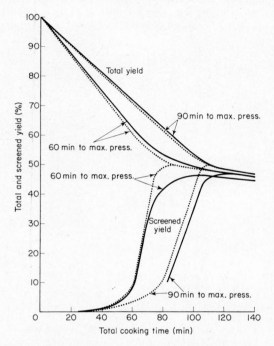

Fig. 9.122. Kraft cooking of slash pine, mill size and shredded chips, 1 and 1.5 h heating time (Nolan)

increase in the yield of screened pulp when the point of fiber liberation is reached, and a pulp low in screenings is obtained at a slightly higher yield in the case of shredded chips. That advantage, however, is more than counter-balanced by the loss of small size wood material formed on shredding, and by the quality decrease. It is also obvious from the figure that the rate of pulping is not appreciably increased by the chip disintegration, only the uniformity is influenced, especially when the cook is heated rapidly. The interrelation of alkali charge, maximum temperature and chip thickness and their influence on the rate of pulping is clearly seen from Figure 9.124 (334a), where these variables are depicted in combinations required to give a pulp of Roe number 6 at constant cooking time. In Figure 9.125 (334a) it is seen that the screenings differ in quantity not only with the Roe number but also with the chip thickness, and for the Roe number 6 level, the influence of chip thickness and temperature is shown in Figure 9.126

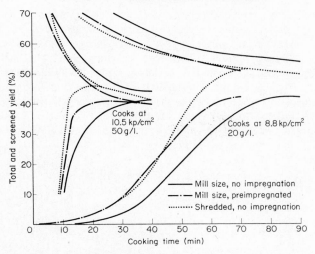

Fig. 9.123. High-speed kraft cooking of slash pine, mill size and shredded chips (Nolan)

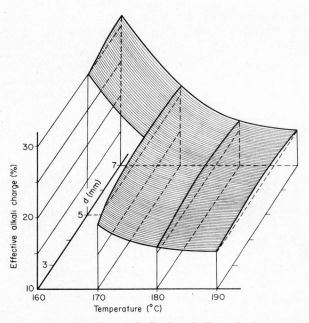

Fig. 9.124. The charge of effective alkali required to reach Roe number 6 using different chip thicknesses and cooking temperatures (Hartler)

633

(334a). Since the screening room and the screenings handling system may often be the capacity-limiting factors, the combinations of chip thickness and maximum temperature to give a certain amount of screenings is of interest, Figure 9.127 (334a). Thinner chips lead to achievement of higher Roe numbers or the tolerance of higher maximum temperatures, both factors of economic importance. Chip thickness does not, however, directly influence the pulp viscosity or strength properties to any degree, in contrast to maximum temperature, Figure 9.128 (334a). The non-uniformity in the degree of cooking caused by varying chip thickness,

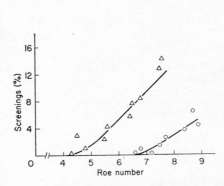

Fig. 9.125. Screenings content versus Roe number. Cooking temperature 170°C. ○ 7 mm, △ 5 mm (Hartler)

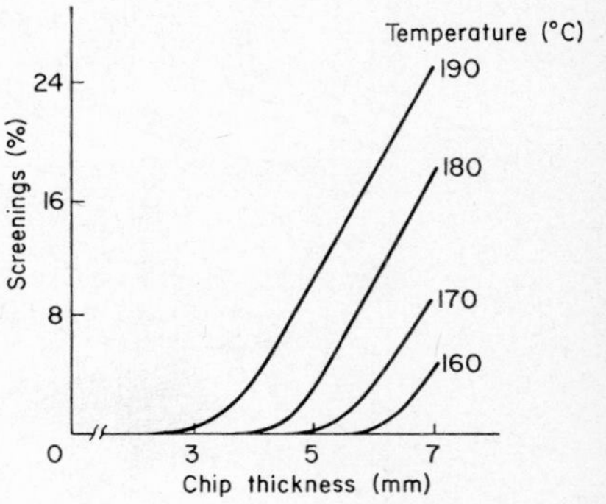

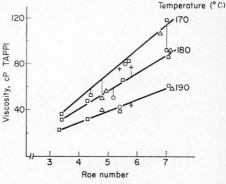

Fig. 9.126. Screenings vs. chip thickness for pulps having Roe number 6 on screened pulp. The laboratory prepared chips had a length of 40 mm and a square cross-section (Hartler)

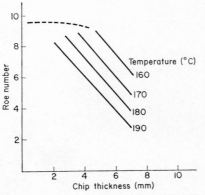

Fig. 9.127. Attainable Roe number on screened pulp at a screenings content of 1% using different chip thicknesses and cooking temperatures (Hartler)

Fig. 9.128. The viscosity in cP TAPPI for delignified unbleached pulps versus original Roe number using different chip thicknesses and temperatures. Symbols indicate chip thicknesses from 3 to 7 mm (Hartler)

634

causing higher screenings from thick chips, can also be met by squeezing the chips in a roll press repeatedly (143), or by using a drum chipper, which gives a uniform thickness (329). An improved yield of screened pulp is also reported when using an alkali-stable wetting agent to improve the penetration (20).

C. Pulp yield and composition

The pulp yield and composition are influenced by all cooking variables. Obviously, any combination of conditions can be chosen to give any desired yield of wood residue. A yield figure should always be related to some other numerical value, such as screenings, lignin content, viscosity or strength properties. Conditions giving a high yield are not ideal unless present at the same time, e.g. a maximal strength or a minimal lignin content is achieved. The amount of screenings obtained, as shown by the previous Figure 9.122–123, is still of considerable interest, but for paper pulps to be processed directly at integrated mills the screenings are often passed through refiners and returned for new screening and consequently add to the yield of accepted pulp. Besides the extra equipment and some additional insignificant power consumption, there is thus no great disadvantage in an increase in the screenings. With such an arrangement it is therefore possible either to increase the digester capacity by allowing less time for heating or to increase the yield and lignin content of the pulp, in both cases converting the higher screenings obtained into useful fibers. A bigger step is taken when the yield is increased above the point of fiber liberation at the 55% yield level. Then refiners for the entire stock are needed and the process turns into a kraft semichemical process.

The relation of total pulp yield to the lignin content of the pulp is shown in Figure 9.129 for various wood species. That relation is especially important for the production of bleached pulp, as the chlorine demand varies in direct proportion to the lignin content of the pulp, as denoted at the abscissa. For unbleached pulps the lignin content gives an approximate indication of how severe the alkaline treatment has been and the extent to which the remaining lignin can be expected to influence the paper properties of the pulp. Further, there is a direct relation between unbleached pulp color and the lignin content, Figure 6.57.

It is seen that hardwoods compare favorably in this respect with softwoods, hardwood kraft pulps being obtained in yields considerably higher than most softwoods even at lower lignin contents than for softwoods.

The same relation of pulp yield and lignin content is shown in Figure 9.130 for Douglas fir (707) and aspen (479) at varying *charge of effective alkali* and constant sulfidity. Obviously, the alkali charge does not affect the relation appreciably as long as the charge is sufficient to leave some residual alkali. If not, the pH of the cooking liquor may drop to a level where acid hydrolysis of some hemicelluloses occurs. However, that is mainly a risk on high-yield kraft pulping, where the high yield can be realized by either a low alkali charge or a low cooking temperature.

635

Normal softwood kraft pulps of 45–50% total yield and a lignin content of 4–5% require an alkali consumption of about 180 kg ptw NaOH, calculated as active alkali, or about 150 kg ptw NaOH as effective alkali. The screenings are then usually only a few per cent of the pulp.

The influence of the *alkali concentration* on the pulp yield at a certain degree of delignification is also insignificant, as seen in Figure 9.131 (707, cf. 135, 165). The large differences in xylan dissolution with varying alkali concentration discussed in Subsection II.2C of this chapter were found in cooking with a continuous liquor flow (817), which removes the dissolved

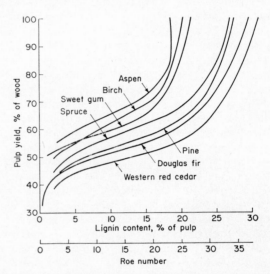

Fig. 9.129. Pulp yield vs. lignin content on kraft pulping of various wood species (various investigators)

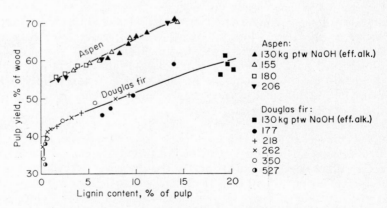

Fig. 9.130. Pulp yield vs. lignin content on kraft cooking of aspen and Douglas fir with varying alkali charge (Legg–Hart and Schwarz–Bray)

636

material from the digester. Within the range of alkali concentrations used in the normal cooks illustrated in the figure, the pentosan content of the pulps at a constant degree of delignification varied by only 0.5–1 %, and consequently did not show up in the pulp yield values. Corresponding differences in the case of hardwoods could be expected to be greater as hardwood kraft pulps always contain more xylan. On cooking scots pine with one low and one high charge of effective alkali, it was found to be, in agreement with the previously discussed experiments in continuous liquor flow digester (Figure 9.105), that for ordinary batch cooks, the dissolution of glucomannan is also barely affected by the alkali charge, whereas the dissolution of glucuronoxylan and of lignin is accelerated by an increase

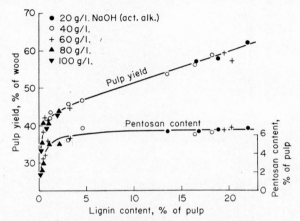

Fig. 9.131. Pulp yield and pentosan content vs. lignin content on kraft cooking of Douglas fir at varying alkali concentration (Schwarz–Bray)

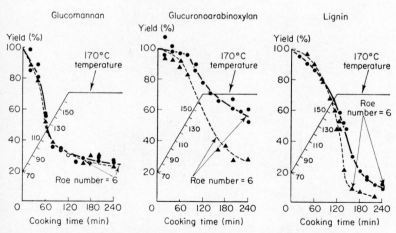

Fig. 9.132. Dissolution of hemicelluloses and lignin during kraft cooking of pine.
● 158 kg ptw NaOH effective alkali, ▲ 250 kg ptw NaOH effective alkali (Aurell)

in the alkali charge, Figure 9.132 (48). As a consequence, the compositions of the kraft pulps from a low and a high alkali charge are different, the former having a higher xylan content and the latter a higher gluco-mannan content, when compared at the same lignin content, Figure 9.133 (48). The net effect is a slightly reduced pulp yield at an increased alkali charge, but the difference is only about 1 % of the wood for a wide range of charges, Figure 9.134 (48). The same general course for the dissolution of the various components of loblolly pine during the kraft cook has been found for both springwood and summerwood (8a).

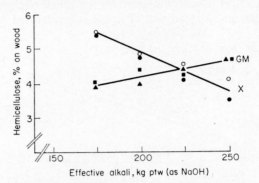

Fig. 9.133. Hemicellulose content of kraft pulp as a function of alkali charge. ■ glucomannan, Na_2S charge 50 kg ptw, ▲ glucomannan, sulfidity 25%, ○ glucuronoarabinoxylan, Na_2S charge 50 kg ptw, ▲ glucuronoarabinoxylan, sulfidity 25% (Aurell)

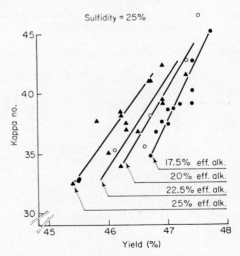

Fig. 9.134. Kappa number vs. yield on kraft cooking of pine at four different charges of alkali (Aurell)

The *sulfidity*, of so great importance for the rate of pulping, also greatly influences the pulp yield, especially from softwoods, as exemplified by Figure 9.135 (134, 296). The differences between kraft and soda cooking are particularly great in the lower yield range of defibrable, chemical pulps. In between the curves for soda and extreme kraft cooking will fall curves for pulping liquors of intermediate, insufficient sulfide content. The explanation for these phenomena has been given in previous sections. The pulp composition at equal lignin content is not appreciably affected by sulfidity variations.

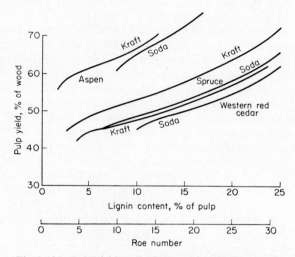

Fig. 9.135. Pulp yield vs. lignin content on kraft and soda cooking of aspen, spruce and western red cedar (Legg–Hart, Hägglund–Hedlund and Christiansen *et al*)

The *cooking temperature* and *time* naturally influence the yield and degree of delignification. However, at least in the interval of 150–170°C (280, 296), the yield of pulp of a certain lignin content is not appreciably changed, provided the pretreatment and time of heating have ensured a uniform cook. The danger of non-uniformities will increase with the maximum temperature and finally, above 170 or 180°C (271, 516, 744), show up in a higher lignin content and more screenings at a certain total yield level, Figure 9.136 (744). As pointed out earlier, these effects will be more pronounced with larger chips.

As shown in a previous section of this chapter, the dissolution of the carbohydrates during the alkaline cooking starts as a peeling reaction from the aldehydic end groups, and possibly also to some extent from occasional keto groups along the chain molecules. It is logical therefore to try to improve the pulp yield of the kraft cook by reacting the carbonyl groups with a reagent prior to or in the early stages of the cook. The most unambiguous reaction is the reduction with sodium tetrahydroborate (sodium borohydride), which yields alcohol groups and tetrahydroborate according to the reaction

$$4 \text{ RCHO} + \text{NaBH}_4 + 2 \text{ NaOH} + \text{H}_2\text{O} \longrightarrow 4 \text{ RCH}_2\text{OH} + \text{Na}_3\text{BO}_3$$

at the same time as the side reaction

$$\text{NaBH}_4 + 2 \text{ NaOH} + \text{H}_2\text{O} \longrightarrow 4 \text{ H}_2 + \text{Na}_3\text{BO}_3$$

A stabilization of carbohydrates towards alkaline peeling degradation was demonstrated by several workers (274, 343, 530, 625). The addition of sodium tetrahydroborate to the kraft cook was suggested recently and investigated on pine pulping (328, 530a, 792a). It was found that the pulp yield increased in proportion to the charge of the reductant, and was about 6% of the wood higher at 20 kg ptw NaBH_4 added. A chromatographic study of the pulp carbohydrate composition showed very interesting results, shedding additional light on the chemistry of the kraft cook. The increase in yield was found to originate entirely from an *increase in glucomannan yield*, 6% of the wood, and possibly *some increase in cellulose yield*, 1% of the wood, whereas the *xylan yield had decreased*, about 1% of the wood. Obviously, a chemical stabilization of both glucomannan and xylan (and cellulose) must occur through the end-group reduction, but the resistance to alkaline degradation is not complete, since cleavage of glycosidic bonds occurs at kraft cooking temperatures. This means that during the later stages of the kraft cook, when the tetrahydroborate is exhausted, there is a new peeling degradation from new end groups formed by the hydrolysis. However, such a hydrolysis must also occur during the conventional kraft

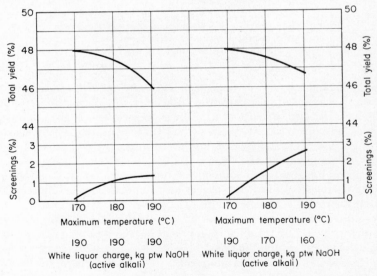

Fig. 9.136. Total yield and screenings vs. maximum temperature at constant or varying white liquor charge when cooking pine kraft pulp of Roe number 6.
(Stockman–Sundkvist)

cook and is no explanation of a decrease in the pulp xylan yield, especially since the effect remains even when the alkali charge is adjusted to give similar alkalinity towards the end of the cook as for a conventional kraft cook. Therefore it seems likely that the stabilized glucomannan is preferentially adsorbed to the cellulose microfibrils and this prevents the adsorption of xylan fragments to the same extent as that occurring during a normal kraft cook. The parallel to the phenomenon observed in the sulfite cook (cf. Chapter 9.I) is striking, where a deacetylation of glucomannan during a neutral sulfite precook or a prolonged acid sulfite impregnation period at low temperature has been found to increase the glucomannan and decrease the xylan yield. That the effect noted in the tetrahydroborate kraft cooks is of a partly physical nature is further confirmed by the observation that in the kraft cooking of birch an addition of sodium tetrahydroborate gives the same increase in pulp yield as with pine, 6–7% of the wood, but that the increase in this case is due to an increase in the xylan yield, together with small increases in the cellulose and glucomannan yields (584), Figure 9.137. Birch contains only relatively small amounts of glucomannan, which are insufficient to cover the microfibril surfaces available for adsorption, and hence the increase in xylan yield is made possible. In contrast, in the kraft pulping of spruce, sodium tetrahydroborate addition gives rise to an increase in glucomannan and a decrease in xylan yield, in analogy with pine cooking (19).

The increase in yield is of practical interest. Sodium tetrahydroborate addition represents one of the few methods known to decrease the wood consumption of a kraft cook. However, the cost of the chemical prevents its practical application at present. The side reaction necessitates

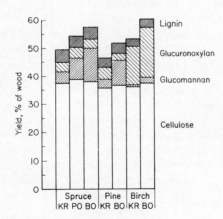

Fig. 9.137. Yield of wood components on pulping to Roe number 4–5, using the kraft process without additions (KR), polysulfide (PO) or tetrahydroborate (BO) additions. Spruce (Annergren, Rydholm, Vardheim), pine (Hartler), birch (Pettersson, Rydholm)

641

considerable charges of tetrahydroborate. A closer study of the variables of the tetrahydroborate kraft cook (48a) revealed that a maximal yield increase of about 10%, wood basis, can be achieved for pine. By a tetrahydroborate pretreatment at 80°C and 7 kp/cm² pressure this effect is obtained with only 10 kg ptw NaBH₄. Lower charges give proportionally lower yield improvement (19, 328). In search of cheaper chemicals to give the same effect interest has first been centered around *polysulfide cooking* (19, 66, 430, 580). When polysulfide is added to the white liquor, a similar yield improvement takes place. This is somewhat lower than can be achieved with tetrahydroborate, or 2–5% of the wood. Also in this case, a fairly linear improvement with chemical charge is obtained (430), and it is obvious that the polysulfide is likewise decomposed in side reaction, mainly to thiosulfate (19). The nature of the carbohydrate reaction leading to stabilization is not quite established since the analogous oxidation of end groups to carboxyls could not be proved for model sugars (156) although degradation products were indicated, which may point to a subsequent decarboxylation to an alkali-stable end group:

$$RCHO \longrightarrow RCOOH \longrightarrow RH + CO_2$$

Other explanations are also conceivable.

Polysulfide kraft cooking is practised to some extent in mills using sulfur in the chemical make-up. These quantities are generally too small to produce any essential yield improvement. 30–40 kg ptw of polysulfide sulfur are required for a substantial effect. The sulfur should not be added to the white liquor in advance since high alkalinity will destroy the polysulfides. The best method is to separate the sulfide and carbonate of the recovered alkali smelt by fractional dissolution, to causticize only the carbonate and to dissolve the sulfur in the sulfide solution, where the alkalinity is not excessive and where the polysulfides formed are fairly stable (789). Polysulfide can also be produced by air oxidation of mixtures of white and black liquor (70).

A systematic search for oxidants does not reveal many substances suitable for mixing with white liquor other than polysulfides. Reductants are more easily found. Most of them, such as pyrocatechol, pyrogallol, ascorbic acid, arsenite, phosphite, hypophosphite, stannite, nitrite, formiate, and hydrazine, have been found without beneficial effect in alkaline cooking, although the delignifying power in the absence of sulfide was mainly tested (580). One of the more closely investigated is *sodium dithionite*, $Na_2S_2O_4$ (396, 400). When added to sodium hydroxide, it was first observed that the rate of delignification was not improved by the dithionite addition, and that 8 h at 180°C were required to achieve pulping. In spite of these harsh conditions, the carbohydrates were remarkably well preserved, and spruce pulps with little screenings were obtained in yields between 60 and 50%. This indicated a specific reaction between dithionite and the carbohydrates. The pulps were also remarkably bright, approaching the brightness of sulfite pulps, which showed that the reducing medium prevented the usual lignin discoloration. Also with beech, high yields of bright pulps were obtained. Since an investigation (546) showed that dithionite is decomposed by alkali into sulfite and thiosulfate under conditions similar to those of an alkali cook, the addition of dithionite was compared to sulfite addition (400), and the former found to give superior effects. The pulping of poplar with neutral sulfite was found to give less bright and strong pulps than when using dithionite and alkali (396).

Although the dithionite addition thus had a positive effect on both carbohydrate and lignin reactions during the alkali cook, the delignification was fairly slow, particularly for softwood pulps. However, kraft cooks were also carried out with dithionite addition (400). The presence of sulfide improved the rate of delignification, and the dithionite only slightly retarded it. The pulps were less bright than with the pure dithionite–alkali cooks but still considerably brighter than kraft pulps. The latter were 25–30%, dithionite–kraft pulps 38–48%, and dithionite–alkali pulps about 60% in brightness. The addition of dithionite to the kraft cook also improved the yield of both unbleached and bleached pulp in proportion to the dithionite charge, at the most 4–5% of the wood for spruce with dithionite concentrations as high as 60 g/l (liquor-to-wood ratio 7.5 : 1) (400). This interesting parallel to tetrahydroborate and polysulfide cooks was also shown to involve a preferential stabilization of the glucomannan fraction (657). Subsequent investigations, e.g. (603), have failed to achieve considerable improvements in yield or pulp brightness upon dithionite additions to kraft cooks. Obviously, an ideal reagent should be stable to alkali in contrast to tetrahydroborate, dithionite and polysulfides. The latter decompose into sulfur and sulfide and are also hydrolyzed by alkali to thiosulfate. Dithionite will decompose into thiosulfate and sulfite, and tetrahydroborate into borate and hydrogen. That effects are still obtained with these chemicals indicates that some carbohydrate carbonyls react during the heating period prior to the total decomposition of the reagent. A pretreatment of wood with tetrahydroborate at room temperature did not, however, improve the yield in comparison with the same charge of tetrahydroborate in a straight kraft cook, which implies that some dissolution of the wood substance is required to make the carbonyls accessible to reduction (657).

Tetrahydroborate thus evolves considerable quantities of hydrogen during the cook. It has also been suggested that *hydrogen* should be used as a pulping agent together with alkali (711). The pressures necessary are high compared with normal practice, or 30–40 kp/cm^2 (729), and metallic nickel in various forms is used as a catalyst. The lignin dissolved is hydrogenated and depolymerized to aromatic hydrocarbons containing an aliphatic side chain with two or three carbon atoms. The lifetime of intermediate reactive products formed has been found long enough to allow the catalyst to be kept separate from the wood on hydrogenation, which is of practical interest (729, cf. 28). As hydrogenation catalysts are sensitive to sulfide, no kraft cooking is possible, and the alkali cooking together with hydrogen did not seem to increase the rate of delignification

643

as compared with normal alkali cooking. The pulping of softwoods is therefore less easy, whereas hardwood pulping is practicable at normal cooking temperatures, 160–170°C (729). The results presented do not allow too many conclusions as to the increase in carbohydrate yield in the presence of active hydrogen, but it has been demonstrated that the degradation of isolated wood hemicelluloses in alkali is retarded by hydrogen and a catalyst (334). It is therefore probable that alkali cooking in the presence of active hydrogen falls in the same category as the tetra-hydroborate, polysulfide, and dithionite cooks. Whether that is also the case with alkali cooking in the presence of *oxygen* is still more difficult to judge from published data (320).

D. *Paper properties of kraft pulps*

In Subsection II.4A the influence of the wood species and condition on the paper properties was considered. It was stressed that some structural

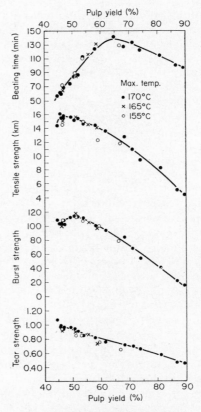

Fig. 9.138. Paper properties of black spruce kraft pulp of varying yield, after beating to 300 C.S. (Kerr–Hart)

details, more or less pronounced in the various wood species, such as fiber dimensions, especially length and wall thickness, summerwood content, etc., will cause large differences in the properties of pulps from various species. However, during the cook, the inherent properties of the fibers are changed to a considerable extent, and therefore the conditions of the cook also influence the final pulp quality. Three main chemical factors are thereby important, as in the case of all paper pulping processes, namely the *degree of delignification*, the *extent of carbohydrate dissolution*, and the *extent of degradation of the remaining carbohydrates*. Also the *location* and *degree of lateral order* of residual hemicelluloses are of importance.

The lignin remaining in the pulp checks the swelling of the fibers on beating, and therefore, the *response to beating* as well as the development of fiber-to-fiber bonds is decreased on increasing the lignin content, as demonstrated in Figures 9.138–139 (429, 479) for spruce and aspen. On prolonged cooking to lower lignin content, the degradation of the carbohydrates becomes noticeable, resulting in a decrease in the tensile and bursting strengths. Therefore there is an optimal degree of cooking, which for normal kraft pulping conditions corresponds to a chlorine number of 5–7 (273e, 324, 429), which is the main level of chemical softwood kraft pulps. Only when special grades are desired, such as unbleached grades of high brightness, is the chlorine number purposely lowered below 4. Pulp for bleaching should be cooked to a degree giving

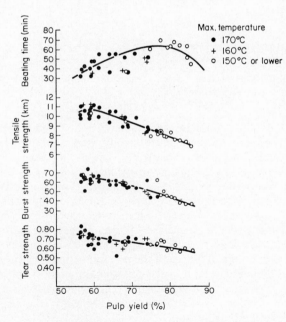

Fig. 9.139. Paper properties of aspen kraft pulp of varying yield, after beating to 300 C.S. (Legg–Hart)

645

the best overall economy and quality, bearing in mind that the wood consumption will increase when the chlorine demand is lowered. With high wood-prices, the comparatively high chlorine consumption of pulps cooked to optimal strength does not motivate a decrease in the chlorine number of pulps for bleaching below 5 (782, cf. 136a). It is the slow beating response and the dark color of the kraft pulps which are their main drawbacks as compared with sulfite pulps, and their superior strength is the dominating advantage.

The dissolution and degradation of the carbohydrates proceed fairly independently of the sulfidity of the cooking liquor, but depend very much on the charge and concentration of sodium hydroxide and on the cooking time and temperature. That is indicated by the decrease in average DP on prolonged cooking, as shown in Figure 9.140 (566), and Figure 9.141

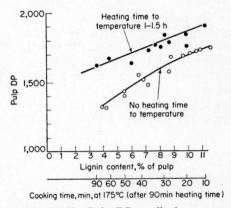

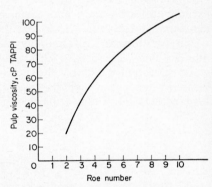

Fig. 9.140, Pulp DP vs. lignin content in kraft pulping of slash pine (Nolan)

Fig. 9.141. Pulp viscosity vs. Roe number in kraft pulping of spruce (Hart–Strapp)

(324). At 150° C, a lower temperature than normally used in kraft cooking, the DP was found to decrease more slowly after an initial heavy drop during the first few minutes of cooking (8a), Table 9.30. Viscosity measurements on unbleached kraft pulps, however, have no direct correlation with their strength properties (e.g. 355, 566), and are only indicative of the degradation of the high-molecular carbohydrates, mainly the cellulose. The alkaline degradation of the hemicelluloses, which is probably more important to the strength properties, is not necessarily parallel to the cellulose degradation but is likely to proceed somewhat in advance of the latter. Furthermore, the influence of the remaining lignin in the unbleached pulps will cause lower strength in the pulps of the highest viscosity levels. A higher charge of effective alkali results at constant cooking temperature and time in a much decreased viscosity (134, 324, 604), whereas changes in sulfidity have only minor effects.

An investigation of the changes of the fiber properties of loblolly pine springwood and summerwood upon kraft cooking (524a) indicated a continually decreasing strength of individual fibers, but an unchanged fiber strength, as expressed in kp/mm^2, i.e., taking into account the shrinkage of fiber cross-sectional area during the dissolution of the carbohydrates, Table 9.30a. Only during the last phase of the kraft cook, beyond the point of fiber liberation, was there a significant loss in specific fiber strength. The dry fiber bond strength was found to decrease continually during the cook. All effects were considerably larger for summerwood than for springwood fibers.

Table 9.30a. Changes in yield, composition, DP, fiber strength and fiber bond strength during kraft cooking of loblolly pine springwood and summerwood (8a, 524a). 150°C, sulfidity 25%, 220 kg ptw active alkali

	Springwood				Summerwood						
Pulp yield, % of wood											
unbleached	100	88	72	46	100	94	71	65	51	48	46
delignified	75	63	54	46	72	64	58	54	47	47	44
Carbohydrate DP											
unbleached	4,670	2,860	1,650	1,540	4,610	2,620	2,010	1,980	1,650	1,590	1,360
delignified	—	—	—	—	—	1,600	1,270	1,140	1,180	1,140	830
Component yield, % of wood											
Lignin	30	27	18	2	28	26	18	13	6	3	2
Cellulose	44	44	41	36	42	43	41	41	38	38	35
Galactoglucomannan	16	12	8	6	18	13	9	7	6	6	6
Glucuronoarabinoxylan	7	6	5	2	8	5	5	5	3	2	3
Delignified fiber properties											
Individual fiber strength, p	17	15	15	11	50	55	38	41	34	35	29
Cross-sectional area, μ^2	386	391	343	292	568	664	458	483	443	472	475
Fiber strength, kp/mm^2	48	40	43	38	88	85	84	86	77	75	60
Fiber bond strength, kp/mm^2	0.27	0.18	0.20	0.18	0.71	0.59	0.60	0.46	0.33	0.47	0.32

As the rate of delignification is increased by the presence of sulfide, it is obvious that for pulps of identical lignin content those cooked in sulfide-free liquor have been subjected to alkali for a longer time or higher temperature. The carbohydrate degradation has therefore proceeded further, and thus soda pulps are invariably weaker than the corresponding kraft pulps. The increase in tensile strength on increasing sulfidity is illustrated in Figure 9.142 (273e) for pine (160°C, 220 kg ptw *active* alkali as NaOH). The curves for constant chlorine numbers at the various sulfidity levels emphasize the fact that the cook of lower sulfidity has to be kept at temperature for a longer period to obtain a certain degree of delignification, and as a consequence pulp strength will decrease. It was stated that quite similar diagrams could be constructed for other paper properties. Similar investigations on western red cedar (170°C, 194 kg ptw *effective* alkali as NaOH) (134) showed that compared at constant yield (or degree of delignification) the pulps made with the highest sulfide charges had the highest tensile and bursting strengths, whereas the tear was comparatively unaffected. It is vital to make the comparison at constant yield or lignin content, and not at constant cooking time–temperature conditions as is often done (e.g. 324, 394), since the change in sulfidity affects the rate of pulping. The conclusion from the above results (134, 273e), as well as others (324), is that for pulps of comparable yield or lignin content there is an improvement in strength properties which is remarkable in the range of 0–20% sulfidity, where the main improvement in the rate of pulping occurs, but also noticeable up to and even above 50% sulfidity (324). However, mill trials (126, 826) indicate an improvement in pulp properties on increasing the sulfidity from 15–25%, but that other variables, especially in the wood raw material, are of greater importance than sulfidity, especially in the fairly small interval of variance in actual practice.

The addition of sulfite to the kraft cook appears for no known reason to lead to pulps with definitely higher strength though somewhat lower yield (580a).

The alkali charge and concentration seems to be of greater influence on the pulp strength than the maximum temperature (at least in the 160–180°C range), as it was found (165, 324) that the bursting strength of pulps of equal chlorine numbers increased with decreasing alkali charge and increasing temperature to keep the cooking time constant, whereas at constant alkali charge and varying time there was no noticeable influence on pulp strength by a change in maximum temperature in the range of 160–180°C (324, 516). Cook at 190°C gave pulps not quite as strong as those cooked at 170°C (744). Therefore, it seems justifiable to keep the maximum temperature relatively high and the charge of alkali correspondingly low, in order to achieve the strongest pulps at a preserved digester cycle. However, a limit is generally set by the color of the unbleached pulp, as very low residual alkali will result in a comparatively dark pulp, and increasing brightness demands on the unbleached kraft pulps have again focused the interest on cooking with increased alkali charges. The yield and composition of such pulps have been discussed previously, and the main consequence of these changes seems to be a slower beating response and slightly higher tear strength, whereas the

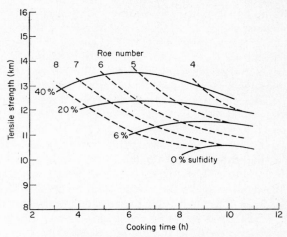

Fig. 9.142. Effect of sulfidity and Roe number on the tensile strength of pine kraft pulp, cooked at 160°C (Hägglund)

tensile and burst strength are insignificantly reduced (48). It has been maintained (635, 800), that continuous injection of white liquor during a kraft cook to keep the alkali concentration at a constant level, lower than that in the beginning of a conventional cook, results in pulps of higher yield and strength, and more recent patents apply a technique in which the cooking liquor is continuously fortified in a separate vessel at full temperature and recirculated at a rapid rate through the digester (569, 807). On the other hand, it has been found that most of the improvements achieved on injection cooking originate from the impregnation treatment necessary (135). However, for practical reasons a dilution of the white liquor required for delignification is always carried out in order to cover most of the chips, and to avoid the introduction of extra water, black liquor is used as a diluent, with no impairing of pulp strength or delignification rate (305). In using injection cooking, an optimum effective alkali concentration was found to be about 20 g/l NaOH (135), lower concentrations giving lower quality and slow pulping, and higher concentrations leading to lower pulp strength.

The addition of reductants or oxidants to the kraft cook, such as sodium tetrahydroborate or polysulfide, which give improved carbohydrate yields by end-group stabilization, also affects the paper properties of the pulp, in that the tear strength is considerably reduced, whereas tensile and burst strength remain unchanged or even improve, Table 9.31 (19, 584, 792a). This is obviously a serious limitation of these processes, another being the reduced brightness of unbleached polysulfide pulp compared with kraft pulp.

Table 9.31. Chemical composition and paper properties of kraft pulps, cooked in the absence and presence of polysulfide or tetrahydroborate (19, 584)

Wood species	Pulping process	Roe no.	Yield, % unbl.	Yield, % bl.	Hemicellulose content, % GM	Hemicellulose content, % GX	Beating time, min	Tensile strength, km	Burst strength	Tear strength
Spruce	Kraft	5	50	46	7	10	76	11.1	112	133
	Polysulfide	5	54	50	16	6	82	12.0	105	110
	Tetrahydro-borate	5	57	53	22	6	65	10.8	95	99
Birch	Kraft	5	54	51	1	27	29	9.0	78	75
	Tetrahydro-borate	5	61	58	4	30	32	9.6	70	62

GM = glucomannan, GX = glucuronoxylan

III. Multistage Cooking Processes (656)

1. INTRODUCTION AND SURVEY

The conventional one-stage chemical pulping processes with all their modifications dealt with hitherto have certain limitations which can be overcome by carrying out the cooking in two or more stages. Thus, *acid sulfite cooking* does not give a very good pulp from most pines or from spruce with tannin damage. Generally it gives paper pulps with comparatively low strength, and dissolving pulps not much above 90% alphacellulose content unless greatly purified in the bleaching. *Kraft cooking*, on the other hand, gives fairly dark pulps, not easily bleached, and unsuitable for dissolving purposes. One-stage cooking allows changes of certain important variables, such as temperature and chemical charges, whereas the concentrations of chemicals during the cook change according to the reactions in a way which is not normally governed by the mill personnel, and which may not always be ideal, e.g. to pulp quality or the yield of by-products.

It is therefore natural that several suggestions have been made to modify the conventional processes so that the composition of the cooking liquor is deliberately affected from the outside, either by the addition of new chemicals or by replacing some of the cooking liquor with a new one of different composition. The border-line between one-stage and multistage processes will therefore not be entirely distinct. For instance, compare *injection alkaline cooking* (135) or *counter-current alkaline cooking* (724) on one hand with the *Raitt* process (597, 723) on the other. In the two former cases, the concentrations of the active chemicals are governed from the outside of the digester, but in a way which does not divide the cooks into separate stages. They are therefore described as modifications of the one-stage kraft process. The Raitt and similar processes, on the other hand, start with a black liquor cook to make more efficient use of the residual chemicals and later replace the black liquor with white liquor. In spite of a general similarity with the former processes, the latter are considered to be two-stage processes.

Likewise, the *bridged acid sulfite cooks* (378), where the gas relief towards the end of the cook is regulated to give a constant acidity, is considered a one-stage sulfite cook modification, whereas a sulfite cook, which is started at moderate acidity or is even alkaline, and eventually gassed up with sulfur dioxide to a more or less acid sulfite stage, as the *bisulfite–acid sulfite*, *neutral sulfite–acid sulfite* and *neutral sulfite–bisulfite* processes, is considered a two-stage cook. More distinctly multistage cooks are cooks where the cooking liquor is withdrawn and replaced by another one. The temperature curve cannot be used as a guide to discriminate between one-stage and multistage cooking as there are often more breaks in the temperature curves of one-stage cooks.

In Table 9.32 most of the suggested multistage cooking processes have been listed.

There are two main types of process which deserve attention and have achieved a commercial application, namely the *two-stage sulfite cook* with less acidity in the initial stage and increased acidity in the final stage, and *processes combining an initial acid treatment with a final alkaline cook*. The former combination has the purpose of allowing a freer choice of wood raw-material for the sulfite pulping and is used by a few Scandinavian

650

mills employing sodium or ammonium base (16, 467, 730, 778), Stora Kopparberg in *Skutskär*, Swedish Cellulose in *Kramfors* and *Ortviken*, Union in *Skien*, and Saugbrugsforeningen in *Halden*, whereas Weyerhaeuser in *Cosmopolis* utilizes magnesium base for a similar process. The acid–alkaline two-stage cooks aim at the production of high-alpha pulps for dissolving and special paper pulp grades and are used by Scandinavian, American and Japanese mills, some of which are of a considerable

Table 9.32. Practised or suggested multistage cooking processes

		Ref.
I. With a final acid cooking stage		
1. Sulfite–sulfite	Improved alcohol yield	270, 562
	Increased waste liquor dry content	676
2. Prehydrolysis–sulfite	Improved rayon pulp quality	107, 178, 478, 573, 733
3. Hydroxide–sulfite	Paper pulp from resinous wood	72, 608, 632
	Improved paper pulp yield	156
4. Neutral sulfite–acid sulfite	Stronger paper pulp	79b, 613
	Paper pulp from pine	248, 721a
	Pulping tannin-damaged wood and improved paper pulp yield	49, 165a, 778, 790
5. Bisulfite–acid sulfite	Paper pulp from pine	16, 53a, 185, 295, 309, 467, 721a, 730
	Stronger paper pulp	613
6. Neutral sulfite–bisulfite	Improved paper pulp yield	18, 789a, 803a
II. With a final alkaline cooking stage		
1. Prehydrolysis–kraft	High alpha pulp. Prehydrolysis with:	
	sulfuric acid	13, 179, 180, 181, 363, 437, 458, 614
	hydrohalogenic acids	151, 152, 398, 544, 688, 811
	water	493, 528, 554, 573, 615, 642, 703, 704, 716, 719
	steam	91, 141, 362, 493, 554, 582, 704, 823
	salt solutions	186, 593
	sulfite waste liquor	503
2. Sulfite–kraft	High alpha pulp	182, 358, 555, 611, 643, 699
3. Sulfite–carbonate	High alpha pulp	465, 578, 600, 610, 655, 720, 721
4. Bisulfite–carbonate	Stronger paper pulp	720, 721
5. Bisulfite–neutral sulfite	Stronger paper pulp	53a, 682
6. Carbonate–kraft	Less causticizing capacity needed	657
7. Carbonate–hydroxide	Stronger paper pulp	231, 356
8. Black liquor–kraft	Lower white liquor consumption	723
9. Hydrosulfide–hydroxide	Paper pulp	680

size (21, 22, 23, 600, 740), such as Uddeholm in *Skoghall*, International Paper Co in *Natchez*, Buckeye in *Foley* and Rayonier in *Jesup* for prehydrolysis–kraft and Rauma–Repola in *Rauma* for sulfite–carbonate. The total production of two-stage processed pulp is of the order of 1 M t/year. Most of the other suggestions of multistage cooking do not have advantages big enough to warrant the increased production costs and technical complications introduced. Only the two important types of multistage cooking processes will therefore be considered below.

2. GENERAL DESCRIPTION OF PROCESSES

Two-stage sulfite cooking employs an initial acid stage, which is subsequently transferred to an acid sulfite stage by introduction of either sulfur dioxide gas or an acid cooking liquor. The first stage is always on a soluble base, the second may also be calcium-based.

Acid–alkaline cooking processes are subdivided into *prehydrolysis–kraft*, *sulfite–kraft*, *sulfite–carbonate* and *bisulfite–carbonate* cooking. Of these, the first is technically dominant. It is carried out with water, steam, or mineral acid in the first stage and this treatment is followed by a conventional kraft cook. The sulfite–kraft process is essentially a prehydrolysis by a limited sulfite cook, followed by a kraft cook. In the latter two processes, delignification is carried out almost to completion in the first stage, and the second stage can therefore be carried out with an uncausticized carbonate solution.

Multistage cooking is still generally performed *batch-wise*, although suggestions for *continuous operation* have been made (12, 458) and carried out on a pilot plant scale (657). Several factors are in favor of continuous operation of these processes. The necessary changes in cooking liquor composition will deduct less time from the effective cooking in continuous operation and the increased numbers of cooking variables of multistage cooking are also more easily controlled in continuous operation.

In order to obtain a complete separation of the cooking liquors of the various stages, *washing* the product of the first stage has been applied prior to the introduction of the second stage cooking liquor. However, this will give a less good heat economy, as well as decreased digester capacity, and is ordinarily not necessary. On the other hand, *removal of varying amounts of the first cooking liquor* is general practice, from a comparatively small liquor side relief, e.g. 0.5 m³ ptw, to allow room for the introduction of a concentrated solution of the second stage chemicals, to a complete drainage of the digester. Without washing, the amount of cooking liquor remaining after drainage will depend on the digester pressure maintained. Completely wet chips will generally contain around 2 m³ ptw, which at an initial liquor ratio of 4 m³ ptw means a liquor removal of only about 50%. If, however, gas formation—steam or sulfur dioxide—is allowed to occur by releasing the digester pressure below the vapor pressure of the cooking liquor, gas bubbles forming within the chips will help to drive out the liquor, resulting in the removal of 66% or even

75% of the original amount. Only in one case, acidification with sulfur dioxide of a neutral sulfite liquor, is no liquor relief necessary, but is yet practised in order to save chemicals and to increase the dry content of the waste liquor. Somewhat analogous is the case of prehydrolysis by high-temperature steaming of the dry chips, followed by a normal liquor charge of a kraft cook.

The *introduction of fresh chemicals* for the subsequent stage does not deviate from normal practice. In the case of sulfur dioxide introduction, this is done in liquid form to the cooking liquor circulation, on the pressure side of the pump. At the introduction of sodium carbonate after an acid cooking stage, formation of carbon dioxide occurs in large amounts. Improved provisions for gas relief must be made in comparison with normal one-stage cooking and special care taken to avoid plugging of the top relief strainer.

Otherwise there are no special features discriminating one-stage and multistage cooking operation. The *cooking cycle* is generally prolonged through the introduction of an extra stage, and digester capacity therefore decreased. However, this deficit can be counter-balanced to some extent by increasing the speed of heating of the cook, which is permissible, e.g. in the case of the initial prehydrolysis or neutral sulfite stages. The speed of heating of the second stage can also be increased because of the complete liquor penetration and the greater accessibility of the remaining wood structure. Figure 9.143 exemplifies the temperature schedules for some of the more important types of two-stage cooking.

The changes in pH during a multistage cook are appreciable and require high corrosion resistance in the *construction materials*. The protective

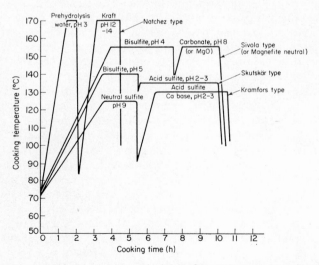

Fig. 9.143. Temperature schedules of some two-stage cooks with industrial application (cooking curves could be adjusted according to quality and capacity demands)

653

scale formation developing in one-stage sulfite or kraft cooks will not occur. Carbon brick linings or high-quality compound steel are used. Also in this respect, continuous operation represents an advantage by keeping the acid and alkaline liquors separate, but instead there is the disadvantage in continuous prehydrolysis–kraft pulping, for example, that resin scaling of the prehydrolysis stage, which tends to block the strainers, is not periodically removed by alkali, as is the case in batch cooking. Vapor phase prehydrolysis is therefore preferred for continuous operation (657).

3. REACTIONS

A. Two-stage sulfite cooking

The reactions of this process have been dealt with in the section on sulfite cooking and its variants, and will only be repeated here in main and special features. Acid sulfite cooking of wood, mainly pines and tannin-damaged spruce, containing certain extractives, is checked by *condensation* of the latter with the lignin (203, 262). This condensation dominates at lower pH over the *sulfonation* of lignin, whereas less acid, neutral or slightly alkaline sulfite solutions favor sulfonation. However, at those higher pH's, only the more reactive and accessible groups of lignin are sulfonated and complete delignification is not achieved. Therefore, a subsequent acid cooking stage is necessary, completing sulfonation and delignification. Then, with the most reactive and accessible groups already sulfonated, there is less tendency for the extractives to condense with the lignin, and good pulp is produced. It may be that the rôle of presulfonation of the first stage has been rather overestimated, as similar results in some cases can be obtained by using sodium bicarbonate instead of a neutral sulfite solution for the first cooking stage (778), but on the other hand it is known that the most reactive groups of lignin are very rapidly sulfonated, and presulfonation could possibly be achieved in the brief period of conversion of the bicarbonate into sulfite and bisulfite before passing into the more acid region where condensation would predominate. The sulfonation of lignin carbonyls could be of importance in this connection (721a).

In order to maintain a fairly constant acidity within the chips, it is beneficial to keep the *concentration* of sodium sulfite–bisulfite in the initial cooking liquor high. To avoid unnecessary consumption of cooking chemicals, the liquor of the initial stage must then be removed to a large extent prior to the acid stage. This will necessitate either the introduction of a second-stage acid cooking liquor, or a vapor-phase cook acidified by sulfur dioxide. However, it is not entirely necessary to operate with an initial cooking liquor concentration higher than that corresponding to the normal consumption of chemicals.

The *pH level* of the initial stage has been the subject of discussions. The lower limit seems to be around pH 4 (measured at room temperature) or corresponding to pure bisulfite solution. Below that pH region, the condensation reactions are favored, probably because of the presence of free sulfur dioxide gas, penetrating the wood structure in advance of the

654

cooking liquor and then creating a higher acidity. The upper pH limit has not been definitely established, but pH 10–11 has been indicated (657). At that level, alkaline intramolecular lignin condensation will impair its subsequent sulfonability. Alternatively, a low-temperature treatment at still higher alkalinity gives the same benefits (156). The rate and extent of presulfonation is not very much affected in the pH range 5–9 (490), and the most suitable pH should therefore depend on the pH-dependence of the condensation reactions as well as physical factors such as the solubility of the extractives, etc. As seen in Table 9.32, both slightly acidic and alkaline sulfite solutions have been suggested and both are in use. In any case, it is obvious that two-stage sulfite pulping requires a *soluble base*, as insoluble metal sulfite would precipitate in the initial stage. Sodium as well as ammonium base is used, ammonium giving somewhat less good results because of side reactions of ammonia or ammonium ion. Magnesium base is also satisfactory in some cases, but is less suitable at high pH's unless supersaturated solution or slurry is applied (562a). However, for the second, acid stage, calcium base can be used as well, provided the liquor side relief after the first stage and the concentration level of that liquor leave sufficiently little combined SO_2 to allow extra additions of base, to a total of 40–50 kg ptw combined SO_2. The *manner of transition to the acid cooking stage* may be of some importance, and it has been suggested in the case of sulfur dioxide addition that it should be done cautiously and over a certain period of time, possibly to prevent re-deposition of dissolved extractives (185).

The *temperature* and *time* of the two cooking stages are not fixed, but depend on raw material and the grade of pulp desired. Figure 9.143 gives two examples. In the case where fairly low temperature and high pH are maintained during the initial stage, the impregnation effect is likely to be more important than the presulfonation, whereas a high temperature and a comparatively low pH will stress the presulfonation effect.

The pulp obtained by two-stage sulfite cooking is very similar to that of one-stage acid sulfite cooking, as long as pH of the first stage is kept below 6. At higher pH, higher yields of carbohydrates and easier fiber-izing at high yields are obtained (778), as part of the glucomannan is stabilized to acid hydrolysis (18). The shives from tannin-damaged wood, which normally cause discoloration on the storage of unbleached pulp, are eliminated and the screening rejects on cooking pine heartwood are considerably reduced. This can be done also with straight bisulfite pulping (165a). The strength properties of paper pulp are unaffected unless the carbohydrate yield is improved (730, 778). The higher hemicellulose content achieved by a neutral sulfite precook tends to reduce the pulp strength of both bisulfite and acid sulfite pulps (18, 682, 790), as exemplified in Table 9.33 (18, 19).

B. Acid–alkaline cooking for high-alpha pulps

Acid sulfite, as well as kraft cooking, involves reactions which may only be influenced to some extent within the limits of the reaction conditions.

Table 9.33. Chemical composition and paper properties of acid sulfite or bisulfite spruce
pulps, cooked with or without an initial neutral sulfite stage (19)

Pulping process	Roe no.	Yield, % unbl.	Yield, % bl.	Hemicellulose content, % GM	Hemicellulose content, % GX	Beating time, min	Tensile strength, km	Burst strength	Tear strength
Acid sulfite	5	53	49	12	5	19	9.3	75	80
Neutral sulfite–acid sulfite	5	57	54	21	4	15	8.5	65	65
Bisulfite	5	52	49	12	5	42	9.6	83	97
Neutral sulfite–bisulfite	5	57	54	21	4	24	9.2	73	77

GM = glucomannan, GX = glucuronoxylan

For instance, this makes it impossible with either process to make a pulp
low in hemicellulose without excessive degradation of the cellulose. In
the acid cook, the hydrolysis reaction, which is active in removing hemicelluloses, will also affect the cellulose to an extent increasing with the
purity of the pulp. The alphacellulose fraction, which is a measure not
only of the purity of the cellulose of the pulp, but also of its state of
degradation, cf. Chapter 20, will therefore reach a maximum of about
90%, beyond which further purification of the hemicelluloses by acid
hydrolysis will be counter-balanced by hydrolytic degradation of the
cellulose. The degradation is accompanied by heavy losses in pulp yield.
This is illustrated in Figure 9.144.

In the kraft cooking process, the dissolution of carbohydrates is still
less selective. The alkaline peeling reaction from the aldehyde end groups
of the carbohydrate molecules preferentially dissolves short-chain material
of both hemicelluloses and cellulose, but stabilizing reactions, including

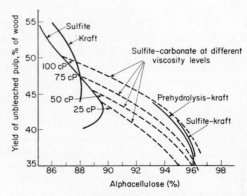

Fig. 9.144. Pulp yield, alphacellulose content
and viscosity level for sulfite, kraft and two-
stage processes. Spruce (Rydholm)

adsorption of xylan on the cellulose microfibrils, will cause more hemicellulose to remain in the pulp than in proportion to their initial molecular size relative to that of cellulose. Prolonged cooking or increased temperature or charge of chemicals will only cause excessive degradation due to alkaline hydrolysis of the glycosidic bonds followed by peeling, and a maximum of about 88 % alphacellulose content is reached (softwoods).

It should be stressed here that the alphacellulose analysis even disregarding its changes upon degradation of the cellulose is an insufficient measure of the purity of the pulp, since the alphacellulose fraction also involves some 'alkali-resistant' hemicelluloses, to an extent varying with the type of process. The alphacellulose fraction of one-stage kraft pulps consists of less pure cellulose than that of sulfite pulps. For dissolving purposes, the purity of kraft pulps is insufficient and they are used neither in the viscose nor in the acetate process. Acid sulfite pulps, cooked to maximal purity in yields of 42–46 %, are sufficiently reactive in the viscose process, but the quality of the end product in both the viscose and especially the acetate process will mostly require an increased purity. This is achieved in the bleachery by hot alkali purification of the sulfite pulp, cf. Chapter 15. That treatment will increase the alphacellulose content, and the reduction in yield will be considerably less than a corresponding effort to increase the alphacellulose content by prolonged sulfite cooking, as is also evident from Figure 9.144.

A similar purification of kraft pulps is not possible since the impurities have been rendered alkali-stable during the kraft cook. Therefore, an entirely different method has been applied to make kraft pulps of sufficient reactivity for dissolving purposes, namely *acid prehydrolysis* prior to kraft cooking. By that treatment, which could be carried out at fairly low temperature with concentrated acids, at intermediate cooking temperature with dilute acids, or high cooking temperature with water only, a considerable part of the hemicelluloses and fairly little cellulose are hydrolyzed to shorter chains, part of which dissolve in the cooking liquor together with a limited fraction of acid-soluble lignin. The hemicelluloses to a considerable extent dissolve in polymer, although degraded, form (65, 573, 731), and are further hydrolyzed to monoses in solution. The latter are partly decomposed to furfural, hydroxymethyl furfural, levulinic and formic acids (465, 666). The remaining hemicelluloses, degraded to a DP of about 30 % of the original (65), are more easily dissolved in the subsequent kraft cook, as the increased number of end groups make the peeling reaction more efficient. In the kraft cook the main delignification reaction will also take place, as well as the normal or somewhat increased alkaline degradation of cellulose. The net result of the two-stage prehydrolysis–kraft cook is therefore a high-alpha pulp of reduced yield, as demonstrated in Figure 9.144. The yield, as well as the alphacellulose content, is very much dependent on the extent of prehydrolysis, all grades between the 87 % alphacellulose of a kraft paper pulp and the 97 % of an extreme high-alpha pulp being obtainable. However, sufficient reactivity for the viscose process does not seem to be reached until the 94–95 % level, although experiments at lower alphacellulose and higher yield level by a limited prehydrolysis are being undertaken.

As will be demonstrated in some detail below, there is also an upper limit to the extent of prehydrolysis other than the economic one set by the decrease in yield. The prehydrolysis stage will cause not only a cleavage of hydrolyzable bonds of carbohydrates and lignin, but also lignin condensation, cf. Chapter 9.I, which on severe conditions may be so extensive that the delignification ability of the kraft cook is impaired. (It may be pointed out here that similar reasons exclude even fairly mild prehydrolysis prior to sulfite cooks, which are more sensitive to pre-condensation of the lignin.) When the delignification of the kraft cook is delayed by too severe a prehydrolysis, low screening rejects and reasonable chlorine numbers can only be achieved by increasing temperature or chemical charges of the kraft cooking stage, and that will lead to increased degradation of cellulose. Therefore, it is logical to consider some means of prehydrolysis by which lignin condensation is limited. Seen in this light, the various suggestions of prehydrolysis with liquors containing small amounts of sulfur dioxide and sometimes also of bisulfite have their justification. However, SO_2 water alone has a reverse effect (unless at very high SO_2 content and low temperature (621)), due to the rapid formation of sulfonic acid groups in the solid phase of the wood, where in the absence of other cations a high local acidity is created, causing lignin condensation at fairly low temperature also. The presence of metal bisulfite will neutralize this effect and as the lignin groups sulfonated are also among those causing condensation, the latter is minimized (182, 358, 555, 611, 620). However, as will be shown below, the increase in the maximal alpha-cellulose content obtainable is fairly small when exchanging water for dilute acid bisulfite cooking liquor.

The modification of the prehydrolysis–kraft process dealt with above does not aim at delignification, only protective pre-sulfonation in the acid cooking stage. However, especially at higher content of total and combined SO_2 of the cooking acid, partial delignification is also achieved. This process could therefore be called the *sulfite–kraft process*. As long as only partial delignification is desired in the first stage, the purity of the acid sulfite cooking chemicals is not very critical, requiring a less complicated regeneration system, cf. Chapter 11. However, at the same time delignification in the second stage requires a normal white liquor and hence a complete kraft regeneration system, including caustization. Only when the acid sulfite cooking stage is carried as far as round the point of fiber liberation is it possible to exchange the white liquor for sodium carbonate solution. This simplifies the regeneration system of the alkaline cooking stage but on the other hand requires that the sulfite cooking chemicals should have normal purity from sulfide and other decomposition catalysts, and consequently a more elaborate regeneration system is needed for the first cooking stage. This process of *sulfite–carbonate cooking*, together with the regeneration system, is known as the *Sivola* process (600, 720), of which a variant (721) also employs an initial neutral sulfite stage prior to the acid sulfite cooking stage to achieve the benefits of two-stage sulfite cooking dealt with in Subsection III.3A of this chapter, turning the two-stage process into a three-stage cooking method.

In the *Sivola* process, only a limited delignification is achieved in the alkaline stage, corresponding to a decrease in the chlorine number with 3–5 units only. Although welcome as a reduction of the chlorine demand in the bleaching, this delignification is not necessary to obtain pulp. In contrast with the *prehydrolysis–kraft* and related processes, the Sivola process therefore allows a choice in the conditions of the alkaline stage, with no regard for delignification requirements and only to give the degree of purification desired. In contrast with other processes, the Sivola process is therefore able to give dissolving pulps of any alphacellulose content from that of sulfite pulps up to around 97%. Therefore, although it represents the one extreme of a number of acid–alkaline pulping processes, the other of which is prehydrolysis–kraft cooking, the Sivola process is also to be compared with acid sulfite cooking combined with hot alkali purification in the bleachery. The difference is that the alkali is recoverable together with the organic matter dissolved, the steam consumption lower and the alkali treatment is carried out in a pressure vessel, the digester, allowing much higher temperatures than ordinary equipment for hot alkali purification in the bleachery. This allows purification of pulps of decidedly higher yields from the sulfite cooking stage. The disadvantages of the process lie in a fairly complicated regeneration system and the high consumption of carbonate, because the acid sulfite waste liquor remaining in the digester has to be neutralized by carbonate in addition to the carbonate quantity required for the purification. This is also considerable for the higher alphacellulose levels. It is also possible to wash the pulp after the sulfite cook prior to carbonate purification. The latter will then require less carbonate and could be carried out before or after screening and chlorination. It is desirable for the purification result that the carbonate should contain some sulfite or sulfide (578). To achieve an economy of these *sulfite–carbonate* processes comparable to that of *Sivola*, it is necessary to recover the waste liquor from the purification and to regenerate its chemicals. This can preferably be done after recirculation of the waste liquor within the carbonate cooking stage to enrich it with organic components (578), or by using the carbonate waste liquor to wash the sulfite pulp prior to carbonate cooking (610), or alternatively the waste liquor of the carbonate stage, containing bicarbonate and sodium salts of weak organic acids, can be used for the preparation of sulfite cooking acid (655). Washing of the pulp prior to the carbonate cook likewise admits an easier alcohol fermentation than does the *Sivola* process. In comparison with the other pulping processes, the relationship of pulp yield to alphacellulose content for the sulfite–carbonate process is also shown in Figure 9.144. Now, in comparing the results of the different processes and different conditions of the same process it must always be kept in mind that alphacellulose content only gives a rough idea about the purity of the pulp and still less about the suitability of the process for dissolving purposes. However, the limitations of the prehydrolysis–kraft and sulfite–kraft processes are clearly demonstrated in Figure 9.144. They yield pulps covering a much narrower range of properties than the sulfite process combined with hot alkali purification or the sulfite–carbonate process. This is mainly because the delignification is virtually left to the alkaline stage, which must therefore be severe. The limitation is still more striking when it is kept in mind that the pulps of lower alphacellulose content obtained by milder prehydrolysis have bad viscose processing properties (e.g. 716), and that, generally speaking, the alphacellulose content after cooking should exceed 95% for this reason. Therefore, prehydrolysis–kraft pulps, and sulfite–kraft pulps are restricted to uses where high-alpha pulps are of advantage, such as for high-tenacity rayon for cord and certain textile filament yarns, as well as for high-grade staple fiber. In the sulfite–carbonate processes, where delignification to yields below the point of fiber liberation is carried out in the first stage, the degree of alkali purification can be chosen at will, and a much wider range of pulps be covered. However, these will virtually resemble sulfite pulps at various levels of purification.

Figure 9.145 makes a comparison between the various types of acid-alkaline cooking processes to high-alpha pulps in the form of staple diagrams representing the amounts of cellulose, hemicelluloses and lignin at various stages of pulping. One extreme is represented by prehydrolysis–kraft pulping, where most of the delignification is performed in the second stage, and the other by sulfite–carbonate pulping, with the delignification done in the first stage. As an intermediate the sulfite–kraft process is found. In all cases, much of the hemicelluloses is removed by acid hydrolysis in the first stage and still more is degraded in order to be dissolvable in the alkaline stage. The cellulose, part of which is dissolved by alkali in the second stage, should be left as unchanged as possible by the first stage, and is largely so, except in the case where a sulfite cook is carried very far, to viscosity levels in the range of 20–50 cP TAPPI (approximately DP 1,000–1,300). On the other hand, where delignification is already fairly complete in the first stage, the conditions of the alkaline (carbonate) cooking stage could be chosen so as to leave part of the alkali-sensitive cellulose fraction together with some hemicelluloses. However, that will decrease the alphacellulose content but increase the pulp yield.

Thus the same reactions are active as known from the sulfite and kraft processes. Lignin is dissolved by *sulfonation* and *acid hydrolysis* of the benzyl–alkyl ether groups in the first stage and by *alkaline hydrolysis* of the phenol ether bonds in the second stage. The dissolution is checked by lignin *condensation* which can be suppressed by *sulfonation* in the acid stage and by *sulfidation* in the alkaline stage. The carbohydrates are removed by *acid hydrolysis* of the glycosidic bonds, as well as by *alkaline peeling* from the aldehyde end groups and *alkaline hydrolysis* of the glycosidic bonds. The acid hydrolysis also serves to degrade some of the carbohydrates, especially the hemicelluloses, to an extent which permits their removal in the alkaline stage by peeling in spite of the tendency to

660

stabilization by the alkaline stopping reaction and by the adsorption to the cellulose microfibrils. In that way pulps consisting of fairly pure cellulose can be obtained which are of particular interest for dissolving purposes. However, the acid–alkali multistage processes are also of some interest in the production of special paper pulps where some of the hemicelluloses are not desired. Papers from such pulps are softer and have a higher tearing strength than those from the corresponding one-stage pulps, whereas burst and tensile strength are lower. As far as is known, the prehydrolysis–kraft process is not used for this purpose, nor is any other acid–alkali process but sulfite cooking followed by hot alkali purification in the bleachery. A variant of the *Sivola* process, the *bisulfite–carbonate process* (721), employing bisulfite instead of acid sulfite as the initial cooking stage, has particular interest for paper pulps, giving

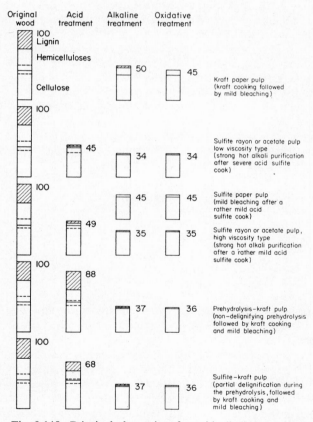

Fig. 9.145. Principal alternatives for acid–alkaline pulping and their effects on the wood components. Broken lines indicate fractions of hemicelluloses and cellulose nonresistant (above) and more resistant (below) to hot alkali. Numbers indicate pulp yield (Rydholm)

661

increased tear strength and opacity (656, 682). The Wegerhaeuser 'two-stage neutral' process on magnesium base employs a bisulfite–magnesium oxide cooking for the same purpose (53a).

4. INFLUENCE OF REACTION CONDITIONS ON PULP YIELD AND QUALITY

This section will be confined to the acid–alkali processes, as the reaction conditions of two-stage sulfite pulping have been dealt with sufficiently in the section on the sulfite process as well as the previous section on the reactions of two-stage sulfite cooking.

A. Wood species

Most wood species, as well as annual plants, such as cereal straw, reed and bagasse, are pulpable by the kraft process, and they can also be used for the production of *prehydrolysis–kraft pulps*. In practical use are pine and possibly spruce (23, 453, 687, 740, cf. 179, 543, 667, 716, 726) and gum (21, 543, 716), and investigations have also included beech (237, 556, 573), birch (582, 620), aspen (716), eucalypt (528), bamboo (244, 363, 554), bagasse (493, 544), salai (255), reed (381, 715), etc. One of the earlier investigations (179) makes the following comparison, Table 9.34, of yield and alphacellulose content of bleached pulp from various raw materials.

Table 9.34. Yield and alphacellulose content for bleached kraft and prehydrolysis–kraft pulps from various raw materials (179)

	Yield, %		Alphacellulose content, %	
Raw material	Kraft pulp	Prehydrolysis–kraft pulp	Kraft pulp	Prehydrolysis–kraft pulp
Pine	40	34	88	95
Beech	33	28	88	94
Birch	38	28	89	97
Aspen	41	29	88	97
Straw	33	24	89	97

Although the yield figures given are decidedly on the low side, they give an idea of the influence of the raw material. Table 9.35 gives some more recent data (657).

Three main categories of raw materials present somewhat different problems in prehydrolysis–kraft pulping. Straw and other annual plants contain silica, which is an undesirable contaminant of dissolving pulps. This problem is dealt with further in Chapter 16. Hardwoods are rich in pentosans, which are normally rendered stable to alkali during the kraft pulp to a considerable extent, cf. Chapter 9.II. Upon prehydrolysis–kraft pulping hardwood pulps also tend to contain more pentosans than softwood pulps. They are also normally obtained in rather lower yields, although this is generally more than compensated by the higher

Table 9.35. Yield and alphacellulose content for bleached kraft and prehydrolysis–kraft pulps from various raw materials (657)

Raw material	Yield, %		Alphacellulose content, %	
	Kraft pulp	Prehydrolysis–kraft pulp	Kraft pulp	Prehydrolysis–kraft pulp
Spruce	46	37	87	96
Birch	52	37	89	94
Poplar	52	41	91	94
Sydney blue gum	51	41	92	97
Blue gum	51	40	91	96
Dowga bamboo	49	38	90	97

density of most hardwoods. On the whole, hardwoods are fairly suitable for this type of process, where the resin troubles encountered are much smaller than in acid sulfite pulping of hardwoods. Softwoods, including pines, are also well suited to the prehydrolysis–kraft process, but their higher lignin content and the greater tendency of softwood lignin to acid condensation makes the conditions of the prehydrolysis more critical, and to avoid screening losses and excessive chlorine consumption in the bleaching, the conditions of the kraft cooking stage should be rather severe. This will cause some degradation of the pulp, resulting in a reduced viscosity level. Especially for softwoods, modifications of the prehydrolysis to depress the lignin condensation are therefore of some interest, such as a limited sulfite cooking stage. If the delignification should be carried further in the acid stage, as in the *Sivola* process, the well known difficulties of pulping pines and tannin-damaged spruce satisfactorily are encountered unless the process is modified to apply an initial, less acid sulfite stage. It should also be noted that especially for the more resinous wood species, deresination is more efficient when the second stage consists of a kraft cook, which has a higher alkalinity than a carbonate cook.

B. *Cooking liquor composition, temperature and time of the two cooking stages*

The dominating carbohydrate reaction during the prehydrolysis is naturally a hydrolysis of glycosidic bonds, causing a chain degradation and partial dissolution of the more accessible material. Therefore, the acidity of the cooking liquor is of great importance, and an addition of mineral acids to the cooking liquor will decrease the time and temperature needed for a certain effect. However, because of hydrolysis of the acetyl groups of the carbohydrates, cooking in pure water will also develop an acidity corresponding to pH 3–4 and hence cause acid hydrolysis. Hardwoods, containing more acetyl groups than softwoods, cause rather higher acidity in the cooking liquor. Obviously, however, the acidity of the cooking liquor does not govern the rate of reaction directly, since it has been shown (29) that the dissolution is almost as rapid in cooks buffered with calcium carbonate as it is in unbuffered water cooks. On the other hand, buffering with soluble chemicals, such as phosphates (145), or sulfite, sulfide, carbonate, ammonia, etc. (620), considerably reduces the rate of dissolution. The acidity developed within the chips is probably the dominating factor.

A further reaction occurring during the prehydrolysis cook is dehydration of the sugars formed, especially of xylose to furfural. This results in the formation of volatile compounds, and a discrepancy in the amount of substance lost from the solid phase, as determined by the yield of prehydrolyzed chips, and the amount found on determination of the dry content of the hydrolyzate. That discrepancy increases upon prolonged treatment or higher cooking temperature. A considerable part of the volatile substances formed at severe conditions is carbon dioxide. Normal conditions of prehydrolysis do not result in much such destruction, however. Figure 9.146 indicates the rate of dissolution and destruction

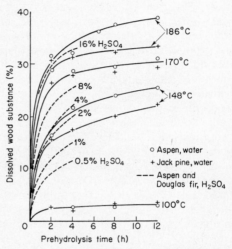

Fig. 9.146. Dissolution of wood substance during the prehydrolysis at different conditions with different wood species (Harris, Aronovsky, Gortner)

at the water hydrolysis of aspen and jack pine at various temperatures (29, cf. also 337, 556, 620, 702, 704, 716). In the same figure the effect of sulfuric acid of various concentrations at 95°C (319) for aspen and Douglas fir is illustrated. A somewhat greater rate of dissolution is indicated for aspen than for pine. To achieve the same effect as water at 170°C, a sulfuric acid concentration of almost 10% seems to be necessary at 95°C. Although it has been suggested that the prehydrolysis be carried out in a pressureless cooking stage (e.g. 386), the high concentrations of acids required make it impractical, and mineral acid hydrolysis also is preferably performed under pressure, at or above 130°C, and at fairly low concentrations (179, 180, 181, 667, 726). Hydrochloric acid hydrolysis below 100°C has also been investigated (151, 152, 542, 695), and is rather more rapid than that of sulfuric acid of corresponding concentration, because of lower equivalent weight and the higher degree of ionization of the hydrochloric acid. However, because of the greater corrosion problems created by hydrochloric acid, sulfuric acid is preferred. The approximate conditions suggested for the prehydrolysis of hardwoods prior to kraft pulping are, 10–30% H_2SO_4 at 70–80°C, or 0.3–0.5% H_2SO_4 at 120–140°C, or 0.5–0.7% HCl at 95°C, or water or steam at 160–170C°, in all cases for 0.5–3 h. Similar conditions apply to the prehydrolysis of softwoods. In general, to obtain high-alpha pulps, water prehydrolysis (pH around 3.5) requires 170–175°C for 0.5–1.0 h, and sulfuric acid hydrolysis 0.25–0.5% concentration (pH 1.2–1.6), 130–140°C for about the same time. The cooking curve is exemplified in Figure 9.136. The dissolution during that stage should be 15–20% for hardwoods and 10–15% for softwoods, of which the main part is carbohydrate components, but also to some extent lignin and extractives. It should be stressed here that the degradation of the hemicelluloses remaining in the chips, which occurs at the same time as the dissolution, is likely to be of equal importance, but the amount dissolved could be taken as a relative measure of the extent of both prehydrolysis effects.

The rate of dissolution during a water hydrolysis will increase by about 200% at a temperature increase of 10°C (520), and a strict temperature control is necessary to achieve reproducible results. Local overheating should also be avoided. Steam hydrolysis seems to proceed with a rate equal to that of hydrolysis in the liquid phase, and is also in commercial use, possibly at higher temperature levels for shorter times (cf. 91, 141), as the exact control of the reaction conditions should be somewhat easier.

The dissolution of wood substance during the kraft cook is largely determined by the alkali charge, temperature and time, and at constant conditions the dissolution in this stage is fairly constant and independent of the extent of prehydrolysis. Thus, at constant conditions of the second stage the prehydrolysis conditions are well reflected by the yield and properties of the final pulp. The severer the prehydrolysis, the lower the yield and pentosan content and the higher the alphacellulose content, as exemplified in Figure 9.147 (657, cf. also 620) for spruce and birch, prehydrolyzed for 0.5 h at varying temperature levels. The lignin content of the final pulp is generally decreased on increasing severity of prehydrolysis to a minimum and then again increasing, as will be further demonstrated below. This is explained in the following way. Prehydrolysis will expose more of the lignin to the alkali and possibly leave rather more alkali to be consumed by the lignin. This will tend to decrease the final lignin content of the pulp. At the same time, there is an increased lignin condensation on increasing severity of the acid cooking stage. With softwoods especially, which contain a readily condensing type of lignin, this phenomenon leads to an increase in the lignin content of the final pulp, and in more severe cases to an increase in screenings (620). Very hard prehydrolysis even results in 'black' or 'burned' cooks, practically

665

impossible to delignify below the point of fiber liberation in the kraft cook. However, this is exceptional and does not occur in normal operation.

The milder symptoms of increase in chlorine number and screenings can be counteracted by increasing the severity of the kraft cook, by increase in white liquor charge, temperature or time. This brings up another problem, namely the degradation of cellulose during the kraft cook. Figure 9.147 shows the change in viscosity of the prehydrolysis–

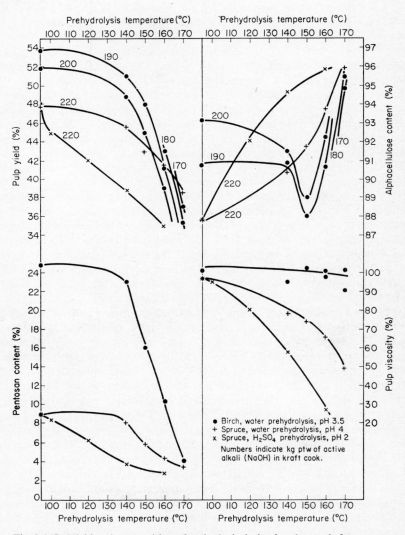

Fig. 9.147. Yield and composition of prehydrolysis–kraft pulps made from spruce and birch at varying prehydrolysis temperature. Time at temperature 0.5 h in the first and 2 h in the second stage (170°C) (Rydholm)

kraft pulps on varying temperature of the prehydrolysis and constant kraft cooking conditions. Superficially this indicates a hydrolytic degradation of cellulose during the prehydrolysis. However, this is not so, as evidenced by Figure 9.148, showing the changes in pulp yield, chlorine number, viscosity and alphacellulose content at constant prehydrolysis and varying time and alkali charge of the kraft cook. Obviously, the main viscosity decrease occurs during the second cooking stage and is an alkaline

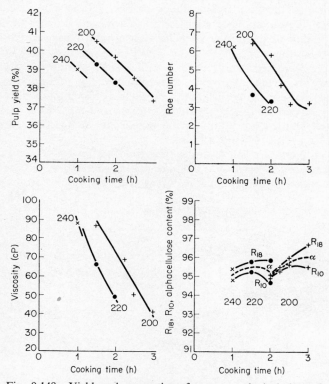

Fig. 9.148. Yield and properties of spruce prehydrolysis–kraft pulps, constant prehydrolysis conditions, 170°C, 0.5 h, water, and varying alkali charge and cooking time at 170°C in the kraft cook. Numbers denote charge of active alkali, in kg ptw NaOH (Rydholm)

hydrolysis of the type experienced during a normal kraft cook to low chlorine numbers, cf. Chapter 9.II on kraft pulping. The effect shown in Figure 9.147 therefore depends possibly on an increased accessibility of the cellulose to alkaline degradation and especially on an increased portion of the alkali charge being available for cellulose degradation, upon a more severe prehydrolysis. The changes in alphacellulose content upon prolonged kraft cooking also indicate cellulose degradation, as the difference in solubility in 10 and 18% NaOH lye increases.

It is obvious that to obtain pulps with lignin contents acceptable for bleaching the conditions of the kraft cook have to be accordingly adjusted. As excessive prehydrolysis will cause lignin condensation, the kraft cook has to employ such severe conditions that the carbohydrate degradation becomes serious. Normal prehydrolysis–kraft pulps of softwoods with an alphacellulose content of 95–96% therefore contain about 3% lignin prior to bleaching, and may have a viscosity as low as 30–50 cP TAPPI. Then conventional kraft cooking conditions, 170–175°C for 1–2 h, although with somewhat increased white liquor charge, 220 kg ptw active alkali (NaOH), have been applied. As these pulps are fairly difficult to brighten and sensitive to oxidants, the viscosity after normal bleaching tends to be rather low, in the range of 10–15 cP TAPPI. Sometimes, the viscosity is deliberately decreased still more, to 7–9 cP TAPPI, to improve the viscose processing properties. However, the cellulose degradation during the kraft cook and especially during the subsequent bleaching is also accompanied by a decrease in alphacellulose content and may result in undesirable chain length distribution in the alphacellulose fraction. Excessive degradation also leads to yield losses.

These problems are less severe in the case of hardwoods, because of the smaller tendency of hardwood lignin to acid condensation and the greater ease of hardwood delignification during the kraft cook. High-viscosity

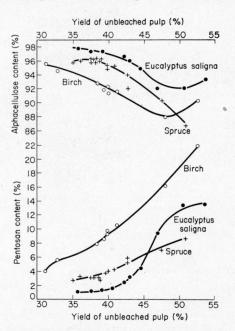

Fig. 9.149. Alphacellulose and pentosan content of prehydrolysis–kraft pulps from spruce, birch and gum at varying yield (severity of prehydrolysis) (Rydholm)

pulps, 90 cP TAPPI, above the 95% alphacellulose level and delignified to around 1% lignin content, can be obtained from hardwoods. The yields are different from different wood species when compared at constant alphacellulose or pentosan content, as exemplified in Figure 9.149. Pentosan contents of 2–3% for softwood and 3–4% for hardwood prehydrolysis–kraft pulps are normal prior to bleaching, where further reduction could be achieved by cold refining, cf. Chapter 15. Alpha-

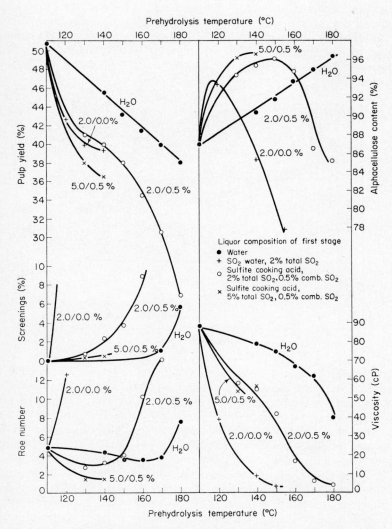

Fig. 9.150. Effect of prehydrolysis temperature and liquor composition in the pulping of spruce. Prehydrolysis time at maximum temperature 0.5 h, kraft cook 170°C, 2 h. Liquor-to-wood ratio 4.0 (Rydholm)

669

cellulose contents of lignin-free pulp after cooking above 96–97% are rare, but could also be improved by cold refining.

To minimize lignin condensation, prehydrolysis can be carried out with a cooking liquor containing sulfur dioxide and bisulfite, i.e. as limited sulfite cooking stages. Figure 9.150 demonstrates the effect of the prehydrolysis temperature on the final cooking result, when water is exchanged for sulfur dioxide solutions with or without small amounts of bisulfite. Obviously, SO_2 water alone leads to increased condensation, as the sulfonation achieved introduces sulfonic acid groups creating a high local acidity in the solid phase. Addition of bisulfite changes this situation, as the sulfonation will then result in sulfonate groups with metal cations instead of hydrogen ions. Sulfonation could in this case suppress condensation, as the same groups are involved in both reactions. Obviously,

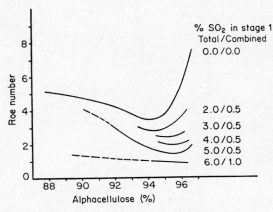

Fig. 9.151. Roe number and alphacellulose content of prehydrolysis–kraft and sulfite–kraft pulps when varying the composition of the prehydrolysis liquor. Spruce (Rydholm)

rather lower chlorine numbers can be achieved. This is accentuated in Figure 9.151, where the chlorine number is plotted against the alphacellulose content for pulps made with various cooking liquors in the prehydrolysis stage. It is seen that increasing content of both total and combined SO_2 will decrease the minimum of the chlorine number curves, obviously an effect of increased sulfonation and decreased condensation during the prehydrolysis. The yield losses during the first stage are in these cases 25–35%, and the process should be termed *sulfite–kraft* pulping instead of prehydrolysis–kraft pulping, as part of the delignification is transfered to the first stage. The final pulp yield, however, is quite similar to that of ordinary prehydrolysis–kraft pulps of corresponding alphacellulose content, as seen in Figure 9.144, which also depicts the yields of conventional one-stage kraft and sulfite pulps, the latter after hot alkali purification.

670

The conditions of the *Sivola* process are essentially those of an acid sulfite cook, cf. Section I, and a sodium carbonate hot purification, cf. Chapter 15, and should be chosen according to the viscosity and alphacellulose levels desired in the unbleached pulp. A lower viscosity requires a more drastic acid stage, and a higher alphacellulose content a more severe carbonate cook. For high-alpha pulps of the same type as prehydrolysis–kraft pulps, 170°C is required for 1–3 h in the alkaline stage, employing a sodium carbonate charge of 150–200 kg ptw to maintain a pH of 9.5–9.0. The cooking curve is exemplified in Figure 9.136. To save carbonate, a substantial removal of waste liquor from the acid cooking stage is required, but enough liquor has to be retained to allow safe uniform mixing of the concentrated carbonate solution introduced. In order to facilitate the bleaching of these pulps, the gas relief of the acid cooking stage should be adjusted to leave 0.5–1 % SO_2 in the liquor remaining during the alkaline stage. When pulps of lower alphacellulose content are desired, both carbonate charge and temperature are decreased. As the pulp viscosity is little changed during the second stage, the conditions of the acid stage can be chosen as for the same viscosity grades of a one-stage sulfite pulp. Normal temperature would therefore be 125–135°C for the high-viscosity grades and 140–150°C for the low-viscosity grades.

The conditions of the *bisulfite–carbonate* process for special paper pulp should also be adjusted according to the grade desired. The carbonate stage should employ 100–150 kg ptw Na_2CO_3, 150–160°C for 1–3 h. If pure bisulfite solution of pH 4 is employed in the first stage, 150–160°C for 3–6 h is suitable. Pulps of strength properties nearly equivalent to those of some kraft pulps and an unbleached brightness approaching that of sulfite pulps can be obtained in yields of 45–50% from softwoods, as exemplified in Table 9.36 (19, 657). The improvement in tear strength achieved by the hemicellulose removal in the second stage for softwoods is

Table 9.36. Effect of hemicellulose removal in the cooking of spruce and birch by the acid sulfite–carbonate, bisulfite–carbonate and prehydrolysis–kraft processes (19, 584)

Wood species	Pulping process	Hemicellulose content, % of pulp GM	GX	Beating time, min.	Tensile strength, km	Burst strength	Tear strength
Spruce	Acid sulfite	12	6	20	9.5	80	70
	Acid sulfite–carbonate	3	3	74	8.1	65	141
	Bisulfite	12	6	41	10.2	87	86
	Bisulfite–carbonate	6	4	64	10.1	92	112
	Kraft	9	11	76	11.2	117	129
	Prehydrolysis–kraft	3	4	140	8.0	65	190
Birch	Acid sulfite	6	18	16	7.9	63	62
	Acid sulfite–carbonate	4	6	57	5.7	41	66
	Kraft	1	28	23	8.5	73	84
	Prehydrolysis–kraft	1	7	65	5.4	42	70

GM = glucomannan, GX = glucuronoxylan

not obtained with hardwoods. As also in this process, like in the acid sulfite–carbonate cook, the unbleached pulp color and the ease of bleaching are improved by the presence of some sulfite in the carbonate stage, the cook has also been called the *bisulfite–neutral sulfite* process (682), although the carbonate charge should preferably be higher than the sulfite charge. Further information on the changes of the strength properties with the pulping conditions and yield is given in Chapter 21 together with a comparison with the strength properties of other types of paper pulp.

IV. Chemical Processes of Minor Importance

1. PROCESSES USING UNORTHODOX CHEMICALS

The chemical processes dealt with so far, which are the main methods of commercial importance, rely on two major lignin reactions, *sulfonation of the α-hydroxyl groups* of the side chain to water-soluble lignosulfonate in all variants of the sulfite processes, and *hydrolysis of the phenol ether bonds* to give alkali-soluble phenolate lignin in the alkaline processes. In the former category of processes, *acid hydrolysis or sulfitolysis of some alkyl ether bonds*, and in the latter category *reaction of the α-hydroxyl groups with hydrosulfide* ions aid the dissolution of the lignin. In Chapter 4, several other lignin reactions were described, some of which might well serve as a base for pulping processes, from a purely technical stand-point. Most of them fail, however, for economical reasons, but some are used on a limited scale in the pulping of straw and other grasses.

A. Solvent pulping

One principle to adopt in removing the wood lignin is to *use other solvents than water* which thus do not necessitate reactions to make the lignin hydrophilic. Such solvents are ethers like *dioxane* (189) and *polyglycols* (254), or alcohols (30, 53) such as *ethanol* (444), *butanol* (30), *glycol* (347), *glycerol* (501) and *phenol* (336) and other compounds, such as *dichloro-propionaldehyde* (236). In those cases, *acid hydrolysis of the alkyl ether bonds of lignin* appears to be a prerequisite for the dissolution, as small amounts of acid and water are necessary for a fast delignification. Likewise, fairly high temperatures, 170–190°C are required in most cases to obtain pulps in a reasonable time. Softwoods are difficult to pulp by this method, but hardwoods are more easily delignified. *HCl* is the acid most commonly used (30, 189, 347, 444, 601) but also $AlCl_3$ (254) or HNO_3 in ethanol (31), SO_2 in *methanol, ethanol, propanol, butanol* and *acetone* (696) or in *dimethylsulfoxide* (243), and Cl_2 in *methanol* (420) have been suggested, in which cases there is also a specific action from the chemical in addition to the hydrolysis and the solvent action. Some degradation of the polymer is thus necessary, but the dissolved product is still high-molecular and can be precipitated from the solution by diluting the solvent with water. The alcohols react to some extent with the α-hydroxyls of lignin, but the remainder is recoverable by distillation. The cost of the solvent through the inevitable losses has made these processes unattractive for industrial purposes, especially as, in general, they offer no advantage in pulp yield or quality over the conventional processes.

To the same principal category belongs the *hydrotropic pulping process*, which has attracted some interest and has been tried on a small industrial scale (474, 525, 581, 652, 771, 772). *Hydrotropic solvents* are water solutions of some salts in high concentration which so change the solvent properties of water that organophilic molecules will dissolve (486, 561). The salts must contain an organophilic molecule substituted by a strongly ionized group, e.g. sodium benzoate, xylenesulfonate, or cymenesulfonate, made from not too expensive chemicals. To be active, the solutions must contain 30–50% salt. The cooking liquor becomes saturated with lignin after 6–7 recyclings. The dissolved lignin is then precipitated completely by dilution to 10–5% salt concentration, and the liquor can be used again after evaporation. It is likely that some chemical reaction is involved, since delignification requires 150–170°C and considerable time, 4–16 h. pH drops from neutrality to 3.5 because of acetic acid formation, and acid hydrolysis is probably one of the necessary reactions here. Condensation of the lignin occurs at the same time, and, as in the case of organic solvents, it is not possible to delignify softwoods by this method within reasonable time and with an acceptable pulp as the end result (652, 771). Hardwoods (581, 652) and grasses (474, 581) are pulped satisfactorily, probably because of lower lignin content and condensation tendency, and pulp yields comparable to those of kraft and sulfite processes are obtained (652, 771). The dissolved hemicelluloses are not precipitated with the lignin, but are probably degraded to low-molecular compounds, which might present a problem in the regeneration of cooking liquor after some cycles. The precipitated lignin could be sold as a by-product or burnt to supply the heat required for the cooking, evaporation of the cooking liquor and drying of the pulp. Inevitable losses of the concentrated salt solutions have also made this process of doubtful interest, especially as no particular advantages are gained, at least as long as there is no qualified use for the lignin obtained (cf., however, 525).

B. *Lignin-degradative pulping*

The other principal method for lignin removal is *degradative*, and starts as a *reaction at the benzene nucleus*, followed by scission of phenolic ether bonds and even carbon–carbon linkages. To this category belong *nitration*, *chlorination* and *chlorine dioxide oxidation*, as well as other halogenations and oxidations. These methods are of greater technical interest, partly because of the smaller amounts of relatively inexpensive chemicals involved, partly because of analogous reactions being used in the bleaching processes, although for products containing less lignin than wood. The literature on *nitric acid pulping* up to 1940 (32), 1950 (804) and 1960 (93) has been covered by surveys and only some of the more essential papers will be discussed here. Though it has been found easier to pulp grasses such as cereal straw (502, 753), cornstalks (365, 753) and bagasse (497) with

673

nitric acid, a large amount of work has been devoted to nitric acid pulping of wood (e.g. 24, 58, 77, 94, 167, 169, 455, 640, 686, 705, 726, 732, 753, 798, 810). Much of the early work was done in Germany, where the first mill with the process was run on beechwood during World War II (726). Two more recently announced methods are those of *Desforges–McLaughlin* (58, 77) and *Delcroix–Desorbay* or *Delbay* (24, 167, 169, 798). Some small straw pulp mills have been based on the latter process. The economic success of all nitric acid pulping methods depends on the amounts of nitric acid consumed, the price of available nitric acid, and the possibility of recovering the spent acid or selling it as a by-product of some value.

The reactions occurring on nitric acid pulping are similar to those of chlorination and have been discussed in Chapter 4. They involve a rapid electrophilic substitution of the aromatic nuclei of lignin with nitro groups, as would occur on a similar treatment of phenol or phenolic ethers. At those phenylpropane monomers containing a free phenolic hydroxyl, substitution will occur in the adjacent 5-position, whereas in etherified monomers, the primary substitution is likely to be in the 6-position. Further nitration brings about scission of the side chain and nitration in the 1-position, and also hydrolysis of the phenolic ether bonds to pyrocatechol configurations, which are rapidly oxidized to quinones. The nitration reaction is therefore accompanied by considerable color reactions. Either as phenols or as quinones, the nitrolignin fragments are soluble in alkali, whereby further degradation occurs, especially removal of nitro groups and possible formation of hydroxynitroquinone configurations. The final reaction products in the nitration of beechwood have been found to be CO_2, CO, N_2, N_2O, NO, NO_2 and HCN, acetic acid, oxalic acid and larger lignin fragments (686). The latter portion corresponded to 16% of the wood, oxalic and acetic acid to 5% each, and the gases to about 1% of the wood. The acetic acid must have originated to a considerable extent from the xylan, which was otherwise found to be mainly hydrolyzed to xylose, or else remain in the pulp. The carbohydrates were not found to be damaged by oxidation. The gas composition has been confirmed by more recent work (94), with the possible reservation that the nitrogen found may have originated from air. The reaction conditions used were in the former investigation 7% HNO_3, 60–100°C, 0.5–1.5 h and 350 kg ptw HNO_3. By adopting an impregnation technique and liquor relief, the nitric acid charged could be decreased to about 250 kg ptw. Pulp yields were about 50%.

Based on this and other German investigations, the *I. G. Farben* plant at *Wolfen*, Germany, was operated (726). It had access to low-cost by-product nitric acid, which was charged to evacuated digesters, filled with beech chips, at a concentration of 15% HNO_3 and a liquor ratio of 3.5 m³ ptw. Pressure air was applied and the chips impregnated at 45°C for 3 h. The digesters were equipped with external circulation through heat exchangers for water cooling. After the impregnation, excess liquor was removed and hot water added to keep further reaction at 70–95°C for 7 h. Then the waste liquor was removed and hot 1% NaOH lye added to react

674

for 1 h at 70°C, followed by 3 h at 80°C in 4% NaOH lye, making a cover-to-cover time of 21 h, including charging and discharging. The excess impregnation acid contained 12% HNO_3 and was strengthened for re-use. The remaining nitric acid gave upon the hot-water addition a concentration of 4% HNO_3, which at the end of the reaction had decreased to below 1%. The total chemical consumption of this process was 0.55 t ptp HNO_3 and 0.75 t ptp NaOH. The yield of the 88% alpha pulp obtained must have been about 40%, since 7.3 m³ of corded beechwood was consumed. The pulp was chlorinated, hot-alkali treated, cold-alkali extracted with 10% NaOH at 25°C for 2 h and cautiously bleached with hypochlorite. The alphacellulose of the bleached pulp was 98%, and the pulp was used for dissolving purposes. Production was about 40 t/d. Stainless steel equipment, V4A, was used in the equipment.

The more recent processes have paid attention to the nitric acid economy. The *Desforges–McLaughlin* process employs a catalyst, which is said to facilitate the recovery of the nitric acid (77). Reaction at 65–70°C and 0.5–2 h are recommended, followed by 1% NaOH lye treatment. The *Delbay* process employs a strong acid, 42% HNO_3, at 15°C (cooling) for 4 h, in a continuously operating nitrator and washer. In order to avoid pressure equipment but obtain a satisfactory impregnation, the chips used should be in the form of very thin wafers, 0.25 mm, produced in a special cutter. The nitration is followed by a 1% NaOH–lye wash and the acid and alkaline waste liquors are combined and said to have some fertilizer value. One of the advantages of the process is the low investment, claimed to be about $100 per yearly ton of pulp, or about half that for conventional pulp mills. The pulp yields are about 50% and the quality similar to that of *sulfite* paper pulp. By proper engineering, the chemical consumption has been considerably reduced. 150 kg HNO_3 and 10 kg NaOH are needed per ton of pulp, as well as 100 kWh (24). The *Reyerson* process applies nitric oxide-containing furnace effluent gases, which are further concentrated and used for pulping at 60–100°C for 5–25 h (605). A comparison between the Wolfen, Desforges–McLaughlin, Delbay and Reyerson processes (810) concluded that all processes still require cheap nitric acid to be economically feasible. The low per-ton investment even for small capacity plants, and the insensitivity to bark, are otherwise ideal for the utilization of waste from timber operations as well as agricultural waste—straw and bagasse. *The utilization of the waste liquor* from the nitric acid pulping has received more attention. Since it is possible (417, 712) to use ammonia instead of sodium hydroxide for the extraction of nitrolignin, it is possible to produce a waste liquor of considerable nitrogen content which has been found to possess normal fertilizer activity (94). Combinations either with an industry producing cheap spent nitric acid or nitric oxides, or with the production of fertilizers from the waste liquor thus seem to be two possibilities for this pulping process. An interesting aspect is the use of nitric acid instead of chlorine in the initial bleaching stage of mills located in districts where the effluence is used in irrigation schemes which cannot tolerate chlorides but would welcome nitrates.

A process similar to nitric acid pulping is *chlorination* in combination with alkali extraction (806). The chemistry of this delignification process is more fully dealt with in Chapter 4 on lignin chemistry and Chapter 14 on bleaching. It is sufficient to state here that lignin degradation is achieved through rapid electrophilic substitution of the aromatic nuclei, followed by scission of the bonds of the phenolic ether groups and the side chain, and then oxidation to chloroquinone derivatives. Alkali treatment will cause solubilization and further degradation of the lignin. In general, this process is considered too expensive for pulping, and for wood not only large amounts of chlorine and alkali are required, but also several repeated chlorinations and alkali extractions are necessary for complete delignification. However, straw and other agricultural residues contain less and more accessible lignin, and an initial alkali treatment at 100–130°C reduces the lignin content still more. This brings down the chlorine consumption to an economically feasible level, and will also remove some silica in the straw cuticula, which would otherwise make chlorine penetration difficult. Another interesting feature of the process is that chlorine and alkali are the only chemicals used, and in about equal proportions (the pulp is bleached with sodium hypochlorite). Therefore, the pulp mill is combined with advantage with an electrolytic plant to produce chlorine and alkali (cf. Chapter 19). Some excess chlorine may be sold as such or converted to hydrochloric acid (574). The process is called *Pomilio* after the inventor (592) and *Celdecor–Pomilio* in its modern form as developed by the Cellulose Development Corp., England (123). It is entirely continuous, using in essence bleachery equipment. The straw is soaked in 2–3% NaOH solution and fed into a reaction tower operated at 110–130°C, with a retention time of about 3 h. The liquor ratio is 3 m^3 per ton of straw, giving an alkali consumption in the first stage of 60–90 kg per ton of straw. The pulped straw is then washed, pressed to a consistency of 30%, fluffed, and fed into a chlorination tower, where it is reacted with 120–180 kg ptp Cl$_2$ for about half an hour. High-consistency operation has been found to give advantages over conventional low-consistency operation for incompletely fiberized materials such as that coming from the alkali cook (350, 590). After washing, the chlorinated pulp is treated with about 40 kg ptp NaOH at 10% consistency and 40°C for 4 h and bleached in one or two hypochlorite stages. The yield of bleached straw pulp is 40–45%, and the total chemical consumption is about 220–300 kg ptp NaOH and 150–190 kg ptp Cl$_2$ (79, 814a). There are about 30 mills in operation, most of which are fairly small, about 10,000 t/year. They have substituted the older *De Vains* process (139). It is a matter of choice whether the Celdecor–Pomilio process should be considered as an unorthodox chemical pulping process or a soda cook, followed by a conventional four-stage bleaching. Anyway, it has been specifically designed to suit the pulping of agricultural residues. Diffusion difficulties make the chlorination processes less attractive for the pulping of wood, although investigations have shown it possible to prepare hardwood pulps in yields of 50% or more (137, 734, 803). The *Isogrand* process, already mentioned

676

in the section on mechanical pulping from chips in Chapter 7, could also be classified as a chlorination pulping process, where the wood lignin is made more accessible to chlorine by defibration of the chips. After the fiberizing in an Asplund Defibrator, the treatment is similar to that of the Pomilio process, i.e. an initial alkali cook, followed by repeated sequences of chlorination, alkali extraction and hypochlorite bleaching. The chlorination is performed at somewhat elevated pH, 3–3.5, with about 50 kg ptp chlorine charge each of three times.ʳ A yield of 'unbleached' pulp of 68 % is reported, and after two additional hypochlorite stages, a bleached grade in 54 % yield from softwoods is obtained (241). In total, about 340 kg ptp of chlorine and 160 kg ptp of alkali, together with 1.5 t ptp of steam and 450 kWh ptp are consumed, which makes the process unattractive from an economic stand-point with normal market price for the chemicals. The process probably becomes more interesting when limited to very high yields, as a variant of a bleached mechanical pulp.

Lignin-degradative *oxidation* is used in the pulping processes with *chlorine dioxide* (483), *sodium chlorite* (649, 792), *peracetic acid* (591), etc. They are all very selectively delignifying and give pulps in high yield, but require large amounts of expensive chemicals and are therefore not economical. An attempt to use cheaper chemicals and achieve a similar effect is the interesting suggestion to impregnate the wood chips with a 20 % solution of *sodium chlorate*, to dry and then react with *hydrochloric acid* at 50°C for some hours (662). Thereby chlorine dioxide and chlorine are formed (cf. Chapter 19) in the chips and the lignin is oxidized. A subsequent alkali treatment at 80°C completes the delignification, to yield a pulp in 70 % of the wood. Even in this case, however, the chemical costs must be high, since the chlorate consumption must be about 150–200 kg ptp, hydrochloric acid 50 kg ptp and alkali 50 kg ptp (241). *Ozonization* of wood also results in a kind of pulp, but simultaneously with the degradation of lignin there is considerable carbohydrate degradation (572a).

Therefore, although numerous attempts have been made during the past 100 years to apply unorthodox pulping chemicals, derived from a rapidly expanding and diversified chemical industry, the basic processes applied by Watt, Burgess and Dahl, by Tilghman, Ekman and Mitscherlich, have held the field, much to their honor.

2. PROCESSES USING RAW MATERIALS OTHER THAN WOOD

A. *Pulping of grasses* (122, 805, 814)

As pointed out in Chapter 1, not all pulp is made from wood. About 3.5 M t, or 6 % of the production originates from other sources, mainly various kinds of grasses, grown either as a crop for pulping, as in the case of *esparto* or *bamboo*, or left as a residue from an agricultural crop, as with *sugar-cane bagasse* and *cereal straw*. The pulp production from grasses is far from proportional to the raw-material supply when comparing the utilization of the forests for wood pulping. The reasons for the unsatisfactory utilization of agricultural residues are to some extent technical but

677

mainly economic. The bulky material is costly to handle, collect and transport, it is produced at scattered fairly small areas, in typical seasonal variations, with a sharp peak at the late summer weeks, and it tends to deteriorate rapidly on storing without special precautions. The material usually has short fibers which do not give a very strong paper, and the presence of an outer cuticula, rich in silica, or a pith consisting of minute cells of low value for paper pulp, present some special technical problems. As advantages, the grasses have a chemical composition comparatively rich in carbohydrates and a fairly low content of an easily accessible lignin, which makes them easy to pulp to good yields when properly cooked. The cost of the fiber material is furthermore low, since there is generally no qualified competitive use. In some cases, especially for bagasse, the material is also for other reasons collected and delivered free of charge at industrial mill sites. The rate of growth of the material is as a rule as high or higher than in the case of wood, 4–5 t/ha year for straw (551) and 7–13 t/ha year (589, 718) or even 10–50 t/ha year (418, 737) for well-managed bamboo crops, and the growth sites are more accessible and suited to mechanized harvesting and transport than most forests. Some fibers, such as from bamboo, are of considerable length and match those of softwoods. It is believed that some grass fibers, especially bamboo and bagasse will increase in importance as a pulping raw material, whereas esparto and straw pulps will suffer from the competition of hardwood pulps.

The principal straw-producing countries, where pulp production is practicable, are Canada, U.S.A., U.S.S.R., Holland, Italy, France, Germany, Greece, Hungary and Spain. *Wheat* and especially *rye* straw are preferred to *oat*. *Rice* straw is produced in several regions, such as South Europe, Egypt, China, Japan, Indonesia, India, Burma, Indochina and South America. For every ton of grain about 1.5 t rice straw is produced, 2.5 t wheat straw and 3.5 t rye straw, at a rate of 4.5 t/ha year. The world production of straw is about 600 M t/year and that of wheat straw about 350 M t/year (215), of which 2 M t were used for pulping. Solely in western Europe, about 80 M t of straw is produced annually and the annual production of rice straw of South Asia is of the same order of magnitude. The largest straw pulping industry is located in southern and western Europe, particularly Holland. *Esparto* (106, 218) is the collective name for two grasses, *Stipa tenacissima* (or alfa grass) and *Lyganum spartum* (esparto proper), growing wild in North Africa and also grown in Spain. They grow leaves to a height of 0.3–1.5 m, which roll up longitudinally to thin pipes, resembling thin stalks, 1–2 mm in diameter. The grass is cut annually and the yield is 0.2–0.7 t/ha year. The roots live for 60–70 years without replanting.

Bamboo (597, 689) grows wild or is grown in India, Burma, Thailand, Indochina, Indonesia, China, Japan, the Philippines, Australia, South Africa, South America and southern North America. Bamboo is a grass of several genera and species (150 in India alone and 70 in America), such as *Dendrocalamus* (*D. strictus* is the most important species in India), *Bambusa* (*B. vulgaris* in India, North America and Africa, *B. arundinacea*

678

in India and Australia) and *Phyllostachys* (*P. bambusoides* in Florida), etc. They grow stalks or stems as high as 40 m with diameters up to 30 cm. The leaves fall off during the ripening and the stalks are cut without leaves. The roots are perennial, and the stalks grow to full size in 7–10 years. Shorter rotations, 2–4 years or even 1 year, are practised. Bamboo flowers at intervals of 30–60 years, and after flowering, the roots usually die. The growth rate is tremendous during the rain season, in 1–2 months of the first year full height is achieved. On average, the annual growth in India is reported to be about 2 t/ha, but figures of 7–13 t/ha are quoted for the first years of growth (589, 597, 718).

Bagasse (45, 216) is the residue of sugar cane, *Saccharum officinarum*, a grass grown in India, China, Indonesia, the Philippines, Hawaii, South Africa, South America, southern North America and the West Indies. It grows to a height of 2–4 m, has a diameter of 4–6 cm, and contains about 15% sugar in the pith cells. The harvest is done on 1- to 2-year rotations, whereby the fields are set on fire to burn off the leaves, and the cane stalks are then piled up with a bulldozer. The cane, having a water content of about 70%, is brought to the sugar mill where it is crushed by a shredder or a series of huge rolls with close-fitting groove patterns, and squeezed and washed to remove the sugar juice. The residue, the bagasse, contains about 50% moisture and 1–2% sugar. The production of bagasse is about 23 M t annually, of which about 2 M t is produced in Oceania, 2 M t in Africa, 2 M t in North and Central America, 4 M t in South America, 4 M t in Asia and 9 M t in the West Indies. Cuba is the largest producer of bagasse with more than 7 M t annually. Only a fraction is converted to bagasse pulp. A related grass, *bhutang*, *Saccharum procerum*, is pulped in India, and a grass of related use, *Arundo donax* in Italy, was for some time extracted for sugar and the residue used for pulping. Another grass used for pulping in India is the *sabai*, *Eulaliopsis binata*, growing on the lower slopes of the Himalayas. A pith-containing agricultural residue of importance in many regions is *cornstalks* from *Zea mays*, and much attention has also been paid to *reed*, *Phragmites communis*, as a raw material for pulping, especially that growing along the Donau River and in Egypt.

One of the greatest disadvantages of grasses as raw material for pulping is the small *cell dimensions*. The enlarged cross section of a straw reveals an outer layer of silica-rich epidermis cells, strengthened by a ring of bast cells. Adjacent is the main tissue of parenchymatic cells, also containing bast and vessel bundles for water transport. Those bundles are sheathed by sclerenchymatic cells. This results in four categories of cells, in the following approximate proportions for *wheat straw* (392): bast and sclerenchyma fibers 50%, parenchyma 30%, epidermis cells 15% and vessels 5%. Another investigation on rye, oat and wheat straw (552) gives about 7% epidermis, 25% sclerenchyma and 68% parenchyma cells. *Bamboo* has the same principal structure, although with a more pronounced and very hard epidermic layer and larger cell dimensions throughout. *Cornstalks* in addition contain a pith fraction, which is 15–25% of the substance and consists mainly of small parenchyma cells,

60%, as compared to 20% in the stalk proper. Therefore, the total substance contains about 50% fibers and 50% parenchyma cells and vessels and only about 1% epidermis cells (439). *Bagasse* resembles in anatomic details the cornstalks, with a considerable pith fraction of 25–30% (174, 379, 447). The fibers therefore constitute only about 40% of the dry substance, parenchyma cells 40% and vessel segments 20%. For comparison, the fiber content of softwoods is 90–95% and that of hardwoods 50–70% (by volume) for the more useful types, as described in Chapter 2.

The cell dimensions vary considerably (26). Compared to softwoods (about 3 mm) and hardwoods (about 1–1.5 mm), the weighted average length of *straw* cells is only 0.3–0.5 mm, with the bast fiber length of 0.5–1.9 mm, parenchyma and epidermis cells 0.06–0.3 mm, and vessel segments up to 0.6 mm. The width of the bast fibers is 10–25 μ, which is not very different from that of hardwood fibers. The bast fibers of *rice* straw are particularly slender, with a length of 0.7–3.5 mm, average 1.5 mm, and a width of 5–15 μ. *Bagasse* fibers are about 1.6 mm long and 20 μ wide, whereas the nonfiber cells are 0.3–0.4 mm long and 8 μ wide (379, 797), and there are about equal parts of each, the total average cell length is therefore about 1 mm. *Cornstalk* cells are similar to those of bagasse, though some fibers may be as long as 5 mm. *Esparto* fibers are 0.4–1.8 mm long and 10–18 μ wide. *Bamboo* fibers are particularly large, approaching the size of softwood tracheids. Average fiber length values of 2–4 mm have been reported, and average width of 15–40 μ (757). Table 9.37 (26, 797) shows a compilation of grass *fiber* dimensions, compared to those of wood fibers. The slenderness of the grass fibers is striking.

Table 9.37. Approximate *fiber* dimensions of grasses as compared to wood (26, 797)

Species	Length, mm			Diameter, μ			Ratio l/d
	Max.	Min.	Average	Max.	Min.	Average	
Cereal straw	3.1	0.7	1.5	27	7	13	110
Rice straw	3.5	0.6	1.5	14	5	9	170
Esparto	1.6	0.5	1.1	14	7	9	120
Bamboo	4.4	1.5	2.7	27	7	14	190
Bagasse	2.8	0.8	1.7	34	10	20	85
Cornstalks	2.9	0.5	1.5	24	14	18	85
Jack pine			3.0			40	75
Red spruce			2.7			32	85
Aspen			1.0			26	40
Red gum			1.6			32	50

The *fine structure of the grass fibers* is similar to that of other bast fibers and of softwood tracheids, with one primary wall and three distinct secondary wall layers (595, 629). The fibrillar structure of these layers is also of the usual type. Thus, on the whole, the fiber fraction of the grasses is similar to that of hardwoods (bamboo fibers similar to softwood tracheids in size). The quantity of nonfiber cells is usually higher, however, which decreases the value of these materials for pulping. The disadvantage is particularly great in the case of *bagasse* and *cornstalks*, where the pith fraction is much larger than for most grasses. Therefore, cornstalks are little used and bagasse is considered a useful raw material only after *depithing*. This operation is carried out in several ways which could be described as either *dry* or *wet*. In both cases, the bagasse is mechanically abraded to break the clusters of pith cells away from the remaining tissue. Dry depithing may use a hammermill, followed by dry screening, as in the *Horton–Keller* or *Horkel* system (367, 422). Wet depithing is carried out with a Hydrapulper (470) or a submerged hammermill or *Rietz* mill (447), in both cases completed by wet screening in rotating cylindrical screens or a screen chamber surrounding the hammermill. Perforations of 2–4 mm are used. In principle, this wet screening resembles the fiber fractionation methods used in removing ray cells from softwood and particularly hardwood pulps (cf. Chapter 10). The material losses of depithing are considerable, 20–25%, and to be operated economically bagasse pulp mills should be combined with sugar mills to burn the pith for steam production, or with a by-product mill to make filter aid, absorbent, filler, etc., out of the pith.

The *chemical composition* of grasses does not deviate materially from that of hardwoods (cf. Chapter 4). A comparison between the various figures given in the literature (33, 446, 471, 552, 554, 626, 767, 814) is complicated by variations in the methods used. Table 9.38 gives some of the more conventional analyses for various grasses. It is seen that the *lignin* content is lowest for rice straw, only 12%, whereas a normal figure for cereal straws on average is 16%, rye straw always being somewhat richer in lignin than the average. The lignin figures may be on the low side because of the solubility of some straw lignin in sulfuric acid. Bagasse contains about 20% lignin, and bamboo has the highest lignin content of all grasses quoted, up to 30%. However, the analytical figures for Klason lignin also comprise the acid-insoluble silica, of which bamboo contains 2–3%. The *pentosan* content is about 26–27%, to which should be added *uronic acid* and *acetyl*, 1 and 2% respectively for straw and much higher for cornstalks. A considerable portion of most grasses is *hot-water soluble*, 12–13%, mainly hemicelluloses and some lignin. Hot-water solubles and lignin are dissolved during the *holocellulose* preparation, and leave about 73% holocellulose. *Alphacellulose*, corrected for ash and pentosans, is generally 36–37%. However, the cellulose fraction is likely to be rather higher since some cellulose in the smallest cells will pass the filter of the alphacellulose analysis. A more complete analysis (767) gave a gross composition of extractive-free material of about 42% *cellulose* for cornstalks and wheat straw, a lignin content of 14 and 22% respectively, and the remainder, 43 and 36% respectively, hemicelluloses, predominantly xylan acetate and also some noncellulosic glucan, mainly starch, as well as some arabinogalactan. This is calculated on ash-free material. Grasses contain a good deal more *ash* than wood. Whereas wood contains about 0.3% ash, of which only 2% is *silica*, the ash content of straw is about 8%, of which one-third is insoluble, mainly silica. Rice straw has as much as

18 % ash. The high silica content introduces some problems in straw pulping, such as difficulties in utilizing straw for rayon pulps, and difficulties in the regeneration of kraft pulping chemicals.

There are four main botanical parts in the straw material, *internodes*, *nodes*, *ears* and *leaves*. Their proportions vary, rye having more than 60% internodes compared with less than 50% for wheat and oat. The nodes are about 4% of the total, ears about 10% for rye and oat but 17% for wheat, and the leaves 20–40% of the material. It is therefore of interest that the chemical composition of these botanically different parts is fairly similar, as is the chemical composition of bagasse pith and fibers.

Table 9.38. Analytical data for some grasses

Species	Total ash, %	Insol. ash, %	Ether sol., %	Total protein, %	Hot water sol., %	Pentosans, %	Lignin, %	Holocellulose, %	Alphacellulose, corr., %	Acetyl, %	Uronic acid, %
European straw (626)											
Barley	9.6	2.3	1.4	2.7	12.2	26.7	16.6	73.3	36.4		
Oat	9.7	1.5	1.3	2.4	14.9	26.2	16.1	71.0	35.9		
Wheat	9.1	3.4	1.2	3.1	12.6	26.8	16.3	73.7	34.7		
Rye	3.8	0.6	1.4	3.5	8.8	27.9	17.8	75.5	39.3		
General average	8.7	2.3	1.3	2.9	12.6	26.8	16.5	73.2	36.0		
American straw (33)											
Barley	6.4		4.7*		16.1	24.7	14.5		33.8		
Oat	7.2		4.4		15.3	27.1	17.5		39.4		
Wheat	6.6		3.7		7.4	28.2	16.7		39.9		
Rye	4.3		3.2		9.4	30.5	19.0		37.6		
Rice	16.1		4.6		13.3	24.5	11.9		36.2		
General average	8.1		4.1		12.3	27.0	16.0		37.4		
European straw (Holland) (552)											
Oat		2.9	2.0		13.8	24.9	15.5		37.1	1.3	1.1
Wheat		7.8	1.5		12.5	24.6	15.6		33.3	2.0	1.0
Rye		1.2	1.4		12.0	25.7	17.6		37.2	2.1	1.0
General average		3.5	1.7		12.5	25.1	16.3		36.2	1.8	1.0
Wheat straw, American (767)	1.6					24.6	22.0		42.0	2.9	2.7
Wheat straw, European (814)	6.3		0.9		7.9	28.9	15.8		36.5	1.9	1.0
Wheat Straw, Denmark (78)	3.7	2.0		2.9		31.3	20.5	72.9	41.6		
European straw (Holland) (552)											
Internodes		1.2	0.8		12.0	24.6	18.9		39.5	2.0	1.0
Nodes		1.1	0.8		16.1	26.4	18.2		30.6	2.2	1.2
Ears		6.1	0.9		12.5	29.4	15.1		29.8	2.0	1.0
Leaves		5.8	3.1		13.6	33.5	13.1		33.5	1.4	1.1
Rice straw, American (214)	18.0		5.2		15.1	25.0	12.8		26.6		
Egyptian	18.1		5.1		16.1	26.5	12.5		28.1		
Hawaiian bagasse (446)											
Pith, average	2.04	1.5	0.3		1.9	28.5	20.2	77.7	34.8		
Fiber, average	0.70	0.5	0.1		0.9	27.9	20.8	77.8	42.5		
Whole, average	1.65	1.1	0.3		2.5	26.7	20.2	76.6	38.1		
American bagasse (471)											
Whole, average	2.3		8.4		10.0	29.0	18.5		33.6		
Cornstalks, American (767)	1.2					26.1	14.0		43.0	4.6	5.6
Bamboo Indian (814)	1–3	0.5–2	0.3–2.0*		4–8	16–21	22–30				
American (554)	2.3	0.14	0.7	4.4	7.8	28.5	23.0		34.8		

* Ethanol–benzene solubles

Leaves are higher in pentosans and lower in lignin than the stalks, as would be expected. Much of the silica is concentrated in the leaves, which explains the comparatively low silica content of rye, which has only about 20% leaves and partly the high silica content of rice straw, which contains as much as 50% of leaf sheaths and blades (214).

To sum up, the chemical composition of grasses resembles that of hardwoods, with a slightly lower lignin and possibly lower cellulose content and a somewhat higher content of non-cellulosic carbohydrates, particularly xylan and starch. Bamboo resembles the more lignin-rich hardwoods in composition. The greatest deviation from the chemical composition of wood is the high ash and especially the high silica content. A high content of hot-water solubles also indicates a higher degree of accessibility of the cell wall components to pulping liquors than for those of the wood.

The processes used for the pulping of grasses are in principle similar to those of wood pulping, but with deviations motivated from the differences in the dimensions, structure and chemical composition of the materials as compared with wood. The original method of straw pulping simply consisted of *burying the straw mixed with lime* for a week, and then washing and treating the material mechanically to achieve fiberizing (cf. 67). *Cooking with lime* is still practised in many mills, followed by mechanical fiberizing. Others have substituted the lime for *alkali* or *sodium sulfite*, to produce semichemical straw pulps. For chemical pulping, *alkali, kraft, neutral sulfite* or *chlorination* processes are used, with subsequent *bleaching. Acid sulfite* pulping gives too brittle papers.

The straw is usually collected within a radius of 50–100 km from the pulp mill. Water transportation allows rather longer distances. For that reason, most straw pulp mills are fairly small, and the processes and equipment chosen accordingly. The straw is baled and the bales are stacked at the farms and mill yards for storage. The normal moisture content of straw is about 10%. Excessive moisture must be avoided because of the danger of rotting during the long storage. In older practice the straw bales were dumped directly into the digesters after removing the baling wires, whereas in modern mills the straw is first cut into 12–30 mm pieces in cutters of special design, such as the *Nyblad* cutter, comprising a roller feeder and a knived drum, for capacities of 3–16 t/d. Magnets remove tramp iron and cyclons separate dust, grain, nodes, etc., before the straw is charged to the digesters. Roll-type presses may also be employed in the cutting operation to crush the nodes and rachises of the straw in order to facilitate the penetration of cooking liquor. Hammermills are likewise used. Usually there are about 5% losses of material in the preparation of straw. *Esparto* is collected in bundles and baled for export from North Africa to pulp mills in England, France and Holland. The cutting and cleaning operations are similar to those of straw. *Bamboo* is river-driven in rafts of 70–80 stalks, having a diameter of 7–10 cm and a length of 6 m. A large number of rafts are collected for one transport (774). River driving is not possible during the monsoon period. At the mill, the rafts are unloosed and the stalks conveyed to storage for drying. Land transportation is also used. Bamboo is chipped in special chippers, or crushed to pieces by passing the stalks through heavy iron rollers, usually three in series. *Bagasse* is the fibrous residue left from the sugar cane after a similar crushing operation and a subsequent extraction. Consequently it has a much higher moisture content, about 50%, than the other materials, which contain 10–15% moisture. The depithing operation, considered essential prior to bagasse pulping, has been described above.

The high bulk of most grass materials presents a special problem in the digester design. Rotary digesters are used for batch pressure cooking. Small, spherical rotating digesters with a volume of 15–30 m^3 for a pressure of 6–7 atm are frequent. To improve the degree of packing, chopped straw and cooking liquor are charged at the same time, and sometimes mechanical packing devices or pressure air packers are used. Often, mills make several complementary fillings with some 20-minute intervals to achieve additional packing. Packing densities of 130–170 kg/m^3 o.d. straw are reached, as compared with 160–250 kg/m^3 for wood chips. Liquor-to-straw ratio is kept at 1.5–3.0 at the beginning, allowing for steam condensate formed in the direct heating. After cooking, the digester pressure is relieved and the content dumped in wash bins or diffusers. Continuous digesters are also being used, either of the multi-tube type with a screw feeder for packing the material in the feeding operation, or vertical tower digesters (Kamyr) with the 'Asthma' steam-packing feeder or a thick stock pump feeder. Both esparto and straw are cooked in this manner. Continuous cooking of bagasse has also been practised early (45, 644) and the Pomolio process applies continuous towers for the initial pressure operation. On the whole, the grasses are well suited to continuous cooking, since the feeding problem is faciliated, and the pressure, temperature and time demands are less severe than in wood pulping.

Lime cooking is carried out with 60–120 kg ptg (per ton o.d. grass) CaO in the case of ordinary lime, or 120–180 kg ptg when using dolomite. In *alkali cooking*, 60–100 kg ptg NaOH is used for coarse, semichemical pulps and 100–150 kg ptg NaOH for chemical pulps. The same charges are suitable for *kraft pulping*. Tables 9.39–40 (33, 35) show the effects of alkali charge and raw material on the result. It is seen that crude yields of about 50% are reached at about 5% lignin content, but that a remarkable amount of material is lost in the screening. In the case of the coarser pulps, much of the losses is in the form of screenings, but a substantial part goes with the white water in the filtration after screening. This is caused by the high amount of minute parenchyma and epidermis cells in straw pulps. In mill practice, these losses amount to 5–10%. The same experience has been had in the alkali or kraft cooking of bagasse (447, 448), and in decreasing the pith content prior to pulping, smaller losses of fines are obtained in the subsequent screening operation. Crude yields of about 55% and screened yields of about 50% are achieved with pulps of less than 5% lignin.

The two most important variables in the alkaline pulping of straw are

684

temperature and alkali charges (33, 34, 35, 212). Normal practice employs 165–170°C for about 2 h and hence necessitates pressure equipment. However, it has been found that the delignification of straw occurs more early than that of wood, and that a contemporary mechanical treatment, e.g. in a Hydrapulper, facilitates the delignification and gives pulp in 60–70% yields at 98°C after 1 h, the *mechanochemical process* (36, 214). The screened yield is about 55%, and 48% yield of bleached pulp can be obtained. Naturally this technique simplifies the pulping equipment but has so far not been generally adopted in the straw pulp mills. The greater ease of delignification has also been utilized to decrease the cooking time, which is of particular interest for continuous cooking methods. A period of 10–15 minutes and even less has been found to be suitable in the pulping of straw (138, 212) and bagasse (447, 448). The temperature and alkali charge still determine the type of pulp, as shown in Table 9.41 (212). It is seen that the yield range of 80–50% is covered, with the lignin content of the pulps varying from 16–6%. However, a high alkali charge and a comparatively low temperature does not give the same pulp type as a high temperature and low alkali charge. The former combination results in pulps with lower ash and lignin contents and higher pentosan content, compared at equal yield basis. For rice straw particularly, this is an argument for low temperature cooking, as the ash content of rice straw pulp is excessive. However, many straw pulp mills operate without alkali recovery, and therefore have to economize with the alkali charge. The reasons for not having a recovery system are primarily the unproportionally high investment in the small-sized mills, and the difficulties experienced

Table 9.39. Effect of alkali charge on the pulping of wheat straw at 170°C for 2 h (35)

Alkali charge, kg ptg NaOH	105	120	140	168
Pulp yield, %				
Crude	53.0	51.9	49.4	45.1
Screened	41.1	40.5	39.8	38.7
Ash content, %	5.2	4.4	3.1	2.3
Lignin content, %	7.6	6.2	4.7	2.7
Pentosan content, %	29.2	26.1	30.9	28.3

Table 9.40. Effect of species on the alkaline pulping of straw at 170°C for 2 h and 120 kg ptg NaOH (33)

Species	Rice	Wheat	Barley	Rye	Oat
Pulp yield, %					
Crude	48.2	53.8	46.1	53.1	52.4
Screened	35.7	34.5	29.4	33.6	39.1
Screenings	2.2	11.0	5.1	5.8	2.7
Ash content, %	15.8	2.9	4.3	2.8	2.7
Lignin content, %	3.5	5.1	5.4	3.8	3.9

685

Table 9.41. Effect of alkali charge and temperature on rapid pulping (15 min) of wheat straw for corrugating medium (212)

Alkali charge, kg ptg NaOH	40	40	40	40	40	60	60	60	60	60	80	80	80	80	80	100	100	100	100	100
Temperature, °C	100	120	140	160	180	100	120	140	160	180	100	120	140	160	180	100	120	140	160	180
Pulp yield, %																				
Crude	84	81	78	75	66	74	69	69	64	60	67	63	63	59	56	66	62	60	54	54
Washed	79	77	74	72	62	71	67	67	62	57	65	61	60	56	54	65	60	58	53	52
Ash content, %	4.2	4.5	4.1	4.7	6.1	3.8	4.3	4.0	5.0	2.4	3.5	3.2	3.6	4.3	2.2	2.8	2.2	2.5	3.2	
Lignin content, %	16.4	16.1	15.7	15.1	14.9	12.9	11.9	12.9	12.4	11.6	10.7	9.4	9.9	9.0	9.9	8.9	8.0	7.8	8.8	6.7
Pentosan content, %	33.6	32.5	31.9	29.8	23.6	32.8	29.6	29.6	26.7	23.6	33.9	32.7	30.0	28.2	24.5	31.8	31.8	30.7	28.1	26.5
Concora test (CMT)	34	38	38	59	77	83	80	80	84	84	(99)	80	80	86	89	75	76	83	84	92

with silica precipitation, scaling and accumulation, when the black liquor from straw pulping is evaporated, burnt and causticized. As a result, the few straw pulp mills having a recovery system operate with as low recovery as 65–80%, as compared with over 90% in the wood pulp kraft mills. One method of overcoming these troubles is to precipitate the silica selectively or with the lignin of the black liquor by stack gases and collect and burn the precipitate separately, whereby the ash of the precipitate is discarded (230, 481). The effect of sulfide addition in straw pulping has been subject to discussion, since it is not as obvious as in alkaline pulping of wood. With wheat straw (137), Table 9.42, rice straw (133, 214, 360, 477), Table 9.43, and bagasse (447, 448), Table 9.44, only small effects have been found, sometimes to the advantage, sometimes to the disadvantage of sulfide. Obviously pulp mills without a recovery system located in populated districts will not find it attractive to apply the kraft process.

Table 9.42. Effect of sulfite or sulfide addition on rapid continuous alkali pulping (11 min) of wheat straw for corrugating medium (138). 170°C

Pulping chemicals	NaOH			NaOH + Na$_2$SO$_3$ 1:1		NaOH + Na$_2$S 2:1	
Alkali charge, as kg ptg	49	62	66	50	72	45	55
Pulp yield, %							
Washed	64	56	59	64	57*	58	64*
Concora test (CMT)	48	76	76	63	81	79	74

* 160°C

Table 9.43. Effect of sulfide addition on alkali pulping of rice straw for bleached paper pulp. 170°C, 2 h, or 98°C, 1 h (in Hydrapulper) (214)

Pulping chemicals	NaOH	NaOH + Na$_2$S	NaOH	NaOH	NaOH + Na$_2$S
Pulping temperature, °C	98	98	170	170	170
Alkali charge, kg ptg	140	140	120	140	140
Pulp yield, crude, %	60.6	63.7	60.0	51.5	56.2
Ash content, %	4.7	6.9	14.3	11.4	15.8
Lignin content, %	5.0	5.3	2.9	1.4	2.8
Burst factor	110	87	96	99	74
Tear factor	40	39	44	50	38

The alkaline pulping of *esparto* is somewhat easier than that of straw, and at alkali charges of 120 kg ptg NaOH, 3–4 atm and 3 h are sufficient. The yields are normally about 40–45% (814), and more crude pulps in 60% yields can be obtained (223, 710). For *bamboo*, kraft pulping is preferred to soda pulping, and alkali charges of 160 kg ptg for unbleached and at least 200 kg ptg for bleachable grades are used, at temperatures of 160–170°C for several hours (25, 735). The *Raitt* process (597) employs two stages, whereby the first utilizes the residual alkali of the black liquor from the second stage, where the normal white liquor is charged. The first stage is thereby performed at about 115°C, the second at about 150°C. The precook could be considered as a buffered soaking at high temperature, to achieve penetration without damage to the carbohydrates prior to the actual cooking reactions. The yields are for unbleached pulps from bamboo 45–50%. The problem of bamboo pulping is to achieve good penetration of the bamboo tissue. The difficulties are caused by the presence of an impenetrable epidermis and strong bundle sheaths, as well as the limited area of conducting channels and complete absence of rays (168). Severe mechanical crushing of the bamboo and chipping to short particles are other means of balancing this deficit.

Room temperature has also been suggested for the alkali treatment of grasses, the *cold caustic* process. The application of this method on straw was suggested fairly early (799), and the *Marsoni* process (43, 508) is a variant using about 2 weeks at room temperature in 2–4% NaOH lye, which gives a pulp well suited to bleached greaseproof and glassine paper. The treatment is carried out in open vessels of 100 m³, taking 20 t straw. To improve the rate of penetration, vacuum and pressure techniques as well as soaking followed by squeezing in a sugar cane press have been studied (213). Semichemical pulps in yields of 75–85% were obtained after fiberizing, with satisfactory crush resistance for corrugating medium paper. With bamboo, cold caustic pulping yields a product which can be used in newsprint (554a).

Alkaline pulping is the most commonly used method for pulping grasses. However, neutral sulfite and chlorination processes have been installed in several mills. The *neutral sulfite process* has been used for *straw* since the 1930's. The cooking liquor is prepared from sulfur dioxide and sodium hydroxide or carbonate. The chemical charges recommended are either 100 kg ptg Na_2SO_3, or 80–100 kg ptg Na_2SO_3 with 30 kg ptg Na_2CO_3 buffer (37, 469), or 80 kg ptg Na_2SO_3 with 35 kg ptg NaOH buffer (42, 43, 784, 791) to keep the final pH at around 7. The maximum temperature is 160–170°C and the time at maximum 1–5 h. Yields are either about 60–70% for unbleached corrugating medium, or about 50% unbleached and 45% bleached pulp for fine paper grades. The cooking is made in stationary or rotary batch digesters, or in multitube (Pandia) or

Table 9.44. Effect of depithing and sulfide addition on alkali pulping of bagasse. Average values for cooks at 171°C for 10 min, alkali charge 155 kg ptg NaOH (447, 448)

| Bagasse type | Whole | | Depithed | |
Pulping process	NaOH	NaOH + Na_2S	NaOH	NaOH + Na_2S
Pulp yield, %				
Crude	56.4	56.1	59.6	60.4
Screened	50.2	52.0	57.3	58.9
Permanganate no.	14.4	10.1	11.0	6.9
Brightness, % GE	30.7	32.2	42.4	45.0
Tensile strength, km	8.5	8.5	8.8	9.6
Burst factor	40	45	53	55
Tear factor	53	58	78	74

vertical (Kamyr) continuous digesters. A preimpregnation with cooking liquor is often used, leading to a liquor-to-straw ratio of only 2.2 : 1 after subsequent squeezing. In the case of semichemical grades, the digester content is passed through disk refiners and washed. No chemical recovery is practised. Neutral sulfite pulping of *bagasse* has also been thoroughly investigated (119) to establish optimal conditions. As with straw (37), the crude and screened yields were found to be fairly independent of chemical charges over a wide range, but higher sulfite charges decrease the lignin content and increase the pentosan content and strength properties. The greatest effect is in the charge interval where the cook becomes sufficiently buffered to keep the pH above 6, in agreement with the experiences of hardwood pulping. 1.5 h at 170°C gave maximal strength properties, and ammonium base was found slightly inferior to sodium base, as is the case in wood pulping. Bisulfite cooking at pH 4 gave less good results, with both unbleached and bleached grades. As shown in Table 9.45, the neutral sulfite process gives somewhat higher

Table 9.45. Comparison of various methods in the production of paper pulp from depithed bagasse (119, 349, 350, 447, 448)

Pulping process	Alkali	Kraft	Neutral sulfite	Bisul-fite	Hydro-tropic	Alkali–chlorine unbl.	bl.
Pulp yield, %							
Crude	59.6	60.4	62.8	67.7	56.2	62.1	60.4
Screened	57.3	58.9	62.2	64.9	—	—	—
Permanganate no.	11.0	6.9	7.9	21.7	38.0	3.5	—
Brightness, % GE	42.4	45.0	46.9	45.0	22.2	38.0	80.6
Tensile strength, km	8.8	9.6	9.2	8.4	5.0	8.5	9.0
Burst factor	53	55	48	48	20	54	53
Tear factor	78	74	65	71	28	68	61

yields, compared at equal lignin content, somewhat brighter pulp but of lower burst and tear strength than alkali and kraft pulping. Similar results have been obtained for oat, rye and wheat straw (552). In the same table the complete inferiority of the *hydrotropic pulping process* is also demonstrated (349). The *Pomilio* or *alkali–chlorine process* gives paper properties similar to that of the neutral sulfite process, and a still more selective delignification (350). The Pomilio process was described earlier in this chapter, Section IV.1, and is therefore only exemplified here in Table 9.46 (350). The main dissolution obviously takes place in the alkali stages.

The *bleaching* of grass pulps is generally easier than the bleaching of corresponding wood pulps. As with the delignification during the cook, the greater accessibility of the grass lignin is probably the cause. Even kraft pulps can be bleached to high brightness without strength losses in only three stages (35, 36, 37). Bamboo pulps require a treatment more similar to wood pulps. The consumption of bleaching chemicals is dependent on the degree of cooking. Continuous tower bleaching is generally practised. The *centrifugal cleaning* is of importance for the final purity and brightness of the bleached grass pulps, to remove impurities originating from the harvest operations. Centrifugal cleaning also brings down the silica content and is of particular value with rice straw pulps.

A comparison of consumption of raw materials in the production of unbleached and bleached pulp grades from straw and bagasse is shown in Table 9.47 (215). The approximate costs of production are shown in

Table 9.46. Conditions and results on the pulping of depithed bagasse by the alkali–chlorine process (350)

Stage	1	2	3	4
Chemical	NaOH	Cl$_2$	NaOH	NaClO
Charge, kg ptg	74	62	30	4
Consistency, %	17	34	12	12
Temperature, °C	110	60	60	35
Time at temperature, h	1	0.3	1	1.8
Yield, % of bagasse	75.4	73.1	61.2	59.8
Permanganate no.	18	—	3.0	—
Brightness, % GE	—	—	40.7	83.2

Table 9.48 (215). The costs of unbleached pulps of the same grade do not deviate materially for different processes, and in the case of bleached grades the kraft and neutral sulfite processes yield the least expensive pulp, assuming recovery in the former process. Alkali–chlorine pulping becomes competitive with alkali pulping upon the installation of a chlorine-alkali electrolytic plant. Bagasse pulp is calculated as being rather less and bamboo pulp rather more expensive than straw pulp. Of course the relation is dependent on the relative prices of the raw materials, which in their turn will be influenced not only by the collection costs but also by the future demand and therefore indirectly by the technical qualities of the pulp products.

Table 9.47. Consumption of raw materials per t of pulp on the production of unbleached and bleached pulps from straw and bagasse (215)

Process	Yield %	Grass t	NaOH kg	Na$_2$S kg	Na$_2$SO$_3$ kg	Na$_2$CO$_3$ kg	Cl$_2$ kg	Steam t	Energy kWh	Water m^3
Alkali, unbl.	60–65	1.6	95					1.2	200	85
Kraft, unbl.	60–70	1.5	70	30				1.2	300	85
Neutral sulfite, unbl.	60–65	1.6			90	35		1.5	200	85
Alkali–chlorine, unbl.	60–65	1.6	150					1.3	160	50
Alkali, bl.	40	2.5	310				80	3	400	175
Cold caustic, bl.	45	2.2	240				75	—	ca.500	175
Kraft, bl.	40	2.5	175	100			80	3	425	350
Neutral sulfite, bl.	46	2.2			180	65	75	3	400	270
Alkali–chlorine, bl.	44	2.3	240				180	2	400	400

The *paper qualities* of the grass pulps, with the exception of the comparatively strong bamboo pulps, are generally inferior to wood pulps, and most investigations have tried to establish how much grass pulp can be tolerated in a certain paper grade. The pulp qualities naturally vary with the raw material, the pulping process and the process conditions chosen. There are two major pulp categories within which several varieties can be discriminated. One is unbleached coarse semichemical pulps for cheaper grades of paper and boards, such as corrugating medium, egg case filler board, and cheap packaging papers, where strength is not essential. The other is bleached semichemical or chemical pulps for glassine and fine papers. In the former category, the yellow-straw pulp made by the lime or alkali processes is dominating, and this is the largest use for straw pulps so far. Coarse bagasse pulps are also used for the same purposes. However, neutral sulfite semichemical pulps from hardwoods are generally superior for corrugating medium paper, especially when compared with lime-cooked straw pulp in the highest yield range, and competition will force the production of alkali and neutral sulfite straw pulps to decreased yield for improved quality, especially in crush resistance (cf. 138, 212). Bleached grades of the four main pulping processes, alkali, kraft, neutral sulfite and Pomilio, are being used in fine papers with up to 100%, but generally not above 50% straw or bagasse pulps. 100% bleached straw or bagasse pulps are used for glassine (79). The gravest objections to the use of straw pulps are the slower drainage at the paper machine wet end, the tendency to stick to the wet presses, and the higher break frequency in the machine. The low tear strength and low extensibility of the resultant paper is a further drawback in all uses where strength is essential, and the tendency to dust in the printing presses is a further disadvantage. Much of the trouble is connected with the high parenchyma content of grass pulps. These cells are disintegrated by the beating to thin membrane-like structures, which greatly slow down the wire drainage (38, 558). Considerable improvement is obtained by selectively removing part of the parenchyma

Table 9.48. Approximate production costs for various types of slush pulps from grasses (215)

Grass type	Pulping process	Yield, % Unbleached	Bleached	Production costs, $ ptp Unbleached	Bleached
Straw	Lime	75	—	50	—
	Alkali–chlorine	65	43	(55)	128 (114*)
	Mechano-chemical	65	48	66	104
	Alkali	60	40	68	118
	Kraft	60	45	66	95
	Neutral sulfite	62	45	64	97
Bamboo	Kraft	50	40	91	124
Bagasse	Kraft	68	—	56	—
	Kraft	55	48	61	84
	Alkali–chlorine	—	46	—	106 (99*)

* Assuming integrated chlorine–alkali production

691

cells, which is considered a necessity for bagasse (447, 448) but of great advantage also for straw, especially rice straw (360). The straw pulps are more easy-beating than wood pulps (559), because of the high content of hemicelluloses, which increase the swelling tendency of the fibers (393, 559). A commercial alkali–chlorine straw pulp was found to have higher overall strength than corresponding kraft and neutral sulfite pulps, whereas the latter gave higher bulk and opacity. However, for widely different fine paper grades, the type of straw pulping process did not significantly affect the paper properties in mixtures of 25 and 50% with softwood pulps (78). These amounts also seemed to be tolerable (78) and improvements in some respects are noted (79). Offset printing papers containing as much as 60% straw pulp were found to have excellent surface smoothness (590). The tear strength is always somewhat decreased by straw pulp additions in larger amounts (641), but even in strong kraft papers up to 20% additions seem tolerable and even of some advantage (81).

The slenderness of the *esparto* fibers has made them a preferred raw material for fine papers where formation, opacity and smoothness are essential properties (523a). It is pulped in batch digesters, as well as in continuous Kamyr or Pandia digesters. The strength of *bamboo* paper pulps allows them to be used for a much wider variety of papers than most other grass pulps. Tear strength is the same as that of softwood pulps, making it possible to produce packaging papers, and because of the slenderness of the fibers, high quality printing papers can be made (2, 735). Bamboo pulping is likely to become of considerable importance in the Asiatic pulp and paper industry of the future.

The *production of dissolving pulp* from grasses is complicated by two circumstances, namely the high silica and high pentosan content. The removal of pentosans can be accomplished by conventional methods, i.e. acid hydrolysis during *sulfite* cooking, as was carried out on *Arundo donax* reed in *Torviscosa*, Italy, during one decade (814b) or by acid *prehydrolysis* followed by *kraft* cooking. The latter method was particularly studied in Germany before and during World War II (13, 179 180) and practised in *Wittenberg* (667), and *Miranda*, Spain, both on cereal straw for viscose rayon. Even for acetate, prehydrolysis–kraft straw pulp has been tried, although the silica content presents special difficulties which can be partly overcome with repeated hot and cold alkali purifications (399). The yields are then below 30% of the straw. Prehydrolysis–kraft pulping of bamboo (244, 363, 405, 418, 419, 554) has also been studied and carried to the mill scale in *Gwalior*, India, and the same process has also been suggested for bagasse, originally as a means of removing the slimy constituents and particles which are responsible for the poor drainage properties of bagasse paper pulp (642, 643), but later to give high-alpha dissolving pulps (31b, 171, 312, 363, 364, 397, 493, 645). Depithing is also preferred here, which causes the pulp yield to decrease to only about 20% of the original weight of the bagasse. Prehydrolysis–kraft pulping of *reed* has also been investigated (381, 715) and carried to the mill scale in *Rumania*.

692

REFERENCES

1. Abrahamsson, B., *et al.*, *Svensk Papperstid.*, **51**, 471 (1948).
2. Adamson, G. A., and G. H. Chidester, *Tappi*, **40**, No. 9, 139A (1957).
3. Adler, E., *Svensk Papperstid.*, **49**, 339 (1946).
4. Adler, E., *Svensk Papperstid.*, **50**, 261, No. 11B, 9 (1947).
5. Adler, E., in E. Hägglund, *Chemistry of Wood*, Academic Press, New York 1951, p. 189.
6. Adler, E., and S. Hernestam, *Acta Chem. Scand.*, **9**, 319 (1955).
7. Adler, E., and L. Stockman, *Svensk Papperstid.*, **54**, 445, 477 (1951).
8. Ahlén, L., and O. Samuelson, *Svensk Papperstid.*, **58**, 421 (1955).
8a. Ahlm, C. E., and B. E. Leopold, *Tappi*, **46**, 102 (1963).
9. Ahlm, E., *Paper Trade J.*, **113**, No. 13, 115 (1941).
10. Ahlojärvi, J., and B. Anthoni, *Paperi Puu*, **38**, 71 (1956).
11. Akamatsu, K., *Kagawa Daigaku Nogakubu Gakuzyuto Hokoku*, **3**, 16, 111 (1951), *C.A.* **46**: 5312.
11a. Akhtar, M., *et al.*, *Swed. Pat.* 152,457 (1955).
12. Allgulander, O., *et al.*, *Svensk Papperstid.*, **57**, 542 (1954).
12a. Alfredsson, B., and O. Samuelson, *Tappi*, **46**, 379 (1963).
13. Alsfeld, M., *et al.*, *Chemiker-Ztg*, **66**, 357 (1942); *Swed. Pat.* 113,076 (1944).
14. Anderson, C. A., *Pulp Paper Mag. Can.*, **47**, No. 1, 43 (1946).
15. Anderzén, O., and B. Holmberg, *Ber.*, **56 B**, 2044 (1923).
16. Anker-Rasch, O., Paper presented at the Sulfite Symposium, N.T.H., Trondheim (Norway), Nov. 12, 1959; cf. *Paper Trade J.*, **138**, No. 42, 33 (1954).
17. Annergren, G. E., and I. Croon, *Svensk Papperstid.*, **64**, 618 (1961).
18. Annergren, G. E., and S. A. Rydholm, *Svensk Papperstid.*, **62**, 737 (1959); **63**, 591 (1960).
19. Annergren, G. E., and S. A. Rydholm, *Svensk Papperstid.*, **66**, 196, (1963) and unpublished.
20. Anon., *Paper Trade J.*, **144**, No. 44, 35 (1960).
20a. Anon., *Paper Trade J.*, **145**, No. 6, 44 (1961).
21. Anon., *Paper Ind.*, **32**, 724 (1950); *Paper Mill News*, **76**, No. 46, 128 (1953).
22. Anon., *Pulp Paper*, **28**, No. 6, 48 (1954).
23. Anon., *Paper Ind.*, **36**, 1084 (1955); *Tappi*, **38**, No. 3, 121A (1955).
24. Anon., *Chem. Eng.*, **62**, No. 1, 104 (1955); *Chem. Weekblad*, **76**, No. 4, 34 (1955); *Paper Trade J.*, **139**, No. 24, 22 (1955); *Wochbl. Papierfabr.*, **85**, 5 (1956).
25. Anon., *Paper Mill News*, **72**, No. 31, 11 (1949).
26. Anon., *Paper Ind. Paper World*, **30**, 244 (1948), cf. ref. (796).
27. Anthoni, B., *Paperi Puu*, **38**, 71 (1956).
28. Arldt, H. G., *et al.*, *Ind. Eng. Chem.*, **49**, 1399 (1957); Thesis, Syracuse, N.Y., 1957.
29. Aronovsky, S. I., and R. A. Gortner, *Ind. Eng. Chem.*, **22**, 264 (1930), Report Univ. of Minnesota, 1934.
30. Aronovsky, S. I., and R. A. Gortner, *Ind. Eng. Chem.*, **28**, 1270 (1936).
31. Aronovsky, S. I., and R. A. Gortner, *Ind. Eng. Chem.*, **29**, 1431 (1937).
31a. Aronovsky, S. I., and D. F. J. Lynch, *Ind. Eng. Chem.*, **30**, 790 (1938).
32. Aronovsky, S. I., *et al.*, *Paper Ind.*, **21**, No. 1, 41; No. 2, 151; No. 3, 335 (1939).
33. Aronovsky, S. I., *et al.*, *Paper Trade J.*, **117**, No. 25, 38 (1943).

34. Aronovsky, S. I., *et al.*, *Paper Trade J.*, **124**, No. 13, 49 (1947).
35. Aronovsky, S. I., *et al.*, *Tech. Assoc. Papers*, **31**, 299 (1948).
36. Aronovsky, S. I., and E. C. Lathrop, *Tappi*, **32**, 145 (1949).
37. Aronovsky, S. I., *et al.*, *Tech. Assoc. Papers*, **31**, 291, 299 (1948); *Tappi*, **35**, 301 (1952); **36**, No. 4, 167A (1953); **37**, No. 12, 24A (1954); *Paper Mill News*, **75**, No. 26, 120 (1952).
38. Aronovsky, S. I., *Paper Ind.*, **32**, 88 (1950).
39. Ashorn, T., *Soc. Sci. Fennica Comm. Phys. Math.* (*Helsinki*), **25**, 8 (1961).
40. Assarsson, A., *et al.*, *Svensk Papperstid.*, **62**, 865 (1959).
41. Asunmaa, S., and P. Lange, *Svensk Papperstid.*, **57**, 501 (1954).
42. Atchison, J. E., *Tappi*, **33**, No. 1, 46A (1950).
43. Atchison, J. E., *Tappi*, **33**, No. 3, 42A (1950).
44. Atchison, J. E., *Paper Trade J.*, **135**, No. 16, 24 (1952).
45. Atchison, J. E., *Paper Trade J.*, **139**, No. 33, 30 (1955); **141**, No. 34, 36 (1957).
46. Aulin-Erdtman, G., *Svensk Papperstid.*, **57**, 745 (1954).
47. Aurell, R., *et al.*, *Svensk Papperstid.*, **61**, 937 (1958).
48. Aurell, R., *et al.*, *Svensk Papperstid.*, **66**, 437, 978 (1963); **67**, 43, 89 (1964).
48a. Aurell, R., and N. Hartler, *Tappi*, **46**, 209 (1963); *Acta Chem. Scand.*, **17**, 545 (1963).
49. Bäckström, C. H., *Swed. Pat.* 142,608 (1953).
50. Bäckström, C. H., and S. Gustafsson, in E. Björkman, *Medd. Statens Skogsforskningsinst.*, **35**, No. 1, 70 (1946).
51. Baker, R. E., and F. Hutton, *Pulp Paper Mag. Can.*, **51**, No. 6, 82 (1950).
52. Baker, R. E., and L. S. Wilcoxson, *Tappi*, **33**, 187 (1950).
53. Bailey, A. J., *et al.*, *Ind. Eng. Chem.*, **30**, 1407 (1938); *Pacific Pulp Paper Ind.*, **14**, No. 3, 24 (1940).
53a. Bailey, E. L., *Tappi*, **45**, 689 (1962).
54. Barsalou, M., *Paper Trade J.*, **141**, No. 3, 34 (1957).
55. Baumann, E., *Ber.*, **23**, 60 (1890).
56. Beazley, W. B., Thesis, McGill Univ., Montreal, 1937.
57. Beazley, W. B., *et al.*, *The Physical Properties of Sulphite Liquors*, Dominion Forest Service Bull. 93, Ottawa 1938.
58. Beazley, W., *Paper Ind.*, **39**, No. 7, 590 (1957).
59. Benjamin, L. R., and J. L. Sommerville, Commonwealth of Australia, Council for Scientific and Ind. Research, Bull. 37, Melbourne 1928.
60. Benson, H. K., *et al.*, *Tech. Assoc. Papers*, **18**, No. 1, 513 (1935).
61. Bergek, T., *Svensk Papperstid.*, **46**, 148 (1943).
62. Bergek, T., *et al.*, *Svensk Papperstid.*, **50**, No. 11B, 22 (1947).
63. Bergek, T., *Norsk Skogind.*, **8**, 372 (1954).
64. Bergström, H., and K. G. Trobeck, *Svensk Papperstid.*, **48**, 49 (1945).
65. Bernardin, L. J., *Tappi*, **41**, 491 (1958).
66. Berthiér, R., *Assoc. Tech. Ind. Papetière, Bull.* **4**, 93 (1953).
67. Bertrand, G., and J. Delga, *Compt. Rend.*, **220**, 805 (1945).
68. Bhat, R. V., *et al.*, *Indian Pulp Paper*, **10**, 307 (1955).
69. Bialkowsky, H. W., *Tappi*, **36**, No. 11, 155A (1953).
70. Bilberg, E., and P. Landmark, *Norsk Skogind.*, **15**, 221 (1961).
71. Bildt, O., *Svensk Papperstid.*, **41**, 261 (1938).
72. Billwiller, J., *U.S. Pat.* 1,649,281 (1928).
73. Binger, H. P., and A. G. Norman, *Tappi*, **40**, 755 (1957).
74. Bishop, F. W., *Paper Ind.*, **37**, 938 (1956).
75. Björkman, A., *et al.*, *Svensk Papperstid.*, **59**, 477 (1956); **60**, 158, 243, 285, 329 (1957).

76. Björkman, E., *et al.*, *Royal Inst. of Forestry, Bull.* No. 4, Stockholm 1949.
77. Bloomberg, W., *Can. Pulp Paper Ind.*, **9**, No. 3, 12 (1956).
78. Boesen, C. E., and E. Flindt-Kruse, *Svensk Papperstid.*, **55**, 885 (1952).
79. Bonavia, M., Paper given at European TAPPI Meeting, Holland, June 1959.
79a. Booth, K. G., *Pulp Paper*, **26**, No. 9, 80 (1952).
79b. Borišek, R., *et al.*, *Svensk Papperstid.*, **64**, 341 (1961).
80. Borlew, P. B., and T. A. Pascoe, *Tech. Assoc. Papers*, **29**, 75, 166 (1946).
81. Botto Micca, G., and E. Grandis, *Tappi*, **43**, No. 11, 168A (1960).
82. Brauns, F. E., and W. S., Grimes, *Paper Trade J.*, **108**, No. 11, 40 (1939).
83. Brauns, O., *Pulp Paper Mag. Can.*, **38**, 148 (1937).
84. Bray, M. W., *et al.*, *Tech. Assoc. Papers*, **21**, 441 (1938).
85. Bray, M. W., *et al.*, *Tech. Assoc. Papers*, **22**, 83, 382 (1939); *Paper Trade J.*, **109**, No. 17, 40 (1939).
86. Bray, M. W., *et al.*, *Paper Trade J.*, **109**, No. 18, 29 (1939).
87. Bray, M. W., and C. E. Curran, *Paper Trade J.*, **105**, No. 20, 39 (1937).
88. Bray, M. W., and P. R. Eastwood, *Paper Trade J.*, **93**, No. 17, 38 (1931).
89. Bray, M. W., and J. S. Martin, *Tech. Assoc. Papers*, **24**, 251 (1941); *Paper Trade J.*, **113**, No. 25, 35 (1941).
90. Bray, M. W., and J. S. Martin, *Paper Trade J.*, **125**, No. 16, 40 (1947).
91. Briggs, B. T., *U.S. Pat.* 2,583,994 (1952).
92. Briggs, D. A. E., *et al.*, *Australian Pulp Paper Ind.*, *Tech. Assoc. Proc.*, **9**, 49 (1955).
93. Brink, D. L., *Tappi*, **44**, 256 (1961).
94. Brink, D. L., *et al.*, *Tappi*, **44**, 263 (1961), **45**, 315 (1962).
95. Brodsky, A. E., and G. P. Miklukhin, in *Radioisotopes in Scientific Research*, Proc. of First (Unesco) Int. Conf., Pergamon Press, London 1958, p. 41.
96. Brookbank, E. B., *Pacific Pulp Paper Ind.*, **36**, No. 52, 17 (1938).
97. Brown, K. J., *Tappi*, **39**, 443 (1956).
98. Bruun, H. H., *et al.*, *Paperi Puu*, **40**, 35 (1958).
99. Bryde, Ö., *Norsk Skogind.*, **1**, 268 (1947).
100. Brude, Ö., and B. Rånby, *Svensk Papperstid.*, **50**, No. 11B, 34 (1947).
101. Buchanan, M. A., and C. M. Koon, *Paper Trade J.*, **115**, T.S. 190 (1942).
102. Bucher, H., and L. P. Widerkehr-Scherb, *Morphologie und Struktur von Holzfasern*, Derendingen (Switzerland) 1948.
103. van Buijtenen, J. P., *et al.*, *Tappi*, **44**, 141 (1961).
104. Bunton, C. A., *et al.*, *J. Chem. Soc.*, **1955**, 4419.
105. Burdynski, R. F., and K. A. Kobe, *Tappi*, **36**, 248 (1953).
106. Burns, I. G., and J. Grant, *World's Paper Trade Rev.*, **137**, 1831 (1952).
107. Byström, S., *Swedish Pat.* 127,269 (1949).
108. Cabott, I. M., and C. B. Purves, *Pulp Paper Mag. Can.*, **57**, No. 4, 151 (1956).
109. Calhoun, J. M., Thesis, McGill Univ., Montreal 1938.
110. Calhoun, J. M., *et al.*, *Can. J. Research*, **B 15**, 457 (1937).
111. Calhoun, J. M., *et al.*, *Can. J. Research*, **B 16**, 242 (1938).
112. Calhoun, J. M., *et al.*, *Can. J. Research*, **B 17**, 121 (1939).
113. Calhoun, J. M., and O. Maass, *Can. J. Research*, **B 15**, 80 (1937).
114. Calkin, J. B., *Tappi*, **34**, No. 9, 108A (1951).
115. Campbell, W. B., and O. Maass, *Can. J. Research*, **2**, 61 (1930).
116. Canadian Standard, CPPA, 1948.

117. Cann, E. D., and W. B. Roberson, *Tappi*, **43**, 97 (1960).
118. Cannon, J. J. R., Thesis, McGill Univ., Montreal 1939.
119. Captein, H. A., *et al.*, *Tappi*, **40**, 620 (1957).
120. Carpenter, C., and G. A. Ritter, *Paper Trade J.*, **110**, No. 3, 29 (1940).
121. Carroll, C. W., *Tappi*, **43**, 573 (1960).
122. Casey, J. P., *Pulp and Paper*, Vol. 1, 2nd Ed., Interscience, New York 1960, p. 398 ff.
123. Cellulose Development Corp., Ltd., *Paper Trade J.*, **115**, No. 22, 32 (1942); *Paper-Maker*, **105**, No. 3, 106 (1943).
124. Centola, G., *Ind. Carta (Milan)*, **11**, No. 10, 119 (1957).
125. Chadeyron, L., *Papier*, **42**, No. 2, 113 (1939).
126. Chesley, K. G., and P. L. Gilmont, *Tappi*, **38**, 279 (1955).
127. Chidester, G. H., *et al.*, *Paper Trade J.*, **106**, No. 23, 37 (1938); **107**, No. 4, 36 (1938).
128. Chidester, G. H., *et al.*, *Paper Trade J.*, **109**, No. 20, 29 (1939).
129. Chidester, G. H., *et al.*, *Tech. Assoc. Papers*, **23**, 661 (1940).
130. Chidester, G. H., *et al.*, *Tappi*, **40**, 8 (1957).
131. Chidester, G. H., and J. N. McGovern, *Paper Trade J.*, **94**, No. 5, 40 (1932).
132. Chidester, G. H., and J. N. McGovern, *Paper Trade J.*, **110**, No. 10, 39 (1940).
133. Chittenden, A. E., and D. Morton, *Colonial Plant Animal Prod.* (Gt. Brit.), **6**, No. 1, 53 (1956).
134. Christiansen, C. B., *et al.*, *Tappi*, **40**, 355 (1957).
135. Christiansen, C. B., and G. W. Legg, *Tappi*, **41**, 216 (1958).
136. Christoffersson, K., and O. Samuelson, *Svensk Papperstid.*, **63**, 729 (1960).
136a. Chollet, J. L., *et al.*, *Pulp Paper Mag. Can.*, **62**, No. 10, T468 (1961).
137. Cittadini, A., *Chem. Ztg.*, **45**, No. 17/18, 193 (1942).
138. Clark, T. F., *et al.*, *Tappi*, **43**, 934 (1960).
138a. Clayton, D. W., *Svensk Papperstid.*, **66**, 115 (1963).
139. Clerk, J. F., *Chem. Met. Eng.*, **30**, 262 (1924).
140. Collin, P. H., *et al.*, *U.S. Pat.* 2,885,317 (1959).
141. Collin, P. H., and H. N. Sköldkvist, *Swed. Pat.* 119,934 (1947).
142. Collins, T. T., *Paper Trade J.*, **129**, No. 8, 29 (1949); **130**, No. 3, 37 (1950); **131**, No. 15, 30 (1950); **136**, No. 12, 37 (1953).
143. Colombo, P., *et al.*, *Svensk Papperstid.*, **63**, 457 (1960).
144. Corbett, W. M., and J. Kidd, *Tappi*, **41**, 137 (1958).
145. Corbett, W. M., and G. N. Richards, *Svensk Papperstid.*, **60**, 791 (1957).
146. Cordingley, R. H., *Tappi*, **42**, 654 (1959).
147. Corey, A. J., *et al.*, *Can. J. Research*, **B 15**, 168 (1937).
148. Corey, A. J., and O. Maass, *Can. J. Research*, **B 13**, 149 (1935).
149. Corey, A. J., and O. Maass, *Can. J. Research*, **B 13**, 289 (1935).
150. Corey, A. J., and O. Maass, *Can. J. Research*, **B 14**, 336 (1936).
151. Correns, E., *Cellulosechem.*, **19**, 105 (1941).
152. Correns, E., and P. Schorning, *Cellulosechem.*, **20**, 29, 33 (1942).
153. Cowan, W. F., *Tappi*, **42**, 152 (1959).
154. Cox, R. D., *et al.*, *Tappi*, **43**, No. 10, 163A (1960).
155. Crandall, H. C., and G. F. Enderlein, *Tech. Assoc. Papers*, **29**, 310 (1946).
156. Croon, I., *Svensk Papperstid.*, **66**, 1 (1963) and unpublished.
156a. Croon, I., *et al.*, *Svensk Papperstid.*, **65**, 693 (1962).
157. Croon, I., and B. Enström, *Tappi*, **44**, 870 (1961).
158. Croon, I., and B. Enström, *Svensk Papperstid.*, **65**, 595 (1962).

159. Cross, C. F., and A. Engelstad, *J. Soc. Chem. Ind.*, **43**, 253T (1924); **44**, 267 (1925); *Papierfabrik*, **22**, 449 (1924); *Brit. Pat.* 12,943 (1922).
160. Crowe, G. A., *Tappi*, **37**, No. 3, 154A (1954).
161. Curran, C. E., *Paper Trade J.*, **88**, No. 3, 66 (1929).
162. Curran, C. E., *Pulp Paper Mag. Can.*, **37**, 646 (1936).
163. Curran, C. E., *Paper Trade J.*, **103**, No. 11, 36 (1936).
164. Curran, C. E., *Fibre Containers Paperboard Mills*, **25**, No. 10, 16 (1940); *Pulp Paper Mag. Can.*, **41**, No. 10, 665 (1940).
165. Curran, C. E., and M. W. Bray, *Ind. Eng. Chem.*, **22**, 830 (1930).
165a. Dahm, H. P., *Norsk Skogind.*, **15**, 421 (1961).
166. Davidson, G. F., *J. Textile Inst.*, **25**, T 174 (1934).
167. Delcroix, P., *Bull. Assoc. Tech. Ind. Papetière*, **3**, No. 2, 32 (1949).
168. Deshpande, P. R., *Indian Pulp Paper*, **8**, No. 3, 167 (1953).
169. Desorbay, G., *U.S. Pat.* 2,571,993 (1951).
170. Detcher, T. E., and R. M. Jones, *Pulp Paper Mag. Can.*, **52**, No. 11, 116 (1951).
171. Dhingra, D. R., *et al.*, *Proc. Sugar Technol. Assoc. India.*, **19**, 242 (1950).
172. Dickerscheid, J. L., *Tappi*, **41**, 526 (1958).
173. Dietzel, R., and S. Galanos, *Z. Elektrochem.*, **31**, 466 (1925).
174. van Dillewijn, C., *Botany of Sugarcane*, Waltham, Mass., 1952.
175. Doriswamy, K., Dissertation, Madison, Univ. of Wisc., 1952.
176. Dorland, R. M., *et al.*, *Pulp Paper Mag. Can.*, **57**, No. 8, 122 (1956).
177. Dorland, R. M., *et al.*, *Pulp Paper Mag. Can.*, **59**, No. C, 236 (1958); **60**, No. 2, T 37 (1959).
178. Dörr, R. E., *Cellulosechem.*, **21**, 49 (1943).
179. Dörr, R. E., *Angew. Chem.*, **53**, 292 (1940); *Papier-Fabrik.*, **39**, 267 (1941); *Svensk Papperstid.*, **46**, 361 (1943).
180. Dörr, R. E., and H. Koch, *Swed. Pat.* 113,579 (1945).
181. Dörr, R. E., and H. Koch, *Swed. Pat.* 113,580 (1945).
182. Dunbar, T. L., *U.S. Pat.* 1,901,706 (1933); Reissue 20,217 (1936).
183. Du Rietz, C., *Über das Ionenbindungsvermögen fester Stoffe*, Dissertation K.T.H., Stockholm 1938, *Svensk Kem. Tldskr.*, **45**, 185 (1933), **49**, 52 (1937).
184. Eftring, K. E., *Swed. Pat.* 153,137 (1956).
185. Eftring, E., *Swed. Pat.* 168,939 (1959).
186. Eggert, J., *Ger. Pat.* 739,668 (1943).
187. Ekman, K., and T. Enkvist, *Paperi Puu*, **37**, 369 (1955).
188. Eliaschberg, M. G., *et al.*, *Bumazh. Prom.*, **30**, No. 9, 10, No. 10, 5 (1955); **31**, No. 1, 8 (1956); *Nauchn. Tr. ZNIIB*, **43**, 59 (1959).
189. Engel, O., and E. Wedekind, *Ger. Pat.* 581,806 (1933).
190. Enkvist, T., *Svensk Papperstid.*, **51**, 225 (1948); *Tappi*, **37**, 350 (1954).
191. Enkvist, T., *Svensk Papperstid.*, **60**, 616 (1957).
192. Enkvist, T., *et al.*, *Svensk Papperstid.*, **52**, 53 (1949).
193. Enkvist, T., *et al.*, *Svensk Papperstid.*, **52**, 517 (1949).
194. Enkvist, T., *et al.*, *Svensk Papperstid.*, **55**, 588 (1952).
195. Enkvist, T., *et al.*, *Paperi Puu*, **39**, 297 (1957).
195a. Enkvist, T., *et al.*, *Paperi Puu*, **44**, 395 (1962); Proc. Wood Chemistry Symposium, Montreal 1961, Butterworths, London 1962, p. 177.
195b. Enkvist, T., *et al.*, *Tappi*, **45**, 128 (1962).
196. Enkvist, T., and B. Alfredsson, *Svensk Papperstid.*, **54**, 185 (1951).
197. Enkvist, T., and B. Alfredsson, *Tappi*, **36**, 211 (1953).
198. Enkvist, T., and B. Alfredsson, *Svensk Papperstid.*, **57**, 159 (1954).

199. Enkvist, T., and E. Hägglund, *Svensk Papperstid.*, **53**, 85 (1950).

200. Enkvist, T., and B. Hougberg, *Paperi Puu*, **37**, 201 (1955).

201. Enkvist, T., and M. Moilanen, *Svensk Papperstid.*, **52**, 183 (1949).

202. Enkvist, T., and M. Moilanen, *Svensk Papperstid.*, **55**, 668 (1952).

203. Erdtman, H., *Svensk Papperstid.*, **42**, 344 (1939); **43**, 241 (1940).

204. Erdtman, H., *Ann.*, **539**, 116 (1939); *Naturwissenschaften*, **27**, 130 (1939); *Svensk Papperstid.*, **42**, 344 (1939); **46**, 226 (1943).

205. Erdtman, H., *Svensk Papperstid.*, **43**, 241 (1940).

206. Erdtman, H., *Svensk Papperstid.*, **43**, 255 (1940); *Tappi*, **32**, 303 (1949).

207. Erdtman, H., *Svensk Papperstid.*, **45**, 374 (1942).

208. Erdtman, H., *Svensk Papperstid.*, **48**, 75 (1945).

209. Erdtman, H., in L. E. Wise and E. C. Jahn, eds., *Wood Chemistry*, Reinhold, New York 1952, p. 1002.

210. Erdtman, H., *et al.*, *Svensk Papperstid.*, **45**, 374 (1942); **46**, 121 (1943).

210a. Eriksson, E., and O. Samuelson, *Svensk Papperstid.*, **66**, 298 (1963).

210b. Eriksson, E., and O. Samuelson, *Svensk Papperstid.*, **64**, 138 (1961); **65**, 600 (1962); **66**, 407 (1963).

211. Eriksson, I., and L. Stockman, *Svensk Papperstid.*, **61**, 545 (1958).

212. Ernst, A. J., *et al.*, *Tappi*, **42**, 235 (1959).

213. Ernst, A. J., *et al.*, *Tappi*, **43**, 34 (1960).

214. Ernst, A. J., *et al.*, *Tappi*, **43**, 49 (1960).

215. FAO, Raw Materials for More Paper, Forestry and Forest Products Study No. 6, Rome 1953.

216. FAO, Bagasse for Pulp and Paper, Rome 1955.

217. Falck, M., and P. A. Giguère, *Can. J. Chem.*, **36**, 1121 (1958).

218. Faldner, J., *Wochbl. Papierfabrik.*, **80**, 394, 633 (1952).

219. Fedorishcheva, I. P., *Tr. Leningrad Lesotekhn. Akad.*, No. 80, 1: 3 (1958).

220. Felicetta, V. F., *et al.*, *J. Am. Chem. Soc.*, **79**, 4499 (1957).

221. Fineman, O., *Svensk Papperstid.*, **60**, 425 (1957); Kamyr Bull. No. 10 (1960), Karlstad, Sweden.

222. Finnish Standard Method.

223. Fischer, E., *Wochbl. Papierfabrik.*, **78**, 432, 461 (1950).

224. Fischler, F., *Z. Physiol. Chem.*, **157**, 1 (1926); **165**, 53 (1927).

225. Flamm, E., and F. Bellak, *Papier-Ztg.*, **63**, No. 6, 17 (1957).

226. Foerster, F., *et al.*, *Z. Anorg. Allgem. Chem.*, **128**, 245 (1923).

227. Forman, L. V., *Paper Trade J.*, **118**, No. 12, 27 (1944); *Paper Ind.*, **25**, No. 12, 1442 (1944).

228. Forss, K., *The Composition of a Spent Spruce Sulphite Liquor*, Diss., Åbo (Finland) 1961.

229. Franzon, O., and O. Samuelson, *Svensk Papperstid.*, **60**, 872 (1957).

230. Franzreb, J. P., Thesis, T.H.D., Darmstadt 1958.

231. Freedman, H., *Paper Trade J.*, **143**, No. 13, 20 (1959).

232. Freudenberg, K., *et al.*, *Ber.*, **80**, 149 (1947); **85**, 78 (1952).

233. Freudenberg, K., *et al.*, *Ber.*, **63**, 1510 (1930); **65**, 484 (1932); **68**, 2070 (1935).

234. Freudenberg, K., *et al.*, *Cellulosechem.*, **22**, 97 (1944).

235. Frisch, H. L., *et al.*, *J. Chem. Phys.*, **21**, 365 (1953); *J. Phys. Chem.*, **57**, 584 (1953); **58**, 507 (1954).

236. Furman, K. E., and P. C. Walt, *U.S. Pat.* 2,760,961 (1956).

237. Gajdos, J., *Papir Celulosa*, **13**, No. 5, 97 (1958); *Zellstoff Papier*, **9**, No. 3, 84 (1960).

237a. Gardon, J. L., and S. G. Mason, *Can. J. Chem.*, **33**, 1477 (1955); *Ind. Eng. Chem. Eng. Data Ser.*, **3**, 115 (1958).
237b. Gasche, U. P., Dissertation THD, Darmstadt 1961; *Papier*, **15**, No. 10a, 538 (1961).
238. Gierer, J. and I. Norén, *Paperi Puu*, **43**, 654 (1961); *Acta Chem. Scand.*, **16**, 1713, 1976 (1962).
239. Gierer, J., and B. Alfredsson, *Acta Chem. Scand.*, **11**, 1516 (1957).
240. Gierer, J., and B. Alfredsson, *Svensk Papperstid.*, **62**, 434 (1959).
241. Giertz, H. W., *Norsk Skogind.*, **11**, 227 (1957).
242. Giertz, H. W., *et al.*, *Norsk Skogind.*, **10**, 344 (1956); **13**, 146 (1959); **14**, 322 (1960); *Papier*, **13**, 185 (1959).
243. Giertz, H. W., and J. McPherson, *Norsk Skogind.*, **10**, 348 (1956).
244. Gohel, V. P., and L. Thoria, *Indian Pulp Paper*, **11**, 33 (1936).
245. Goldfinger, G., *Paper Trade J.*, **112**, No. 24, 29 (1941).
246. Goliath, M., and B. O. Lindgren, *Svensk Papperstid.*, **64**, 109, 469 (1961).
247. Gordon, L. J., *Tappi*, **39**, No. 4, 172A (1956).
248. Graham, J. A., *Brit. Pat.* 5,365 (1882).
249. Gralén, N., *J. Colloid Sci.*, **1**, 453 (1946).
250. Green, H., *et al.*, *Pulp Paper Mag. Can.*, **38**, 108 (1937).
251. Green, H., and F. H. Yorston, *Pulp Paper Mag. Can.*, **40**, No. 4, 244 (1939); **41**, No. 2, 123 (1940).
252. Green, J. W., *Tappi*, **39**, 472 (1956).
253. Grögaard, L., *Swed. Pat.* 163,175 (1958).
253a. Grögaard, L., *Svensk Papperstid.*, **49**, 271 (1946).
254. Grondal, B. L., and P. Zenczak, *U.S. Pat.* 2,772,968 (1956).
255. Guha, S. R. D., *et al.*, *Indian Pulp Paper*, **14**, 565 (1960).
256. Gustafsson, C., *et al.*, *Paperi Puu*, **35**, 409 (1953).
257. Gustafsson, C., and R. Soila, *Paperi Puu*, **38**, 9 (1956).
258. Hachihama, Y., *et al.*, *J. Chem. Soc. Japan.*, *Ind. Chem. Sect.*, **54**, 195, 397 (1951); **55**, 151 (1952).
259. Hägglund, E., *Cellulosechem.*, **5**, 81 (1924).
260. Hägglund, E., *Paperi Puu*, **7**, 361 (1925).
261. Hägglund, E., *Svensk Kem. Tidskr.*, **37**, 116 (1925).
262. Hägglund, E., *Cellulosechem.*, **8**, 25 (1927), **9**, 38 (1928).
263. Hägglund, E., *Medd. Åbo Akademi Inst. Träkemi* (*Finland*), No. 33 (1927).
264. Hägglund, E., *Ber.*, **62**, 437 (1929).
265. Hägglund, E., *Zellstoff Papier*, **11**, 338 (1931).
266. Hägglund, E., *Svensk Papperstid.*, **34**, 838 (1931).
267. Hägglund, E., *Papierfabrik.*, **33**, 73 (1935).
268. Hägglund, E., *Papierfabrik.*, **34**, 313 (1936).
269. Hägglund, E., *Svensk Papperstid.*, **41**, 194 (1938).
270. Hägglund, E., *Ger. Pat.* 663,911 (1938).
271. Hägglund, E., *Svensk Papperstid.*, **48**, 195 (1945).
272. Hägglund, E., *Tappi*, **32**, 241 (1949).
273. Hägglund, E., *Chemistry of Wood*, Academic Press, New York 1951; (a) p. 415 ff., (b) p. 434, (c) p. 449, (d) p. 450, (e) p. 479.
274. Hägglund, E., *Holz Roh Werkstoff*, **11**, 254 (1953).
275. Hägglund, E., CCL, Stockholm, Yearly report 1956, Appendix 1, p. 7.
276. Hägglund, E., *et al.*, *Svensk Kem. Tidskr.*, **36**, 284 (1924); *Svensk Papperstid.*, **32**, 815 (1929).

277. Hägglund, E., *et al.*, *Svensk Kem. Tidskr.*, **37**, 116 (1925); *Paperi Puu*, **16**, 282, 383 (1934); *Svensk Papperstid.*, **40**, 23 (1937).
278. Hägglund, E., *et al.*, IVA Handl. (Stockhom), No. 86 (1928); *Ber.*, **62**, 84, 437, 2046 (1929); **63**, 1387 (1930); *Svensk Kem. Tidskr.*, **41**, 8, 55 (1929); *Papierfabrik.*, **26**, 657 (1928); **29**, 161 (1931); *Zellstoff Papier*, **14**, 490 (1934); **15**, 482 (1935); **16**, 12 (1936).
279. Hägglund, E., *et al.*, *Ber.*, **63**, 1387 (1930).
280. Hägglund, E., *et al.*, *Svensk Papperstid.*, **34**, 719 (1931); **36**, 632 (1933).
281. Hägglund, E., *et al.*, *Biochem. Z.*, **250**, 321 (1932); *Paperi Puu*, **16**, 383 (1934); *Svensk Papperstid.*, **40**, 23 (1937).
282. Hägglund, E., *et al.*, *Paperi Puu*, **16**, 282 (1934).
283. Hägglund, E., *et al.*, *Svensk Papperstid.*, **37**, 133, 164, 196 (1934); **38**, 454 (1935); *Papierfabrik.*, **33**, 81 (1935); cf. *Chemistry of Wood*, Academic Press, New York 1951, p. 442.
284. Hägglund, E., *et al.*, *Svensk Papperstid.*, **38**, 659 (1935).
285. Hägglund, E., *et al.*, *Svensk Papperstid.*, **39**, Special issue, Sept. 7, 37 (1936).
286. Hägglund, E., *et al.*, *Svenska Skogsvårdsfören. Tidskrift*, (Stockholm), **1940**, 105.
287. Hägglund, E., *et al.*, IVA Handl. (Stockholm), No. 2 (1942).
288. Hägglund, E., *et al.*, Medd. CCL (Stockholm), Ser. B, No. 11, No. 12 (1946–47).
289. Hägglund, E., and N. Aarsrud, *Svensk Papperstid.*, **36**, 807 (1933).
290. Hägglund, E., and S. Arnold, *Papierfabrik.*, **36**, 266 (1938).
291. Hägglund, E., and C. B. Björkman, *Acta Acad. Aboensis, Math. Phys.*, **3**, No. 3 (1923).
292. Hägglund, E., and H. Boedecker, *Acta Acad. Aboensis, Math. Phys.*, **4**, No. 4 (1927).
293. Hägglund, E., and I. Eidem, *Svensk Papperstid.*, **36**, 632 (1933).
294. Hägglund, E., and U. Ekman, *Svensk Papperstid.*, **41**, 3 (1938).
295. Hägglund, E., and F. Hedborg, *Svensk Papperstid.*, **38**, 318 (1935).
296. Hägglund, E., and R. Hedlund, *Papierfabrik.*, **30**, No. 5, 49; No. 6, 61 (1932); *Svensk Papperstid.*, **34**, 719 (1931).
297. Hägglund, E., and A. Johansson, *Svensk Papperstid.*, **35**, 475 (1932).
298. Hägglund, E., and T. Johnson, *Svensk Papperstid.*, **31**, 263 (1928).
299. Hägglund, E., and B. Nelson, *Svensk Papperstid.*, **47**, 226 (1944).
300. Hägglund, E., and H. Nihlén, *Svensk Papperstid.*, **37**, 754 (1934); cf. *Paperi Puu*, **10**, 737 (1928).
301. Hägglund, E., and H. Nihlén, *Svensk Kem. Tidskr.*, **47**, 141 (1935).
302. Hägglund, E., and E. Ringström, *Svensk Papperstid.*, **44**, 183 (1941).
303. Hägglund, E., and O. Sandelin, *Svensk Kem. Tidskr.*, **46**, 83 (1934).
304. Hägglund, E., and G. Schollin-Borg, *Papierfabrik.*, **30**, 359 (1932).
305. Hägglund, E., and G. Schollin-Borg, *Paperi Puu*, **14**, 368 (1932).
306. Hägglund, E., and L. Stockman, *Svensk Papperstid.*, **57**, 409 (1954).
307. Hägglund, E., and H. Urban, *C.A.*, **23**, 4067 (1929).
308. Häggroth, S., *et al.*, *Svensk Papperstid.*, **56**, 660 (1953).
309. Haglund, G., *Swed. Pat.* 79,840 (1931); 79,842 (1931); *Svensk Pappersmassetidn.*, **1934**, 124 (Annual issue).
310. Haglund, G., *Swed. Pat.*, 82,751 (1933).
311. Haglund, G., *Swed. Pat.* application 4266/1953.
312. Hamaguti, E., *et al.*, *J. Trop. Agr.*, *Taihoku Imp. Univ.*, **11**, 309 (1939); **12**, 9 (1940); **14**, 1 (1942).

313. Hamilton, J. K., *et al.*, *Pulp Paper Mag. Can.*, **59**, No. 10, 233 (1958); **61**, No. 4, T 263 (1960).
314. Hamilton, J. K., *et al.*, *Tappi*, **41**, 803, 811 (1958).
315. Hamilton, J. K., and N. S. Thompson, *Pulp Paper Mag. Can.*, **61**, No. 4, T 263 (1960).
316. Hamilton, R. P., *Tappi*, **44**, 647 (1961).
317. Hanson, F. S., *Tech. Assoc. Papers*, **23**, 163 (1940).
318. Hanson, F. S., *Paper Trade J.*, **112**, No. 2, 32 (1941).
319. Harris, E. E., in L. E. Wise and E. C. Jahn, eds., *Wood Chemistry*, Reinhold, New York 1952, p. 910.
320. Harris, G. C., *U.S. Pat.* 2,673,148 (1954).
321. Harris, G. R., *Pulp Paper Mag. Can.*, **58**, No. 3, 284 (1957).
322. Harris, G. R., and M. Wayman, *Pulp Paper Mag. Can.*, **57**, No. 3, 231 (1956).
323. Hart, J. S., *et al.*, *Pulp Paper Mag. Can.*, **55**, No. 10, 114 (1954).
324. Hart, J. S., and R. K. Strapp, *Pulp Paper Mag. Can.*, **49**, No. 3, 151 (1948).
325. Hart, J. S., and R. K. Strapp, *Pulp Paper Mag. Can.*, **52**, No. 7, 148 (1951).
326. Hart, J. S., and J. M. Woods, *Pulp Paper Mag. Can.*, **56**, No. 9, 95 (1955).
327. Hart, J. S., and J. M. Woods, *Pulp Paper Mag. Can.*, **57**, No. 5, 158 (1956).
328. Hartler, N., *Svensk Papperstid.*, **62**, 467 (1959); **65**, 513 (1962).
329. Hartler, N., *Svensk Papperstid.*, **64**, 101 (1961).
330. Hartler, N., *et al.*, *Svensk Papperstid.*, **64**, 336 (1961).
330a. Hartler, N., *Paperi Puu*, **44**, 365 (1962).
330b. Hartler, N., *Svensk Papperstid.*, **66**, 443 (1963).
330c. Hartler, N., *Svensk Papperstid.*, **66**, 412 (1963).
330d. Hartler, N., *et al.*, *Svensk Papperstid.*, **66**, 301, 309 (1963).
330e. Hartler, N., *Svensk Papperstid.*, **66**, 526 (1963).
331. Hartler, N., *et al.*, *Svensk Papperstid.*, **63**, 263, 279 (1960).
331a. Hartler, N., *et al.*, *Svensk Papperstid.*, **64**, 106, 336 (1961).
332. Hartler, N., *et al.*, *Svensk Papperstid.*, **64**, 699 (1961).
333. Hartler, N., and A. Lund, *Svensk Papperstid.*, **65**, 951 (1962).
334. Hartler, N., and A. Lund, unpublished.
334a. Hartler, N., and W. Onisko, *Svensk Papperstid.*, **65**, 905 (1962).
335. Hartler, N., and O. Sundberg, *Svensk Papperstid.*, **63**, 263 (1960).
336. Hartmuth, R., *Ger. Pat.* 326,705; 328,783 (1919).
337. Hasche, R. L., *Ind. Eng. Chem.*, **37**, 52 (1945).
338. Hästbacka, K., *Soc. Sci. Fennica Comm. Phys. Math.* (*Helsinki*), **26**, 4 (1961).
339. Hata, K., *J. Japan. Forestry Soc.*, **32**, 383 (1950).
340. Hata, K., *et al.*, *J. Japan. Forestry Soc.*, **33**, 1 (1951); **34**, 320, 357, 386 (1952); **35**, 74, 133 (1953).
341. Hatch, R. S., *U.S. Pat.* 1,852,011 (1932).
342. Hatch, R. S., *Pulp Paper Mag. Can.*, **47**, No. 9, 80 (1946).
343. Head, F. S. H., *J. Textile Inst.*, **46**, T 584 (1955).
344. Hedlund, I., *Svensk Papperstid.*, **50**, No. 11B, 109 (1947).
345. Heiwinkel, H., *Svensk Papperstid.*, **47**, 265 (1944).
346. Hentola, Y., and R. Räsänen, *Paperi Puu*, **33**, B 71 (1951).
347. Hibbert, H., and H. J. Rowley, *Can. J. Research*, **2**, 357 (1930).
348. Hilz, H., *Zellstoff Papier*, **13**, 602 (1933).
349. Hinrichs, D. D., *et al.*, *Tappi*, **40**, 626 (1957).
350. Hinrichs, D. D., *et al.*, *Tappi*, **40**, 634 (1957).

351. Hinrichs, D. D., *et al.*, *Tappi*, **40**, 637 (1957).

352. Hoge, W. H., *Tappi*, **37**, 369 (1954).

353. Holzer, W. F., *Paper Trade J.*, **112**, No. 19, 38 (1941).

354. Holzer, W. F., *et al.*, *Tappi*, **33**, 95, 110 (1950).

355. Holzer, W. F., in E. Ott and H. M. Spurlin, eds., *Cellulose and Cellulose Derivatives*, Vol. 2, Interscience, New York 1954, p. 548; cf. Heuser, E., *et al.*, *Tappi*, **33**, 101 (1950); Atchison, J. E., *Paper Trade J.*, **116**, No. 21, 23 (1943).

356. Hooper, H. S., *U.S. Pat.* 1,887,241 (1932).

357. Hooper, J. F., and B. T. Briggs, *U.S. Pat.* 2,747,995 (1956).

358. Hooper, J. F., and B. T. Briggs, *Swed. Pat.* 164,827 (1958).

359. Höpner, T., *Cellulosechem.*, **22**, 38 (1944).

360. Höpner, T., *Tappi*, **43**, No. 5, 211A (1960).

361. Horio, M., *J. Soc. Chem. Ind. Japan*, **45**, 581, 583, 586 (1942).

362. Horio, M., and Y. Fukuda, *Japan. Pat.* 157,964 (1943); *J. Chem. Ind. Japan*, **46**, 1088 (1943); **47**, 127 (1944); *Japan. Pat.* 3,452 (1952).

363. Horio, M., and M. Takahama, *Bull. Inst. Chem. Res., Kyoto Univ.*, **36**, No. 5, 157 (1958).

364. Horio, M., and M. Takahama, *Bull. Inst. Chem. Res., Kyoto Univ.*, **36**, No. 5, 172 (1958).

365. Horváth, E., and G. Eber, *Cellulosechem.*, **12**, 85 (1931).

366. Horton, J. L., *Pulp Paper Mag. Can.*, **54**, No. 3, 205 (1953).

367. Horton, P. M., and A. G. Keller, *Paper Trade J.*, **142**, No. 26, 28 (1958); *U.S. Pat.* 2,729,856 (1956).

368. Hougberg, B., and T. Enkvist, *Paperi Puu*, **36**, 381 (1954).

369. Hrubesky, C. E., and G. H. Chidester, *Paper Trade J.*, **98**, No. 7, 34 (1934).

370. Hull, W. Q., *et al.*, *Ind. Eng. Chem.*, **43**, 2424 (1951).

371. Hull, W. Q., *et al.*, *Ind. Eng. Chem.*, **46**, 1546 (1954).

372. Hultsch, K., *Angew. Chem.*, **60**, 179 (1948); *Chemie der Phenolharze*, Berlin 1950.

373. Husband, R. M., *Tappi*, **36**, 529 (1953); **38**, 577 (1955); **40**, 412 (1957).

374. Husband, R. M., *Tappi*, **40**, 452 (1957).

375. Il'in, N. A., *Bumazh. Prom.*, **30**, No. 11, 24 (1955); **31**, No. 3, 25 (1956).

376. Immergut, B., and B. Rånby, *Svensk Papperstid.*, **60**, 573 (1957).

377. Ingold, C. K., *Structure and Mechanism in Organic Chemistry*, Bell, London 1953, p. 313.

378. Ingruber, O. V., *Pulp Paper Mag. Can.*, **55**, No. 10, 124 (1954); **58**, No. 10, 161 (1957); *Tappi*, **41**, 764 (1958); *Svensk Papperstid.*, **65**, 448 (1962).

379. Isenberg, H., *et al.*, *Tappi*, **40**, 597 (1957).

380. Ivancic, A., and S. A. Rydholm, *Svensk Papperstid.*, **62**, 554 (1959).

381. Ivanow, H. I., *Zellstoff Papier*, **6**, 102 (1957).

382. Jackson, G. E., *Pulp Paper*, **27**, No. 13, 60 (1953).

382a. Jansson, L. B., *Tappi*, **46**, 296 (1963).

383. Jayme, G., in H. Hesmer, *Das Pappelbuch*, Bonn 1951, p. 237.

384. Jayme, G., *et al.*, *Papierfabrik.*, **37**, 229, 240, 353, 361, 392 (1939).

385. Jayme, G., *et al.*, *Wochbl. Papierfabrik.*, **71**, 689 (1940); *Papierfabrik.*, **39**, 9, 89, 141, 149, 161 (1941); *Chem. Ztg.*, **65**, 30 (1942); *Ind. Chemist*, **24**, No. 276, 30 (1948).

386. Jayme, G., *et al.*, *Holz Roh Werkstoff*, **3**, 273 (1940); *Papierfabrik.*, **39**, 161 (1941); *Chemie*, **55**, 326 (1942); *Cellulosechem.*, **21**, 22 (1943); *Angew. Chem.*, **59**, 150 (1947); *Papier*, **7**, 223 (1953).

387. Jayme, G., *et al.*, *Holz Roh Werkstoff*, **6**, 1 (1943); *Cellulosechem.*, **22**, 65 (1944).
388. Jayme, G., *et al.*, *Papier*, **2**, 45, 95 (1948).
389. Jayme, G., *et al.*, *Papier*, **10**, 495, 540 (1956).
390. Jayme, G., and F. Braunschied, *Papier*, **13**, 284 (1959).
391. Jayme, G., and L. Grögaard, *Cellulosechem.*, **18**, 34 (1940); *Papierfabrik.*, **38**, 93, 101, 113 (1940).
392. Jayme, G., and M. Harders-Steinhäuser, *Papierfabrik.*, **39**, 89 (1941).
393. Jayme, G., and H. Krüger, Paper given at the European Meeting, Nordwijk, Holland, June 1959.
394. Jayme, G., and W. Licht, *Papier*, **6**, 33, 450, 510 (1952); *Holzforschung*, **9**, 33 (1955).
395. Jayme, G., and E. Lochmüller-Kerler, *Holz Roh Werkstoff*, **5**, 10, 377 (1942); *Papierfabrik.*, **42**, 223 (1944).
396. Jayme, G., and R. Nischk, *Wochbl. Papierfabrik.*, **85**, 7 (1957).
397. Jayme, G., and K. H. Rosenstock, *Papier*, **11**, 7 (1957).
398. Jayme, G., and P. Sarten, *Ger. Pat.* 744,868 (1940); *Chemie*, **55**, 323 (1942); *Swed. Pat.* 105,901 (1942).
399. Jayme, G., and L. Scheuring, *Papier*, **7**, 223, 298, 347 (1953).
400. Jayme, G., and G. Wörner, *Papier*, **6**, 80, 220, 381 (1952); *Holz Roh Werkstoff*, **15**, 244 (1952).
401. Jensen, W., *Paperi Puu*, **33**, 4, 333 (1951).
402. Jensen, W., *et al.*, *Svensk Papperstid.*, **54**, 739 (1951); *Paperi Puu*, **35**, 35 (1953); **36**, 387 (1954); **37**, 451 (1955).
403. Jensen, W., and C. E. Bruun, *Paperi Puu*, **36**, 321 (1954).
404. Jensen, W., and P. Rainio, *Paperi Puu*, **34**, 53 (1952).
405. Joglekar, H. H., and C. P. Donofrio, *Tappi*, **34**, 254 (1951).
406. Johansson, D., *Svensk Papperstid.*, **36**, 137 (1933).
407. Johansson, D., *Svenska Skogsvårdsfören Tidskrift*, **33**, 77 (1935); Norrlandsutredningen (Stockholm), 1942, p. 71.
408. Johansson, D., *Paperi Puu*, **21**, Special No. 54 (1939).
409. Johansson, D., *Holz Roh Werkstoff*, **61**, T 515 (1960).
410. Johansson, S., and G. Olson, *World's Paper Trade Review*, **144**, 793 (1955).
411. Johnstone, H. F., and P. W. Leppla, *J. Am. Chem. Soc.*, **56**, 2233 (1934).
412. Jonas, K. G., and P. Walter, *Wochbl. Papierfabrik.*, **62**, No. 23A, 55 (1931).
413. Jones, E. A., *et al.*, *Tappi*, **41**, 721, 727 (1958).
414. de Jong, J. J., *et al.*, *Rec. Trav. Chim.*, **72**, 497 (1953).
415. Jörgensen, L., *Studies on the Partial Hydrolysis of Cellulose*, Dissertation, NTH, Trondheim, 1950.
416. Kalinina, T. I., *Bumazh. Prom.*, **27**, No. 12, 5 (1952).
417. Kampf, G. A., and G. Rutz, *Ger. Pat.* 694,947 (1940).
418. Karnik, M. G., *Indian Pulp Paper*, **13**, No. 6, 283 (1958); *Tappi*, **46**, 130 (1963).
419. Karnik, M. G., and D. L. Sen, *J. Sci. Ind. Research (India)*, **7**, No. 8, 35 (1958).
420. Katzen, R., *et al.*, *Tappi*, **33**, 67 (1950).
421. Kaufmann, Z., *Über die chemischen Vorgänge beim Aufschluss von Holz nach dem Sulfitprozess*, Dissertation, ETH, Zürich 1951.
422. Keller, A. G., *Sugar J.*, **51**, No. 3 (1956).
423. Kenner, J., *Chem. & Ind.*, **1955**, 727.
424. Kenner, J., *et al.*, *J. Chem. Soc.*, **1954**, 278, 1784, 3277; **1955**, 1431, 1709; **1956**, 2921; **1957**, 2916, 3019; *Chem. & Ind.*, **1954**, 1483.

425. Kerp, W., *et al.*, *Arb. Kaiserl. Gesundheitsamte*, **21**, 180, 372 (1904); **26**, 231, 269 (1907); **32**, 89, 120 (1909).

426. Kerp, W., and E. Bauer, *Arb. Kaiserl. Gesundheitsamte*, **26**, 297 (1907).

427. Kerr, W. D., and S. A. Harding, *Pulp Paper Mag. Can.*, **56**, No. 9, 102 (1955); *Tappi*, **39**, 308 (1956).

428. Kerr, W. D., and J. S. Hart, *Pulp Paper Mag. Can.*, **58**, No. 4, 139 (1957); *Tappi*, **40**, 681 (1957).

429. Kerr, W. D., and J. S. Hart, *Tappi*, **42**, 254 (1959).

429a. Kesler, R. B., and S. T. Han, *Tappi*, **45**, 534 (1962).

430. Kibrick, A. C., and I. W. Scopp, *U.S. Pat.* 2,944,928 (1960); *Paper Trade J.*, **144**, No. 40, 39 (1960).

431. Kirchner, E., cited in E. Hägglund, *Chemistry of Wood*, Academic Press, New York 1951, p. 443.

432. Kiato, N. *Wood Research* (*Kyoto*), **1950**, No. 5, 8.

433. Klason, P., *Tek. Tidskr.*, **23**, 33 (1893).

434. Klason, P., *Svensk Papperstid.*, **19**, 180 (1916).

435. Klason, P., *Ber.*, **56**, 300 (1923).

436. Klason, P., and B. Segerfeldt, *Arkiv Kemi*, **4**, No. 6, 1 (1911).

437. Klauditz, W., *Holz Roh Werkstoff*, **4**, 314 (1941).

438. Klauditz, W., *Holzforschung*, **11**, 158 (1958).

439. Klauditz, W., and K. Bergling, *Papierfabrik.*, **39**, 139, 145 (1941).

440. Klein, A., and N. N. Kurzhalls, *Zellstoff Papier*, **15**, 486 (1935).

441. Kleinert, T. N., *et al.*, *Pulp Paper Mag. Can.*, **58**, No. 5, 154, No. 6, 131, No. 7, 215, No. 10, 147 (1957); *Tappi*, **40**, 813 (1957); **41**, 372 (1958).

442. Kleinert, T. N., *et al.*, *Tappi*, **44**, 440 (1961).

443. Kleinert, T. N., and C. S. Joyce, *Tappi*, **40**, 813 (1957).

444. Kleinert, T., and K. Tayenthal, *Angew. Chem.*, **44**, 788 (1931); *U.S. Pat.* 1,856,567 (1932).

445. Klingstedt, F. W., *Paperi Puu*, **15**, 258 (1933).

446. Knapp, S. B., *et al.*, *Tappi*, **40**, 595 (1957).

447. Knapp, S. B., *et al.*, *Tappi*, **40**, 602 (1957).

448. Knapp, S. B., *et al.*, *Tappi*, **40**, 609 (1957).

449. Knutsson, T., and L. Stockman, *Svensk Papperstid.*, **61**, 424 (1958); *Tappi*, **41**, 704 (1958).

450. Koch, R. O., *et al.*, *Tappi*, **41**, 349 (1958).

451. von Koeppen, A., *Tappi*, **41**, 460 (1958).

452. von Koeppen, A., and W. E. Cohen, *J. Appl. Sci. Australia*, **6**, 105 (1955).

453. Korchemkin, F. I., *Zh. Prikl. Khim.*, **29**, 1440, 1542 (1956).

454. Koshijima, T., *et al.*, *Wood Research* (Kyoto), **1954**, No. 13, 150.

455. Krais, P., *Papierfabrik.*, **29**, Fest-u. Auslandsheft, 71 (1931); *Ger. Pat.* 391,173; 395,191; 395,192; 464,240 (1924).

456. Kress, O., *et al.*, *U.S. Dep. Agr.*, *Forest Prod. Lab. Bull.*, No. 1298 (1926).

457. Kress, O., and G. H. McGregor, *Paper Trade J.*, **96**, No. 24, 40 (1933).

458. Kroupa, R., and L. Skark, *Swed. Pat.* 148,368 (1954).

459. Kulkarni, G. R., and W. J. Nolan, *Paper Ind.*, **37**, 142 (1955).

460. Kullgren, C., *Svensk Kem. Tidskr.*, **44**, 15 (1932); *Svensk Papperstid.*, **36**, 499 (1933); **55**, 1 (1952).

461. Küng, A., *Svensk Papperstid.*, **49**, 145 (1946).

462. Kurth, E. F., *Tappi*, **39**, 520 (1956).

463. La Fond, L. A., *Tappi*, **36**, No. 8, 131A (1953).

464. La Fond, L. A., and W. F. Holzer, *Tappi*, **34**, 241 (1951).

465. La Forge, F. B., *Ind. Eng. Chem.*, **15**, 499 (1923).
466. Lagergren, S., *et al.*, *Svensk Papperstid.*, **60**, 632, 664 (1957).
467. Lagergren, S., and B. Lundén, *Pulp Paper Mag. Can.*, **60**, No. 11, T 338 (1959).
468. Lagergren, S., and S. A. Rydholm, *Svensk Papperstid.*, **62**, 103 (1959).
469. Lathrop, E. C., *Pulp Paper Mag. Can.*, **50**, No. 3, 167 (1949).
470. Lathrop, E. C., *et al.*, *Methods for Separating Pith-Bearing Plants into Fiber and Pith*, U.S. Dep. Agr., A.R.S. 71–4, March 1955.
471. Lathrop, E. C., and S. I. Aronovksy, *Tappi*, **37**, No. 12, 24A (1954).
472. Latimer, W. M., *The Oxidation States of the Elements and Their Potentials in Aqueous Solutions*, New York 1952, p. 71.
473. Laroque, G. L., and O. Maass, *Can. J. Research*, **B 19**, 1 (1941).
474. Lau, H., *Paper Ind. Paper World*, **23**, 247 (1941).
475. Laue, H. C., *Wochbl. Papierfabrik.*, **45**, 1858 (1914).
476. Lauer, K., *Tappi*, **41**, 337, 339 (1958).
477. Lauer, K., and A. F. M. Ghoneim, *Wochbl. Papierfabrik.*, **80**, No. 7, 211 (1952).
478. Lautsch, W., *Cellulosechem.*, **20**, 119 (1942), **21**, 51, 148 (1943).
478a. Lea, D. C., *Tappi*, **37**, 393 (1954).
479. Legg, G. W., and J. S. Hart, *Pulp Paper Mag. Can.*, **60**, No. 7, T 203 (1959); *Tappi*, **43**, 471 (1960).
479a. Legg, G. W., and J. S. Hart, *Pulp Paper Mag. Can.*, **61**, No. 5, T 299 (1960).
480. Legg, G. W., and J. S. Hart, *Pulp Paper Mag. Can.*, **61**, No. 1, T 19 (1960).
481. Lengyel, P., *Zellstoff Papier*, **9**, No. 3, 89 (1960).
482. Leopold, B., *Acta Chem. Scand.*, **6**, 55, 64 (1952).
483. Levitin, N., and H. Schwartz, *Pulp Paper Mag. Can.*, **55**, No. 8, 128 (1954).
484. Lewin, M., and A. Lengyel, *Bull. Research Council Israel*, **5 C**, 151 (1956).
485. Ley, H., and E. König, *Z. Physik. Chem. (Frankfurt)*, **B 41**, 365 (1938).
486. Lindau, N. N., *Naturwissenschaften*, **20**, 396 (1932).
487. Lindberg, B., *et al.*, *Svensk Papperstid.*, **59**, 531, 870 (1956); *Acta Chem. Scand.*, **12**, 340 (1958).
487a. Lindberg, B., and O. Theander, *Svensk Papperstid.*, **65**, 509 (1962).
488. Lindberg, J. J., and T. Enkvist, *Soc. Sci. Fennica Comm. Phys. Math. (Helsinki)*, **17**, 4 (1953).
489. Lindgren, B. O., *Acta Chem. Scand.*, **5**, 603 (1951).
490. Lindgren, B. O., *Svensk Papperstid.*, **55**, 78 (1952).
491. Lindner, C., *Monatsh.*, **33**, 613 (1912).
492. Linkhart, R., *Paper Trade J.*, **144**, No. 27, 28 (1960).
493. Locus, A. H., *Tappi*, **43**, 11 (1960).
494. Logan, K. C., *et al.*, *Pulp Paper Mag. Can.*, **61**, No. 11, T 515 (1960).
495. Lundberg, A. H., *Paper Trade J.*, **92**, No. 20, 53 (1931).
496. Lusby, G. R., and O. Maass, *Can. J. Research*, **B 15**, 536 (1937).
497. Lynch, D. F. J., and M. J. Goss, *Ind. Eng. Chem.*, **24**, 1249 (1932).
498. MacLaurin, D. J., and J. R. Peckham, *Tappi*, **38**, 283 (1955).
499. Machell, G., *et al.*, *Chem. & Ind.*, **1957**, 467.
500. Machell, G., and G. N. Richards, *J. Chem. Soc.*, **1957**, 4500; *Tappi*, **41**, 12 (1958).
501. Machell, G., and G. N. Richards, *J. Chem. Soc.*, **1960**, 1944.
502. Mainguet, H., *Fr. Pat.* 989,191 (1951).
503. Mannbro, N. V., *Swed. Pat.* 130,004 (1950).
504. March, R. E., *Paper Trade J.*, **127**, No. 17, 51 (1948).

505. Marchessault, R. H., and B. G. Rånby, *Svensk Papperstid.*, **62**, 230 (1959).
506. Marchlewska-Szrajerowa, J., cited in ref. 421.
507. Mariani, E., and G. Torraca, *Ind. Carta (Milan)*, **7**, 47 (1953).
508. Marsoni, S., *Brit. Pat.* 533,423 (1941).
509. Martin, G. E., *Tappi*, **33**, 84 (1950).
510. Martin, H. C., *Tappi*, **42**, 108 (1959).
511. Martin, J. S., *Southern Pulp Paper J.*, **6**, No. 7, 13 (1943).
512. Martin, J. S., *Forest Prod. J.*, **9**, 359 (1959).
513. Martin, J. S., and M. W. Bray, *Tech. Assoc. Papers*, **26**, 253 (1943).
514. Martin, J. S., and K. J. Brown, *Tappi*, **35**, 7 (1952).
514a. Marton, J., and E. Adler, *Tappi*, **46**, 92 (1963).
515. Mattsson, V. F., Dissertation, Inst. Paper Chem., Appleton, Wis. 1954.
516. May, M. N., *Paper Ind.*, **37**, 935 (1956).
517. May, M. N., and J. R. Peckham, *Tappi*, **40**, 914 (1957).
518. McGovern, J. N., *Paper Trade J.*, **103**, No. 20, 29 (1936).
519. McGovern, J. N., *U.S. Dep. Agr.*, *Forest Prod. Lab. Report*, 1792 (1951).
520. McGovern, J. N., *et al.*, *Tappi*, **32**, 440 (1949).
521. McGovern, J. N., and G. H. Chidester, *Paper Trade J.*, **98**, No. 18, 41 (1934).
522. McGovern, J. N., and G. H. Chidester, *Am. Pulp Paper Mill Supts. Assoc. Yearbook and Program*, **1939**, 274.
523. McGovern, J. N., and G. H. Chidester, *Tech. Assoc. Papers*, **25**, 679 (1942).
523a. McGovern, J. N., and J. Grant, *Tappi*, **45**, 343 (1962).
524. McIlhenny, N., in Eng. Exp. Station Georgia Inst. Tech., Bull. No. 18, V, *A Survey of the Bamboos*, 11 (1953).
524a. McIntosh, D. C., *Tappi*, **45**, 273 (1963).
525. McKee, R. H., *U.S. Pat.* 2,308,564 (1943); *Ind. Eng. Chem.*, **38**, 382 (1946); *Pulp Paper Mag. Can.*, **55**, No. 2, 64 (1954).
526. McKinney, J. W., *Paper Trade J.*, **122**, No. 4, 58 (1946).
526a. Meier, H., *Svensk Papperstid.*, **65**, 299, 589 (1962).
527. Meller, A., *Paper Trade J.*, **125**, No. 11, 57 (1947).
528. Meller, A., *Tappi*, **33**, 248 (1950); **35**, 178 (1952).
529. Meller, A., *Tappi*, **34**, 171 (1951); **35**, 72 (1952).
530. Meller, A., *Tappi*, **36**, 366 (1953); **38**, 682 (1955).
530a. Meller, A., *Tappi*, **46**, 317 (1963).
531. Menzinsky, G., *Ber.*, **68**, 822 (1935).
532. Merewether, J. W. T., *Tappi*, **37**, 483 (1954).
533. Migita, N., *et al.*, *J. Japan. Tech. Assoc. Pulp Paper Ind.*, **5**, 399 (1951); **6**, 476 (1952); *J. Japan. Forestry Soc.*, **37**, 448 (1955).
534. Mikawa, H., *Bull. Chem. Soc. Japan*, **27**, 50 (1954).
535. Mikawa, H., *et al.*, *J. Chem. Soc. Japan, Ind. Chem. Sect.*, **54**, 299 (1951).
536. Mikawa, H., *et al.*, *Bull. Chem. Soc. Japan*, **29**, 265 (1956).
537. Mikawa, H., and H. Okada, *J. Chem. Soc. Japan, Ind. Chem. Sect.*, **54**, 239 (1951).
538. Miller, R. N., *Paper Trade J.*, **81**, No. 23, 55 (1925).
539. Miller, R. N., *et al.*, *Pcper Trade J.*, **77**, No. 15, 51 (1923); **82**, No. 9, 58 (1926); *Chemistry of the Sulphite Process*, Lockwood, New York 1928.
540. Miller, R. N., and W. H. Swanson, *Paper Trade J.*, **74**, Apr. 13 (1922); **76**, Mar. (1923).
541. Miller, R. N., and W. H. Swanson, *Paper Trade J.*, **78**, No. 15, 178 (1924); **79**, No. 16, 48 (1924); **81**, No. 11, 53 (1925).

542. Miller, R. N., and W. H. Swanson, *Ind. Eng. Chem.*, **17**, 843 (1925).
543. Mitchell, R. L., *et al.*, *Tappi*, **39**, 571 (1956).
544. Mitra, D. N., *Tappi*, **42**, 366 (1959).
545. Monsson, W. H., *Paper Trade J.*, **86**, No. 17, 59 (1928).
546. Montano, J., and R. Hossfeld, *Tappi*, **34**, 468 (1951).
547. de Montigny, R., *Pulp Paper Mag. Can.*, **34**, No. 2, 109 (1933).
548. Moore, T. R., and F. H. Yorston, *Pulp Paper Mag. Can.*, **46**, No. 3, 161 (1945).
549. Morud, B., *Studies on the Chemistry of the Sulphite Cooking*, Thesis, NTH, Trondheim 1958.
550. Most, D. S., *Tappi*, **40**, 705 (1957).
551. Müller, F. M., *Papier*, **12**, 461 (1958).
552. Müller, F. M., *Tappi*, **43**, No. 2, 209A (1960).
553. Murray, F. E., *Can. J. Chem. Eng.*, **36**, No. 2, 69 (1958); *Tappi*, **42**, 761 (1959).
554. Naffziger, T. R., *et al.*, *Tappi*, **43**, 591 (1960).
554a. Naffziger, T. R., *et al.*, *Tappi*, **44**, 472 (1961).
555. Nakao, M., *Japan. Pat.* 3,451 (1952).
556. Nakao, M., and M. Tatsumi, *J. Chem. Soc. Japan, Ind. Chem. Sect.*, **54**, 639 (1951).
557. Neale, S. M., *J. Textile Inst.*, **20**, T 373 (1929); **21**, T 225 (1930); **22**, T 230, T 349 (1931).
558. van Nederveen, G., *et al.*, *Papier*, **9**, 1 (1955).
559. van Nederveen, G., and G. H. Hellenberg, *Tappi*, **39**, 631 (1956).
560. Nepenin, Y. N., *Bumazh. Prom.*, **26**, No. 2, 6, No. 4, 11 (1951); **32**, No. 7, 5 (1957).
561. Neuberg, C., *Biochem. Z.*, **76**, 107 (1916).
562. Nihlén, H., *Svensk Papperstid.*, **42**, 593 (1939); cf. R. Schepp, *Papier*, **1**, 140 (1947).
562a. Nilsson, O., and L. Stockman, *Svensk Papperstid.*, **65**, 711 (1962).
563. Nokihara, E., *et al.*, *J. Am. Chem. Soc.*, **79**, 4495 (1957).
563a. Nokihara, E., *et al.*, *J. Japan. Tech. Assoc. Pulp. Paper Ind.*, **8**, 14 (1954).
564. Nolan, W. J., *et al.*, *Tappi*, **33**, 338 (1950); **34**, No. 3, 38A (1951); **35**, 29 (1952).
565. Nolan, W. J., *et al.*, *Tappi*, **35**, 29, 505 (1952).
566. Nolan, W. J., *et al.*, *Paper Ind.*, **37**, 926 (1956); *Tappi*, **40**, 170 (1957).
567. Noyess, A. A., and R. Stewart, *J. Am. Chem. Soc.*, **32**, 1133 (1910).
568. Nylinder, P., and E. Hägglund, *Medd. Statens Skogsforskningsinst.*, **44**, No. 11 (1954).
569. Obenshain, D. N., *U.S. Pat.*, 2,789,051 (1957).
570. Öhrn, O., *et al.*, *Svensk Papperstid.*, **63**, 762, 817 (1960).
571. Öhrn, O., and I. Croon, *Svensk Papperstid.*, **63**, 601 (1960).
572. O'Meara, D., and G. N. Richards, *J. Chem. Soc.*, **1960**, 1944.
572a. Osawa, Z., *et al.*, *Tappi*, **46**, 84 (1963).
573. Overbeck, W., and H. F. Müller, *Papierfabrik.*, **40**, 136 (1942); *Ber.*, **75**, 547 (1942).
574. Packard, R. A., *Tappi*, **37**, No. 3, 38A (1954).
575. Palczewski, T., and J. Rutkowski, *Prace Inst. Celuloz-Papier*, **5**, No. 1 (1956).
576. Palmrose, G. V., *Paper Trade J.*, **100**, No. 3, 38 (1935).
577. Parck, C., and O. Samuelson, *Svensk Papperstid.*, **58**, 31 (1955).

578. Parrett, A. N., *U.S. Pat.* 2,823,119; 2,823,120; 2,823,121 (1958); *Swed. Pat.* 163,857 (1958).
579. Patterson, R. F., *et al.*, *Pulp Paper Mag. Can.*, **52**, No. 12, 105 (1951).
580. Peckham, J. R., and M. N. May, *Tappi*, **43**, 45 (1960).
580a. Peckham, J. R., and V. van Drunen, *Tappi*, **44**, 374 (1961).
581. Pelipetz, M. G., Dissertation Columbia Univ., 1937.
582. Perilä, O., *Paperi Puu*, **43**, 521 (1961).
583. Pettersson, G., *Svensk Papperstid.*, **27**, 384 (1924).
584. Pettersson, S. E., and S. A. Rydholm, *Svensk Papperstid.*, **64**, 4 (1961).
585. Pew, J. C., *Tappi*, **32**, 39 (1949).
586. Pictet, R., *et al.*, *Ger. Pat.* 26,331 (1883), 504,667 (1926); *Norweg. Pat.* 42,934; 43,337; 43,338 (1926).
587. Pillow, M. Y., and M. W. Bray, *Paper Trade J.*, **101**, No. 26, 31 (1935).
588. Ploetz, T., *Holz Roh Werkstoff*, **4**, 380 (1941).
589. Podder, V., *Paper Industry in India*, National Printing Works, Delhi, 1959, p. 32, 57.
590. Poggianti, U. and G. Moltedo, *Paper Technol.*, **1**, 413 (1960).
591. Poljak, A., *Angew. Chem.*, **60A**, No. 2, 45 (1948).
592. Pomilio, U., *Paper Trade J.*, **87**, No. 18, 49 (1928); *Ind. Eng. Chem.*, **31**, 657 (1939).
593. Porphire, P., *Swed. Pat.* 119,389 (1947).
594. Potter, G. C. J., and F. H. Yorston, *Pulp Paper Mag. Can.*, **38**, 103 (1937).
595. Preston, R. D., and K. Singh, *J. Exptl Bot.*, **1**, 214 (1950).
596. Pulpwood, Stands, Procurement and Utilization, TAPPI Monograph Series No. 4, New York 1947.
596a. Quick, R. H., *Tappi*, **39**, 357 (1956).
597. Raitt, W., Report on the Investigation of Bamboo as Material for the Production of Paper Pulp, Indian Forest Records, Calcutta 1912, *Indian Forest Records*, **11**, No. 9, 271 (1925); *The Digestion of Bamboo and Grasses for Papermaking*, Crosby, Lockwood & Son, London 1931.
598. Rånby, B. G., Fine Structure and Reactions of Native Cellulose, Dissertation, Uppsala Univ. (Sweden), 1952; *Svensk Papperstid.*, **55**, 115 (1952).
599. Rånby, B. G., and E. Ribi, *Experientia*, **6**, 12 (1950).
600. Räsänen, R. H., and L. I. Luotonen, *Zellstoff Papier*, **9**, 340 (1958), **10**, 375 (1959); *Paper Mill News*, **83**, No. 3, 16 (1960).
601. Rassow, B., and H. Gabriel, *Cellulosechem.*, **12**, 227, 249, 290, 318 (1931).
602. Regestad, S. O., and O. Samuelson, *Svensk Papperstid.*, **61**, 735 (1958).
603. Regnfors, L., *Svensk Papperstid.*, **60**, 178 (1957).
604. Regnfors, L., and L. Stockman, *Svensk Papperstid.*, **59**, 509 (1956).
604a. Reid, H. A., *Appita*, **15**, 102 (1962).
605. Reyerson, L. H., *U.S. Pat.* 2,733,992 (1952), cf. 2,301,314 (1942).
606. Richards, G. N., *et al.*, *J. Am. Chem. Soc.*, **80**, 4888 (1958).
607. Richards, G. N., and H. H. Sephton, *J. Chem. Soc.*, **1957**, 4492.
608. Richardson, R. W., *Swed. Pat.* 82,599 (1935).
609. Richter, G. A., *U.S. Pat.* 1,427,125 (1922); *Tappi*, **36**, 228 (1953).
610. Richter, G. A., *U.S. Pat.* 1,654,603 (1928).
611. Richter, G. A., *U.S. Pat.* 1,787,953; 1,787,954; 1,819,002; 1,819,003 (1931); 1,917,545 (1933); *Tappi*, **39**, 193 (1956).
612. Richter, G. A., *Can. Pat.* 328,260 (1932).
613. Richter, G. A., *U.S. Pat.* 1,848,661; 1,880,042 (1933).
614. Richter, G. A., *U.S. Pat.* 1,880,043 (1933); *Tappi*, **39**, 193 (1956).

615. Richter, G. A., *U.S. Pat.* 1,880,048 (1933).
616. Richter, G. A., *Ind. Eng. Chem.*, **33**, 532 (1941).
617. Richter, G. A., *Ind. Eng. Chem.*, **33**, 75 (1941).
618. Richter, G. A., *Tappi*, **32**, 553 (1949).
619. Richter, G. A., *Tappi*, **36**, 228 (1953).
620. Richter, G. A., *Tappi*, **39**, 193 (1956).
621. Richter, G. A., and R. H. MacClaren, *U.S. Pat.* 2,694,631 (1954); *Tappi*, **38**, 129 (1955).
622. Richter, G. A., and L. H. Pancoast, *Tappi*, **37**, 263 (1954).
623. Richter, J., *Svensk Papperstid.*, **61**, 741 (1958); *Kamyr Bull.* No. 10 (1960); No. 11 (1961).
624. Richtzenhain, H., *Svensk Papperstid.*, **53**, 644 (1950); *Acta Chem. Scand.*, **4**, 206, 589 (1950); *Ber.*, **83**, 488 (1950).
625. Richtzenhain, H., *et al.*, *Svensk Papperstid.*, **57**, 363, 538 (1954).
626. Ritman, E. L., *et al.*, *Paper Ind.*, **29**, No. 12, 1751 (1948).
627. Robinson, M. D., and D. W. Harris, *Pulp Paper Mag. Can.*, **60**, No. 8, T 243 (1959); *Pulp Paper*, **33**, 87 (1959).
628. Roe, R. B., *Ind. Eng. Chem.*, **16**, 808 (1924); TAPPI Standard T 202 m-45, CCA 9.
629. Roelofsen, P. A., *Papierwereld*, **14**, No. 3, 403 (1959).
630. Roschier, H., *Paperi Puu*, **4**, 108 (1922).
631. Roschier, H., and E. Aaltio, *Paperi Puu*, **32**, 189 (1950).
632. Rosén, G. E., *Swed. Pat.* 89,152 (1937).
633. Rosenberger, N. A., *Bumazh. Prom.*, **31**, No. 3, 6 (1956).
634. Rosenberger, N. A., *Bumazh. Prom.*, **32**, No. 10, 4 (1957); *Zellstoff Papier*, **6**, 361 (1957).
635. Ross, J. H., *U.S. Pat.* 1,922,262 (1933); *Pulp Paper Mag. Can.*, **33**, No. 4, 35 (1932).
636. Ross, J. H., *et al.*, *Pulp Paper Mag. Can.*, **52**, No. 10, 116 (1951).
637. Roth, W. A., *Z. Physik. Chem.*, A **173**, 313 (1935).
638. Rothrock, C. W., and W. J. Nolan, *Tappi*, **34**, No. 3, 38A (1951); **35**, 29 (1952).
639. Routala, O., and A. Pohjola, *Paperi Puu*, **16**, 289 (1934).
640. Routala, O., and J. Sevón, *Cellulosechem.*, **7**, 113 (1926).
641. van Royen, A. H. H., *Straw pulp in paper*. Paper given at European TAPPI Meeting, Holland, June 1959.
642. de la Roza, J. J., *U.S. Pat.* 1,782,869 (1930).
643. de la Roza, J. J., *U.S. Pat.* 1,864,985 (1932).
644. de la Roza, J. J., *Pulp Paper Mag. Can.*, **38**, No. 4, 296 (1937).
645. de la Roza, J. J., *Mem. Assoc. Tech. Azucar.*, Cuba, **11**, 349 (1937).
646. Rue, J. D., *et al.*, *Paper Trade J.*, **78**, No. 4, 45, No. 20, 46 (1924).
647. Rue, J. D., and S. E. Nagel, *Paper Trade J.*, **115**, No. 6, 29 (1942).
648. Runkel, R. O., *Wochbl. Papierfabrik.*, **71**, 93 (1940); *Holz Roh Werkstoff*, **5**, 413 (1942); *Zellstoff Papier*, **21**, 139 (1941); *Tappi*, **35**, 174 (1952).
649. Runkel, R. O., and P. Schoeller, *Papierfabrik.*, **40**, 201 (1942); *Holzforschung*, **2**, 1 (1948), **3**, 47 (1949).
650. Running, K. D., *Pulp Paper Mag. Can.*, **41**, 181 (1940); **42**, 104 (1941).
651. Rusten, D., Thesis, NTH, Trondheim (Norway) 1960.
652. Rydholm, S. A., Thesis, KTH, Stockholm 1948.
653. Rydholm, S. A., *Svensk Papperstid.*, **57**, 427 (1954).
654. Rydholm, S. A., *Svensk Papperstid.*, **58**, 273 (1955).

655. Rydholm, S. A., *Fr. Pat.* 1,228,690 (1960).
656. Rydholm, S. A., *Papier*, **14,** 535 (1960).
657. Rydholm, S. A., unpublished.
658. Rydholm, S. A., *et al., Svensk Papperstid.*, **64,** 386 (1961).
659. Rydholm, S. A., *et al., Svensk Papperstid.*, **66,** 110 (1963).
660. Rydholm, S. A., and S. Lagergren, *Svensk Papperstid.*, **62,** 103 (1959).
661. Rys, L. J., *et al., Tappi*, **35,** 147 (1952).
662. Rys, L. J., *U.S. Pat.* 2,783,590 (1957).
663. Saarnio, J., *et al., Acta Chem. Scand.*, **8,** 825 (1954).
664. Saarnio, J., and C. Gustafsson, *Paperi Puu*, **35,** 65 (1953).
665. Sadler, H., and O. Trantina, *Holzforsch. Holzverwert.*, **9,** No. 3, 37 (1957).
666. Saeman, J., *Ind. Eng. Chem.*, **37,** 43 (1945).
667. Saeman, J. F., *et al.*, PB–7736 (1945), Officer of Tech. Services, U.S. Dept. Comm., Wash. D.C.
668. Samuels, R. M., and D. W. Glennie, *Tappi*, **41,** 250 (1958).
669. Samuelson, O., *Svensk Papperstid.*, **45,** 516 (1942).
670. Samuelson, O., *Svensk Papperstid.*, **46,** 583 (1943).
671. Samuelson, O., *et al., Svensk Papperstid.*, **65,** 363, 685, (1962).
672. Samuelson, O., *et al., Svensk Kem. Tidskr.*, **61,** 234 (1949).
673. Samuelson, O., *et al., Svensk Papperstid.*, **56,** 779 (1953); **57,** 827 (1954).
674. Samuelson, O., *et al., Svensk Papperstid.*, **61,** 1043 (1958).
674a. Samuelson, O., *et al., Svensk Papperstid.*, **65,** 767 (1962).
675. Samuelson, O., and A. Wennerblom, *Svensk Papperstid.*, **56,** 745 (1953).
676. Samuelson, O., and E. A. Westlin, *Swed. Pat.* 121,439 (1947).
677. Samuelson, O., and E. A. Westlin, Medd. CCL, B, No. 12 (1947), Stockholm.
678. Samuelson, O., and A. Westlin, *Svensk Papperstid.*, **50,** No. 11 B, 149 (1947).
679. Samuelson, O., and A. Westlin, *Svensk Papperstid.*, **51,** 179 (1948).
680. Sandberg, E. S., *Swed. Pat.* 95,984 (1939).
681. Sander, A., *Paper Trade J.*, **81,** No. 10, 50 (1920).
681a. Sanyer, N., *et al., Tappi*, **44,** No. 8, 180A (1961).
682. Sanyer, N., *et al., Tappi*, **45,** 90 (1962).
683. Saponitskii, S. A., *Bumazh. Prom.*, **32,** No. 8, 5 (1957).
684. Sarie, S. P., and R. K. Schofield, *Proc. Royal Soc. (London)*, A **185,** 431 (1946).
684a. Sarkanen, K. V., *et al., Tappi*, **46,** 375 (1963).
685. Saunderson, H. H., and O. Maass, *Can. J. Research*, **10,** 24 (1934).
686. Schaarschmidt, A., and P. Nowak, *Cellulosechem.*, **13,** 143 (1932).
687. Schenker, C., and M. A. Heath, *Tappi*, **42,** 709 (1959).
688. Schieber, W., *Jentgens Kunstseide u. Zellwolle*, **23,** 228 (1941); *Wochbl. Papierfabrik.*, **72,** 575 (1941).
689. Schmeil, W., Bambus als Papierrohstoff, Dissertation, Dresden, Schulze, Gräfenhainichen 1921.
690. Schmidt, E., *Papierfabrik.*, **36,** 565 (1938).
691. Schmidt, J., *Wochbl. Papierfabrik.*, **83,** 1025 (1955).
691a. Schmidt, U., *Papier*, **15,** 79 (1961).
692. Schöberl, A., *Angew Chem.*, **53,** 227 (1940).
693. Schoettler, J. R., *Tappi*, **37,** 686 (1954).
694. Schöön, N. H., *Svensk Papperstid.*, **64,** 235, 624 (1961); **65,** 729, 965 (1962), Diss. CTH, Gothenburg (Sweden), 1962.

695. Schorning, P., *Chemie*, **55**, 62 (1942).
696. Schorning, P., *Faserforsch. Textiltech.*, **8**, 487 (1957).
697. Schuerch, C., *et al.*, *Anal. Chem.*, **30**, 518 (1958).
698. af Schultén, K., *Paperi Puu*, **38**, 181 (1956).
699. af Schultén, K., *Swed. Pat.* 117,257 (1945).
700. Schur, M. O., and R. E. Baker, *Tech. Assoc. Papers*, **24**, 405 (1941); **25**, 453 (1942).
701. Schur, M. O., and E. G. Ingalls, *Tech. Assoc. Papers*, **26**, 296 (1943).
701a. Schüssler, F., *Zellstoff Papier*, **4**, No. 2, 49 (1955).
702. Schütz, F., *Ber.*, **75**, 703 (1942).
703. Schütz, F., *Ger. Pat.* Appl., cited in Schütz, F., and P. Sarten, *Cellulosechem.*, **21**, 47 (1943).
704. Schütz, F., and P. Sarten, *Cellulosechem.*, **21**, 35 (1943), **22**, 1 (1944).
705. Schwalbe, C., *Ger. Pat.* 204,460 (1909).
706. Schwarz, S. L., and M. W. Bray, *Paper Trade J.*, **107**, No. 12, 24 (1938).
707. Schwarz, S. L., and M. W. Bray, *Tech. Assoc. Papers*, **22**, 600 (1939).
708. Shaw, A. C., *Pulp Paper Mag. Can.*, **57**, No. 1, 95 (1956); **58**, No. 10, 170 (1957); *Pulp Paper Ind.*, **10**, No. 11, 49 (1957).
709. Shaw, A. C., and M. Dignam, *Can. J. Chem.*, **35**, 322 (1957).
710. Shaw, M. B., *et al.*, *Paper Trade J.*, **81**, No. 12, 119 (1925).
711. Sherrard, E. C., and E. E. Harris, *U.S. Pat.* 2,328,749 (1943).
712. Shimoda, I., and K. Kotani, *J. Soc. Textile Cellulose Ind.*, *Japan*, **2**, No. 2, 73 (1946).
713. Sihtola, H., *et al.*, *Paperi Puu*, **40**, 493 (1958).
714. Sillén, L. G., *et al.*, *Acta Chem. Scand.*, **12**, 878 (1958).
715. Simionescu, C., *et al.*, *Papeterie*, **79**, 589 (1957); *Celuloza Hirtie* (*Bucharest*), **5**, No. 7, 156 (1956); **7**, No. 5, 171 (1958).
716. Simmonds, F. A., *et al.*, *Tappi*, **35**, 166 (1952); **36**, 103 (1953); **38**, 178 (1955); **39**, 641 (1956).
717. Simon, A., *et al.*, *Z. Physik. Chem.*, **204**, 235 (1955); *Z. Anorg. Allg. Chem.*, **281**, 113, 135 (1955); **283**, 359 (1956); **284**, 36, 47 (1956); *Ber.*, **89**, 2442 (1956).
718. Sindall, R. W., *Bamboo for Papermaking*, Marchant Singer, London 1909, p. 38.
719. Sirakoff, G., *Holz Roh Werkstoff*, **4**, 205 (1941).
720. Sivola, G., *U.S. Pat.* 2,710,763 (1948); *Can. Pat.* 480,404 (1952); cf. *Tappi*, **42**, 265 (1959).
721. Sivola, Y. (G.), *Swed. Pat.* 146,535 (1952).
721a. Sjöström, E., *et al.*, *Svensk Papperstid.*, **65**, 885 (1962).
722. Slavik, I., *Svensk Papperstid.*, **64**, 427 (1961).
723. Sloman, A. R., *Australian Pulp Paper Ind. Tech. Assoc.*, **3**, 49 (1949).
724. Sloman, A. R., *Pulp Paper International*, **3**, No. 6, 18 (1961); *Appita*, **14**, No. 2, 57 (1960).
725. Smith, D., and A. C. McCorry, *Tappi*, **41**, No. 6, 247A (1958).
726. Smith, L. H., ed., *Synthetic Fiber Developments in Germany*, P.B. 7416, Textile Research Inst., New York 1946.
727. Smith, R. W., *Australian Pulp Paper Ind. Tech. Assoc.*, **10**, 60 (1956).
728. Smithsonian Physical Tables.
729. Sobolev, I., and C. Schuerch, *Ind. Eng. Chem.*, **49**, 1399 (1957); *Tappi*, **41**, 545 (1958).
730. Söderquist, R., *Swed. Pat.* Appl., 4,378/1929; *Svensk Papperstid.*, **58**, 706

(1955); *Paperi Puu*, **37**, 301 (1955); *Paper Trade J.*, **139**, No. 42, 30 (1955); *Papier*, **11**, 487 (1957).
731. Sohn, A. W., and P. O. Lenel, *Papier*, **3**, 109 (1949).
732. Solechnik, N.Y., *Bumazh. Prom.*, **14**, No. 4, 30 (1935).
733. Somer, V., unpublished.
734. Somerville, J. L., *Australian Pulp Paper Ind. Tech. Assoc.*, **1**, 74, 95 (1947).
735. Sproull, R. C., *Tappi*, **38**, 593 (1955).
736. Stangeland, G. E., *Kgl. Norske Videnskabers Selskabs Handl.*, No. 1, Oslo 1932.
737. Stevens, R. H., *Chemurgic Dig.*, **17**, No. 1, 8 (1958); *Southern Pulp Paper Mft.*, **21**, No. 3, 93, 130 (1958).
738. Stevens, R. J., *Pulp Paper Mag. Can.*, **59**, No. 1, 96 (1958).
739. Stockman, L., *Svensk Papperstid.*, **54**, 621 (1951).
740. Stockman, L., *Svensk Papperstid.*, **56**, 525 (1953).
740a. Stockman, L., *Svensk Papperstid*, **65**, 978 (1962).
741. Stockman, L., *et al.*, *Svensk Papperstid.*, **61**, 871 (1958), **64**, 33, 67 (1961).
742. Stockman, L., and E. Edlund, Paper presented at the Annual Meeting of SPCI (Stockholm) 1961.
743. Stockman, L., and E. Hägglund, *Svensk Papperstid.*, **51**, 269 (1948).
744. Stockman, L., and E. Sundkvist, *Svensk Papperstid.*, **61**, 746 (1958).
745. Stone, J. E., *Tappi*, **40**, 539 (1957).
746. Stone, J. E., *et al.*, *Pulp Paper Mag. Can.*, **59**, No. 6, 165, No. 7, 191 (1958); **62**, No. 6, 517 (1961); *Tappi*, **42**, 51 (1959).
747. Strapp, R. K., *et al.*, *Pulp Paper Mag. Can.*, **58**, No. 3, 277 (1957).
748. Studeny, J., and C. E. Libby, *Paper Trade J.*, **109**, No. 20, 29 (1939).
749. Sundman, J., *Paperi Puu*, **29**, 52 (1947); *Medd. Ind. Centrallab.*, No. 71, Helsinki 1949.
750. Sundman, J., Dissertation, Helsinki 1949.
751. Sundman, J., *Paperi Puu*, **32**, 267 (1950).
752. Sundstedt, N. J., *Svensk Papperstid.*, **40**, 107, 111 (1937).
752a. Surewicz, W., *Tappi*, **45**, 570 (1962); *Przegl. Papiern.*, **7**, No. 12, 272 (1951); **16**, No. 7, 198 (1960).
753. Suida, H., *et al.*, *Papierfabrik.*, **25**, *Fest- u. Auslandsheft* 93 (1927), **26**, *Fest- u. Auslandsheft* 71 (1929), **28**, 363 (1930).
754. Svedberg, T., *Svensk Papperstid.*, **52**, 157 (1949).
755. Swanson, W. H., *Paper Trade J.*, **83**, No. 22, 198 (1926).
756. Swedish Standard CCA 18.
757. Tamolang, F. N., *et al.*, *Tappi*, **40**, 671 (1957).
758. Tamolang, F. N., and F. F. Wangaard, *Tappi*, **44**, 201 (1961).
759. TAPPI Standard T 206 m-44, CCA 13, CCA 16.
760. TAPPI Standard O-400 p-44.
761. TAPPI Standard T 214 m-50, CCA 9.
762. TAPPI Standard O-400 p-54.
763. Tartar, H. V., and H. H. Garretson, *J. Am. Chem. Soc.*, **63**, 808 (1941).
764. Tatsuyama, B., *J. Japan. Tech. Assoc. Pulp Paper Ind.*, **2**, No. 2, 16, 64 (1948).
765. Theiss, B., *Zellstoff Papier*, **5**, 217 (1956).
766. Tilghman, B. C., *Brit. Pat.* **385** (1867).
767. Timell, T. E., *Tappi*, **40**, 749 (1957).
768. Toda, H., and T. Hamada, *J. Japan. Tech. Assoc. Pulp Paper Ind.*, **11**, 429, 489, 515 (1957).

769. Tomlinson, G. H., in J. N. Stephenson, ed. *Pulp Paper Manufacture*, Vol. 1, McGraw-Hill, London 1952, p.364.
770. Tomlinson, G. H., *et al.*, *Pulp Paper Mag. Can.*, **59**, No. C, 247 (1958); *Tappi*, **43**, No. 8, 674 (1960).
771. Traynard, P., and A. Eymery, *Papier, carton et cellulose*, **3**, No. 5, 87 (1954); *Holzforschung*, **9**, 172 (1955); **10**, 6, 43 (1956).
772. Traynard, P., and A. Robert, *Tappi*, **38**, No. 9, 149A (1955).
773. Trobeck, K. G., *Svensk Papperstid.*, **54**, 632 (1951); **56**, 636 (1953); *Pulp Paper Mag. Can.*, **53**, No. 3, 225 (1952).
774. Trost, E., *Indian Pulp Paper*, **4**, 355 (1950).
775. Turner, C. H., *Australian Pulp Paper Ind. Tech. Assoc.*, **6**, 89 (1952).
776. Turner, G. B., *The Thermal Decomposition of Aqueous Solutions of Sulphur Dioxide*, Dissertation, London Univ. 1954, p. 44.
777. Tydén, H., *Norsk Skogind.*, **6**, 175 (1952).
778. Tydén, H., *Svensk Papperstid.*, **59**, 296 (1956).
779. Ulfsparre, S., *Svensk Papperstid.*, **31**, 642 (1928).
780. Ulfsparre, S., The Svedberg Celebration, Uppsala 1944, p. 379.
781. U.S. Forest Products Lab., *Fiber Containers Paperboard Mills*, **34**, No. 11, 66 (1949).
782. Valeur, C., *Svensk Papperstid.*, **54**, 613 (1951).
783. Valeur, C., *Svensk Papperstid.*, **55**, 776 (1952).
784. Vamos, G., and P. Lengyel, *Papierwereld*, **14**, No. 5, 447, 456 (1959/60).
785. Vassie, J. E., *Tappi*, **36**, 367 (1953).
786. Venemark, E., *Svensk Papperstid.*, **51**, 418 (1948).
787. Venemark, E., *Svensk Papperstid.*, **59**, 629 (1956).
788. Venemark, E., *Svensk Papperstid.*, **60**, 73 (1957).
789. Venemark, E., *Swed. Pat.* 160,736 (1957).
789a. Wennerås, S., *Norsk Skogind.*, **16**, 118 (1962).
790. Vethe, A., *et al.*, *Norsk Skogind.*, **14**, 167 (1960).
791. Vidal, I. P., and H. Bonnier, *A Straw Pulp Plant*, Paper presented at Eucepa Meeting, Nordwijk, Holland, June 1959.
792. Vincent, G. P., and J. F. White, *Paper Ind.*, **27**, 880 (1945).
792a. Virkola, N. E., and A. A. Alm, *Papier*, **15**, 522 (1961).
793. Vroom, K. E., *Pulp Paper Mag. Can.*, **58**, No. 3, 228 (1957).
794. Walters, W. Z., and M. N. May, *Tappi*, **43**, 881 (1960).
795. Walton, H. F., in F. C. Nachod, ed., *Ion Exchange, Theory and Application*, Academic Press, New York 1949, p. 13.
796. Wangaard, F. F., *Paper Ind.*, **19**, No. 7, 777 (1937).
797. Weber, E. A., *Pulp Paper Mag. Can.*, **35**, No. 6, 307 (1934).
798. Weber-Marshall, J., *Chem. Eng.*, **62**, No. 3, 320 (1955).
799. Wells, S. D., *U.S. Pat.* 1,769,811 (1930).
800. Wells, S. D., *et al.*, *U.S. Pat.* 1,949,669 (1934); *Tech. Assoc. Papers*, **24**, 156 (1941); **27**, 167 (1944).
801. Wells, S. D., and K. Arnold, *Tech. Assoc. Papers*, **24**, 156 (1941).
802. Wells, S. D., and J. D. Rue, *The Suitability of American Woods for Paper Pulp*, U.S. Dep. Agr. Forest Prod. Lab. Bull. 1485, Madison 1927.
803. Welte, C. T., and C. E. Libby, *Paper Ind.*, **21**, 1075 (1940).
803a. Wennerås, S., *Norsk Skogind.*, **16**, 118 (1962).
804. West, C. J., *Pulping Processes*, Part I, *Nitric Acid Processes*, Bibliographic Series No. 172, Inst. Paper Chem., Appleton, Wis. 1950.
805. West, C. J., *Papermaking Materials, I. Cereal Straws*, Bibliographic Series No. 171, Inst. Paper Chem., Appleton, Wis. 1949.

806. West, C. J., *Pulping Processes*, Part II, *Chlorine Process*, Bibliographic Series No. 173, Inst. Paper Chem., Appleton, Wis. 1950.
807. Westcott, D. B., *U.S. Pat.* 2,671,727 (1954).
808. Wilson, J. W., *et al.*, *Pulp Paper Mag. Can.*, **61**, No. 1, T 19 (1960).
809. Wilson, J. W., and D. O'Meara, *Pulp Paper Mag. Can.*, **61**, No. 4, T 259 (1960).
810. Wither, R. P., and H. A. Captein, *Forest Prod. J.*, **10**, 174 (1960).
811. Wohl, A., *Ger. Pat.* 707,725 (1941).
812. Wolf, R. B., *et al.*, *U.S. Pat.* 1,699,556 (1929); 1,772,792 (1930); 1,780,638 (1931); 1,804,967 (1931).
813. Wolfrom, M. L., and A. Thompson, in W. Pigman, ed., *The Carbohydrates*, Academic Press, New York 1957, p. 208.
814. Wurz, O., *Zellstoff Papierherstellung aus Einjahrespflanzen*, Roether, Darmstadt 1960. (a) p. 47, 53, (b) p. 100, cf. Rogers, A.C., *Pulp Paper Mag. Can.*, **41**, 607 (1960).
815. Wurz, O., *Papierfabrik.*, **27**, 495, 576 (1929).
816. Yllner, S., *Acta Chem. Scand.*, **10**, 1251 (1956).
817. Yllner, S., *et al.*, *Svensk Papperstid.*, **60**, 795 (1957).
818. Yllner, S., and B. Enström, *Svensk Papperstid.*, **59**, 229 (1956), **60**, 549 (1957).
819. Yorston, F. H., *Studies in Sulphite Pulping*, Dom. Forest Service Bull. (Ottawa), **97** (1942).
820. Yundt, A. P., *Tappi*, **34**, 91 (1951).
821. Zaitseva, A. F., *et al.*, *Tr. Inst. Lesa, Akad. Nauk*, SSSR, **45**, 70 (1958).
822. Zebbs, F. L., *Tappi*, **39**, No. 4, 180A (1956).
823. Zellstoff-Fabrik Waldhof, *Fr .Pat.* 875,279 (1941).
824. Zentner, T. G., *Tappi*, **36**, 517 (1953).
825. Ziegelmeyer, F., and O. Feischl, *Papier*, **12**, 122 (1958).
826. Zimmerman, W. P., and J. J. Holt, *Paper Trade J.*, **146**, No. 23, 28 (1962).

10

FURTHER TREATMENT OF
UNBLEACHED PULP

I. General Principles

After leaving the grinder, the refiner or the digester, the pulp is far from made, even if the aim is unbleached grades. Firstly, in the case of semichemical and chemical pulps, the organic and inorganic components dissolved in the waste liquor have to be removed, and in most cases be further treated by evaporation and combustion to utilize the heat value of the organic components and recover the inorganic chemicals for re use (cf. Chapter 11). Therefore, washing of the pulp has to be performed as completely as possible, with a minimum of dilution of the waste liquor. Secondly, the washed pulp has to be freed from solid impurities, which are mineral particles, resin particles, bark fragments, as well as coarse fiber bundles, which owing to the heterogeneous structure of wood and deficiencies in the pulping processes remain in the bulk of separated, acceptable fibers. Thirdly, the cleaned unbleached pulp is present as a suspension in water, or as a wet pulp web, and if it is not going to be further processed at the mill most of the water has to be removed. These three processes, the removal of soluble impurities, the removal of solid impurities, and the removal of water, or *washing*, *screening* (cleaning) and *dewatering* of pulp, will be treated in this chapter. Closely connected with the washing and screening sequence is *refining*, which sometimes to some extent is performed after washing and some screening. However, refining is definitely a process of *pulping* and was therefore treated together with other pulping processes in Chapters 6 and 8. *Beating* and other phases of stock preparation, as well as the *drying of beaten pulp* on the paper machine, belong to paper technology and will not be dealt with in this book. The same applies to the *final operations in the production of hardboards*. Reference is made to the standard monographs on paper and board production (e.g. 20a, 91).

II. Washing

1. INTRODUCTION AND HISTORY

Washing is needed as soon as chemicals have been used and wood substance dissolved in the production of pulp, i.e. for chemical and semichemical pulps. The first pulp industry to rationalize pulp washing with the aim of chemicals recovery was the *kraft industry*, which used larger quantities of

715

more expensive chemicals than the *sulfite industry*. In the latter, the waste liquor was allowed to drain to the sewers in the blow pits until later recovery became economically interesting, in some cases because of waste liquor utilization for the production of *organic chemicals* or *heat*, but lately because of the use of more expensive *cooking chemicals* which can and have to be regenerated. Further, with the increase of the pulp industry the *stream pollution* problems have become accentuated, in extreme cases making waste liquor recovery a necessity by law for permission to run the mill. Although the economic utilization of waste liquor from *semichemical pulping* processes is more difficult than in the case of chemical pulping, the reasons for and the process of their waste liquor recovery are essentially the same.

The primary reason for washing, *to obtain a pulp free of soluble impurities*, is of course most essential, but has made less impression on the washing methods used since the subsequent operations, especially pulp screening, involve repeated dilution and concentration of the pulp and, consequently, a washing. Leaving out the ordinary washing process, however, would affect the efficiency of both screening and bleaching, and would not be acceptable from the viewpoint of stream pollution or chemicals and heat recovery.

The problems involved in waste liquor recovery are essentially the same as those of separation of dissolved substances from suspended particles, which are met in most processing industries. The young kraft industry in the 1880's solved the technical problem by borrowing equipment from the older sugar industry, where *diffusers* had been introduced in 1865. In the sulfite industry the liquor was drawn from the digesters and replaced with hot water, or drained from the blow pits, where the pulp was washed with water. This technique of *washing in the digester* or *blow pit* is used predominantly today, with improvements in structural details and by using weak liquor for a primary washing to obtain a higher dry content of the waste liquor recovered.

Filter washing was first introduced in connection with bleaching, where the problem was limited to that of getting a clean-washed pulp, but from 1930 onwards filter washing was becoming increasingly used as an operation for black liquor recovery, where minimum dilution of the recovered liquor was also required. Since World War II this has been the generally adopted system for new installations in America, whereas diffusers still dominate the kraft industry of Europe, although the most recent installations have been filter washers, as is the case in other parts of the world. The sulfite and semichemical pulping industries have also adopted filter washing. The new trend towards making the cooking operation continuous is a strong argument for leaving the discontinuous washing techniques in diffusers and blow pits. Some washing is already carried out in the bottom of the Kamyr continuous digesters, in one case almost eliminating the need of a special washing operation, cf. Chapter 9.II.

Lately, *press washing* on multistage installations of screw, roll or disc presses has been advanced, although only a few mills have adopted the system exclusively. Some combinations of press and filter washing are also in use.

Part or the entire screening is sometimes carried out prior to washing, so-called *black stock screening*, in which case the washing operation has to be performed continuously, with filters and presses.

2. FUNDAMENTAL PRINCIPLES

It is a general rule that to gain something another thing has to be sacrificed. In washing, the factors opposed are *the recovered amount of dry substance* and *the dilution of the recovered liquor*. As the latter has to be evaporated prior to combustion, every volume of washing water accompanying the waste liquor to the evaporation station will cost steam. *To increase the efficiency* of the washing process is to increase the recovery of dry substance with preserved or decreased dilution of the recovered liquor. *To choose*, at a given washing efficiency, *the extent of recovery and dilution* is a matter of economy, and the choice will be influenced by the prevailing costs of heat and the inherent value of the substances to be recovered (16, 85, 97). For instance, in *a sulfite mill with alcohol plant only*, an increase in fuel price will limit the economic recovery of dry substance to a level where the dilution and steam consumption in the distillation are relatively low, whereas an increase in alcohol price will have the reverse effect. If *evaporation and burning only* of the sulfite waste liquor is performed, an increase in fuel price will admit a more complete washing, and if *alcohol production together with evaporation and burning* is undertaken, changes in fuel prices do not affect the limits of economical washing appreciably. If *recovery of inorganic cooking chemicals* is aimed at, as in the case of magnesium or sodium base sulfite waste liquors or in the case of kraft black liquors, it is profitable to wash to much more complete recovery of dry substance than in the other cases. Therefore, the ways of expressing the washing result are quite different. In the kraft industry the recovery is expressed in *losses of sodium sulfate per ton of pulp*, usually 5–30 kg Na_2SO_4 ptp, corresponding to a recovery of 96–99 % of the cooking chemicals used, whereas the sulfite industry speaks of *substance yield factor*, called U (70), of about 0.75–0.95, complete recovery being expressed as $U = 1.0$. The dilution in the kraft industry is expressed with the *dilution factor* (42, 52, 58, 59), or the amount of wash water counted in unit weight per unit weight of air-dry pulp, which accompanies the recovered black liquor to the evaporation, whereas the sulfite industry counts in terms of *concentration quotients*, f, or the concentration ratio of the liquor recovered to the liquor from the digester (28, 70, 85, 96). In the kraft industry, dilution factors of 2–4 m^3 ptp are general, corresponding to concentration quotients around 0.8–0.6, whereas in efficient sulfite waste liquor recovery an f factor below 0.8 is seldom economically motivated. Another term of sulfite pulp washing is the *relative liquor volume* or the total liquor volume recovered in relation to the liquor volume in the digester. This value, which in sulfite pulp washing may be above or below 1.0, is in the kraft industry always larger than 1.0, approximately 1.25–1.5. Substance yield, concentration quotient and relative liquor volume are interrelated according to the formula

$$U = f \cdot (v_0 + V)/(v_0 + V_0)$$

where the fraction $(v_0 + V)/(v_0 + V_0)$ is the relative liquor volume, composed by the terms v_0, liquor volume recovered by drainage before introduction of washing liquor; V_0, liquor volume remaining in the pulp after drainage; and V, liquor volume recovered after introduction of washing liquor to the pulp (85, 96).

The process of washing can be of two essential types, either a *displacement*, or *washing by successive dilution and thickening*, and a practical washing case is likely to consist of both (6). A displacement washing may be figured as a number of *partial volumes* (85), where in each one *instantaneous mixing of waste liquor and washing liquor occurs*. The greater the number, n, of partial volumes in the pulp layer, the more efficient the washing. The theory of partial volumes has been mathematically treated

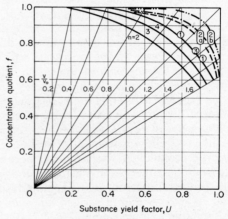

Fig. 10.1. *U–f* diagram for sulfite waste liquor recovery, principal figures and a few practical results. V/V_0, relative liquor volume recovered; n, number of partial volumes in pulp layer (Scholander)

Theoretical curves:
—— displacement with hot water only
— — displacement with weak waste liquor $(V/2)$, followed by hot water
—·— displacement with weak waste liquor (V), followed by hot water
—··— displacement with two weak waste liquors $(V + V)$, followed by hot water
Practical results: (1) digester wash, one weak liquor (2a) digester wash, two digesters in series, (2b) digester wash, two weak liquors, (3) blow pit wash

(85), and resulted in the schematic Figure 10.1, where the relation of substance yield and concentration quotient is given for different values of *n*. In the diagram lines for the relative liquor volume have also been drawn and some practical results (15, 17, 18, 42, 43, 44, 52, 70, 85, 96, 99, 100, 105). It is seen that in sulfite washing practice both digester and blow pit washing results correspond to a number of partial volumes varying from four upwards. Figure 10.2 is an enlargement of the same principal figure, indicating by the shadowed areas the results of sulfite and kraft washing practice (50, cf. 15, 17, 18 etc).

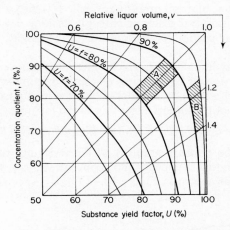

Fig. 10.2. *U–f* diagram for waste liquor recovery in practice. (A) sulfite industry, Ca base, digester washing; (B) kraft industry, diffuser washing (Jönsson)

The theory of partial volumes has been discussed mainly in connection with sulfite waste liquor recovery, although it could also be applied to diffusers and to some extent to filters. To achieve a good displacement efficiency, i.e. a high number of partial volumes, is obviously essential to *avoid channelling* in the pulp layer, and also to *avoid excessive mixing* of original liquor and washing liquor. The former aim is fulfilled by a uniform pulp packing in the blow pit or diffuser. To avoid mixing liquors it is important to maintain as great a difference as possible in the *specific gravity* of original liquor and washing liquor. If the liquor to be recovered is heavier than the washing liquor, as in the case of black liquor, and in most cases of sulfite waste liquor, displacement with washing liquor should be carried out from above, whereas with very cold washing liquor and hot sulfite waste liquor the reverse is true and the best displacement is carried out from below. Figure 10.3 will illustrate this in a diagram for the temperature dependence of waste liquor density. It must be kept in mind that displacement is frequently carried out first with a weak waste

719

liquor with a density between that of original liquor and water, and with a temperature lower than that of the original liquor.

Another factor to prevent excessive mixing between washing liquor and the original liquor is the *rate of flow*, which is as important as the density difference. Besides the risk of channeling at high flow rates it is found that a uniform flow even results in less washing efficiency at a higher rate, probably because of turbulence around individual fibers. Slow *diffusion* from the interior of the fibers into the surrounding liquor may also be a limiting factor for higher flow rates (84). Obviously these circumstances limit the displacement efficiency of the filter wash (74), and also affect the capacity of digester, blow pit or diffuser wash. It is also seen in Figure 10.1 that for instance simple digester or blow pit washing does not correspond to more than four partial volumes, although the height of the pulp layer is several meters.

The rate of flow in a diffuser, which determines diffuser washing capacity, is limited not only by washing efficiency requirements but also by other factors such as the pressure gradient, the resistance of the medium and the viscosity of the liquor, according to the formula (97):

$$v = F_1(dp/dh)/F_2(R\eta) = F_1'(dp/dh, T)/F_2'(RC)$$

where dp/dh is the pressure gradient, R the resistance to flow and η the viscosity, which in turn is dependent on concentration, C, and temperature, T, of the liquid, as shown in Figure 10.4 (97).

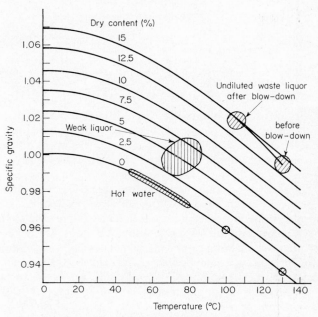

Fig. 10.3. Temperature dependence of the density of liquors involved in the recovery of sulfite waste liquor (Scholander)

720

As the resistance of the pulp layer increases with the degree of packing, the filling of the diffuser is important. The resistance tends to increase during the process of washing because of tighter packing. To compensate for this and maintain the rate of flow, pressure is applied on the top of the diffusers, up to 2.5 kp/cm² towards the end of the washing. Pressure vessels are not used in the blow pit washing of the sulfite industry, and open diffusers in the kraft industry have also been reported.

The extent of displacement in filter washing is likely to be less because flow rates 10–100-fold that of a diffuser (with flow rates in the order of 0.5–1.0 m/h) (32), are applied. Therefore, multistage washing on filters is necessary to achieve the same result as in a diffuser (79), and it has also been suggested that a retention volume for diffusion be placed between the different filters (71, 79). The term *displacement ratio* has been introduced to characterize washing shower efficiency (74), which on modern filters has been shown to be considerable. The displacement concept is then connected to the fraction of soluble matter in the unwashed pulp that migrates to the filtrate during washing. By that concept the wash water acts solely as a diluent for the filtrate. A different concept of the washing process defines *displacement* as that part of the original liquor which is actually displaced in an unchanged form by an equal volume of the wash water, and then diluted by another portion of the wash water, which has initially come in equilibrium with the residual wash liquor through *diffusion* processes and has received a concentration of solids corresponding to that of the liquor remaining in the pulp after washing (80). These assumptions, which obviously contain simplifications, allow the calculation of a *displacement factor* and a *washing efficiency* as well as the resulting recovery and dilution effects in studying single- or multistage washing, e.g. on filters.

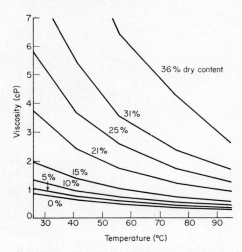

Fig. 10.4. Viscosity of kraft black liquor at varying concentration and temperature (Vene-mark)

A practical concept used to describe the shower water flow is the *shower wash factor* which expresses the flow of added wash water in multiples, usually 0.8–1.4, of the liquor volume remaining in the pulp web at the moment of washing. As the consistency of the web is not so easily determined at that point, it is generally assumed that it equals the pulp consistency of the web leaving the drum. The shower wash factor is more frequently used in connection with bleachery filters. In the multistage washing of unbleached pulp for waste liquor recovery, the concept of *dilution factor* is used more frequently. As already mentioned, this concept describes the portion of the wash water which actually passes through the pulp web to dilute the wash liquor, and equals the total wash water added, minus that leaving the last filter with the pulp.

Screw, roll, or disk presses are not normally equipped for displacement operations, and the effect here is entirely limited to dilution and compression of the pulp. However, they have the advantage of guaranteeing a forced flow from the luminae of the fibers, the content of which in the other types of washing processes is left mainly to diffusion and capillary flow. Even with presses the entire liquor volume of the pulp does not mix with the dilution liquor. Practical experience indicates that up to about 0.3 m³ ptp does not take part in the mixing before and under a press stage (50), although there is evidence of almost complete mixing in other cases (101), probably depending on the mixing device prior to the press and on the manner of liquor addition, which ought to follow directly upon the previous pressing stage. If the mixing is complete, the following principal formulae are valid for serial press washing (50):

Stage 1.
$$U = \frac{1 + y - x}{1 + y}$$

Stage 2.
$$U = \frac{1 + y - x}{1 + y^2/(x + y)}$$

Stage 3.
$$U = \frac{1 + y - x}{1 + y^3/(x^2 + xy + y^2)}$$

Stage 4.
$$U = \frac{1 + y - x}{1 + y^4/(x^3 + x^2y + xy^2 + y^3)}$$

Stage 1.
$$f = \frac{1}{x + y}$$

Stage 2.
$$f = \frac{1}{1 + y^2/(x + y)}$$

Stage 3.
$$f = \frac{1}{1 + y^3/(x^2 + xy + y^2)}$$

Stage 4.
$$f = \frac{1}{1 + y^4/(x^3 + x^2y + xy^2 + y^3)}$$

where $x = L_i/L_o$ and $y = V/L_o$, V being the wash water added, L_o the original waste liquor volume and L_i that after i presses.

3. WASHING PRACTICE

For details on machinery constructions, the reader is referred to appropriate textbooks, such as (69, 91) and to manufacturers' bulletins. Here only a *diffuser*, a *screw press*, a *filter washer*, a *drum press* and a *disk press* are depicted, Figures 10.5–9.

In the *sulfite* industry, digester washing, blow pit washing, filter washing and pressing are in use. The digester washing decreases cooking capacity and is used in mills where the digester house is not the bottleneck of the production, and where the digesters are comparatively small and numerous. Usually one intermediate washing with weak waste liquor should be applied before hot water is introduced. A high temperature in the washing liquors is beneficial, especially when displacement from the top is practised. Blow pit washing has the advantage of working on defibrated pulp, which is easier to wash (85). However, practically the same results have been achieved with digester and blow pit washing carried out at optimal conditions. Early reports of digester, blow pit and filter washing (70) gave U values of 0.87, 0.81 and 0.90, respectively, at f values of 0.89, 0.83 and 0.74. The best result reported on blow pit washing so far is $U = 0.93$, $f = 0.93$ (18), with a more long-term average of $U = 0.935$,

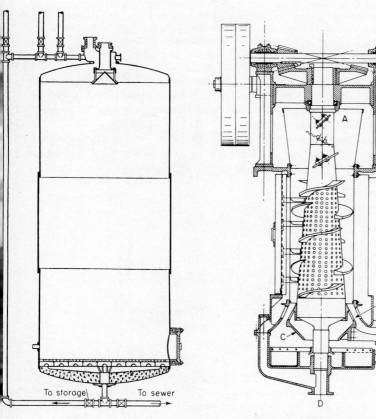

Fig. 10.5. Diffuser   Fig. 10.6. Zenith screw press

723

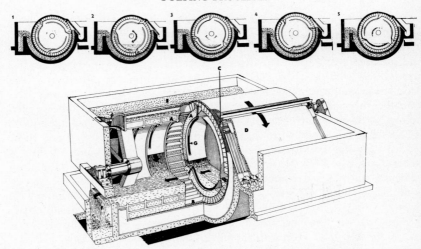

Fig. 10.7. Sund-Lindblad valveless filter washer. Picture strip shows the creation of vacuum in the suction cells and finally the emptying of white water through the canals. Filter trough and drum are sectioned to show: (A) suction canal, (B) suction cell, (C) doctor roll, (D) pulp web, (E) pulp inlet, (F) white water outlet, (G) vent pipe

$f = 0.86$. Figure 10.10 summarizes the average results of digester washing and blow pit washing, the latter in general being superior. Figures 10.11 and 10.12 show more detailed results and also the principal arrangements of digester and blow pit washing.

To achieve recovery values of $U = 0.97–0.99$, which are necessary in the recovery of cooking chemicals, in a reasonable time, diffusers or filters probably have to be used in the sulfite industry. Filter washing is

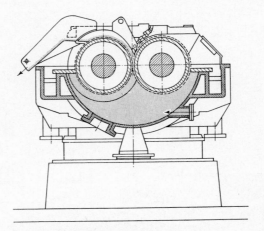

Fig. 10.8. Sund-Impco dewatering press

already used by some mills operating on Mg and Na base. The results reported for Mg base waste liquors correspond to $U = 0.95$ (7).

Disk presses have also been introduced in the recovery of Na base waste liquors.

In the *kraft industry* several investigations have been published on diffuser washing (e.g. 8, 10, 32, 41, 43, 81, 97) as well as filter washing (e.g. 19, 21, 24, 32, 39, 42, 43, 52, 58, 68, 71, 73, 74, 99, 100) and press washing (5, 15, 25a, 43, 50, 101, 105). In diffuser studies it was found that the flow rate decreases with increasing lignin content of the pulp (8, 43), to about 50% on a change in Roe number from 3 to 6.5 (97). On average, a newly filled diffuser contains around 0.1 t/m³ pulp, in a consistency of 17%. The flow rate is 0.5–1.0 m/h through the diffuser, which means about 0.5–1.0 m/min in the strainer holes at the bottom of the diffuser (97). The strainers are conical bottom plates with a perforation of 1–2.5 mm diameter holes. Most of the resistance to flow occurs

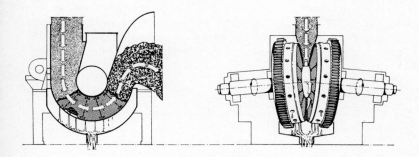

Fig. 10.9. Davenport or Defibrator DKP conical dewatering disk press

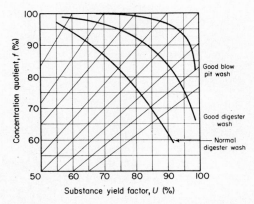

Fig. 10.10. Average results of spruce sulfite waste
liquor recovery by blow pit and digester washing
(Brunes)

725

in the neighborhood of the strainers, where the pulp mat is most compressed. The compression and flow resistance will increase on the application of gauge pressures to the diffuser top to maintain the flow rate during the washing process. An optimum pressure differential of 1.5–2 kp/cm² has been found (8). The packing of the diffuser is also most important (8, 97), and it has been found (41) that simple horizontal crossed angle iron supports in the lower part of the diffuser to relieve some of the pressure against the strainer increases washing capacity by 10–20%. Still better is a method of placing vertical strainers at approximately the same place instead of the iron supports, Figure 10.13 (10). This arrangement increased the washing capacity by 30–60% (41) and in some cases by 100% (10), without changing washing efficiency, Figure 10.14 (10). To place vertical strainers around the periphery of the lower part of the cylinder walls does not lead to the same result because of irrational flow of washing liquor along the walls. A similar method of increasing the diffuser capacity by decreasing the pressure against the strainer is to introduce a conical, perforated false bottom in the lower part of the diffuser (43). At optimal conditions normal sulfate losses in diffuser washing of Scandinavian softwood pulps are 15–20 kg ptp Na_2SO_4, at a dilution factor around 2.5, corresponding to

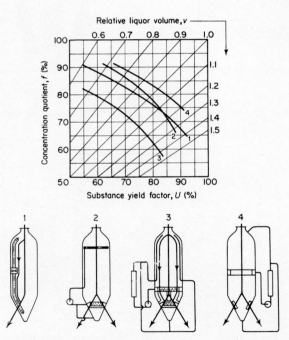

Fig. 10.11. Results and arrangements of spruce sulfite waste liquor recovery by digester washing in digesters of various circulation systems (Brunes)

$U = 0.97$–0.98 and $f = 0.75$ (43). For southern pine pulp sulfate losses as low as 10 kg ptp are quoted (41). To maintain optimal flow conditions it is advisable to install flow regulators on the washing liquor (43). Optimum wash water temperature is 50°C (8) or higher. Approximately twice the digester volume is needed for the diffuser volume in a mill, and the space requirement is therefore great, a factor which has had significance in the development of other methods of brown stock washing in the larger kraft mills. Diffusers have also been suggested in combination with filters (64). A development to come may be the *continuous diffuser*, an upflow tower, where rotary strainers in the bottom remove the black liquor, and wash liquor is introduced at the top (48). A similar development is the

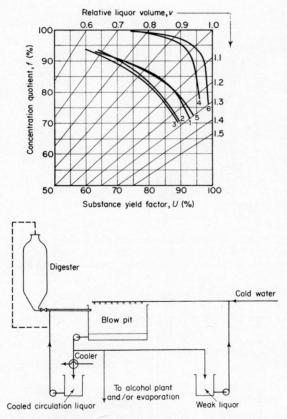

Fig. 10.12. Results and arrangements of spruce sulfite waste liquor recovery by blow pit washing. (1) cold water only, mill A, (2) cold water only, mill B, (3) hot water only, mill B, (4) weak liquor followed by hot water, mill B, (5) cold water only, mill C, (6) weak liquor followed by hot water, mill C (Brunes)

727

counter-current washing in a continuous digester (66, 87), Figure 10.15. One advantage of digester washing would be that the diffusion velocity is considerably higher than at filter washing temperature, since the diffusion coefficients of sodium compounds in kraft-cooked chips were found to be about 1.10^{-5} cm^2/sec at 40°C, hot water temperature, about 2.10^{-5} at 70°C, maximal filter washing temperature, and by extrapolation $5-7.10^{-5}$ at cooking temperature, all figures referring to longitudinal direction, transversal diffusion rate being 30–50% of those values (66).

Since the brown stock washing on filters was introduced about 1930 (68), considerable improvement has been made and many studies on filter

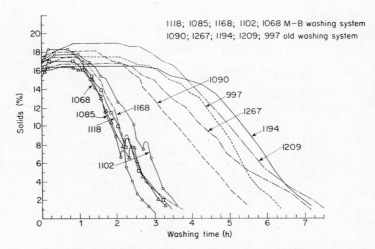

Fig. 10.13. Washing time–concentration curves in diffuser washing of pine kraft pulp according to conventional systems as well as to the Markila–Brax system (Brax–Markila)

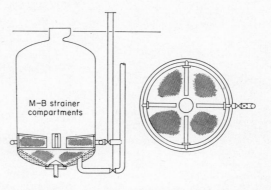

Fig. 10.14. M–B diffuser system (Brax–Markila)

728

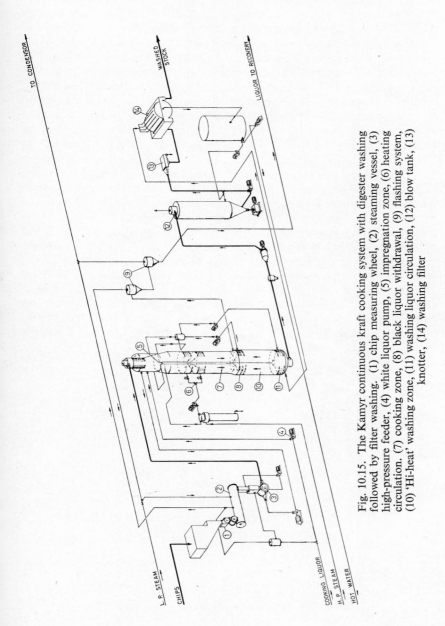

Fig. 10.15. The Kamyr continuous kraft cooking system with digester washing followed by filter washing. (1) chip measuring wheel, (2) steaming vessel, (3) high-pressure feeder, (4) white liquor pump, (5) impregnation zone, (6) heating circulation. (7) cooking zone, (8) black liquor withdrawal, (9) flashing system, (10) 'Hi-heat' washing zone, (11) washing liquor circulation, (12) blow tank, (13) knotter, (14) washing filter

washing published (e.g. 19, 32). It was found necessary to wash in several stages, on a multistage filter or several one-stage or multistage filters, applying counter-current principles. Since the introduction of the dilution factor concept (42, 58, 99), several studies on filter efficiency have contributed greatly to the knowledge of what can be achieved in filter washing and which factors will influence the results. By measuring the flow of wash water on the final filter, and subtracting the wash water leaving with the washed pulp, the dilution factor can easily be calculated and compared with the sulfate losses determined on the washed pulp. These are determined preferably by colorimetrical, spectrometrical or conductometrical methods, and it should be observed, that a small quantity, corresponding to about 5 kg ptp Na_2SO_4, is chemically attached to the pulp and can be removed only after acidulation (cf. 24). By starting with a low dilution factor and high sulfate losses, and increasing the flow of wash water step-wise while keeping all other factors constant, the *dilution curve* is determined (99), analogous to the *U–f* diagrams of sulfite waste liquor recovery. The dilution curve characterizes the washing result, and by taking up dilution curves for different filter loads, different pulps and different filter types and filter assemblies, the influence of these factors on the washing result can be studied. Figure 10.16 shows some dilution curves taken on various pulps and various filter combinations (44, 52, 99, 100). The generally adopted system in modern kraft mills is a four-drum four-stage or a three-drum five-stage washing, in the latter case with two stages on each of the first two filters. The filters are of the vacuum type, preferably valveless because of their ease of operation (39). Low lignin content

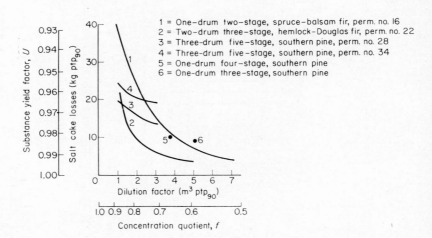

Fig. 10.16. Dilution curves at brown stock filter washing, with various numbers of drums and stages, and with pulps of various types (Harper–Paul, Klein *et al*, Waters–Bergström, West *et al*)

730

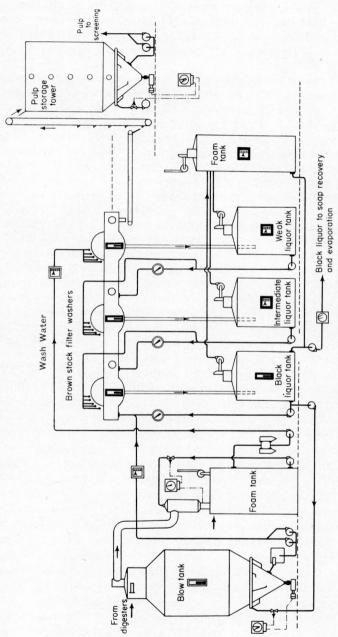

Fig. 10.17. Brown stock filter washing (Esila–Hakkarainen)

731

pulps are also easier to wash on filters (58, 73, 99). The beneficial effect of press rolls, good water showers and high wash water temperature, around 60°C, has been emphasized (42, 58, 74), as well as even, regulated flow of pulp and washing liquor (21, 42, 43). Foaming is one of the most important sources of trouble (42, 58) in both kraft and sulfite pulp washing on filters.

Improvements in machinery and operation have thus decreased the sulfate losses, which in the 1930's and 1940's were normally 40–50 kg ptp (42, 71), to 5–25 kg ptp at a dilution factor of 2–4, corresponding to $U = 0.96–0.99$ and $f = 0.65–0.80$ (43, 71, 99, 100). Figure 10.17 shows the arrangement of a modern brown stock filter washing. The pulp arrives at the blow tank in a consistency of 12 % or lower, is diluted in the bottom cone with black liquor from the first washer to 2–3.5 % consistency, which is kept constant by a consistency regulator, usually taking the impulse from the bottom stirrer of the blow tank. The level of the blow tank is recorded. The pulp flow from the blow tank is regulated. Since filter operation is improved by de-knotting, the pulp is often diluted with black liquor to about 1 % consistency and passed over vibratory knotters (cf. Section III) before the filters. To avoid foaming the knotters are run immersed in black liquor, with the pulp flow charged below the liquor surface. The pulp is then washed on three filter drums counter-currently, with flow-regulated wash water arriving at the last filter, and black liquor leaving the first zone of the first filter. This arrangement will require as many liquor tanks as washing stages, and a foam tank connected to the tops of the liquor tanks. The shower flow to the last filter may be regulated by impulse from a conductivity cell in the filter trough (63).

Data on press washing are more scarce (15, 25a, 26a, 43, 50, 101, 105) although the process is used at several kraft mills. Three or four stages are required, the pulp entering at 10–11 % consistency and leaving at 37–40 %. Up to 90°C is used (or even 110°C in one case of screw pressing in the Kamyr continuous cooking system), a high temperature permitting concentration to higher consistency. The use of such high temperatures is an advantage of press washing, whereas vacuum filters do not allow more than 70°C in the black liquor for evaporation. Another advantage is that foaming is avoided. To give 10 % consistency prior to the first press the pulp from the blow tank is passed over a filter. A screw press followed by washing filters has also been installed in some mills using continuous cooking, whereby the consistency of the pulp leaving the digester is high enough to allow the direct application of a press.

Figure 10.18 shows three systems of press washing, with presses only, or press in combination with filter (50). Dilution factors for a three-stage press system of around 2.1 m³ ptp have been reported, at a loss of 25 kg ptp Na_2SO_4 (15, 105, cf. 25a), corresponding to $U = 0.96$ and $f = 0.78$. In general, the efficiency follows the theoretical expectance assuming complete mixing of black liquor and wash liquor followed by squeezing (101). Figures 10.19–21 (50) show the theoretical expectance for the washing results applying up to four presses in series with a final consistency of 50 % in each stage, for complete mixing or with 0.3 m³ ptp remaining un-mixed in each stage, and for three different liquor-to-pulp ratios after the cook, 10, 6 and 2 m³ ptp. The latter figures correspond approximately to sulfite rayon pulp, very high yield chemical paper pulp and drained or vapor phase semichemical pulp cooking. Kraft cooks contain about 8 m³ ptp as do normal sulfite paper pulp cooks. The normal results of sulfite and kraft pulp washing systems are indicated for comparison. It is obvious that high liquor-to-pulp ratios facilitate the achievement of a good washing result. With one press only it is possible to obtain with chemical pulps the washing result of a conventional sulfite bin wash. For kraft pulp washing results, at least three press stages are required. Figure

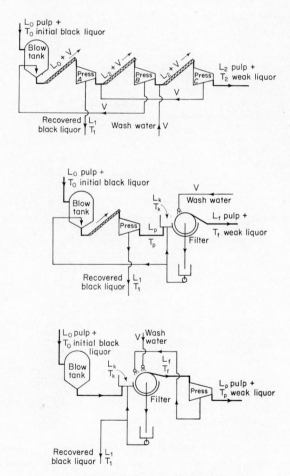

Fig. 10.18. Multi-press and press–filter brown
stock washing systems (Jönsson)

733

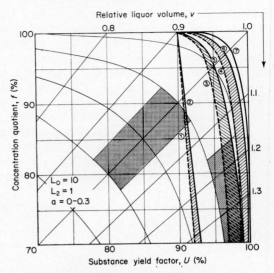

Fig. 10.19. Washing result when applying one or
more press stages. Liquor quantity 10 t ptp;
press consistency 50%. (1) one press, a = 0.3,
(2) one press, a = 0, (3) two presses, a = 0.3,
(4) two presses, a = 0, (5) three presses, a = 0.3,
(6) three presses, a = 0, (7) four presses, a = 0,
where a = liquor not mixed with wash water
(Jönsson)

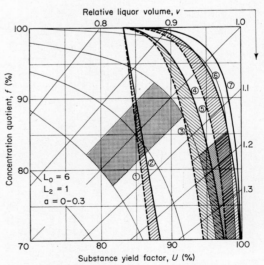

Fig. 10.20. Washing result when applying one or
more press stages. Liquor quantity 6 t ptp;
press consistency 50%. Key as for Figure 10.19
(Jönsson)

10.22 shows what happens when the press consistency drops from 50 to 40%. Figures 10.23–25 compare at the same liquor-to-pulp ratios the expected results of a one-stage filter press wash and the combinations filter–press and press–filter. It is seen that practical considerations can be allowed to dictate whether the filter should precede or follow the press. It is believed that the combination of one filter and two efficient high-capacity presses has considerable future interest. However, future systems for pulp washing using *displacement* with only little consistency changes may lead to decreased machinery costs. One earlier suggestion, involving screw conveyors without pressing (46), has been found fairly costly, but counter-current displacement washing in a continuous digester followed by a limited filter wash or a simple pressing operation, or alternatively a continuous diffuser, are now being developed and should represent a considerable saving in capital. Displacement in combination with one pressing to 50% consistency is illustrated in Figure 10.26.

The washing of *semichemical pulp* has to consider the combination with refining. As long as stream pollution presents no objection, the soft chips in the blow tank are passed over a drainer conveyor to the refiner and the waste liquor is allowed to drain to the sewer. The refined pulp is washed clean during the screening operations. However, where stream pollution is a problem, or where combination with a chemical pulp mill makes waste liquor recovery profitable, the soft chips are refined in the hot waste liquor, maybe after passing through a breaker trap for coarse fiberizing, and the waste liquor is recovered from the refined pulp by

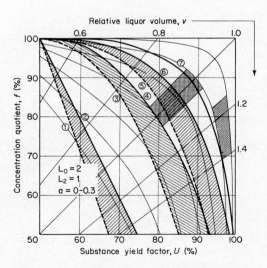

Fig. 10.21. Washing result when applying one or more press stages. Liquor quantity 2 t ptp; press consistency 50%. Key as for Figure 10.19
(Jönsson)

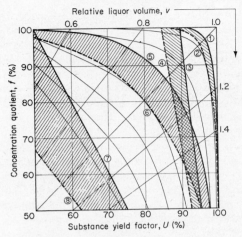

Fig. 10.22. Washing result when applying one or more press stages. Liquor quantity 10 t ptp or 2 t ptp; press consistency 40 or 50%. Complete mixing assumed for each stage (a = 0). (1) 3 presses, 50%, 10 t ptp, (2) 3 presses, 40%, 10 t ptp, (3) 1 press, 50%, 10 t ptp, (4) 1 press, 40%, 10 t ptp, (5) 3 presses, 50%, 2 t ptp, (6) 3 presses, 40%, 2 t ptp, (7) 1 press, 50%, 2 t ptp, (8) 1 press, 40%, 2 t ptp (Jönsson)

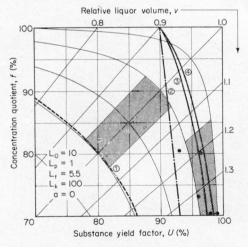

Fig. 10.23. Washing result using one press in combination with one filter. Liquor quantity 10 t ptp; press consistency 50%. (1) filter only (theoretical), (2) press only (theoretical), (3) filter and press (theoretical), (4) press and and filter (theoretical), (•) press and two-zone filter (measured) (Jönsson)

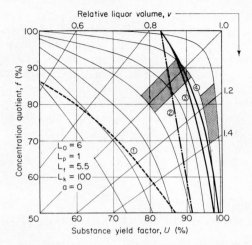

Fig. 10.24. Washing result using one press in combination with one filter. Liquor quantity 6 t ptp; press consistency 50%. (1) filter only, (2) press only, (3) filter and press, (4) press and filter (Jönsson)

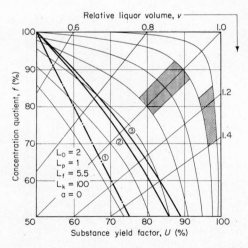

Fig. 10.25. Washing result using one press in combination with one filter. Liquor quantity 2 t ptp; press consistency 50%. Filter only, $U = f = 44\%$, (1) press only, (2) filter and press, (3) press and filter (Jönsson)

737

conventional methods. As continuous cooking is general for semichemical pulps, the continuous washing systems on filters or presses, or combinations thereof, are natural. In batch cooking of high yield chemical or semichemical kraft pulp for liner board etc., the blow tank stirrer may be equipped for a mild fiberizing action, and the coarse pulp is pumped through closed breaker traps and refiners to *black* or *hot stock submerged screening* prior to washing. In the production of cold caustic pulp, where considerable quantities of useful chemicals are retained in the swelled chips, the application of a roll press (21a) or a screw press (26a, 40) is frequent prior to fiberizing, and this is of course applicable to semichemical pulp chips in general (40).

III. Screening and Cleaning

The purpose of screening and cleaning is to remove solid impurities from the acceptable pulp fibers. These impurities would otherwise show up as spots in the final paper, or cause processing difficulties in the case of dissolving pulps. Advantage is taken of deviating size or specific gravity of the impurities in comparison with the fibers, and the means are perforated or slotted plates in various types of *screens*, or equipment using gravity or centrifugal forces, *rifflers* and *cleaners*. To avoid too much particle interaction, the screening and cleaning operations are performed in very

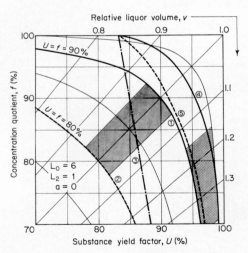

Fig. 10.26. Washing result using one press after a displacement operation (such as digester or blow pit wash). Liquor quantity 6 t ptp; press consistency 50%. (1) displacement only, $U = f = 90\%$, (2) displacement only, $U = f = 80\%$, (3) press only, (4) displacement $U = f = 90\%$ and press, (5) displacement $U = f = 80\%$ and press (Jönsson)

dilute pulp suspensions, with consistencies varying from 0.2 to 2%. Therefore they consume fairly large quantities of mill water, electrical power, and building volume. However, their importance has increased with the demand for pulpwood, as lower grade pulpwood unavoidably leads to a less pure pulp prior to screening. The mill water demand can be substantially decreased by white water recycling, and the building volume has been considerably reduced by the introduction of modern high-efficiency screens.

1. ACTION OF THE SINGLE SCREEN OR CLEANER

A. Fundamental principles

The fundamentals of screening and cleaning are still incompletely known, and until only recently fundamental research was completely lacking in this field. However, a long period of practice and applied research and development work has created several efficient tools to separate the impurities from the pulp fibers. There is no detailed description of machinery in this book but reference is made to (69, 91). However, Figure 10.27 shows the classification and symbols in use to describe the screening operations and machinery, and Figures 10.28–33 illustrate the design of *centrifugal, vibratory rotating, vibratory flat* and *pulsatory flat screens*, as well as the *vibratory knotter screen*.

To study the fundamentals involved in screening fairly complicated statistical mathematics has been used, both for the simpler case of pulp suspensions of infinite solutions and to correct for particle interaction (3, 22, 54, 55, 56, 89, 90). The principles are, however, straightforward. The terms *charge, accept* and *reject* are used to describe the pulp fractions entering and leaving a screen or a cleaner. The probability factors α and β are used to describe the chances of impurities being accepted and of good pulp fibers being rejected. The former factor is thus an expression for the expected cleanliness of the accepted pulp, and the latter for the expected fiber losses. Both α and β are <1 and should be low for a good screen and cleaner. A screening result has to give both factors to be sufficiently defined. The fiber losses are fairly easy to determine, and the changes in cleanliness are determined by dirt counting according to various methods (cf. Chapter 20).

Three parameters are of importance for the screening result, (a) the nature and amount of impurities in the pulp charged, (b) the consistency at every point near the screen membrane, and (c) the time of contact between pulp and screen membrane. At a given α, the purity of the accept is proportional to the *purity of the charge*. The accept of a flat screen is least pure towards the end of the screen. The *consistency* will influence the rate of clogging of the screen openings with fibers, and hence the chances for both fibers and impurities to pass. The vibrations of the old low frequency and the modern high frequency screens aim to keep the screening surface free and break network fiber structures temporarily formed.

739

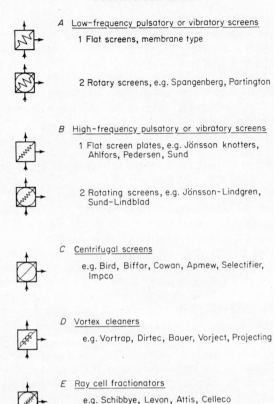

A Low-frequency pulsatory or vibratory screens

  1 Flat screens, membrane type

  2 Rotary screens, e.g. Spangenberg, Partington

B High-frequency pulsatory or vibratory screens

  1 Flat screen plates, e.g. Jönsson knotters, Ahlfors, Pedersen, Sund

  2 Rotating screens, e.g. Jönsson-Lindgren, Sund-Lindblad

C Centrifugal screens

  e.g. Bird, Biffar, Cowan, Apmew, Selectifier, Impco

D Vortex cleaners

  e.g. Vortrap, Dirtec, Bauer, Vorject, Projecting

E Ray cell fractionators

  e.g. Schibbye, Levon, Attis, Celleco

Fig. 10.27. Classification and symbols of screening room equipment (Ranhagen)

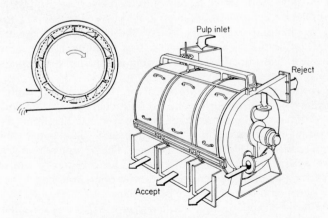

Fig. 10.28. Biffar centrifugal screen

In the centrifugal screens such structures are utilized as a screening medium, but are controlled and limited by the hydraulic conditions created by the rotating device inside the screen and the flow of water through the screen. The *time of contact* between the pulp and the screen membrane determines the number of chances both fibers and impurities get to pass through the screen openings. This time is related to the *overscreening percentage* or the amount of reject flow discharged relative to the charge flow. As the chances for the pulp fibers to pass during a certain time period are greater than those for the impurities, the cleanliness of the accepted pulp increases with decreasing time of contact, or increasing overscreening percentage. A factor of importance for the screening result is the phenomenon of *back flow* through the membrane of particles once accepted (90). This is affected by the hydraulic conditions around the membrane, and related to the construction details of the screen, as well as the load of the screen.

B. *Nature of impurities*

The *varying shape and nature* of the impurities greatly influence the α factor of a given screen. The impurities are of the following kind (2, 11, 75):

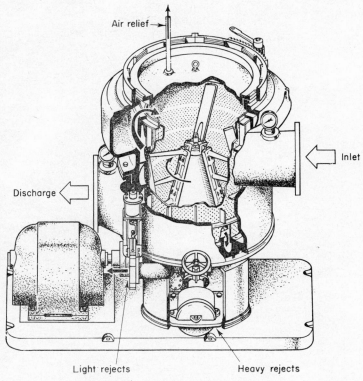

Fig. 10.29. Selectifier centrifugal screen

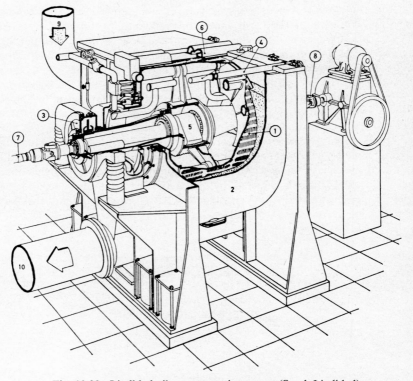

Fig. 10.30. Lindblad vibratory rotating screen (Sund–Lindblad)

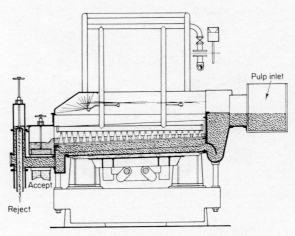

Fig. 10.31. Ahlfors vibratory flat screen

742

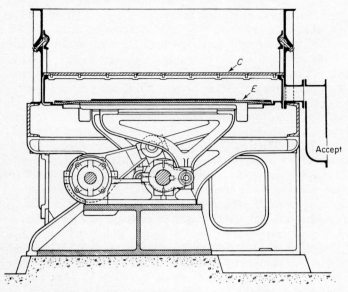

Fig. 10.32. Sherbrooke pulsatory flat screen. Cross section, not showing pump inlet and reject ends of the screen. C screen plate; E rubber diaphragm (Stephenson)

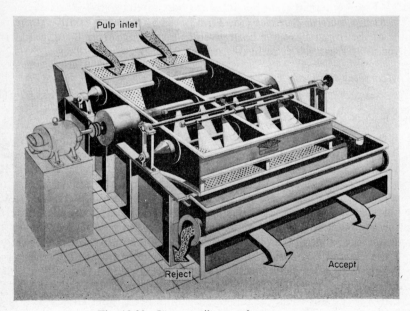

Fig. 10.33. Jönsson vibratory knotter screen

Bark fragments arise from deficiencies in the barking as well as from bark around knots and branches which have been embedded in the wood. They are of approximately spherical form. Larger fragments are easily removed on all sorts of screens and by most cleaners, medium-sized fragments are better removed on *slotted* than on perforated *screen plates*, whereas smaller bark impurities present a difficult problem, partly solved by the construction of the modern *vortex cleaners* (93, 95, 103). *Bast fragments* are often longish in shape and may be difficult to remove on slotted plates, whereas *perforated plates* or the larger types of vortex cleaners are more effective. The same is true for *fiber bundles* kept together by transversal ray cells or *shives* occurring in sulfite pulp from pine or tannin-damaged spruce, as well as in insufficiently refined semichemical pulp. *Wood fragments* of larger dimensions, up to *undercooked chips* and *knots*, are removed at an early stage of the screening, usually on high frequency vibratory flat screens with coarsely perforated plates, so-called *knotters*. In the case of semichemical pulps, which have passed a refiner before screening, the undercooked or burnt centres of the chips and especially of the knots, are disintegrated to small, short and hard fragments, sometimes called chops, which have to be removed from the unbleached and especially the bleached paper grade pulps, e.g. for printing papers. This is only possible in vortex cleaners (103), which have been of singular importance for the development of acceptable semichemical pulps. Free, *resin-containing parenchymatic cells* are better removed later in the screening process, on *ray-cell filters*, operating with fine mesh metal cloth, which allows the small impurities but not the good fibers to pass. Free, spherical *resin particles* are best removed by vortex cleaners (77), as are *mineral particles* (31, 37, 53). The following relative proportions of the impurities have been given as an average from 8 sulfite mills: shives 49%, bark 44%, resin 5%, misc., 2% (2).

C. Geometry involved

The *dimensioning of the slots and perforations* must take several factors into account, such as the *load of the screen*, and *pulp consistency*, and the *dimensions of fibers and impurities*. The capacity of a vibratory screen with slotted plates decreases to 50% when the slot width is decreased from 0.50 to 0.25 mm (59, 60) or in some cases from 0.35 to 0.25 mm (75). For a vibratory knotter the same is true at a decrease in hole diameter from 6 to 3 mm (4). The capacity of a vibratory screen is also reduced to 50% by a decrease in pulp consistency from 1.2 to 0.6% (59, 60). The relation is not altogether linear, as is seen from Figure 10.34, as particle interaction at higher consistency tends to slow down the rate of screening.

In the slot range of 0.25 to 0.45 mm paraná pine pulp screens with only half the capacity of spruce pulp because of longer fibers (75), and it is well known that hardwood pulps generally screen much faster than softwood, e.g. birch twice or three times as fast as spruce. Groundwood pulp screens faster than chemical pulps and sulfite needs finer slots and holes than kraft.

744

The softwood fibers are usually 2.5–3.5 mm long and 0.03–0.06 mm in diameter, cf. Chapters 2–3. The slots are generally 0.20–0.40 mm wide and the hole diameter of the perforations is about 1.0–1.5 mm (with the exception of the knotter plates). The smallest speck noticeable by the naked eye in a sulfite pulp sheet is around 0.2 mm in diameter or has the area 0.03 mm², and the smallest particle counted according to the TAPPI standard method has 0.3 mm diameter or 0.08 mm² area. Evidently impurities in the size range 0.2–0.5 mm must present a problem to screening. However, in the case of perforated centrifugal screens, particles far below the size of the holes are removed because of the filtering loose network of fibers formed at the screen surface during proper operation of the screen (34). Mineral particles down to a size of 0.02 mm are removed by vortex cleaners, and from a bark fraction with the average size of 0.06 mm a one-stage vortex cleaning was found to remove 50% (93). Ray cell filters usually apply metal cloths with meshes about 0.3 mm for softwood pulps and 0.1–0.2 mm for hardwood pulps (26), through which the ray cells, having a size 0.02–0.2 mm, pass, leaving the bulk of the pulp fibers.

D. Differences in action of the various types of machinery

The older type of *pulsatory screens*, such as the *diaphragm flat screen*, use frequencies about 500 c/min at amplitudes of 3 mm (83) for the diaphragm pulsating beneath the screen plates. Fairly low consistencies are required, 0.25–0.50%, and as laminar flow of maximum 1 m/s (83) and rather thin layers of pulp suspension, 3–4 mm (12), are necessary for a good screening result, these types of screens have low capacity and require

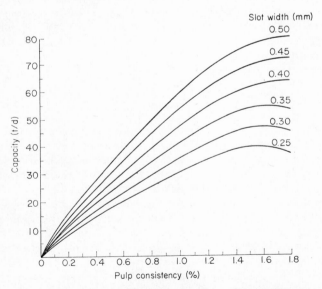

Fig. 10.34. Influence of pulp consistency and slot width on vibratory screening capacity (Lindblad)

745

much space. Their efficiency also decreases with the length of the screen (83), provided no water is added consecutively along the screen (20, 76), which is, however, normally the case. Slotted plates are preferred to hole perforation (12) and normal slot widths are 0.3–0.4 mm for kraft and 0.2–0.3 mm for sulfite pulp.

To overcome these drawbacks, modern vibratory screens (1, 33, 34, 47, 59, 60) use higher consistencies, up to 2%, but usually 1.0–1.5%, which require higher frequency of the vibrations to prevent fiber inter-action, usually 1,000–1,500 c/min, at an amplitude of 2–3.5 mm. In this case the very plates are vibrating. These screens also use plates of similar or somewhat wider slots, 0.3–0.5 mm, except for the knotters which use coarse hole perforation, 3–8 mm diameter. Some of these *high frequency vibratory screens* are *flat*, such as the *Ahlfors* screen, others cylindrical and slowly *rotating*, such as the *Lindgren* and *Lindblad* screens. The main disadvantages of these screens are capacity too low for the large modern mills, and building construction problems caused by the vibrations.

The *centrifugal screens* (13, 27, 29, 34, 35, 38, 86, 92, 102), such as the *Impco*, *Cowan* and *Biffar* screens, are in contrast to the vibratory screens not constructed to destroy the fiber interaction at the membrane, but to maintain, control and utilize it (34, 76). Therefore, it is not necessary to dimension their membrane openings according to the size of the pulp fibers and impurities, but they can be allowed to have holes with fairly large diameters, up to 2.4 mm (102) or even 2.8 mm for kraft pulps but usually 1.0–2.0 mm. The screens consist of a cylindrical stationary membrane, against which the pulp suspension is forced by means of a device, rotating at a speed of 200–500 rpm. The charge enters the center of one end of the screen drum and the reject leaves at the other. Consistencies of 0.6–0.8% are normally used (cf. below). One category of centrifugal screens works with fully drowned screen plates and overhead reject discharge, and another with free discharge of both accept and reject. The former seems to be better suited to defibrator pulps for hardboard (86) and other semichemical pulps, as well as for hot stock screening in the presence of black liquor prior to washing, whereas the latter gives a better result on washed chemical pulps (34).

A special rotary screen, originally designed for the removal of fiber knots ahead of the paper machine without introducing air, is the *Selectifier*, which is a vertical, totally enclosed screen, which operates completely full of stock and under pressure (23, 25). It consists of a stationary, perfor-ated cylinder and a non-contacting airfoil-bar rotating element. The closed construction makes it suited to so-called *black stock* screening, i.e. screen-ing of kraft pulp in the black liquor prior to washing (98). A re-design has also made other screens, such as the *Impco* screen, well suited to black stock screening, working at 1.5% consistency and with reject consistencies of about 4%.

Riffling is the old method of trapping sand or other heavy particles by grav-ity. Rifflers are very spacious and are therefore now being substituted by the more efficient *centrifugal cleaners*. The first of these, e.g. the *Erkensator*, were constructed with moving parts and *forced vortex*, resulting in the same angular speed for all particles. The tangential speed was proportional to the radius, i.e. $v = v_1 . R/R_1$, where v_1 and R_1 are velocity and radius of the charged flow. Then the centrifugal forces were $C = m . R . (v_1/R_1)^2$, and therefore, to get a high degree of separation large dimensions of the cleaner were required. Cleaners with a *free vortex*, such as the *Vortrap, Dirtec, Bauer Cleaner*, etc. (30, 31, 36, 37, 51, 53, 77, 78, 93, 95, 103) behave quite differently. There, the tangential speed is inversely proportional to the radius, i.e. $v = v_1 . R_1/R$, and $C = m . (v_1 . R_1)^2/R^3$. Therefore, the centrifugal forces are greatest near the center of the vortex, where a speed of 18 m/s at 5 mm radius has been measured, corresponding to a centrifugal force of almost 7,000 G (51). Some of these cleaners are cylindrical, equipped with intercepting rubber membranes, but the most modern and efficient cleaners are conical, to provide for a relatively large inlet radius R_1 (cf. formula) and still maintain a small inner diameter of the vortex, which is determined by the size of the bottom outlet for the reject. A *vortex finder* is placed at the top outlet for the accepted pulp, somewhat wider than the empty cylindrical space, which stretches centrally from the bottom to the top of the cone. The construction principle and the assumed flow conditions are seen in Figure 10.35. The heavier impurities are forced to the walls of the cone, where the centrifugal force is almost nil, and move slowly downwards with the flow caused by the reject outlet. Mineral

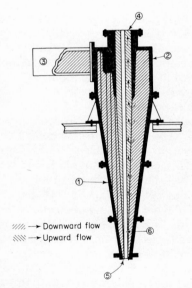

Fig. 10.35. Vortex cleaner. (1) conical part, (2) cylindrical head, (3) pulp inlet, (4) accept (upward flow within the vortex finder), (5) reject (downward flow along the conical walls), (6) free vortex air column (Bauer)

747

particles down to a size of 20 μ are thus removed. Pulp fibers, which are also subject to the centrifugal forces, behave differently because of their long shape, which reacts to the shear forces between the water layers of different radius and speed, and are finally urged into the inner parts of the vortex and discharged at the top outlet as accept. However, towards the apex of the cone there is also a risk of the impurities being urged into the upflow of the inner vortex, provided they are large and of similar shape. Therefore, such particles require a fairly large bottom outlet to be properly removed, but do not need excessive centrifugal forces. In contrast, small, light and round particles are not sensitive to the shear forces but need large centrifugal forces. Obviously, two types of free vortex cleaners can be used with advantage, one larger type with fairly large bottom outlet and fairly large void central space, which removes shives and other coarse and longish fragments, whereas another smaller type with narrow bottom outlet and high centrifugal forces removes small resin and bark specks and disintegrated knot fragments in spite of the fact that resin particles are lighter and bark fragments have about the same specific gravity as the pulp fibers. One investigation, using small vortex cleaners, gave a purification efficiency of 95% with added bark particles, 0.9 mm in diameter, 80% for 0.5 mm and 50% for 0.06 mm (93) in the case of chemical pulp. Another, using both small and large cleaners on groundwood gave a speck reduction of 95% in the size class 0.15 mm, 85% for 0.10 mm and 50% for 0.06 mm (38a), with little difference between the cyclone types, at 5–10% rejects. The chop removal was about 50%, and formulas were developed for the influence of pressure, nozzle diameter and inject chop content. Both cleaner types, but especially the smaller one, remove mineral particles, some of which, entering with the mill water, can be extremely small and cause great difficulties in the use of dissolving pulps if they are not removed in the screening room.

Vortex cleaners are used in consistencies of up to 1.5% but usually 0.5–1.0%, with an inlet pressure of 2.5–3.5 kp/cm². The capacity of each unit is relatively small, 75–750 l/min, and consequently large assemblies have to be installed. The power consumption of the operation is also considerable. However, in spite of these drawbacks, vortex cleaners have become a great success especially for hardwood pulps (95) and semi-chemical pulps (103,104), but increasingly so for mechanical (14, 38a) and ordinary chemical pulps, *sulfite* (77), *kraft* (49) and *soda* (95), paper and dissolving grades. To avoid contamination of the pulp suspension with air, combinations with vacuum tanks or injectors are sometimes used, e.g. in the *Deculator-Cleaner, Vorvac, Vorject*, etc. (8a, 9, 31).

The theory of *fiber fractionation*, which essentially coincides with that of screening, has been further elaborated and the variables of fiber fractionation on ray cell filters thoroughly studied (26). It is important to choose the mesh of the metal cloth, the load of the filter, and the consistency of the charge in such a way that a consistency of the accept of 4–5% is obtained. Thereby 80–95% of the ray cells have been given a chance to pass the filter, since the water is to be regarded simply as their transport medium.

748

In order to increase the de-watering capacity of the filter, and to keep the filter clear of pulp and impurities, the charge should be sprayed on the filter at a certain, moderate pressure, around 0.3 kp/cm². Higher pressures result in too tight a network of fibers on the filter. More recent constructions are the *Attis* (26) and the *Celleco* (31a) ray cell filters.

2. COMBINATION OF SCREENS AND CLEANERS

A. Fundamental principles

Returning to the basic concepts of single-stage screening and cleaning, the principles of combinations in multistage screening will now be discussed (3, 22, 89). It was stated that the probability factors α and β, indicating the chances for the impurities to be accepted and for good pulp fibers to be lost in the reject, together describe the expected screening result. They stand in opposition, because when the screening conditions are chosen to give an extremely low β factor, the impurities in the accept tend to increase; and the α factor can be lowered by allowing the over-screening percentage and hence the β factor to increase. These phenomena are related to the time of contact between screen membrane and the charged flow. In fact, most screen and cleaner constructions have to work with over-screening percentages between 10–30% to deliver an accept of sufficient purity. This immediately introduces the necessity of multistage screening, as fiber losses to that extent cannot be tolerated. Therefore, screening of the reject, or *secondary screening*, was introduced to complete the *primary screening* in order to reduce the fiber losses. Sometimes it was even found necessary to rescreen the reject from the secondary screens on *tertiary screens* for further reduction of the fiber losses. Figure 10.36 will illustrate these concepts. However, returning to the purity of the accept after primary screening, it was soon found that after reaching a certain

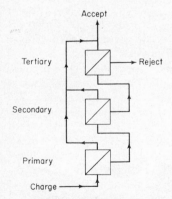

Fig. 10.36. Diagram illustrating the concepts of primary, secondary and tertiary screening (Steenberg)

overscreening percentage, which allowed the screen to work under optimum conditions, the purity of the accept could not be further increased by additional overscreening (34). The purity level was different for different screens, different consistency and different purity of the charge, but only minor improvements could be achieved by choosing optimum consistency and changing the construction. But by rescreening the accept, *double screening*, the purity of the final accept was much higher, Figure 10.37. This follows from probability laws which require that the net result to be expected as regards the purity of the final accept can be expressed as the product of the α factors of the two screens coupled in series, or $a_1 . a_2$. As each factor is fairly low the product is extremely low, much lower than could be obtained by changing the conditions or improving the construction of a single-stage screen.

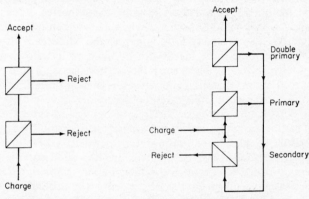

Fig. 10.37. The double screening concept (Steenberg)

Fig. 10.38. Double screening and secondary screening (Steenberg)

With double screening of the accept and secondary screening of the reject, Figure 10.38, conditions have been created for a good screening result, as regards both factors α and β. However, this is not necessarily achieved. In using several screening stages, several pulp fractions of different purity are obtained, and *proper combination* of these fractions is necessary lest the good result should be destroyed. It has been customary to combine the accepts from secondary and tertiary screening with the primary accept, Figure 10.36. However, with identical screening conditions in each stage, the accepts from the secondary and tertiary screens must be less pure than that from the primary screen, because of less pure charge, and the coupling therefore decreases the purity of the primary accept. A more correct coupling would be that of Figure 10.39, where the accept from the secondary stage is combined with the primary charge and rescreened. For the same reason which speaks for double screening on the primary side, *double screening on the secondary side*—not to be confused with tertiary screening—may be beneficial. Figure 10.40 shows the theoretically

750

correct coupling of double screening in the primary stage, one secondary screening, and one tertiary screening stage. The principles of coupling are called the *cascade coupling* (89), and the way of drawing the coupling scheme gives the process a similarity to distillation, with stripper and rectifier parts. An infinite number of stages can be added, but in practice even double screening is fairly rare. The cascade coupling principles have been mathematically treated to find out optimum conditions, including optimum number of stages of the stripper and rectifier sides (3). It was found that for a given total number of stages the number of stages on the rectifier side should exceed that of the stripper side by one stage. The optimum overflow on each screen was found to be rather high, between the limits of 18–51 % at 5 % total fiber losses and between 10–50 % at 2 % total fiber losses.

B. Practical applications

The theoretical calculations assume identical screening units in all stages and impurities of homogeneous nature. In actual practice allowance has to be made for the facts mentioned in Section III.1, the varying nature and shape of the impurities, and the different ability of different types of screens and cleaners to reject them. For instance, double screening on the primary, as well as on the secondary side should take advantage of the different work done by a vibratory screen with slotted plates and a centrifugal screen with hole perforation. Both may be completed by vortex cleaners. In this way round, coarse particles are mainly removed first, then longish shives and finally small bark, resin and mineral particles. This means

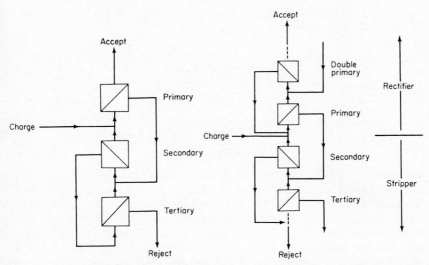

Fig. 10.39. Correct coupling principles of primary, secondary and tertiary screening stages (Steenberg)

Fig. 10.40. Correct coupling principles of an infinite number of screening stages, the cascade coupling principle (Steenberg)

751

that only inspection and analysis of the different pulp fractions obtained in a multistage screenery can judge how these fractions should be combined. However, the existing couplings of screens in many mills call for a stricter observation of the basic principles forwarded in the theories of screening, the most common fault being the combining of secondary and tertiary accepts with that of the primary screens (75) as in figure 10.36.

The *combination of slots and hole perforation in double screening* should preferably begin with the slotted vibratory screens and be followed by centrifugal screens (61, 75, 76). The latter have a slight disintegrating action on brittle impurities such as bark fragments, and therefore these should be removed on slotted plates prior to centrifugal screening. Only in the case of insufficiently slushed hard pulp may it sometimes be beneficial to start the screening with the centrifugal screens. On the other hand, where double screening is not practised, which is in the majority of cases, centrifugal screening is the most general principle in use, and admittedly is sufficient for most grades of pulps.

The *combination of pulp opener and screens* in the case of sulfite pulps has been discussed (75). The opener, a cylindrical wooden construction equipped with rotating wooden bars and stationary baffles, should liberate the bulk of the well-cooked fibers but leave the knots as undamaged as possible to avoid contamination of the pulp and allow the knotters to remove them, Figure 10.41. A conceivable variation in the case of

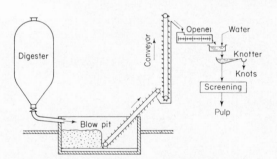

Fig. 10.41. Treatment of chemical pulp by high-consistency opener prior to screening (Wultsch)

soft pulps would be to place the knotters before the openers to de-knot the pulp as it comes from the washing bin by pumps, Figure 10.42. To avoid extra losses of fibers, the reject from the knotters is then passed through an opener, the resultant pulp is rescreened on knotters with finer hole perforation, and the accept combined with the original charge or with the accept from the primary knotters. In the case of harder chemical pulps, this arrangement would result in such quantities of pulp on the secondary knotters that it is feasible to limit the screening of the clean pulp on the primary side to a one-stage screening but to carry out a qualified double screening on the secondary side. In the case of high yield

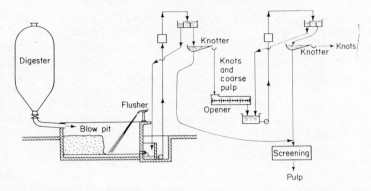

Fig. 10.42. Treatment of chemical pulp by high-consistency opener, placed after primary knotters and delivering the treated coarse fraction to secondary knotters (Wultsch)

chemical or semichemical pulping, the opener may be substituted by a *breaker trap* and *pump-through refiners* prior to screening in submerged centrifugal screens, the rejects of which are recycled for completion of the fiberizing.

Conventional openers are run at fairly high consistency, and if the pulp is pumped from the washing bins, a filter preceding the opener is needed, whereas one modern low-consistency opener (45) works directly on the pulp pumped from the washing bin at 1–4% consistency, Figure 10.43.

Vortex cleaners are usually assembled in batteries of often several hundred units, arranged in three to five stages, the *reject* from each stage being passed on to the next one for reduction of the fiber losses. Within each stage, the units are coupled in parallel with a common feed pump. Increasing degree of cleanliness may be obtained by placing sets of cleaners with their *accepts* in cascade. However, this arrangement obviously

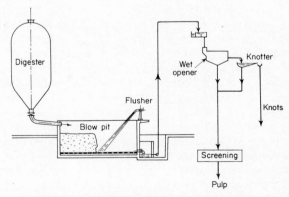

Fig. 10.43. Treatment of chemical pulp at low consistency by means of a 'wet opener' before screening (Wultsch)

753

greatly increases the installation and operating costs, since then the main flow is treated repeatedly, whereas the reject treatment involves a large reduction in the number of units for each stage, the rejected 'overflow' being only 5–15% of the total flow and the rejected fiber quantity 10–30% per stage. Cascading the accepts is therefore not customary, but when used, the highest order of cleanliness of the final accept is achieved by recirculation of the reject flow of all but the first sets to the inlet of the first set. On the reject side, the accepts from each stage should be recycled to the inlet of the previous stage. Since there is a noticeable concentration of the pulp suspension on the reject side, dilution with water should be provided in order to run each stage at optimal consistency, 0.5–0.7%. An arrangement according to the above-mentioned principles is illustrated in Figure 10.44 (72). It has been found that the accept of the second stage

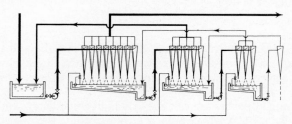

Fig. 10.44. Cascade coupling of vortex cleaners in four stages (Eie)

is often as clean as from the first one and therefore these accepts may be combined (31, 77). The cleaning efficiency and fiber losses of any combination can be calculated under certain assumptions (72), as exemplified here for the most interesting combinations. A typical result of a cleaning stage may be said to be 85% dirt removal at 10% reject. In Table 10.1, the expected performance of various battery combinations has been calculated, assuming the first set of each stage to be operating at either 90 or 75% dirt removal, and the second set at 75 and 60%. The fiber reject to achieve that result is assumed to be 10, 15, 20 and 25% for the first, second, third and fourth stages. As shown by Table 10.1, the addition of reject stages will decrease the fiber losses with little influence on the cleaning efficiency. Two sets in stage 1, double cleaning, improves the cleanliness considerably with little increase in operating costs. Quite often, double cleaning is carried out in a sense, since both unbleached and bleached stock may be passed through cleaners (95). This gives less possibility of combination but, instead, a removal of particles introduced during the bleaching operations.

The *combination of screens and vortex cleaners* is still rather undecided. The difference in action between the larger and smaller types should be noticed. A battery of *small cleaners* complete an ordinary screening equipment for the removal of small specks; in the case of bleached pulp this is preferably done after bleaching, immediately prior to the machine chest.

754

Table 10.1. Expected performance of vortex cleaner batteries at various assumptions and cleaner combinations (72)

Battery, number of sets per stage				Fiber rejects, %	Dirt removal, %	Proportional pumping cost
Stage 1	Stage 2	Stage 3	Stage 4			
1	–	–	–	10	90	62
1	1	–	–	1.64	88.9	75
1	1	1	–	0.38	88.9	85
1	1	1	1	0.11	88.9	95
2	1	–	–	1.82	97.0	135
2	1	1	–	0.46	97.0	145
2	1	1	1	0.13	97.0	155
1	–	–	–	10	75	62
1	1	–	–	1.64	68.6	75
1	1	1	–	0.38	67.5	85
1	1	1	1	0.11	66.0	95
2	1	–	–	1.82	84.3	135
2	1	1	–	0.46	83.8	145
2	1	1	1	0.13	83.4	155
1	–	–	–	10	75	62
1	2	–	–	1.87	71.8	90
1	2	1	–	0.44	71.6	100
1	2	1	1	0.13	71.2	110
2	2	–	–	2.18	86.2	150
2	2	1	–	0.55	86.1	160
2	2	1	1	0.16	86.0	170

It has been found that in this case the cleaners ought also to be preceded by screens, such as Lindgren, Lindblad or Ahlfors screens with slotted, vibratory drums or plates to remove coarser impurities, which would otherwise clog the apices of the cleaners. The *larger type of vortex cleaner* is in use on the secondary side of the screening of unbleached pulp, not only to complete, but also often to substitute the screens. It has been maintained (31) that secondary purification should not be carried out by screens, and several mills have substituted their secondary screens with cleaners (95).

In many cases, especially with groundwood pulp, hardboard pulp and coarse paper pulps, the reject is passed through refiners to convert coarser wood fragments and fiber bundles into useful fibers, as exemplified in Figure 10.45 (67). At the same time, non-fiber impurities are disintegrated to smaller particles and become difficult to remove on screens. The vortex cleaners here represent the solution to the problem, as in the case of semichemical pulp screening. Another possibility for kraft screening rejects is recooking, which results in a brighter pulp than with accepting the refined rejects, but also a lower yield. The screening rejects of *sulfite* pulp mills are normally fiberized, wet-lapped and sold as a secondary pulp grade.

Fiber fractionation on ray cell filters is preferentially carried out after the

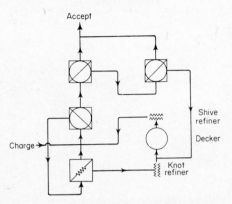

Fig. 10.45. Screening system with refining
of rejects (Millar *et al*)

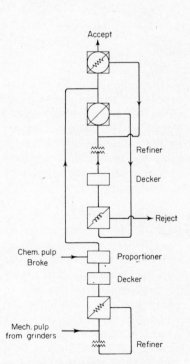

Fig. 10.46. Screening of groundwood
(Lindgren)

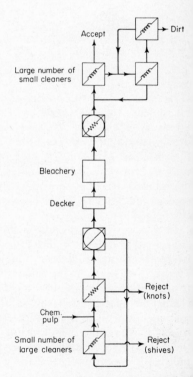

Fig. 10.47. Screening of chemical
pulp

conventional screening. Modern equipment makes it possible to obtain the accepted pulp in consistencies of 3–5 % (26), thus eliminating the need for special deckers after the screening equipment. Attention has also been drawn to the fact that the main part of the ray cells pass with the accepted pulp at the earlier sections of the centrifugal screens, and it has been suggested that the fiber fractionation should be limited to this part of the pulp (102).

Descriptions and suggestions for the design of screening and cleaning of *groundwood* (13a, 52a, 88), *hardboard* (57, 65, 86), *semichemical* (56a, 103, 104), *kraft* (76, 98), *sulfite* (47a, 75, 94) and *waste paper* (62) pulps are frequent, and Figures 10.46–47 are believed to represent the modern solution to the different purification problems encountered in some of the processes mentioned. However, there are obviously an infinite number of possible variations which may be as good or better. The design of a screening room has to take not only quality requirements, but factors such as investment costs, power consumption and mill water consumption into account. However, there is no doubt that as inferior qualities of pulpwood have to be accepted, the importance of screening and cleaning is accentuated.

IV. Dewatering, Drying and Other Operations with Unbleached Pulp

After washing and screening, the unbleached pulp is ready for use in integrated mills, or to be passed on to the bleachery. However, a paper mill is not a steady consumer of pulp, because of changes in grade and basis weight, as well as voluntary and involuntary breaks in the production. In order not to disturb the operation of the pulp mill by these changes in the pulp consumption, and in the same way to eliminate disturbances in the paper production originating from the pulp mill, a certain *buffer storage of pulp* is necessary. In order to limit the space required for the pulp buffer, the pulp should be concentrated from the screening consistency of 0.5–1.5 % to 5–15 % or even more. This reduces the volume demand from 200–66 m³ ptp to 20–6.6 m³ ptp. Another desired achievement is to *equalize the pulp quality*, which is subjected to unavoidable changes because of variation in raw materials and pulping conditions, e.g. freeness and strength of groundwood pulp, degree of delignification, strength and color of unbleached chemical pulp, degree of polymerization of dissolving pulp. These changes are partly rhythmic, in time with the sharpening cycles of the grinding stones and the batches of cooking, and partly of a less regular occurrence, such as those caused by mistakes in the operation or by changes in the raw materials, i.e. the freshness of the pulpwood, the concentration of the cooking liquor, the steam pressure or the power voltage. It is impossible to design a pulp system which equalizes all these variations of different frequency, but most pulp buffer systems try to fulfil this demand to a certain extent. Some systems thereby use huge chests of pulp in fairly low consistency, 3–5 %, to and from which chests pulp is continuously pumped and where mixing is attempted during the retention by external pump recirculation or internal stirring. Inadequate mixing is usually obtained through insufficient power input and unsuitable design of the vessel. Furthermore, varying level of the buffer chest, which is unavoidable if the chest is to fulfil its buffer function, is another cause of variation in the mixing efficiency. A different system employs medium consistency storage in down-flow towers, similar to bleach towers. This takes care of the buffer storage aspect, but the mixing effect is achieved only if there are several towers coupled in parallel, with simultaneous charge or discharge of several of these towers. Both systems have advantages and drawbacks, but in view of the fairly long variation periods, the medium consistency system is perhaps to be preferred, especially after the development of the modern high-consistency pumps which ensure a convenient transport of the pulp in filter consistency.

For the concentration of the pulp slurry after screening, *deckers* or *filters* are used. Both machine types are in principle rotating steel drums, on the periphery of which a 30–70 mesh metal cloth has been spanned. The pulp stock enters a trough at low consistency, 1.5% or lower, and the water passes through the meshes of the cloth, whereas the main fiber fraction is retained and subsequently discharged at the other side of the drum in thickened form. The final consistency depends on the force applied to expel the water. Deckers have open drums and the driving force of the drainage is just the difference in water level on the outside and inside of the drum. By closing the ends of the drum a filter construction is obtained. The whole interior of the drum could then be set under vacuum by means of a drop leg or by a vacuum pump. So-called valveless filters generally operate without such accessories, and the vacuum is created by channels extending over the drum periphery behind the cloth, at an angle to the generatrix. These channels are filled with water in their submerged position, and by rising during the rotation of the drum they tend to evacuate and thereby create a vacuum behind the pulp pad corresponding at most, to the barometric leg equal to the diameter of the drum. The valveless filters are valued because of their ease of operation and low fiber losses with the back water. They give a pulp consistency of 10–14%, as compared with about 5% from a decker. The consistency can be increased somewhat by applying extra vacuum, and up to 20% by application of one or more press rolls at the top of the drum. The pulp web is finally removed from the drum by a blade or preferably by a pick-up roll, and disintegrated by a rotating mixer screw at the discharge.

In non-integrated pulp mills, the de-watering has to be carried further in order to decrease the transportation costs. This is done by either *wet-lapping* or drying. In the former, the pulp web of a filter drum is picked up by an endless woollen felt carried by a couch roll, and then passed through one or several pairs of press rolls which remove more water and deliver the pulp web in a consistency of 30–45%, to be taken up in rolls or normally passed through slitters and cutters to give wet sheets or laps, which are further piled and hydraulically compressed to *bales*. An alternative to the wet-lapping machine is the similar but feltless Kamyr wet

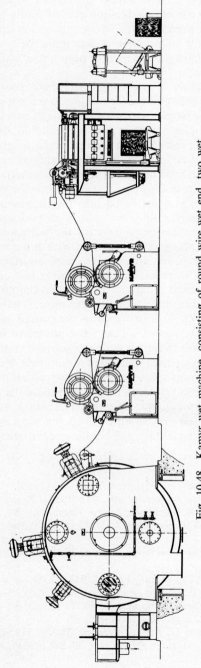

Fig. 10.48. Kamyr wet machine, consisting of round wire wet end, two wet presses, cutter, hydraulic press and baler (Sandy Hill–Kamyr)

machine, Figure 10.48, which is very commonly used for de-watering groundwood and also sometimes for unbleached sulfite pulp. The baling press is also shown in Figure 10.48. Metal strings are applied during the bale pressing operation to preserve a minimum bale volume. A bale usually contains 150–250 kg dry weight of pulp fibers, and measures about $0.5 \times 0.7 \times 1.0$ m.

A quite different manner of preparing pulp for transportation is *noduliz-ing* (25b) or *pelletizing* (86a) for bulk storage and transport. Both methods apply press dewatering to give particles of grain size or somewhat larger. Nodulizing in its simplest form is just a shredding of the press cake emerging from a pulp press, usually a screw press, to give a fairly loose-packing bulk pulp. Pelletizing makes use of a special machine, or pellet-izer, which is in commercial operation for other materials, such as cattle food. It consists of a rotating, perforated drum on a vertical axis. The pulp at the desired dry content is fed into the interior of the drum and pressed through the perforations by means of two static doctor rolls. Outside the drum other devices scrape off the pulp worms formed into suitable lengths. The machine can operate with both wet and dry pulp, but in the latter case the pellets appear glazed at the surface and are difficult to disperse in water. The pellets can be blown or belt conveyed with the same equipment as is used for grain transport in the ports, and thus de-crease the costs of loading and unloading the ships. The packing density is still much lower, 0.25–0.35, than for properly stowed bales, 0.5–0.7, and this new form of pulp transport is thus most attractive for short shipping distances, where the time in port is a significant part of the costs.

With the comparatively high density of a pulp bale, the bale weight is a decisive factor in the pulp transportation costs, which makes *pulp drying* attractive. Most chemical pulp of non-integrated mills leaves in the dry form, with 85–95% dry content. For quality reasons, sulfite pulp of the greaseproof type is often only dried to 70%, and most mechanical pulp is not dried at all. Drying methods and equipment are treated in Chapter 18.

REFERENCES

1. Ahlfors, S. E:son, *Svensk Papperstid.*, **53**, 447 (1950).
2. Alhojärvi, J., *Svensk Papperstid.*, **56**, 451 (1953); *Papier*, **12**, 523 (1958).
3. Almin, K. A., and B. Steenberg, *Svensk Papperstid.*, **57**, 37 (1954).
4. Anon., Jönssons Vibrationssilar, A. B. Ekströms Advert. Bull., Stockholm 1950.
5. Armstrong, B., *Paper Mill News*, **77**, No. 30, 11 (1954); *Paper Ind.*, **38**, 854 (1957).
6. van Arsdel, W. B., *Paper Ind.*, **17**, 725, 943 (1936).
7. Baker, R. E., and F. Hutton, *Pulp Paper Mag. Can.*, **51**, No. 6, 82 (1950).
8. Björkman, C. B., *Svensk Papperstid.*, **49**, 27 (1946); **50**, 43 (1947).
8a. Boadway, J. D., *Tappi.*, **45**, 265 (1962).
9. Boadway, J. D., and H. Freeman, *Tappi*, **39**, 797 (1956).
10. Brax, A. J., and L. Markila, *Paperi Puu*, **33**, 284 (1951); *Svensk Papperstid.*, **55**, 139 (1952).
11. Brecht, W., *et al.*, *Wochbl. Papierfabrik.*, **83**, 347 (1955).

12. Brecht, W., and H. Schröter, *Wochbl. Papierfabrik.*, **75**, 67, 88 (1947).
13. Brecht, W., and H. Schröter, *Wochbl. Papierfabrik.*, **76**, 261 (1948).
13a. Brecht, W., and A. Weidhaas, *Tappi*, **45**, 383 (1962).
14. Brecht, W., and K. Weishaupt, *Wochbl. Papierfabrik.*, **86**, 221, 281 (1958).
15. Brumley, G. W., *Tech. Assoc. Papers*, **30**, 569 (1947).
16. Brunes, B., *Svensk Papperstid.*, **51**, 336 (1948).
17. Brunes, B., *Svensk Papperstid.*, **54**, 96 (1951); *Paperi Puu*, **33**, 273 (1951).
18. Brunes, B., *Svensk Papperstid.*, **57**, 317 (1954).
19. Calhoun, T. B., *et al.*, *Paper Trade J.*, **141**, No. 2, 30 (1957).
20. Calkins, D. L., *Paper Trade J.*, **127**, 49 (1948).
20a. Casey, J. P., *Pulp and Paper, Chemistry and Chemical Technology*, 2nd Ed., Interscience, New York 1962.
21. Chandler, J. B., *Southern Pulp Paper Mfr*, **13**, No. 4, 54 (1950).
21a. Colombo, P., *et al.*, ATIP Bull. No. 3, 61 (1956); No. 4, 133 (1960).
22. Corte, H., *Zellstoff Papier*, **7**, No. 4, 116 (1958).
23. Cross, R. H., *Tappi*, **43**, No. 3, 240A (1960).
24. Dedert, W. G., and H. K. Waters, *Paper Trade J.*, **141**, No. 2, 34 (1957).
25. Dentremont, A. E., and R. S. Swenson, *Tappi*, **43**, No. 1, 249A (1960).
25a. Dozier, E. L., and P. D. Van Derveer, *Paper Trade J.*, **142**, No. 51, 32 (1958).
25b. Diehl, W. F., *Pulp Paper*, **31**, No. 13, 64 (1957).
26. Dubach, M., and M. Rutishauser, *Papier*, **11**, 37 (1957); *U.S. Pat.* 2,748,951 (1956), *Svensk Papperstid.*, **61**, 754 (1958).
26a. Dunning, J. W., and C. W. Converse, *Paper Ind.*, **38**, 950 (1957).
27. Ebersole, W. M., and W. B. Simmons, *Tappi*, **38**, 442 (1955).
28. Eidem, I., *Medd. CCL (Stockholm)*, B No. 12 I, 1947.
29. Eie, R., *Svensk Papperstid.*, **53**, 402 (1950).
30. Eie, R., *Svensk Papperstid.*, **58**, 325 (1955).
31. Eie, R., *Norsk Skogind.*, **10**, 247 (1956).
31a. Ellesfen, Ö., *Norsk Skogind.*, **16**, 175 (1962).
32. Esilä, A. J., and N. H. Hakkarainen, *Paperi Puu*, **40**, 325 (1958).
33. Fahlgren, S., *Pulp Paper Mag. Can.*, **55**, No. 3, 217 (1954).
34. Foster, J., *Pulp Paper Mag. Can.*, **53**, No. 3, 259 (1952).
35. Fraser, R. L., *Pulp Paper Mag. Can.*, **50**, No. 6, 112 (1949).
36. Freeman, H., and J. D. Boadway, *Pulp Paper Mag. Can.*, **54**, No. 4, 102 (1953).
37. Freeman, H., and C. H. Skelton, *Pulp Paper Mag. Can.*, **38**, No. 2, 170 (1937).
38. Gardner, W. S., *et al.*, *Tappi*, **37**, 314 (1954).
38a. Gavelin, G., and L. Sikström, *Svensk Papperstid.*, **63**, 398 (1960).
39. Gilles, T. L., and M. B. Pineo, *Tappi*, **37**, 46 (1954).
40. Ginaven, M. E., and A. H. Adams, *Paper Trade J.*, **141**, No. 4, 40 (1957); *Tappi*, **40**, No. 10, 212A (1957).
41. Göthner, K. F., and H. T. Robson, *Tappi*, **35**, 370 (1952).
42. Grieve, J. R. W., *Pulp Paper Mag. Can.*, **46**, No. 8, 601 (1945).
43. Hannunkari, L., *Svensk Papperstid.*, **56**, 435 (1953).
44. Harper, E. A., and F. C. Paul, *Tappi*, **37**, 206 (1954).
45. Heese, F., *Paperi Puu*, **37**, 258 (1955).
46. von Hildebrandt, P. G., *Paper Trade J.*, **137**, No. 4, 20 (1953).
47. Homans, R., and M. B. Pineo, *Tappi*, **37**, 257 (1954).
47a. Hooper, S. W., *Pulp Paper Mag. Can.*, **59**, No. 7, 115 (1958).

48. Jalkanen, M. J., *U.S. Pat.* 2,916,346 (1959).
49. Johnson, T. R., *Tappi*, **41**, No. 3, 152A (1958).
50. Jönsson, S. E., *Svensk Papperstid.*, **62**, 425 (1959).
51. Kelsall, D. F., *Trans. Inst. Chem. Engrs* (*London*), **30**, 87 (1952); *Chem. Eng. Sci.*, **2**, 254 (1953).
52. Klein, M., *et al.*, *Tech. Assoc. Papers*, **30**, 562 (1947).
52a. Klemm, K. H., *Wochbl. Papierfabrik.*, **83**, 261, 266, 349 (1955).
53. Klinga, I., *Svensk Papperstid.*, **53**, 495 (1950); *Papier*, **6**, 135 (1952).
54. Kubát, J., *Papier*, **9**, 83 (1955).
55. Kubát, J., *Svensk Papperstid.*, **59**, 175, 251 (1956).
56. Kubát, J., and B. Steenberg, *Svensk Papperstid.*, **58**, 319 (1955).
56a. Kubinek, V., *et al.*, *Papir Celulosa*, **12**, No. 6, 127 (1957).
57. Lee, J. A., *Chem. Met. Eng.*, **48**, No. 8, 88 (1941).
58. Lientz, J. R., *Paper Ind.*, **28**, No. 6, 806 (1946).
59. Lindblad, R., *Svensk Papperstid.*, **53**, 93, 442 (1950).
60. Lindgren, K., *Svensk Papperstid.*, **53**, 366 (1950).
61. Lindgren, K., *Paper Trade J.*, **139**, No. 13, 30, No. 15, 22, No. 16, 33 (1955).
62. Madsen, F., *Svensk Papperstid.*, **56**, 338 (1953).
63. Mann, A. A., *Tappi*, **39**, 790 (1956).
64. Mannbro, N., *Svensk Papperstid.*, **54**, 535 (1951).
65. McGinn, E. P., *Paper Trade J.*, **132**, No. 17, 30 (1951).
66. McKibbins, S. W., *Tappi*, **43**, 801 (1960).
67. Millar, R. E., *et al.*, *Tappi*, **38**, 604 (1955).
68. Morrison, H. A., *Tech. Assoc. Papers*, **13**, No. 1, 92, 122 (1930).
69. Nepenin, Y. N., *Chemie und Technologie der Zellstoffherstellung*, German Ed., Vol. 1, Academie-Verlag, Berlin 1960.
70. Nilsson, T., *Svensk Papperstid.*, **44**, 449 (1941).
71. Noble, J. H., and J. P. Rich, *Paper Trade J.*, **117**, No. 20, 35 (1943).
72. Nuttall, G. H., and I. F. Hendry, *Tappi*, **40**, 951 (1957).
73. Orr, W. L., *Tappi*, **37**, 162 (1954).
74. Perkins, J. K., *et al.*, *Tappi*, **37**, 83 (1954).
75. Ranhagen, G., *Svensk Papperstid.*, **56**, 565 (1953).
76. Ranhagen, G., *Tappi*, **37**, 363 (1954).
77. Rastatter, E. L., and A. H. Croup, *Tappi*, **35**, 223 (1952).
78. Reynolds, V. T., *Tappi*, **32**, 454 (1949).
79. Richter, J., *Svensk Papperstid.*, **48**, 545 (1945).
80. Robertson, J. D., *Tappi*, **39**, No. 12, 158A (1956).
81. Russell, R., *Pacific Pulp Paper Ind.*, **11**, No. 2, 21 (1937).
82. Rydholm, S. A., *Swed. Pat. Appl.*
83. Schenk, H. F., *Tappi*, **37**, 283 (1954).
84. Schippel, H. W., *Papier*, **10**, 233 (1956).
85. Scholander, A., *Svensk Papperstid.*, **53**, 95 (1950); *Norsk Skogind.*, **4**, 64 (1950).
86. Segring, S. B., *Svensk Papperstid.*, **56**, 363 (1953).
86a. Shook, R. E., *Pulp Paper Int.*, **1**, No. 11, 36 (1959).
87. Sloman, A. R., *Pulp Paper Int.*, **3**, No. 6, 18 (1961).
88. Starborg, E., *Svensk Papperstid.*, **56**, 412 (1953).
89. Steenberg, B., *Svensk Papperstid.*, **56**, 771 (1953).
90. Steenberg, B., and J. Kubát, *Papier*, **10**, 227 (1956).
91. Stephenson, J. N., *Preparation and Treatment of Wood Pulp*, Vol. I, McGraw-Hill, London 1952.

92. Stevens, W. C., *et al.*, *Tappi*, **36**, 372 (1953).
93. Stockman, L., and L. Ruus, *Svensk Papperstid.*, **58**, 483 (1955).
94. Sulphite Committee, Can. Pulp Paper Assoc., Tech. Sect., Factors Contributing to sulphite pulp cleanliness, Montreal 1945.
95. Tomlinson, G. H., and N. G. M. Tuck, *Pulp Paper Mag. Can.*, **53**, No. 12, 109 (1952).
96. Ulfsparre, S., *Waste and Byproducts in the Forest Industry*, Norrlandsutredningen, Stockholm 1942, p. 145.
97. Venemark, E., *Svensk Papperstid.*, **46**, 315 (1943).
98. Wagner, R., *Tappi*, **42**, No. 1, 115A (1959).
99. Waters, H. K., and R. E. Bergström, *Tappi*, **38**, 169 (1955).
100. West, P. H., *et al.*, *Tappi*, **37**, 137 (1954).
101. Wieters, J. D., *Tappi*, **40**, 667 (1957).
102. Wikman, S. A., *Svensk Papperstid.*, **53**, 492 (1950).
103. Wiley, A. L., *et al.*, *Tappi*, **37**, 164 (1954).
104. Wiley, A. L., *et al.*, *Tappi*, **38**, 600 (1955).
105. Zimmerman, E., and H. Vranian, *Tappi*, **33**, 561 (1950).

11

PREPARATION OF COOKING CHEMICALS AND TREATMENT OF WASTE LIQUORS

I. General Principles

In the preparation of chemical and semichemical pulps, considerable quantities of cooking chemicals, 200–500 kg ptp, are used. Some are present in unchanged form after the cook, others are changed during the pulping reactions. It is of vital economic interest to recover them for preparation of new cooking liquor. The waste liquor from the cooks contains the chemicals in a dilute solution, which has to be concentrated prior to the regeneration process. Thus, in most cases a vast quantity of water has to be evaporated. The heat economy then requires that part or all of the organic substance dissolved during the cook should be burnt under generation of heat. The combustion of the organic substance is necessary from another point of view. The large pulp production presents an accentuated problem of stream pollution, especially for those mills located in mid-country or important fishing or oyster-growing districts. Quite often legislation will force pulp mills to solve the stream-pollution problem or else limit, or even close down, production. Furthermore in most cases the cooking chemicals are recovered in a form which makes additional operations necessary in order to prepare a cooking liquor of desired composition. Sometimes it is possible to obtain valuable by-products during the operations. Thus, the complete preparation of cooking liquors involves:

(1) evaporation of waste liquor;
(2) combustion of waste liquor;
(3) recovery of inorganic chemicals;
(4) preparation of cooking liquor;
(5) manufacture of by-products.

These leading principles are applied quite differently, according to the different needs and possibilities of the various pulping processes. The kraft process, using the largest amount of expensive chemicals, has been compelled to develop the most advanced technology, resulting in a complete and expensive system for the recovery of heat and chemicals. The acid sulfite process, long operating on calcium base, which was comparatively cheap, lacked a corresponding incitement, and as considerable technical difficulties were involved in the evaporation of calcium-based sulfite waste liquors, the chemicals recovery of the sulfite process was long confined to the excess sulfur dioxide needed in the cooking acid for good impregnation and rapid cooking, and which was comparatively easy to recover. However, with the introduction of soluble bases, which were more expensive, a more complete recovery was necessary, and systems have been worked out or are under development, which aim at a satisfactory recovery of both heat and chemicals. Stream-pollution problems have enforced this development, and even mills operating on calcium base have built facilities for the evaporation and combustion of the waste liquors, in spite of the useless calcium compounds obtained. At the same time, the heat economy of the sulfite process has been improved. A complete recovery of chemicals is, however, quite complicated because of the purity required for the recovered chemicals in the acid sulfite process. The neutral sulfite process, requiring less pure chemicals, faces another problem, namely the lack of sufficient organic matters in the waste liquors for combustion, as the neutral sulfite pulps are always made in high yields. This has also led to the suggestion of a principally different system, namely that of *wet combustion*, or the treatment of the waste liquor without previous evaporation, in order to improve the heat economy. Then the organic matter of the original waste liquor is oxidized at high temperature and pressure, and stream pollution minimized. Systems for the recovery of chemicals in combination with wet combustion have been suggested but are not easily realized. Wet combustion has also been applied to acid sulfite waste liquors. At certain conditions, wet combustion is incomplete, and some organic matter is obtained in a precipitated form of a high carbon content, which could be burnt separately. The method then approaches the *pyrolysis processes*. Another process, involving pyrolysis after previous evaporation of the waste liquor, is the *A.S.T.* (atomized suspension technique) process suggested for acid sulfite waste liquors. Part of the organic matter is thereby obtained in gaseous form and is subsequently burnt, and the remainder yields a dry powder, also containing most of the inorganic chemicals. A variant of the process uses partial or complete *gasification* in the reactor by introducing varying amounts of air, thus decreasing or eliminating the carbon content of the solid residue, which is treated with water to dissolve the inorganic chemicals. Pressure heating and pyrolysis of *kraft* black liquors was attempted by the *Rinman* and similar processes, in combination with the recovery of valuable organic by-products, such as organic acids and ketones, but has not met with commercial success.

The production of other by-products in treating the wastes from the cooking has been established. The condensates of the top gas and blow-down reliefs of kraft cooking yield *turpentine*, which is redistilled and sold, whereas the *methanol* produced at the same time is not economically recoverable. The *dimethyl sulfide* of the condensate can be removed and converted to the valuable solvent *dimethyl sulfoxide*. After some evaporation the black liquor yields *tall oil skimmings*, sodium soaps of fatty and resin acids of the wood, together with some neutral substances, all of which

765

Table 11.1. Recovery principles for chemicals used in various cooking processes

Recovery method	Cooking process	Evaporation	Recovery furnace	Combustion of organics in reactor	Chemicals recovery	Preparation of cooking liquor
Loddby–Malm	Acid sulfite Ca base	Yes	Combustion, no reduction zone	Complete	Only reabsorption of SO_2 from digester. No base recovery	From fresh chemicals and from digester SO_2
Lebanon	Acid sulfite, bisulfite, neutral sulfite, NH_4 base	Yes	Ibid.	Complete	Reabsorption of SO_2 from digester and flue gases. No base recovery	From fresh chemicals and from digester SO_2 and flue gas SO_2.
Tomlinson–Weyerhaeuser	Acid sulfite, bisulfite, Mg base	Yes	Ibid.	Complete	Reabsorption of SO_2 from digester and flue gases. Base recovery from ashes	Absorption of flue gas SO_2 in a suspension of recovered ashes (MgO)
Stora, Sivola, Mead, IPC, Western Precipitation	Acid sulfite, bisulfite, neutral sulfite, Na base	Yes	Combustion, reduction zone	Complete	Dissolution of molten $Na_2CO_3 + Na_2S$. Absorption of SO_2 from flue gases	Conversion of Na_2S to $NaHSO_3$ by various methods. Absorption of SO_2 from flue gases or from Na_2S conversion
Tomlinson	Kraft	Yes	Ibid.	Complete	Dissolution of molten $Na_2CO_3 + Na_2S$	Caustization of dissolved melt. Regeneration of the lime by reburning carbonate sludge obtained

A.S.T.–Gauvin	Acid sulfite, bisulfite, neutral sulfite, Na base	Yes	Pyrolysis reactor, carbon sludge and gas furnace	No	Washing of carbonized residue, which is then burnt. The Na_2CO_3 solution obtained is used to absorb flue gas SO_2 from burnt pyrolysis gases	Conversion of Na_2CO_3 obtained from pyrolysis residue, into sulfite cooking liquor by absorption of digester SO_2 and flue gas SO_2
Billerud–S.C.A.	Acid sulfite, bisulfite, neutral sulfite, Na bases	Yes	Gasification reactor, carbon sludge and gas furnace	Partial	Ibid.	Ibid.
Billerud–S.C.A.	Acid sulfite, bisulfite, neutral sulfite, Na base	Yes	Gasification reactor and gas furnace	Complete	Dissolution of carbon-free Na_2CO_3, absorption of flue gas SO_2	Conversion of Na_2CO_3 obtained into sulfite cooking liquor by absorption of digester SO_2 and flue gas SO_2
Cederquist	Acid sulfite, any base, neutral sulfite, Na or NH_4 base	No	Wet combustion reactor	Partial	No recovery. Carbonaceous residue burnt	From fresh chemicals and from digester SO_2
Zimmermann–Hammermill–Borregaard	Acid sulfite, any base, neutral sulfite, Na or NH_4 base	No	Wet combustion reactor	Complete	No recovery	From fresh chemicals and from digester SO_2

can be recovered separately after additional treatments. The tall oil is a valuable by-product of the kraft industry.

The sulfite waste liquors contain varying amounts of monosaccharides, which can be fermented to *ethanol*. Especially in Europe, alcohol plants have been added to the sulfite mills, and in some cases an organic-chemical industry based on sulfite alcohol has been established. Some methanol is also recovered with the ethanol. The *cymene* occurring in the top gas and blow-down relief of sulfite cooks is sometimes recovered and purified, but only in insignificant amounts. On the whole, the by-product recovery is fairly unimportant compared with the value of the pulp produced. The principal by-product, the *lignin* dissolved, which is a potential raw material obtained in quantities comparable to those of the pulp, is predominantly used for fuel. It thereby fulfills the purpose of making the cooking chemicals economically recoverable. Exceptionally, some lignin is converted to useful chemicals, such as *dispersants*, *tanning aids*, *plastics*, or *vanillin*. The use of sulfite waste liquor as a *road binder* should also be mentioned in this connection. The by-products of the pulping industry will be discussed further in a subsequent section. For *neutral sulfite pulping*, the recovery of *acetic acid* from the waste liquor has been tried on a pilot plant scale but found economically unattractive (21).

Table 11.1 surveys the various principles for the recovery of cooking chemicals and waste liquor treatments. The following sections of this chapter will consider them in some detail. In addition, the possibility of so-called *cross-recovery* should be observed, i.e. combinations of the recovery systems of different pulping processes. For instance, the waste liquor from *sodium-based acid sulfite or neutral sulfite cooking* could be combined with the black liquors from a *kraft mill* prior to evaporation and burning. The inorganic content of the former liquor will join the bulk of inorganics and occur in the smelt from the furnace, substituting the sodium sulfate normally added in the kraft recovery cycle to cover losses of chemicals. In the preparation of the sulfite cooking liquor from fresh chemicals, a value corresponding to the sodium sulfate costs could then be deducted from the total costs of chemicals. The system has several drawbacks, one being that the production of the sulfite mill is limited to a fraction of the kraft pulp production. A similar type of cross-recovery has been suggested (103), where the sulfite waste liquor is used instead of water to dissolve the smelt from the combustion furnace, which would save steam in the evaporation plant. In *combining acid sulfite and neutral sulfite mills*, the waste liquor of the first could be used in the preparation of the neutral sulfite cooking liquor by the addition of fresh or recovered chemicals.

II. Evaporation of Waste Liquors

1. KRAFT PROCESS

The black liquor coming from the diffusers or filter washers contains most of the organic substance removed from the wood during the cook, as well

768

as the inorganic chemicals charged, mainly in the form of salts with organic acids. The approximate composition of a normal black liquor from a pine kraft cook is shown in Table 11.2 (70). The total content of solids is thus around 20%, but varies with the moisture content of the wood used, the amount of liquor charged to the cook, and the pulp yield, and may be as low as 15%. In order to get proper ignition and burning of the organic substance in the recovery furnace, it is necessary to concentrate the liquor up to a dry content of 50–70%, most of which operation is carried out in multiple-effect evaporators to get the best heat economy. The evaporation required per ton of pulp varies with the pulp yield, the washing efficiency etc., but is generally in the order of 6–8 m^3 ptp.

The principles of evaporation as well as the equipment used will not be treated in detail (cf. 17 for further information), but some fundamental concepts must be given. The two principal categories of evaporators are the *film type* and the *forced-circulation type*. In both, the liquor is heated by steam and then allowed to expand for evaporation, but they differ in the way in which the flow through the heat exchangers is maintained. The rate of heat transfer is governed by (i) the area of the heating surface, (ii) the existing temperature difference between the steam side and the liquor side, and (iii) the coefficient of heat transfer. The first factor is naturally limited by the cost of heat exchangers. The second factor is limited by the fact that multiple-effect evaporation uses the steam from one effect to heat the next one, and that the total temperature difference between the steam used in the first effect and the liquor leaving the last is limited by other factors, namely the pressure of the steam at disposition and the vacuum achieved in the last effect. The total temperature difference is generally between 50° and 100°C. Another circumstance, the increase in the boiling point of the liquor during evaporation, causes a substantial reduction in the temperature differences available for each effect. The coefficient of heat transfer is composed of three factors, the heat transfer from steam to wall, the heat conduction through the wall and the heat transfer from wall to liquor. Of these, the last-mentioned has the dominating influence. Therefore it makes little difference if the walls of the heat exchanger are thick or thin, or whether they are made of copper, mild steel or stainless steel. Other considerations, such as those of mechanical damage or corrosion, are more important in that respect (80). Neither is the heat transfer from steam to wall very critical but it should be improved by adequate removal of condensate and non-condensable gases. The heat transfer from wall to liquor, which mainly determines the overall coefficient of heat transfer, can be improved by a higher rate of flow of the liquor passing the heating surface, e.g. by forced circulation. It is further influenced by the viscosity of the liquor, which increases with increasing concentration but decreases with increasing temperature. That is a major reason for maintaining a counter-current flow through the evaporation plant, so that the thickest liquor will meet the hottest steam. Other considerations may modify the straight counter-current coupling.

Quite often two evaporation units will be coupled in parallel to facilitate the final evaporation stage.

The major cause of decreased heat transfer is *scaling* on the evaporator heating surface. There are different types of deposits. One is of mainly organic nature, and appears as a result of polycondensation and carbonization when circulation of the thickest liquor is insufficient and excessive steam temperature is applied. Another consists of sodium sulfate at insufficient reduction in the furnace, and can be removed by water boiling. More serious are scales consisting of calcium carbonate containing some organic polycondensates, and those of aluminium silicate. The former could be removed by acid washing followed by drilling, the latter is more resistant. Repeated acid washings may cause corrosive damage on the heat exchangers. The aluminium silicate scales are prevented by using chrome bricks instead of high-alumina refractory in the smelting zones of the recovery furnace. The most common type of scaling is the formation of iron sulfide at the steam side of those exchangers using steam from previous effects, unless stainless steel is used or careful venting of hydrogen sulfide is performed (80, 156).

The principle of multiple-effect evaporation allows the utilization of the latent heat of the evaporated water in one effect to be used in a subsequent one for heating. Thus, quadruple-effect stations evaporate more than 3 tons of water per ton of steam used, quintuple effects almost 4 tons and sextuple effects somewhat less than 5 tons of water. The steam used in the first effect is saturated with a pressure of up to 4.5 kp/cm^2, and the vacuum obtained in the last effect is generally around 600–650 mm Hg, achieved in a condenser for the steam leaving the last effect.

The principal coupling and conditions of a seven-body, sextuple-effect evaporation station is illustrated in Figure 11.1 (17). The initial concentration of the black liquor is around 15–20% total solids and the final concentration 55–60%. At some of the intermediate effects, the tall oil skimmings are removed. Their minimum solubility occurs when a concentration of around 25–28% of total solids is reached, and as the temperature is still below the boiling point of the liquor at atmospheric pressure, the liquor can be sent to open settling tanks for the skimming operation and then returned to the evaporation station.

For improved heat economy, evaporation is often carried as far as 60–70% or even higher. This cannot be done with the conventional types of evaporators. Specially constructed forced-circulation steam evaporators, or else gas contact evaporators are required. The latter are constructed to utilize some of the heat of the stack gases for the final evaporation, in special cases even to dryness. An old type was the *disk evaporator*, consisting of several series of rotating vertical disks, which were partly submerged in the pre-evaporated liquor and partly subjected to contact with the hot combustion gases. A development of that type are the *cascade evaporators*, which mainly differ from the old type by a more efficient distribution of the black liquor surface in contact with the stack gases. The *cyclone evaporator* solves that problem in a different manner

770

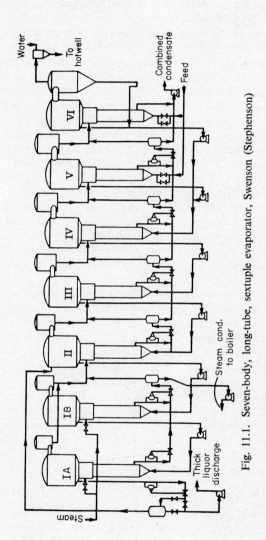

Fig. 11.1. Seven-body, long-tube, sextuple evaporator, Swenson (Stephenson)

by spraying the pre-evaporated liquor through tangential nozzles into a cyclone, into which the hot gases are introduced near the bottom.

The so-called *B.T. system* (15, 151) uses a specially designed final evaporator, which operates at a pressure of 10 kp/cm², through which steam, superheated to 400–450°C in the furnace, is recirculated and an amount of saturated steam, corresponding to the evaporated water, is continually removed to a low-pressure steam generator. The black liquor enters at a concentration of 55% and leaves the evaporator with about 80% under expansion to atmospheric pressure, whereby it is converted to a dry powder of only 10–15% moisture content, which is then fed to the furnace. In order to avoid pitch deposition in the combustion, the black liquor should be oxidized by air prior to evaporation, a process which gives other advantages, cf. below. Several advantages are claimed for the B.T. system, the major being a higher efficiency of heat recovery (45, 151), around 75%, as compared to 66–72% for the modern black liquor injection system and 50–55% for the old rotary furnace system.

There are certain modifications of the kraft process which may influence the evaporation plant. The introduction of a prehydrolysis stage changes the amount of organics dissolved as well as the water quantities to be evaporated. In some cases a cold alkali refining of the prehydrolysis–kraft pulp is also practised, where the reclaimed refining liquor is sent to be used as cooking liquor, preferably after some concentrating. Therefore, such a mill includes a *concentration of white liquor* in one or two effects of the evaporation plant.

The *black liquor oxidation* (40) converts sodium sulfide and hydrosulfide to thiosulfate and methyl mercaptan to disulfide. The odor problem of the kraft mill is thereby reduced (19, 152) and sulfur losses in the evaporation decrease from about 12 kg ptp S to zero (150). This increases the sulfidity of the white liquor, in spite of increased sulfur losses in the recovery furnace, from 26 to 29% (150) or 25 to 32% (16), which is of little value. In this respect, black liquor oxidation is more important to mills which, because of low sodium losses, have a low sodium sulfate make-up and therefore tend to lose in sulfidity continually, whereby the lower limit is approached that affects the rate of pulping and the pulp quality (19), cf. Chapter 9.II. Less corrosion in the evaporator tubes is another advantage of black liquor oxidation (51, 150). The oxidation of sulfide and hydrosulfide to thiosulfate,

$$2\,Na_2S + 2\,O_2 + H_2O \rightarrow Na_2S_2O_3 + 2\,NaOH, \ \Delta H = -215$$

is exothermic and responsible for 3–6% of the heat value of the black liquor. In the oxidation equipment, that heat can only be used for hot water production, instead of steam generation (155), which is a noticeable disadvantage. In addition to the thiosulfate reaction, oxygen is consumed in other reactions, such as sulfate formation (54), which are particularly accentuated as the sulfide oxidation nears completion (155). The oxidation of sulfide by oxygen in inorganic buffers occurs much more slowly than in black liquor (162), and it has been demonstrated (22, 48) that the probable oxidation catalysts are pyrocatechol configurations of the thiolignin. The rate of oxidation is maximal at 60° to 70°C for sulfide concentrations higher than 2.5 g/l and at 90°C for low concentrations such as occur towards the end of the oxidation (109). It is essential that a good contact is provided between gas and liquid and there are two essential principles used in the design of the commercial equipment to secure this contact. In one system, air is passed up a packed column counter-current to the black liquor flow. The packing is designed to prevent foaming (19, 148). The other system creates foam by means of a fan in an oxidation tower, whereafter the foam is passed through a foam separator and a foam tank equipped with foam breakers (150). Defoaming creates a problem and has initiated investigations using oxygen instead of air (54), which at low oxygen prices may become economically feasible. An interesting variant of black liquor oxidation is the aeration of a mixture of white and black liquor (22). This creates pH conditions which on cautious aeration favors the oxidation to *polysulfide*, which only in the presence of excess oxygen is oxidized further. Polysulfides in the cooking liquor favor the preservation of the wood polysaccharides and increase the pulp yield, cf. Chapter 9.II. The presence of polysulfides in the cooking liquor will likewise influence the corrosion velocity of the digester, cf. Chapter 6.VI. It was observed (22) that both polysulfide and sulfite were formed during the aeration, and that some changes occurred subsequently, such as formation of thiosulfate from polysulfide and sulfite. It was thus assumed, that the thiosulfate formation occurs in two steps

$$4\ S^{2-} + O_2 + 2\ H_2O \rightarrow 2\ S_2^{2-} + 4\ OH^-$$
$$2\ S^{2-} + 3\ O_2 \rightarrow 2\ SO_3^{2-}$$
$$2\ S_2^{2-} + 2\ SO_3^{2-} \rightarrow 2\ S_2O_3^{2-} + 2\ S^{2-}$$

$$4\ S^{2-} + 4\ O_2 + 2\ H_2O \rightarrow 2\ S_2O_3^{2-} + 4\ OH^-.$$

The formation of polysulfide is in its turn probably preceded by quinone formation of the pyrocatechol groups of the thiolignin.

2. SULFITE PROCESSES

The concentration of a sulfite waste liquor in the digester prior to pulp washing is around 11–17%, depending on the pulp grade and the liquor-to-wood ratio, cf. Table 11.2 (55). After washing, the concentration has normally decreased by 10–15%, and a further reduction is caused if the liquor is used for alcohol production. In the case of sulfite waste liquors, therefore, the main combustion processes require pre-evaporation in order to get proper ignition and burning, as well as good heat economy. The same principle of multiple-effect evaporation is used as in the evaporation of kraft black liquor, but some features differ, especially in the case of calcium-based liquors. In that case the scaling problem dominates the construction and operation of the stations. Furthermore, the waste liquor from the conventional sulfite process is acidic, less so after having

Table 11.2. Components of kraft black liquor and sulfite waste liquor (55, 70)

Black liquor (total solids 17–22%)		Sulfite waste liquor (total solids (12–16%)		
	% of total solids			% of total solids
Alkali lignin	41	Lignosulfonate (of which 43 lignin		
Extractives	3	and 9 sulfonate)		52
Hydroxy acids and lactones	28	Extractives		3
Acetic acid	5	Poly- and oligosaccharides		6
Formic acid	3	Monosaccharides		23
Methanol	1	Galactose	3	
Sulfur	3	Glucose	3	
Sodium	16	Mannose	11	
	——	Arabinose	1	
Total	100%	Xylose	5	
		Glucuronic acid		1
		Aldonic acids		4
		Sugarsulfonates		3
		Acetic acid		2
		Methanol		1
		Calcium		5
		Total		100%

been used for alcohol manufacture or if the cooking process was modified to bisulfite cooking. In all these cases, acid-resistant steel is required in the evaporation plant. Only when the finishing cooking stage is alkaline, as in one of the recent modifications of the sulfite process, or in neutral sulfite pulping, can the waste liquor be concentrated in conventional kraft black liquor evaporators but here also corrosion is serious enough to require stainless steel.

The scaling problem, which made evaporation of calcium-based waste liquors difficult, caused some mills, especially in America, to convert the operation to soluble bases, particularly ammonium or magnesium. However, in Sweden special attention was paid to the scaling problem (cf. 154 for further refs.), and in cooperation between the Swedish cellulose industry and manufacturers of evaporation plants, two systems were developed, the *Ramén* and the *Rosenblad* systems, which have now been installed in a large number of sulfite mills, not only in Scandinavia.

The main reason for the scaling difficulties depends on the peculiar solubility behavior of calcium sulfate in its three forms, the dihydrate, the semihydrate, and the anhydrite, as illustrated by Figure 11.2 (126, 135). As sulfate ions are formed during the acid sulfite cook, especially towards the end of the cook, and especially in dissolving pulp cooks (Chapter 9.I), there is always a danger of calcium sulfate precipitation. As a matter of fact some gypsum is precipitated on the pulp fibers already in the digester, and as the solubility of calcium sulfate is higher at low temperature, a considerable part of that precipitate is redissolved in the washing and waste liquor reclaiming operations (29, 125, 135, 138). In contrast, oxidation of bisulfite to sulfate ions in the same operations causes only minor troubles (135, 153). However, although there is always an excess of calcium ions, it has been found that trying to keep down the sulfate ion content is not always the best method of preventing scale formation. It may be true for vacuum evaporation stations, but at the higher temperatures of the back pressure evaporation stations, the solubility limits will always be exceeded. Therefore, in some cases it has been of advantage to *add* sulfuric acid in limited quantities to produce precipitation within the whole liquor volume instead of at the heating surface. Precipitation is accelerated by seeding with calcium sulfate (126, 131), a method which is now practised in the form of neutralization of the waste liquor for alcohol fermentation by adding ashes from the combustion furnace, containing about 50% CaO and 50% $CaSO_4$. Also pressure heating in special equipment prior to evaporation might prevent scaling on the heating surface.

As the anhydrite forms at temperatures above 130°C and the dihydrate at temperatures below 100°C, it is fortunate that the scale originally consists of semihydrate and only eventually passes into the anhydrite form which dissolves with difficulty. Frequent washing of the heating surface is therefore advisable. The scale removal is facilitated at low pH, and one of the evaporator systems, *Rosenblad*, makes use of frequent acid washings by the so-called channel-switching method (67). Hereby, the liquor and steam sides of the heat exchanger are interchanged, and the steam condensate, containing the strong α-hydroxysulfonic acids formed from volatile aldehydes (formaldehyde, methyl glyoxal and furfural) and SO_2, removes the slight scales formed at the liquor side during the previous period. The *Ramén* system instead systematically removes one effect at a time from the production to be washed with the acid condensate. In some cases, however, the scaling gets more serious, e.g. after some faulty operation of the effects containing the most viscous liquor. Then anhydrite together with organic incrustants is formed, and has to be removed by boiling with nitric acid combined with mechanical cleaning.

Both film-type and forced-circulation evaporators are used in sulfite waste liquor concentration. They are operated as multiple effect stations

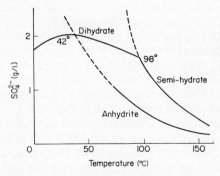

Fig. 11.2. Solubility curves for the system
$CaSO_4–H_2O$

containing 4–6 effects. They could be run in three principally different ways, as *vacuum, thermo-compression*, or *back pressure* stations. The choice between these alternatives has to consider the relation of fuel to electrical energy prices, as well as the demands for hot water and low pressure steam at other departments of the mill (154). Back pressure operation, where all effects are kept under pressure and low pressure steam leaves the last effect, gives the best heat economy in cases where there is a steady use for the low pressure steam. That is so when an alcohol plant is connected to the mill. The scaling problem is generally more serious in back pressure operation, and in the case of ammonium-based liquors, which tend to undergo polycondensation at elevated temperature and thereby increase in viscosity, it has been found necessary to refrain from the conventional counter-current flow of liquor and steam through the effects in back-pressure evaporation, and instead permit the concentrated liquor to leave the evaporation plant at the low temperature end. The evaporation of magnesium- and sodium-based sulfite waste liquors does not involve similar viscosity difficulties and the scaling problem is also decidedly reduced though not eliminated, as there is normally enough calcium of wood origin to accumulate to a critical concentration unless removed by a special operation in the recovery cycle.

III. Combustion of Waste Liquors

Table 11.3 gives the approximate composition of the waste liquors from the three main cooking processes. In excess of the inorganic components from the original cooking liquor there is a considerable quantity of carbon and hydrogen as well as oxygen and unevaporated water. The approximate heat value of the total *organic* substance dissolved is about 4,700 Mcal/t, or roughly 5,000 Mcal ptp for chemical pulps of normal yields (33, 55, 124). In the combustion, that heat is partly used to evaporate the residual water of the concentrated waste liquor, partly to reduce some of the sulfur compounds to sulfide, and some heat also escapes with the stack gases. The largest quantity, however, is utilized for steam generation, thus contributing to a substantial part of the entire steam requirement of the pulp mill. The demand of electrical energy is also covered to some extent by generation in turbines using high pressure steam. The energy balance of the various types of pulp mills has been subjected to several studies (e.g. 30, 45, 149, 154) but will not be considered here except as illustrated in Table 11.4.

The conditions of combustion determine the course of the chemical reactions, the amount of heat evolved, and the form in which the cooking chemicals can be recovered. The development of the combustion furnaces has on the whole been purely empirical from a chemical point of view, and only recently has a more fundamental basis been developed for the understanding of the reactions taking place at the high temperatures of combustion. That can be anticipated to facilitate the choice of conditions favorable for each special type of pulp mill.

776

Table 11.3. Composition of pulping waste liquors for evaporation and combustion

	Acid sulfite rayon pulp	Acid sulfite paper pulp	Bisulfite paper pulp	Neutral sulfite (semi-chemical)	Kraft
Total solids:					
% of wood	68	64	74	46	74
% of waste liquor	13–17	12–16	14–18	9–11	17–22
Ashes, % of total solids	10–12	12–14	18–20	35–45	35–45
Carbon, % (resp. atomic proportions)	43 (10)	40 (10)	35 (10)	29 (10)	42 (10)
Hydrogen, % (resp. atomic proportions)	5 (14.6)	5 (14.4)	4 (14.4)	4 (16.5)	5 (15.5)
Oxygen, % (resp. atomic proportions)	42 (7.7)	42 (7.9)	42 (9.2)	44 (11.2)	35 (7.5)
Sulfur, % (resp. atomic proportions)	6 (0.5)	8 (0.7)	11 (0.9)	8 (1.0)	3 (0.1)
Sodium, % (resp. atomic proportions)	4 (0.5)	5 (0.7)	8 (0.9)	15 (2.8)	15 (1.9)
Heat value, Mcal/t total solids	4,500	4,300	3,500	3,000	3,900

Table 11.4. Heat balance of kraft and sulfite pulp mills, Mcal ptp (45)

	Kraft paper pulp Min. Mean Max.			Sulfite paper pulp Min. Mean Max.			Sulfite rayon pulp Min. Mean Max.		
Heat produced:									
in recovery furnace	2,700	2,950	3,150		2,350			3,200	
Heat consumed:									
in waste liquor evaporation	720	720	720	950	950	950	1,300	1,300	1,300
in cooking	810	1,060	1,660	720	960	1,480	1,010	1,330	1,600
in pulp drying	680	860	970	680	860	970	680	860	970
Total	2,210	2,640	3,350	2,350	2,770	3,400	2,990	3,490	3,870

Bleaching will in addition consume 300–600 Mcal ptp
Bark and wood refuse fuel will produce about 400 Mcal ptp
Pyrite combustion of sulfite mills gives about 200 Mcal ptp

The earlier types of combustion furnaces used for the recovery of kraft chemicals were of the rotary type, concentrated black liquor entering at one end and a half-burned black ash substance leaving at the other for further combustion in a smelt pot. In comparison with the modern type of combustion furnace, operation was more complicated, labor consuming and untidy, the steam production lower and the losses of chemicals considerable. A technically more convenient and efficient form of combustion furnace was developed during the late 1920's and early 1930's, particularly by the contributions of *Tomlinson* (146). The Tomlinson furnace, illustrated

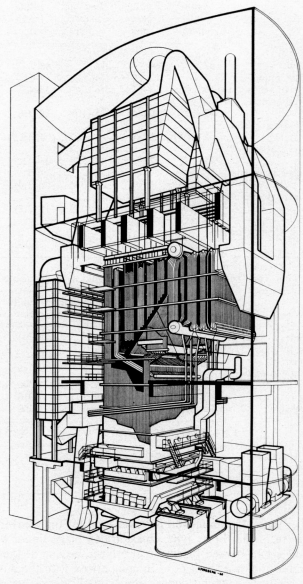

Fig. 11.3. Tomlinson-type kraft recovery furnace (Combustion Engineering)

in Figure 11.3, uses concentrated black liquor, which is sprayed in liquid form into the lower part of the furnace through oscillating nozzles across the furnace, to strike the rear wall and the two side walls of the furnace (149). There the residual water evaporates and the 'black ash' accumulates and finally falls down to the hearth, through which preheated *primary air* is forced. The organic matter burns out, and the molten inorganic chemicals leave the bottom of the furnace at the smelt spouts. To avoid excessive oxidation of the inorganic sulfur compounds, the primary air is limited to maintain a *reduction zone*. Then the smelt contains mainly sodium carbonate and sulfide with a minimum of sodium sulfate. The combustion of the gasified organic components is completed higher up in the furnace by the introduction of secondary air. The walls of the furnace are there clad with water-cooled tubes, connected with the boiler, for protection against the heat evolved. After a screen of tubes to protect for chemicals deposits, the combustion gases pass a number of platens of tubes, forming the super-heater, the boiler, and the economizer, whereby high-pressure steam is produced. After utilizing a large part of the residual heat of the gases by the gas air heater and sometimes cascade or cyclone evaporators for black liquor, mechanical dust collectors and electrical inorganic fume collectors (of the *Cottrell* type) or wet scrubbers are applied to recover some inorganics, mainly sodium sulfate, which would otherwise cause losses of 50–100 kg ptp Na_2SO_4.

During the late 1930's and the 1940's, a similar combustion furnace was developed by *Tomlinson* for *magnesium-based sulfite waste liquors*, with the important exception that no smelt was obtained, but the entire base quantity was recovered as MgO in dust collectors and subsequently the sulfur as SO_2 by absorption in scrubber towers (6, 43, 79). The combustion of concentrated *calcium-based* sulfite waste liquors was developed in the 1940's and 1950's with the introduction of the *Loddby* or the *Lurgi* primary furnaces forming an extension of an ordinary cooled furnace, Figure 11.4 (30, 31, 130, 132, 136a). The ashes, containing a mixture of calcium sulfate and oxide in roughly equal amounts (130), cannot be reused in the cooking process but have sometimes to be recovered in dust collectors in order to reduce air pollution. *Ammonium-based* sulfite waste liquors could be burnt in the same type of furnaces, and as the base is decomposed and converted to nitrogen and water there is no fly ash problem and the sulfur could be recovered as SO_2 by scrubbing the stack gases. Recently, the combustion of *sodium-based* sulfite waste liquors has also been performed industrially, in the Tomlinson type of furnace (138). The sodium compounds are recovered as a smelt of sodium carbonate and sulfide, whereas considerable quantities of SO_2 can be recovered from the stack gases.

To facilitate subsequent conversion to cooking chemicals, the conditions of the combustion should be chosen appropriately. In the case of kraft chemicals recovery, the formation of sodium sulfate, which is inert in the cooking process, must be avoided, and as much as possible of the make-up sulfate, added prior to combustion to cover the sodium losses of the recovery cycle, should be reduced to sulfide. Further, the sulfur losses

779

through volatile sulfur compounds in the stack gases should not be excessive, as otherwise the sulfidity of the white liquor will decrease to an extent which will affect the result of cooking adversely. The losses of sodium sulfate in the form of fumes in the stack gases will also increase at unfavorable conditions (excessive temperatures). In the recovery from magnesium-based liquors, there are no specially disadvantageous side reactions during the combustion, nor in the case of ammonium-based liquors, although the well known and undesirable reversion of SO_2 to SO_3 on cooling the combustion gases prior to absorption must be depressed. On the combustion

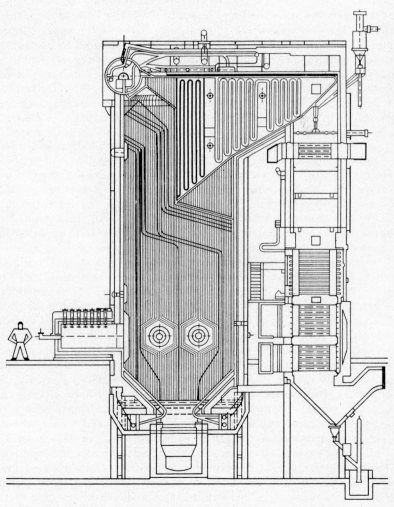

Fig. 11.4. Loddby extension furnace attached to an ordinary boiler for the combustion of calcium-based sulfite waste liquor (Motala Verkstad)

of calcium-based liquors, it might be feasible to change the conditions to decrease or avoid the formation of calcium sulfate and thereby to increase the content of useful calcium oxide in the ashes and sulfur dioxide in the gases. Similarly, it would be most desirable to recover the chemicals from the combustion of sodium-based sulfite waste liquors not in the form of a sulfide–carbonate smelt, but as pure carbonate, thereby recovering all the sulfur as dioxide over the stack gases. As will be seen in a subsequent section, that would highly simplify the regeneration of the cooking chemicals to a usable state. One method, that of pyrolysis in the presence of steam (*atomized suspension technique, A.S.T.*, method), seems to have approached that goal, but will simultaneously contaminate the carbonate recovered by a considerable amount of carbonaceous residues, which necessitates further operations (62, 115) and requires external heating, which is a severe complication. It is also vital that the desirable improvements outlined above should not introduce such changes in the combustion conditions that the heat economy is sacrificed, as one of the important tasks of the combustion operation is steam production. Further, the furnace must not get too complicated.

In order to facilitate the understanding of the chemistry of combustion of the waste liquors from the pulping industry, some thermodynamic data have been collected and treated mathematically to describe the systems involved in the combustion reactions (9, 106, 120, 136, 160). These reactions and their approximate equilibrium constants are given in Table 11.5. Depending on the combustion conditions, carbon will occur as carbon dioxide, monoxide, or elementally, hydrogen as water or hydrogen sulfide, and sulfur as sulfur dioxide or trioxide, as well as in hydrogen or metal sulfide, further as sulfate or elemental sulfur. The metals will occur as oxide, sulfide, sulfate, carbonate, or elementally. Obviously the independent variables are several, such as *temperature, addition of oxygen*, and the original *composition of the waste liquor*, including also the unevaporated *water*. To describe the complicated system, logarithmic equilibrium diagrams have been applied (9, 136). The following assumptions have been made to define the composition of the waste liquors:

$$p_{CO_2} + p_{CO} = 0.15 \text{ atm.}$$
$$p_{H_2O} + p_{H_2} = 0.10 \text{ atm.}$$
$$p_{H_2S} + 1/2 \, p_{S_2} + p_{SO_2} + p_{SO_3} \leq 0.01 \text{ atm.}$$

Metals are assumed to be present in excess of sulfur, so that it is theoretically possible to convert all sulfur to sulfate or sulfide, and this assumption is only important in some parts of the diagrams.

The variable of oxygen addition is illustrated as $-\log p_{O_2}$ on the abscissa, and the resulting concentrations of the various compounds are plotted on the ordinate. There are different diagrams for each temperature of combustion, and each base, Figures 11.5–14. In the diagrams, a close study reveals the essential quantitative composition of the gas phase at any conditions, as well as the qualitative composition of the solid phase. Generally speaking, at low oxygen content the solid phase becomes free from carbon

781

at a certain minimum temperature, and will contain, according to the temperature and base used, carbonate or oxide together with sulfide. At the same time hydrogen sulfide will appear in the gas phase. At still higher oxygen contents, SO_2 appears in the gas phase and sulfate in the solid phase. Of special interest are those conditions, where the theoretical partial pressure of the volatile sulfur compounds will exceed the maximum partial

Table 11.5. Logarithm of equilibrium constants of reactions at various temperatures

Reaction	Temperature, °K			
	800	1,000	1,200	1,500
$C(s) + 1/2 O_2 \rightleftharpoons CO$	11.9	10.5	9.5	8.5
$CO + 1/2 O_2 \rightleftharpoons CO_2$	13.9	10.2	7.8	5.3
$C(s) + O_2 \rightleftharpoons CO_2$	25.8	20.7	17.2	13.8
$H_2 + 1/2 O_2 \rightleftharpoons H_2O$	13.3	10.1	7.9	5.7
$1/2 S_2 + O_2 \rightleftharpoons SO_2$	19.7	15.0	11.9	8.8
$SO_2 + 1/2 O_2 \rightleftharpoons SO_3$	1.5	0.2	−0.5	(−1.5)
$H_2 + 1/2 S_2 \rightleftharpoons H_2S$	3.2	2.0	1.3	0.5
$H_2S + 3/2 O_2 \rightleftharpoons H_2O + SO_2$	29.9	22.8	18.4	14.0
$Na_2O(s) + CO_2 \rightleftharpoons Na_2CO_3(s, l)$	14.0	10.2	7.9	6.0
$Na_2S(s, l) + 2 O_2 \rightleftharpoons Na_2SO_4(sII, sI, l)$	47.6	34.6	26.1	17.5
$Na_2S(s, l) + 3/2 O_2 + CO_2 \rightleftharpoons Na_2CO_3(s, l) + SO_2$	30.9	22.4	16.8	11.3
$Na_2S(s, l) + 1/2 O_2 + CO_2 \rightleftharpoons Na_2CO_3(s, l) + 1/2 S_2$	11.2	7.3	4.9	2.5
$Na_2S(s, l) + H_2O + CO_2 \rightleftharpoons Na_2CO_3(s, l) + H_2S$	1.1	−0.7	−1.7	−2.7
$Na_2O(s) + H_2O \rightleftharpoons 2 NaOH(s, l)$	7.7	6.0	5.0	4.2
$Na_2CO_3(s, l) + H_2O \rightleftharpoons 2 NaOH(s, l) + CO_2$	−6.2	−4.1	−2.8	−1.6
$Na_2SO_4(sII, sI, l) + CO_2 \rightleftharpoons$ $Na_2CO_3(s, l) + SO_2 + 1/2 O_2$	−16.7	−12.7	−9.2	−6.2
$Na_2SO_4(sII, sI, l) + CO_2 + H_2O \rightleftharpoons$ $Na_2CO_3(s, l) + H_2S + 2 O_2$	−46.6	−35.3	−27.8	−20.0
$Na_2SO_4(sII, sI, l) + CO_2 \rightleftharpoons$ $Na_2CO_3(s, l) + 1/2 S_2 + 3/2 O_2$	−36.4	−27.5	−21.1	−15.0
$Na_2CO_3(s, l) \rightleftharpoons Na_2 + CO + O_2$	−50.6	−35.8	−26.1	−16.4
$Na_2S(s, l) \rightleftharpoons Na_2 + 1/2 S_2$	−25.5	−18.2	−13.4	−8.8
$Na_2 \rightleftharpoons 2 Na$	−0.6	0.3	1.0	1.7
$CaO(s) + CO_2 \rightleftharpoons CaCO_3(s)$	3.4	1.2	−0.3	−1.9
$CaS(s) + 2 O_2 \rightleftharpoons CaSO_4(s)$	43.2	30.8	22.8	14.7
$CaS(s) + 3/2 O_2 \rightleftharpoons CaO(s) + SO_2$	25.3	19.6	15.4	11.5
$2 CaS(s) + O_2 \rightleftharpoons 2 CaO(s) + S_2$	11.2	9.0	7.2	5.6
$CaS(s) + H_2O \rightleftharpoons CaO(s) + H_2S$	−4.5	−3.6	−3.0	−2.4
$CaS(s) + H_2O + CO_2 \rightleftharpoons CaCO_3(s) + H_2S$	−1.1	−2.4	−3.3	−4.3
$CaSO_4(s) + H_2O \rightleftharpoons CaO(s) + H_2S + 2 O_2$	−47.7	−34.8	−25.8	−17.1
$2 CaSO_4(s) \rightleftharpoons 2 CaO(s) + S_2 + 3 O_2$	−75.4	−52.4	−38.4	−24.0
$CaSO_4(s) \rightleftharpoons CaO(s) + SO_2 + 1/2 O_2$	−17.9	−11.7	−7.4	−3.2
$CaSO_4(s) \rightleftharpoons CaO(s) + SO_3$	−16.4	−11.3	−7.9	(−4.7)
$MgO(s) + CO_2 \rightleftharpoons MgCO_3(s)$	−1.1	−2.5	−3.4	(−4.5)
$MgS(s) + 2 O_2 \rightleftharpoons MgSO_4(s)$	41.9	30.0	21.9	14.1
$MgS(s) + 3/2 O_2 \rightleftharpoons MgO(s) + SO_2$	31.6	24.8	19.6	14.9
$2 MgS(s) + O_2 \rightleftharpoons 2 MgO(s) + S_2$	23.8	19.7	15.6	12.2
$MgS(s) + H_2O \rightleftharpoons MgO(s) + H_2S$	1.8	1.5	1.2	0.9
$MgSO_4(s) + H_2O \rightleftharpoons MgO(s) + S_2 + 3 O_2$	−40.1	−28.5	−20.7	−13.2
$2 MgSO_4(s) \rightleftharpoons 2 MgO(s) + S_2 + 3 O_2$	−60.2	−42.0	−28.2	−16.0
$MgSO_4(s) \rightleftharpoons MgO(s) + SO_2 + 1/2 O_2$	−10.3	−5.2	−2.3	0.8
$MgSO_4(s) \rightleftharpoons MgO(s) + SO_3$	−8.8	−5.3	−2.8	(−0.7)

782

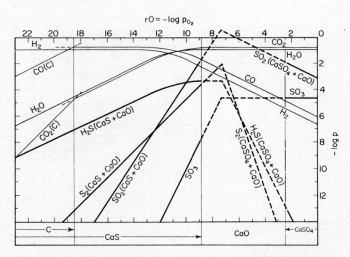

Fig. 11.5. Equilibria with Ca compounds at 1500°K: log p for each gas as a function of r0 $= -\log p_{O_2}$. The broken lines are invalid because of sulfur shortage; in these parts of the diagrams the solid sulfur compounds have disappeared, and the only solid present is CaO (Sillén–Andersson)

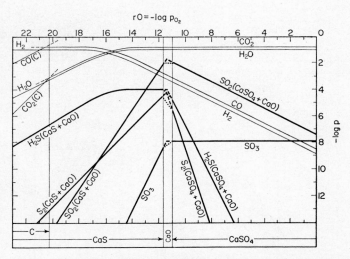

Fig. 11.6. Equilibria with Ca compounds at 1200°K and varying r0. The broken lines are invalid for the same reason as in Figure 11.5. The dotted lines for the sulfur compounds give the (homogeneous) equilibrium pressures that would really be obtained (Sillén–Andersson)

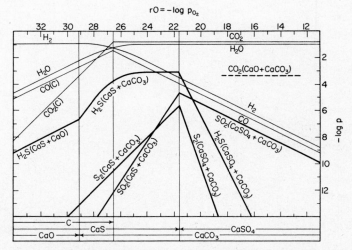

Fig. 11.7. Equilibria with Ca compounds at 800°K and varying rO
(Sillén–Andersson)

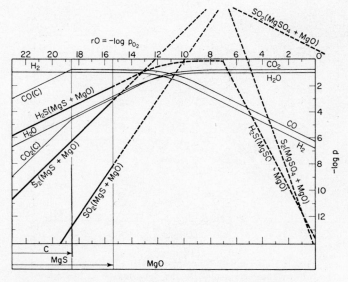

Fig. 11.8. Equilibria with Mg compounds at 1500°K and varying rO
(Sillén–Andersson)

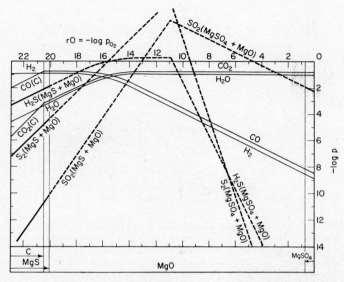

Fig. 11.9. Equilibria with Mg compounds at 1200°K and varying rO
(Sillén–Andersson)

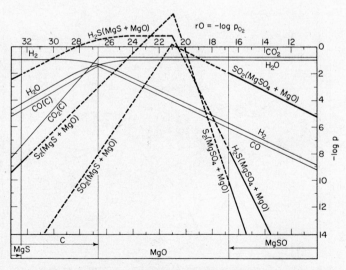

Fig. 11.10. Equilibria with Mg compounds at 800°K and varying rO
(Sillén–Andersson)

785

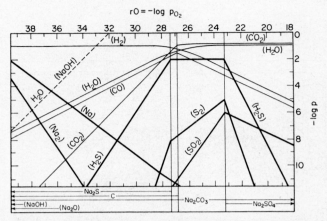

Fig. 11.11. Condensed phases and partial pressures of gases at 800°K. The small regions where Na₂O and NaOH can exist lie just outside the left-hand margin of the diagram. In the central portion of the diagram there exists a region where all sulfur present will be in the gas phase, mainly as H₂S (Bauer–Dorland)

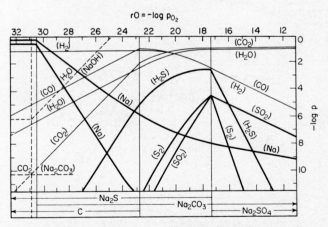

Fig. 11.12. Condensed phases and partial pressures of gases at 1000°K. NaOH and Na₂O cannot exist at this or higher temperatures (Bauer–Dorland)

786

pressure assumed to correspond to the total sulfur content of the system. Then all sulfur will disappear with the gases and leave a sulfur-free solid. As seen from the diagrams, that is the case for *magnesium-based* liquors over a wide range of temperatures and oxygen contents. This is also demonstrated by Figure 11.15. The gas escaping will contain either H_2S or SO_2. The main reactions responsible for this favorable result are at low oxygen pressures the easy conversion of the sulfide to oxide: $MgS + H_2O \rightleftharpoons MgO + H_2S$ and at higher oxygen pressures the thermal instability of the sulfate: $MgSO_4 \rightleftharpoons MgO + SO_2 + 1/2\ O_2$. Obviously, there are good possibilities

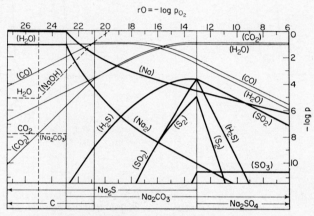

Fig. 11.13. Condensed phases and partial pressures of gases at 1200°K (Bauer–Dorland)

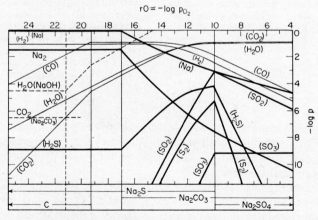

Fig. 11.14. Condensed phases and partial pressures of gases at 1400°K. The partial pressure of metallic sodium is becoming more and more important as the temperature increases, and will lead to high fly ash losses (Bauer–Dorland)

for a simple conversion of chemicals, as MgO and SO_2 can be used directly for the preparation of cooking acid.

In the case of *calcium*, the corresponding equilibria are far less favorable, and high temperatures are needed for the decomposition of the sulfate or conversion of the sulfide to oxide, as shown in Figure 11.16. Therefore, normal combustion ashes of calcium-based liquors are a mixture of sulfate and oxide, which cannot be used for cooking acid preparation. In some

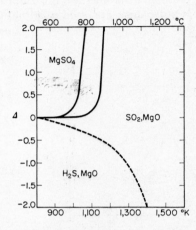

Fig. 11.15. Δ, T diagram for magnesium. Δ is roughly the oxygen excess or deficiency in percent. In the areas so marked, sulfur would at equilibrium be obtained chiefly as $MgSO_4(s)$, as $SO_2(g)$, or as $H_2S(g)$. In an intermediate area (without text), sulfur would be divided between SO_2 and $MgSO_4$ (Sillen–Andersson)

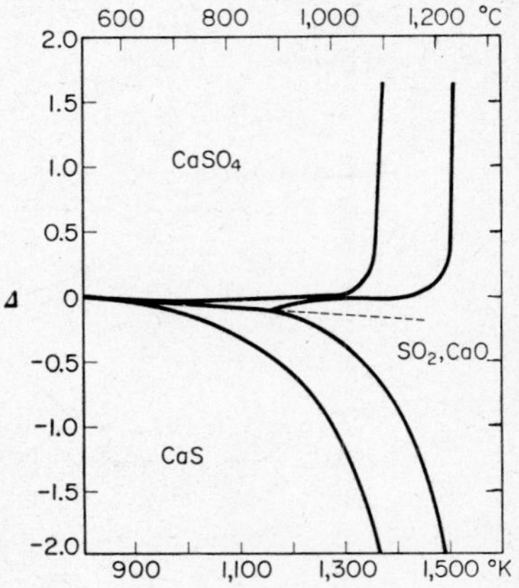

Fig. 11.16. Δ, T diagram for calcium. In the areas so marked, and limited by full-drawn lines, the sulfur would at equilibrium be obtained chiefly as $CaSO_4(s)$, as $SO_2(g)$, or as CaS(s). In the intermediate area (without text) appreciable amounts of sulfur would be present both as $CaSO_4$ and SO_2 (upper part), or both as CaS and SO_2 (lower part). In points on the broken line, $CaSO_4$ and CaS could be in equilibrium (Sillén–Andersson)

mills the oxide is utilized by adding the ashes in the neutralization of waste liquor prior to alcohol fermentation. The use of extremely high temperature of combustion would yield pure oxide but would probably introduce problems of maintenance.

The interesting case of *sodium-based* liquors (9, 106) will be considered rather more closely, Figure 11.17, cf. Figures 11.11–14, as it involves the kraft regeneration problems as well as those of neutral and acid sulfite cooking with the most promising base. Due to the considerable thermal stability of sodium sulfate, there is obviously no possibility of removing the sulfur from the smelt at oxidizing conditions. In the case of a kraft mill, where a high degree of reduction of sulfate is desired and yet the sulfur should be preserved in the smelt as sulfide, reducing conditions and a fairly high temperature should obviously be chosen. Excessive temperature must be avoided to prevent losses from volatile sodium compounds, including sodium in elemental form. Normal temperatures in the reduction zone of a kraft mill combustion furnace are likely to be around 1,000°C. The diagrams further reveal that at comparatively low temperature and not too reducing conditions there is an area where all sulfur is obtained in the form of H_2S, leaving a solid residue of pure carbonate, which is of the utmost interest for sodium-based sulfite waste liquors. This is mainly due to the reaction equilibrium of

$$Na_2S + H_2O + CO_2 \rightleftharpoons Na_2CO_3 + H_2S$$

being favorable at certain conditions. At higher oxygen contents, the oxidation will proceed to sulfate, and at lower oxygen contents the carbon dioxide content will be insufficient. At higher temperatures, the CO_2 content at reducing conditions will also be depressed, and, consequently, so will the favorable reaction. At still lower temperature (and oxygen contents) *carbon* threatens to contaminate the solids. Thus, the conditions of the combustion must be chosen carefully to deliver the chemicals in the form which is most desirable for sulfite cooking acid preparation, namely solid, pure carbonate and gaseous hydrogen sulfide, which is subsequently burned to sulfur dioxide, either in the regeneration furnace, or possibly after absorption separately to facilitate the final absorption of sulfur dioxide in the cooking liquor. The best conditions have been the subject of further consideration (3a, 11a, 97), while the question of heat generation in the reduction zone and the influence of the water remaining in the evaporated waste liquor has also been looked into, Figures 11.18–19.

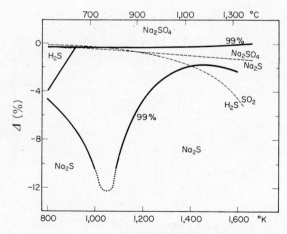

Fig. 11.17. Compounds obtained at various temperatures and oxygen deficiencies (Bauer–Dorland)

789

It must be observed that the above considerations apply to *equilibrium* conditions. As their result is that the temperature of the reaction zone should be kept fairly low, the question arises whether the reactions will be fast enough to reach equilibrium. That will depend greatly on the construction of the furnace, and it is possible that the gasification of the organic substance and separation of the inorganic solids should be carried out in one reactor and the final combustion of the reaction gases in another

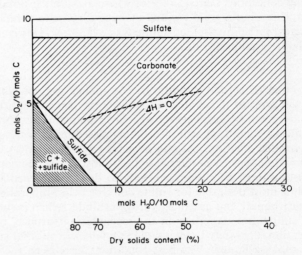

Fig. 11.18. Equilibrium composition as a function of water and oxygen content, 627°C (Andersson–Björkman, cf. 11a, 97)

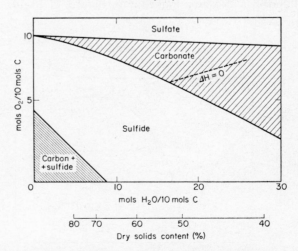

Fig. 11.19. Equilibrium composition as a function of water and oxygen content, 727°C (Andersson–Björkman, cf. 11a, 97)

(97). Such a path has already been trodden by the construction of the pyrolysis reactor (62, 115) which, however, suffers from the need for external heating. Development work in progress on the so-called 'shock pyrolysis' upon the introduction of limited amounts of air and oil for the heating (11a) will be commented on below.

An entirely different approach to convert the organics of waste liquor to energy is *wet combustion*, or heating the unconcentrated waste liquor under pressure to reaction temperature, at which air or oxygen is introduced and oxidation takes place. This can be complete (163) or leave a carbonaceous residue (36), which has to be burnt separately. The heat evolved by the reactions is used to generate steam and electrical energy, as well as for preheating the uncombusted liquor. The system has the advantage of avoiding evaporation of the liquor, and is also said to require less capital costs than the conventional installations but involves many unknown elements and does not seem to present great possibilities for the recovery of chemicals, especially as it is necessary to make the liquors alkaline prior to combustion to avoid the formation of corrosive sulfuric acid, which is quite aggressive at the temperatures in question (25, 32, 87). One neutral sulfite and one acid sulfite mill have tried the process, in the latter case on a large scale. Calcium-based waste liquor is charged with lime sludge, treated with steam at 130°C for gypsum precipitation, and then reacted, with preheated, compressed air at 300°C, 140 atm. Gas and steam leave the continuous reactor at the top and exhausted liquor below. A complicated system of heat exchangers, steam and gas turbines complete the equipment.

IV. Recovery and Conversion of Cooking Chemicals

1. PRINCIPLES

The chemicals are recovered from the combustion furnace in three different forms, namely as a smelt (or crystals) at the bottom, as collected dust and fumes from the cyclones and electro-filters at the top of the furnace, and as gases to be absorbed from the remainder of the combustion gases. The chemicals from the *soda process* present the simplest case, where sodium carbonate is the only chemical recovered, and where the losses are covered by the addition of sodium carbonate. As the active cooking chemical in the process is sodium hydroxide, the carbonate is causticized by means of lime addition. In the *kraft process*, the smelt consists mainly of sodium carbonate and sulfide, and the losses are made up by the addition of sodium sulfate, which must be added prior to combustion to be reduced to sulfide, which is an active cooking chemical. Also, in that case *causticizing* is necessary to produce the cooking liquor, which consists mainly of hydroxide and sulfide. The dust and fumes collected consist of sodium sulfate and are returned to the evaporated black liquor for combustion. There are further losses of sulfate as well as sulfur dioxide and some organic sulfur compounds with the stack gases.

791

These losses tend to decrease the sulfidity (percentage of sulfide in the smelt), which is roughly 30% in most mills. That is counteracted by the fact that the sodium losses are entirely covered with sulfate, which after reduction in the combustion yields mainly sulfide. However, when the sodium losses are low elsewhere in the system, the sulfate additions are small and sulfidity tends to decrease. To avoid the need for elemental sulfur additions, which are also sometimes practised, and then preferably to the white liquor (140b), the black liquor is oxidized in towers prior to evaporation and combustion. That operation will decrease the sulfur losses with the stack gases and at the same time reduce air pollution, cf. Section II.

The lime needed for causticizing was formerly often produced from limestone in conventional lime kilns and in some cases slaked prior to use. The calcium carbonate emerging from the causticizing in the form of a blue-green lime sludge was a practically valueless by-product which presented a disposal problem. It was stored in large ponds. Since the introduction of rotary kilns for lime sludge reburning, this by-product is re-used, and to make up for calcium losses, sludge from the ponds provides a long-lasting raw material for many mills. The recovery cycles for sodium, sulfur and calcium in the kraft process are illustrated in Figure 11.20.

Sodium-based waste liquors from the *acid* and *neutral sulfite processes*, combusted in a similar furnace as used in kraft mills, yield chemicals in similar form. As the sulfur content introduced to the combustion would

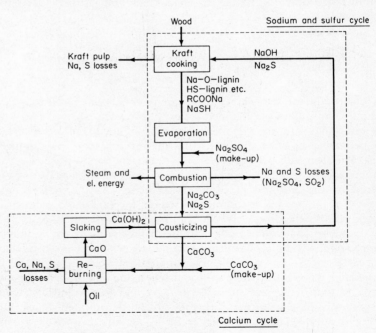

Fig. 11.20. Recovery cycles of a kraft mill

be approximately 1 S/Na instead of around 0.15 S/Na in the kraft process, the sulfur quantities leaving the furnace with the combustion gases are much higher, especially as the sulfidity of the smelt does not increase more than up to around 75%. To recover an appreciable part of the sulfur, around 75% of the total amount to be recovered, absorption of sulfur dioxide from the combustion gases is necessary. Although this presents some special problems, especially because of the comparatively low SO_2 concentration of the gases, as well as the danger of SO_3 formation from residual oxygen on cooling the gases, the absorption medium of sodium carbonate from the recovery cycle is rather suitable for this purpose. A more serious problem is that of purification of the smelt to useful chemicals. Sulfide-containing sodium compounds are detrimental to cooking acid stability in the acid sulfite process, and although some quantities could be tolerated in neutral sulfite pulping, the pulp quality will be affected in some respects. The complete removal of sulfide from the smelt chemicals is fairly complicated and has delayed the introduction of sodium base to sulfite cooking. Now, several recovery systems based on the chemicals from a conventional kraft combustion furnace are developing, which will be described in a subsequent section. Perhaps still more interesting are the processes under development, which require a change in the furnace construction to employ a first stage of partial or complete gasification of the organic components together with removal of all sulfur in the form of H_2S and reclaiming the sodium in the form of pure carbonate. Subsequent complete combustion of the gases will leave the sulfur in the form of dioxide in the gases for absorption. Figure 11.21 illustrates the recovery cycles of sodium and sulfur in a sodium-based sulfite mill. More detailed schemes will be given later which disclose that some of the alternative systems also require recovery cycles of auxiliary chemicals, such as carbon dioxide, analogous to the calcium cycle of a kraft recovery system.

In the case of *magnesium-based waste liquors*, combustion in a modern recovery furnace leaves magnesium oxide in the dust collectors and sulfur dioxide to be absorbed from the combustion gases, Figure 11.22. As magnesium hydroxide is sparingly soluble in water, the absorption of the sulfur dioxide from the dilute stack gases in milk of magnesia liquors presents a greater problem than for the sodium-based mills. In the case of *calcium-based* mills, no recovery is practised as yet, as the theoretical possibility of obtaining calcium oxide and sulfur dioxide by using high combustion temperatures has not been technically realized. In normal operation, the fly ashes collected contain around 50% calcium oxide and 50% sulfate. The remaining sulfur dioxide has too low a concentration, and milk of lime too little absorption ability to motivate a recovery. In comparison, the sulfur recovery of *ammonium-based liquors* is simplified in two ways. All sulfur is then obtained in the combustion gases as sulfur dioxide and can be absorbed by the alkaline ammonia (110a), which is more ideal for absorption than milk of magnesia but presents a problem because of its volatility, which puts a limit on the alkalinity allowable. At high pH the ammonia losses will exceed the increased SO_2 recovery. To recover

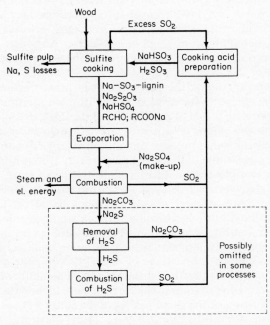

Fig. 11.21. Principal Na base recovery cycles of a sulfite mill

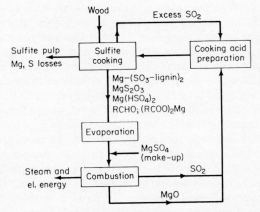

Fig. 11.22. Principal Mg base recovery cycles of a sulfite mill

ammonia from the waste liquor, on the other hand, is very difficult. Unless removed previously, it will decompose and burn during the combustion, and its removal by the addition of any other base to make the waste liquor sufficiently alkaline will consume at least as much chemicals as would be required when using that base directly for cooking acid preparation, and would further complicate the sulfur recovery. To recover any base by *ion exchange*, be it ammonium or sodium ions (20, 117), must for a large pulp mill present great practical problems and has not yet been applied industrially, although a system has been suggested which uses SO_2–water to recover the base cations from the ion exchanger after saturation of the latter. That would leave the waste liquor with only hydrogen cations, which might introduce problems of polycondensation and corrosion in the further handling.

It is observed in Figures 11.21–22, that apart from the recovery cycle of base and sulfur consumed in the cooking process, there is a separate, economically very important recovery cycle for excess sulfur dioxide, relieved from the digester during the cook. That cycle is necessary at acid sulfite cooking on any base.

The so-called *cross recovery systems* should also be observed. The most common is a combination of the waste liquors from two adjacent mills, one of which is a *kraft mill* and the other an *acid sulfite* or a *neutral sulfite mill*. The recovery process is that conventional for kraft pulp mills, with the exception that the inorganics of the sulfite waste liquor are used as a make-up for the sodium and sulfur losses instead of sodium sulfate. The chemicals used in the sulfite cooking have to be bought, although the sulfite mill gets a credit from the kraft mill corresponding to the cost of sodium sulfate saved. The essential drawback of such a system is that the sulfite pulp mill capacity will be limited to correspond to the sodium losses of the kraft mill, generally meaning to less than half the kraft mill production. Another type of cross recovery has been suggested, the '*silfate*' system (103), where waste sulfite liquor is used instead of water to dissolve the smelt from the recovery furnace. As before, the sulfite cooking chemicals are not regenerated but used as make-up chemicals in the kraft recovery cycle. The advantage with such a system would be that there is less water to remove in the evaporation station of the combined mills. The possible disadvantages of having the organics of the sulfite cook present during the caustization and kraft cook have been investigated. It should be an advantage in this process, if the sulfite waste liquor has passed an alcohol plant, whereby it is neutralized, and sugars are removed, which would otherwise consume alkali. There is a possibility of recovering some SO_2 for the sulfite process from the stack gases. The system is illustrated in Figure 11.23. It has not been industrially applied, as far as is known.

An analogous system for the combination of a *neutral sulfite* and an *acid sulfite mill* has been suggested, the '*silfite*' process (103), where the waste liquor from the acid sulfite pulp mill is used to prepare the cooking liquor of the NSSC mill. As in the former case, the organics and inorganics of the sulfite waste liquor could be tolerated in the subsequent cooking

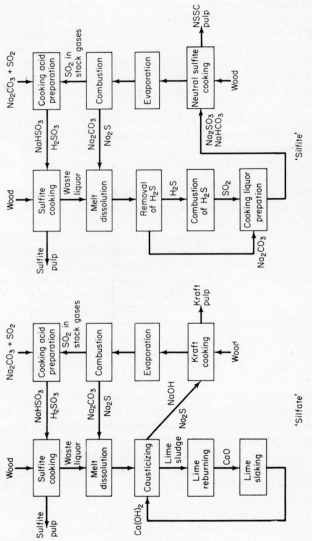

Fig. 11.23. Modified cross-recovery systems (Mannbro)

without too great a disadvantage, and the advantage of combining the organic matter from the two processes in one waste liquor is obvious. The regeneration of cooking chemicals for the two processes is, however, fairly complicated. In a variation of the process, the sulfite waste liquor is not used to dissolve the smelt but, instead, the regenerated chemicals, to prepare the NSSC cooking liquor. The smelt is treated in various ways to recover the chemicals in a form usable in both processes.

2. KRAFT PROCESS

A. Causticizing (91)

A normal causticizing system such as that developed by *Dorr Co*, is outlined in Figure 11.24 (38). The smelt leaving the combustion furnace by the spout is dissolved in water in a tank beneath the furnace. The *green liquor* formed will then have approximately the following composition, Table 11.6.

The presence of thiosulfate, sulfite and polysulfides is disregarded here. Causticizing is required to convert the green liquor to a usable cooking

Table 11.6. Typical green liquor composition, g/l Na_2O

Sodium carbonate	95
Sodium sulfide	33
Sodium sulfate	2
Total	130

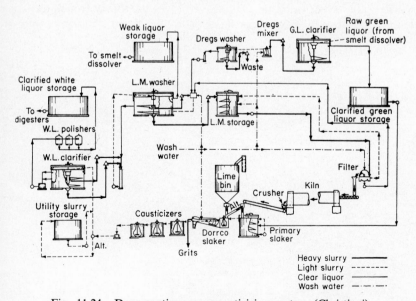

Fig. 11.24. Dorr continuous recausticizing system (Christiani)

liquor, *the white liquor*. The main reactions involved are the following:

$$CaO + H_2O \longrightarrow Ca(OH)_2$$
$$Ca(OH)_2 + NaCO_3 \rightleftharpoons 2\,NaOH + CaCO_3.$$

Thus lime, usually from the recovery kiln of the mill, is slaked in the green liquor and causticizing subsequently takes place. There are four important features in the operations required:

   (*a*) *Causticizing efficiency* should be high, in order to avoid excessive circulation of sodium carbonate, which can be regarded as an inert cooking chemical.

   (*b*) *White liquor concentration* should be high, in order to decrease the amount of heat needed in the cooking.

   (*c*) *White liquor purity* should be high, in order to prevent scaling troubles in the digester house and the evaporation plant.

   (*d*) *Sodium losses* should be low, which means that the wastes that leave the causticizing should be washed substantially free of sodium compounds. In the case where the major waste, the calcium carbonate sludge, is reburned for re-use, the need for washing remains, as excessive amounts of sodium compounds cause trouble in the lime kiln.

Some of these features are controversial, and the design of the equipment and the choice of operating conditions will determine the overall result. Causticizing efficiency is bound to decrease on increasing concentration of green and white liquor, since the reaction equilibrium is unfavorably affected by the decrease in calcium hydroxide solubility at high hydroxyl ion concentrations. Dilute carbonate solutions can be causticized almost to 100%, whereas 85–90% is the theoretical maximum at

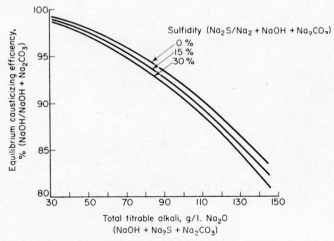

Fig. 11.25. Influence of sulfidity and alkali concentration on the causticizing efficiency (Goodwin)

normal white liquor concentrations (64, 85). Figure 11.25 demonstrates the influence of liquor concentration as well as sulfidity. In actual practice, the causticizing efficiency is always some 5–7% below the theoretical values and averages 80% (63). Thereby other factors, such as reaction time, quantity and quality of the lime added, the slaking conditions etc., contribute to the decrease (121). The specific surface of the lime, which is influenced by the reburning as well as the slaking conditions, is important to the causticizing efficiency and the amount of unreacted particles left in the lime sludge. Normally, 2–3% CaO is left in the sludge. Increased addition of lime improves the causticizing efficiency somewhat. *Two-stage causticizing* (63) takes advantage of this by adding excess lime in the first, main, stage, and using the residual calcium hydroxide of the lime sludge so obtained in a second stage to causticize either strong or weak green liquor.

The white liquor leaving the causticizing department thus contains the following components, Table 11.7.

Table 11.7. Typical white liquor composition, g/l Na_2O

Sodium hydroxide	76	
Sodium carbonate	19	
Sodium sulfide	33	
Sodium sulfate	2	
Total alkali	130	
Total titrable alkali	128	
Total active alkali	109	(= 141 as NaOH)
Total effective alkali	93	(= 120 as NaOH)
Sulfidity ($Na_2S/(Na_2S + NaOH)$)	30%	
Causticity	60%	
Causticizing efficiency	80%	

The purity of the white liquor is regulated by two purification systems, one for the green liquor and one for the white liquor. The impurities of the green liquor, called the *dregs*, consist of substance from the brick linings of the combustion furnace as well as from corroded metals, and are around 30 kg per ton of pulp in systems using the old rotary furnaces and about 3 kg per ton of pulp in mills using modern spray-type combustion systems (63). It is a matter of discussion whether in the latter case green liquor clarification is necessary, especially where the lime sludge is not reburned. The dregs are removed in a green liquor clarifier, a settling tank equipped with a slow-moving scraper, an overflow for clarified green liquor to storage, and a bottom outlet for the dregs suspension, which should contain 10–20% of solids. This suspension is pumped to the dregs washer, a multitray continuous thickener for counter-current washing, to which wash water is introduced at the bottom and from which a weak green liquor is recovered at the overflow. The latter joins the weak white liquor from the lime sludge washing and is used for the dissolution of the smelt. The washed dregs are discharged and generally very little sodium losses occur at those operations.

The clarified green liquor is pumped to the lime slaker, which can be constructed for one or two stages of operation. A rotary 'dry slaker' to convert the calcium oxide to hydroxide with small amounts of liquor thus sometimes precedes the slurry mixer tank, where additional green liquor is added. The operation is nowadays predominantly continuous as is the subsequent causticizing and clarifying system. The slaker is generally combined with a sloping classifier to remove the *grits*, or impurities entering with the lime. The slaking conditions will determine the settling characteristics of the calcium carbonate sludge formed, and a high temperature in the slaking, around 100°C, gives the most rapid settling. A high temperature is maintained by a low liquor-to-lime ratio, around 3:1, but the exothermal slaking reaction then has to be carefully controlled to avoid explosions. Excessive additions of lime should be avoided, unless two-stage causticizing is practised, as calcium hydroxide will decrease the rate of settling.

Causticizing occurs to a large extent already in the slaking operation, but additional time, 1–2 h, is generally allowed to approach the equilibrium. This is achieved in three overflowing stirring tanks, coupled in series, preceding a white liquor *clarifier*, a multitray continuous *settling* tank, equipped with slow-moving scraper arms, which discharge the carbonate sludge at the bottom and deliver from the overflow box a clarified white liquor to storage tanks. The white liquor then contains only about 0.1–0.2 g/l of suspended solids. When necessary, additional purification

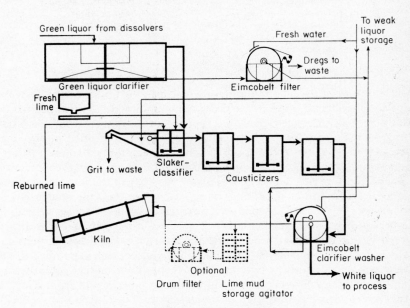

Fig. 11.26. Eimcobelt causticizing system

of the white liquor, 'polishing', is subsequently performed by *filtration* through anthracite coal, *centrifugation* or *vortex cleaning*.

The underflow from the white liquor clarifier, called *lime sludge* or *mud*, is contaminated by white liquor. The total quantity of dry sludge is around 500 kg per ton of pulp, and to avoid sodium losses, which could be quite considerable at this stage, the sludge is washed in a multitray continuous thickener, and subsequently on filters in one or two stages, to leave a final filter cake of about 60–75% dry content and less than 3% Na_2O, as determined spectrometrically (121), and which is likely to be in part chemically combined with the solids, as titrimetric analysis gives lower figures, 0.3–1.0% Na_2O. A recent space-saving system, by *Eimco-belt*, employs a belt-type drum filter instead of the white liquor clarifier and mud thickener, Figure 11.26 (90a). Mills operating a lime-sludge reburning kiln have to be particularly careful to wash the sludge, since sodium components tend to give clogging difficulties in the kiln. The weak liquor resulting from the counter-current lime-sludge washing is sent to storage and used for dissolution of the smelt. The sodium recovery of the causticizing cycle is about 97%, and figures as high as 99% can be achieved (38).

B. Lime-sludge reburning (39, 61, 145)

Around 250 kg lime per ton of pulp are needed for the causticizing. To buy such a quantity represents a considerable cost, and with the tremendous growth of the kraft industry, it would occasionally also present a raw material problem, in addition to the waste disposal problem of the lime sludge. Therefore it is natural that the majority of kraft mills today include lime-sludge reburning, converting their calcium carbonate by-product into useful calcium oxide. The first experimental kiln was erected in Sweden in 1905, but the major development took place in America after 1935 and in Europe after 1950. The kilns, Figure 11.27, operate according to the same principles as rotating cement kilns, including steel chains for heat recuperation. They are fired either with oil or coal, to supply the heat required for the reaction

$$CaCO_3 \rightleftharpoons CaO + CO_2; \quad \Delta H = +43,500 \text{ cal}$$

The dissociation temperature of calcium carbonate, at which the partial

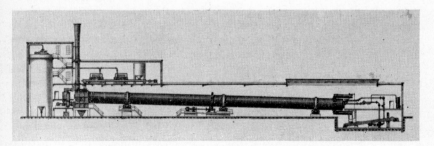

Fig. 11.27. Lime kiln (F. L. Smidth & Co)

pressure of carbon dioxide reaches 1 atm, is 910°C. The modern, long lime kilns are usually operated at around 1,100°C, but shorter kilns have to apply up to 1,300°C. Thereby the danger of 'dead-burning' will increase, involving physical changes in the oxide structure, which gives lower reactivity in the slaking process. A retention time of up to 4 h is provided in the long kilns, which are built up to or above 120 m in length and 3.5 m in diameter. The speed of rotation is usually about 1 rpm. and the inclination 1 : 20–1 : 40. Depending on the dimensions and load of the kiln, its recuperation equipment etc., the combustion gases leave at 150–350°C, and the burned lime at 800–1,200°C. These heat losses, together with radiation losses, approach 40% of the entire heat consumption of modern kilns, which is slightly above 2,000 Mcal per ton of lime product, or 0.2 t oil. The other 60% is divided approximately equally into decomposing the carbonate to oxide and heating and evaporating the water contained in the lime sludge. The sludge filter cake had a moisture content of around 40% unless centrifuged; recently, however, the pre-coat filtration technique has reduced this figure to 25%, or even lower. Calculated on its dry substance, the calcium carbonate content is around 90–93%, the remainder being 1–2% SiO_2, 2–3% Na_2O, and 1–3% CaO. The substance leaving the kiln has the following approximate composition, Table 11.8.

Table 11.8.   Typical composition of reburned lime, %

CaO	93
MgO	1
Na_2O	2
Al_2O_3	1
Fe_2O_3	1
SiO_2	1
CO_2	1
Total oxides	100

The occurrence of aluminium oxide is partly caused by attack on the alumina brick layer of the kiln, which, however, should be started up in a manner giving a protective layer of lime inside the bricks.

The size of the lime nodules leaving the kiln should preferably be 5–15 mm, smaller particles causing dusting troubles and oversize particles causticizing inefficiency. Generally, the operation of the kiln should be so regulated that subsequent grinding is unnecessary. A buffer storage of lime should be kept to eliminate irregularities between kiln and causticizing departments. A large slaker tank is an alternative suggestion (63) for buffer capacity. The losses of the calcium cycle will always necessitate the addition of external calcium oxide or carbonate, in a quantity of about 25 kg per ton of pulp, i.e. 90% recovery. As much as 97% lime recovery has been reported (38). Often the source of that addition is old lime-sludge ponds, previously made from the by-product lime sludge in periods prior to the lime kiln installation.

3. SULFITE PROCESS

A. *Recovery of consumed cooking chemicals*

As pointed out earlier, the base recovery of *calcium-based* liquors is not practised although some theoretical possibilities exist, if the conditions of combustion could be favorably changed. The ashes normally obtained, containing about equal amounts of calcium oxide and sulfate, are either permitted to leave with the stack gases or separated from them in dust collectors of the cyclone type. *Magnesium-based* waste liquors give ashes of magnesium oxide, which are similarly separated and recovered for cooking acid preparation. An overall base recovery of 75–88 % (6) is reported, depending on the load of the regeneration department (6, 43, 79), corresponding to an MgO consumption of only 20–10 kg ptp. The sulfur losses were about 50–25 kg ptp, i.e. a recovery of 64–70 %. Table 11.9 gives an

Table 11.9. Distribution of chemical losses in a magnesium-based sulfite mill, kg ptp

	Organic matter	MgO	S
Dump tank vents	—	—	2.0
Knotter rejects	3	0.3	0.4
Pulp after washers	37	4.4	6.5
Evaporator condensate	5	0.3	0.4
Evaporator vents	75	8.9	8.9
Acid settling tanks	—	0.1	0.1
Backwashing acid filters	—	1.3	3.0
Sewer	4	2.0	0.5
Total known losses	124	17.3	21.8
Unaccounted for		1.2	23.2
Make-up chemicals		18.5	45.0
Chemicals present in acid		85	150
Chemicals recovery		78%	70%

example of how the losses can be distributed on the various recovery operations, and is valid in part also for other systems for base and sulfur recovery. The oxide is washed on a filter to remove potassium which originates from the wood and tends to accumulate, thereby causing troubles in the magnesium recovery. Figure 11.28 illustrates the recovery cycle of the *Magnefite* process, or magnesium-based bisulfite pulping (43). *Ammonium-based* waste liquors do not permit base recovery, at least with methods practised up to date, whereas sulfur dioxide can be recovered from stack gases by absorption in dilute ammonia. *Sodium-base* recovery requires elaborate equipment, unless combustion conditions and equipment are radically changed to leave a pure sodium carbonate in the solid phase from the furnace. As those changes have not yet been carried to

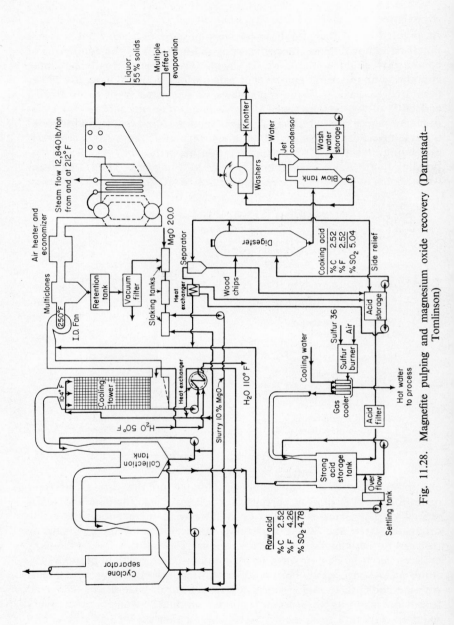

Fig. 11.28. Magnefite pulping and magnesium oxide recovery (Darmstadt–Tomlinson)

mill scale operation, the methods of removal of sulfur from the carbonate–sulfide smelt of a conventional furnace should be analyzed here (cf. 24).

One principal method suggests *controlled oxidation* of the sulfide to sulfite, another *separation of the carbonate from the sulfide* and return of the latter to the combustion furnace, whereas the remaining methods all include an acidification of the green liquor solution with sulfur dioxide or carbon dioxide. The oxidation method, in one design called the *Sulfox* process (5), involves the addition of green liquor in an oxidation reactor to a solid 'sulfite' powder in excess. The water evaporates and the sulfide is converted to sulfite in the presence of air oxygen. The fine fraction of the powder after oxidation, said to consist of mainly sulfite and carbonate, is separated from the remainder, which is recycled. It has also been suggested to oxidize the cooled smelt to sulfite directly with air under continuous pulverizing and stirring (66a). It is questionable whether these methods can give chemicals, sufficiently pure of sulfide to permit sulfite cooking, whereas they may be of interest for neutral sulfite cooking.

The *Western Precipitation* method (17a, 28, 110, 111), Figure 11.29 (28),

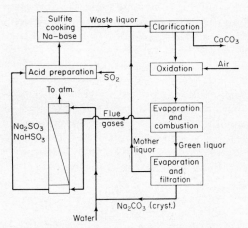

Fig. 11.29. Western Precipitation method
(Björkman)

which has been tested on a fairly large scale, is based on the fact that sodium sulfide on combustion will lose a substantial amount of sulfur to the combustion gases, thus being to some extent converted to carbonate, so that a smelt of approximately equimolar proportions of carbonate and sulfide is obtained. In the method, sodium carbonate is accordingly separated from the green liquor by crystallization after some evaporation, and the mother liquor, containing all the sulfide, is returned to the combustion furnace. The latter will therefore be loaded much higher than in the other processes. A low sulfidity in the smelt is desired in the combustion. The purity of the carbonate crystals obtained from the green liquor is high, 95+ %, and they could be used directly for cooking acid preparation. Similar methods for carbonate crystallization were suggested in an earlier patent (128) and studied on a pilot plant scale. Trials have also been performed (110) to separate carbonate crystals directly from the green liquor by using only small quantities of water for the dissolution of the smelt. Thereby a 'smelt jetting' principle was applied to disperse the smelt by steam jets prior to contact with water. The sulfide has a higher solubility than carbonate, and the mother liquor has a sulfidity of 60%, whereas the crystals after 'isothermal recrystallization' contained only 2% sulfide. A similar method of carbonate separation by partial dissolution of the smelt in a mother liquor of high sulfidity has been mentioned in some patents (e.g. 137). Another feature of the process is the reaction of sodium sulfide of the mother liquor with bisulfite and loosely combined sulfur dioxide of the sulfite waste liquor, to form thiosulfate, in order to eliminate evaporator corrosion. A special aeration stage, similar to that of black liquor oxidation, completes this treatment.

The *Institute* process (161) is used in some neutral sulfite mills in the U.S.A. It involves acidification of the green liquor with SO_2 to expel H_2S. Thereby the main difficulty is to avoid the formation of thiosulfate. SO_2-containing gases are brought in contact with the green liquor at almost 100°C co-currently in a reaction tower. It is claimed that the thiosulfate formation can be limited to 5% of the entire sulfite formed, and therefore the solution could be used for neutral sulfite pulping. The expelled H_2S is burned to SO_2.

Although the last-mentioned process is beautifully simple, it is questionable whether it could be developed for use in bisulfite or acid sulfite mills because of unavoidable contamination with thiosulfate. For that purpose, CO_2 is used instead of SO_2 to expel the H_2S from the green liquor. The *Mead* process (34, 105), Figure 11.30 (105), thereby utilizes stack gases only. They are first freed from SO_2 by absorption in sulfide-free carbonate

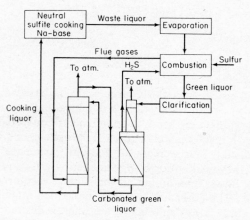

Fig. 11.30. Mead process (Björkman)

solutions to avoid thiosulfate formation and to recover SO_2, and then passed to a carbonating tower, to which green liquor is introduced at the top and from which H_2S disappears to be combusted in the waste liquor furnace. The stack gases from the furnace will therefore contain all the SO_2 of the process. In the upper part of the carbonation tower there are two gas exits, the lower of which allows the main part of the gases to escape together with most of the H_2S for combustion, whereas about a third of the gas volume is further treated with fresh green liquor, which absorbs the remaining H_2S and allows the rest of the gases to escape to the atmosphere. One weak point in this rather simple process is that the carbonated green liquor is obtained in the form of a solution, with no further purification operation. Therefore, complete carbonation is necessary, and that is not performed easily when using dilute carbon dioxide in the form of stack gases. The latter also contain some oxygen, which may cause undesirable oxidation of sulfide to thiosulfate. At present the process is only used for the recovery of neutral sulfite chemicals. A recovery of sodium of 80%, and 85% of sulfur is reported (34, 105).

The recovery process used by *Stora Kopparbergs Bergslags AB* (37, 94, 133, 138), Figure 11.31, for sodium-base acid sulfite pulping employs pure carbon dioxide for the carbonation of the green liquor. The sulfide-free

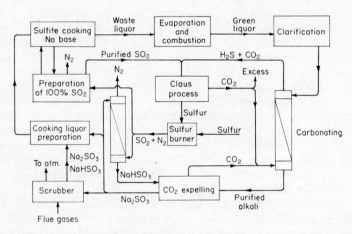

Fig. 11.31. Stora Kopparberg process, Skutskar (Björkman)

bicarbonate solution obtained is reacted with a bisulfite solution to give CO_2 for re-use in the carbonation tower and a sulfite solution, which is used for the absorption of SO_2 from the combustion gases. The mixture of H_2S and unabsorbed CO_2 leaving the top of the carbonation tower is reacted with SO_2 in a *Claus* furnace to yield sulfur and unreacted and undiluted CO_2, which is sent back to the carbonation. The sulfur is burned in a conventional sulfur burner together with purchased sulfur to cover the losses, and the SO_2 gas obtained is used for cooking acid preparation together with the sulfite–bisulfite solution obtained from the absorption of the gases from the waste liquor combustion. A preparation of liquid SO_2 is also included, part of which is used for addition to the digester in the two-stage process used, and part sent to the Claus furnace to be reacted with H_2S. It should be observed that the green liquor must be substantially free from thiosulfate in order to give a pure cooking acid, and therefore the green liquor preparation must avoid any oxidation.

To ensure a very pure alkali from the carbonation, not only pure CO_2 should be used, but the carbonation could also be carried out at a concentration which causes bicarbonate to precipitate. The bicarbonate crystals are then filtered off and washed. Such a system was earlier included in the *Stora* process (138), and is also practised in the *Sivola* process (112, 137), which in a modified form is used at a Finnish acid sulfite mill (116) and also at a neutral sulfite mill (100a). The bicarbonate is then calcined by steaming to give pure CO_2 and a carbonate solution, which is used for the cooking acid preparation. The mixture of H_2S and CO_2 from the carbonation is burned in a furnace to yield SO_2, which is then absorbed in carbonate, and the CO_2-containing residual gases are either lost or reused after removal of the inert gases by selective absorption. The gases from the waste liquor combustion are also treated for absorption of SO_2 and some CO_2. Due to a unique feature in the cooking process, which uses carbonate in a final stage for some carbohydrate removal, the Sivola process also includes a separation of carbonate from the smelt by partial crystallization. As high purity is not required for this alkali, such a separation appears logical. As the Sivola process does not employ a Claus process, the carbon dioxide contaminating the H_2S from the carbonation will not be recovered in pure form, and therefore the CO_2 recovery requires special attention. One source of CO_2 will be the stack gases, which having been subjected to SO_2 absorption are sent through the green liquor for pre-carbonation prior to the final expulsion of H_2S by pure CO_2. Another source is the carbonate added instead of sulfate to cover the sodium losses. It should also be observed, that although crystallization and washing of bicarbonate will permit an intense purification of the alkali, the calcination of the bicarbonate involves steam costs.

Two systems try to get around the complication of hydrogen sulfide removal by choosing the conditions of pyrolysis and combustion so that no sulfide is formed, according to the principles described previously. The *A.S.T.* (*atomized suspension technique*) *process* (62), Figure 11.32, employs a reactor operating at a slightly elevated pressure, into which superheated waste liquor is atomized. The reactor walls are gas heated, and the radiant heat decomposes the organic substance at about 750°C to carbon, carbon monoxide, hydrogen and hydrogen sulfide, whereas the sodium content of the liquor is recovered as carbonate, which can be separated together with the carbon dust and then removed by leaching. The gases of the pyrolysis are in principle used for heating the reactor and are then passed through a boiler for heat generation. An additional heat source is, however, needed.

The reactor construction material problems of the A.S.T. process are partly avoided in the *Billerud-SCA process* (11a), Figure 11.33, where air and oil are introduced directly into the reactor together with the atomized waste liquor. After dust separation, the pyrolysis gases, including hydrogen sulfide, are burnt in an ordinary boiler, whereas the sulfide-free sodium carbonate is recovered from the dust by leaching. If present in considerable quantities, the carbon has to be dried and burnt separately, but some possibilities exist for nearly eliminating the carbon by increasing the temperature of this 'shock pyrolysis' without impairing the purity of the carbonate. With a suitable droplet size, about 100μ, the decomposition occurs within a fraction of a second, which also allows operation at conditions where the thermodynamical equilibrium data indicate sulfide formation. However, at temperatures above the melting point of sodium carbonate, 851°C, the hydrogen sulfide initially formed tends to combine with the carbonate to form sodium sulfide. The process has not yet reached the mill scale.

The *absorption of sulfur dioxide* from the combustion gases is a problem in common for all recovery processes from waste sulfite liquors with soluble bases. In a wider sense, the absorption of dilute SO_2 gases also applies to the preparation of calcium-based cooking acids, except that the concentration of SO_2 in gases from sulfur or pyrite burners is decidedly higher. The problem will therefore be treated in the following section.

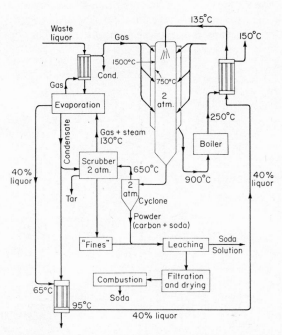

Fig. 11.32. Atomized suspension technique (Björkman)

Here it is sufficient to state that the sulfur lost in the chemicals recovery department of a sodium-based acid sulfite mill is reported to be about 10 kg ptp and the sodium losses about 2 kg ptp (133), to which figures should be added the unavoidable losses in pulp washing, evaporation, recovery furnace, etc. The recovery of sulfur from the combustion is about 75% (94).

A system of sodium-base recovery different in principle is the *Abitibi-Permutit* and similar ion exchange systems, Figure 11.34 (102a). The waste liquor is passed through cation exchange columns to recover the sodium ions, which are subsequently eluted by a sulfur dioxide solution prepared from sulfur burner gas. The eluate constitutes the raw acid after addition of make-up carbonate. The decationized waste liquor is concentrated and burnt, and additional sulfur dioxide can be recovered from the flue gases. Likewise, the drawbacks of this system remain to be seen when tested on a large scale.

B. Absorption of SO_2, excess SO_2 cycle, and preparation of cooking acid

The sulfur dioxide necessary for sulfite cooking liquor preparation is derived from several sources. The most convenient supply is that of purchased *liquid sulfur dioxide*, which can be added directly at any stage of liquor preparation and cooking, without the need for any absorption equipment (92, 98). However, it is also the most expensive form and is not in adequate supply for the sulfite industry. In some cases it is produced within the sulfite pulp mill, to facilitate the direct addition of sulfur dioxide to the digester in multistage cooking as well as to purify the digester relief gases of undesirable organic components, The devices for the

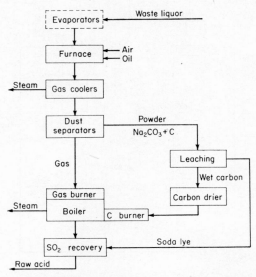

Fig. 11.33. SCA–Billerud process (Bergholm)

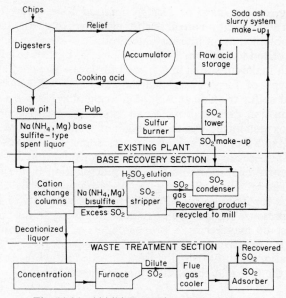

Fig. 11.34. Abitibi–Permutit recovery process

production of liquid SO_2 from digester relief gases are shown in Figure 11.35 (140).

In all other cases, the sulfur dioxide is obtained in a mixture of combustion gases from the burning of *sulfur, pyrite, hydrogen sulfide,* or *sulfite waste liquor.* The sulfur burners are usually of the *rotary* type, whereas the pyrite roasters are of the *Herreshoff etage* type, the *Nichols–Freeman*

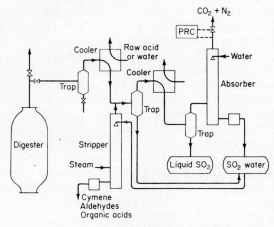

Fig. 11.35. Production of liquid sulfur dioxide according to the Somer–Celleco system

811

flash-roasting, or the *Lurgi* or *Dorrco fluidized bed-roasting* type. Their construction and operation are described elsewhere (e.g. 101, 102). Hydrogen sulfide obtained as an intermediate product of some recovery systems is either converted to sulfur in a *Claus* furnace, or burned to sulfur dioxide together with make-up sulfur in a special furnace. The combustion gases from any type of furnace and starting material will contain oxygen, nitrogen and sulfur trioxide as well, and in the flue gases from the waste liquor combustion carbon dioxide and monoxide are also present. The presence of oxygen introduces the problem of *avoiding secondary formation of sulfur trioxide* from sulfur dioxide, and sometimes makes *removal of sulfur trioxide* necessary to avoid excessive consumption of base in the cooking liquor preparation and gypsum precipitation in the case of calcium base. The presence of inert gases necessitates *selective absorption of sulfur dioxide* for its recovery. Finally, to ensure stability of the cooking liquor, the presence of hydrogen sulfide, sublimated sulfur and selenium dioxide must be avoided by a proper choice of combustion conditions combined with selective removal of selenium dioxide.

The formation of sulfur trioxide from dioxide in the presence of oxygen depends on the fact that the equilibrium of the reaction

$$SO_2 + 1/2\ O_2 \rightleftharpoons SO_3$$

is moved to the right at low temperatures and to the left at high temperatures. Therefore, the combustion gases of around 1,000°C originally contain relatively little of trioxide. At low temperature the rate of oxidation to trioxide is slow. Thus, a rapid cooling of the combustion gases is essential through the critical temperature interval, 500–900°C, where the rate of oxidation is rapid and the equilibrium favors trioxide formation. Cooling is accomplished in lead pipe coolers, e.g. of the *Jenssen* type, or spray coolers, e.g. the *Chemipulp–Kimberley Clark* system. The two types of cooler are often combined. In the spray coolers, water is sprayed into the top of one or two towers, where it meets the hot combustion gases, which rapidly cool down to the wet-bulb temperature of the gas. The hot water is removed from the bottom of the towers, cooled in a heat exchanger and recirculated to eliminate losses of dissolved sulfur dioxide. At the same time, the small amounts of sulfur trioxide formed during and after combustion are dissolved in the cooling water to form sulfuric acid, which leaves the system as an overflow from a weir box, where eventually a red sludge of selenium dioxide is obtained. Electro-precipitation of gas impurities by Cottrell filters is also practised. In the case of flue gases from waste liquor combustion, more elaborate types of cooling scrubbers are used (cf. Section 3).

Thus cooling has the effect of limiting sulfur trioxide formation, eliminating the trioxide formed, and removing the cooking acid decomposition catalyst of selenium dioxide (the other two potential catalysts, hydrogen sulfide and sublimating sulfur are eliminated by ensuring sufficient supply of secondary air to the furnace). Another important object of cooling is to facilitate the absorption of sulfur dioxide, as the solubility of the latter

812

in water will decrease on increasing temperature of the water (11, 60, 159) as shown in Figure 11.36.

The SO_2 content of the gases delivered to the absorption system varies with the raw material and the conditions used in the combustion. Theoretically, burning sulfur in air according to the reaction

$$S + O_2 \longrightarrow SO_2$$

should give an SO_2 content by volume corresponding to that of oxygen in air, or 21%. In burning pyrite in air according to the reaction

$$2 \, FeS_2 + 5\tfrac{1}{2} \, O_2 \longrightarrow Fe_2O_3 + 4 \, SO_2$$

only a maximum of 15.3% SO_2 could be reached. In actual practice, 14–19% SO_2 is obtained in sulfur burning and 10–14% in pyrite roasting.

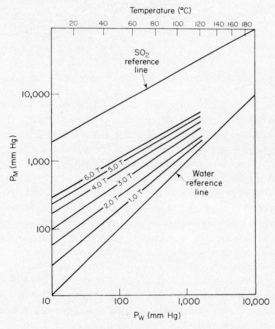

Fig. 11.36. Modified Othmer–Cox chart showing equilibrium concentration–vapor pressure–temperature relationships for the system SO_2–H_2O–CaO; combined SO_2 concentration 0.5 g SO_2/100 g H_2O; P_M, total pressure over solution; P_W, vapor pressure of water; T, total SO_2, g/100 g aq.

After combustion of ammonium- or magnesium-based sulfite waste liquors, an SO_2 content of around 1% could be expected, provided no additive fuel is used in the combustion. Similar conditions are expected in the case of sodium-based liquors in such combustion as yields a sulfide-free carbonate.

813

Absorption is facilitated by the fact that not only SO_2-water but also bisulfite (in some cases monosulfite) is required, whereby the sulfur dioxide is combined with a base. As defined in Chapter 9.I, the sulfite cooking liquor is said to be *based* on calcium, magnesium, ammonium or sodium, i.e. the corresponding bisulfite (in some cases monosulfite) is an important component of the cooking liquor. The fraction of sulfur dioxide, theoretically combined as monosulfite, is called *combined SO_2*, the remainder of the total SO_2 is called *free SO_2*, and the amount in excess of bisulfite, which means in excess of twice the combined SO_2, is called *excess SO_2*. The latter is present in the form of hydrated or unhydrated, dissolved SO_2 and is only used in the acid sulfite process. Obviously, in order to obtain a neutral sulfite cooking liquor, it is only necessary to absorb sulfur dioxide in an excess of alkaline chemicals, such as ammonia, sodium hydroxide or sodium carbonate. The reactions are then

$$2\ NH_4OH + SO_2 \longrightarrow (NH_4)_2SO_3 + H_2O$$
$$2\ NaOH + SO_2 \longrightarrow Na_2SO_3 + H_2O$$
$$H_2O + 2\ Na_2CO_3 + SO_2 \longrightarrow Na_2SO_3 + 2\ NaHCO_3.$$

The absorption is carried out in packed towers with the gas entering and liquor leaving at the bottom. In the case of sodium base there is no particular difficulty. With ammonia, the absorption of SO_2 is easily made complete, but at the expense of ammonia losses, since the latter is a volatile compound with a certain partial pressure and therefore appears in a corresponding amount in the inert gases leaving the top of the tower. Consequently, there is an optimum composition, approximately corresponding to the ammonium sulfite, where the losses of ammonia are balanced against the losses of sulfur dioxide. The exact economical pH of the liquor is thereby determined by the relative prices of ammonia and sulfur. As a slightly alkaline cooking liquor is required in the neutral sulfite cooking process, the pH is afterwards adjusted with extra additions of ammonia. To maintain a comparatively high concentration and still preserve an adequate amount of absorption liquor in the tower, some liquor is recycled.

In the preparation of *bisulfite cooking* liquor, the absorption of sulfur dioxide is somewhat, but not seriously, more difficult. The bisulfite liquors are made from ammonia, sodium bicarbonate or carbonate, or from milk of magnesia

$$Mg(OH)_2 + 2\ SO_2 \longrightarrow Mg(HSO_3)_2$$

by absorption of SO_2 in packed towers, applying virtually counter-current flow. In the preparation of *acid sulfite cooking* liquor, a still more efficient absorption is needed, as SO_2 in excess of bisulfite must be absorbed. In addition to the above-mentioned chemicals calcium and magnesium carbonate and calcium hydroxide are also used. The reactions involved are

$$CaCO_3 + H_2O + 2\ SO_2 \longrightarrow Ca(HSO_3)_2 + CO_2$$
$$Ca(OH)_2 + 2\ SO_2 \longrightarrow Ca(HSO_3)_2$$
$$H_2O + SO_2 \longrightarrow H_2SO_3$$

The operation principles are the same as in the previous cases. The dilute sulfur dioxide gas is introduced at the base of an absorption tower and the inert gases as well as carbon dioxide evolved in the reactions are released at the top of the tower. As a rule two towers, 'the weak acid' and 'the strong acid tower', are coupled in series to minimize SO_2 losses. Two principally different absorption systems are applied (3, 8, 65, 68, 102). In one of them, as exemplified by the *Barker 'milk-of-lime system'* (7), the gases are passed as bubbles through a liquid phase, in the other, exemplified by the *Jenssen system* (89, 90), the absorption liquor is sprayed into a packed tower containing a coherent gas phase, Figure 9.1. The packing is either various types of inert Raschig rings or of active chemicals, mainly limestone. Also, the milk-of-lime system is sometimes combined with a pre-absorption tower of the gas-phase type. In the *N.A.F.–Haglund system* (75), a suspension of calcium carbonate is used for cooking acid preparation. This involves previous grinding of the limestone and is preferably used where soft limestone is available, which is not suited to the Jenssen system as it gives excessive pressure drop in the absorption towers.

The theory of absorption developed for these operations assumes a multilayer system (18, 90). Next to the interface between the gas and the liquor two thin layers develop, one of gas and one of liquid, through which matter can pass only by diffusion, whereas turbulence and convection occurs in the rest of the system. At the interface equilibrium is assumed between the partial pressure of the gas to be absorbed from the gas film, and the concentration of the gas dissolved in the liquid film. There is a gradient of partial pressure through the gas film and a gradient of concentration through the liquid film which govern the rate of diffusion. The thinner the films, the less the resistance to diffusion. The thickness of the films will decrease with the rate of flow of gas and liquid, respectively. The rate of absorption will depend on the rate of diffusion through the gas and liquid films. In some cases, where the solubility of the gas in the liquor is high, the rate of diffusion through the gas and liquid film will then govern the rate of absorption. In such cases a spray tower is preferential, where the droplets move rapidly through the gas and are considered to have a thin gas film but a relatively thick liquid film. Where the diffusion through the liquid film is rate-governing, i.e. when the solubility of the gas in the liquid is low, a bubble-cap or sieve-plate tower is preferred, in which the moving gas bubbles will invariably meet fresh liquid where no thick liquid film has been developed.

The mechanism of absorption is rather more complicated in those systems, where a rapid reaction occurs between the dissolved gas and some component of the liquor. Then a zone of reaction must be assumed to occur somewhere in the liquid film, introducing new diffusion gradients of the reaction products. If the gas reacts in a way which virtually eliminates its partial pressure at the interface, the mechanism will not deviate much from that of a readily soluble gas. This is the case in the preparation of neutral sulfite and, essentially, bisulfite cooking liquors. However, in the case of acid sulfite cooking liquor, where dissolution of excess SO_2 is

815

required, the latter will exert a considerable pressure at the interface. Therefore, the sieve plate absorption tower should be of the type of equipment best suited for this purpose. For practical reasons, however, a special type of packed tower is generally preferred for calcium-based cooking acid preparation, where limestone fills the tiled concrete tower from a wooden grate about 5 m above the bottom, up to the top, where water is introduced. Figure 11.37 illustrates one theory of the mechanism (18) when SO_2-containing gases are introduced at the tower base. In the

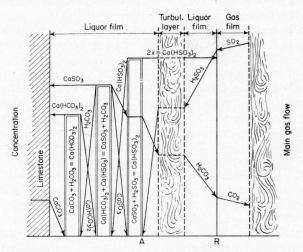

Fig. 11.37. Diagrammatic representation of the processes involved in the preparation of calcium-base sulfite cooking acid (Beuschlein–Conrad)

gas film there is a diffusion of SO_2 towards the liquid film at the same time as an outward diffusion of one of the reaction products, the carbon dioxide gas. In an outer layer of the liquid film there are corresponding movements of sulfurous and carbonic acids. The interior of the liquid film contains successive reaction zones for the formation of bisulfite and possibly monosulfite as well as bicarbonate. Somewhere in the liquid film there is also a turbulent zone, where the liquid moves down through the absorption tower, eventually assuming the desired content of calcium bisulfite and excess sulfur dioxide. The proportions of these components will vary with the reaction conditions. An increase in temperature will decrease the solubility of sulfur dioxide and increase the rate of diffusion in the liquid film layers (decreasing viscosity of the liquid layer and increasing solubility of some reactants). The net result is that an increased temperature tends to decrease the content of excess SO_2 and to increase that of combined SO_2. At some localities it is therefore difficult to maintain the strength of the cooking acid in the summertime, and to keep the base content down at the desired level. The quality of the limestone is also of importance in this

816

connection. Too hard a stone is slow in reaction, but a too loose one tends to give a sludge of particles, which is undesirable. An increase in the water input will decrease, especially the combined, but also the excess SO_2 content, and the latter could be increased by an increased gas load or by a 'free acid tower' containing no limestone, and coupled in series with one or two limestone towers. In the case of soluble bases, the combined SO_2 content is controlled by the concentration of the charged chemicals, such as sodium carbonate or ammonia, and is also easily adjusted.

The efficiency of a tower depends on the contact area of gas to liquid. That area depends on the shape of the stone or ring fillings and on the gross volume of the tower. It is vital that the entire cross section is wet, which requires a certain ratio of tower diameter to stone size, as well as a satisfactory distribution of liquor at the top of the tower. The height of the tower is considered to determine the efficiency of SO_2 removal according to the formula (12, 86) $K_s = K_b \cdot 0.5 \, h/H$ where K_b is initial and K_s final SO_2 content of the gases, h the height of the tower and H the height where the SO_2 content is half of the initial one. h/H should exceed 7. In the first of an ordinary two-tower system, 75–95 % of all SO_2 is absorbed, and the total losses are less than 1 %. The cross-sectional area determines the flow rate of gas and liquor which can be passed through the tower without causing 'flooding' of the tower. Obviously, the absorption towers for flue gases from waste liquors have to have an entirely different shape from those for sulfur or pyrite combustion gases, as the gas volume to be treated is 10–20 times higher in the former case. The design of packed towers for the adsorption of SO_2 in water or dilute *alkali* considers in a similar manner the principles of mass transfer from dilute gases to liquid films (140a). Problems connected with the absorption of SO_2 in milk of *magnesia* in packed towers led to the development of a venturi scrubber system, where the stacked gases are passed through a packed cooling tower and then through two venturi scrubbers in series, where the magnesia slurry is introduced (105a).

When leaving the towers a calcium-based acid contains considerable amounts of mineral particles, which are removed by subsequent filtration on sand filters or similar types (4, 42, 50). Especially important is the removal of silicate particles from the acid in rayon pulp mills. A typical analysis of the 'tower acid' obtained from a calcium-based acid sulfite mill for rayon pulp production is 4.0 % total and 1.5 % combined SO_2, whereas the corresponding figures of a greaseproof pulp mill are 4.2 % total and 1.6 % combined SO_2. It will be observed that the content of combined SO_2 is kept higher in the paper pulp production, and that in both cases the content is higher than in the acid normally charged to the digester. The latter difference depends on the fact that side reliefs from the digesters will dilute the acid before charging to a new cook. Most striking, however, is the low content of total SO_2 in the tower acid. The technique of building up an acid of 'high strength', i.e. a high content of total SO_2, 5–10 %, which admits good penetration and a rapid cooking, will be described below (cf. 26, 56, 93, 100, 119, 139, 144). It should be observed that unless there are extra 'free acid towers' or supplies of purchased liquid sulfur dioxide, it is only the excess SO_2 of the tower acid, i.e. 1.0% in the above-mentioned cases, which is used in building up the strength of the acid. In the cook, the sulfur dioxide consumed largely corresponds to the bisulfite, i.e. twice the combined SO_2, and the excess SO_2 can be relieved during the cook, or during the blow-down period, and recovered. The manner in which that relief is done and the relief gases absorbed in the acid preparation system determines, together with the excess SO_2 of the tower acid, the resulting strength of the cooking acid, the SO_2 losses, as well as the heat economy. If all gases are recovered under cooling, cooking acid charged to the digesters will have a temperature not far from that of the mill water. In the hot-acid system, only little cooling is applied, and the cooking acid temperature raised to around 70°C. This requires pressure tanks for acid storage.

The gases relieved during the cook have a pressure and temperature corresponding to the maximum digester pressure and temperature. They contain mainly sulfur dioxide (93) together with some carbon dioxide, organic acids and aldehydes, methanol and cymene. The sulfur dioxide could be recovered in liquid form by cooling these gases under maintained pressure (140). At the same time some of the impurities can be removed, which is claimed to improve the stability of the cooking acid. Normally, however, the top relief gases are passed over to a 'high-pressure acid' accumulator, and absorbed there. Modern accumulators have a working pressure of about 3 kp/cm². Unabsorbed SO_2 passes further on to a 'low-pressure acid' accumulator of around 1 kp/cm² and from that to an 'eductor tank' and to the acid towers. Blow-down gases pass over a cooler to the low-pressure accumulator during the initial blow-down period, and later to the eductor tank, which is under atmospheric pressure. Only so much heat is removed as is necessary to maintain the desired total SO_2 content of the high-pressure acid. The condensate from the cooler contains much sulfur dioxide together with volatile organic acids, aldehydes as well as a cymene phase. Cymene could be recovered here (cf. Section V) and the aqueous phase is either rejected or passed on to the acid system.

The sulfur dioxide gases thus go counter-current to the acid, which after leaving the towers is filtered and stored in pressureless raw-acid tanks, from which it is pumped over the eductor tank to the low- and high-pressure accumulators. The eductor tank or the low-pressure accumulator receives the side relief from the digesters, whereas normally the waste liquor from the cook is sent to separate buffer tanks prior to further treatment in the alcohol plant or evaporation station. Only in special cases, such as some magnesium-based mills, is there a recirculation of waste liquor to the acid system, the reason being that the sulfate content of the waste liquor will cause gypsum precipitation in calcium-based cooks, and the thiosulfate and polythionate ions of the waste liquor cause a catalytic decomposition of the cooking acid prior to and under the acid sulfite cook. In neutral sulfite cooking, a considerable waste liquor recirculation is permissible.

818

Thus the bisulfite solution of the tower acid, with its fairly small content of excess SO_2, absorbs considerable quantities of sulfur dioxide on its way to the digester, so that the final composition is normally 6–7% total SO_2 and 0.9–1.2% combined SO_2. An equilibrium is reached, where the sulfur losses together with the sulfur consumed in the cook balance the amounts of sulfur dioxide absorbed in the towers. The arrangements of this hot-acid system are illustrated in Figure 11.38, which also includes the towers system. Considerable local variations occur. A Sankey-diagram of the sulfur dioxide cycle is presented in Figure 11.39 (46). The interrelation of partial SO_2 pressure, and combined and total SO_2 is shown in Figure 11.40 for one temperature.

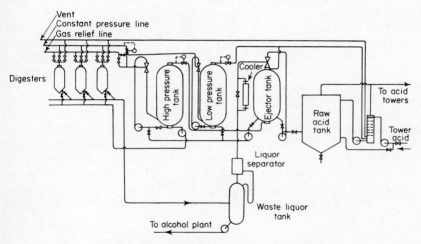

Fig. 11.38. Pressure acid system (Eidem)

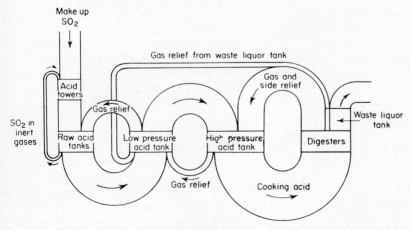

Fig. 11.39. Sulfur dioxide cycles in pressure acid system and digester house (Eidem)

To maintain the desired cooking acid composition in the various stages of a multistage cook it is sometimes necessary to pass some of the SO_2-containing gases to a free acid tower, often operating under pressure, and then strip off the absorbed SO_2 in a stripper column. The received, concentrated sulfur dioxide is then passed on to a suitable point in the acid system or charged directly to the digester.

V. By-Products

1. SULFITE PROCESS

Approximately half the wood substance is lost during the chemical pulping processes, and considerable efforts have been made to convert some of the waste material to useful products. Although the dominant use of the dissolved substance is definitely as a fuel, preferably combined with the recovery of cooking chemicals, there are several other minor uses, some of which are fairly important. The quantities of the various compounds available after the sulfite cook are listed in Table 11.10. Only a few of these compounds are utilized. Most common is fermentation of the *sugars*, which is standard in most European sulfite mills. In the subsequent alcohol distillation some *methanol* is also recovered. *Acetic acid* which is obtained in considerable quantities, especially in hardwood sulfite and especially neutral sulfite cooking, is difficult to isolate economically from the comparatively dilute solution. The same is true for the minor, water-soluble components. Crude *cymene* can be separated from the condensates removed from the digester gas relief system (157) and refined by simple distillation. If spruces and firs have been the wood raw material, the distilled

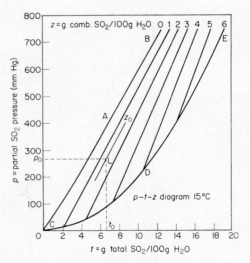

Fig. 11.40. Partial SO_2 pressure and cooking acid composition

product is 99 % *p*-cymene, the terpenes from which it is derived being α-pinene and some monocyclic terpenes. If pines containing Δ3-carene were used, the *p*-cymene will be contaminated by up to 30 % *m*-cymene, which makes the product less attractive for chemical conversion. The crude cymene is often used within the sulfite mill as a resin-cleaning solvent, and the distilled product finds some use in the paint and varnish industry. Minor quantities of *borneol* and *sesquiterpenes* are also found in the crude cymene.

The utilization of the lignosulfonates has been a standing project for generations of industrial wood research chemists, but no generally valid solution has been presented, mainly because the quantities of lignosulfonates produced as a waste are so immense that most products which could be derived from lignosulfonates, even from a few sulfite mills, will saturate the market. There are two main types of product made, namely:

(i) more or less purified lignosulfonates;
(ii) degradation products.

In the first category fall lignosulfonates for *tanning, dispersing, soil-improving* and other purposes, in the second category *oxidation products* such as vanillin, and *hydrogenation products* intended to be useful as solvents or liquid fuel. A comparatively large use of crude lignosulfonate together with the other components of the waste liquor in areas not too remote from the sulfite mills is as a *dust-binder* for gravel roads.

The most important way of isolating and purifying lignosulfonates is the *Howard* process used by *Marathon* (10, 76, 84, 104). After removal of most sulfite and sulfate by lime addition to pH 10.5, more lime is added to the filtrate to give a basic calcium lignosulfonate (27), which precipitates in the pH interval of 10.5–12.2. More than half the lignosulfonate quantity is thereby recovered, and separated by filtration. By the addition of sulfuric acid and magnesium or sodium sulfate to the filtercake, most of

Table 11.10. By-products (both commercial and non-commercial) of the sulfite cook

Compound	Origin	Quantity, kg per ton of pulp	Ref.
Methanol	Methoxyl groups of the glucuron-oxylan	7–10	13
Acetic acid	Acetyl groups of the xylan	30–90	71
Formic acid	Bisulfite oxidation of formaldehyde	0.5–1	71
Formaldehyde	Hydroxymethyl groups of lignin	2–6	2, 59
Methyl glyoxal	Degradation of hexoses	5–6	2
Furfural	Dehydration of pentoses	5–6	2
Sugarsulfonic and aldonic acids	Bisulfite substitution and oxidation of sugars	150–250	1, 73, 127
Sugars	Hemicellulose and cellulose	200–400	143
Cymene	Bisulfite oxidation of terpenes	0.3–1	122
Lignosulfonates	Lignin	600–800	10, 49, 84

the calcium is removed as gypsum, whereupon the neutral magnesium or sodium lignosulfonate can be obtained as a light brown powder upon evaporation and drying. The purified product can be used as a *tanning aid* together with vegetable tannins or synthetic tanning agents. However, because of the scarcity of phenolic groups in the lignosulfonates, only about 0.3 per monomer, their own combination with the hide will merely be through the sulfonate groups and therefore no water-proof tanning is achieved by lignosulfonates alone (69). A chemical combination of lignosulfonates with formaldehyde and phenolic compounds has been tried on an industrial scale, but does not represent an economically or technically satisfactory solution. Purification is necessary to remove calcium and iron, which react with the vegetable tannins, and sugars, which increase the hygroscopity of the leather, but purification costs, although low, in combination with the poor tanning properties prevent a more universal acceptance of lignosulfonates in an industry which is otherwise large enough to absorb very considerable quantities. Sulfite mills operating on bases other than calcium could possibly eliminate the need for purification, however, but with the exception of ammonia such mills will need the fuel value of the lignin for the recovery of the cooking chemicals. Some mills based on ammonia are able to sell evaporated waste liquor for tanning purposes, whereby it is vital to operate a fermentation plant to eliminate a maximal amount of sugar prior to the evaporation. As the pentoses are not removed by the conventional alcohol fermentation process, it is advantageous to combine *Saccharomyces* and *Torulopsis* fermentation (cf. below) to remove the sugars more completely.

The use of lignosulfonates as *dispersants* for oil-well drilling mud and similar purposes seems to be more promising but still a comparatively local outlet for the product (76). *Soil-improvement* with lignosulfonates is achieved at certain types of soil, but has not met with general success.

Vanillin is obtained from both sulfite and kraft lignin on heating with alkali (129, 149a). The yield of vanillin is only around 5% of the lignin. Condensed lignin, such as high-molecular lignosulfonates or kraft lignin gives lower yields, and highly sulfonated (and less condensed) lignin higher yields (74). Simultaneous oxidation, especially with nitrobenzene, considerably improves the vanillin yield, up to 25% of the lignin (57, 96). Vanillin is extracted from the reaction mixture either by benzene after acidification or as the sodium salt with butanol directly from the alkaline solution. The latter procedure eliminates some technical difficulties such as foaming. Purification is obtained through the sodium bisulfite compound. Only softwood lignin is suitable for vanillin production, since hardwood lignin yields 2–3 times as much syringaldehyde as vanillin (e.g. 83, 114) because of its high content of syringyl groups. Other aromatic products could also be derived from lignin upon oxidative treatment, such as *vanillic acid* (113), but only *pentamethylphenol* and similar compounds, obtained on high-temperature treatment of lignin with methanol (108), have been obtained in yields approaching those of vanillin, and none have reached the commercial production stage.

Catalytic hydrogenation of lignin has also remained a project in the laboratory and pilot plant scale. Substantial quantities of aromatic or alicyclic compounds are obtained (17, 78, 82, 141), but the hydrogenation products from lignosulfonates contain combined sulfur, which makes them less suitable for fuel purposes and gives them a foul smell (23, 58, 95). The sulfur compounds also tend to poison the metal catalysts.

Large-scale fermentation of the sugars of the sulfite waste liquor (35) was commenced in 1909 in Skutskär, Sweden, and is now practised by most European sulfite mills in order to reduce stream pollution and to obtain valuable products, especially *ethanol*. Ordinary baker's yeast, *Saccharomyces cerevisiæ* Hansen, is used for fermentation (47). Glucose and mannose are directly fermentable by the yeast, and after a certain adaptation period for the yeast, galactose also becomes fermentable, whereas the pentoses remain unfermented. The quantity of fermentable sugars arriving with the waste liquor at the alcohol plant depends on the cooking conditions (cf. Chapter 9.I) as well as the efficiency of the liquor recovery. It is important for the economy of the subsequent distillation, as well as for the liquor evaporation and combustion, that the liquor should be reclaimed without excessive dilution. Equipment is generally provided to recover 90 % of the substance at a dilution of 10–15 %, cf. Chapter 10.II. As the aldonic acid formation during the sulfite cook results in the destruction of approximately one-third of the sugars, the quantities of sugars available for fermentation in the alcohol plant are reduced to about 100 kg per ton of wood for strong paper pulping and 140 kg for rayon pulp cooking. 10–15 m³ of waste liquor per ton of pulp thus go to the alcohol plant, containing 30–50 g/l sugars, 25–35 g/l being fermentable by *Saccharomyces* yeast. Around 2 % of the fermented sugars are lost at the neutralization of the waste liquor prior to fermentation, 5 % left unfermented, 8 % lost in side reactions during the fermentation and 2 % lost in the form of ethanol escaping distillation. The stoichiometrical yield of alcohol from the hexoses according to the reaction

$$C_6H_{12}O_6 \longrightarrow 2\ C_2H_5OH + 2\ CO_2$$

is 51 %. Consequently, the total amount of ethanol obtained is about 100–130 l 95 % ethanol/t of rayon pulp and 50–100 l/t of paper pulp. The fermentation requires a pH of around 5, and the degassed and aerated waste liquor is therefore neutralized with calcium carbonate, usually in the form of lime mud from an adjacent kraft mill, about 1 t/t of alcohol produced. Batch as well as continuous neutralization operations are used, and the precipitated calcium sulfite is separated from the liquor in settling tanks, to which some nutrient salts are also added, about 10 kg ammonium sulfate and 25 kg superphosphate per ton of alcohol produced. The hot waste liquor should then be cooled down to the optimal temperature for fermentation, or 33°C. The adaptation of the yeast to small amounts of sulfur compounds, such as bisulfite and hydrogen sulfite, has been investigated (44).

The fermentation is carried out during a continuous flow of liquor

823

through large vats to allow a retention time of 8–24 h. The higher the concentration of yeast, the more rapid the fermentation. The yeast is either detained by mechanical means, or separated by centrifuges from the fermented liquor and returned to the fermentation. A small amount of yeast, corresponding to the cell growth, is removed from the system continuously and sold as *fodder yeast* after drying. The alcohol is recovered by distillation, usually in two columns, one for stripping and one for rectification. In the rectifier column the main product, 95% ethanol, is received from some bottoms below the top. In the top some aldehydes and methanol are recovered to be returned to the fermentation vats (142), and some bottoms are obtained from the base of the column *fusel-oil*, which contains C_3–C_5 alcohols together with borneol, some cymene, etc. The ethanol sold for consumption and even for some industrial purposes has to be demethanolized in a special column, and for the production of absolute alcohol for motor fuel, etc., dehydration columns of various types are in use, such as azeotropic distillation with benzene or trichloroethylene, as well as systems using absorption of water by dehydrated sodium-potassium acetate or calcium sulfate, which are then recycled for regeneration.

The waste liquor leaving the base of the stripping column is passed to the evaporation plant. To minimize heat consumption, special combinations of distillation and evaporation have been designed. Without such systems, steam consumption is considerable, or 15 t steam/t of ethanol produced. Figure 9.1, as well as figures 11.41–42 give flow sheets for the production of sulfite alcohol. Some mills include in addition a considerable organic chemical industry based on sulfite alcohol, mainly over *acetaldehyde* to *butanol, acetic acid, esters, etc.*, as well as over *ethylene oxide* to glycols and ethylene oxide polycondensates with phenols, etc.

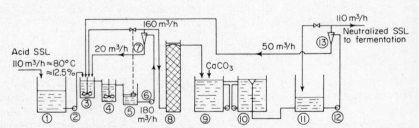

Fig. 11.41a. Flow sheet and specification of apparatus for the neutralization, clarification and sulfate precipitation operations at the Domsjö alcohol plant. (1) acid liquor storage, 250 m³; (2) acid liquor pump; (3) and (4) seeding tanks, diam. 3 m, H = 4 m, liquor volume 20 m³, with Stamo agitators type 1, 1,400 rpm, 10 hp; (5) buffer tank, diam. 3 m, H = 4 m; (6) pump; (7) seeding cyclones 4-8 units, diam, 200 mm, conical angle 15°, inlet opening 12 × 100 mm², reject opening diam. 14 mm, accept opening diam. 36 mm; (8) limestone towers, 4 units, diam. 2.3 m, H = 10 m; (9) and (10) final neutralization tanks, diam. 6 m, H = 5.6 m, pump capacity 12,000 1/min; (11) buffer tank, diam. 6 m, H = 5.6 m; (12) pump; (13) clarification cyclones, 5-8 units, same as seeding cyclones but with reject opening diam. 20 mm (Carlson *et al*)

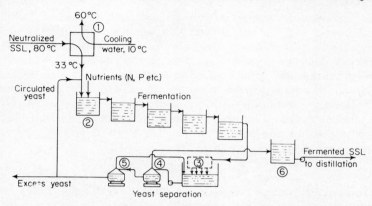

Fig. 11.41b. Flow sheet and specification of apparatus for the fermentation at the Domsjö alcohol plant. (1) heat exchanger, (2) three lines of five fermenters (155 m³) each, (3) two screens, 60 mesh, (4) six primary separators, de Laval DDB 6M, (5) one secondary separator, (6) tank for fermented SSL, 155 m³ (Modén)

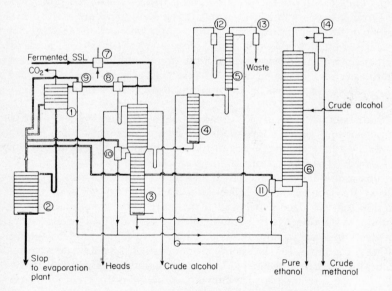

Fig. 11.42. Flow sheet and specification of apparatus for distillation at the Domsjö alcohol plant. (1) CO_2-stripping column, diam. 2.2 m, 3 plates; (2) alcohol stripping column, 3 units diam. 2.2m, 20 plates each; (3) alcohol rectifying column, lower part diam. 1.2 m, 30 plates, upper part diam. 1.7 m, 25 plates; (4) stripping column, diam. 1.0 m, 25 plates; (5) hydro-selection column, diam. 0.6 m, 30 plates; (6) methanol-ethanol-separating column, diam. 1.7 m, 70 plates; (7–14) heat exchangers (Carlson *et al*)

825

Other fermentation methods have been tried, such as butanol–acetone as well as acetic and lactic acid fermentation, but with little commercial success. Only yeast production by means of *Torulopsis utilis* fermentation, which can consume both hexoses and pentoses for its growth, is now operated on the large scale from sulfite waste liquor.

Furfural is obtained from pentoses on acid distillation. However, the pentose and furfural quantities present in the sulfite waste liquor are not sufficient to make a furfural production economically feasible. Instead the furfural production utilizes hardwood wastes and oat hulls.

2. KRAFT PROCESS

The two principal commercial by-products of the kraft pulping industry are *crude sulfate turpentine* and *crude tall oil*. Some of the mills also include refineries for these products, but normally refining is done elsewhere, often in the paint and lacquer industry, which is the chief consumer of the refined products. About 1,000,000 t of tall oil is produced yearly, half of which in North America (92a).

The content of terpenes in the wood depends on species, geographical location of the forests, as well as the wood handling, especially the storage of the wood. A fair yield of turpentine in a kraft mill is around 10 kg/t of pulp. The quantity of tall oil produced is dependent on the same factors, but is much larger, a fair yield being at least 50 kg/t of pulp in the northern regions of Sweden and half that amount in middle or southern Sweden, in both cases from kraft mills using scots pine. The tall oil yields from southern pines in southern United States agree with the higher figure (28a) and those from Douglas fir at the Pacific Coast are only about 30 kg/t (33a, 161a). There are also seasonal variations, especially in the ease of recovery (28a).

Crude sulfate turpentine, obtained as a digester relief condensate, contains some sulfur compounds, which give the product a very foul smell. Distillation endeavours to remove the smell by taking out a light and a heavy fraction containing most of the malodorous compounds and yielding a middle fraction called refined turpentine, which is used as a solvent for lacquers, etc. Since some of the components of the heavy fraction tend to decompose and form more volatile sulfur compounds, the middle fraction has to be re-distilled to get rid of all odour. Another drawback has caused considerable resistance to the general acceptance of sulfate turpentine for lacquers. Some sensitive persons develop skin irritations on handling lacquers containing sulfate turpentine. Investigation of the phenomena has shown that the skin-toxic compound is an hydroperoxide formed by the Δ3-carene on exposure to air. Freshly distilled turpentine does not show such effects, nor does stored turpentine containing no carene.

The light fraction removed on distillation constitutes about 5–10% of the crude turpentine and contains terpenes contaminated by organic sulfur compounds, such as methyl mercaptan and *dimethyl sulfide* (52), the

826

latter being of industrial interest for the production of dimethyl sulfoxide (76a, 79a, 107), an excellent solvent. The heavy fraction, about 15 % of the crude turpentine, besides some sulfur compounds, also contains sesquiter-penes, diterpenes and terpene alcohols, which can be recovered by vacuum distillation. The middle fraction, about 75 % of the crude turpentine, contains terpenes and a small amount of terpene alcohols. If pine is the principal wood raw material, the terpenes are α-pinene, β-pinene, Δ3-carene and some monocyclic terpenes such as dipentene, carvestrene, terpinene and terpinolene. In the case of scots pine the pinene fraction is 50–60 % of the refined turpentine, α-pinene being the dominating compon-ent, and the carene fraction 35–40 %, whereas in turpentine from southern pines there is no carene and considerable amounts of β-pinene. In some cases, the individual terpenes are isolated for further processing to other chemicals of some importance for the perfumery and lacquer industry, etc. p-Cymene can be produced by de-hydrogenation of pinene and the p-substituted monocyclic terpenes, whereas carene yields a mixture of p- and m-cymene (123).

The *tall oil* is recovered from the black liquor at some early stage of its concentration (134). Because of the salt content, the tall oil separates from the water phase and is removed as 'soap skimmings'. The recovery of tall oil with the skimmings depends on the retention time and black liquor solids content, 3 h and 36 % being recommended (161a). The recovery is subject to seasonal variations between 60 and 90 % (28a). About 10 % black liquor solids and 30–40 % water are occluded in the skimmings. These contain the tall oil components as their sodium salts, and the tall oil is obtained from the soap skimmings after acidification with sulphuric acid. The water phase containing sodium sulfate and some water-solubles are returned to the black liquor. The tall oil, which in the case of scots pine consists of about 50 % fatty acids, about 40 % resin acids and some 10 % 'unsaponifiables', can only be used in crude form in exceptional cases and is normally fractionated by vacuum distillation. This yields about 10 % *light oil*, consisting of neutral com-ponents and some saturated fatty acids, 40 % *fatty acid fraction*, mainly unsaturated fatty acids contaminated by resin acids, 20 % *resin acid fraction*, mainly abietic acid, and finally about 30 % *pitch residue* and other losses. The pitch contains polymerization products from the components, and this amount could be decreased by improved distillation technique, such as continuous operation and higher vacuum. It further contains phytosterols, mainly β-*sitosterol* and β-*sitostanol*, which have been subject to interest for commercial production of sex hormones otherwise made from cholosterol. The latter has proved the superior raw material and little, if any, tall oil phytosterols are now produced on the large scale.

The fatty acid fraction is the most valuable and is sometimes redistilled for higher purity. It is then very lightly colored and a suitable base for drying oils, after esterification with glycerol or preferably pentaerythritol. It is also used for soap production. The resin acid fraction is applied in paper sizing, etc. after partial saponification with alkali, or in the paint and laquer industry after chemical modification, such as hydrogenation, dimerization, esterification, etc. The resin acid fraction predominates in the tall oil from many North American wood species (33a, 161a). Hardwoods yield only small amounts of tall oil, with no resin acids.

Methanol is obtained in the digester gas relief condensates in amounts of 2–5 kg/t of pulp, but its isolation is not considered economically justified. As seen from Table 11.11, the main by-products of the kraft cook are

Table 11.11. By-products (both commercial and non-commercial) of the kraft cook

Compound	Origin	Quantity, kg per ton of pulp	Ref.
Methanol	Methoxyl groups of lignin and possibly glucuronoxylan	5	14
Acetate	Acetyl groups of the xylan as well as degraded carbohydrates	100–200	158
Formiate	Degradation of carbohydrates	40	41, 158
Lactate	Degradation of carbohydrates	100	41, 53, 66
Saccharinic acids and lactones	Degradation of carbohydrates	250	41, 66
Aliphatic sulfur compounds (methyl mercaptan, sulfide, disulfide)	Methoxyl groups of lignin and possibly glucuronoxylan	1	52, 107
Turpentine	Terpenes	8–10	52, 107
Tall oil (fatty and resin acid salts, phytosterols, etc.)	Wood resin components	20–100	88
Alkali lignin	Lignin	400–600	53, 147

the *degradation products of carbohydrates and lignin*. However, these are mainly utilized as fuel in the regeneration of cooking chemicals. Considerable effort has been spent on obtaining more valuable chemicals from these compounds, but with only very limited success as in the case of the sulfite process by-products. The most consistent efforts on the carbohydrate degradation products were made between 1910–20 using *dry distillation* of the alkaline black liquor powder together with excess lime or alkali (81, 118), to obtain methanol, acetone, methylethylketone, higher ketones and other components of light and heavy oils, in appreciable quantities (60–70 kg/t of pulp each of the low-molecular and the high-molecular compounds). The radical changes needed in the chemical recovery equipment, as well as the large heat consumption and the contamination of the products by foul-smelling sulfur compounds has prevented common acceptance of the process. Similarly, a process for *pressure heating* of aqueous black liquor in the presence of excess alkali (72), although giving high yields of methanol, acetic acid and tars, has not been exploited commercially. This idea has more recently received renewed attention (48a), in that heating of the black liquor for 10–20 min at 250–290°C together with small amounts of alkali and sulfide gave up to half of the organic substance in low-molecular form, Table 11.12.

Lignin, which in the above-mentioned processes is changed to less valuable oil and tar products, could also be isolated by acid precipitation prior to processing to more useful products. Wood lignin is considerably changed by kraft or soda cooking. Condensation of carbonyl and alcohol groups to the aromatic parts of the molecules tends to increase the molecular weight, at the same time as a degradation by alkaline cleavage of the phenolic ether linkages occurs. Alkali lignin is thus dissolved in phenolate form in the black liquor. The acidification is preferably carried out with carbon dioxide (stack gases), whereby the phenolic groups are liberated and the lignin precipitates, much because of the salting-out effect of inorganics of the black liquor. The precipitated lignin can be removed by filtration, which should preferably be carried out at elevated temperature, 60–80°C, to increase filter capacity, as the lignin precipitate will then loose some of its gelatinous hydrated structure. At still higher temperatures the precipitate melts and separates as a heavy, semi-solid phase, which can be removed mechanically (106a, 147). There is no melting in its strict sense, but merely a formation of an aqueous lignin phase of high viscosity. Hardwood alkali lignin, melting at 90–100°C, is conveniently handled in this way, whereas softwood lignin, which has a higher softening temperature interval, is more easily removed by filtration. The isolated crude alkali lignin contains considerable quantities of sodium, probably attached to the carboxyl groups, and can be further purified by dissolution in water and reprecipitation by sulfuric acid addition to pH 2–3. The acidified black liquor filtrate may be extracted for the recovery of formic, acetic and saccharinic acids before it is returned to the conventional chemical recovery system (53).

Table 11.12 By-products of the kraft cook and from subsequent pressure heating of the black liquor with alkali and sulfide at 250–285°C (48a)

Before pressure heating	kg ptp	After pressure heating	kg ptp
Tall oil	50	Acetic acid	60
Turpentine	17	Formic acid	60
Acetic acid	40	Methyl sulfide	40
Formic acid	40	Methyl mercaptan	8
Methanol	5	Pyrocatechol	30
Vanillin	2	Methyl catechol	11
Acetoguaiacone	2	Ethyl catechol	9
Guaiacol	2	Other ether-soluble phenols	150
Pyrocatechol	1	Homoprotocatechuic, protocatechuic and other phenol carboxylic acids, perhaps	150
Other phenols	42		
Phenol carbonic acids	45		
Nonvolatiles and lactic acids	145	Ether soluble acids of carbohydrate origin	150
Total	391	Demethylated lignin of novalac properties	100
		Butanol-soluble lactones	35
		Total	803

Numerous suggestions for the use of isolated alkali lignin have been investigated. Sulfur-free hardwood soda process lignin is free of malodour and useful as an extender in *molding plastics composition*. Condensation of alkali lignin with formaldehyde gives thermosetting products which, however, tend to stick to the molding equipment unless co-condensed with phenols. It is still used in the production of *paper laminates*, etc., where its discoloration is no objection. The phenolic groups of alkali lignin make it a potentially more valuable *tanning agent* than lignosulfonates, but its insufficient hydrophility makes the introduction of sulfonate groups necessary. This can be done by sulfite treatment in alkaline solution in combination with either formaldehyde or oxygen, The processing costs hitherto seem to have prevented acceptance of the product as a commercial tanning agent. Addition of alkali lignin as a *reinforcing pigment in rubber* has also been tried with some success, as well as to *asphalt emulsions*, etc. However, the main utilization of lignin remains as a fuel in the cooking chemicals recovery.

The formation of methanol, methyl mercaptan and dimethyl sulfide in the kraft cook occurs through demethylation of the lignin by hydroxyl, hydrosulfide and methyl mercaptide ions respectively (48a). The formation of the two malodorous compounds, methyl mercaptan and dimethyl sulfide, is one of the few big disadvantages of the kraft process. Air pollution prevents the kraft industry from becoming established in more heavily populated districts or tourist regions. Kraft mills are not allowed, for example, in Western Germany. Considerable effort has been devoted to odor abatement. The sources of odor are digester blow gases, stack gases and evaporation station vents. In order to reduce the blow gas odor, the gases after the condenser are collected in so-called 'vapor spheres' on the digester roof, from which there is a more uniform blow gas flow to either the drop leg of a chlorination filter or a furnace for catalytic combustion of gases (19). To reduce the odor from evaporation and combustion, black liquor oxidation is practised (150, 152), cf. Section II. In spite of these efforts, which by no means are common for the entire kraft industry, some odor remains, which in serious cases has to be eliminated by spraying expensive odor counteractants into the stack gases (149b, 156a).

REFERENCES

1. Adler, E., *Svensk Papperstid.*, **49**, 339 (1946).
2. Adler, E., *Svensk Papperstid.*, **50**, No. 11B, 9 (1947).
3. Anderson, O. E., *Paper Trade J.*, **135**, No. 20, 161 (1952).
3a. Andersson, P. E., and A. Bjorkman, unpubl.
4. Anon., *Pulp Paper Ind.*, **19**, No. 2, 32 (1945).
5. Aries, R. S., and A. Pollak, *U.S. Pat.* 2,640,758; 2,642,399 (1953).
6. Baker, R. E., and F. Hutton, *Pulp Paper Mag. Can.*, **51**, No. 6, 82 (1950).
7. Barker, E. R., *Paper Trade J.*, **131**, No. 22, 136 (1950).
8. Barsalou, M., *Paper Trade J.*, **135**, No. 20, 135, 141 (1952).
9. Bauer, T. W., and R. M. Dorland, *Can. J. Technol.*, **32**, 91 (1954).

10. Baum, M., *et al.*, *Paper Trade J.*, **126**, No. 9, 130 (1948).
11. Beazley, W. B., *et al.*, *The Physical Properties of Sulphite Liquors*, Dominion Forest Bull. 93, Ottawa 1938.
11a. Bergholm. A., *Svensk Paperstid.*, **66**, 125 (1963).
12. Bergson, C. R., *Beiträge zur Kenntnis der Sulfitzellstoff-Verfahrens*, Günther-Staib, Biberach-Riss 1937.
13. Bergström, H., *Papierfabrik.*, **7**, 1314 (1909); **8**, 506 (1910); **10**, 677 (1912).
14. Bergström, H., *Papierfabrik.*, **11**, 427 (1913).
15. Bergström, H., *Swed. Pat.* 50,740 (1917).
16. Bergström, H., and K. G. Trobeck, *Svensk Papperstid.*, **42**, 554 (1939); *Swed. Pat.* 118,750; 120,998; 128,263.
17. Bergström, R. E., in J. N. Stephenson, Ed., *Pulp and Paper Manufacture*, Vol. 1, McGraw-Hill, London 1952, p. 535 ff.
17a. Berry, L. R., and A. D. Larsen, *Tappi*, **45**, 887 (1962).
18. Beuschlein, W. L., and F. H. Conrad, *Paper Trade J.*, **99**, No. 12, 75 (1934); **105**, No. 4, 37 (1937).
19. Bialkowsky, H. W., and G. G. De Haas, *Paper Mill News*, **74**, No. 35, 14 (1951); *Pulp Paper Mag. Can.*, **53**, No. 11, 99 (1952).
20. Bickell, L. K., and G. D. Tretheway, *Pulp Paper Mag. Can.*, **54**, No. 13, 110 (1953).
21. Biggs, W. A., *et al.*, *Tappi*, **44**, 385 (1961).
22. Bilberg, E., and P. Landmark, *Norsk Skogind.*, **15**, 221 (1961).
23. Björkman, A., Transactions KTH (Stockholm) No. 31 (1950).
24. Björkman, A., *Svensk Papperstid.*, **61**, 760 (1958).
25. Blikstad, F., *Norsk Skogind.*, **10**, 172, 292 (1956).
26. Bloomen, T., *Tech. Assoc. Papers*, **20**, 346 (1937).
27. Borisek, R., and V. Stanik, *Tappi*, **41**, No. 5, 188A (1958).
28. Boyer, R. Q., *Tappi*, **43**, 688 (1960).
28a. Bristow, O. J., *et al.*, *Tappi*, **40**, 809 (1957).
29. Brunes, B., *Svensk Papperstid.*, **54**, 96 (1951).
30. Brunes, B., *Paperi Puu*, **33**, 273, 302 (1951); *Paper Trade J.*, **133**, No. 25, 24, No. 26, 18 (1951).
31. Brunes, B., *Svensk Papperstid.*, **57**, 317 (1954).
32. Brunes, B., *et al.*, *Svensk Papperstid.*, **58**, 332 (1955).
33. Brunes, B., *et al.*, *Svensk Papperstid.*, **61**, 726 (1958).
33a. Burch, G. H., *et al.*, *Pulp Paper Mag. Can.*, **48**, No. 3, 127 (1947).
34. Campbell, J., and P. E. Shick, *Tappi*, **40**, No. 9, 202A (1957).
35. Carlson, G., *et al.*, *Svensk Papperstid.*, **61**, 815 (1958).
36. Cederquist, K. N., *Svensk Papperstid.*, **58**, 154 (1955); **61**, 38 (1958); *Swed. Pat.* 143,765; *U.S. Pat.* 2,668,099 (1954).
37. Cederquist, K. N., *et al.*, *Tappi*, **43**, 702 (1960).
38. Christiani, W., *et al.*, *Tappi*, **43**, No. 6, 211A (1960).
39. Cliff, W. R., *Pulp Paper Mag. Can.*, **48**, No. 10, 88 (1947).
40. Collins, T. T., *Paper Trade J.*, **136**, No. 12, 37, No. 13, 19 (1953); *Tappi*, **38**, No. 8, 172A (1955).
41. Corbett, W. M., and G. N. Richards, *Svensk Papperstid.*, **60**, 791 (1957).
42. Corey, A. J., *Pulp Paper Mag. Can.*, **44**, 168 (1943).
43. Darmstadt, W. J., and G. H. Tomlinson, *Tappi*, **43**, 674 (1960).
44. Dillén, S., *Svensk Papperstid.*, **64**, 283, 545, 819 (1961).
45. Edling, G., *Svensk Papperstid.*, **55**, 863 (1952); *Papier*, **7**, 159 (1953); *Paper Trade J.*, **136**, No. 15, 14 (1953).
46. Eidem, I., *Svensk Papperstid.*, **45**, 239 (1942).

47. Enebo, L., *et al.*, *Svensk Papperstid.*, **50**, No. 11B, 72 (1947); **52**, 101 (1949); **61**, 162 (1958).
48. Enkvist, T., and K. Ekman, *Finska Kemistsamfundets Medd.*, **64**, 47 (1955).
48a. Enkvist, T., *et al.*, *Tappi.*, **45**, 128 (1962).
49. Erdtman, H., *Svensk Papperstid.*, **45**, 315, 374, 392 (1942).
50. Erickson, A. E., *Paper Ind.*, **26**, 729 (1944).
51. von Essen, C. G., *Tappi*, **33**, No. 7, 14A (1950).
52. Falk, H., *Papierfabrik.*, **7**, 469 (1909).
53. Findley, M. E., *Tappi*, **43**, No. 8, 183A (1960).
54. Fones, R. E., and J. E. Sapp, *Tappi*, **43**, 369 (1960).
55. Forss, K., *The Composition of a Spent Spruce Sulfite Liquor*, Dissertation, Åbo (Finland) 1961.
56. Fotiev, S. A., *Bumazh. Prom.*, **17**, No. 1, 8 (1939).
57. Freudenberg, K., *et al.*, *Naturwissenschaften*, **27**, 227 (1939); *Ber.*, **73**, 167 (1940).
58. Freudenberg, K., *et al.*, *Ber.*, **74**, 171 (1941).
59. Freudenberg, K., *Ber.*, **80**, 149 (1947); **85**, 78 (1952).
60. Friese, G., *Papier*, **5**, 410 (1951).
61. Friis-Hansen, J., *Svensk Papperstid.*, **55**, 397 (1952).
62. Gauvin, W. H., and J. J. O. Gravel, *Tappi*, **43**, 678 (1960); cf. *Tappi*, **40**, 866 (1957).
63. Gillespie, D. C., *Tappi*, **36**, 147 (1953).
64. Goodwin, L. F., *J. Soc. Chem. Ind.*, **45**, T362 (1926).
65. Grangård, G., *Svensk Papperstid.*, **57**, 605 (1954).
66. Green, J. W., *Tappi*, **39**, 472 (1956).
66a. Greenwalt, J. E., *U.S. Pat.* 2,642,336 (1953).
67. Grewin, F. W., and S. Lindberg, *U.S. Pat.* 2,490,750 (1949).
68. Griffee, D., *Paper Trade J.*, **135**, No. 20, 157 (1952).
69. Gustavson, K. H., IVA Handl. (Stockholm) No. 177 (1944); *Svensk Papperstid.*, **50**, No. 11B, 101 (1947).
70. Hägglund, E., *Cellulosechem.*, **5**, 81 (1924).
71. Hägglund, E., *Svensk Kem. Tidskr.*, **36**, 133 (1924).
72. Hägglund, E., *et al.*, *Papierfabrik.*, **31**, 493 (1925); *Paperi Puu*, **13**, 508, 569 (1931).
73. Hägglund, E., *et al.*, *Ber.*, **62**, 84, 437, 2046 (1929); *Svensk Kem. Tidskr.*, **41**, 8, 55 (1929).
74. Hägglund, E., *et al.*, *Svensk Papperstid.*, **39**, 347 (1936); **40**, 236 (1937).
75. Haglund, G., *Swed. Pat.* 82,865 (1932).
76. Hall, L., *Svensk Papperstid.*, **59**, 716 (1956); **60**, 199 (1957).
76a. Haller, A. K., *Tappi.*, **45**, No. 8, 132A (1962).
77. Harris, E. E., *et al.*, *J. Am. Chem. Soc.*, **60**, 1467 (1938); **68**, 2507 (1946).
78. Harris, E. E., *et al.*, *Ind. Eng. Chem.*, **41**, 2063 (1949).
79. Hazelquist, S. E., *Pulp Paper*, **24**, No. 7, 39, 102 (1950).
79a. Hearon, W. M., *et al.*, *Tappi.*, **45**, No. 1, 28A (1962).
80. Hedström, B., *Svensk Papperstid.*, **56**, 645 (1953); **59**, 561 (1956).
81. Heuser, E., *Papierfabrik.*, **21**, 325 (1923).
82. Hibbert, H. H., *et al.*, *J. Am. Chem. Soc.*, **63**, 3061 (1941); **65**, 1192 (1943).
83. Hibbert, H. H., *et al.*, *J. Am. Chem. Soc.*, **66**, 32, 37 (1944).
84. Howard, G. C., *Paper Trade J.*, **103**, No. 1, 84 (1936); *Ind. Eng. Chem.*, **22**, 1184 (1930); **26**, 614 (1934); *Paper Mill News*, **62**, 37, 70 (1939); *U.S. Pat.* 1,699,845 (1929); 1,856,558 (1932).

85. Hughey, G. B., et al., *Paper Trade J.*, **114**, No. 9, 25 (1942).
86. Humm, W., *Beiträge zur Kenntnis der Sulfitzellstoff-Verfahrens*, Günther-Staib, Biberach-Riss 1937.
87. Jackson, D. T., and R. W. Brown, *Pulp Paper*, **32**, No. 2, 69 (1958).
88. Jakobson, T., *Svensk Papperstid.*, **55**, 432, 460, 483 (1952); **56**, 456, 491 (1953); **57**, 883, 925 (1954); **58**, 16 (1955).
89. Jenssen, G. D., *Paper*, **21**, No. 23, 72 (1918).
90. Kenetti, A., *Svensk Papperstid.*, **55**, 477 (1952).
90a. Knight, C. H., and C. F. Cornell, *Pulp Paper Mag. Can.*, **64**, No. C, T133 (1963).
91. Knight, C. H., and J. N. Stephenson, Ed., *Pulp and Paper Manufacture*, Vol. 1, McGraw-Hill, London 1952, p. 626 ff.
92. Kopantsev, M. H., *Bumazh. Prom.*, **26**, No. 6, 119 (1951).
92a. Krohnstad, W., *Svensk Kem. Tidskr.*, **72**, 509 (1960).
93. Krüger, A., *Paperi Puu*, **17**, 58 (1935); **18**, 787 (1936).
94. Lagergren, S., and B. Lundén, *Pulp Paper Mag. Can.*, **60**, No. 11, T338 (1959).
95. Lautsch, W., *Cellulosechem.*, **19**, 69 (1941).
96. Leopold, B., *Acta Chem. Scand.*, **6**, 39, 49 (1952).
97. Lindberg, S. G., and B. T. Brunes, *Swed. Pat.* Appl. No. 5863/58 (1961).
98. Lougheed, E. H., *Pulp Paper Mag. Can.*, **49**, No. 3, 215 (1948).
99. Lundberg, H. A., *Acid Making in the Sulphite Pulp Industry*, G. D. Jenssen Co, Watertown, N.Y., 1949.
100. Lundberg, A. H., *Paper Trade J.*, **131**, No. 22, 147 (1950).
100a. Lüthgens, M. W., *Tappi*, **45**, 837 (1962).
101. McGinn, E. P., et al., *Paper Trade J.*, **132**, No. 21, 21 (1951).
102. McGregor, G. H., in J. N. Stephenson, Ed., *Pulp and Paper Manufacture*, Vol. 1, McGraw-Hill, London 1952, p. 252.
102a. Manchester, D. F., and J. P. Termini, *Pulp Paper Mag. Can.*, **62**, No. 9 T415 (1961).
103. Mannbro, N., *Svensk Papperstid.*, **54**, 19, 61, (1951); **55**, 665 (1952); **58**, 525, 571 (1955).
104. Marathon Corp., Chem. Div., Bull. 110 and M-1151.
105. Markant, H. P., *Tappi*, **43**, 699 (1960).
105a. Markant, H. P., et al., *Tappi.*, **45**, 849 (1962).
106. May, M. N., Diss., Appleton, Wis. 1952; *Tappi*, **35**, 511 (1952).
106a. Merewether, J. W. T., *Tappi.*, **45**, 159 (1962).
107. Meyer, W. G., and J. G. Coma, *Chem. Eng. Progr.*, **54**, No. 5, 178 (1958).
108. Monnberg, R., et al., *Paperi Puu*, **35**, 8, 189 (1953); *Svensk Papperstid.*, **56**, 46 (1953).
109. Murray, F. E., *Tappi*, **42**, 761 (1959).
110. Nugent, R. A., and R. Q. Boyer, *Paper Trade J.*, **140**, No. 18, 29, No. 19, 30 (1956).
110a. Palmrose, G. V., and J. H. Hull, *Tappi*, **35**, 193 (1952).
111. Parsons, S. R., and R. Q. Boyer, *Tappi*, **42**, 565 (1959).
112. Pascoe, T. A., et al., *Tappi*, **42**, 265 (1959).
113. Pearl, I., et al., *Tappi*, **33**, 508, 544 (1950); **39**, 171 (1956); **40**, 45 (1957); **42**, 800 (1959); *J. Am. Chem. Soc.*, **74**, 614 (1952); **76**, 6106 (1954).
114. Pepper, J. M., *Pulp Paper Mag. Can.*, **59**, No. 10, 253 (1958).
115. Rabinovitch, W., et al., *Pulp Paper Mag. Can.*, **56**, No. 13, 118 (1955); **57**, No. 2, 59, No. 13, 123 (1956); **59**, No. 3, 140 (1958).

116. Räsänen, R., and L. Luotonen, *Zellstoff Papier*, **8**, 340, 375 (1959); *Paper Mill News*, **83**, No. 3, 16 (1960).
117. Rayonier Inc., *U.S. Pat.* 2,656,244; 2,656,249 (1953).
118. Rinman, E. L., *Svensk Papperstid.*, **26**, 158 (1923); *Paper*, **35**, No. 6, 224 (1924).
119. Rosenblad, C., *Paper Trade J.*, **106**, No. 26, 78 (1938).
120. Rossini, F. D., *et al.*, U.S. Nat. Bur. Stand., Circular 500, Washington, D.C., 1952.
121. Rothrock, C. W., *Tappi*,, **41**, No. 6, 241A (1958).
122. Routala, O., and A. Pohjola, *Paperi Puu*, **16**, 289 (1934).
123. Rydholm, S. A., unpublished.
124. Sadler, H., *et al.*, *Papier*, **7**, 416 (1953).
125. Samuelson, O., *Svensk Papperstid.*, **49**, 575 (1946).
126. Samuelson, O., *Svensk Papperstid.*, **52**, 283 (1949).
127. Samuelson, O., *et al.*, *Svensk Papperstid.*, **61**, 1043 (1958), and to be published.
128. Sandberg, E. S., *Swed. Pat.* 95,984 (1937).
129. Sandborn, L. T., *et al.*, *U.S. Pat.* 2,057,117 (1936); Re-issue 12,268 (1936).
130. Scholander, A., *Svensk Papperstid.*, **53**, 35 (1950).
131. Scholander, A., *Svensk Papperstid.*, **53**, 681 (1950).
132. Scholander, A., *Paperi Puu*, **34**, 140 (1952).
133. Scholander, A., *Tappi*, **43**, 706 (1960).
134. Shelow, W. S., and A. L. Pickens, *Tappi*, **41**, No. 5, 148A (1958).
135. Sillén, L. G., *Svensk Papperstid.*, **49**, 387 (1946); **50**, 339 (1947).
136. Sillén, L. G., and T. Andersson, *Svensk Papperstid.*, **55**, 622 (1952).
136a. Simmons, T., *Svensk Papperstid.*, **56**, 121 (1953).
137. Sivola, Y. (G), *U.S. Pat.* 2,710,763 (1948); *Swed. Pat.* 146,535 (1952).
138. Söderquist, R., *Svensk Papperstid.*, **58**, 706 (1955); *Papier*, **11**, 487 (1957).
139. Soltau, G., *Papierfabrik.*, **26**, 550 (1928).
140. Somer, V. H., *U.S. Pat.* 2,564,452 (1951).
140a. Spalding, C. W., and S. T. Han, *Tappi*,. **45**, 192 (1962).
140b. Stacie, J. H., and R. G. Guide, *Tappi*, **46**, 141 (1963).
141. Stumpf, W., *Svensk Papperstid.*, **50**, No. 11B, 164 (1947).
142. Sundman, J., *Paperi Puu*, **31**, 309 (1949).
143. Sundman, J., *Paperi Puu*, **32**, No. 9B, 267 (1950).
144. Swartz, J. N., *Pulp Paper Mag. Can.*, **44**, 139 (1943).
145. Swartz, J. N., in J. N. Stephenson, ed., *Pulp and Paper Manufacture*, Vol. 1, McGraw-Hill, London 1952, p. 648.
146. Tomlinson, G. H., *Chem. Ind.*, **1948**, No. 24, 371; *Pulp Paper Mag. Can.*, **49**, No. 7, 63 (1948).
147. Tomlinson, G. H., and G. H. Tomlinson II, *U.S. Pat.* 2,406,867 (1946); *Can. Pat.* 448,476 (1948).
148. Tomlinson, G. H., *et al.*, *Pulp Paper Mag. Can.*, **47**, No. 9, 71 (1946).
149. Tomlinson, G. H., *et al.*, in J. N. Stephenson, Ed., *Pulp and Paper Manufacture*, Vol. 1, McGraw-Hill, London 1952, p. 568.
149a. Töppel, O., *Papier.*, **15**, 81 (1961).
149b. Tremaine, B. K., *et al.*, *Tappi.*, **36**, 154, No. 8, 41A, 143A (1953).
150. Trobeck, K. G., *Svensk Papperstid.*, **54**, 632 (1951); *Pulp Paper Mag. Can.*, **53**, No. 3, 225 (1952); *Paper Trade J.*, **135**, No. 1, 27 (1952).
151. Trobeck, K. G., *Svensk Papperstid.*, **53**, 8 (1950).
152. Trobeck, K. G., *et al.*, *Tappi*, **42**, 425 (1959).

153. Ulfsparre, S., *Svensk Papperstid.*, **49**, 383 (1946).
154. Ulfsparre, S., *Svensk Papperstid.*, **61**, 803 (1958).
155. Venemark, E., *Svensk Papperstid.*, **59**, 629 (1956).
156. Venemark, E., *Svensk Papperstid.*, **61**, 881, 983 (1958); **62**, 381 (1959); **63**, 387 (1960).
156a. Van Bergen, J. M., *Tappi*, **39**, No. 7, 194A (1956).
157. Waller, A., *Svensk Papperstid.*, **44**, 427 (1941).
158. Wells, S. D., *et al.*, *Paper Trade J.*, **76**, No. 24, 49 (1923).
159. White, C. K., *et al.*, *Tech. Assoc. Papers*, **31**, 141 (1948); TAPPI Data Sheet 148 A–B, 1948, 165–171 (1956); *Tappi.*, **39**, No. 7, 135A (1956).
160. Whitney, R. P., *et al.*, *Tappi*, **34**, 396 (1951).
161. Whitney, R. P., *et al.*, *U.S. Pat.* 2,802,791 (1953); *Tappi*, **40**, 587 (1957).
161a. Wilhelmsen, L. A., *Tappi*, **45**, 910 (1962).
162. Wright, R. H., *et al.*, *Tappi*, **35**, 276 (1952); **36**, 180 (1953); *Pulp Paper*, **26**, No. 1, 89 (1952); *Paper Trade J.*, **139**, No. 41, 22 (1955).
163. Zimmermann, F. J., *U.S. Pat.* 2,665,249 (1954).

PART III

PREPARATION OF BLEACHED PULP

12

GENERAL PRINCIPLES OF
BLEACHING

I. Classification of Bleaching Processes and Historical Development

The *purpose of the bleaching operations* is to impart the desired final
physical and chemical properties to the pulp, the most obvious being the
whiteness or brightness. This is done by removal of some constituents of
the unbleached pulp and by modification of the remainder. The operations
and processes applied depend entirely on the character of the unbleached
pulp and the quality desired of the bleached pulp. In some instances only
a higher brightness is desired, with as little removal of matter as possible
to preserve a high pulp yield. This is the case for mechanical and some
semichemical pulps. As the coloring matter in those pulps is predominantly
lignin, the processes required could be classified as *lignin-bleaching
methods*, where chromophors of lignin are destroyed without considerable
removal of substance. This is usually done by one stage of bleaching
with *dithionite* (hydrosulfite) or *peroxide* or two-stage combinations of
them. These methods do not impart a very high brightness to the pulp, nor
any greater brightness stability, but are sufficient for their purpose, to
improve the eye appeal of pulps for newsprint and certain grades of board,
or to give a base paper for coating which does not require excessive
amounts of pigment for a satisfactory white coated paper.

When higher brightness is desired it is necessary to apply *lignin-removing
methods*, which are of interest for chemical and some grades of semichemical pulps. The removal of lignin also improves the paper properties
of semichemical and high yield chemical pulps and is necessary for obtaining good processing properties of dissolving pulps. The lignin removal
is usually done in several stages for economic as well as qualitative reasons,
multistage bleaching. In principle, it consists of chlorination in one or
two stages, for the degradation of lignin, followed by an alkali stage for
the neutralization and dissolution of the degradation products, and finished
by one or more oxidative stages with intermediate alkaline extraction.
Only after the oxidation is the final discoloration removed and full high
brightness obtained. In essence, bleaching of this type represents a continuation of the cooking processes, although with more selective, but also
more expensive, chemicals.

However, the multistage bleaching has purposes in addition to that of
giving brightness to the pulp, namely *carbohydrate removal, deresination*,
and *viscosity adjustment*. The carbohydrate removal, carried out mainly in

the alkali extraction stages, modifies the paper properties of paper pulps and improves the quality of dissolving pulps. Deresination, or pitch removal, also occurs mainly in the alkali stages and is important in obtaining a high brightness. Viscosity adjustment, or depolymerization, of the remaining carbohydrates, is mainly carried out in the oxidative stages. In the case of most paper pulps this is a non-desirable reaction which decreases the paper strength properties, but it is desired for dissolving pulps to achieve a uniform viscosity level of the production, which is vital in the further processing.

These various aspects of bleaching have only gradually appeared. From the beginning bleaching was done for brightness alone. The bleaching of textile cellulose involved exposure to sunlight in the open air, with intermediate washings and alkali (potash or soda ash) treatments and final acidulation. The discovery of chlorine in 1774 and the subsequent preparation of potassium, sodium and calcium hypochlorite introduced new and powerful bleaching agents, which were eventually found efficient for wood pulp. The handling and transportation of liquid chlorine was learnt during World War I and introduced to the pulping industry shortly afterwards. As the demand for bleaching chemicals increased in this industry, some mills integrated electrolytic chlorine–alkali production in their operations. The use of chlorine dioxide was investigated during the 1920's and 1930's and introduced to the pulping industry during the 1940's. World War II brought about a development of peroxide research and production, and peroxide as a bleaching agent was introduced to the pulping industry shortly afterwards.

Until the end of the 19th century the technique of bleaching was a *one-stage hypochlorite* bleach, carried out in *washing drums* or *hollanders* at low consistency (3–4%) for about 10 h. With the beginning of the new century, bleachers were introduced which made medium consistency bleaching possible, first at 7% (the *Bellmer bleacher*), and eventually at 15–25%, the *Wolf* and the *VW bleachers*. A continuously operating bleacher was introduced by *Thorne* in the 1920's. Also in the 1920's multistage bleaching began to gain ground, first as a *two-stage hypochlorite* bleach, but later, with the development of acid-proof steel, as *combined chlorination and hypochlorite bleaching*. This was around 1930, and as a result pulps which were formerly considered as unbleachable or bleachable only with difficulty, could now be bleached. The effect on these types of pulp was improved by *intermediate alkali extraction*, and also by repeated chlorinations, and the increased number of stages accelerated the development of *continuous bleaching in towers*, which were introduced during the 1930's. Although a large percentage of the existing bleacheries still apply a discontinuous last stage, fully continuous bleaching is rapidly gaining ground in the re-building of bleacheries and in all new mills.

The quality of the bleached pulps has been ever increasing. With the introduction of medium-consistency bleaching it was possible to make a kraft pulp with a brightness which today could be described as semibleached, but at a sacrifice in strength. Multistage bleaching permitted considerable gain in both brightness and strength for sulfite as well as for kraft pulps. With the introduction of *chlorine dioxide*, kraft pulp could be bleached to the same brightness as sulfite pulps without any strength loss at all. Until lately super-bleaching of sulfite pulps has been carried out with the aid of chlorine dioxide to still higher brightness, at a level where purity of the mill water is the only limitation. The bleaching of semi-chemical and mechanical pulps has also been developed for special purposes, as has the purification by alkali extraction during the bleaching operations for dissolving and special paper pulps.

Before entering into details of the various processes, some general problems will be treated in the following sections of this chapter.

II. Optical Properties of Pulp

1. FUNDAMENTAL DEFINITIONS

The most important concepts of optical pulp properties are those of *whiteness*, *brightness* and *opacity*. They all refer to the ability of the pulp to *reflect* and *absorb* light. Figure 12.1 shows the reflexion of visible light over the entire wavelength range for different types of pulp. On the whole, their shape corresponds to the absorption of visible light by lignin (cf. Chapter 9.I, Figure 9.5), and the dominating source of discoloration is

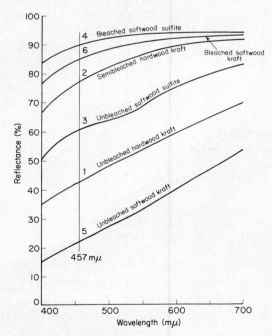

Fig. 12.1. Spectral reflectivity curves for some pulp samples (Van den Akker)

definitely condensed and degraded lignin. The absorption of light is therefore greatest in the short-wave part of the spectrum, and measurement of the reflected blue light hence gives the best differentiation between the pulps. Of the many methods for brightness determination, the one most generally adopted is that of General Electric (9, 54), utilizing a blue glass filter with a transparency peak at 457 mμ. Other filters are also supplied, making it possible to estimate the course of the total reflectancy curve in the visible light region, but the term *brightness* is reserved for the determinations with the blue filter. The fraction of reflected light in per cent of incident light being less easy to determine, all reflexion measurements are related to the light reflected by a standard plate of magnesium oxide, which gives nearly total reflection. The standard G.E. meter, as most reflectancy meters, is constructed for direct reflection of the light beam. This has the drawback of rendering the brightness value dependent on the smoothness of the sample surface. Machine-dried pulp sheets with felt marking therefore give different brightness values for the two sheet sides when measured in the G.E. meter. The brightness meters applying the integrating sphere principle, such as the Zeiss Elrepho instrument (57a), overcome this difficulty and show higher brightness figures for such sheets. For smooth handsheets, specially prepared for brightness testing, the difference is almost negligible (57c). To eliminate any influence from the background, the sheets should be made sufficiently thick. For practical reasons the test sheets are prepared with a basis weight limited to around 150 g/m^2, and instead four sheets are piled on top of each other (54). The light reflected from a layer of infinite thickness is denoted R_∞ and called the *reflectivity*. In the special case of blue light of 457 mμ, the reflectivity is equal to brightness.

Brightness, although a physical concept, does not describe a simple physical phenomenon but involves the effects of surface reflection, absorption, repeated macro-optical reflection by the inhomogeneities within the sheet and within the fibers, as well as true light scattering (50), even disregarding the transparency of the sheet of limited thickness. All effects are not identically registered by different instruments. This is why it has been considered necessary to make the definition precise by choosing a standard instrument. In contrast to the physical concept of brightness, *whiteness* is a physiological phenomenon. Whiteness is the impression on the eye created by the light reflected from the sheet. A sheet of given brightness could be made to appear whiter to the eye by the addition of a blue dyestuff, which in fact *decreases* the reflexion of light over the entire wavelength region, even at 457 mμ, although the decrease is much larger in the yellow region. The resulting reflectancy curve thus becomes more horizontal, and the color impression is whiter. Therefore, attempts have been made to relate the concept of whiteness to the reflectancy values at two or more wavelengths, e.g.

$$W = 2\,B - R \quad (53) \text{ or } W = 1 + B - R \quad (19)$$

where B is the reflectancy in blue and R that in red light. A more satisfactory approach, if somewhat complicated, applies the principles of color measurement. The *C.I.E. system* for trichromatic colorimetry (18a, 22, 49) applies three *stimuli* or standard colors of fictive, high saturation and defined composition, as described in Figure 12.2, from which colors, by mixing, all other colors can be prepared. One of the stimuli, denoted $\bar{y}$, corresponds to the sensitivity curve of the human eye. By choosing three standard color filters of similar quality (57b), measurement of reflectancy will give three figures for any colored paper, the so-called *trichromatic indices*, X, Y, and Z. The Y figure has been called the *luminosity* value of the color, i.e. how bright a color appears to the eye. The trichromatic indices thus define the color in a three-dimensional system, the projection of which in the plane is obtained by calculation of the *trichromatic coordinates*, x and y, through the expressions

$$x = \frac{X}{X + Y + Z} \quad \text{and} \quad y = \frac{Y}{X + Y + Z}$$

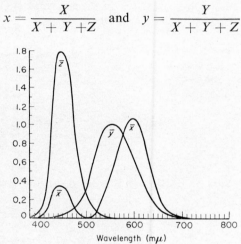

Fig. 12.2. Spectral distribution of the three stimuli of the C.I.E. system (Stenius)

The projection is given in Figure 12.3. All colors fall within a 'color triangle', two sides of which are limited by the saturated spectral colors. Color of lower saturation falls within the limits, saturation decreasing towards the center of the figure, where the so-called *white point* is situated. Several investigations have been carried out to correlate the physiological reaction on whiteness of a large number of test subjects with the colors as defined by the color triangle, for a large variety of white test papers of varying hue and saturation. The distance, Δs, from the white point, indicating the degree of saturation, and the luminosity, Y, were found to enter the expression of whiteness, W, as follows:

$$W = \sqrt{Y - 6700(\Delta s)^2} \quad (23), \text{ or}$$
$$W = 100 \cdot [1 - \sqrt{(1 - Y)^2 + 120(\Delta s)^2}] \quad (45), \text{ or}$$
$$W = 100 \cdot [1 - \sqrt{(1 - \sqrt{Y})^2 + 40\sqrt{Y}(\Delta s)^2}] \quad (32)$$

843

Whiteness determinations are of interest mainly for the finished paper, to which color-modifying dyestuffs and pigments have been added. In the case of pulps the brightness determination is usually sufficient for the characterization, as the reflectancy curves for pulps of different brightness are largely congruent. However, this is not always the case, e.g. when comparing unbleached sulfite with semibleached kraft pulps, as further discussed in a subsequent section.

Opacity likewise requires a closer definition. It is a paper property, related to the light scattering, which is important for many grades of papers, especially printing papers, where a high opacity is desired, and glassine papers, where a high *transparency*, the inverse function, is necessary. Opacity could be measured in reflected (5, 8, 10, 24, 44) as well as transmitted light (31), as further discussed in several surveys (11, 15, 20, 55).

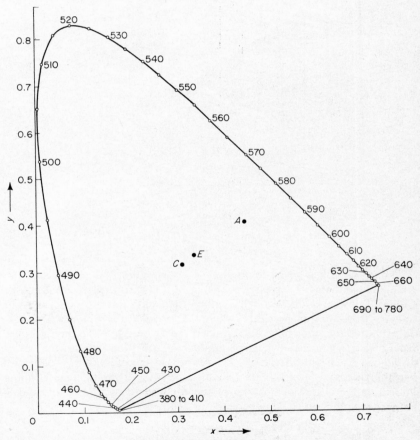

Fig. 12.3. Chromaticity diagram with the spectrum locus. *E* is chromaticity of equal-energy spectrum, *A* and *C* chromaticities of C.I.E. Standard Sources *A* and *C* (DIN Standard 5033)

It is given in terms of *contrast ratio* or *printing opacity*, which are slightly different functions. In both cases, opacity obviously denotes a sheet property. The contrast ratio is the ratio of light intensities on reflection from the paper kept above black and white backgrounds. The black background should be absolutely black, and the white one should, according to TAPPI Standards (54), be 91.5% GE in brightness. Experimentally more practical is the concept of printing opacity, denoted R_0/R_∞, which is the reflectancy of the paper on black background divided by the reflectivity of the paper as previously defined, e.g. the reflectancy of a pile of papers of infinite thickness. For most papers, R_∞ is lower than the reflectancy on a 91.5% GE background, and consequently printing opacity has a higher numerical value than the contrast ratio. The printing opacity value tells how much '*show-through*' is to be expected, i.e. extent to which the print on the subsequent paper will appear through the first one. The phenomenon of '*print-through*' of the text on the opposite page of the first paper is further dependent on other qualities of the paper as well as the ink, and is no true optical property.

As pointed out earlier, these opacity concepts denote properties of paper sheets, and to achieve a function describing the scattering properties of a pulp the term *light scattering coefficient* has been developed. The relation between reflection, scattering and absorption in a sheet is described by the *Kubelka–Munk* theory (28, 48, 57). In a sheet of a translucent, diffusing material of thickness X, an infinitesimal layer of the thickness dx parallel to the surface receives light of the intensity i_t from above and i_r from below. When passing dx, i_t is decreased by the fraction $i_t(S + K)dx$ and increased by $i_r S dx$, whereas i_r is decreased by $i_r(S + K)dx$ and increased by $i_t S dx$, where S is the scattering coefficient and K the absorption coefficient. Thus

$$- di_t = - (S + K)i_t dx + S i_r dx \quad \text{and}$$
$$di_r = - (S + K)i_r dx + S i_t dx$$

These equations lead to

$$R_\infty = 1 + K/S - \sqrt{K^2/S^2 + 2\,K/S} \text{ and}$$

$$R_0 = \frac{\exp\left[SX(1/R_\infty - R_\infty)\right] - 1}{1/R_\infty \exp\left[SX(1/R_\infty - R_\infty)\right] - R_\infty}$$

where R_∞, as before, denotes the reflectivity (or brightness if the light used is of 457 mμ) and R_0 the reflectancy from a sheet with an absolutely black background. Obviously, the brightness of a pulp sheet is not only dependent on the amount of light absorbed (K), but also on the extent of light scattering (S). Decreasing light scattering will decrease the brightness, which is the case when a pulp is beaten to form a paper sheet. In the same way, the printing opacity, R_0/R_∞, is not only dependent on the light scattering, but also on the light absorption, a lower absorption giving a somewhat lower opacity, as in the case of pulp bleaching. The coefficients S and K, however, should be regarded as independent variables. The

845

relationship of opacity, brightness and scattering coefficient has been described graphically in various publications (3, 15, 25, 38, 48), and usually not S but SX, sometimes called the *scattering power*, is used, as exemplified by Figure 12.4 (15).

As the thickness X of a pulp or paper sheet is not well defined, its measurement is not quite satisfactory, and the *Kubelka–Munk* equations have therefore been modified (25, 57) to contain the basis weight W instead of thickness. The light scattering and absorption coefficients are

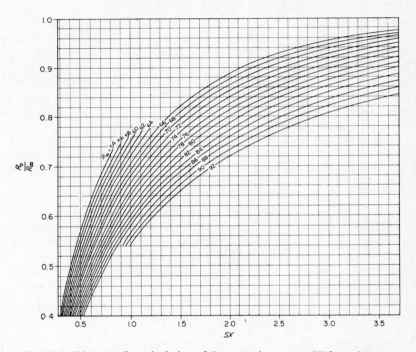

Fig. 12.4. Diagrams for calculation of the scattering power SX from the measured values of printing opacity, R_0/R_∞, and brightness, R_∞ (Giertz)

then denoted s and k, and called *specific* scattering and absorption coefficients. Thus,

$$s = SX/W \text{ and } k = KX/W.$$

If W is expressed in terms of g/cm^2, the value of s becomes conveniently high (15). The light scattering and opacity phenomena at the different pulping processes will be further treated in a subsequent section. The relationship between k, s, R_0/R_∞ and R_∞ can be presented in diagrammatic form, Figure 12.5 (52).

The *Kubelka–Munk* theory has proved very useful in understanding the optical phenomena in a sheet of fibers. However, it involves the idealization of a constant light scattering and absorption throughout the sheet.

846

This is not quite the case. In contrast to earlier results (e.g. 15, 48), it has been shown (51) that the scattering coefficient decreases somewhat with decreasing basis weight, indicating that the surface layers of hand-made sheets are less opaque and dense than the central layers. The scattering coefficient should therefore be determined with a comparatively thick sheet. This phenomena also leads to rather (around 1%) higher brightness values of a pulp sheet than would be expected from the average density of the sheet (51).

The light scattering of a pulp sheet tends to increase somewhat with decreasing wavelength (20), Table 12.1 (15). At the same time, the printing opacity increases still more, in accordance with the influence of the increasing light absorption indicated by the *Kubelka–Munk* equations. The determination of light scattering coefficient and printing opacity should therefore preferably be carried out at standardized conditions such as with the G.E. meter or a corresponding instrument employing a blue filter. This is also convenient as the opacity determination is carried out together with the brightness determination. Table 12.1 also indicates some differences between various pulp types. The hemicellulose-rich paper grades are less opaque than the rayon grades. Hardwood sulfite pulp is more

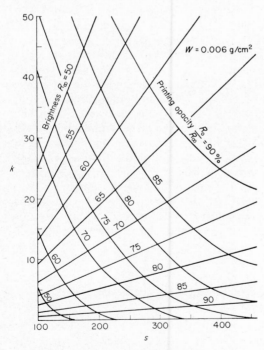

Fig. 12.5. Relationship between the specific scattering and absorption coefficients, brightness and printing opacity (Stenius)

Table 12.1. Specific scattering coefficient and printing opacity at different wavelength for dried pulps (15)

Wave length, mμ	400	500	600	700
Specific scattering coefficient for				
Aspen sulfite paper pulp	530	529	527	525
Spruce sulfite rayon pulp	406	421	409	401
Spruce sulfite paper pulp	376	369	362	361
Pine kraft paper pulp	419	406	391	388
Printing opacity for				
Aspen sulfite paper pulp	0.946	0.868	0.827	0.804
Spruce sulfite rayon pulp	0.869	0.806	0.773	0.747
Spruce sulfite paper pulp	0.877	0.789	0.753	0.733
Pine kraft paper pulp	0.867	0.802	0.764	0.745

opaque than softwood pulps. The influence of pulping on opacity will be discussed further in a subsequent section.

The *nature of the light scattering* in a pulp sheet is complex. Part of the effect is caused by repeated macro-optical refraction and reflection at the surface of the larger particles, whereas the remainder is caused by diffraction by much smaller particles about the size of a half wavelength or 2,000–4,000 Å. Such particles are abundant in the form of fibril bundles at the fiber surface. Empirical formulae (e.g. 6), indicate that apart from particle size the *refractive index* will also influence the extent of scattering. For the components of the fiber wall, that value is around 1.55 and changes little with the chemical composition (16, 40). However, the particle concentration must be very much dependent on the manner of drying the sheet, since the extent of hydrogen bonding between interacting surfaces will increase during drying. A pulp sheet dried from butanol has a considerably higher opacity than one dried from water. Therefore, measurement of opacity and the specific scattering coefficient must standardize the conditions of sheet formation and drying as well. As the amount of residual water tends to decrease opacity by overbridging two adjacent surfaces, the conditioning of the sheet prior to measurement is also standardized, preferably the same as prior to paper testing.

It is possible to calculate the scattering coefficient of a mixture of different pulps by applying the following mixing rule (39, 57):

$$s = \frac{s_1 W_1 + s_2 W_2 + s_3 W_3 + \dots}{W_1 + W_2 + W_3 + \dots}$$

where s_n is the specific scattering coefficient and W_n the part of weight of the component.

2. BRIGHTNESS OF UNBLEACHED AND BLEACHED PULPS

Figure 12.1 gives reflectancy curves over the whole visible spectrum for various unbleached and bleached plups. The values at 457 mμ, i.e. the brightness values, especially those of unbleached and semi-bleached pulps, do not quite give a satisfactory description of the color of the pulp, as they only give the reflectancy in the blue wavelength region. The brightness level of semibleached kraft pulps is similar to that of unbleached sulfite pulp, but whereas the former is yellow to the eye, the latter is reddish-grey. To some extent this difference is indicative of the color of chlorinated and unchlorinated lignin. However, during alkaline, and especially kraft cooking, the lignin color is changed to dark brown, and kraft pulps are brown.

In spite of this deficiency, the brightness determination has the advantage of giving an indication of a property related to the pulp color in one single figure, which could be used for comparisons between various types of pulp.

The dominating source of color in the unbleached pulp is lignin, although in pulps from some special wood species the color of certain extractives are also of noticeable importance (21, 47). Some recent investigations (7, 34) imply that heartwood constituents in the ray cells as well as in many heartwood vessels and fibers is one of the major causes of color in *unbleached mechanical* and *semichemical* pulps. These constituents form a 'gum'-like exudation of unknown chemical composition, possibly from lignin precursors, which in the dead cells of the heartwood follow a different transformation pattern to more colored compounds than the normal lignification. The protolignin of the wood is lightly cream-colored only, and most of the unbleached, as well as semi-bleached, color of *chemical* pulps are due to changes in the lignin molecules during cooking and bleaching, producing chromophoric groups. The nature of these changes are not known. Some suggestions were forwarded in Chapter 9.I for the changes on the acid condensation of lignin, which is thought to produce configurations similar to those of triphenylmethane dyestuffs. Also, alkaline condensation occurring during the alkaline pulping processes, is likely to produce similar color changes in the lignin. The reason for the fairly bright color of the sulfite pulps is that the condensation only occurs to a considerable extent when most of the lignin has been removed from the pulp. Prolonged cooking will also affect other pulp properties and is thus avoided. The color reactions of the lignin during the sulfite cook are therefore more noticeable in the cooking liquor than in the pulp, only overcooked pulps showing a decrease in brightness. In contrast, the color reactions of the alkaline cooks occur already at an early stage, and brightness increases with increasing degree of cooking, as the dark lignin and other discoloring substances are removed from the pulp, Figure 6.57. As considerable amounts of lignin have to be left in the pulp after cooking to avoid the carbohydrate degradation of prolonged cooking, the alkaline pulps are much darker than sulfite pulps. The role of sulfur in the kraft cook for final pulp color is still obscure, but kraft pulps are somewhat darker than soda pulps of the same lignin content.

On bleaching, the lignin and other discoloring substances are either brightened, or removed. In the former case, reduction or oxidation changes the configurations of the discoloring compounds to less colored structures,

849

often without substances removal. In the latter case, reactions occur, which first change the lignin structure to make it soluble in water or alkali. Thereby the color of the lignin changes first to intense yellow on chlorination, to red or brown on alkalization, and finally white on oxidation, with more or less intense shades of yellow from remaining chlorinated lignin. The brightest pulps have a bluish-white tinge which is agreeable to the eye. They contain very little lignin and extractives.

Table 12.2 classifies the various pulp grades according to brightness. Within each range, there is a variation according to wood species used and the process conditions. Thus, unbleached groundwood pulp, as well as sulfite and kraft pulp from spruce, is considerably brighter than that from pine and most hardwoods. It is likely that these differences are to a large extent caused by extractives, rather than differences in the lignin color.

Table 12.2. Brightness ranges of various pulp types

Brightness range, % GE	Ground- wood	Acid sul- fite and bisulfite	Neutral sulfite	Cold caustic	Kraft	Paper products
15–30			Unbl. (NH$_4$)		Unbl.	Coarse pack- aging
40–50		Unbl. (NH$_4$)	Unbl. (Ca, Na)	Unbl.		
55–65	Unbl.	Unbl. (Ca, Na)	Semibl.	Semibl.	Semibl.	Newsprint, tissue
70–85	Semibl.	Semibl.	Fully bl.		Fully bl.	Coated papers
87–93		Fully bl.			Superbl.	Fine papers
95–99		Superbl.				and bl. boards, bl. tissue

Cold grinding produces pulp of higher brightness than hot grinding. High combined SO$_2$ content causes a considerably brighter pulp than is obtained with less chemicals, as does a purer mill water and absence of contaminating iron equipment. The reddening of unbleached sulfite pulps has been investigated considerably and is treated in Chapter 13. Unbleached sulfite paper pulps are produced which have a brightness of up to 75% GE. Ammonium-based sulfite pulps are considerably darker than sodium- or calcium-based pulps. This is still more striking in the case of neutral sulfite pulps, which are quite dark on ammonium base. These color differences must be caused by selective actions of ammonia or ammonium ions on lignin, and resemble similar phenomena in tri-phenylmethane dyestuff chemistry. As pointed out above, kraft pulps are brighter at a lower lignin content. At preserved degrees of deligni-fication, an increase in alkali charge and residual alkali of the kraft cook gives a brighter pulp. This might depend on better removal of discoloring extractives, as well as on preventing lignin precipitation on the fiber surface.

The brightness of the unbleached pulp is of great importance in those bleaching methods which preserve most of the colored substances converted to a less colored form. Those methods which *remove* the coloring matter are naturally not very dependent on the color intensity of these substances.

3. BRIGHTNESS STABILITY

The brightness of both unbleached and bleached pulps is not permanent, and *brightness reversion* is accelerated by exposure to light, heat, chemicals, and high humidities. The tendency of brightness reversion, or *yellowing*, is an important property of pulps for both paper and chemical conversion. The yellowing of newsprint on exposure to *light* or on *storage* is one of the major objections to this type of paper for many purposes, and the brightness reversion of bleached pulps on *transport* and storage causes disputes between seller and buyer of pulp and gives a less good end product than anticipated from the brightness arrived at in the bleachery with the aid of expensive chemicals. Further color deterioration of the paper on storage or in use is also objectionable. The *heat stability* of pulp brightness is of special importance for pulps used as plastic fillers and laminates, as heating is required in the processing. Stability of pulp brightness towards *alkali* and *acids* is required in the production of textile rayon and staple, as well as acetate products.

The problem of brightness reversion has been studied for a long time, and its causes and prevention are still not entirely known. Obviously, a large number of compounds and reactions are involved, different for different pulp types and different treatments. For instance, the main cause of brightness reversion of newsprint is lignin reactions, as is the case for most unbleached pulps, whereas the reversion of a bleached pulp is caused to a considerable extent by the carbohydrates as well as by residual resin, and in sized papers by the rosin size. A survey of the studies on the subject up to 1938 (56) revealed largely qualitative investigations, much because of lack of suitable methods for evaluation and comparison of the reversion effects. The decrease in brightness is easily measured, although the method to bring about the reversion could be discussed. However, in order to evaluate, for example, how much of the reversion on heating of a sized paper is caused by the rosin, the brightness decrease of unsized and sized paper have to be compared, although the brightness level of the unsized paper is considerably higher. To do this on a theoretically sound basis, the *Kubelka–Munk* theory was made use of (56). In any brightness reversion, the increase in light absorption, as expressed by the absorption coefficient, k, is the main primary variable, and this should be proportional to the amount of coloring matter formed. As the first *Kubelka–Munk* equation could be written

$$k/s = (1 - R_\infty)^2/2\,R_\infty$$

the change in the k/s value is easily computed from the two brightness values before and after the treatment, and as the scattering coefficient was found to be constant during the treatment producing reversion, the

851

change in the k/s value is indicative of the increase of coloring matter. Figure 12.6 (14) graphically relates k/s to brightness, and it is easily seen that a small amount of coloring matter (a small change in k/s) produces a fairly large brightness reversion of bright sheets, and a modest one in a less bright sheet. Figure 12.7 (14) demonstrates the direct proportionality between the k/s value and the amount of dyestuff added to the pulp. For

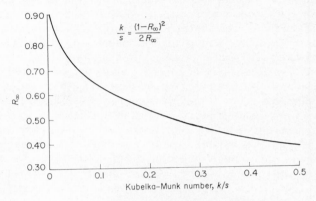

$$\frac{k}{s} = \frac{(1-R_\infty)^2}{2R_\infty}$$

Fig. 12.6. Relation between brightness and Kubelka–Munk number

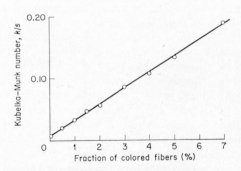

Fig. 12.7. Relation between Kubelka–Munk number and dye content of pulp (Giertz)

pulps *of the same scattering coefficient*, therefore, the change in k/s value upon aging under standard conditions (14, 43), sometimes called the *p.c. (post color) value* (14), should represent a comparable figure, However, as s remains in the denominator of the difference, the function should not be used to compare the yellowing tendency of different pulp types with widely differing scattering coefficients, as has been sometimes done, if by yellowing tendency one means the tendency towards increased light absorption. To achieve a true comparison it is then necessary to determine s for each pulp and compute the changes in k. Another thing is that a

852

change in k is much more striking to the eye in the case of a low scattering coefficient, as could also be derived from the *Kubelka-Munk* equations.

The manner of accelerated aging is questionable, and should be chosen in relation to the conditions of the end use of the paper. An increase in the relative moisture content of the air surrounding the test sheet has sometimes been found to increase the brightness reversion (33, 43, 56), in other cases to be of little consequence (14). A temperature increase (14, 56) naturally accelerates aging, and 100 (41b) or 120°C (14) has been suggested for standard. Although the correlation between the reversion on long storage at room temperature and that of heat-accelerated aging is none too good (33), many end-use conditions of paper make heat stability tests justified. However, 75–95°C seems a better temperature level than 120°C. Acceleration by ultraviolet light is said mainly to influence color changes in the lignin molecules (29) and is less suitable for bleached pulps although an effect is observed also on the latter (47a). The stability towards alkali of rayon pulp brightness is tested by steeping in 18 % NaOH solution, pressing under standardized conditions, and normal brightness determination.

The extent of brightness reversion depends on the type of pulp and the conditions of the test (47a). Normal reversion on long-term storage of bleached pulps is only one or a few units. Among the effects of the pulping processes on brightness stability, the following are of greater importance (cf. 4, 14). *Removal of lignin* by sulfite pulping tends to decrease the yellowing and reddening tendency of *unbleached* pulps. As these color phenomena are caused by air oxidation in the presence of *heavy metal catalysts*, cf. Chapter 13, elimination of the latter means an improvement (1). *Removal of hemicelluloses* during sulfite pulping (14, 43, 56), or by subsequent alkali extraction (18), may increase the brightness stability of *bleached* pulps. *Kraft pulping* yields better bleached brightness stability than *sulfite pulping* to corresponding yield. Cold or hot *alkali extraction* of sulfite or kraft pulps prior to bleaching increases brightness stability, as does *ethanol extraction to remove resins* (14, 26, 41a, 56). Introduction of *carbonyl* groups by *hypochlorite bleaching* at too low a pH will cause a decrease (4, 14, 30, 35, 43, 56), and conversion of carbonyl groups to carboxyls by *acid chlorite treatment* (30, 41, 43, 46, 58a) or to alcohol groups by *tetrahydroborate reduction* will increase the brightness stability (18, 26, 30, 41, 46, 58a). One investigation indicated that carbonyl groups are responsible for about half the color reversion of cautiously bleached pulps and the pulp resin for another 15 % (26), whereas the cellulose component was responsible for less than 10 %. In agreement with this, the alpha- and betacellulose fractions of a heat-treated, yellowed pulp were found to be white, whereas the gamma fraction was yellow to brown (18). The best practical method of brightness stabilization of overbleached pulps has been shown to be alkali–chlorine dioxide treatment, which was superior to a peroxide stage or to an alkali stage alone (48). Prolonged diffusion to improve *washing* after the bleaching has a favorable effect only at technically impossible retention times. Most of these effects apply to brightness stability on treatment with mercerizing lye as well. *Iron contamination* is detrimental only in fairly high amounts for pulps with a low lignin content (43), and an acidification or complexing agent addition therefore has little effect on normal bleached pulps. The influence of the *short-fiber fraction* is sometimes found to be considerable (14, 27), but not always (14, 43), probably depending on wood raw material and pulping method. In spite of the complexity of the problem, much of the information gathered stresses the importance of avoiding carbohydrate degradation, especially of the easily accessible hemicelluloses, for the brightness stability of bleached pulps, and also that resin removal is essential.

The brightness reversion phenomenon of greatest consequence is that of groundwood, which can be considered one of the main causes for the development of the chemical pulping industry. Exposed to light, groundwood-containing paper turns yellow, whereas its brightness is rather stable to heat (30a). Obviously lignin, being an aromatic compound with a strong absorption of ultraviolet light in contrast to the carbohydrates, cf. Chapter 4, takes up irradiation energy, which results in a radical reaction mechanism in which air oxygen takes a part (36a). This leads to a loss of methoxyl groups (12a), probably rupture of the aliphatic side chain and the formation of hydroperoxide radicals, semiquinones and quinoid configurations (30b). In addition, lignin probably acts as a photosensitizer, like certain dyestuffs (10a), causing oxidative degradation of the cellulose by a hydroperoxide radical mechanism, since newsprint and other papers containing groundwood eventually become brittle and disintegrate.

4. OPACITY

As pointed out under the heading 'Fundamental definitions', opacity, as usually defined, depends on both the scattering and absorption coefficients. Decreased scattering naturally decreases opacity. Decreased absorption likewise gives a decrease in opacity, even at constant light scattering. However, the specific scattering coefficient, s, has the dominating influence on opacity. As s denotes a pulp property of both theoretical and practical interest in paper-making, some studies have been devoted to its changes on pulping and subsequent treatments. Figure 12.8 shows the scattering coefficients for a large number of softwood pulps, prepared by kraft and acid sulfite pulping under varying conditions, followed by chlorite delignification (17). The dominating influence is exerted by the extent of carbohydrate removal, whereas changes in the pulping conditions *within each process* are of little importance in this respect. However, kraft pulping gives considerably higher opacities over the entire yield range. As already shown in Table 12.1, hardwoods tend to give low-yield sulfite pulps of higher opacity than do softwoods. On the other hand, hemicellulose-rich hardwood pulps prepared by the neutral sulfite semichemical process, have a low opacity. It seems fairly safe to assume that the removal of hemicelluloses during the pulping processes creates new optically active surfaces, and that in the absence of hemicelluloses many of those surfaces remain even after drying of the sheet, a process which otherwise causes the

854

components of the cell wall surface to stick together by hydrogen bonding. The reason for kraft pulps being more opaque than sulfite pulps of the same yields is obscure, but may have something to do with the removal of amorphous cellulose in the kraft cook or with the crystallization tendency observed for the xylans during kraft pulping, which would have the same consequence as regards opacity as a removal of the amorphous hemicelluloses by dissolution. Table 12.3 (43a) gives more recent data on the influence of the wood species and the pulping on carbohydrate yield and specific scattering coefficient of bleached pulp after beating.

The influence of lignin removal by bleaching on the scattering coefficient is very slight, as seen from Table 12.4 (13), whereas the opacity figure continually decreases as a consequence of the decreased light absorption. The changes of the carbohydrate composition caused by bleaching (hot alkali extraction disregarded) are not of much consequence for the light scattering (16), cf. Section II.1 of this chapter. It is therefore not surprising to find that no matter how the bleaching is carried out (sequence, bleaching agent), the scattering coefficient remained virtually unchanged (17).

The specific scattering coefficient thus turns out to be quite difficult to alter by changes in the cooking or bleaching conditions, unless the content of hemicelluloses, and therefore the pulp yield, is varied. However, a great change in the opacity properties is experienced on drying the pulp before slush making and sheet formation, as seen in Figure 12.8 (17). This effect is utilized by paper mills buying dried pulp, and sometimes even by integrated mills making opaque papers. The explanation is likely to be the irreversible syneresis of the amorphous carbohydrate gel on drying, creating cracks and new optically active surfaces, some of which remain unaffected by subsequent slushing and drying. At the same time, however,

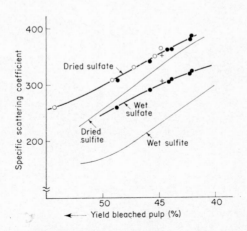

Fig. 12.8. Relationship between the specific scattering coefficient and the yield after cooking and bleaching, for spruce sulfite and kraft pulps
(Giertz)

the fiber bonding tendency is decreased and many paper strength properties are affected adversely. As a matter of fact there exists a close correlation between the mechanical properties of a paper and its light scattering properties. This correlation, as well as the opacity changes on beating, however, has no direct connection with the pulping processes and could not therefore be treated in detail in this book. However, some description of the phenomena is given in Chapter 21 on pulp properties and uses.

Table 12.3. Specific scattering coefficient for bleached pulps, beaten for paper testing without previous drying (43a)

Wood species	Pulping process	Roe no.	Pulp yield, %		Spec. scattering coefficient	
			Unbleached	Bleached	at 25° SR	at 45° SR
Spruce	Acid sulfite	12	58	51	145	105
		8	56	50	150	105
		6	53	49	160	110
		3	51	48	160	125
	Neutral sulfite–acid sulfite	11	64	57	135	100
		8	62	56	140	105
		5	57	54	155	105
		3	55	53	155	110
	Bisulfite	12	58	51	150	110
		8	56	50	160	130
		6	53	50	170	145
	Neutral sulfite–bisulfite	10	63	55	140	105
		8	59	55	155	120
		5	57	54	160	130
	Bisulfite–carbonate	11	53	47	190	160
		8	50	46	200	165
		5	47	44	210	185
		3	44	42	245	220
	Kraft	12	56	48	160	140
		8	53	48	175	150
		6	51	47	180	155
		3	48	45	185	165
Pine	Bisulfite	11	57	50	160	110
		8	53	48	165	125
		6	51	47	190	145
		3	49	45	210	155
	Kraft	12	53	46	185	150
		8	50	45	195	155
		5	47	43	200	160
		3	45	43	210	185
Birch	Acid sulfite	10	59	54	150	110
		4	49	47	180	140
		2	45	44	220	180
	Acid sulfite–carbonate	2	39	38	290	250
	Kraft	11	60	53	170	130
		7	56	52	185	145
		3	51	50	215	175
	Prehydrolysis–kraft	2	38	37	290	250

856

Table 12.4. The optical properties of sulfite pulps on one-stage hypochlorite bleaching and multistage bleaching respectively (13)

Charge, kg ptp act. Cl	Lignin content, %	Brightness, % GE	Spec. scatt. coeff. at 560 mμ	Spec. absorption coeff. at		Opacity (TAPPI)
				410 mμ	560 mμ	
0	2.0	57.9	275	25.7	8.4	0.59
4	2.0	52.8	286	41.1	9.4	0.60
8	1.9	54.2	285	37.0	7.2	0.60
12	1.5	57.8	290	37.9	5.7	0.52
20	0.8	67.7	288	22.0	2.5	0.49
28	0.5	72.9	292	15.0	1.9	0.48
44	—	81.4	295	5.6	1.2	0.55

Multistage bleaching	Roe no.	Spec. scatt. coeff. at 457 mμ	Opacity (TAPPI)
Unbleached	10.1	268	0.806
Bleached	—	257	0.730
Unbleached	4.7	261	0.813
Bleached	—	258	0.734
Unbleached	1.8	265	0.784
Bleached	—	278	0.745

III. Chemical Aspects of Bleaching

Bleaching must be considered as a continuation of the fiberizing process to achieve the final properties desired. The *lignin-bleaching methods* described in Chapter 13 endeavour to preserve the substances in the pulp but to remove some of its chromophors by reduction, oxidation or a combination of both. Those methods are especially sensitive to the process by which the unbleached pulp was produced, and to the color of the unbleached pulp. The *lignin-removing methods* described in Chapter 14 are less sensitive to the unbleached pulp color but are nevertheless influenced by the previous pulping conditions in many ways. The amount of lignin left in the unbleached pulp will determine the consumption of bleaching chemicals. They are more expensive and less easy to recover than the cooking chemicals and should only be used in an amount which is motivated by quality considerations. Prolonged lignin removal in the cooking, however, will also affect the carbohydrates and change the quality, in most cases for the worse. If a bleached greaseproof grade is wanted, it has to be accepted that the chlorine consumption must be quite high, 50–70 kg ptp for sulfite and up to 250 kg ptp for neutral sulfite semichemical pulps. A strong bleached kraft pulp cannot be produced unless the total chlorine consumption is at least 40 and preferably 70 kg ptp. The saving of bleaching chemicals by a prolonged cooking is also often off-set by the increased wood consumption. Unfavorable cooking conditions, such as too low a sulfidity in the kraft cook or too little combined SO$_2$ during the sulfite

857

cook, cause lignin condensation and make the pulp less easy to bleach. The *carbohydrate-removing methods* carried out in the bleachery, which are described in Chapter 15, are also influenced by the manner of cooking, much in the same way as the lignin removal. Thus, to obtain a certain alphacellulose content of a sulfite rayon pulp, it is necessary to use more alkali, and sometimes higher temperature also, if more hemicelluloses have been left in the pulp by limiting the cooking. However, there is often at the same time an improvement in final overall yield or quality which makes the increased cost of the alkali purification justified. Unfavorable cooking conditions, e.g. the prolonged cooking at low temperature when a digester is left over a weekend stop, may increase the resistance of some hemicelluloses not only to the subsequent acid sulfite cook but also to alkali purification and necessitate harsher purification conditions. The *removal of impurities*, particularly *resins*, which is dealt with in Chapter 16, is also affected by the cooking and washing conditions, although in most cases it seems possible to do comparatively little in the cooking to improve deresination.

Not all lignin, carbohydrate or resin removal desired can be accomplished with a one-stage operation, however efficient the stage and the previous cooking. *Multistage bleaching*, described in Chapter 17, gives the best overall economy for the best technical result of the bleaching. Chlorine, the cheapest of the bleaching chemicals, is efficient in removing large quantities of lignin, especially in combination with a subsequent alkali extraction stage. However, it does not remove highly condensed lignin, nor resin, at least at the mild conditions, low temperature and short reaction time normally applied. Although harmless to the carbohydrates at those conditions, chlorine would be dangerous if applied at the more severe conditions necessary to remove the last part of the residual lignin and resin. Therefore, hypochlorite bleaching is added to the sequence to give an oxidative degradation of the impurities. There is always a risk of carbohydrate damage, although it is minimized by keeping a high pH during the entire stage. The hypochlorite stage is capable of imparting brightness to the pulp, which is not the case with chlorination and alkali treatment, and shows its efficiency in removing traces of colored material. However, as the demands on brightness have increased, it is now often necessary to apply such intense oxidation that even well-buffered hypochlorite will cause excessive carbohydrate degradation. Instead, a superbleaching stage with peroxide or chlorine dioxide is introduced. Chlorine dioxide is especially selective in its action, causing little damage to the carbohydrates but efficiently removing residual impurities. For better results, chlorine, hypochlorite as well as chlorine dioxide stages are often doubled, with an intermediate alkali stage. This introduces the question of *accessibility* and *reactivity* of the impurities, especially of the lignin.

Insufficient is known of the detailed *location in the fiber wall* of the residual lignin left after pulping, and still less about the detailed *structure* of the coloring matter, such as residual lignin and resin left in the unbleached pulp, which certainly deviates from the structure of the

858

corresponding wood components. In sulfite pulping, delignification is believed to start from the middle lamella, cf. Chapter 6.V, whereas the swelling caused by the alkali in the kraft cook is likely to guarantee a more homogeneous delignification. In spite of that, and in spite of the fact that resin removal is much more efficient in the kraft cook, kraft pulps are decidedly more difficult to bleach than the sulfite pulps. One likely explanation of that is the higher degree of lignin condensation occurring during the kraft cook as compared with that during sulfite cooking. Lacking more accurate methods of determining the extent of condensation, it is difficult to judge the validity of this hypothesis, but in any case kraft lignin is much *less high-molecular* than are the lignosulfonates. Furthermore, prolonged cooking to lower lignin content, or a prehydrolysis, which certainly does not exclude condensation, makes kraft pulp more easy-bleaching. Another explanation is believed to have a higher validity, namely the lower *hydrophility* of kraft pulp lignin as compared with sulfite pulp lignin. The latter is at least partly sulfonated, to an extent of about 0.2–0.3 S/OCH_3 on average, and is therefore water-soluble if cut to smaller fragments. Kraft pulp lignin, on the other hand, contains considerably more phenolic groups than the lignosulfonate, but is still not hydrophilic enough to be water-soluble upon degradation with chlorine. Chlorination of sulfite pulps (neutral sulfite, bisulfite, as well as acid sulfite) involves the dissolution of chlorinated lignosulfonate fragments during the chlorination stage and exposure of more lignosulfonate to the chlorine. In this way the majority of lignin, 80% or more, depending on the pulp grade, is removed in the chlorination stage and only a minor portion left undissolved for alkali extraction or further oxidation. In kraft chlorination, the reverse is true. Only about 20% of the lignin of an ordinary kraft paper pulp dissolves during the chlorination, whereas the remainder has to be removed in the alkali extraction stage. It is thus likely that not all of the lignin was accessible to the chlorine and some will therefore resist even the alkali extraction. However, the extraction makes it accessible to a second chlorination and extractable by a second alkali stage. Double chlorinations and alkali extractions have often been applied in the bleaching of kraft pulp. However, there is a danger that the second chlorination will affect the carbohydrates, partly because the acidity of the second stage may not develop as fast as in normal chlorinations, thus allowing more hydration of the chlorine to hypochlorous acid. Therefore, hypochlorite is nowadays generally preferred to a second chlorination. Even for hypochlorite, and especially for the acidic chlorine dioxide bleaching, an intermediate alkali extraction between two oxidation stages will improve the result. This is also likely to be caused by topochemical effects. It is safe to assume that during the course of bleaching, the remaining impurities will be less and less reactive and located at the originally least accessible parts of the fiber wall, and correspondingly the carbohydrates will be more and more exposed to oxidative degradation. This dilemma is solved by applying increasingly selective bleaching agents.

As will be further discussed in Chapter 14.III on chlorine dioxide bleaching, the *redox potential* is a poor guide to the action of an oxidant in pulp bleaching. Redox potentials refer to reversible reactions, and pulp bleaching involves irreversible oxidations, often preceded by intermediate compound formation between oxidant and pulp component. The special advantages with chlorine dioxide may be that it is a neutral compound not forming esters with the hydroxyl groups of the carbohydrates, whereas it is capable of attacking aromatic compounds containing phenolic hydroxyl or ether groups. Therefore it is also possible to use much higher temperatures in chlorine dioxide bleaching than in other bleaching stages, which is also of advantage for the oxidation of resin, which seems to require fairly severe conditions. To remove lignin with chlorine dioxide in the earliest stages of a bleaching sequence only requires room temperature, and in the intermediate stages, where hypochlorite is generally used, chlorine dioxide could be applied with hypochlorite conditions. However, for the finishing chlorine dioxide bleach, 70°C is suitable. Although there are several exceptions, a thumb rule for the bleaching philosophy is therefore to make the conditions of bleaching stages increasingly severe as regards the oxidative effect on lignin and resin, but choosing the oxidant so as to prevent carbohydrate degradation. An obvious exception is the viscosity adjustment of rayon pulps, where a certain oxidative degradation of the cellulose is desired and where the hypochlorite stages often come at the end of the bleaching sequence, after a chlorine dioxide stage. Another exception is the bleaching of sulfite pulps from resinous hardwoods, where an initial chlorination will give chlorinated fatty acids which are subsequently difficult to remove. Then an oxidative treatment with hypochlorite or chlorine dioxide is to be preferred. Some advantages are also gained with a finishing hypochlorite stage with a small charge of active chlorine to improve brightness stability.

There is not sufficient knowledge of the fundamental chemical reactions of bleaching to allow any general description of the mechanism. Details are given in each section of the particular bleaching agents. It may be safe to state that the *reactions at the lignin molecule start in the aromatic part*, especially in those monomers containing free phenolic groups, in many cases as a chlorine substitution and in all cases involving oxidation. Degradation occurs through scission of both alkylaryl ether bonds and carbon–carbon bonds, and the aromatic system is converted to a considerable extent to quinoid and aliphatic configurations soluble in alkali. The *oxidation of the carbohydrates starts at the hydroxyl groups, in many cases via ester formation*, to give carbonyl groups which labilize the glycosidic bonds of the particular monomer. The strong pH dependence displayed by the action of most ionized oxidants gives an opportunity to regulate the speed and selectivity of these oxidation reactions.

IV. Technical Aspects of Bleaching

1. TERMS AND DEFINITIONS

The technical operations of bleaching, apart from pulp *transport*, essentially consist of *mixing* pulp with chemicals and heat, *retention* of the mixture in suitable reactors, and *washing* the pulp after reaction to remove the organic substance dissolved, together with the inorganic chemicals. The sequence of mixing, retention and washing constitutes a bleaching stage, and may be repeated several times in the case of multistage bleaching, whereas in other cases one stage is sufficient.

The technique of bleaching, and the equipment used, vary considerably. Older mills use methods different to those of the more modern mills. *Batch-wise* or *continuous* operation is used, with quite different machinery. The rate of reaction of different bleaching chemicals is varying, requiring varying retention time and varying reaction temperature, which is reflected in the equipment needed. The flow properties of a pulp suspension are quite different at different consistency, and operation at low, medium, and high consistency requires different means of transport, different types of mixers and reactors, as well as different arrangements at the previous washers to produce the consistency desired.

Before discussing the equipment used in the various bleaching operations, some terms have to be defined to facilitate the description.

The following *conditions of bleaching* are important in any bleaching stage:

A. Charge of chemicals

Most of the chemicals charged are usually consumed during the stage. The charge is given in kg active chemicals/t of dry, unbleached pulp, *kg ptp*. In the case of chlorine and alkali (sodium hydroxide), no misunderstanding is possible. In the case of hypochlorite, chlorite and chlorine dioxide, the usual manner of expression is *kg ptp act. Cl* (active chlorine), which really means oxidation equivalents times 35.5 (the atomic weight of chlorine). This was an especially practical concept when hypochlorite was the only oxidant used, as the hypochlorite is prepared directly from alkali or lime and chlorine, one chlorine atom always giving one oxidation equivalent. For chlorite and chlorine dioxide, this meaning has been lost, but it is still practical for comparisons to apply the basis of oxidation equivalents, and just as well expressed as kg ptp act. Cl. For economic comparisons it may be of value to keep the conversion factors from kg of chemical to kg of active chlorine in mind, as given in Table 12.5, but as the bleaching chemicals are frequently made at the mill or, when bought, still analyzed by titration of oxidation equivalents, expressed as active chlorine, this is not often necessary. The non-chlorine containing oxidants, such as peroxide or permanganate, are less naturally expressed in terms of active chlorine. Instead they are given as kg ptp 100% chemical or as kg ptp active oxygen (act. O). These conversion factors are also given in Table 12.5

Other chemicals charged, such as acids, surface active agents, etc., are expressed as kg ptp 100% chemical. The special addition of buffering alkali to calcium or sodium hypochlorite oxidation is sometimes given as *excess alkali* in per cent of the hypochlorite charge. For instance, 35% excess alkali at a hypochlorite charge of 10 kg ptp act. Cl is 3.5 kg ptp NaOH. The excess alkali could also be given directly in kg ptp. In both cases, the figure includes all alkali in excess of that used up at the preparation of the hypochlorite, i.e. the residual alkali of the hypochlorite solution as well as the extra alkali added.

Table 12.5. Conversion factors for bleaching oxidants to terms of active chlorine or active oxygen

Oxidant, 1 kg	Active chlorine, kg	Active oxygen, kg
$NaClO$	0.93	0.21
$NaClO_2$	1.57	0.35
ClO_2	2.63	0.59
Na_2O_2	0.91	0.20
H_2O_2	2.09	0.47
$KMnO_4$	1.11	0.25

B. Consistency

The consistency* of the pulp suspension is defined as the content of pulp in a given weight of suspension, including both the weight of the water and the weight of the pulp. Thus, 10% consistency means 1 t of pulp in 9 m^3 of water. At a given charge of chemicals, in kg ptp, the *concentration of chemicals* in g/l and hence the rate of reaction will obviously increase with consistency. This makes a high-consistency operation desirable in the case of slowly-reacting chemicals. At the same time, space is saved in increasing the consistency, and likewise heat and chemicals. The consistency is therefore an important variable in pulp bleaching, and as the equipment needed for the operations is rather different for different consistency levels, there is a need for classification of the operations in low-, medium- and high-consistency operations. As the technique has been improved, the meaning of high consistency has gradually become transferred towards higher values. In this book, the following concepts are used:

(1) Low consistency, 0–6%. Suspension pumpable in ordinary pulp transport pumps. Consistency obtainable by deckers and filters without press rolls.
(2) Medium consistency, 6–20%, usually 10–18%. Suspension pumpable with special machinery. Still mainly a coherent, liquid phase, at least at higher temperature and some compression. Consistency

* The term *consistency* is preferred to the term *density*, which is also used in the same meaning, and to the term *concentration* which should be preserved to indicate chemical concentrations of real solutions.

obtainable by filters, for higher consistencies than 15% equipped with press rolls.

(3) High consistency, 20–40%, usually 25–35%. Liquid phase completely absorbed by the fibers. Non-pumpable but for very short distances. Consistency obtainable only by presses.

C. Temperature

Temperature of reaction, usually maintained constant from the moment of mixing pulp with chemicals and heat to the moment the cooler water of dilution enters the zone of reaction.

D. Time

Time of reaction, the time between the just-mentioned moments of mixing and dilution. Time of retention is somewhat longer, as it may include the brief periods for mixing and dilution. In contrast with cooking, the period of heating to maximum temperature is usually very short, as no time for penetration is required.

With the four independent variables mentioned, i.e. charges of chemicals, consistency, temperature and time, the chemical conditions of a bleaching stage are sufficiently defined, especially if the important adjustments of pH are included in the concept of charges of chemicals. Initial and final pH are then often added as a further description, although they may also be classed among the dependent variables.

To describe a multistage bleaching, a set-up of these four variables for each stage is necessary, together with a *bleaching schedule*, describing in which order the different treatments occur, including the washings. A system to give a bleaching schedule in a brief and yet explicit way is given in Chapter 17.III, from which one example should be cited here:

/C/E/DH/, meaning a sequence of chlorination, alkali extraction, chlorine dioxide and hypochlorite oxidations, where washing is performed before and after each stage except between D and H, where the intermediate washing has been excluded.

The *results of the bleaching* are given in terms of *pulp yield*, as well as *analysis of pulp and liquor* after each stage. To the latter analysis figures belong *pH*, *residual chemicals* and sometimes liquor color, oxygen demand or some other property to describe the organic substance dissolved. The pulp analysis includes *brightness* and sometimes *brightness stability* and *opacity*, as well as *residual chlorine (or oxygen) demand* (chlorine or permanganate number), *viscosity*, *alphacellulose*, *pentosan* and *resin* content, sometimes *carbonyl* and *carboxyl* content, and often *paper properties*. The properties of the unbleached pulp should always be given.

An example of a satisfactory account for a bleaching is given in Table 12.6.

2. BLEACHING EQUIPMENT

A. Means of pulp transport

For the pulp transport in the bleachery pumps and band conveyors are mainly used. As in the case of the screening room, additional transport is obtained from machinery of additional functions, such as filter drums and screws.

For the lowest consistencies, up to about 0.5%, ordinary water centrifugal pumps can be used. At somewhat higher consistency the pump used should have more open impellers, the so-called pulp stock pumps, Figure 12.9, with the preferred consistency range of 1–3% but usable up to around 6% in special constructions. In the lower medium-consistency range, 6–12%, a special device of *Kamyr* design is used, consisting of a low-pressure star feeder, combined with a pressure chamber. Air or steam pressure supplies the necessary force for pulp flow. At still higher consistency, 10–18%, or covering the entire medium-consistency range, the *Impco* thick stock pump is used, Figure 12.10. A similar recent *Kamyr* construction works in the same consistency range and can be used at even 35% consistency for short transport distances. At high consistency, the pulp may be blown by air transport, or conveyed on rubber bands, which are also used at medium consistency.

The need for pumping or conveying in the bleachery exists for the following purposes:

> from the bottom of a downflow tower to the next filter, usually placed on the top floor;
> from a filter to the bottom of an upflow tower, whereby also the flow resistance of the tower must be overcome;
> from a filter to the alternative bleachers of a batch bleachery.

Table 12.6. Account of bleaching conditions and results

Schedule	/	C	/	E	/	D	H	/
Consistency, %		3.0		15.0		10.0	6.0	
Temperature, °C		20		100		70	60	
Time, h		1		1		2	4	
Charge, kg ptp act. Cl		12		—		20	5.0	
kg ptp NaOH		—		39		—	6.5	
Initial pH		—		—		—	10.9	
Final pH		1.9		9.8		3.2	10.4	
Residual chemicals, kg ptp		1.2		1		7	4.5	

	Unbleached	Bleached
Wood	Spruce	—
Pulp type	Sulfite	—
Yield, %	—	90.7
Roe chlorine number	1.0	—
Viscosity, cP Tappi	24.5	14.0
Alphacellulose, %	89.7	91.6
Resin content, %	1.2	0.15
Brightness, % GE,		
of pulp	61.0	98.9
of alkali cellulose	—	88.4

For the latter purpose, band conveyors are usual. Apart from the special devices to pump medium-consistency pulp, there is the gravity transport from the filter through a downflow tower, and the same is used for high-consistency pulp.

B. Mixers

The mixing of chemicals and heat to the pulp suspension is of determining importance for the uniformity of the bleached pulp, and thus, it requires close attention. The mixing problem is more difficult at higher consistency, which requires more elaborate machinery.

Batch mixing presents a special problem, connected with the considerable time required for filling a bleacher. In some mills, the chemicals are charged continuously during the filling, in mixers similar to those of continuous bleaching. This ensures a satisfactory mixing with the pulp,

Fig. 12.9. Kamyr low-consistency pulp transport pump, with impeller unit separated from the pump housing

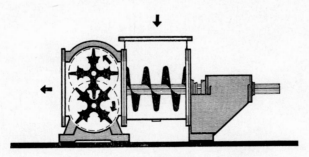

Fig. 12.10. Sund–Impco thick stock pump

but results in a considerably longer bleaching time for the pulp first arriving at the bleacher than the average, and consequently in non-uniformity. In other mills, the chemicals are charged after filling the bleacher, whereby, to avoid excessive charging times, the chemicals have to be added at a rate which must lead to local excess of chemicals and hence to non-uniformity. Actually, this is a principal drawback of batch bleaching in comparison with continuous bleaching, unless the filling time can be made very short in comparison with the time of reaction, which would require heavily overdimensioned filters or many very small batches. The mixing of heat in batch bleaching encounters the same principal problems.

The *continuous mixing of chemicals with low-consistency pulp* is easily done in the transport pumps, the inlet of chemicals preferably being placed immediately prior to the pump. In the case of a low-consistency alkali or hypochlorite stage, the pump is placed directly after a washing filter, and the chemical is added to the filter shredder or at the last shower. Chlorination requires an especially efficient mixing, as the reaction is initially very rapid, and the main part of the chlorine therefore reacts directly after the introduction. Local excess due to inefficient mixing would then produce overchlorination, as well as insufficiently chlorinated regions. Furthermore, unreacted chlorine may cause troubles on the subsequent filter. Three systems are in use. The simplest is an *impeller* on a horizontal shaft, placed in the bottom of the upflow chlorination tower. The chlorine is introduced as a gas or as chlorine water close to the pulp inlet at the tower

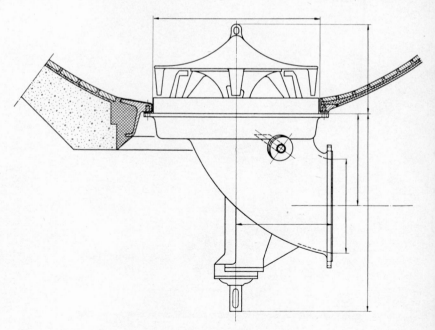

Fig. 12.11. Kamyr radial mixer for low- and medium-consistency upflow towers

base, cf. Figure 12.19. In the case of neutral sulfite pulps, two impellers on top of each other, and two chlorine inlets for the large amounts of chlorine, are sometimes recommended. A further development is the *radial mixer*, Figure 12.11, a pump wheel placed on a vertical shaft concentric in the bottom of an upflow tower. The pulp is introduced into the center of the mixer and chlorine gas nearby. A third possibility is a *special chlorine mixer* outside the chlorination tower, Figure 12.12.

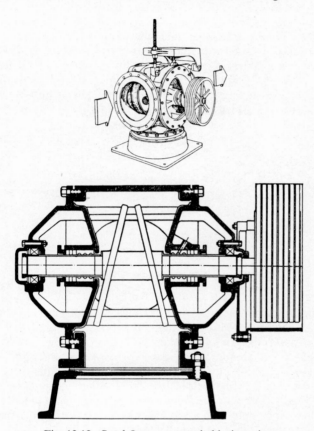

Fig. 12.12. Sund–Impco external chlorine mixer

The *mixing of heat with low-consistency pulp* is usually done by hot water showers on the filter prior to the bleaching stage. Low-consistency stages are for economical reasons always low-temperature stages, with temperatures of 10–50°C and seldom up to 70°C. Steam heating is avoided as much as possible, but often a steam mixer is placed after the filter for minor temperature adjustments on top of the temperature supplied by the hot water. This mixer is usually a single-shaft horizontal, or sometimes vertical mixer for direct steaming, cf. Figure 12.20. Radial mixers also have a steam inlet.

The *mixing of chemicals with medium-consistency pulp* can be done by a radial mixer to a consistency of 12%. For the higher consistencies in this range, the single- or double-shaft mixer is used, Figure 12.13 and Figures 12.20–21. The charging of the chemicals is then done at the previous filter, either at the shredder or at the last shower. In the case of hot alkali refining for high alpha pulps, considerable quantities of alkali are used, but too high concentration of the added lye, which could produce local mercerization, should be avoided. A method of ensuring good mixing at medium-consistency hot refining is to add an excess of alkali to the pulp at low consistency after the first filter, and then remove the excess at a second filtration to the consistency required. However modern double-shaft mixers are considered to supply adequate mixing of chemicals and heat with the pulp. A method, similar to the double filtration, was used in a system employing a vertical screw press in the bottom of an upflow tower, the 'concentrator'. The excess lye expelled was returned to dilute the pulp to

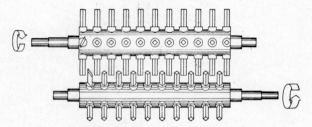

Fig. 12.13. Rotors of Sund double shaft mixer for medium- and high-consistency pulp

low consistency after the previous filtration. Due to pulp knot formation in the press, this system has been abandoned by several mills. The single- or double-shaft mixer is sometimes also used for the introduction of chlorine gas to alkali-containing pulp for direct production of sodium hypochlorite. The alkali is then added at the previous filter, in an amount corresponding to the chlorine plus the excess alkali desired.

The *mixing of heat with medium-consistency pulp* is done as in the case of low-consistency pulp with a hot water addition to the filter prior to the bleaching stage in question, and an addition of live steam to a mixer. The medium consistency allows higher reaction temperatures, 50–120°C, as less heat is required to achieve a certain temperature. Considerable amounts of steam are consumed, which are introduced through double rows of nozzles at the sides of the mixer. Usually the same mixers are used as for the chemicals, but sometimes it is an advantage to use a separate steam mixer prior to the introduction of chemicals. Thus, a horizontal steam mixer may precede a horizontal or radial mixer for chlorine dioxide solution, Figure 12.21, prohibiting the chlorine dioxide gas from escaping and preventing the corrosive gas phase in the mixer when chlorine dioxide is introduced prior to the steam mixer.

The *mixing of chemicals and heat with high-consistency pulp* is the most difficult problem. In some instances a drum press or a horizontal screw press is incorporated between the mixer of chemicals and the mixer of steam. In that case, the mixing of chemicals is done in a conventional medium-consistency mixer or even in the double-filter system. The expelled liquor containing chemicals is returned to the filter showers, to displace some of the pulp web water, and the high-consistency pulp is steamed in an ordinary mixer, possibly after having passed a low-pressure star feeder, Figure 12.14. The star feeder could be replaced by a thick stock pump. In other systems, the press expels a hard cake of pulp of 40–45% dry content, which is then disintegrated in a vertical-shaft disk refiner,

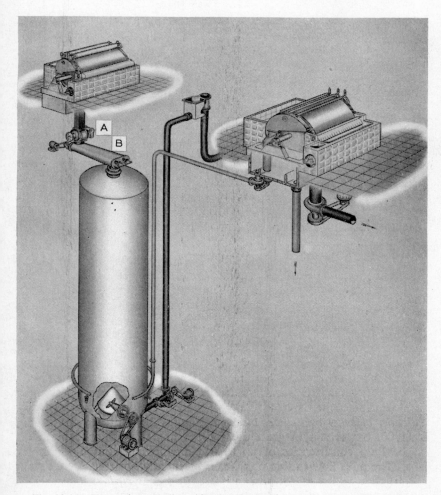

Fig. 12.14. Kamyr hot alkali purification system for medium- or high-consistency operation, including low-pressure star feeder (A) and double shaft mixer (B)

869

the so-called *Rotopulper*, Figure 12.15. If the chemicals have not been introduced prior to the press, they are charged through nozzles situated at some distance from the center of the disks. The chemical solution is said to be atomized at the introduction and uniformly distributed to the pulp. The formation of knots in both press and Rotopulper (37) has so far prevented a more general acceptance of the system.

A special mixing system in high consistency is the 'cold steeping' in peroxide bleaching, of a pulp web at 35–50% dry content by passing it through a pair of press rolls, to which the bleach solution is applied (2, 59).

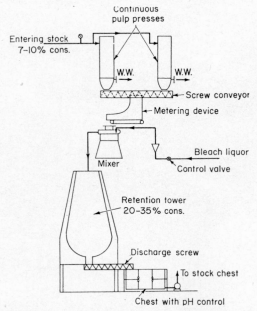

Fig. 12.15. Continuous high-density tower system

C. Reactors

The present *batch reactors* were developed from the hollander beater, the beater roll of which was exchanged for a paddle wheel and finally for an impeller. At the same time, the design of the tub was somewhat changed and constructed in tile-lined concrete. This development ended in the *hollander bleacher* or *Bellmer bleacher*, Figure 12.16, already constructed by 1900, but is still in great use for the final hypochlorite bleaching stage. Pulp consistencies of up to 8% are possible, but 6–7% is the rule. The pulp flow in this bleacher is essentially horizontal. A similar construction with vertical flow, called the *vertical bleacher*, Figure 12.17, was developed somewhat later on, and is also still used.

Some types of true medium-consistency batch bleachers were also developed, commencing with the *Wolf horizontal bleacher*, consisting of a system of long, horizontal screw conveyors. This construction was improved to become the vertical-flow *Wolf–Fletcher* or *VW bleacher*, Figure 12.18, which allows consistencies of up to 18%. Such constructions are also in use.

Attempts to construct *continuous bleachers* had already been made in the beginning of this century, but continuous bleaching did not receive

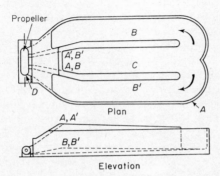

Fig, 12.16. Bellmer bleacher

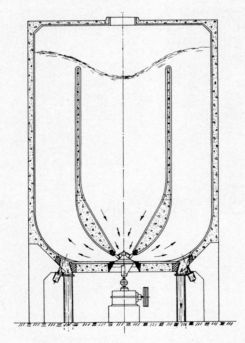

Fig. 12. 17. Kamyr vertical bleacher

closer attention until the 1930's, with the construction of high-capacity multistage bleacheries, where the advantages of continuous operation were more obviously realized. The continuous *bleaching tower* was constructed, with upwards flow at low consistency and downwards flow for medium consistency. The best-known construction of *upflow towers* is that of *Kamyr*, Figure 12.19, and of downflow towers that of *Thorne*, later improved by *Kamyr* and *Impco* by substituting the mechanical discharger with a system of dilution water nozzles and one or preferably two impellers, Figure 12.20.

There are two more remarkable deviations from the rule that upflow towers are used for low-consistency and downflow towers for medium-consistency bleaching. The *Impco chlorination tower* uses a narrow upflow leg with a retention time of only some minutes, whereas the main retention time is in a downflow tower. This arrangement allows an easy control of the chlorine dosage at an early stage. The main limiting factor for the *upflow* towers as regards consistency is the friction resistance in the pulp transport through the pipeline from the filter to the tower, and through the tower. With the construction of the thick stock pumps, Impco and Kamyr have succeeded in increasing the pulp consistency for upflow towers to 10–18%. In those cases, the horizontal-shaft impeller in the bottom of the tower is exchanged for a radial mixer, Figure 12.21.

The reactors for high-consistency bleaching are downflow towers. To eliminate the tendency of bridging and plugging, in some cases they have been designed conically, with a broader base. However, bleaching in 30% consistency is also carried out in ordinary cylindrical towers with conventional dilution discharge. Some experience seems to indicate that the

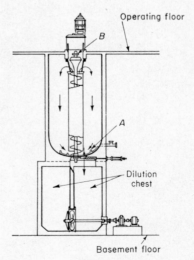

Fig. 12.18. VW bleacher (Pulp Bleaching Co., Seattle)

danger of plug formation in a downflow tower is greatest in the region of 20–25%, at the same time as the disappearance of free water.

There are different opinions about the advantages of a consistency increase, and the advantages and drawbacks of upflow and downflow towers. As will be shown below the gain in space on increasing the consistency is considerable up to around 15% and equal to the theoretical gain assuming complete filling of the space with pulp and liquid. Further increase in consistency means additional but minor gains in space demand. This is an effect of the increasing presence of void spaces between the moist pulp crumbs. Processes requiring long retention times should therefore preferably be carried out at medium consistency. On increasing the consistency, savings in heat and chemicals are also possible. The heat savings are essentially proportional to the decrease in the water present and therefore continue through the high-consistency range. High temperature processes should therefore be carried out at medium consistency at least, and preferably at high consistency. To the latter processes belong above all the hot alkali refining (including carbonate cooking at 150–170°C) and to some

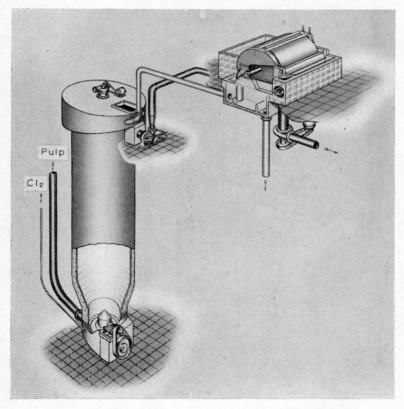

Fig. 12.19. Kamyr low-consistency upflow chlorination tower

extent also chlorine dioxide bleaching, whereas normal alkali extraction is carried out at low or medium consistency, as is hypochlorite bleaching. Although medium-consistency chlorination has been investigated, the rapidity of reaction as well as the importance of instantaneous perfect mixing suggest low-consistency operation for this process. Peroxide bleaching as a separate stage is according to some findings best carried out at high consistency in order to achieve the highest brightness increases, which also underlines the fact that reaction rate is accelerated at an increase in consistency. In discussing the justification for bleaching at higher consistency, the increased costs of investment must also be considered, not only for pulp transport and mixing, but for the equipment used to achieve the higher consistencies, such as filter press rolls or separate presses.

The downflow towers allow higher consistency than upflow towers and

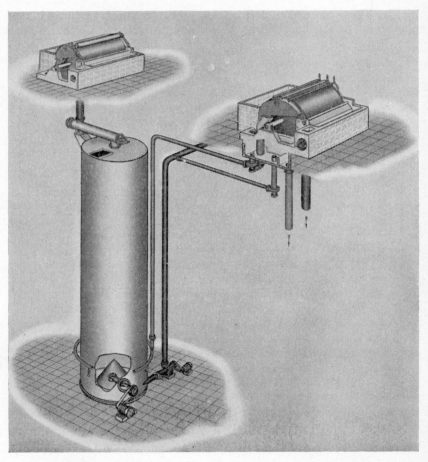

Fig. 12.20. Kamyr medium-consistency downflow tower, with single-shaft mixer

874

are often preferred for medium-consistency bleaching. One of their advantages is that the retention time can be varied simply by increasing or decreasing the pulp level. However, although of value for minor adjustments in viscosity, there is generally nothing to be gained by lowering the time of retention, that cannot be achieved by decreasing temperature or charge of chemicals. It is therefore more economical to run the towers with high pulp levels. The drawbacks of downflow towers have been their tendency to plug when run at consistencies approaching 20%, the difficulty of level control and, finally, the tendency of the cooler dilution zone to wander upwards irregularly, thereby prematurely stopping the reaction. However, these drawbacks have been largely overcome by better instrument control and improved equipment for intense stirring in the bottom.

The advantage of a medium-consistency upflow tower, in spite of the

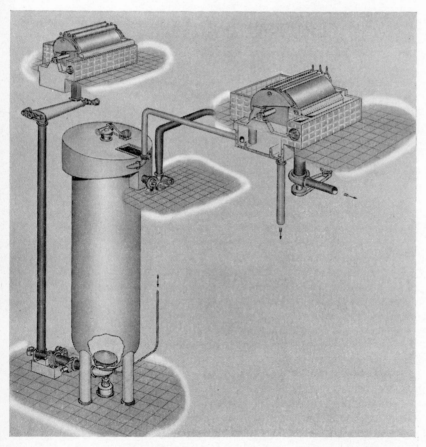

Fig. 12.21. Kamyr medium-consistency upflow tower, with double-shaft mixer and radial mixer

somewhat lower consistency practicable, would be less danger of wandering dilution water, as well as easier level control, as upflow towers work with overflow. A further definite advantage is that the discharge is principally possible without dilution of the pulp suspension. This is important at the combination of two bleaching stages without intermediate washing, as in the case of double hypochlorite addition, or of a combined chlorine dioxide–hypochlorite bleaching. In these cases, which result in heat saving and lower investments, an upflow tower in combination with a downflow tower is ideal, for bleaching at around 10–15% consistency, Figure 12.22.

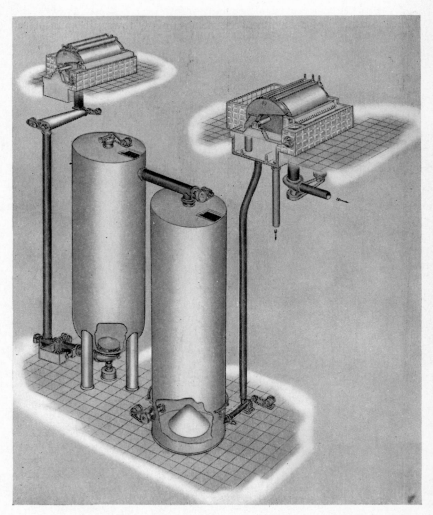

Fig. 12.22. Combined upflow-downflow medium consistency bleaching (Kamyr)

Another advantage with the medium-consistency upflow towers would be that they permit operation on the ground floor, no filters or mixing machinery being necessary at the tower top, which could therefore be placed outdoors, properly insulated. This means a saving in building costs. However, with the Impco feeder and mixer, the same is true for the downflow towers at the same or higher consistency. A condition in both cases are modern filters needing no extra suction drop-legs. To date, however, most bleacheries are built with operation on the top floor. Figures 12.23–24 show examples of both alternatives.

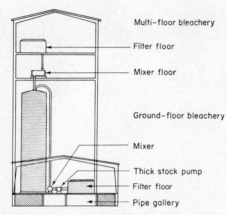

Fig. 12.23. Section showing bleacheries operated from top or ground floor (Sund)

The retention time in a bleach tower depends on the rate of production, the effective tower volume, the consistency and degree of packing, and the uniformity of the pulp flow. The effective tower volume is almost 100% in an upflow tower but only about 75–80% in a normal downflow tower due to the volume lost in the dilution zone as well as at the top cone of pulp. The degree of packing is 100% at low consistencies, so that the pulp–water suspension fills out the entire volume. At medium and high consistency, void air spaces appear, which detract from the advantage of increasing the consistency. Figure 12.25 indicates that at the top of the towers where the packing pressure is small, the advantages of a higher consistency are already lost at about 12%, but that in the main part of the tower the packing is sufficient to utilize consistency increases up to about 18–20%, although it must be stressed that different pulp types may pack differently, and that the temperature and chemicals employed may also influence the degree of packing. A minimum of 5 m³ ptp tower volume is therefore required, and 7–8 m³ ptp is normal for medium-consistency operations, As pointed out previously, there are advantages other than retention time to be gained by increasing the consistency, such as heat economy and higher reaction velocity.

877

The uniformity of flow in the tower can be tested with a flame spectro-photometer technique (58) or with radioactive tracers (12) involving the injection of a known quantity of potassium chloride or radioactive sodium bicarbonate immediately prior to the tower and determining the amounts leaving the tower after a suitable interval. Examples of both techniques tried on the same tower are given in Figure 12.26 (12, 36), together with

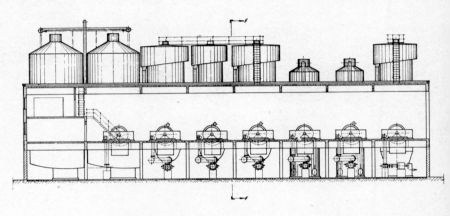

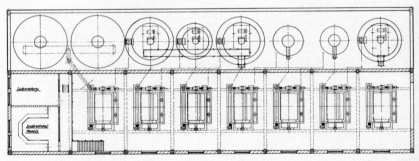

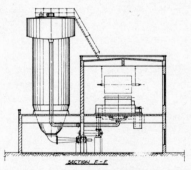

Fig. 12.24. Kamyr bleachery arranged for ground-floor operation and outdoor towers. Kraft bleaching sequence (right-to-left) /C/E/H/D/E/D/ followed by two storage towers (cf. Chapter 17)

878

a comparison of different types of tower. The uniformity of flow is best evaluated by the standard deviation from the average value

$$S = \sqrt{\frac{\overset{i}{\underset{1}{\Sigma}}(X_i - \bar{X})^2}{n - 1}} \text{ and as the skewness } k = \sqrt[3]{\frac{\overset{i}{\underset{1}{\Sigma}}(X_i - \bar{X})^3}{n \cdot S^3}}.$$

The standard deviation, expressed as the percentage variation coefficient, is about 3% for towers with good performance and 5–10% for less good. The skewness is usually positive, i.e. some pulp tends to lag behind, but sometimes approaches zero, or symmetrical distribution.

D. *Washers*

As washing in bleaching operation, in contrast to that after cooking, does not have to consider spent liquor recovery, the main purpose is to remove impurities at a reasonable consumption of fresh water. Additional achievements of the washers are to deliver the pulp to the next bleaching stage at proper consistency, and in some cases to mix in heat or chemicals.

Washing is achieved by *dilution and thickening*, as well as by *displacement*. As in the case of unbleached pulp washing, the efficiency is decreased by the fact that considerable amounts of liquid are imbibed in the capillary system of the fiber, and that some impurities are retained on the fibers by absorption or ionic attraction.

On leaving the bleacher or tower, the pulp is diluted to a consistency of around 2%, to flow more freely, and then further to around 1% before

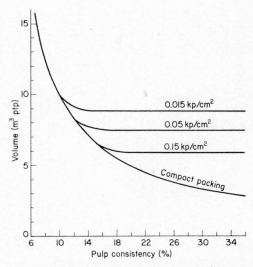

Fig. 12.25. Space demand of one ton of spruce pulp at varying consistency, packed at different top pressures (approximately corresponding to 0.3, 1 and 3 m tower depth)

879

washing. With a simple thickening of this suspension to 10% consistency, up to 90% of the impurities are removed. This is often the main effect obtained in filter washing in the bleachery. To increase the effect, there are two possibilities. One is repeated dilution and concentration, the other addition of wash water to the thickened pulp for displacement. The former alternative, for which *deckers*, coupled in series of several units have been used, needs a lot of water and has the additional drawback of achieving far from the theoretical results because of the retention phenomena mentioned. The other is practised on the various types of *filters*, which are the dominating equipment of the bleachery. The action of *disk*, *drum* or *screw presses* could be utilized to eliminate some of the difficulties connected with the capillary imbibition, but are little used, and mainly in connection with the realization of high consistencies.

The filters used in the bleacheries are either *vacuum* or *pressure filters*. The former are more frequent, the vacuum being obtained with a separate pump, with a suction drop-leg, or in more recent constructions by suction channels in the filter drum, the so-called *valveless* filters, Figure 10.6.

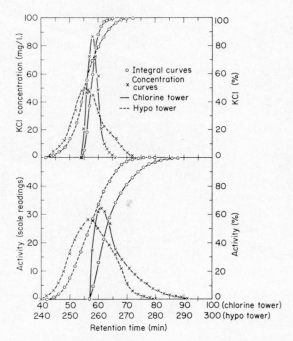

Fig. 12.26. Two tracer techniques for establishing the retention time and uniformity of pulp flow of one low-consistency upflow chlorination tower and one medium consistency upflow hypochlorite bleach tower. Upper half, spectrophotometry tracing of KCl; lower half, tracing of radioactive $Na^{24}HCO_3$ (E. Nilsson–O. Fineman)

These are now preferred to other types because of their ease of operation, and because they could be placed at any floor, whereas the drop-leg necessitates a height of 10–15 m above the ground floor. As pointed out in the previous section, the operation floor including the filters is usually at the top of the towers, but could now also be placed at the ground floor.

The filters are preferably equipped with a variator, for adjustment of the speed of rotation, which is usually 1–4 rpm. The wash water for displacement is supplied by the *showers*, which could be sprinkler pipes, or more elaborate constructions, such as slot extruders, or washing boxes. The latter, which keep a constant and calm zone of wash water on top of the pulp layer, are believed to create the best conditions for displacement, as they leave the structure of the pulp layer undisturbed and do not create unfavorable channeling. There is an optimum thickness of the filter cake, which is sufficient to minimize the channeling tendency of a thin cake but thin enough to allow the water of displacement to penetrate the layer during the time determined by the speed of rotation and the drum diameter. Therefore, there is an optimum load on a filter washer, different for different types of pulp and for different washing stages, but generally around 6 t/d.m^2 filter area. However, most filters are run overloaded, up to 10 or even 15 t/d.m^2 (42), because of the general tendency to increase the production of a bleachery without change of equipment, which in the case of filters involves a considerable capital investment.

The problem of filter mixing of chemicals and heat is in principle similar to that of washing by displacement. One or more of the showers are then utilized to introduce hot water or a chemical solution, such as alkali lye. Generally, there is no complete displacement through the filter cake in these cases to avoid losses of chemicals, mixing being completed subsequently in the filter shredder or in a mixer.

A normal vacuum filter will deliver a consistency of 10–15%. If equipped with press rolls, the pulp leaves the filter with a consistency of up to 20%. Presses achieve consistencies of 30–50%, varying with the type of pulp, the load, and the temperature.

To save fresh mill water, a multistage bleachery applies a type of *counter-current washing*. To dilute the pulp at the discharge of the tower, as well as the further dilution prior to filtration, the filtrate, or '*white water*' from the subsequent filter is often used, Figures 12.19–20. This is not advisable where larger amounts of impurities have to be removed, as it eliminates the washing effect of dilution and thickening mentioned previously. If practised, the only white water in excess corresponds to the amounts of wash water added at the showers. This quantity of white water is then often added as the first shower of the preceding filter. Such a procedure is thus avoided where too many impurities are present, as in the case of white water from the first alkali extraction of a kraft pulp. With water recirculation, it is also less costly to keep up the temperature at the filtration, which is of importance for both filter capacity and washing efficiency. In systems not practising a consequent counter-current washing principle, heat exchangers are applied to preheat the wash water to a filter with the white water flowing from the same filter (1a).

The construction material of most filters is usually nowadays best-quality stainless steel. To avoid a corrosive atmosphere and gas hazards, it is becoming the practice to equip each filter with a hood, connected to ventilation.

Modern filters have reached a high degree of perfection, as have mixers and bleaching towers. However, with high-grade construction materials and the costly procedures of manufacture involved, the investment costs for a multistage bleachery are appreciable, $2–3 M for a 300 t/d six-stage kraft bleachery. Some efforts have been made lately to decrease the number of stages necessary, and to simplify the equipment required. Examples of the reduction of stages are given in Chapter 17.IV. An example of the search for simplified equipment will be given here. It is possible, in a construction similar to the continuous diffuser (cf. Chapter 10.II) to obtain one or more washings *and* bleachings in the same continuous tower, using counter-current chemical treatment. For instance, the diluted unwashed pulp from an alkali stage is introduced in the bottom of the tower. There, the spent bleaching liquor is withdrawn through the perforated plate bottom, which is kept clean by a doctor blade, circulating from a vertical shaft. The displacing liquor moves slowly downwards, whereas the pulp flow is upwards. At a certain level, bleach liquor, chlorine dioxide or hypochlorite is introduced, and at a still higher level hot water or steam, on top of that cold water. Above the washing zone new chemicals, such as sulfur dioxide for acidification, could be introduced. The effect of counter-current bleaching will tend to lower the reaction times necessary. Working at a constant capacity, the control of the reactions will depend on the charge of chemicals, but especially of temperature. Interesting possibilities are realized if the construction can be engineered to work at well-defined flow, at substantial savings in investment costs.

REFERENCES

1. Adler, E., and S. Häggroth, *Svensk Papperstid.*, **53**, 287, 321 (1950).
1a. Alm, N. O., *Tappi*, **45**, 188 (1962).
2. Anon., *Pulp Paper*, **24**, No. 9, 70 (1950); cf. L. A. Beeman and J. S. Reichert, in TAPPI Monograph Series No. 10, New York 1953, p. 242.
3. Campbell, W. B., and J. Benny, *Pulp Paper Mag. Can.*, **47**, No. 7, 75 (1946).
4. Chadeyron, L., *Bull. Assoc. Tech. Ind. Papetiere*, **1**, 21 (1954).
5. Clark, J. d'A., *Paper Trade J.*, **89**, No. 20, 62 (1929).
6. Clewell, D. H., *J. Opt. Soc. Am.*, **31**, 521 (1941).
7. Côté, W. A., and R. Marton, *Tappi*, **45**, 46 (1962).
8. Davis, M. N., *Paper Trade J.*, **93**, No. 16, 39 (1931).
9. Davis, M. N., *Paper Trade J.*, **101**, No. 1, 36 (1935).
10. Doughty, R. H., *Paper Trade J.*, **87**, No. 19, 66 (1928).
10a. Egerton, G. S., *J. Soc. Dyers Colorists*, **64**, 336 (1948); *J. Textile Inst.*, **39**, T293 (1948).

11. Farebrother, T. H., *World's Paper Trade Rev.*, **107**, No. 25, T.S. 38 (1937).
12. Fineman, O., unpublished.
12a. Forman, L. V., *Paper Trade J.*, **111**, No. 21, 34 (1940).
13. Forni, P. A., *Tech. Assoc. Papers*, **28**, 399 (1945).
14. Giertz, H. W., *Svensk Papperstid.*, **48**, 317 (1945).
15. Giertz, H. W., *Svensk Papperstid.*, **53**, 673 (1950).
16. Giertz, H. W., *Svensk Papperstid.*, **54**, 267 (1951).
17. Giertz, H. W., *Svensk Papperstid.*, **54**, 769 (1951); **55**, 72, 897 (1952).
18. Giertz, H. W., and J. McPherson, *Svensk Papperstid.*, **59**, 93 (1956).
18a. Hardy, A. C., *Handbook of Colorimetry*, Technology Press, Cambridge, Mass. 1936.
19. Harrison, V. G. W., P.A.T.R.A. Reports No. 2 (1938), No. 3 (1939).
20. Harrison, V. G. W., *Measurement of Opacity of Paper, A Theoretical Survey*, Paper Makers' Assoc. of Great Britain and Northern Ireland, 1940.
21. Holzer, W. F., *Paper Trade J.*, **99**, No. 12, 91 (1934).
22. Johansson, T., *Färg*, Natur och Kultur, Stockholm 1952.
23. Judd, D. B., *Paper Trade J.*, **100**, No. 21, 40 (1935).
24. Judd, D. B., *Paper Trade J.*, **100**, No. 1, 28 (1935).
25. Judd, D. B., *Paper Trade J.*, **106**, No. 1, 39 (1938).
26. Jullander, I., and K. Brune, *Svensk Papperstid.*, **62**, 728 (1959).
27. Keller, R., et al., *Svensk Papperstid.*, **61**, 754 (1958).
28. Kubelka, P., and F. Munk, *Z. Tech. Physik*, **12**, 593 (1931).
29. Launer, H. F., and W. K. Wilson, *Paper Maker Brit. Paper Trade J.*, **105**, 16 (1943).
30. Lekander, K. E., and L. Stockman, *Svensk Papperstid.*, **58**, 775 (1955).
30a. Lewis, H. F., et al., *Paper Trade J.*, **121**, No. 8, 44, 76 (1945).
30b. Luner, P., *Tappi*, **43**, 819 (1960).
31. Maass, O., and R. Richardson, *Pulp Paper Mag. Can.*, **34**, 457 (1933).
32. MacAdam, D. L., *Tappi*, **38**, 78 (1955).
32a. MacClaren, R. H., et al., *Tappi.*, **45**, 789 (1962).
33. McIntyre, J. W., *Paper Trade J.*, **109**, No. 24, 29 (1939).
34. Marton, R., *Tappi*, **43**, 826 (1960).
35. Marum, E. B., *Tappi*, **39**, 390 (1956).
36. Nilsson, E., unpublished.
36a. Nolan, P. A., et al., *Paper Trade J.*, **121**, No. 11, 33 (1945).
37. Nolan, W. J., and B. Armstrong, *Paper Mill News*, **77**, No. 27, 160, No. 39, 14 (1954); **78**, No. 13, 70 (1955); *Paper Trade J.*, **139**, No. 1, 23 (1955).
38. Nordman, L., *Svensk Papperstid.*, **52**, 441 (1949).
39. Parsons, S. R., *Paper Trade J.*, **115**, No. 25, 34 (1942).
40. Patel, G. M., *Makromol. Chem.*, **7**, 12 (1951).
41. Rapson, W. H., et al., *Tappi*, **41**, 442 (1958); *Pulp Paper Mag. Can.*, **58**, No. 8, 151 (1957).
41a. Rapson, W. H., and C. B. Anderson, *Pulp Paper Mag. Can.*, **61**, No. 10, 495 (1960).
41b. Rasch, R. H., *J. Research Natl. Bur. Standards*, **3**, 469 (1929); **7**, 465 (1931), cf. TAPPI Standard T453 m–48.
42. Richter, J., *Svensk Papperstid.*, **56**, 548 (1953).
43. Rollinson, S. M., *Tappi*, **38**, 625 (1955).
43a. Rydholm, S. A., et al., *Svensk Papperstid.*, **66**, 196 (1963) and unpublished.
44. Sammet, C. F., *Paper Trade J.*, **81**, No. 5, 49 (1925).

45. Selling, H. J., and L. F. C. Friele, *Whiteness Relations and Their Application*, Vezelinst. T.N.O., Delft 1950.
46. Sihtola, H., *et al.*, *Paperi Puu*, **40**, 579, 627 (1958); **41**, 35 (1959).
47. Shriner, R. L., *A Review of Natural Coloring Matters in Wood*, TAPPI Monograph Series, No. 6, 182 (1948).
47a. Spinner, I. H., *Tappi*, **45**, 495 (1962).
48. Steele, F. A., *Paper Trade J.*, **100**, No. 12, 37 (1935).
49. Stenius, Å. S:son, *Svensk Papperstid.*, **63**, 1 (1960).
50. Stenius, Å. S:son, *Svensk Papperstid.*, **59**, 172 (1956).
51. Stenius, Å. S:son, *Svensk Papperstid.*, **54**, 663, 701 (1951); **56**, 607 (1953).
52. Stenius, Å. S:son, *Svensk Papperstid.*, **64**, 20 (1961).
53. Stephansen, E., *Papir Journalen*, **23**, 244 (1935).
54. TAPPI Standard T452 m-58, CCA 26:55; *Svensk Papperstid.*, **59**, 12, 650 (1956); cf. C. Valeur, *Svensk Papperstid.*, **57**, 789 (1954).
55. The Institute of Paper Chemistry, *Paper Trade J.*, **109**, No. 4, 29 (1939).
56. Tongren, J. C., *Paper Trade J.*, **107**, No. 8, 34 (1938).
57. Van den Akker, J. A., *Tappi*, **32**, 498 (1949).
57a. Van den Akker, J. A., *et al.*, *Tappi*, **43**, No. 2, 230A; No. 5, 253A (1960).
57b. Van den Akker, J. A., *et al.*, *Tappi.*, **46**, No. 1, 179A (1963).
57c. Van den Akker, J. A., *et al.*, *Tappi*, **46**, No. 5, 202A (1963).
58. Venemark, E., *Svensk Papperstid.*, **58**, 78 (1955).
58a. Virkola, N. E., *et al.*, *Paperi Puu*, **40**, 579, 635 (1958); *Norsk Skogind.*, **12**, 87 (1958).
59. Wultsch, F., and W. Gärtner, *Die Peroxydbleiche von Zellstoff und Holzschliff*, Degussa Bull., 1956.

13

LIGNIN-BLEACHING METHODS

I. General Description of Processes

As shown in Table 12.2, most unbleached pulps have a brightness of 40–65%GE, and kraft pulps less than 30%GE. To a considerable extent the pulp color determines the usefulness of the pulp. The eye appeal aspect of the paper products has been extended from the fine paper and normal printing paper fields into the packaging papers and boards, which are increasingly used for printing. Although there is a recent tendency for clay coating of many products, the color of the base paper is still important for the coating economy. Many of the pulps used in these fields are lignin-rich pulps obtained in high yields, and to preserve the pulp economy these pulps have to be bleached without substantial yield losses, i.e. to remove chromophors rather than the whole body of the colored compounds.

To start from the darker side of the register, unbleached kraft pulps sell better for both wrapping paper and liner board if they can be made just a few points brighter, or could be made with more economy, at a higher yield, if it were not for the darker shade obtained when increasing the yield. A limited amount of lignin-preservative bleaching chemical is desired here and sometimes used, for example, for envelope papers. Newsprint requires a brightness of about 60%GE. This can be obtained without bleaching for both groundwood and sulfite pulp when using spruce and fir, whereas darker pulpwood, such as from pine or western hemlock, tends to give about 5%GE lower brightness. Because of the competitive situation, groundwood pulp producers using the darker softwood species have to bleach their stock to equivalent brightness. Hardwoods generally give unsatisfactory groundwood from more than the color aspect, but aspen and poplar can be used. Although tree breeding has given poplars with very satisfactory brightness, other stands give a darker groundwood which requires bleaching to achieve the required brightness standard.

Other hardwoods are pulped by the cold caustic and neutral sulfite semichemical processes, some pulp of which is also used for newsprint and still higher grades. Cold caustic pulps generally fall in the 40–50%GE range, and sometimes even lower, whereas neutral sulfite pulps are somewhat brighter. These pulps, like groundwood, contain much lignin which has to be preserved during the bleaching required.

Speciality grades of printing paper require still higher brightness. Primarily the 65–70%GE range was the target, but present trends aim at 75+%GE for certain book grades etc. This requires not only a more qualified bleaching for both groundwood and semichemical pulps, but also that special attention be paid to the pulpwood, which must be fresh and sound to give maximal unbleached brightness. Lignin-rich pulps bleached to those high brightness levels tend to become serious competitors of bleached chemical pulps in many fields, particularly where brightness permanence and strength are not critical qualities. Substantial quantities of such pulps are now produced, Table 13.1 (23), and rapid development is expected.

Table 13.1. Approximate production of peroxide-bleached pulp grades in relation to total production of bleached pulp in U.S.A., 1959–60 (23)

Pulping process	Total bleached production, Mt	Peroxide-bleached	
		Mt	%
Groundwood*	0.86	0.65	76
Kraft	4.00	0.74	18
Sulfite	1.85	0.24	17
Cold caustic	0.15	0.15	100

* Excluding news grade (and therefore excluding a large quantity of dithionite-bleached hemlock and pine groundwood, about 0.9 Mt).

There are two principal types of lignin-preservative bleaching, *reductive* and *oxidative*. In reductive bleaching, *sodium bisulfite*, $NaHSO_3$, or *sodium* or *zinc dithionite*, $Na_2S_2O_4$ or ZnS_2O_4, are used (4, 11, 18, 19, 27, 50, 52, 81, 82). Dithionite is also called *hydrosulfite* or *hyposulfite*, and can be purchased or produced at the mill by passing sulfur dioxide through a slurry of zinc powder. Another reductant, *sodium tetrahydroborate*, also called *borohydride*, is also efficient, but too expensive for practical use. Among the *oxidants*, *hypochlorite* is used in groundwood and semichemical pulp bleaching (36, 59) but is not true lignin-preservative bleaching and is therefore discussed in Chapter 14. Oxidants of a more truly preservative type are *sodium* and *hydrogen peroxide* (12, 80). Both oxidants and reductants are unstable chemicals and require additional chemicals for maximal efficiency. Thus, *sequestrants* are required to remove metal ions, which otherwise impair the result by direct discoloration, or act as decomposition catalysts. *Tetrasodium ethylenediaminetetraacetate*, Na_4EDTA, or preferably *pentasodium diethylenetriaminepentaacetate*, Na_5DTPA, are efficient for both peroxide (75) and dithionite (11, 52), and *sodium tripolyphosphate*, $Na_5P_3O_{10}$, for dithionite (10). These chemicals should preferably be added to the pulp as a *pretreatment* prior to the bleaching operation, with 2–5 kg ptp. Another principle for the removal of metal ions and other impurities is the acidification of groundwood pulp to pH 3, followed by washing (55). Operations to destroy peroxide-decomposing enzymes in the pulp or mill water is a slight chlorination (54) or hypochlorite pretreatment (41). As a stabilizer for peroxides further *sodium silicate* together with *magnesium sulfate* is necessary. In addition, chemicals for pH adjustment are needed, *sodium hydroxide* in the case of hydrogen peroxide, *sulfuric acid* for sodium peroxide, and sodium bisulfite or *sulfur dioxide* for dithionite bleaching after an alkaline operation.

886

A subsequent section will deal with the influence of the reaction variables on the bleaching result and here only some typical data will be given. *Bisulfite* bleaching, where practised, is preferably carried out at pH 4–5, under conditions which agree with existing equipment. Some success has been experienced with grinder pit additions in quantities of 10–20 kg ptp. *Dithionite* is the preferred chemical in reductive bleaching, and it has been found eventually that remarkable results can be obtained by certain precautions, such as pretreatment of the pulp with sequestrants, adjustment of pH (11), exclusion of air (9, 11, 73, 74), and keeping a fairly high temperature. Recommended conditions (10) are 2–5 kg ptp $Na_5P_3O_{10}$, sulfur dioxide addition to pH 5–6 at ZnS_2O_4 or pH 6–7 at $Na_2S_2O_4$, 50–60°C, 1–2 h, and 3–6% consistency. The dithionite charge can be 5–10 kg ptp, seldom 20 kg ptp. The brightness increase experienced is then 5–12% GE.

For *peroxide bleaching*, the best results are obtained at an initial pH of 10.5–11.0. The sulfuric acid necessary in sodium peroxide bleaching, 2–20 kg ptp H_2SO_4, is sometimes added directly to the pulp suspension prior to the addition of bleach solution. This acidification may destroy peroxide-decomposing catalysts, especially enzymes. When hydrogen peroxide is used, alkali is added to the bleach solution for pH adjustment. Sometimes the correct pH is obtained by mixing sodium and hydrogen peroxide. Hydrogen peroxide is available in 35 or 50% solution, sodium peroxide as free-flowing granules of 98–99% purity. The latter chemical is somewhat less expensive. For lignin-preservative bleaching 10–30 kg ptp Na_2O_2, 50 kg ptp sodium silicate (40% solution) and 0.1–0.5 kg ptp Epsom salt ($MgSO_4$, 7 H_2O) are recommended. The Epsom salt can be omitted where the mill water contains sufficient magnesium ions. For the super-bleaching of chemical pulps, another application of peroxide, which will be described in this chapter for the sake of simplicity, 5–10 kg ptp Na_2O_2 and 20–30 kg ptp silicate are recommended. In the preparation of the bleach solution, equipment yielding metal decomposition catalysts, such as copper, should be avoided. Efficient stirring is recommended to avoid local high concentrations of peroxide in dissolving the granules, which should be added to the solution *after* the charge of the stabilizers. Long storage of peroxide bleach solutions must be avoided, and this necessitates small batches or continuous preparation. Two types of automatic equipment have been constructed for this, for batch (80) and continuous operation (12), where metering tanks, dry feeders and proportioning pumps mix the chemicals with water in the following order: magnesium sulfate, sodium silicate, sodium peroxide, and sulfuric acid. The production is easily adjusted by changing the rate of water flow. For peroxide bleaching, 2–4 h at 30–50°C are recommended with medium consistency bleaching (10, 23, 68). High consistency, 30–50%, in the web (34, 66, 80) or crumb form (34, 61) at about 20°C for long retention times, offers certain advantages (12, 77). As the principle of peroxide bleaching of *groundwood* is also applicable to *unbleached sulfite* pulps (70), integrated mills often bleach groundwood and sulfite pulps in mixtures as used in the paper production (62). The same technique is also used for *neutral sulfite* (35, 45) and *cold caustic*

887

pulp (23). For the *superbleaching of kraft pulp* in medium consistency (16, 17, 37, 40, 46, 53, 58), 4 h at 85°C is practised, with 10–15 kg ptp H_2O_2, 1–2 kg ptp NaOH, 0.2 kg ptp Epsom salt and 20 kg ptp sodium silicate, after a delignifying prebleaching (23). Other recommendations are 60–70°C as a finishing stage, or at a still lower temperature as an addition to the last alkali stage prior to a final chlorine dioxide stage (3), with about 10 kg ptp each of Na_2O_2 and silicate. For prebleached sulfite pulps, 5–10 kg ptp Na_2O_2 at 40°C is sufficient (13, 80, 81). On the whole, however, other chemicals, especially chlorine dioxide, are generally preferred for the super-bleaching of chemical pulps.

Combinations of peroxide and dithionite, i.e. *two-stage bleaching*, of groundwood have been developed through the increased brightness demands, after finding that the oxidative and reductive effects are additive to a considerable extent, whereas increasing the charge of either chemical outside the normal limits gives only slight brightness increase. Although a reductive pretreatment improves the result of peroxide bleaching (e.g. 10, 31), it is generally preferred to let the peroxide treatment precede the dithionite bleaching (8, 10, 23, 29, 34, 69). The second stage could also use sodium bisulfite (21). The total brightness increase for groundwood is about 16 %GE (10, 34) and for the darker cold caustic pulp up to 35 %GE (23, 34, 72). 20–30 kg ptp Na_2O_2 and 10 kg ptp $Zn_2S_2O_4$ or $Na_2S_2O_4$ respectively are average charges. The pH of the pulp suspension should be adjusted to about 6 after the peroxide stage, preferably with sulfur dioxide, which also eliminates the residual peroxide, prior to the charge of dithionite. The bleaching sequence thus becomes: pretreatment with acid or sequestrants, peroxide bleaching, neutralization with sulfur dioxide, and dithionite bleaching.

The equipment and operations used to satisfy the increasing demands vary widely and are still partly under development. Dithionite can be added directly to the *grinder pit*, or preferably to the *decker chest*, where the pulp is still hot from the grinding (11, 82), Figure 13.1. This gives practically no extra investment costs but suffers from some disadvantages, such

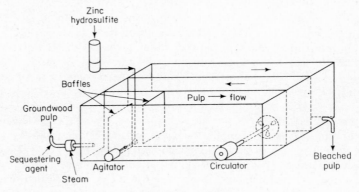

Fig. 13.1. Chest bleaching system (Barton)

as the fact that the stock contains air oxygen and mixing may not be adequate (sequestrants for a pretreatment have to be added to the grinder). The deficiencies lead to increased consumption of dithionite, about 50% more than needed at ideal conditions (11). These could be approached in chest bleaching by special arrangements for the addition of sequestrants, steam and dithionite. A low-consistency *upflow tower* is preferred, where the pulp is mixed with sequestrants, passes a pre-retention leg for de-aeration and then a pump for mixing it with the dithionite and for transport through the bleach tower.

In spite of the alkaline conditions used in peroxide bleaching, stainless steel equipment is recommended. Much experience indicates the advantage of high-consistency bleaching, and the high-consistency technique has been considerably improved during the development of peroxide bleaching (12, 77). Screw pressing is followed by high-consistency mixing in a Roto-pulper (23a, 57), Figure 13.2, a Condux disk refiner or a conventional

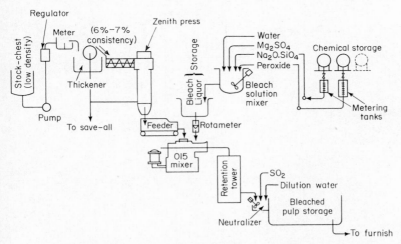

Fig. 13.2. High-consistency peroxide bleaching (Jackson–Church)

double-shaft mixer, and retention is achieved in a conical *down-flow tower* (57), or in *storage bins*, *trucks* or *freight cars*, to which the pulp crumbs are blown for further transport to the paper mill (34), during which transport further bleaching is achieved. This is also the case where peroxide solution is added to the wet pulp web in the wet-lapping machine, the *cold steep* bleaching, Figure 13.3 (12, 80). With groundwood, special attention is given to the application of the chemicals, either by spray pipes and nylon brushes (6) or by a special trough (80) to the applicator rolls, as the ground-wood pulp does not wet well by the peroxide solution. With sulfite pulp a roll and a trough is mainly sufficient for this operation. Some bleaching of kraft pulp is also carried out in the *drying machine* by hydrogen peroxide addition together with phosphate at the wet end (34).

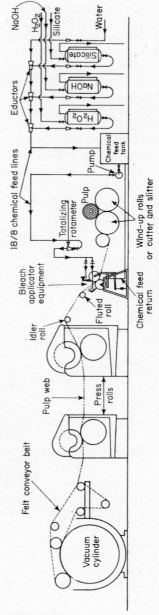

Fig. 13.3. Steep bleaching of continuous pulp web

More recent experience indicates (80) that provided the water is free from peroxide-decomposing catalysts, there is not a very great advantage in high-consistency operation, and hence low or medium consistency is recommended because of less investment and easier mixing. Both batch and continuous operation are used, applying *hollander-bleachers* as well as *upflow* or *downflow towers*. In order to allow a high concentration of chemicals, it has also been suggested that the spent liquor be recycled from the subsequent washer for the dissolution of fresh chemicals (37). A medium consistency downflow or upflow tower is probably the optimal form for peroxide bleaching operation, and Figure 13.4 describes this system in combination with the previously mentioned equipment for dithionite bleaching (10, 82). Since such arrangements are fairly costly, small-sized groundwood mills are better served with very simple equipment for peroxide bleaching, consisting of a *thick stock pump* and a *retention pipe*, Figure

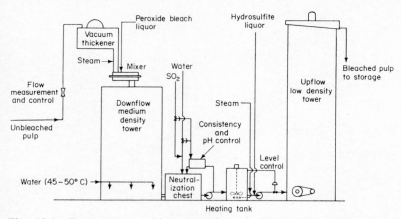

Fig. 13.4. Two-stage peroxide–hydrosulfite groundwood bleaching system (Barton)

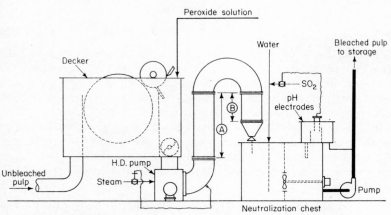

Fig. 13.5. High-temperature groundwood bleach process (Fennell)

891

13.5 (23). The pulp arrives from the filter, where preferably a sequestrant is added, and the thick stock pump serves as a mixer for the peroxide solution and steam. In order to achieve complete reaction within 10 minutes, 95°C is applied, and the result is said to be only slightly inferior to conventional operation (23).

A variant of the decker chest bleaching of groundwood is *refiner bleaching* of mechanical or semichemical pulp from chips (30, 34), Figure 13.6 (34). The bleach solution is added to the drained and preferably washed chips prior to the refiner, which serves both as a mixer and a heater. One or more chests after the refiner gives satisfactory retention.

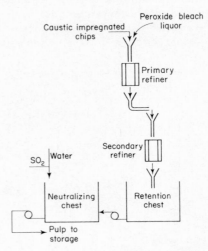

Fig. 13.6 Refiner bleaching (Kindron–Rosebush)

II. Reactions

1. INORGANIC REACTIONS

The active agent of *bisulfite* bleaching is the bisulfite ion, and bisulfite bleaching should therefore be carried out around pH 4, where the bisulfite ion concentration is at maximum. The addition of bisulfite ions to carbonyl groups occurs rapidly even at low temperature, whereas the possible reduction requires a somewhat higher temperature.

In *dithionite* bleaching, the active agent is likely to be the dithionite or bidithionite ion, and the *tetrahydroborate* ion in borohydride bleaching. The dithionite can be consumed in two side reactions, which detract from the bleaching efficiency, namely air *oxidation* and *decomposition* according to the formulae:

$$Na_2S_2O_4 + O_2 + H_2O \longrightarrow NaHSO_3 + NaHSO_4$$
$$Na_2S_2O_4 + H_2O \longrightarrow Na_2S_2O_3 + 2\,NaHSO_3$$

At normal bleaching conditions, an aerated dithionite solution is consumed in 2 minutes, during which period only a minor part of the bleaching reaction has occurred (11). The oxidation can be prevented by deaeration of the stock prior to the charge of the bleach solution. The disproportionation reaction is accelerated at lower pH, is noticeable at pH 5 and almost instantaneous at pH 4, so that pH should be adjusted to about 6 for the bleaching.

Peroxide bleaching involves the action of the OOH^- ion (43, 64). Hydrogen peroxide is a very weak acid with its first ionization constant about $2 . 10^{-12}$ at room temperature and $2 . 10^{-11}$ at 80°C, the maximal bleaching temperature region (26). Its redox potential, -0.2 V at pH 10–11, as shown in Figure 14.53, indicates a mild oxidizing action. Apart from the oxidation of organic compounds, mainly the phenolic groups of lignin, and some attack at the carbohydrates, there is a decomposition reaction, which under unfavorable conditions may dominate and greatly reduce the bleaching effect. The decomposition also involves the OOH^- ion and leads to formation of oxygen gas:

$$2\ OOH^- \longrightarrow O_2 + 2\ OH^-$$

The detailed mechanism involved in preventing this reaction is not elucidated, but several catalytic effects have been studied, such as the influence of the container walls and the presence of metal ions. Iron vessels accelerate the decomposition, and so do even glass walls, although to a less extent (26). Polyethylene vessels are, as would be expected, fairly inert (26). Uncatalyzed decomposition increases with pH because of the higher concentration of hydroperoxide ions, and follows approximately the shape of the neutralization curve of hydrogen peroxide, Figure 13.7 (26). However, in glass vessels a decomposition maximum often occurs at pH 11 or slightly lower. *Cupric ions* greatly catalyze the decomposition without changing the shape of the uncatalyzed decomposition curve,

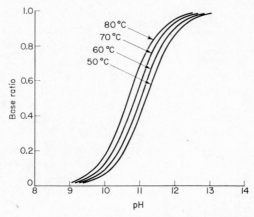

Fig. 13.7. Dissociation of hydrogen peroxide with
pH (Hartler)

893

whereas *manganese ions* give a sharp maximum at pH 10 in addition to the normal pH influence at higher pH. It is believed that the formation of manganese hydroxide at higher pH decreases the catalytic action. The presence of *calcium ions* together with manganese ions increases the catalytic action of the latter, and an acid wash is recommended prior to peroxide bleaching if calcium hypochlorite has been used in the pre-bleaching. *Iron ions* will increase the decomposition at high pH (26,56), whereas *lead ions* and *aluminium ions* are inert in this respect.

To stabilize peroxide solutions, some complexing agents are used (40, 48, 65). *Magnesium sulfate* alone seems to stabilize peroxide solutions at high pH in the absence of manganese ions (26), but gives some protection from manganese catalysis only in a limited pH interval around 10.2. *Sodium silicate* alone gives a stabilizing effect on peroxide solutions in a manner shown in Figure 13.8 (26). Obviously, the effect is very much dependent

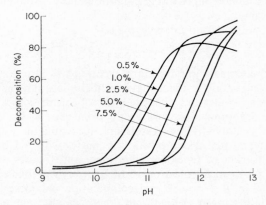

Fig. 13.8. Decomposition in three hours at 60°C of hydrogen peroxide solution containing sodium silicate (Hartler)

on the silicate charge, and it is assumed that a complex is formed between the silicate and the peroxide in a reversible reaction, the equilibrium of which will also influence the ionization equilibrium of hydrogen peroxide and decrease the concentration of OOH^- ions (22, 26, 60). It has also been assumed that the active component in the silicate is the colloidal silica, whereas metasilicate was found to have no stabilizing effect (26). The action of magnesium sulfate in combination with silicate is decidedly more stabilizing than either component alone (12, 26) and eliminates the catalytic action of, for example, manganese ions. It is assumed that colloidal magnesium hydroxide or silicate absorbs catalyzing metal ions.

The standard composition of bleach liquor is therefore magnesium sulfate, sodium silicate and sodium peroxide, with the pH adjusted to around 10.5 with sulfuric acid. Chelating agents of the type ethylene-diamine tetraacetic acid (EDTA) and diethylenetriaminepentaacetic acid (DPTA) likewise have a stabilizing action on peroxide solutions

894

contaminated by manganese (75), but the action is off-set by the presence of calcium, which competes with manganese for the chelating agent (26). Pyrophosphate likewise has a pronounced stabilizing effect (28, 33).

2. ORGANIC REACTIONS

The characteristic feature of the lignin-*bleaching* methods, in contrast with the lignin-*removing* methods, is that an improved pulp brightness is obtained without substantial loss in yield. The reactions involved must therefore deal with the chromophors of lignin and certain extractives without destroying the molecules to such a degree that they are rendered water-soluble. It is also evident that the final result must depend on the amounts of chromophors to be eliminated, and their nature. Therefore, the color of the unbleached pulp is of importance for the final brightness of the bleached pulp, in contrast with the case of the lignin-removing methods. The color of unbleached pulp was discussed to some extent in Chapter 12.II, and lignin color reactions in Chapters 4.IV and 9.I. Some additional aspects have to be discussed here.

The protolignin of wood is faintly cream-colored and about the same shade as the brightest unbleached groundwood and sulfite pulps of about 70%GE. After diazomethane methylation, which concerns the phenolic and enolic groups, lignin practically becomes white. The following groups in lignin are likely to take part in color changes, Figure 13.9. Few of these configurations are colored as such, but they constitute systems, which are easily changed by chemical treatment into chromophors. The exact nature of these changes is not known. However, the *reddening* of unbleached sulfite pulps which occurs on storage, eventually leaving a more stable brown color, has been shown to be connected with quinoide or quinone methide groups (1). The reddening is caused by air oxidation, accelerated by metal catalysts, mainly copper and iron. The same color changes are brought about by a slight addition of hydrogen peroxide. The guaiacylpropane monomers may be oxidized to a quinoid configuration of the type

$$O=\langle\rangle=CH-CH=C\begin{smallmatrix}\diagup\\\diagdown\end{smallmatrix}$$
$$CH_3O$$

The reddening is prevented by removal of metal ions through acidification and washing, or addition of sequestrants, such as EDTA. The same phenomena of reddening may be observed on neutral sulfite pulps. Oxidation of lignin by *Fremy's* salt has been shown (2) to produce red color through oxidation of uncondensed monomers containing a free phenolic group to an *o*-quinoid configuration, Figure 13.10. The presence of pyrocatechol configurations in pulp lignin upon some demethylation in the cooking will also lead to chromophoric *o*-quinoid structures upon subsequent air exposure, or alternatively form bluish-grey complexes with iron

895

Type	Formula	Occurrence in *proto*lignin; per phenylpropane monomer
1 Coniferylaldehyde groups	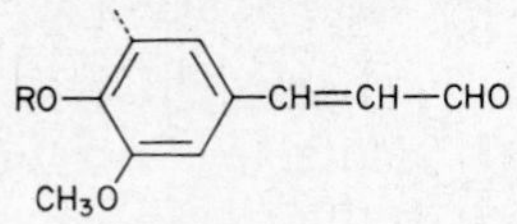 RO—⟨ring, CH_3O⟩—$CH{=}CH{-}CHO$	0.03
2 α-Carbonyl groups	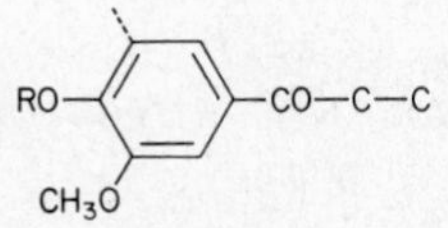 RO—⟨ring, CH_3O⟩—$CO{-}C{-}C$	0.07
3 Phenolic groups	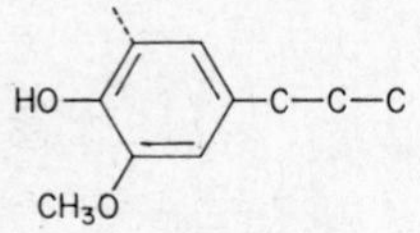 HO—⟨ring, CH_3O⟩—$C{-}C{-}C$	0.30
4 Condensed systems of the type	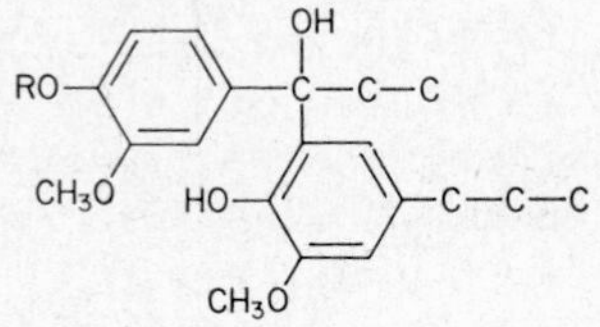 RO—⟨ring, CH_3O⟩—$\overset{OH}{C}{-}C{-}C$; HO—⟨ring, CH_3O⟩—$C{-}C{-}C$	Probably none
5 Condensed systems of the type	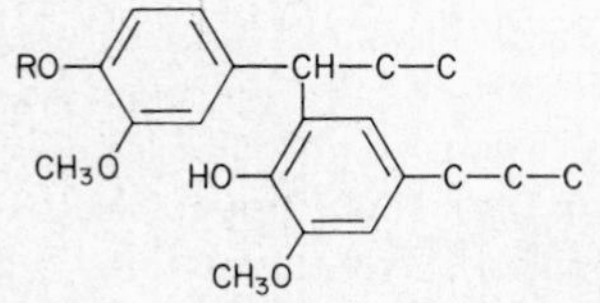 RO—⟨ring, CH_3O⟩—$CH{-}C{-}C$; HO—⟨ring, CH_3O⟩—$C{-}C{-}C$	Probably none
6 Condensed systems of the type	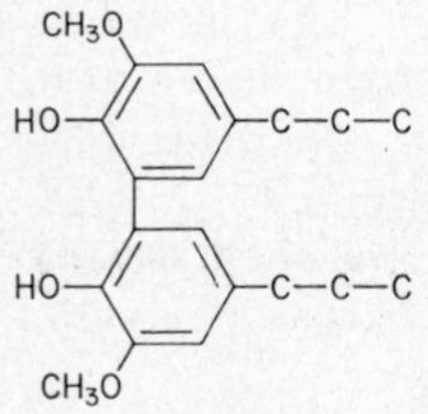 CH_3O, HO—⟨ring⟩—$C{-}C{-}C$; HO—⟨ring, CH_3O⟩—$C{-}C{-}C$	0.12
7 Quinoidal systems of the type	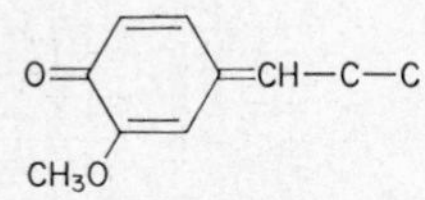 $O{=}$⟨ring, CH_3O⟩$={=}CH{-}C{-}C$	0.05
8 Quinoidal systems of the type	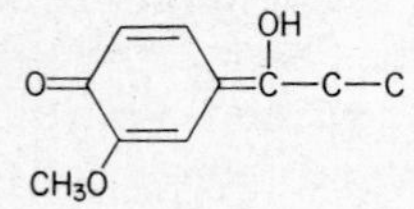 $O{=}$⟨ring, CH_3O⟩—$\overset{OH}{C}{-}C{-}C$	<0.01
9 Quinoidal systems of the type	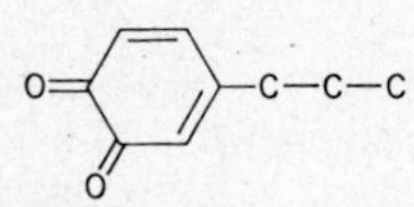 $O{=}$⟨ring, $={=}O$⟩—$C{-}C{-}C$	Probably very little

Fig. 13.9. Potentially chromophoric configurations in lignin

contaminant (21a). The *yellowing* of groundwood pulp on storage in the presence of air and light is also likely to be an oxidation. A proposed mechanism (38) involves a free radical attack leading to scission of the aliphatic side chain with formation of a hydroquinone, which may form a red-colored semiquinone on contact with alkali and oxygen, Figure 13.11.

The carbonyl groups and systems containing phenolic groups may condense at elevated temperature in acid and possibly also in alkaline medium to configurations of type 4 in Figure 13.9, which may also be present to some extent in the protolignin. Such systems, resembling the carbinol bases of triphenylmethane dyestuffs, are likely to give rise to color in both acid and alkaline media, as well as by further oxidation. Condensed systems of type 5, which are likely to occur in the protolignin after further condensation, would correspond to the leuco bases of the same dyestuffs, and lead to color on oxidation and acidification. The quinoidal system present in the protolignin, type 7, corresponds to the *p*-hydroxybenzyl alcohol monomers, which are known to react in the quinone methide form. This configuration may be partly responsible for the native hue of lignin and wood, and might easily lead to more colored systems upon reaction, such as oxidation or condensation. It should also be remarked, that additional *p*-hydroxybenzyl alcohol (and thus quinone methide) configurations may form upon acid hydrolysis, possibly up to about 0.3 per monomer, since there exist substantial quantities of *p*-hydroxybenzylalkyl ethers in the protolignin. Inasmuch as these are not sulfonated they form the easily condensed quinone methide configuration during even a mild sulfite or bisulfite cook.

Obviously, the configurations contributing to the color of the unbleached pulp are formed on:

(i) *condensation* in acid or alkaline medium, and to some extent already in the biogenesis of lignin, partly upon a *hydrolysis* of *p*-hydroxybenzylalkyl ether bonds,

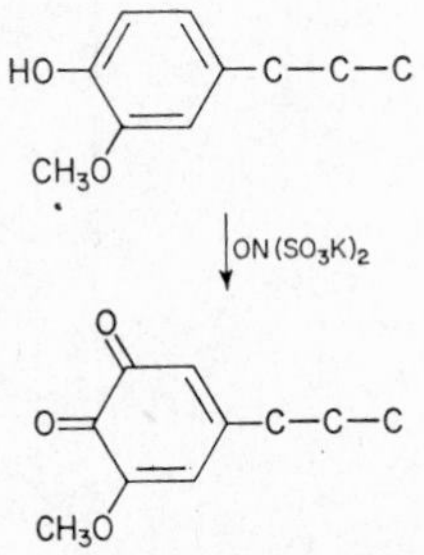

Fig. 13.10. Specific oxidation reaction of uncondensed lignin monomers containing a free phenolic hydroxyl (0.16 per monomer in protolignin) (Adler)

897

(ii) limited *oxidation,* to some extent possibly already in the woods.

(iii) possibly *degradation* of the protolignin to form colored structures.

The condensation reactions occur in the case of mechanical pulp only to a limited extent because of the mild chemical conditions. However, in hot grinding, and especially in the Asplund and Mason processes, as well as in steamed groundwood pulping, an increasing acid condensation occurs, accompanied by a gradual discoloration. In the sulfite and neutral sulfite processes, where the chemical conditions are at least as severe as in the previous cases, the unbleached pulps are fairly bright, because the reactive carbonyl groups are protected by the formation of α-hydroxy-sulphonates with bisulfite ions. The lignin-rich semichemical bisulfite and neutral sulfite pulps, although comparatively bright initially, tend to turn brownish on exposure to air. This has been ascribed to small amounts of pyrocatechol groups formed by demethylation during the cook (21a). In

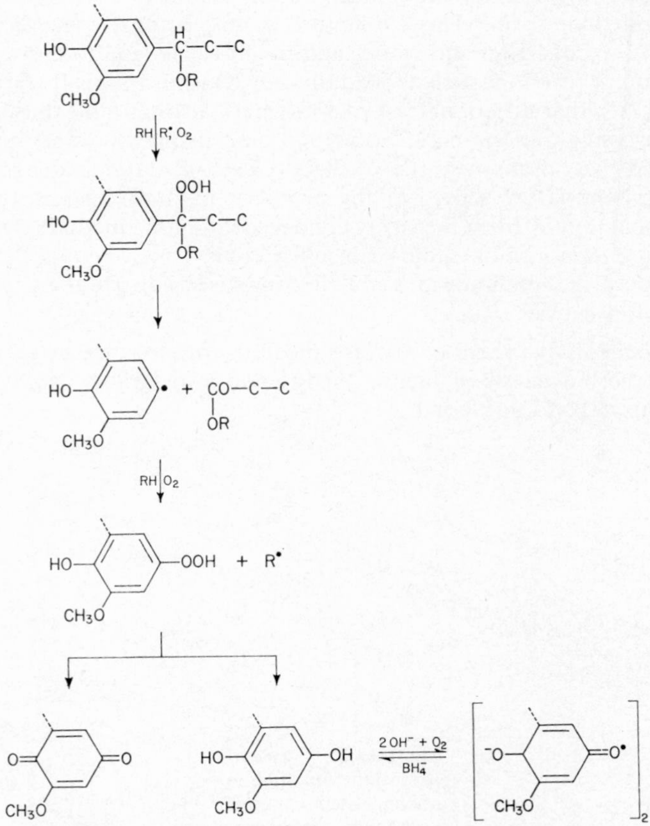

Fig. 13.11. Proposed mechanism for the formation of colored quinoidal configurations in lignin by the action of air and alkali (Luner)

the ammonium-based sulfite and neutral sulfite processes, the ammonium ion or ammonia react with carbonyl groups to form readily condensable chromophor-containing structures, and those pulps are therefore darker than the corresponding pulps from sodium- or calcium-based cooks. Condensation in alkaline cooking is favored by the formation of additional phenolic groups and formaldehyde in degradation reactions.

To decrease the content of chromophors, four principally different methods are possible. One is *protection of carbonyl* and coniferylaldehyde groups by bisulfite to α-hydroxysulfonate adducts. Another is the *reduction* of the colored configurations to leuco bases and similar phenol-containing structures. The third method is *further oxidation* of the colored configurations, containing phenolic and quinoid groupings, to carboxyl groups and carbon dioxide, etc. Finally, *substitution* of some critical groups through methylation or acetylation is conceivable. *Bisulfite bleaching* involves protection and possibly some reduction, *dithionite bleaching* involves a probably more powerful reduction, *tetrahydroborate bleaching* a decided reduction of carbonyls (39, 78), especially α-carbonyls (51), and *peroxide bleaching* applies oxidation of the chromophors. It is obvious that the reductive bleaching does not prevent re-oxidation to colored configurations and therefore could not be expected to yield the same brightness *stability* as peroxide bleaching. It is also possible that not all of the chromophoric groups are readily reduced by bisulfite and dithionite, and that therefore only a limited degree of brightening can be obtained. In the case of oxidative bleaching, a minor initial decrease in brightness is to be expected, at the conversion of some systems to a colored state. Further oxidation should then bring about a considerable brightening. However, in contrast to other oxidants, peroxide oxidation stops at a comparatively early stage, involving little losses of substance from the lignin molecule, at least under the conditions normally applied. It is also logical, as is done in the combined peroxide–dithionite bleaching, to reduce those configurations which by the peroxide treatment were only carried to the colored state.

The tendency of lignin-containing pulps, especially groundwood pulp, to *yellow in alkaline medium* in the presence of air or small amounts of oxidants should also be observed. The reaction mechanism indicated in Figure 13.11 has not been established, but is likely to involve the formation of additional oxidized systems from phenolic ether groupings. Consequently, in peroxide bleaching, which is performed in alkaline medium, two reaction mechanisms compete, one an elimination and the other a formation of chromophors. For that reason, the reaction conditions should be chosen so that there is little residual alkali and some residual oxidant at the end of the bleaching.

The following reaction may approximately describe peroxide bleaching of lignin, or at least indicate one of several possibilities, Figure 13.12. In this case one carboxylate or phenolate ion is formed for every hydroperoxide ion consumed, and as the corresponding carboxyl or phenolic groups are stronger acids than hydrogen peroxide, pH during the bleaching

899

is reduced. One investigation indicated that peroxide oxidation of lignin eliminated phenolic or enolic hydroxyl but not methoxyl groups (32). Methylation of native lignin with *diazomethane* or *methanol–hydrochloric acid* strongly inhibited the peroxide reaction. Furthermore, such methylation makes both lignin and pulps much brighter (14, 47), and also eliminates almost all (carbonyl) groups capable of reduction with tetrahydroborate (39), which on the other hand has been found to make both groundwood (51) and cold caustic pulps (38, 39) considerably brighter. The conclusion has been drawn (39) that 1,2-dicarbonyl groups, such as *o*-quinones, are the chromophors eliminated. The activity of methanol–hydrochloric acid in this connection, however, rather suggests 1,4-configurations of the quinone methide type 7 in Figure 13.9 or possibly the condensed systems of type 4 and 5. *Acetylation* (47) has also been found to cause a similar increase in the brightness of groundwood, possibly for similar reasons, although acetylation in addition causes strength reduction due to reduced hydrogen bonding in the carbohydrate portion of the fiber.

Therefore the situation of lignin-preservative bleaching from the standpoint of lignin chemistry is the following. The protolignin contains some chromophors, possibly of quinone methide type, and a fair amount of potential chromophors, which give rise to color upon oxidation or condensation. The chromophors form redox systems, in which the reduced forms are colorless, motivating reductive bleaching with dithionite. They are also

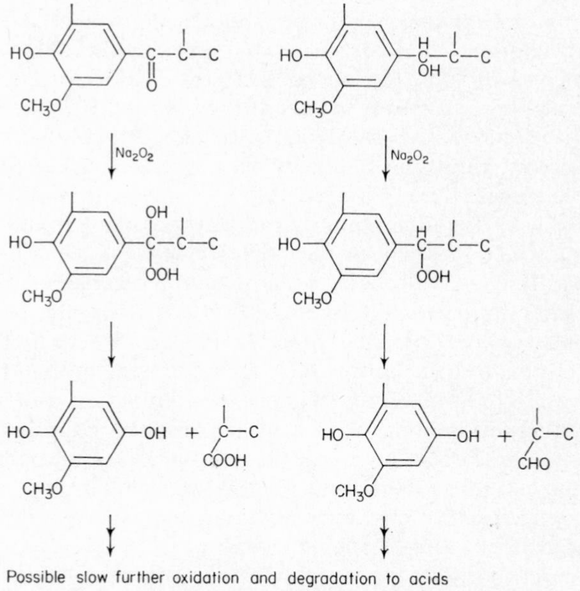

Possible slow further oxidation and degradation to acids

Fig. 13.12, Possible reaction mechanisms in the peroxide treatment of lignin

capable of destructive oxidation to colorless compounds, motivating peroxide bleaching. Some of the chromophors, however, may be physically
inaccessible or chemically non-convertible. It is the dilemma of semichemical pulping, that the cooking process tends to produce groups of
this kind, especially with softwoods. Whereas mechanical and chemical
pulps may be bleached to considerable brightness, about 80%GE, with
lignin-preservative methods, semichemical bisulfite pulps are extremely
difficult to brighten at all with similar methods (25), unless produced in
very high yields, above 80%, where the strength properties are again less
interesting. Semichemical hardwood pulps represent a more promising
alternative. However, this is a relatively new field of research, which may
still prove fruitful. As a matter of fact, recent studies (21a) have indicated
that the semichemical bisulfite pulps are easily bleached with dithionite
after elimination of the iron from the refiner plates and the mill water,
although there is a rapid color reversion on exposure to air. This is
believed to reflect the reactions of pyrocatechol configurations formed
during the bisulfite or neutral sulfite cook.

The influence of peroxide bleaching on the *extractives* containing
phenolic groups should be similar to that on lignin. Anthocyanine rings
are opened up to form a double ester, which is subsequently hydrolyzed
to hydroxyphenylacetic acid (71). Leucoanthocyanadins are present in,
for example, western hemlock (26a) and may give rise to a colored flavylium
salts, which have been shown to be reduced by dithionite to colorless
compounds (76a). Some of the most unsaturated fatty acids are likely
to be oxidized at the double bonds. Finally, recent investigations (20,
49) imply that some *heartwood constituents* may be major causes of discoloration. These may be formed from lignin precursors, which during
the heartwood formation follow a different transformation pattern to
that of normal lignification. The *carbohydrates* are left almost entirely
unchanged after a peroxide bleaching stage in the cold (e.g. 76), but as a
hot finishing stage peroxide bleaching leads to a definite degradation, as
shown by the viscosity decrease and the increase in carbonyl content (37),
whereas the carboxyl content remains constant.

III. Reaction Conditions and their Influence on Pulp Yield and Properties
(5, 7, 12, 24, 37, 44, 67, 76, 80, 83)

1. PULPWOOD AND UNBLEACHED PULP TYPE

As discussed above, only part of the colored matter in wood can be
bleached without removal, and the majority of chromophors formed during
the treatment with chemicals cannot be eliminated with lignin-preservative
bleaching. Therefore, it is not surprising that in both reductive and
oxidative bleaching of this type, the brightness *increase* at defined conditions is fairly independent of the *initial pulp brightness* for a certain
category of pulps, as exemplified in Figure 13.13 for peroxide bleaching
of a large number of *groundwood* pulps with unbleached brightness from

55–72 % GE (80). Similar results are obtained with *sulfite* pulps of varying brightness and lignin content (80). A darker unbleached pulp will thus require more bleaching chemicals for the same brightness and may never reach the brightness levels now required for some papers even when charging excessive amounts of chemicals. In this connection attention has been focussed on the wood quality. Experiments with grinding and bleaching spruce and fir cut at various seasons and stored for various periods gave the following result (79). The season for cutting does not materially influence the changes observed on storage. Both species behaved similarly on storage. Storage did not appreciably change the brightness gain for a standard bleach but decreased the brightness for both unbleached and bleached groundwood. This decrease was approximately linear with storage time and amounted to about 2–3 % GE per year for storage of barked wood and 5–6 % GE for rough wood. Average values for barked and rough wood are given in Table 13.2, which also shows the results from a similar investigation on poplar (50). Identical results were obtained with sodium peroxide and zinc dithionite on both the 5 and 10 kg ptp charge level. The storage effect may be caused by air oxidation, but the influence of fungi is also important, as shown in the investigation on poplar. That poplar pulpwood can vary considerably in color is also shown in other studies (e.g. 52), and thereby the species or hybrid clone also has a considerable influence. Poplar hybrids with particularly white wood have been cultivated specifically for groundwood production in Italy. The influence of wood species on the groundwood color is further illustrated in Table 13.3. Obviously, data for different species give a

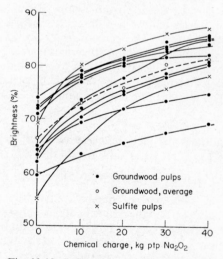

Fig. 13.13. Influence of initial pulp brightness on the result of peroxide bleaching of spruce groundwood and two extreme sulfite pulps (Wultsch–Gärtner)

somewhat uncertain basis for comparisons unless the storage time and wood condition is known, but the results shown can be regarded as fairly representative. Thus poplar offers the best brightness possibilities, and spruce-fir the best among the softwoods. Western hemlock and southern pines normally give somewhat darker groundwood and usually require a slight peroxide or dithionite treatment, varying from 2–6 kg ptp (cf. 19), also for news grades. The hardwood *cold caustic* pulps are very dark compared with the groundwood pulps but, on the other hand, have a better response to bleaching and achieve a brightness comparable to that of the bleached groundwood pulps from the softwood species. The response to bleaching is also somewhat better for unbleached chemical *sulfite* pulps than for groundwood (80), whereas *neutral sulfite* semi-chemical pulps are equivalent to groundwood in this respect (36). *Bisulfite* semichemical pulps from softwoods have been found very difficult to bleach with these methods (25), and a few results on one-stage peroxide

Table 13.2. The effect of pulpwood storage on the brightness, %GE, of unbleached and bleached groundwood pulps (50, 79)

Months of storage	Balsam fir Unbleached	Bleached	Spruce Unbleached	Bleached	Poplar Unbleached	Bleached
0	64	71	65	70	68	73
3	64	69	64	69	—	—
6	63	69	64	69	—	—
9	63	68	63	68	—	—
12	61	68	62	67	63	68
24	—	—	—	—	60	63

Table 13.3. The influence of wood species on the brightness, %GE, of unbleached and bleached groundwood pulps (10, 23, 34)

Bleaching chemical Bleach charge, kg ptp Wood species	— 0	H_2O_2 12	$H_2O_2 + Na_2S_2O_4$ 12 + 10
Spruce—balsam fir	62	74	78
Western hemlock	55	66	69
Southern pines	56	68	71
Aspen*	47	68	71
Beech–birch–maple*	46	74	77
Southern hardwoods (oak etc.)*	43	67	71

Bleaching chemical Bleach charge, kg ptp Wood species	— 0	Na_2O_2 20	ZnS_2O_4 10	$Na_2O_2 + ZnS_2O_4$ 20 + 10
Spruce	58	68	70	75
Southern pines	56	66	66	72
Poplar	67	75	77	82
Spruce–poplar 60/40	62	71	75	78

* Cold caustic pulps.

903

bleaching of *kraft* pulps give a quite low brightness level of the bleached pulp, although there was some increase. Dithionite brightening of kraft pulps for certain grades is sometimes practised.

The *age* of the unbleached pulp has some importance for the peroxide bleaching result, particularly if the content of mold and bacteria has increased during the storage. The enzymes, such as catalase, produced by the biological activity, decompose the peroxide during the bleaching. This effect can be counteracted by addition of some sulfuric acid to the pulp prior to bleaching (42). The acid decreases enzyme activity, whereby almost the same bleaching result as with freshly ground pulp is obtained. According to some investigations the *metal content* of the unbleached pulp is of little significance for the bleaching result, since the heavy metal ions are attached to the acidic groups of the pulp and therefore catalytically inactive, in contrast to those of the mill water, whereas other investigations stress the importance of removing the metal ions of the pulp prior to bleaching. As stressed previously, metal contamination is particularly undesirable with pulps containing pyrocatechol configurations, such as semichemical bisulfite pulps.

2. CHARGE OF CHEMICALS

Figure 13.14 (12, 23, 80) and 13.15 (11, 52) show the brightness increase as a function of the charge of dithionite and peroxide for some different types of pulp. The previously mentioned differences in bleaching response for different pulp types are noted. All curves approach a definite limit in the brightness increase at charges between 10–20 kg ptp for dithionite and between 20–40 kg ptp for peroxide (15, 37, 80). For groundwood, a gain of 14 %GE with peroxide and 12 %GE with dithionite is considered maximal. At 20 kg ptp applied, about 10 %GE brightness increase is achieved for groundwood with sodium peroxide, sodium dithionite and sodium tetrahydroborate (cf. 51). For cold caustic pulps, about twice as high gain is

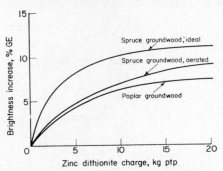

Fig. 13.14. Response to dithionite bleaching by spruce and poplar groundwood at varying chemical charge, in the absence and presence of air (Barton and Merlo *et al*)

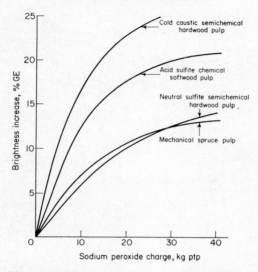

Fig. 13.15. Response to peroxide bleaching by various pulps at varying chemical charge (Beeman–Reichert, Fennell, Kingsbury *et al*, and Wultsch–Gärtner)

achieved with both peroxide and tetrahydroborate (cf. 38, 39). When combining peroxide and dithionite, the brightness increments are found additive to a certain extent, but not completely, as shown in Figures 13.16–17

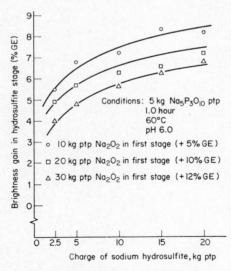

Fig. 13.16. Effect of dithionite charge on groundwood, prebleached with varying charges of peroxide (Barton)

905

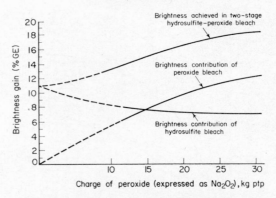

Fig. 13.17. Effect of sodium peroxide concentration on the brightness gains obtained by bleaching groundwood pulp with peroxide combined with hydrosulfite (Barton)

(10). The total brightness increase, however, approaches 20%GE and is about 17%GE for 20 kg ptp Na_2O_2 followed by 10 kg ptp $Na_2S_2O_4$ with properly chosen conditions. These results are clearly summarized in Figure 13.18 (10), which gives the approximate cost of chemicals for separate as well as combined bleaching with peroxide and dithionite as a function of the brightness increase. The figure indicates that for brightness levels attainable with dithionite, this chemical is to be preferred, whereas for still brighter pulps a combination of peroxide and dithionite is suitable. Obviously, the investment needed for two-stage operation will influence

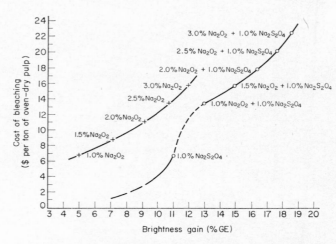

Fig. 13.18. Cost of bleaching groundwood pulp with peroxide, hydrosulfite, and combinations of peroxide and hydrosulfite (Barton)

the decisions as well, but future production is likely to expand in this direction with the increased brightness demands.

The increase in brightness obtained for lignin-rich pulps is permanent only in the absence of light. Peroxide-bleached pulp lost 1 %GE during two years of storage in the dark (12). On exposure to light, new chromophors are formed in the lignin, which remains in the pulp, although in bleached form. The brightness stability is larger for the unbleached pulp, as illustrated in Figure 13.19 (80), but if sufficient amounts of peroxide have been used, the pulps are still brighter after exposure to light than

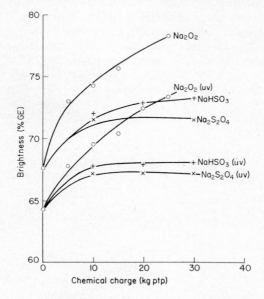

Fig, 13.19. Brightness of spruce groundwood before and after bleaching by various charges of sodium peroxide, bisulfite and dithionite and before and after 'aging' in UV-irradiation for two hours (Wultsch–Gärtner)

the initial, unbleached pulp, in contrast to the pulps bleached by reducing agents (82). Brightness stability of pulps given a finishing peroxide bleach after a lignin-removing bleaching sequence is high compared with conventional bleaching, or even chlorine dioxide bleaching (16, 17, 37).

The pH-dependence of peroxide bleaching is shown in Figure 13.20, which indicates an optimum at about an initial pH of 10.5–11.0 (12, 37, 63). The drop in pH during the bleaching depends on the initial level, but is about two units. The importance of low alkalinity and high residual peroxide at the end of the bleaching to avoid alkaline discoloration has been stressed previously. In the case of superbleaching of prebleached pulps, the cause of the pH-optimum has been shown to be that the consumption of peroxide at higher pH in the main and side reactions is more rapid and leaves an alkaline reaction mixture without residual peroxide (37). Small additions of peroxide to maintain the oxidant concentration during the bleaching allow as good a result at pH 12, after an equal bleaching period. At pH lower than 9 little brightening occurs, mainly because the active bleaching agent, the hydroperoxide ion, is practically absent.

Normally, the consumption of alkali and peroxide should proceed in parallel, Figure 13.21 (12), where alkali refers to total alkali, including NaOOH and silicate. If considerable amounts of peroxide are consumed in reactions which do not consume alkali, mainly by unexpectedly high decomposition, an excess of alkali is obtained towards the end of the bleaching, leading to color reversion. In industrial bleaching, where the catalytic action of metal ions is difficult to avoid, the charge of stabilizers, especially sodium silicate, is therefore important, Figure 13.22 (80, cf. 37). Silicate retards not only the decomposition of peroxide but also the bleaching reaction, although the utilization of the oxidant for the bleaching is improved (48).

Optimal pH for dithionite bleaching is 5–7, since higher pH gives alkali

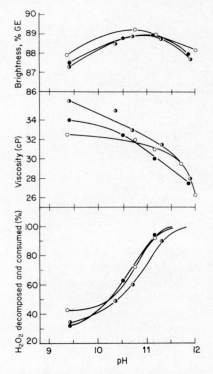

Fig. 13.20. Brightness, viscosity, and peroxide decomposition and consumption as a function of pH. Super-bleaching of kraft pulp (Hartler)

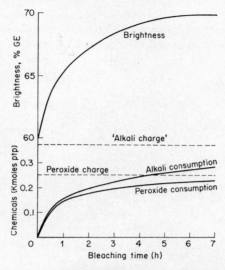

Fig. 13.21. Brightness development and chemicals consumption during peroxide bleaching of groundwood. Conditions: 32°C, 5% consistency, 20 kg ptp Na_2O_2, 50 kg ptp 40° Be silicate, 15 kg ptp H_2SO_4. 'Alkali charge' is total alkali minus sulfuric acid (Beeman–Reichert)

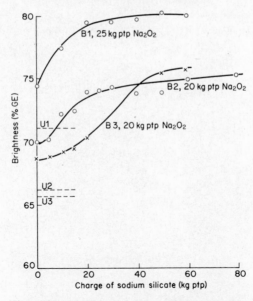

Fig. 13.22. Bleaching of three groundwood pulps (U1, U2 and U3) with sodium peroxide and varying charge of sodium silicate (Wultsch–Gärtner)

909

color and lower pH decomposition of dithionite through disproportion-ation (73), Figure 13.23. The stabilizer sodium tripolyphosphate charge necessary in dithionite bleaching has been shown to be 2–5 kg ptp $Na_5P_3O_{10}$.

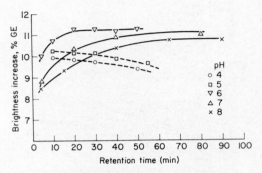

Fig. 13.23. Brightness increase versus time at varying pH in the dithionite bleaching of ground-wood (Sparrow)

3. CONSISTENCY

The influence of consistency on the peroxide bleaching result is shown in Figure 13.24. It is thus seen that some investigations indicate a better result at high consistencies (12, 23a, 37), whereas other investigators main-tain that there are practically no differences in the bleaching of groundwood

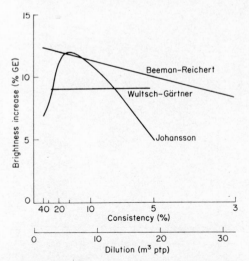

Fig. 13.24. Effect of consistency on brightness increase in the bleaching of groundwood with a constant peroxide charge (Beeman–Reichert, Johansson and Wultsch–Gärtner)

910

pulps (31, 80), although high-consistency bleaching of sulfite pulps is favorable (80). Several factors are likely to contribute to these discrepancies. An obvious reason for better results at high consistency is the influence of the mill water. A high content of lead, copper, manganese or iron in the water will cause peroxide decomposition, and consequently a less pure water will give a deficient result at low consistency, whereas in a clean water, this effect of the consistency will not show up. Another reason for the discrepancies is the difficulty of getting a uniform distribution of chemicals when charged to high-consistency pulps. A less good distribution of chemicals will off-set the other advantages of high-consistency operation. Finally, as the reaction is slower at low consistency, the comparison between different consistencies must be made either at varying time or temperature. In the latter case, temperature dependence enters into the picture. However, on the whole, high-consistency operation could be recommended for peroxide bleaching in new mills, provided good mixing is assured, whereas older mills with existing equipment for medium consistency operation generally get satisfactory results also. In bisulfite bleaching, the consistency is not critical, and the consistency of dithionite bleaching should be low (15), 3–5%, in order to facilitate air removal prior to bleaching.

4. TEMPERATURE

There are some indications of decreased peroxide bleaching effect at increased temperature (31, 80), at least in the range 35–70°C. However, these results must be judged with caution, since they are usually obtained with constant charges of chemicals, and the consumption of alkali in carbohydrate reactions is bound to increase with the temperature. However, one-stage peroxide bleaching should preferably be carried out in the range 20–50°C, the lower values being suitable in high-consistency bleaching. 50–85°C is used in peroxide bleaching of prebleached sulfite or kraft pulps (12, 37). For dithionite bleaching, both as a separate stage and in combination with peroxide, a temperature increase has been found to give increased brightness, other conditions being equal, Figure 13.25. A gain of 3%GE is achieved when increasing the temperature from 30–75°C (10).

5. TIME

The time required in one-stage oxidative and reductive bleaching obviously varies with consistency, temperature, and charge of chemicals. For dithionite bleaching, 1 h at 50°C or 0.5 h at 70–80°C gives the main effect. The results shown in Figure 13.26 indicate that prolonged time of reaction gives some improvement in peroxide bleaching. Table 13.4 (80) gives the approximate times for total consumption of different peroxide charges at typical low-, medium- and high-consistency bleaching conditions. Ordinarily, some residual peroxide should be preserved to guarantee no color reversion occurs. In the peroxide super-bleaching of prebleached pulps at high temperature, retention times of about 4 h are suitable (37).

911

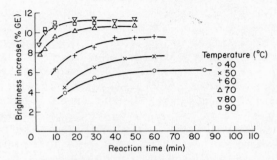

Fig. 13.25. Brightness increase versus time at various temperatures in the dithionite bleaching of groundwood (Sparrow)

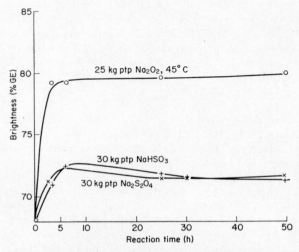

Fig. 13.26. Influence of reaction time on brightness in the bleaching of groundwood with sodium peroxide, bisulfite or dithionite (Wultsch–Gärtner)

Table 13.4. Approximate duration, h, for total peroxide consumption in groundwood peroxide bleaching at various charges and consistencies (80)

Charge, kg ptp Na_2O_2	Low- and medium-consistency conditions (e.g. 6% and 40°C)	High-consistency conditions (e.g. 30% and 20°C)
5	0.5	1.7
10	1.3	3.8
15	2.7	5.3
20	4.8	7.8
25	6.5	11.5

6. PULP PROPERTIES OTHER THAN BRIGHTNESS

In the foregoing, the influence of reaction conditions on the optical properties of the pulps were described. In the case of lignin-bleaching methods it is natural to concentrate on these, as other properties are little affected. Pulp yield for all pulps is nearly quantitive when bleached with one-stage bisulfite, dithionite or peroxide, 96–100% being reported for groundwood pulp, cold caustic, neutral sulfite and sulfite pulps. The *paper properties* are largely unaffected, as, in general, are the figures for *lignin content, viscosity, copper number* etc. In most cases, this must be considered an advantage. However, in the case of lignin-rich pulps, a considerable improvement is possible in beating response and physical paper properties when using lignin-removing methods and multistage bleaching, for example, in the case of neutral sulfite pulps. This must then be done at the sacrifice of yield, and is of interest for entirely different paper types than those obtainable with one-stage bleaching of lignin-rich pulps.

In the peroxide superbleaching of prebleached pulps at high temperature, the carbohydrates do not remain unaffected, and considerable degradation has been registered by the decrease in pulp viscosity (37, 63) as well as the increase in carbonyl groups. Remarkable enough, in spite of the increase in carbonyl content, the brightness stability to heat was improved by the treatment. Compared to chlorine dioxide superbleaching, peroxide bleaching seems to give less good results and be more expensive. Some benefits may be obtained by a combination of the two bleaching agents (16, 17, 34). However, peroxide bleaching seems to offer more distinct advantages in the brightening of lignin-rich, unbleached pulps.

A bleaching method, which must also be characterized as a lignin-bleaching method, is the one-stage *hypochlorite* bleaching of lignin-rich pulps, such as neutral sulfite or cold soda semichemical pulps, as well as groundwood pulp (36, 59). About 100 kg ptp active chlorine at an initial pH of 12 and 30°C gives 70-80%GE, varying with the type of groundwood pulp. Hardwood pulps, groundwood as well as semichemical, are especially suitable. As the chemistry of such bleaching has much in common with the conventional hypochlorite bleaching, although the yield is 98–100%, a discussion of this point is saved for Chapter 14.

REFERENCES

1. Adler, E., and S. Häggroth, *Svensk Papperstid.*, **53**, 287, 321 (1950).
2. Adler, E., and K. Lundquist, *Acta Chem. Scand.*, **15**, 223 (1961).
3. Aitken, K. G., *Pulp Paper Mag. Can.*, **55**, No. 6, 125 (1954).
4. Andrews, I. H., *Pulp Paper Mag. Can.*, **46**, 679 (1945).
5. Anon., *Peroxide Bleaching of Sulfate Pulp*, Du Pont de Nemours Bull.
6. Anon., *Pulp Paper*, **24**, No. 9, 70 (1950).
7. Anon., *Sodium Peroxide, Use in Bleaching of Wood Pulp*, I.C.I. Bull.
8. Armstrong, N., *Tappi*, **39**, No. 11, 194A (1956).
9. Back, S., *Tappi*, **39**, No. 4, 170A (1956).

10. Barton, R. W., *Tappi*, **41**, No. 3, 161A (1958).
11. Barton, R. W., *Tappi*, **44**, No. 8, 161A (1961).
12. Beeman, L. A., and J. S. Reichert, in *The Bleaching of Pulp*, TAPPI Monograph Series No. 10, New York 1953, p. 210.
13. Bradley, L., and E. P. McKeefe, *U.S. Pat.* 1,768,820; 1,768,821; 1,768,822; 1,768,823 (1930).
14. Brauns, F. E., *Paper Trade J.*, **111**, No. 14, 35 (1940).
15. Brecht, W., *et al.*, *Papier*, **4**, 174 (1950).
16. Casciani, F., and G. K., Storin, *Tappi*, **33**, 588 (1950); *U.S. Pat.* 2,424,797 (1947); 2,494,542 (1950).
17. Chadwick, A. F., *et al.*, *Tappi*, **42**, 308 (1959).
18. Chidester, G. H., *et al.*, *Tappi*, **43**, 876 (1960).
19. Cogan, E., *Tappi*, **40**, No. 5, 170A (1957).
20. Côté, W. A., and R. Marton, *Tappi*, **45**, 46 (1962).
21. Craig, K. A., *U.S. Pat.* 2,187,016 (1940).
21a. Croon, I., and B. Swan, *Svensk Papperstid.*, **66**, 812 (1963); **67**, 177 (1964).
22. Fells, H. A., and J. B. Firth, *Proc. Royal Soc. London*, **114 A**, 517 (1927).
23. Fennell, F. L., *et al.*, *Tappi*, **43**, 903 (1960).
23a. Ferguson, D. M., *et al*, *Tappi*, **45**, 702 (1962).
24. Gärtner, W., *Tappi*, **41**, No. 10, 178A (1958).
25. Giertz, H. W., *Tappi*, **44**, 1 (1961).
26. Hartler, N., *et al.*, *Svensk Papperstid.*, **62**, 269 (1959); *Tappi*, **43**, 806 (1960).
26a. Hergert, H. K., *Forest Products J.*, **10**, 610 (1960).
27. Hirschkind, W., *Pulp Paper Mag. Can.*, **33**, 489 (1932).
28. Husain, S., *Z. Anorg. Allg. Chem.*, **177**, 215 (1928/29).
29. Jacques, H., and R. W. Barton, *Pulp Paper Mag. Can.*, **59**, No. 10, 154 (1958); *Tappi*, **43**, No. 1, 235A (1960).
30. Jahne, J. F., and C. E. Price, *Tappi*, **43**, No. 7, 226A (1960).
31. Johansson, O. S., *Svensk Papperstid.*, **53**, 649 (1950).
32. Jones, G. W., *Tappi*, **33**, 149 (1950).
33. Kauffmann, H. O., *U.S. Pat.* 2,191,431 (1940).
34. Kindron, R. R., and F. J. Rosebush, *Tappi*, **44**, No. 10, 158A (1961).
35. Kingsbury, R. M., *et al.*, *Paper Trade J.*, **123**, No. 11, 50 (1946); **124**, No. 4, 53 (1947).
36. Kingsbury, R. M., *et al.*, *Paper Trade J.*, **126**, No. 24, 49 (1948); *Pulp Paper Mag. Can.*, **50**, No. 5, 98 (1949).
37. Lindahl, E., *et al.*, *Svensk Papperstid.*, **62**, 308 (1959).
38. Luner, P., *Tappi*, **43**, 819 (1960).
39. Luner, P., and R. Supka, *Tappi*, **44**, 620 (1961).
40. McEwen, J. M., *et al.*, *Tappi*, **38**, No. 10, 162A (1955).
41. McEwen, R. L., *Can. Pat.* 442,196 (1947).
42. McEwen, R. L., *U.S. Pat.* 2,465,327 (1949).
43. McEwen, R. L., *Paper Trade J.*, **135**, No. 20, 244 (1952).
44. McEwen, R. L., *et al.*, *Tappi*, **34**, 193 (1951).
45. McEwen, R. L., and I. C. MacGugan, *Paper Trade J.*, **139**, No. 3, 18 (1955).
46. McEwen, R. L., and F. R. Sheldon, *Pulp Paper Mag. Can.*, **55**, No. 8, 109 (1954).
47. Manchester, D. F., *et al.*, *Svensk Papperstid.*, **63**, 699 (1960).
48. Martin, D. M., *Tappi*, **40**, 65, 72 (1957).
49. Marton, R., *Tappi*, **43**, 826 (1960).
50. Masak, E., *Tappi*, **43**, No. 1, 166A (1960).

51. Mayer, W. C., and C. P. Donofrio, *Pulp Paper Mag. Can.*, **59**, No. 10, 157 (1958); *Tappi*, **43**, No. 1, 238A (1960).
52. Merlo, L., *et al.*, *Tappi*, **41**, No. 5, 216A (1958).
53. Miller, R. L., *et al.*, *Tappi*, **39**, 826 (1956).
54. Mills, R. T., and W. O. Stauffer, *Can. Pat.* 458,399 (1949).
55. Neale, F. R., *Paper Trade J.*, **135**, No. 11, 26 (1952).
56. Nicoll, W. D., and A. F. Smith, *Ind. Eng. Chem.*, **47**, 2548 (1955).
57. Nolan, W. J., and B. Armstrong, *Paper Mill News*, **77**, No. 39, 14 (1954).
58. Noreus, R. E., and R. P. Hella, *Tappi*, **38**, No. 10, 168A (1955).
59. Parsons, S. R., and H. J. Lausman, *Tappi*, **34**, 97 (1951).
60. Penner, S. S., *J. Am. Chem. Soc.*, **74**, 2754 (1952).
61. Pierce, L. A., *Paper Trade J.*, **131**, No. 22, 203 (1950).
62. Premo, R. A., *Tappi*, **34**, 270 (1951).
63. Rapson, W. H., *Tappi*, **39**, 284 (1956).
64. Reichert, J. S., *Paper Trade J.*, **135**, No. 20, 230 (1952).
65. Reichert, J. S., *et al.*, *Paper Trade J.*, **118**, No. 14, 45 (1944).
66. Reichert, J. S., *et al.*, *Paper Trade J.*, **118**, No. 11, 45 (1944).
67. Reichert, J. S., *et al.*, *Paper Trade J.*, **119**, No. 16, 49 (1944).
68. Richardson, C. A., *Paper Mill News*, **72**, No. 52, 64 (1949).
69. Richardson, C. A., *Tappi*, **39**, No. 6, 189A (1956).
70. Sheldon, F. R., *Pulp Paper Mag. Can.*, **52**, No. 10, 104 (1951).
71. Shriner, R. L., *A Review of Natural Coloring Matters in Wood*, TAPPI Monograph Series, No. 6, 182 (1948).
72. Smedberg, G. E., and N. J. Stalter, *Paper Trade J.*, **141**, No. 51, 20 (1957).
73. Sparrow, D. B., *Tappi*, **39**, 486 (1956).
74. Sparrow, D. B., *Pulp Paper Mag. Can.*, **56**, No. 12, 148 (1955).
75. Spitz, R. D., *Tappi*, **44**, 731 (1961).
76. Stobo, W. E., and J. K. Russell, *Pulp Paper Mag. Can.*, **48**, No. 3, 224 (1947).
76a. Trotter, P. C., *Tappi*, **45**, 449 (1962).
77. Ullman, E. V., *Paper Trade J.*, **118**, No. 25, 35 (1944).
78. Varshney, M. C., and P. Luner, *Tappi*, **44**, 285 (1961).
79. Whitman, F. A., *Tappi*, **40**, 20 (1957).
80. Wultsch, F., and W. Gärtner, *Die Peroxydbleiche von Zellstoff und Holzschliff*, Degussa Bull., 1956.
81. Wultsch, F., *Tappi*, **42**, 313 (1959).
82. Yankowski, A. A., *Tappi*, **40**, 717 (1957).
83. Yankowski, A. A., *Southern Pulp Paper Mfr.*, **18**, No. 4, 60 (1954).

14

LIGNIN-REMOVING METHODS

I. Chlorination and Alkali Extraction

1. GENERAL DESCRIPTION OF PROCESS

Chlorination is carried out in the bleachery as one or more stages of a multistage bleaching sequence, but it has no actual bleaching effect in the sense of yielding a white pulp. Therefore it could be considered as a method to continue the delignification that was interrupted after the cooking process to a degree varying with the type of process and the type of pulp. Chlorination is considerably more selective in delignification than the cooking processes, but also more expensive. Therefore, the cooking is carried to the lowest lignin content allowable for the particular type of pulp with respect to degradation and dissolution of carbohydrates. The unbleached pulps with the lowest lignin content are therefore the sulfite dissolving pulps, where a certain attack on the carbohydrates is allowable and even desirable. Sulfite paper pulps of the soft type should also contain fairly little hemicelluloses and are therefore comparatively low in lignin content. With increasing hemicellulose content in the pulp of stronger grades, more lignin has to be left in the pulp. Kraft pulping is a less selective delignification method than sulfite pulping and has to be interrupted at a higher lignin content to avoid excessive carbohydrate degradation. The neutral sulfite semichemical pulps are the most hemicellulose- and also lignin-rich pulps bleached. The initial lignin content of the wood, widely varying with species, also influences the final lignin content of the unbleached pulp. The chlorine demand of the pulp sent to the bleachery is thus widely varying, and determines the chemical charge and yield of the chlorination process. Table 14.1 gives a survey of the approximate Roe numbers

Table 14.1. Roe chlorine numbers of pulps for bleaching

Pulping process	Pulp grade	Softwood pulps	Hardwood pulps
Acid sulfite	Dissolving	1.0–2.0	2.0–4.0
	Soft paper	1.5–3.0	2.0–4.5
	Strong paper	2.5–5.0	3.0–5.0
	Greaseproof paper	4.0–8.0	4.0–8.0
Kraft	Dissolving	2.0–4.0	1.5–2.5
	Paper	3.0–8.0	2.0–6.0
Neutral sulfite	Paper		10–15
	Greaseproof		15–18

of technical pulps. The Roe chlorine number roughly describes the chlorine demand, expressed in per cent of the pulp (29, 98). The chlorine demand thus varies from 10 to 180 kg ptp.

The chlorine number bears a certain relation to the lignin content, as most of the chlorine is consumed by the lignin. Resin also takes up chlorine (cf. Chapter 16), and the resin content will influence the chlorine number noticeably in the case of some hardwoods. However, for kraft pulps it has been found that the lignin content in per cent of the pulp is roughly 0.8 times the Roe number (59), and for acid and neutral sulfite pulps the corresponding factor is around 0.9–1.0 (71). Other rapid methods of estimating the lignin content are also used, such as various types of permanganate numbers (e.g. 128, 129), but often they are directly converted into terms of chlorine demands with the use of curves, such as illustrated in Figure 14.1, different for sulfite and kraft pulps.

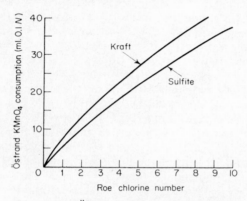

Fig. 14.1. Östrand permanganate number versus Roe chlorine number for sulfite and kraft pulps

Chlorination is a rapid reaction and cold water temperature is sufficient. In the same way the reactions go to completion even at dilute chlorine solutions, and low-consistency technique can be used. Hence upflow towers or downflow towers with an initial upflow leg are used. Reaction times of 15–90 minutes are sufficient, normally around 0.5 h for sulfite pulps and somewhat longer for kraft pulps. Because of the rapid reaction, instantaneous uniform distribution of the chlorine is necessary to avoid over-chlorination of some parts of the pulp and insufficient chlorination of the remainder. Mixing is accomplished either with one or two horizontal-shaft impellers at the base of the upflow tower, or in a special mixer outside the tower. The chlorine is supplied from pressure drums or tanks of liquid chlorine, from which it is drawn from the gas phase through a suitable meter, such as the rotameter, either directly to the pulp suspension or, less often, to a mixer of chlorine water. The amounts of chlorine charged are related to the chlorine demand of the pulp and some excess, such as 10–20% more than that corresponding to the Roe number (expressed in kg ptp this means 11–12 times the Roe number) for pulps low in lignin, and 10 times the Roe number plus 1–3 kg ptp in excess at high lignin contents. Too large excess of chlorine should be avoided, for economic as well as technical reasons. Excess chlorine might cause foaming difficulties at the filter wash after chlorination and also some degradation of the pulp. As the lignin content of the unbleached pulp is bound to vary somewhat, a current control of the chlorine demand and adjustment of the charge is necessary. Quite often residual chlorine after chlorination is determined. In some cases devices for earlier control have been installed for rapid adjustment of the charge, such as color measurement of the suspension leaving the upflow leg of a twin tower after a few minutes' retention time, or by automatic electrometric (redox) analysis of the residual chlorine at a similar early stage of the process.

Part of the lignin dissolves during chlorination and can be removed on the subsequent wash filter. However, a substantial additional quantity is made alkali-soluble during the chlorination, and to achieve the full benefit of the chlorination this must be followed by an *alkali extraction stage*. An alkali stage also has other functions, such as carbohydrate and resin removal. These are dealt with in Chapters 15 and 16. In this chapter only the delignifying functions of the alkali stage are considered. Since they are closely connected with the efficiency of the chlorination stage, both stages will be discussed together.

As will be explained below, there is a fundamental difference in the solubility of the chlorinated lignin from kraft and sulfite pulps. Little of the kraft lignin dissolves during the chlorination and subsequent wash, but enters into solution in the alkali stage. The main part of the acid and neutral sulfite pulp lignin, on the other hand, is rendered water-soluble by chlorination and only minor quantities remain to be dissolved by the alkali. This difference does not motivate very different conditions of chlorination but suggests more severe conditions in the alkali stage of the kraft pulps. That the carbohydrate fraction has been rendered stable to hot alkali during the kraft cook makes it possible to choose the conditions of the alkali stage exclusively from the delignification point of view. In the alkali extraction of sulfite pulps, more notice has to be taken of the carbohydrate fraction. For dissolving pulps, where a dissolution of hemicellulose is desired, the conditions are severe enough to remove most residual lignin, but for paper pulps, especially of the stronger types, the hemicellulose fraction is extremely sensitive to alkali treatment, and the conditions must be accordingly mild. It is therefore fortunate, that the lignin of those pulps does not require very severe conditions to be removed. Actually, deresination is the only reaction in the alkali stage which would motivate more drastic conditions in the case of sulfite paper pulps of the hemicellulose-rich type (cf. Chapter 16).

Thus the temperature of the alkali extraction is preferably 50–60°C in the case of kraft pulps and 20–40°C for sulfite paper pulps. The alkali charge depends greatly on the efficiency of the preceding wash, removing hydrochloric acid and chlorolignin. With perfect washing, 15–20 kg ptp NaOH is sufficient for both kraft and sulfite pulps, and 20–25 kg ptp NaOH are regarded as normal charges, for sulfite pulps often considerably lower. The consistency can be quite low, 4–6%, for low-temperature extraction, whereas in the case of kraft pulps higher consistency is required to save hot water. Steam, supplied in a simple mixer is used only for temperature level adjustment. The hot water and the alkali are charged to the pulp web at the last showers and in the shredder screw of the preceding filter. The towers may be upflow or downflow, allowing a retention time of 0.5–2 h, provided no hot alkali purification to high-alpha pulp is desired at the same time, cf. Chapter 15.

As will be explained below, repeated chlorinations may be required, especially of kraft pulps, followed by alkali extractions. The chlorine charge is then adjusted to correspond to the chlorine or permanganate number of the pre-extracted pulp and is consequently lower than in the first stage. Alkali stages are also used for lignin extractions after oxidative treatments, such as hypochlorite or chlorine dioxide stages. The temperatures used are then the same, but the charges lower, 5–15 kg ptp NaOH, since less lignin is then removed. The intermediate alkali treatments are of considerable importance for the ultimate brightness. The combinations of different types of treatment are dealt with further in Chapter 17.

2. REACTIONS

A. The system of chlorine, alkali and water

In this section, the inorganic chemistry of chlorination and hypochlorite stages will be treated, the understanding of which is essential for the explanation of many of their most important features.

Chlorine, dissolved in water, forms the following equilibrium:

$$Cl_2 + H_2O \rightleftharpoons HClO + H^+ + Cl^-$$

Thus, hypochlorous and hydrochloric acids are formed to an extent depending on the total chlorine concentration and the equilibrium constant, the latter of which is changing lightly with temperature. The hydrochloric acid is completely ionized, whereas the hypochlorous acid, being fairly weak, is mainly undissociated at the pH of the chlorine water solution. On the addition of alkali to the solution, increasing amounts of hypochlorite ion are formed, the point of half neutralization being reached at around pH 7.5 Thus the concentration of hypochlorous acid is governed by two equilibria, giving the following equations:

$$K_h = [H^+] . [Cl^-] . [HClO]/[Cl_2]$$
$$K_a = [H^+] . [ClO^-]/[HClO]$$
$$[Cl^-] = [HClO] + [ClO^-]$$
$$C = 0.5 . (2[Cl_2] + [HClO] + [ClO^-] + [Cl^-]) = [Cl_2] + [HClO] + [ClO^-]$$

919

where C is the molar concentration of the chlorine added, K_h is the equilibrium constant for chlorine hydrolysis, and K_a the ionization constant of hypochlorous acid.

Solving this system with respect to hypochlorous acid content gives:

$$[HClO] = -\frac{K_h}{2[H^+]} + \sqrt{\frac{K_h^2}{4[H^+]^2} + \frac{C \cdot K_h}{[H^+] + K_a}}$$

which is simplified at pH above 5 to the expression:

$$[HClO] = C \cdot [H^+]/([H^+] + K_a)$$

K_h has been determined for various temperatures (53) and the recalculated values (68) are given in Table 14.2.

Table 14.2. Hydrolysis constant of aqueous chlorine
solutions at varying temperatures

Temperature, °C	$K_h \cdot 10^4$
0	1.45
10	2.58
20	4.06
30	5.65
35	6.43
40	7.15
50	8.51
60	9.75

More recent investigations (143) indicate a somewhat lower value, 3.5×10^{-4}, at 25°C. K_a is 3.47×10^{-8} (50, cf. 20) at 18°C. Its variation with temperature is not known.

C will vary during the chlorination as chlorine is consumed, and the initial concentration will vary with the chlorine charge. For a normal paper pulp chlorination, the molar chlorine concentration will be around 0.03 initially and about 0.001 finally.

The concentration of molecular chlorine, as well as of hypochlorous acid and hypochlorite at various pH, is shown in Figure 14.2 in the form of a *Bjerrum* diagram (25) as well as a percentage diagram (47). It is seen that the concentration of hypochlorous acid is at a maximum at pH 4–5; in the more acidic region the chlorine concentration increases, in the more alkaline region the hypochlorite ion concentration increases. A decrease in total concentration leads to an increase in the relative amounts of hypochlorous acid. An increase in temperature has the same effect. Obviously a lower consistency gives a higher percentage of hypochlorous acid at a constant chlorine charge, and at constant consistency a lower chlorine charge results in a higher proportion of hypochlorous acid. Less evident is how the proportions change during the chlorination period. The decrease in total chlorine concentration tends to increase the proportion of hypochlorous acid, whereas the increased hydrogen and

920

chloride ion concentrations through the reactions tend to suppress the formation of hypochlorous acid. The net effect, shown by calculations for normal conditions, should be that the proportion of hypochlorous acid decreases during the reaction period.

When no additions to the chlorine water are used, the hydrogen ion concentration initially equals that of hypochlorous acid. As shown by the *Bjerrum* diagrams, pH should then be around 1.8 for a 0.04 *M* chlorine water and 2.1 for a 0.01 *M* at 18°C and 1.7 and 2.0 at 50°C. As hydrochloric acid is formed by the reactions, pH drops to around 1.3 for a high and 1.7 for a low chlorine charge. Additions of acids or chlorides to chlorine water will depress the formation of hypochlorous acid. The effect of acidity is shown in the previous figures, and the effect of chloride addition is analogous, as evident from the equilibrium equation.

It should also be pointed out here that the hydrolysis of chlorine is a rapid reaction (119), taking only a few minutes to reach equilibrium. As, however, chlorination takes place during the first few minutes of the stage, hypochlorous acid concentration may still be somewhat lower in technical chlorinations than indicated by the figures, which assume equilibrium conditions. A possible difference is thus indicated between the techniques of adding chlorine gas and chlorine water, although no great differences in the practical result have been observed.

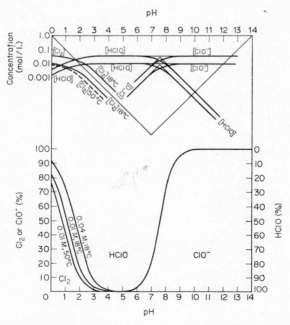

Fig. 14.2. Concentrations and existing forms of chlorine at varying pH and temperature, for realistic conditions of chlorination and hypochlorite bleaching

921

B. Reaction kinetics

A remarkable number of studies have been devoted to the problem of how much of the total chlorine consumption has taken part in chlorination and how much in oxidation. As would be expected from the foregoing section, the ratio of chlorination to oxidation varies considerably with the reaction conditions, and with the type of pulp, and ratios from 100:0 to 30:70 have been quoted (9, 27, 31, 32, 41, 43, 47, 63, 64, 65, 116). With increasingly refined technique of analysis, the figures for the oxidation have tended to increase, but an important reason for the wide variations in the results is obviously the varying raw materials and conditions used. It seems fairly safe to conclude that in unbuffered technical chlorinations of lignin-rich sulfite and neutral sulfite pulps, the dominating reaction is chlorination, whereas in the case of sulfite pulps low in lignin content, and also for kraft pulps, the oxidation reaction may be equally important or even dominate. This may have some connection with the changes of the proportions of elemental chlorine to hypochlorous acid described in the previous section, but might also be due to less reactivity to chlorine in the case of the condensed lignin in sulfite rayon pulps or less accessibility in the case of kraft pulp lignin. Attempts to increase the proportion of chlorination by changing the proportions of chlorine to hypochlorous acid show that chlorides have little effect, whereas the addition of acids increases the percentage of chlorination to a certain small extent (32, 43). Pretreatment of the pulp with acid had the same effect, which seems to indicate that the proportions of chlorine to hypochlorous acid do not determine the proportions of chlorination to oxidation to any considerable degree, and that unknown physical or chemical changes of the pulp caused by the hydrogen ions may be more important, although the effect is not very great either. This may be true in the acidic medium of technical chlorination, but the effect of decreasing chlorination, increasing oxidation and decreasing overall reaction rate on the addition of increasing amounts of alkali, Figure 14.3 (9, 31, 47), must be explained in terms of changing composition of the chlorine water. The same explanation is also probable

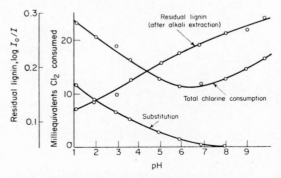

Fig. 14.3. Chlorination at varying pH of a sulfite pulp
for one hour (Giertz)

for the observation that if only small quantities of chlorine are added to the pulp, they seem to be almost entirely consumed in oxidation, Figure 14.4 (31, 32, 41). In those cases pH is higher than normal and the proportion of hypochlorous acid high. It is clear from the figure that a pulp has a certain demand of chlorine, which is consumed reasonably rapidly, whereupon further amounts are only consumed slowly, and by oxidation.

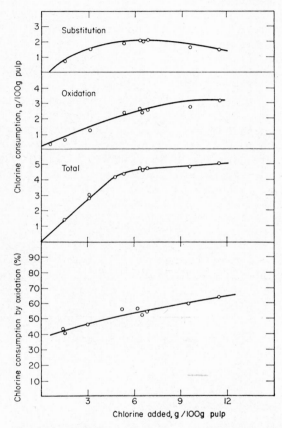

Fig. 14.4. Chlorine consumption by substitution and oxidation on the chlorination of a balsam fir sulfite pulp with varying chlorine charge (Grangaard)

Little extra lignin is dissolved by super-charging of chlorine, whereas the danger of carbohydrate degradation is increased. The proper charge corresponds to somewhat more than the Roe number, or around 1.5 g/g of lignin, consumed in approximately equal amounts in chlorination and oxidation.

It is evident from most investigations that chlorination is the more rapid, initial reaction in acid medium, Figure 14.5 (32). Chlorination occurs during the first few minutes and is, according to some results (31), complete after around 15 minutes. According to other, more recent results (32), it is so rapid that any increase in substitution is hardly measurable. On the contrary, a slight decrease is noticed, which may depend on a further decomposition of the chlorolignin initially formed. Oxidation is also quite rapid, an initial oxidation reaction involving up to half the amounts consumed by chlorination takes place during the first few minutes, and a considerable part during the first half hour, whereafter in contrast to the chlorination reaction the oxidation continues to proceed for several hours, although at a lower speed.

Temperature influences the speed of oxidation but not that of chlorination, within the range of 0–25°C, Figure 14.6 (32). At higher temperatures an increasing amount of chlorine is consumed in oxidation.

The influence of the pulp type on the proportion of chlorination to oxidation reactions is seen in Figure 14.7 (32). It is seen that for pulps of lower lignin content, the oxidation reaction becomes increasingly important and very little chlorination seems to occur at pulps of Roe number below 2 (cf., however, 31). The lignin of those pulps may be fairly condensed and accordingly rendered less reactive to substitution.

The important question of whether chlorination or oxidation contributes to the water- and alkali-solubility of the residual lignin of the unbleached pulps has also received much attention. Figures 14.8–9 (31, 32) illustrate this for sulfite pulps. It is seen that there is a very rapid decrease in the lignin content of the washed or alkali-extracted pulp. It may be argued whether the initial decrease is more closely related to the chlorination or oxidation reactions. Probably both contribute, but it is obvious that

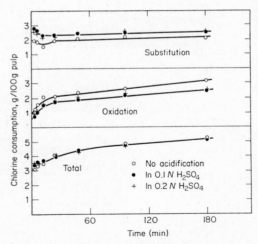

Fig. 14.5. Effect of reaction time and acidification on the chlorine consumption of a balsam sulfite pulp (Grangaard)

prolonged treatment, which mainly involves oxidation, results in further decreased residual lignin content. The lignin content after alkali extraction is affected by the concentration of the alkali applied, and therefore the dissolution of lignin seems to be a question of accessibility. Swelling of the fibers in lye of corresponding strength prior to chlorination and using normal alkali concentration for the extraction does not have any beneficial effect (32), and the conclusion has been drawn that the factor limiting lignin removal during the chlorination and alkali extraction is the hindrance for the chlorolignin to diffuse out of the fiber rather than hindrance to the

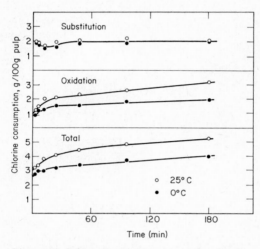

Fig. 14.6. Effect of temperature on the chlorine consumption of a balsam sulfite pulp (Grangaard)

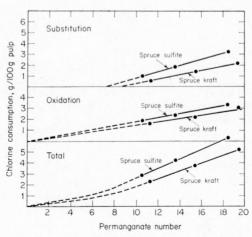

Fig. 14.7. Chlorine consumption versus permanganate number; reaction time one hour (Grangaard)

925

chlorine reaching the lignin (32). This may be especially true for sulfite pulps, where only fairly small amounts of lignin remain after one combined treatment of chlorine and alkali extraction. In the case of kraft pulps, the diffusion of chlorolignin out of the fibers during the chlorination is much more limited, which seems to cause the remainder of the lignin to be less accessible to the chlorine. Figure 14.10 shows the residual lignin of three sulfite and three kraft pulps of varying unbleached lignin content, after chlorination in an excess of chlorine for 3 minutes or 3 hours and subsequent

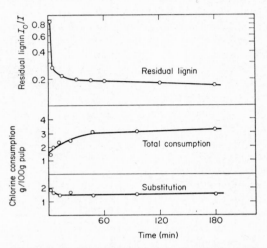

Fig. 14.8. Residual lignin content after alkali extraction versus time of chlorination of a balsam sulfite pulp (Grangaard)

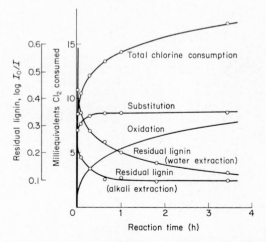

Fig. 14.9. The course of the chlorination of a sulfite pulp with an excess of chlorine (Giertz)

alkali extraction. It is seen that the lignin content is appreciably decreased in the sulfite pulps, already after the short chlorination period, whereas considerably more lignin remains in the kraft pulps. Prolonged treatment with chlorine, which involves mainly oxidation, causes further reduction in the residual lignin content, but still leaves the kraft pulps with appreciable quantities of lignin. Repeated chlorination after the alkali extraction rapidly reduces the lignin content further. The alkali extraction of the chlorolignin has obviously exposed new regions of less chlorinated and oxidized lignin to the chlorine. The considerable difference between sulfite and kraft lignin may be due to a higher degree of condensation in the latter case (31) but is more likely dependent on the fact that the sulfite lignin is sulfonated and its fragments, after chlorination, are therefore considerably water-soluble, in contrast with those of the kraft pulp lignin. Therefore they dissolve during the chlorination stage, thus exposing new regions of the pulp lignin to chemical attack. Only the last traces of residual lignin in the sulfite pulp are not water-soluble, and their extraction in alkali will leave some of the least accessible lignin in the pulp, which may be removed by repeated chlorination and alkali extraction. However, in the case of sulfite pulps, the residual lignin content after one chlorination and alkali extraction is so small that repeated chlorination will mainly consist of a hypochlorous acid oxidation in neutral or weakly acid medium. As further discussed in the section on hypochlorite bleaching, the oxidative degradation of the carbohydrates is maximal at around pH 6. Therefore, in most cases sulfite pulps are only chlorinated once, and the last traces of lignin removed by alkaline hypochlorite bleaching subsequent to the alkali extraction stage. Kraft pulps, especially those of high initial

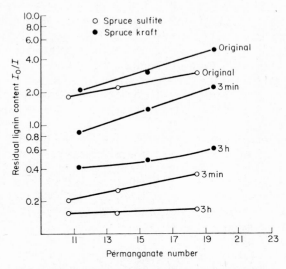

Fig. 14.10. Residual lignin content versus permanganate number at varying reaction time (Grangaard)

lignin content, on the other hand, contain so much lignin that a repeated chlorine–alkali sequence is motivated from both the technical and economic points of view. However, in kraft pulps the risk of oxidative attack on the carbohydrates is also remarkable, and the second chlorination is often exchanged for a less dangerous oxidative stage, usually hypochlorite.

The degree of condensation of the residual lignin of unbleached sulfite pulps also affects the amount left after chlorination and alkali extraction, a decrease in combined SO_2 of the cooking acid as well as in impregnation time causing a higher residual lignin content (31). A higher residual lignin content is also found after normal chlorination and alkali extraction of both sulfite and kraft pulps of higher unbleached lignin content (31), as was shown in Figure 14.10.

There has been much discussion of how much unbleached pulp lignin should be left to subsequent removal by hypochlorite. From 55–90% of the total chlorine consumption has been recommended to be charged in the chlorination stage. However, both for sulfite (104) and kraft pulps (72) the best final results are obtained when a maximum of lignin is removed by the first stage. The limiting factor is the degradation of the carbohydrates on prolonged treatment with excess chlorine, and the exact point can be found by pulp viscosity measurements in any individual case. Normally, little degradation is caused by the chlorination stage, a usual decrease of a 100 cP viscosity pulp being around 5 cP. No hydrolytic degradation takes place at such mild conditions, and the viscosity decrease must be caused by oxidative damage.

The amounts of active chlorine charged in the hypochlorite stage will depend on the type of pulp and the brightness and viscosity level desired. However, normally a hardwood neutral sulfite pulp requires 15–20 kg ptp in the hypochlorite stage or around 10% of the total chlorine demand, greaseproof sulfite and kraft pulps from softwoods nearly as much, which corresponds to around 25%, whereas sulfite dissolving pulps need 5–10 kg ptp or around 30% of the total chlorine consumption. Thus the figures of 55–90% of the total chlorine to be used in the chlorination stage, which have been suggested in the literature, are fairly close to the truth of industrial practice, except that there is no real technical reason for connecting the two figures for chlorine consumption of the chlorination and hypochlorite stages.

The importance of the oxidation reaction for the dissolving of lignin during the chlorination and subsequent alkali stages, especially for kraft pulps (34, 35), has led to experiments for increasing the effect by combining the chlorination stage with a hypochlorite stage without intermediate washing (33, 55, 77, 100, 102, 126), with the main oxidation carried out either prior to (77, 126) or after (100, 102) chlorination, and with additions of acids and chlorine, as well as sodium or calcium hydroxide (54a), to effect the pH changes.

The result of the delignification by combined chlorine–alkali treatment of pulp is thus dependent on a number of factors, which could be assigned to one of the following three categories (cf. 79):

928

(1) Factors affecting the physical or chemical nature of the fibers, such as wood species, cooking process, degree of cooking, degree of swelling in the alkali extraction etc.

(2) Factors influencing the physical nature of the lignin, mainly the degradation obtained by the chlorination, oxidation and alkali treatment, as well as the conditions used in the alkali treatment to facilitate its conversion to the dissolved state and its diffusion through the fiber wall.

(3) Factors influencing the chemical nature of the lignin, such as the condensation prior to chlorination, introduction or removal of hydrophilic groups etc., as well as the ionization of hydrophilic groups by the use of suitable alkaline reagent in optimal concentration.

C. Lignin reactions

The main possibilities of reactions between lignin and chlorine water are *addition* of chlorine to double bonds, *substitution* of a hydrogen atom of the benzene nuclei with chlorine, and *oxidation* of both lignin and the chloro-lignin formed. As the double bonds are only likely to occur at two phenylpropane monomers out of a hundred, the discussion can be limited to oxidation and chlorination by substitution.

Studies on the halogenation of lignin (e.g. 6, 28, 41, 45, 46, 65, 66, 114) have shown that chlorine replaces the hydrogen atom at the 5- and 6-position of the benzene nucleus, probably at the 5-position if the phenolic hydroxyl in 4-position is unetherified (46), which occurs in three monomers out of ten in the protolignin, probably the same in sulfite pulp lignin, and considerably more in kraft pulp lignin. Almost instantly the methoxyl group in the 3-position is hydrolyzed, Figure 14.11 (46), yielding a pyro-catechol configuration, which is rapidly oxidized to an *o*-quinone (46).

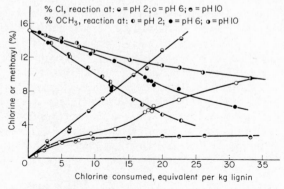

Fig. 14.11. Effect of the amount of chlorine consumed and the pH of chlorination upon the methoxyl and chlorine content of chlorinated alkali lignins (Hibbert *et al*)

929

Substitution of the phenylpropane units etherified in the 4-position probably occurs in the 6-position and will cause cleavage of the alkylaryl ether bond, analogous to the demethylation, followed by demethylation and oxidation of the pyrocatechol configuration (46). These changes are accompanied by color reactions, in yellow, orange and red, to turn into dark reddish brown upon alkalinization. The demethylation and the cleavage of the alkylaryl ether bond has been extensively studied and found to be a hydrolysis catalyzed by polarized molecular chlorine, upon the partial chlorination of the benzene ring (111, 112). About 25% of these bonds appear to remain unhydrolyzed, possibly because of previous condensation, which makes the ring less reactive towards chlorine.

It must be emphasized, that on the average 1.5 g chlorine/g lignin are consumed in technical chlorinations charged with an amount slightly exceeding the Roe number. This means that approximately 8 chlorine atoms are consumed per phenylpropane monomer. Since about half of them have reacted in substitution (cf. Figure 14.4), two chlorine atoms per phenylpropane monomer must enter the benzene nucleus, probably in the 5- or 6-positions under simultaneous formation of two molecules of hydrochloric acid. This is in accordance with the observation that 20–25% of the total chlorine consumption is bound to the organic substance dissolved on the chlorination of sulfite pulp (41) or wood (45); and also that around 1.5–2 chlorine atoms per phenylpropane monomer are combined in the chlorolignin of softwood (45) or jute (114). Two further chlorine atoms must be involved in the oxidation of the pyrocatechol configuration and must constitute the rapid oxidation reaction noticed. These reactions thus account for 6 of the approximately 8 chlorine atoms consumed. The remaining 2, consumed in the slower, but important oxidation leading to more complete dissolution of residual lignin, are likely to cause cleavage of carbon–carbon bonds.

A large part of the chlorine can be removed by *treatment of the chlorinated lignin with alkali*, some already in the cold. Chlorinated jute lignin containing almost 2 Cl/OCH_3 lost around 0.8 Cl/OCH_3 on treatment with alkali at room temperature (114). The different lability of the chlorine towards alkali was interpreted to mean that a considerable part of the substituting chlorine in chlorolignin is aliphatically combined (88), whereas the remaining alkali-stable part is connected to the aromatic system, as comparison with the model compounds benzyl chloride and *p*-chlorophenol showed somewhat similar alkali lability and stability respectively. However, it should be observed that half the chlorine in compounds such as tetrachloroquinone is very rapidly removed by alkali, forming hydroxychloroquinones such as chloranilic acid, even at room temperature (26, 51).

Therefore, besides the carboxyl groups possibly formed in the slower oxidation reaction, which are neutralized in the alkali stage and aid the dissolution of the remaining chlorolignin, the first reaction with alkali is likely to be a hydrolysis of the chlorine atoms of the benzene nucleus, at least the one in the 5–position, into hydroxyl groups of considerable acid strength, which are then neutralized by alkali. This reaction, which should be analogous to the formation of chloranilic acid from tetrachloroquinone, might be the main cause of the alkaline dissolution of the chlorolignin. The o-quinone configuration, although possibly stabilized by the chlorine substitution, may be alkali-labile and further degraded. It can be calculated that approximately 0.5 g NaOH per g of remaining lignin of a well-washed chlorinated kraft pulp are needed in the alkali stage, corresponding to 2–3 molecules per phenylpropane monomer. It is suggested that these are consumed in the hydrolysis of the chlorine in the 5-position and the acidic hydroxyquinone groups thus formed, as well as in the neutralization of the carboxyl groups formed in the slower oxidation reactions.

These possible reactions are illustrated schematically by Figure 14.12. It should be stressed that in spite of the cleavage of most alkylaryl ether bonds, fragmentation to *monomers* does not necessarily follow, because of carbon–carbon bonds especially between the α-carbon atom of the side chain of one monomer and the 5- or 5-carbon atom of another, co-condensed monomer. These bonds must also decrease the possibilities of chlorination according to the reactions suggested, and consequently decrease the corresponding cleavage of alkylaryl ether bonds, as was pointed out earlier. This is indicated by the reactions at pulps of low Roe numbers and kraft pulps, with fairly condensed lignin, where oxidation is favored. Oxidation is likely to start at the free phenolic groups of the lignin and proceed according to reactions further described in the section on hypochlorite bleaching.

It is also indicative of the basic correctness of the reaction scheme suggested, that the ultraviolet spectrum of lignin completely changes on chlorination, whereas the hypochlorite treatment preserves the typical features of the spectrum, although the absorbency values decrease in proportion to the monomers oxidized (81).

The formation of quinoid configurations in lignin on chlorination should cause spectral changes in the regions of both ultraviolet and especially visible light. Degradation of those configurations by spontaneous decomposition or by the slower oxidation reactions should decrease the absorbency, and alkaline hydrolysis of substituting chlorine to hydroxyquinoid configurations should considerably increase the absorbency. Those changes have been followed quantitatively by chlorination at room temperature of a technical lignosulfonate, originating from a mild sulfite cook (51). By choosing a soluble lignosulfonate for the study instead of a sulfite pulp, the reactions could be investigated in a homogenous phase. Figure 14.13 shows the consumption of chlorine at different charges and reaction times. It is clear that chlorine charges of up to 5–6 Cl/OCH_3 are immediately consumed to more than 90%. Higher charges

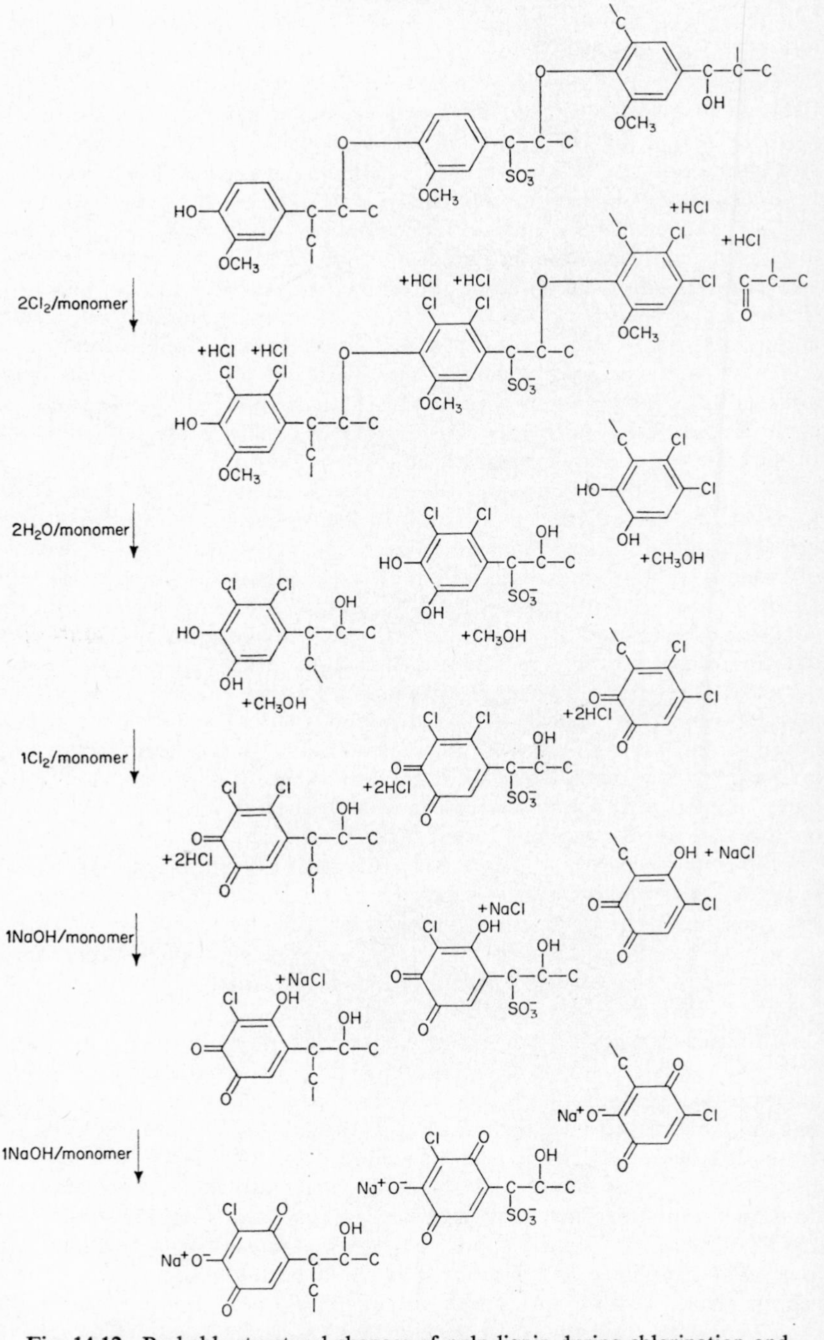

Fig. 14.12. Probable structural changes of pulp lignin during chlorination and subsequent alkali extraction (Ivancic–Rydholm)

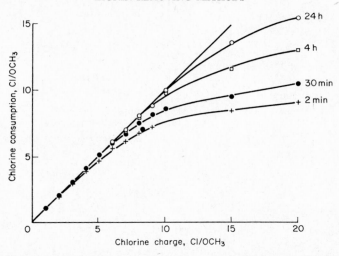

Fig. 14.13. Chlorine consumption versus chlorine charge at different
times of reaction at room temperature (Ivancic–Rydholm)

result in still more chlorine immediately consumed, up to 9 Cl/OCH_3,
but also leave residual chlorine for slower consumption. The corresponding spectral changes are illustrated in Figure 14.14 as the absorbency at

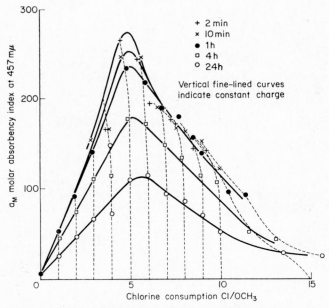

Fig. 14.14. Molar absorbency index versus chlorine consumption at
different times of reaction (Ivancic–Rydholm)

933

457 mμ (the wavelength of the GE brightness determination) after various times and chlorine consumptions. The following facts are evident:

(1) Absorbency increases sharply until a chlorine consumption of around 5 Cl/OCH$_3$ is reached, and then sharply decreases on further consumption, indicating formation and oxidative degradation of chromophors.

(2) Absorbency at a constant chlorine consumption decreases with time, indicating the lability of the chromophors even without oxidation. However, the decomposition is slow in comparison with the oxidative degradation indicated.

Figure 14.15 shows the spectral changes over the main range of visible

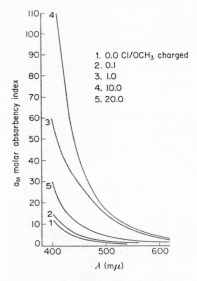

1. 0.0 Cl/OCH$_3$ charged
2. 0.1
3. 1.0
4. 10.0
5. 20.0

Fig. 14.15. Molar absorbency index versus wavelength of visible light for lignosulfonate, chlorinated with varying chlorine charges after 24 hours reaction (Ivancic–Rydholm)

light on chlorination. There are no characteristic peaks but an even slope over the entire interval.

Figure 14.16 shows the effects of alkali treatment. If no chlorination has been carried out, there is a considerable increase in the absorbency because of the ionization of the phenolic groups of lignin. Heating in alkali will cause some additional increase in absorbency, and some of the changes caused will remain upon acidification to the low pH used when measuring the absorbency of the original lignosulfonate preparation. However, the changes in absorbency caused by the alkali treatment of

934

the chlorinated lignosulfonate are much greater. Even in that case, heating will cause some additional, but fairly small increase in absorbency, indicating that the main reaction already occurs in the cold. If the chlorination has been carried out with a large excess of chlorine, the destruction of chromophors is also indicated by the comparatively small changes caused by an alkali treatment.

The corresponding changes in the ultraviolet spectrum by chlorination and subsequent alkali treatment are illustrated by Figure 14.17 (51). Obviously chlorination will cause considerable changes in the characteristic lignin spectrum, but the absorption at 280 mμ is comparatively unchanged at chlorine charges causing the highest absorbency in visible light, whereas excess charges will decrease the absorbency over the entire wavelength range. These observations are not in opposition to the assumption that the chlorination converts the lignin molecule to quinoid configurations, which may subsequently be destroyed by excess chlorine. It is clearly shown that the alkali treatment which causes such great changes in visible light, does not change the ultraviolet absorbency remarkably, and especially not at 280 mμ. That is also in agreement with the concept that

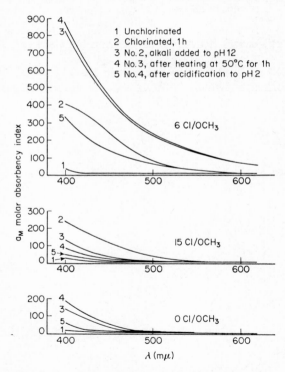

Fig. 14.16. Molar absorbency index versus wavelength of visible light for lignosulfonate and its changes on chlorination and subsequent alkali treatment (Ivancic–Rydholm)

935

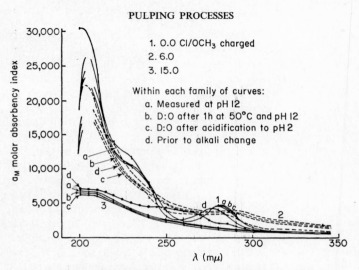

Fig. 14.17. Molar absorbency index versus wavelength of ultraviolet light for lignosulfonate and its changes on chlorination and subsequent alkalization (Ivancic–Rydholm)

alkali treatment causes hydrolysis of chlorine but does not degrade the ring system.

Figure 14.18 again shows the changes in the ultraviolet spectrum of lignin on chlorination with one optimal and one excess charge of chlorine,

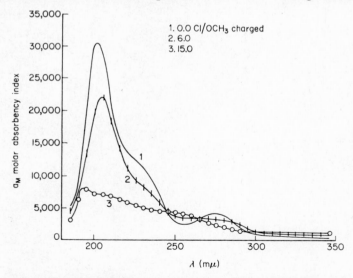

Fig. 14.18. Molar absorbency index versus wavelength of ultraviolet light for lignosulfonate and its chlorination products after 24 hours reaction, as measured in a recording spectrophotometer, Beckmann DK2 (Ivancic–Rydholm)

936

as measured by a modern recording spectrophotometer able to extend the measurement below 200 mμ. With the same instrument, absorbency against time curves were recorded during chlorination, Figure 14.19 (51). The chlorine water was in that case introduced directly into the cuvette containing the lignosulfonate solution, which together with a brief shaking to mix the liquids only took about 20–30 seconds. Still, with excess chlorine present, the initial color change was so rapid that it was not recorded, and with a more limited charge only the last part of the absorbency increase could be recorded. The subsequent decrease in absorbency is, on the other hand, slow enough to be conveniently measured.

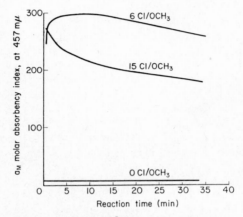

Fig. 14.19. Molar absorbency index versus reaction time at two different chlorine charges, as measured in a recording spectrophotometer, Beckmann DK2 (Ivancic–Rydholm)

The spectral changes observed indicate that there are very rapid, indeed almost instantaneous reactions, which lead to a remarkable increase of the absorbency in visible light and a change in the ultraviolet spectrum, which indicates a change in the aromatic system without considerable destruction of the six-membered ring. A chlorine consumption of around 5 Cl/OCH_3 produces the maximal increase in the visible light absorbency. Subsequent reaction takes place in the presence of more chlorine, which is fairly rapid up to around 9 Cl/OCH_3 but slower than the initial reactions. Thereby absorbency in the visible region as well as in ultraviolet is decreased. This type of reaction, probably an oxidative degradation, proceeds with retarding rate for more than 24 h. A fairly slow decomposition of chromophors in the absence of excess chlorine is also indicated. Alkali treatment produces changes of less consequence for the ultraviolet spectrum but which greatly increase the absorbency of visible light. Those changes already occur rapidly at room temperature and are only slightly enhanced by heating.

937

All observations are in agreement with the picture of the reaction mechanism presented above, involving an initial rapid chlorine substitution of the hydrogen atoms of 5- and 6-position of the aromatic ring, followed by rapid oxidation of the pyrocatechol configuration to an *o*-quinone and a slower oxidation of the latter to non-aromatic compounds in the presence of excess chlorine. It should be remarked here that the latter type of oxidation may be more rapid than perhaps previously assumed, at least in the presence of appreciable amounts of excess chlorine. Also in the absence of oxidant, the *o*-quinones are unstable. The assumed mechanism of hydrolysis of substituting chlorine without further destruction of the six-membered ring is also quite possible in the light of the spectral evidence obtained.

In addition to the degradation of the lignin macromolecule caused by the cleavage of the alkylaryl ether bonds, one important further degradation mechanism has been elucidated (23). As a result of the introduction of chlorine in the 6-position of the benzene nucleus, a *scission of the side chain* may occur, followed by chlorination in the 1-position. This is especially the case for units with free phenolic groups, containing a benzyl alcohol group. Condensed or sulfonated monomers would not react in that manner. The reaction may therefore involve the quinone methide configuration as an intermediate structure, which is subsequently oxidized by chlorine, leaving an aldehyde end group at the side chain and a chlorine substituent in the 1-position of the benzene ring. This degradation mechanism has also been included in the reaction scheme of Figure 14.12.

The heterogeneity of the chlorolignin, at least in respect of molecular size and probably also as to chemical composition, is indicated by the fact that of the kraft pulp lignin dissolved by the alkali treatment after chlorintion, one part is precipitable by acids, whereas the remainder stays in solution even at low pH levels (72). Precipitation is also possible by divalent and trivalent metal ions, even in alkaline medium, under formation of insoluble salts. This phenomenon explains the inefficiency of lime as an extracting agent (1, 65, 87). Further studies on the aggregation tendency of alkali-treated chlorolignin have been carried out by means of paper electrophoresis and by sedimentation in the ultracentrifuge (73). As demonstrated in Figures 14.20–21, the kraft pulp chlorolignin, after extraction by alkali, is electrophoretically immobilized at about pH 3, indicating that the acidic groups of the material are rather strong, which is to be expected for hydroxychloroquinones. Figure 14.21 also shows the relative amounts of chlorolignin extractable from a kraft pulp at varying pH, and thereby illustrates the circumstance that not only should these groups be *neutralized* but *formed* through the hydrolysis of chlorine from the chlorolignin, which requires alkaline conditions. Topochemical effects may also contribute to the shape of the curve. Whenever the potential acidity of the chlorolignin is greater than that corresponding to the pH of the surrounding liquid, hydroxyl ions will migrate into the fiber to neutralize the hydrogen ions. This will give rise to a potential gradient,

938

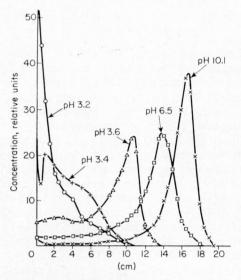

Fig. 14.20. Electrophoresis of alkali-extracted kraft chlorolignin at different pH values; time 3.5 h, temperature 24°C (Löschbrandt–Wetlesen)

which together with the concentration gradient of the chlorolignin will be the main driving force for its dissolution. If the chlorolignin particles are too large to pass through the fiber structure, they will remain in the fiber, unless disaggregated by the alkali.

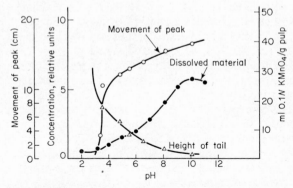

Fig. 14.21. Influence of pH on movement of peak, amount of slow-moving material in the vicinity of the starting point (height of tail) during electrophoresis, and on acid-precipitable material dissolved during extraction (Löschbrandt–Wetlesen)

939

3. INFLUENCE OF REACTION CONDITIONS ON PULP YIELD AND PROPERTIES

As in all bleaching stages the main variables of chlorination and alkali extraction are consistency, temperature, time and charge of chemicals. The positive effect of the treatments is *lignin removal*, the negative one is *carbohydrate degradation and removal*, and methods of estimating both have been worked out. The dissolved lignin is sometimes determined by permanganate oxidation (72) or color measurements (72), but more often the residual lignin in the pulp is determined by permanganate oxidation using normal standard methods (128, 129) or by colorimetric methods. The latter do not measure the color of the pulp itself, which is related to the lignin content only within a series of pulps of one certain type. Instead, the pulp is dissolved in sulfuric or phosphoric acid and the absorbence in visible light (31), or at 280 mμ (2, 71) measured. The degradation of the carbohydrates is estimated by determination of the changes in pulp viscosity, copper number, hot alkali solubility, alphacellulose content, and paper strength.

The influence *in the chlorination stage* of temperature, time and charge of chlorine for various types of pulp upon the ratio of substitution to oxidation reactions as well as upon lignin removal have already been dealt with in the previous section. It was demonstrated that up to a certain amount, all chlorine charged is fairly rapidly consumed at room temperature or lower, in fairly short times. This chlorine demand corresponds to slightly more than the Roe number, and should normally be charged. Increasing the charges above this chlorine demand does not substantially contribute to the lignin removal but increases the danger of carbohydrate degradation. Increasing the period of chlorination does aid in lignin removal, up to reaction times of around an hour. Further prolonging of the chlorination will increase the danger of carbohydrate degradation, provided excess chlorine has been charged. Increasing the reaction temperature does not increase lignin removal, unless excess chlorine has been added, and then carbohydrate degradation will also occur, as noticed for both kraft (25, 40, 46a, 87, 127) and sulfite pulps (17, 24a, 62, 137a). Figure 14.22 (25) shows the viscosity of kraft pulp, chlorinated at various temperatures, either with two constant levels of chlorine charge, corresponding to the chlorine demand of 30% excess, at a constant time, or also at varying times to constant chlorine consumption. It is seen that the main effect of temperature is to increase the rate of chlorine consumption, which is doubled for an increase of 8°C (25), the viscosity decrease at a constant chlorine consumption being about the same at temperatures up to 50°C. At constant temperature, an increase in chlorine consumption by prolonged treatment results in a similar degradation. Therefore, the essential factor determining the carbohydrate degradation seems to be the chlorine consumption in excess of the chlorine demand of lignin, irrespective of temperature and time, and is likely to be almost exclusively an oxidative degradation rather than hydrolysis. The attack on the carbohydrates is

940

also shown by the hot alkali solubility analysis, Figures 14.47–48, and the copper numbers, Figure 14.23 (109), both increasing as the viscosity decreases. Finally, chlorite oxidation or borohydride reduction after the chlorination have been shown to diminish the viscosity decrease (25). Therefore, carbohydrate degradation during the chlorination seems to involve the same type of oxidative damage as in the case of hypochlorite oxidation and will be treated in detail in the section on hypochlorite bleaching. The effect of the degradation on paper strength properties and on the alphacellulose content of dissolving pulps will also be dealt with in that section.

The influence of consistency changes on the chlorination reactions is little investigated because of the experimental difficulties. An increase in consistency will favor the substitution reaction, as the chlorine concentration and acidity will increase at a constant chlorine charge (46a). Reaction rate will also increase, the first 10 seconds giving the major reaction. However, the instant mixing of chlorine to pulp suspensions of higher than 4% consistency involves mechanical difficulties, and non-uniform distribution of the chlorine more than offsets the possible benefits of increased consistency. The special high-density mixer, called Rotopulper, has been suggested for chlorination at 15% consistency, whereby the charging of chlorine into a double-disk refiner facilitates the mixing. Another problem in high- or medium-consistency chlorination is the removal of the heat evolved in the exothermic reaction. Disregarding the complications caused by the machinery, optimal consistency for gas phase chlorination is 20–50%, higher or lower levels giving less rapid reaction (46a). Carbohydrate degradation at a certain degree of

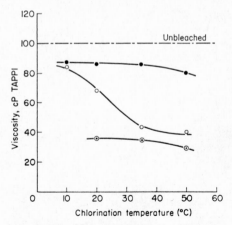

Fig. 14.22. Viscosity of chlorinated kraft pulp (Roe number 5.0) after washing (Eriksson–Stockman)

- • chlorine charge 50 kg ptp, reaction time 1 h
- ○ chlorine charge 65 kg ptp, reaction time 1 h
- ◉ chlorine charge 65 kg ptp, varying reaction time to 2 kg ptp residual chlorine

delignification was found to be slightly lower than with low-consistency chlorination, but this advantage disappeared at the final bleaching.

The *conditions of the alkali stage* are obviously of great importance for the lignin removal. Increased concentration of the extracting lye improves the delignification even up to the mercerizing concentration range, as was pointed out in the previous section. This indicates that swelling phenomena are of importance for the outward diffusion of the chlorolignin. However, the main improvement in the lignin removal is achieved by increasing pH from neutrality to pH 12, Figure 14.24 (72, 105). Then, as some alkali is consumed at the decomposition of the chlorolignin, the initial alkali charge per ton of pulp rather than the initial alkali concentration is of importance. That charge is proportional to the amount of lignin left in the pulp and therefore highest in the case of kraft pulps, where at least 15 kg ptp NaOH and usually 20–25 kg ptp are needed (62). For well-cooked and well-chlorinated sulfite paper pulps as little as 10 kg ptp or even less may be needed. The higher the consistency, the less residual alkali is needed to maintain a certain pH, but the savings in alkali obtainable by an increase in consistency from 6–12 % are not so substantial that medium-consistency operation is obligatory, especially not in the case of sulfite paper pulps. For sulfite dissolving pulps, as well as for kraft paper pulps, heat economy requires medium consistency, 10–18 %.

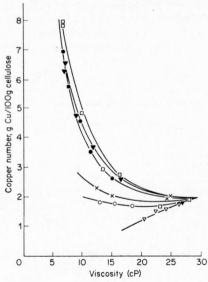

Fig. 14.23. Relationship between copper number and viscosity on bleaching with 2 % chlorine at varying pH (Samuelson–Ramsel)

pH	3	4	7	8.5	10	12
	□	▼	●	×	○	▽

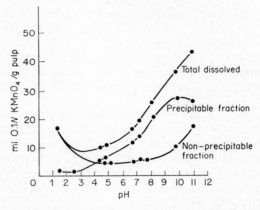

Fig. 14.24. Relation of pH of extraction liquor to quantity of dissolved organic substances on the alkali extraction of chlorinated kraft pulp (Lösch-brandt)

The temperature is of considerable importance for the efficiency of lignin removal, especially from kraft pulps, as is demonstrated in Figure 14.25 (72). The same figure, as well as Figure 14.26 (72), shows that the period of alkali extraction is far less important. For a kraft pulp a temperature of at least 50–60°C is therefore required in the alkali stage, and is achieved mainly by using hot water. Higher temperatures usually require steam heating, the cost of which has to be balanced against the additional savings in hypochlorite or chlorine of subsequent stages which could be obtained by a further increase in alkali extraction temperature. A period of 1–1.5 h is generally considered sufficient.

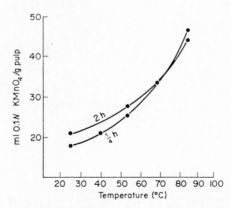

Fig. 14.25. Relation of the temperature of alkali treatment of chlorinated kraft pulp to the quantities of organic substances dissolved in 0.25 and 2 hours (Löschbrandt)

943

For sulfite paper pulps, in contrast to kraft pulps, a high temperature in the alkali stage will cause dissolution of carbohydrates, thereby decreasing yield and strength. Therefore, fairly low temperatures have to be maintained, especially in the case of pulps rich in hemicelluloses. The same is true for neutral sulfite pulps, where room temperature is maintained in the alkali extraction, as compared with 20–40°C for sulfite paper pulps.

The nature of the alkaline reagent has been varied in laboratory experiments. Ammonia (40) as well as lime (1, 65, 87), has been found less efficient than sodium hydroxide in lignin removal. Sodium sulfite has been used as a mild lignin extractant for alkali-sensitive pulps such as neutral sulfite (133) or chlorinated wood preparations (3). However, as far as is known, sodium hydroxide is the only chemical in technical use for the alkali extraction stage.

The yields obtained after bleaching of paper pulps are largely proportional to the lignin content of the unbleached pulp. Even in cautious lignin removal some losses of carbohydrates are unavoidable. The yields after bleaching of normal softwood kraft pulps, with an unbleached lignin content of 4–5%, are around 93%, showing a loss of 2–3% of carbohydrates. Bleaching of soft sulfite paper pulps with 1.5–2% lignin gives a yield of around 98%. Neutral sulfite hardwood pulps of around 12% lignin yield on bleaching around 83% bleached pulp, indicating a loss of 5% carbohydrates and resin. The main yield losses occur in the chlorination and alkali extraction, as the lignin left to the oxidative stages is usually quantitatively insignificant, although of dominating influence in pulp brightness. The oxidative treatments, although often degrading the carbohydrates, seldom cause any considerable carbohydrate dissolution.

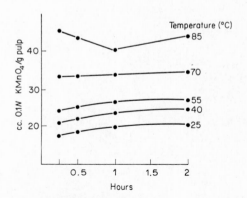

Fig. 14.26. Relation of the duration of alkali treatment of chlorinated kraft pulp to the quantities of organic substances dissolved at various temperatures (Löschbrandt)

II. Hypochlorite Oxidation

1. GENERAL DESCRIPTION OF PROCESS

Hypochlorite oxidation was originally used as a one-stage bleaching process of most types of pulp, although with limited success in the case of alkaline-cooked pulps. Originally a low-consistency process, it was eventually discovered that increase in consistency gave considerable improvement. Later on it was found that savings in chemicals and improved brightness could be obtained by dividing the bleaching into two stages with intermediate washing. 70% of the total chemicals were added to the first stage. After the introduction of liquid chlorine handling and stainless steel equipment, it was found that chlorination followed by alkali extraction was preferable to the initial hypochlorite stage for both economic and technical reasons, and consequently hypochlorite oxidation became the final bleaching stage of a three-stage schedule. This is still the most common place for the hypochlorite treatment, but there are many variations. Sometimes, the third hypochlorite stage is followed by another hypochlorite stage, either with or without intermediate washing, and often, especially at kraft pulp bleaching, with an intermediate alkali extraction. With the introduction of the modern bleaching agents, especially chlorine dioxide, the latter have often taken over the role of hypochlorite as finishing bleaching stages, sometimes entirely replacing it. In other cases, as in the super-bleaching of sulfite pulps, the hypochlorite treatment may be placed after the chlorine dioxide bleach, sometimes without intermediate washing, which will result in a mixed oxidation by hypochlorite and chlorine dioxide. There are also methods of combining hypochlorite oxidation with chlorination, with the chlorination either before or after the hypochlorite stage, and without intermediate washing.

However, although one-stage hypochlorite bleaching is scarce for chemical pulps, it is used to some extent for mechanical and semichemical pulps, particularly from hardwoods. In those cases, lignin removal is not desired but only a limited brightening of the pulp as discussed in Chapter 13.

Hypochlorite bleaching is carried out either batchwise or continuously in towers. The lowest consistencies used in modern practice are 5–6%, in hollander bleachers. Tower bleaching is practised in both upflow towers in 6–12% consistency or downflow towers using 10–18% or even higher. High-consistency operation of up to 40% consistency has been suggested but not commercially applied. The bleaching chemical is either calcium or sodium hypochlorite, usually plus a sodium hydroxide buffer. It is added to the pulp in the shredder screw of the preceding washing filter, and mixed in a conventional single- or double-shaft mixer or radial mixer. In some cases it is also produced in the mixer by introducing chlorine gas to the pulp, which has previously received the alkali in the shredder screw, in an amount corresponding to the hypochlorite formation as well as to the buffer needed. In the case of hollander bleachers the chemicals may be added at the filter, but are more often charged directly into the bleacher, immediately before the circulation impellers. The charges vary from 3–150 kg ptp active chlorine, with alkali added in amounts to keep the final pH above 8, and preferably above 9. For chemical pulps, the charges are usually only 5–15 kg ptp active chlorine.

The temperature of the hypochlorite stage varies between 30–60°C, and the time from 2–8 h or more. Normal conditions are 40°C and 6 h for a hollander bleach and 50°C and 3–4 h for a tower bleach. The conditions are adjusted to meet the brightness and viscosity demands. The heat is mainly supplied by hot water, added at the last filter showers and in the shredder screw prior to the mixer, where steam may be added for final adjustment of the temperature. In the case of hollander bleachers, direct steaming in the hollander is provided for but mostly avoided. Figures 12.20–21 are examples of the machinery used in hypochlorite bleaching.

The control of the hypochlorite stage involves tests on the liquor and the pulp. Residual oxidant and alkali are determined, as well as final pH. Brightness of the bleached pulp is frequently tested to ensure that the proper level is kept, both at an intermediate and final moment. Carbohydrate degradation is closely followed, chiefly by viscosity tests, but sometimes also by copper number determinations or similar tests as well as by paper strength testing. In the case of paper pulps, carbohydrate degradation is kept at a minimum, but some degradation has to be allowed to admit the gain in brightness. With dissolving pulps, hypochlorite oxidation is an important means of viscosity adjustment to the level desired, thus compensating for variations obtained after the preceding treatments affecting viscosity.

2. REACTIONS

A. Inorganic reactions

Hypochlorite bleaching involves a complicated system of reactions, which can be subdivided into inorganic reactions, lignin (and resin) reactions, and carbohydrate reactions. The latter two categories are influenced by the first one. As was shown in Figure 14.2, there are two pH-dependent equilibria in chlorine and hypochlorite solutions, the hydrolysis of chlorine

$$Cl_2 + H_2O \rightleftharpoons HClO + H^+ + Cl^-$$

and the ionization of hypochlorous acid

$$HClO \rightleftharpoons H^+ + ClO^-$$

At low pH, chlorine concentration dominates, but already in dilute chlorine water and more so upon addition of alkali, hypochlorous acid concentration increases to reach a maximum around pH 4–5, where almost all chlorine is in the form of chloride ions and hypochlorous acid. The pK_a of the latter is around 7.5, and consequently a further increase in pH

946

results in increased ionization, 50% at pH 7.5, 90% at pH 8.5 and 99% at pH 9.5. A pure hypochlorite solution at a concentration initially prevailing during a normal bleaching stage has a pH of about 10.5. Generally, however, excess sodium hydroxide is added to maintain a reasonably high pH during the bleaching, which results in an initial pH of 11 or above. As will be shown below in more detail, both lignin and carbohydrate reactions change their character if pH is allowed to drop, and pH does drop if no excess hydroxide is added, because in addition to the formation of hydrochloric acid from hypochlorous acid, which at this high alkalinity should not cause any great change in pH, the organic reactions give rise to carbonic acid and carboxyl groups. The latter are immediately converted to salts, consuming alkali. As they are stronger acids than hypochlorous acid, the latter will be formed from the hypochlorite ions, thereby changing the equilibria described, if no excess hydroxide has been charged.

Chlorate formation also occurs during the hypochlorite bleaching at high temperature and represents an undesirable loss of oxidant, as chlorate is not oxidizing the pulp components in alkaline solution. The chlorate formation is especially rapid in less alkaline medium, probably because of the hypochlorous acid being the actual compound undergoing disproportionation, $3 \ HClO \longrightarrow ClO_3^- + 2 \ Cl^- + 3 \ H^+$. Metal catalysts such as iron, manganese and copper accelerate the decomposition.

The hypochlorite is supplied in the form of sodium or calcium hypochlorite, as will be further described in Chapter 19.

The term *available* or *active chlorine* is used in the bleaching technique to indicate oxidation equivalents, expressed as weight of chlorine, because the origin of the oxidant is chlorine in the case of hypochlorite. Thus, NaClO has two oxidation equivalents, and a 1 M solution of hypochlorite is thus said to contain $2 \times 35.5 = 71$ g/l active chlorine. The solution could also have been prepared by the addition of 71 g/l chlorine to a 2 M solution of sodium hydroxide, giving rise to 1 mole hypochlorite and 1 mole chloride/l. The analysis of a bleach solution is made by an iodometric titration with thiosulfate in the presence of iodide and starch.

The nature of the actual oxidant in hypochlorite bleaching has been discussed. Hypochlorous acid is in all probability the active agent, but the hypochlorite solutions are more agressive at pH 6–7 than at pH 4–5, where the concentration of hypochlorous acid is at a maximum. This has been explained by the increasing accessibility of the fiber at higher pH (139) or by a hypothetical complex of hypochlorous acid and hypochlorite ion (58). Modern concepts on carbohydrate oxidation, cf. below, do not necessitate such assumptions.

B. Lignin reactions

As described in a previous section of this chapter, lignin, or at least chlorolignin, is oxidized by hypochlorous acid. The oxidation of the pyrocatechol configuration to *o*-quinoid compounds occurs rapidly, and is followed by a slower oxidation and cleavage of carbon–carbon bonds. However, the alkali treatment following chlorination probably removes most of the chlorinated lignin, leaving the least accessible, most condensed and least reactive lignin for further oxidation in the hypochlorite stage. As little oxidation takes place after diazomethane methylation, this oxidation is likely to start at the free phenolic groups and proceed in a sort of peeling reaction (97), cf. Chapter 4.IV on lignin oxidation. However, chlorine analysis of lignin preparations treated with hypochlorite at pH 11 (46, 97) indicates that initial chlorination may also take place in very alkaline solution, analogous to chlorination of certain phenols (90). Up to 8 moles of hypochlorite per lignin monomer are consumed. Hypochlorite oxidation of guaiacol should yield methanol, oxalic acid and maleic acid, and lignin has been found to yield about 0.2 mole of carbon dioxide per mole of hypochlorite and the rest organic acids (96), as well as methanol, since demethoxylation at a fairly early stage of hypochlorite oxidation has been observed.

Therefore it seems likely that the main difference between the lignin degradation in the chlorination and hypochlorite stages is the lack of chlorination of monomers coupled with aryl ether bonds, and/or the lack of chlorine-induced hydrolysis of the latter. The monomers containing free phenolic groups are presumably chlorinated, their methoxyl groups split off, and oxidation of the pyrocatechol group formed occurs as in the chlorination stage. In contrast to acid chlorination, the chlorine substituting the o-quinone formed is then split off by alkali, exposing the monomer to further oxidation, which would eventually lead to destruction of the entire monomer and formation of a new phenolic group at the adjacent monomer. This sequence of reactions is schematically illustrated in Figure 14.27. It is obvious that such degradation of the lignin molecule must be slower than that of acid chlorination, where all or nearly all monomers are simultaneously open to attack, cf. Figure 14.12. The slower lignin removal in a hypochlorite stage as compared with a chlorination stage is demonstrated by Figure 14.28, which also shows the more severe carbohydrate degradation from a lignin-rich pulp in the hypochlorite stage.

If the reaction mechanism of Figure 14.27 is principally valid, it is obvious that part of the chlorine once consumed in substitution eventually appears in the alkaline hypochlorite solution as chloride, Therefore, the method adopted to discriminate between substitution and oxidation reactions, i.e. determination of chloride in per cent of total chlorine consumption, is not adoptable in alkaline medium. The earlier results obtained with this technique (9, 31), that substitution of lignin by chlorine-containing solutions ceases at around pH 7, is probably incorrect. The amount of acids formed on the hypochlorite oxidation of lignin is indicated by the consumption of excess alkali added to maintain the pH. A minimum of around 25–30% excess alkali, calculated as weight of NaOH on the weight of active chlorine charged and consumed, is required to maintain pH above 8.3 at finished bleaching. At pH 8.3 the carbon dioxide formed on oxidation is entirely in the bicarbonate form, and all carboxyl groups in

948

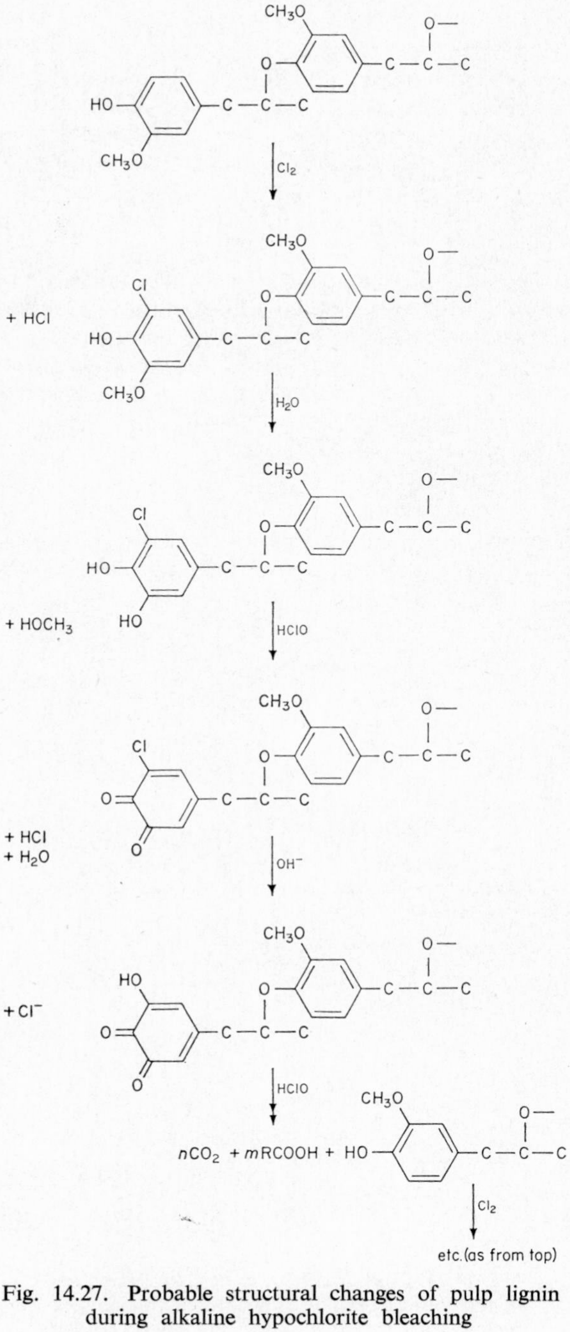

Fig. 14.27. Probable structural changes of pulp lignin during alkaline hypochlorite bleaching

949

carboxylate form. This means, that if 8 moles HClO have been consumed per monomer in oxidation (about 3 kg act. Cl per kg lignin), around 4 moles of excess NaOH are needed to neutralize the acids formed, which is about what is to be expected when one of the main oxidation products is carbon dioxide. For instance, on limited hypochlorite oxidation of guaiacol (97), 1 mole methanol, 1 mole oxalic and 1 mole maleic acid, or 4 carboxyl equivalents, are formed on the simultaneous consumption of 6 moles HClO, whereas continued oxidation ought to give 1 mole methanol and 6 moles CO_2 at a total consumption of 13 moles HClO and 6 moles NaOH.

Thus, a consumption of 7 kg ptp active chlorine, which is a fairly normal figure for a hypochlorite stage following chlorination and alkali extraction, means an oxidation of around 2–2.5 kg ptp lignin (0.2–0.25% of the pulp) with formation of about as much carbon dioxide and organic acids and a consumption of around 2 kg ptp NaOH. For single-stage hypochlorite bleaching, 19 kg ptp act. Cl per Roe number unit or about 2–2.5 kg act. Cl per kg lignin is considered suitable (29).

C. Carbohydrate reactions

The formation and structure of oxidized celluloses was dealt with in Chapter 4.II. Two main types exist, *reducing* and *acidic*. No strict

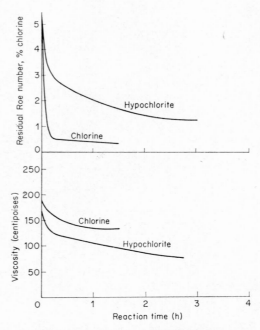

Fig. 14.28. Reaction velocity of chlorination and hypochlorite bleaching as measured by lignin removal and carbohydrate degradation (Hatch)

950

borderline exists between the two and it is more correct to describe the products as carbohydrates containing oxidized groups of reducing and acidic nature. Both cellulose and hemicelluloses can contain such groups. The acidic groups are *carboxyls* and the reducing groups *aldehyde* or *keto* groups. They can be located at any of the hydroxyl-bearing atoms, or in the 1-, 2-, 3- or 6-position (132). Some lactone and carbonic acid ester groups are also formed (123). Some oxidants are selective, e.g. periodate, giving dialdehyde monomers oxidized at C_2 and C_3 (52), whereas nitrogen dioxide–tetroxide mainly gives C_6 oxidation to carboxyls (61). Hypochlorite is not selective, and does not give the dialdehyde type of oxidized cellulose (52, 123), possibly for steric reasons (91). The dialdehyde type of oxidation is considered to be preceded by a cyclic ester formation between the glycol group and the oxidant, Figure 14.29. Similarly, esterification may precede oxidation with hypochlorous acid.

The oxidized groups, whatever their localization, change the behaviour of the carbohydrates, and may lead to degradation and eventually to formation of yellow structures, i.e. to reduction of the strength properties of paper pulp as well as to color reversion on storage. The carbonyl groups in either 2-, 3- or 6-position form β-alkoxycarbonyl configurations, Figure 14.30 (60), which are rapidly hydrolyzed by alkali to give chain rupture and a fragment, which may rearrange to saccharinic acid unless further oxidized. Therefore, carbonyls are more frequent in cellulose subjected to chlorine or hypochlorous acid in neutral and acid solution than to hypochlorite in alkali. On determining the viscosity on cuoxam or cuen solutions of a carbonyl-containing pulp, chain rupture occurs, which gives a lower viscosity than motivated by the actual DP of the undissolved pulp. Furthermore, these alkali-sensitive groups form new starting points for the hot-alkali peeling reaction, cf. Chapter 9.II and Chapter 15, and there is a direct correlation between the hot-alkali solubility of a pulp and its carbonyl content (69, 109), expressed by its copper number or by its capacity for tetrahydroborate reduction.

On the other hand, further oxidation of the carbonyl-containing monomer may lead to scission of the C_2–C_3 bond upon formation of two carboxyl groups (21, 141). which also causes chain rupture in alkali, with the formation of *erythronic* and *glyoxylic acids* from the oxidized monomer, both of which may be further degraded by oxidation. These acids, together with *gluconic acid*, have been isolated from oxidation of methyl glucoside (132) and of cellulose (42), and present evidence is of *direct cleavage of the glucosidic bonds* induced by chlorine or hypochlorous acid. This is of principal interest in understanding the oxidative degradation of cellulose in acid medium. Such a degradation is negligible during a normal chlorination, where chlorine is rapidly consumed by the lignin, but can be appreciable at a second chlorination stage or at elevated temperatures.

The degradation of the carbohydrates during hypochlorite bleaching is mostly undesired for paper pulps, whereas a controlled degradation is practised for dissolving pulps. As hypochlorous acid is likely to be the active oxidant, the degradation is limited by keeping a relatively high

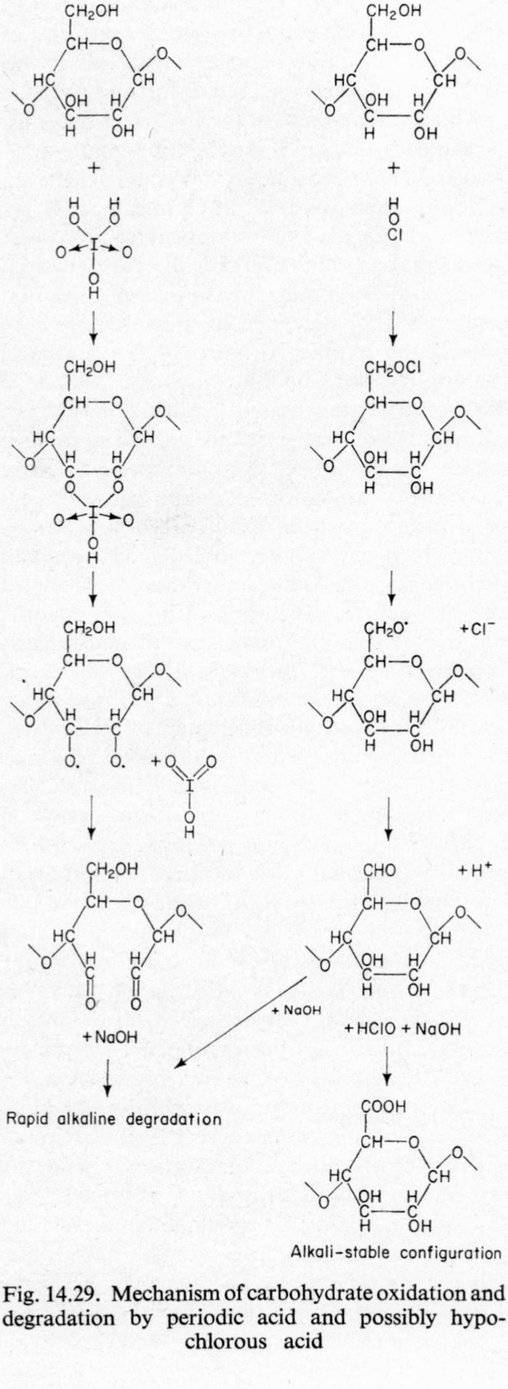

Fig. 14.29. Mechanism of carbohydrate oxidation and degradation by periodic acid and possibly hypochlorous acid

alkalinity to maintain the majority of the active chlorine in the hypochlorite form. The oxidized groups then formed are mainly carboxyls, Figure 14.31 (109), whereas in acidic and neutral medium the carbonyl formation dominates (123), as already shown in Figure 14.23. The rate of degradation of carbohydrates obtained on treatment with chlorine-containing solutions of varying pH, at constant charge of active chlorine and constant other reaction conditions, clearly has a maximum at neutrality, as shown by Figure 4.19 (15, 94), in agreement with the rate of oxidation of methyl glucoside (132). An obvious reason for a higher rate of reaction at neutrality, as compared to the maximal hypochlorous acid content at pH 4–5, is that the carbonyl compounds are more rapidly degraded at higher pH. To prevent the pH dropping to the dangerous range during hypochlorite bleaching, *excess alkali* is added (82) to neutralize the acids formed on oxidation. Even when a limited degradation is desired, it is preferable to perform it at comparatively high pH, where it is easier to control the reaction.

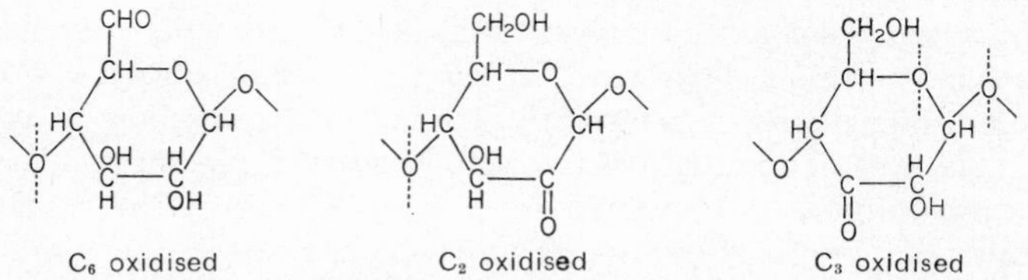

Fig. 14.30. β-alkoxycarbonyl configurations of oxidized cellulose (alkali-labile linkages indicated)

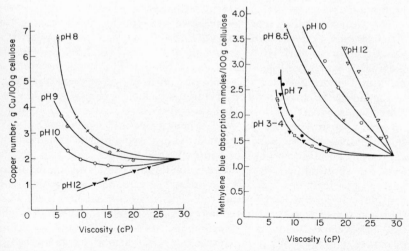

Fig. 14.31. Formation of carbonyl groups (copper number) and carboxyl groups (methylene blue absorption) at the degradation (viscosity decrease) of cellulose by chlorine or hypochlorite (Samuelson–Ramsel)

953

The extent of oxidation of the carbohydrates will thus vary with the bleaching conditions and the total amount of oxidant reacted, and these variations will later be described in some detail. It is sufficient here to state that a low-viscosity pulp after cooking contains about 0.003 reducing carbonyl groups and as many carboxyls per glucose monomer, and that the carbonyls are slightly increased during chlorination and somewhat decreased during the alkali treatment, more so on increasing degrees of purification. Finally, during the hypochlorite bleach with a normal alkalinity, carbonyls decrease somewhat, whereas carboxyls increase considerably. The content of oxidized groups of the final bleached pulp may be about 0.002 carbonyls and 0.005–0.007 carboxyls per glucose monomer. Hypochlorite oxidation of cotton at pH 10–11 showed that the degraded material contained about two oxidized groups per molecule, mainly carboxyls, irrespective of the state of degradation (110). About 15 oxidation equivalents were consumed per oxidized groups, or 17–30 per alkali-resistant molecule. There was only little hypochlorite consumption in the liquor on prolonged heating in the absence of fibers, allowing the conclusion that the main oxidation takes place within the fiber and only little further oxidation of the reaction products occurs outside. Complete oxidation of one glucose monomer to carbon dioxide involves 24 oxidation equivalents. An increase of 0.002 oxidized groups per monomer should mean a consumption of about 6 kg ptp active Cl, assuming 15 oxidation equivalents per oxidized group. Therefore, a considerable part of the total hypochlorite consumed in a hypochlorite stage belongs to carbohydrate reactions. On the other hand, the yield loss experienced with these 6 kg ptp act. Cl would only be about 1–2 kg ptp, or 0.1–0.2%. The main yield losses in bleaching are thus caused by delignification, especially that of the preliminary stages of chlorination and alkali extraction.

The two competing types of reaction of hypochlorite bleaching, the *delignification* and the *carbohydrate degradation* can be correlated in various manners to describe the result of the bleaching and to elucidate the reaction mechanism. The essential criteria describing the result is brightness gained and the paper strength sacrificed. As an indirect measure of the latter, the viscosity drop during the bleaching can be given. For a closer interconnection with the consumption of oxidant, the fluidity (inverse viscosity) change per oxidation equivalent has been studied (85). If the fluidity of the pulp is plotted against hypochlorite consumption, curves are obtained, which are approximately composed of two straight lines, one showing that little change in the fluidity occurs during the initial part of the reaction, the other showing an essential degradation with continued hypochlorite consumption. This is illustrated in Figure 14.32 (85), which also depicts the initial hypochlorite charges and the final brightness achieved, as functions of the hypochlorite consumption. Each family of curves represents one pulp, chlorinated with various charges in the first stage and then alkali extracted prior to the hypochlorite stage. It is seen that the initial period of hypochlorite consumption with only insignificant fluidity increase is dependent on the pretreatment, so that a well chlorinated

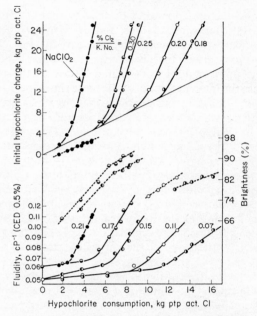

Fig. 14.32. Brightness and fluidity changes at varying hypochlorite charge and consumption for a pulp previously chlorinated to a varying extent (% Cl₂/K number) and alkali extracted. Reference delignified by chlorite (Paulson)

pulp has only a relatively small consumption of hypochlorite before the viscosity begins to drop (fluidity to increase). It is also obvious that the slope of the curves becomes steeper as more chlorine is used in the chlorination pretreatment. This means that less hypochlorite is needed to cause a certain viscosity drop, the pulp has become more 'sensitive' to the hypochlorite bleaching. It is also seen that the brightness level finally achieved improves with increasing quantities of chlorine in the pretreatment. A chlorite pretreatment, however, gives superior brightness levels.

A basically more meaningful manner of expressing the result of a hypochlorite bleaching is to plot the function $1/DP-1/DP_0$ against the hypochlorite consumption, Figure 14.33 (44). This function should be reasonably proportional to the number of bonds broken in the carbohydrate molecules. The figure shows the same subdivision into two periods, the initial one consuming hypochlorite without carbohydrate degradation, the following period causing a degradation proportional to the hypochlorite consumption. The slope of the curve during the latter period, however, depends on the purity of the pulp. Table 14.3 (44) compiles the influence of various factors on the intercept with the abscissa, and the slope of the curve, from which the following conclusions may be drawn,

955

in agreement with the previous work on fluidity changes during the hypochlorite stage. The intercept is larger, and the slope less steep the higher the lignin content of the unbleached pulp, and the less chlorination or chlorine dioxide pretreatment it has received. A similar effect has addition of lignin to the pulp. Addition of hemicellulose to the pulp, however, does not increase the intercept but does decrease the slope, whereas removal of hemicellulose by hot alkali purification will increase the slope. Obviously, oxidation of lignin without carbohydrate degradation accounts for the intercept, the initial hypochlorite consumption. The slope expressing the quantity of bond breaks per hypochlorite consumption is influenced partly by the residual lignin, which continues to consume hypochlorite during the latter period, but also by the residual hemicelluloses, which are degraded in the same way under hypochlorite consumption but do not appear in the degradation figures, which are based on viscosity determinations. The subdivision of the lignin reactions into the two periods may express a variation of lignin accessibility, but is also likely to have chemical reasons. Obviously, the slope of the curve is a true expression for bond breakage per oxidant in the carbohydrate reaction only in the case of cotton linters, which is free of lignin and hemicelluloses. The slope figure of 1.82 corresponds to a consumption of 25 oxidation equivalents per chain rupture, i.e. complete oxidation to carbon dioxide of the attacked glucose monomer in the chain.

The degradation of carbohydrates during the hypochlorite bleaching has considerable influence on the paper strength. This is one of the main reasons for the use of chlorine dioxide, which oxidizes the lignin without much degradation of the carbohydrates. The effect on the paper strength

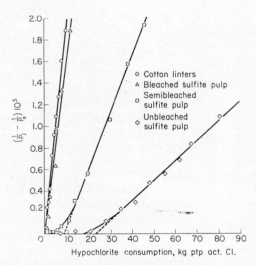

Fig. 14.33. Degradation of pulps, delignified to a varying extent, versus hypochlorite consumption (Herbst–Krässig)

956

Table 14.3. The course of hypochlorite bleaching as influenced by the pulp origin and pretreatment (44)

Type of pulp	Type of pretreatment	Pretreatment, kg ptp act. Cl	Intercept, kg ptp act. Cl	Slope of curve, DP^{-1}/kg ptp act. Cl $\times 10^4$
Cotton liners	—	—	0	1.82
Bleached softwood sulfite viscose pulp	Full bleach		0	1.58
Semibleached hardwood–softwood sulfite pulp	Chlorine–alkali		9.0	0.51
Unbleached hardwood–softwood sulfite pulp	—	—	24.0	0.18
Unbleached hardwood–softwood sulfite pulps	Roe no. 1.9	—	17.8	0.198
	Roe no. 2.3	—	23.9	0.180
	Roe no. 2.6	—	28.3	0.149
Semibleached hardwood–softwood sulfite pulps	Chlorine–alkali	29.0	7.8	0.18
		36.0	5.2	0.22
		44.0	2.4	0.25
Semibleached hardwood–softwood sulfite pulps	Chlorine dioxide	0	27.7	0.09
		21.0	6.1	0.18
		34.2	5.5	0.29
		78.9	1.7	0.40
		Excess	2.2	0.43
Bleached hardwood–softwood sulfite pulp	None	—	2.2	0.43
	60 kg ptp NaLS* added	—	48.3	0.09
Unbleached softwood sulfite pulp				
NaClO bleach at 60°C		—	27	0.09
NaClO bleach at 25°C		—	26	0.11
Semibleached softwood sulfite pulp NaClO bleach at	Chlorine–alkali			
pH 9.5–10				0.43
10.5–11				0.34
11.5–12				0.22
Bleached softwood sulfite pulp	Hot alkali purification	40 (NaOH)	0	0.67
		20	0	0.61
		0	2	0.43
	100 kg ptp hemicelluloses added	0	0	0.27
Unbleached	Never dried		26	0.11
	Dried		29	0.21
Bleached	Never dried		0	2.13
	Dried		0	2.14

* NaLS = sodium lignosulfonate.

properties can be correlated with the viscosity decrease, and viscosity is often used as a quality control in the bleaching of paper pulps, although there is probably no direct connection between cellulose DP and strength properties of the paper.

3. INFLUENCE OF REACTION CONDITIONS ON PULP YIELD AND PROPERTIES

As the hypochlorite oxidation is mainly concerned with the removal of small quantities of lignin from the pulp, usually less than 0.5%, and little carbohydrates are dissolved even on fairly excessive degradation, the *yields* obtained in hypochlorite bleaching are normally almost quantitative. Exceptions would be neutral sulfite semichemical pulps, containing large amounts of alkali-sensitive hemicelluloses and sometimes rather more lignin than usual. Then a few per cent losses may be experienced, the higher alkalinity during the bleaching the more losses. But, generally, the conditions used during the bleaching do not materially influence the yield. The *properties* of the pulps, both for paper and dissolving purposes, are in contrast very much dependent on the extent and manner of hypochlorite bleaching. Two properties are of immediate interest, namely *brightness* and *viscosity*, the former describing the removal of impurities, predominantly lignin but also resin, and the latter indicating the carbohydrate degradation, desired or unwanted. The introduction of oxidized groups, *carbonyls* and *carboxyls*, is also followed by analysis, as are the changes in *cold and hot alkali solubility*. The changes in *brightness stability* and *paper properties* are likewise often recorded.

The reaction conditions as in any bleaching stage involve *consistency*, *temperature, time,* and *charge of chemicals.* The latter includes both *hypochlorite* charge, reported as *active chlorine*, and *alkali* charge, reported in *per cent excess alkali* (calculated on the weight of active chlorine charged) or *initial and final pH.* The *residual active chlorine* is analyzed, and the *consumption* of active chlorine calculated. Of these reaction variables, most effects observed in hypochlorite bleaching can be referred to hypochlorite consumption and pH (cf. 120).

A. *Hypochlorite consumption*

As most pulp properties are dependent in some way on the consumption of active chlorine, it is preferred to start the description by showing how the hypochlorite consumption is affected by the reaction variables. Figure 14.34 (103) demonstrates the degree of reaction of a 7.5 kg ptp active chlorine charge to a sulfite rayon pulp, previously chlorinated and extracted, at *various consistencies and reaction times*, at constant temperature. Figure 14.35 shows the degree of reaction at the same charge, with *various consistencies and reaction temperatures*, at constant time. Figure 14.36 shows the degree of reaction at *various charges and consistencies*, at constant reaction temperatures and times. It is seen that an increase in consistency from hollander bleacher level of 6% to medium

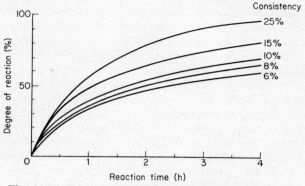

Fig. 14.34. Rate of hypochlorite consumption at varying consistency. Hypochlorite charge 7.5 kg ptp act. Cl, temperature 40°C, pulp prebleached spruce sulfite (Rydholm)

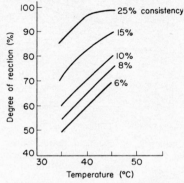

Fig. 14.35. Influence of temperature consistency on the rate of hypochlorite bleaching. Constant charge of 7.5 kg ptp act. Cl (Rydholm)

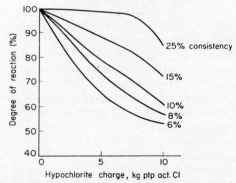

Fig. 14.36. Influence of charge and consistency on the rate of hypochlorite bleaching. Constant temperature 40°C (Rydholm)

959

consistency of 15% in towers will decrease the necessary reaction time by 50%, or the necessary reaction temperature by 10°C. A direct proportionality between the reaction velocity and the consistency is generally stated (18, 48, 67). An increase of reaction temperature by 10°C will double the rate of reaction (cf. 18, 67, 101). An increase in the hypochlorite charge at other constant conditions will decrease the degree of reaction, as calculated in per cent of the charge, but increase the absolute amount of hypochlorite consumption, in kg ptp. The latter phenomenon depends on the higher concentration of chemicals in the bleaching liquor at the higher charges, and the effect is almost balanced by a corresponding dilution of the liquor when decreasing the consistency at the higher charge of chemicals, as seen by Figure 14.37. For the slower, later part of the

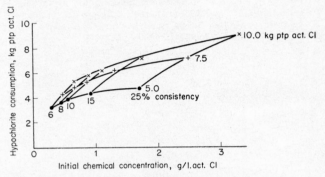

Fig. 14.37. Influence of chemical concentration, charge and consistency on the rate of hypochlorite bleaching. Constant temperature 40°C (Rydholm)

hypochlorite oxidation reaction the velocity has been found proportional to the square of the hypochlorite concentration (9, 46). Catalysts such as copper and nickel not only accelerate hypochlorite oxidation but also carbohydrate degradation (43a). On decreasing the *excess alkali* or final pH, the reaction rate is increased, although not much time could be gained by lowering the excess alkali within the range of 100–30%, Figure 14.38, which are about the widest variations allowable for qualitative reasons. The rate of reaction has been found to be at maximum at pH 7 in some investigations (15, 67, 94), whereas in others a decrease of reaction velocity with increasing pH has been found for the entire pH range (94, 109, 117). Hypobromite oxidation has a slightly different pH dependence (67a).

Something should be said here about the rôle of excess alkali. Evidently to keep pH at a constant level during the bleaching would require either the use of salt buffers or continuous additions of alkali as the acid oxidation products are formed. The former way has been applied in certain investigations (e.g. 67, 94), but no cheap buffers are available for technical application in the desired pH range of 9–10, other than ammonia, which should

960

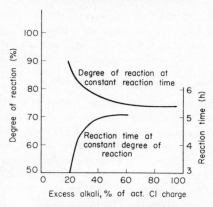

Fig. 14.38. Influence of the charge of excess alkali on the rate of hypochlorite bleaching (Rydholm)

be avoided because of its specific reactions with the hypochlorite, and sodium carbonate, which rather buffers at around pH 10–11 and has to be applied in considerably greater amounts than the generally used sodium hydroxide. The other solution of the problem could be realized in batch bleaching using a pH automatic controller, but not in continuous tower bleaching. However, no particular disadvantage is usually connected with only one single addition of excess alkali as applied in technical bleaching, although it must be remembered that the continuous decrease in pH will then somewhat accelerate the bleaching and therefore tends to exaggerate the influence of any reaction variable.

To connect the figure for excess alkali with that for the hypochlorite *charge* by expressing it in per cent of available chlorine is practical and responds fairly well to the actual need of neutralization chemicals. Actually, it would be still more accurate, although less practical, to connect the

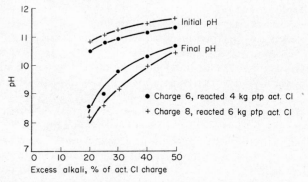

F g. 14.39. pH conditions of hypochlorite bleaching at varying additions of excess alkali (Rydholm)

figure with the hypochlorite *consumption*, which would indicate the exact need of neutralization chemicals to keep a constant final pH. In Figure 14.39 the pH conditions of a hypochlorite oxidation stage are given for different amounts of excess alkali at constant hypochlorite consumption.

B. Brightness and brightness stability

The brightness increase is related to the hypochlorite consumption in the bleaching stage and will therefore increase with time, temperature and consistency at a constant charge of chemicals, and with increasing charges. The amount of *prebleaching* obviously influences both the final brightness level and the brightness increase for a certain hypochlorite stage, as illustrated previously in Figure 14.32. *Drying* of a kraft pulp prior to bleaching does not materially influence brightness response nor brightness stability of the bleached pulp (138). Compared at constant hypochlorite consumption, the effects are considerably smaller and also dependent on other factors. For instance, at increased consistency, the result will be dependent on the efficiency of chemicals mixing. At satisfactory mixing, low-consistency bleaching gives slightly higher brightness than medium-consistency bleaching (67). A change in temperature below 60°C only slightly influences the brightness achieved at a certain hypochlorite consumption, but the brightness stability seems to be somewhat increased with the temperature (67).

There is an optimal alkalinity for brightness. Bleaching at around 30–35% excess alkali, resulting in a final pH of 9–9.5, seems to give higher brightness than bleaching at higher alkalinity to the same chlorine consumption, possibly because of secondary lignin reactions, whereas lower pH tends to give some discoloration and especially lower brightness stability due to carbohydrate degradation (29b, 67, 98a). This is illustrated in Figure 14.40 for a sulfite low-grade dissolving pulp and in Figure 14.41 for a sulfite paper pulp (67), in both cases compared at constant consumption of hypochlorite. Corresponding brightness curves for prebleached sulfite and kraft pulps, as well as unbleached neutral sulfite pulps, all compared at constant charge and other constant bleaching conditions but pH, are shown in Figure 14.42 (84, 94).

As brightness stability to storage, heat or chemicals is closely connected with the content of carbonyl groups (29b, 67), it is further discussed in a subsequent section, but it should be stressed here that in order to obtain a better brightness stability it might often be advantageous to increase the final pH of the hypochlorite stage above that of maximum brightness at pH 9–9.5.

One of the most important variables for the brightness obtainable in the hypochlorite stage is the pulp type and pretreatment. A pulp rich in lignin when entering the hypochlorite stage requires more oxidant to achieve a certain brightness. Kraft pulps require somewhat more oxidant than acid or neutral sulfite pulps of the same lignin content, and show also different brightness stability (98a). The resin content of the pulp entering the hypochlorite stage, as well as the nature of the resin, will also influence the bleaching result, and the deresination in the alkali stage (cf. Chapter 16) is of considerable importance for the final brightness. Brightness stability has been found to increase with the duration of the alkali extraction prior to the final bleaching (98a).

The purity of the water in the hypochlorite stage, and especially at the subsequent dilution and washing operations, is also a great influence on the final brightness result.

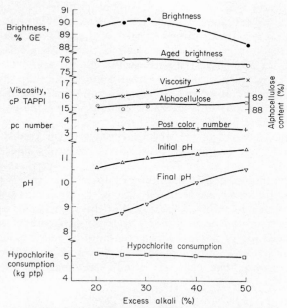

Fig. 14.40. Influence of excess alkali on the result of hypochlorite bleaching of a prebleached spruce sulfite rayon pulp (Rydholm)

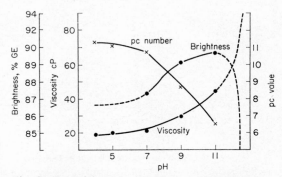

Fig. 14.41. Brightness, viscosity and yellowing as influenced by pH of hypochlorite bleaching of a sulfite paper pulp (Lekander–Stockman)

963

As stated above, the brightness achieved is proportional to the amount of hypochlorite reacted. However, the factor limiting the brightness achieved in the hypochlorite stage is not the cost of chemicals. The hypochlorite consumption must be limited to an amount which does not cause excessive carbohydrate degradation. How the reaction variables affect that degradation is dealt with in the following section.

C. Carbonyl and carboxyl group formation

The changes in carbonyl and carboxyl content of the pulp are of interest as a measure of the oxidative degradation of the carbohydrates, as well as for their importance for certain properties of the pulp, such as brightness stability during storage, heating or treatment with chemicals, as well as the tendency to absorb metal ions. Although the content of oxidized groups is affected in most chemical treatments of the pulp, hypochlorite oxidation is one of those with dominating influence, and the survey of the changes in carbonyl and carboxyl content during the entire pulping process is therefore preferably made here.

The carbonyl content of the wood carbohydrates is almost exclusively due to the aldehydic end groups of the chain molecules, and thus mainly inversely proportional to the DP. The hemicelluloses therefore contain considerably more carbonyls than the cellulose. The same is true for the carboxyl groups, which are originally limited to the uronic acid fraction. During the cooking process, a great deal of the uronic acids and the low-molecular part of the hemicelluloses is removed, thereby lowering the content of these native groups, which could not be called oxidized groups in the technical sense, although they are included in that concept for analytical reasons. The carboxyl groups are analyzed with methods

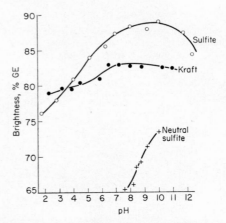

Fig. 14.42. Brightness of neutral sulfite, pre-bleached sulfite and kraft pulps on bleaching with hypochlorite at varying pH and otherwise constant conditions (Parsons–Lausman and Rapson)

employing ion exchange (7, cf. Chapter 20), and the carbonyl groups by measuring the reductive properties of the pulp (7) by selective reduction with tetrahydroborate, by selective oxidation to carboxyls with chlorite or hypoiodite and determination of the increase in carboxyl content, or by selective substitution with carbonyl reagents, such as hydroxy lamine or Girard reagent. The latter method is preferred as it gives a fairly stoichiometrical reaction and a direct measure of the carbonyl content per glucose unit, whereas the older analytical methods, the copper number determinations, give only relative values, although they have all the same been of much use in the study of the changes in carbonyl content.

The nature of the new types of carbonyl and carboxyl groups formed has been touched upon in a previous section. Figures have also shown the change in hot alkali solubility during sulfite cooking, Figure 9.54 (107), and in copper number on treatment with chlorine-containing solution of varying pH, Figure 14.23 (109, cf. 4, 14, 117). The changes in carboxyl content in the latter type of treatment were also shown, Figure 14.31. To make possible an estimation of the total amounts of oxidized groups formed, the stoichiometrical methods for carbonyl determination must be applied, and the values added to those found for carboxyls. It is then found that the total amount of oxidized groups at a certain viscosity does not vary considerably with the alkalinity of the bleaching stage, but that the carbonyls decrease and carboxyls increase at increased pH. This indicates that an initial carbonyl formation also occurs in more alkaline hypochlorite solution, which leads to cleavage of a glycosidic bond in the alkaline medium and consequently a shortening of the chain before stabilization of the oxycellulose has occurred through further oxidation of the carbonyl to carboxyl groups. Figure 14.43 shows the approximate carbonyl and carboxyl groups of two sulfite pulps at various bleaching stages, with a fairly limited hot alkali purification and a rather alkaline hypochlorite bleaching. Higher degree of cooking results in less carboxyl groups and more carbonyl

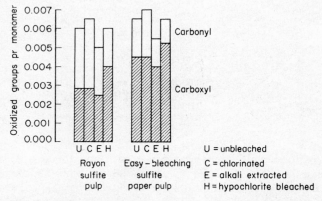

Fig. 14.43. Oxidized groups in spruce sulfite pulps at various stages of bleaching (Rydholm)

965

groups. Higher degree of purification leads to less carbonyl groups. Less alkaline hypochlorite stage gives more carbonyls and less carboxyls. Figure 14.44 shows the increase in oxidized groups during a severe oxidative degradation of a sulfite pulp as a function of viscosity. It is obvious, that more groups are formed than could possibly be end groups. A detailed study on the nature and content of oxidized groups after excessive degradation of cellulose by acid and alkaline hypochlorite oxidation (123), revealed the following composition, Table 14.4.

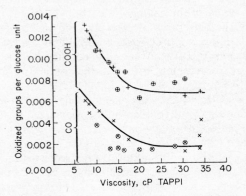

Fig. 14.44. Formation of oxidized groups during hypochlorite degradation of a soft sulfite paper pulp. Encircled symbols denote a final pH above 9, the remainder a final pH of 6–8 (Rydholm)

Table 14.4. Nature and content (per glucose monomer) of oxidized groups after excessive degradation of cellulose with hypochlorite (123)

Group	Original pulp	Oxidized at pH 4.6 to DP 500	to DP 220	Oxidized at pH 11 to DP 180
Carboxyl, uronic	0.0015	0.0026	0.0074	0.0071
non-uronic	—	—	0.0030	0.0076
total	0.0015	0.0026	0.0104	0.0147
Carbonate ester	0.0002	—	0.0022	—
Carbonyl, aldehydic	0.0020	0.0032	0.0102	0.0017
hydroxyketonic	0.0031	0.0182	0.0145	0.0133
total	0.0051	0.0214	0.0247	0.0150
Grand total	0.0068	0.0240	0.0373	0.0297

The brightness stability to heat has been found to decrease with the copper number (29a, 67), and the brightness stability to chemicals, as measured in terms of alkali cellulose brightness, is also related to the carbonyl content.

The variables in the hypochlorite stage, apart from pH and hypochlorite

966

consumption, do not considerably influence the carbohydrate degradation, as measured as carbonyl and carboxyl groups at constant hypochlorite consumption. Temperature has no influence, and consistency only a little (67).

D. Changes in viscosity, cold alkali solubility and paper strength

The degradation of the carbohydrates during the hypochlorite oxidation is also manifested in the decrease of viscosity and paper strength, as well as increase in alkali solubility. The main influence on these properties, as on the carbonyl and carboxyl content, is exerted by the amount of hypochlorite reacted, as well as by the pH during the oxidation. The pulp consistency and the temperature during the bleaching are of little significance (103, 109), if good mixing of chemicals is provided for.

The influence of pH on viscosity and alphacellulose content at constant hypochlorite consumption is demonstrated in Figures 14.45–46 (67, 103,

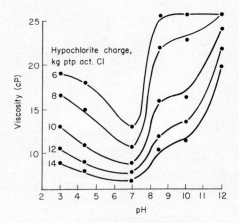

Fig. 14.45. Degradation of a rayon pulp (original viscosity 30cP TAPPI) by bleaching with varying hypochlorite charges at different pH's (Samuelson–Ramsel)

109), showing maximal degradation at neutrality. In the pH range of technical bleaching, with excess alkali of 25–50%, the effect on viscosity is slight and on alkali solubility negligible, Figure 14.40 (103, cf. 117). The interaction of the variables temperature, alkalinity and consistency with regard to alphacellulose decrease has been studied when bleaching rayon sulfite pulp to a constant viscosity level (81a). At low alkalinity (initial pH10), the alphacellulose losses increased with temperature, the reverse being true for high alkalinity (initial pH11). The losses were at a minimum at medium consistency (10%). Figures 14.47–48 (94) show the influence of pH on the viscosity of sulfite and kraft pulps at constant hypochlorite charge and other variables but varying consumption. The decrease in viscosity at approaching neutrality is pronounced by the increased rate of reaction in the same region.

The dominating variable affecting carbohydrate degradation is that of hypochlorate consumption. Figure 14.32 showed the viscosity decrease as a function of hypochlorite consumption for various types of pulps. It is seen that the viscosity decrease is affected by the previous treatment. This effect is likely to depend on the fact that more residual lignin has been removed from the pulp by the more extensive chlorination. Naturally, the hypochlorite consumption of the residual lignin will correspondingly protect the carbohydrates. The removal of lignin as well

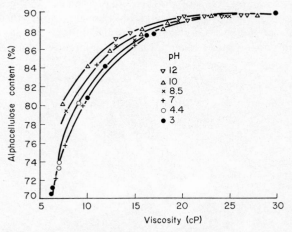

Fig. 14.46. Alphacellulose versus viscosity on the degradation of rayon pulp by hypochlorite bleaching at different pH's (Samuelson–Ramsel)

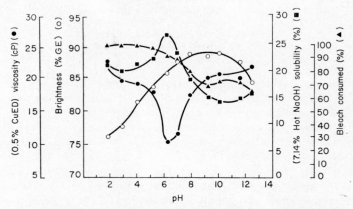

Fig. 14.47. Effect of pH on bleaching chlorinated and extracted sulfite pulp with chlorine (Rapson)

as of low-molecular carbohydrates by increasingly severe alkali purification will expose the high-molecular portions to oxidation. The combined effect of swelling and high degree of purification renders the cold alkali purified pulps extremely sensitive to hypochlorite bleaching.

In Figure 14.49 the increase in cold alkali solubilities is shown as a function of viscosity at pulps of various unbleached viscosities and degrees

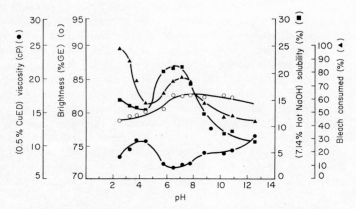

Fig. 14.48. Effect of pH bleaching with chlorine a kraft pulp purified in a preliminary stage (Rapson)

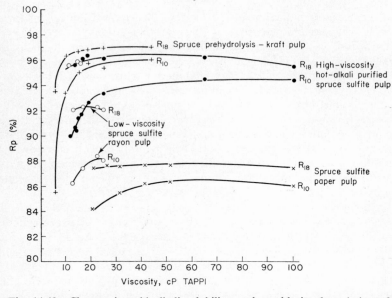

Fig. 14.49. Changes in cold alkali solubility on hypochlorite degradation of various pulp types. R_{18} and R_{10} denote non-solubility in 18 and 10% NaOH (Rydholm)

of purification. These changes are of great economic interest for dissolving pulps. It is seen that R_{18} is fairly unchanged until rather low viscosity levels, whereas R_{10} and therefore the conventional alphacellulose content decrease even at fairly small changes in viscosity. This indicates that the carbohydrate degradation by hypochlorite oxidation is partly decidedly heterogeneous, leading to a considerable fragmentation of microfibrils. In comparison with the hydrolytic degradation during the sulfite cook, the oxidative degradation during the bleaching is somewhat, but insignificantly, more uniform. The greater uniformity in the oxidative degradation during the aging of alkali cellulose has been stressed (106, 118a). Therefore, in the case of some early dissolving pulps for tire cord manufacture, where a homogeneous chain length distribution is desired, the pulp after a fairly mild sulfite cook and a hot alkali purification to a high alphacellulose level was mildly bleached and delivered at fairly high viscosity, leaving the necessary degradation to the viscose plant. In other cases, where a low-viscosity rayon pulp is desired, the main degradation is carried out by some mills in the digester and by others in the hypochlorite stage, both methods having advantages and disadvantages.

The loss in paper strength during the oxidative degradation in the hypochlorite stage has been the subject of numerous investigations and has been of great technical consequence. First of all, it has motivated multistage bleaching and the introduction of the acid chlorination and alkali extraction stages. Furthermore, it has for many years limited bleached kraft pulp brightness especially to a fairly low level and still at the loss of much of the unbleached pulp strength. Finally, it has motivated the introduction of the modern bleaching chemicals, chlorine dioxide, chlorite and peroxide.

To minimize the loss in paper strength, all variables of hypochlorite bleaching have been investigated. However, but for the influence of hypochlorite consumption and pH, no differences in paper strength losses have been clearly demonstrated. The influence of pH on the hypochlorite stage is considerable, both for sulfite and kraft pulps (74, 75, 83) and for neutral sulfite pulps (84). To a considerable degree this depends on the increased rate of oxidation in neutral medium, but even at constant hypochlorite consumption a lower strength is obtained if the pH has been allowed to drop too low. Within the variations of technical well-buffered hypochlorite stages, the effects are minimal. Then the strength loss is related mainly to the hypochlorite consumption.

The decrease in paper strength properties has often been related to the viscosity decrease. Although the decrease in the chain length of cellulose is likely to mean little to paper strength, viscosity is a good measure of the main progress of oxidative degradation, which is probably fairly parallel to the attack on the strength-bearing elements of the fibers, whether being fiber wall layers, microfibrils, or the chain molecules of the hemicelluloses. Therefore, a fair correlation exists between paper strength properties and pulp viscosity (12, 103, 134), as demonstrated in Figure 14.50 for kraft and in Figure 14.51 for sulfite pulp. Therefore, viscosity determination is often

970

used in bleaching control to follow the changes in paper strength of a certain pulp type. The viscosity of an isolated pulp sample, however, tells little about the paper properties, as the correlation between strength and viscosity is different for different types of pulp (e.g. for sulfite and kraft), for different types of degradation to a certain viscosity (e.g. hydrolytic or oxidative) and even for oxidative degradation with different bleaching agents.

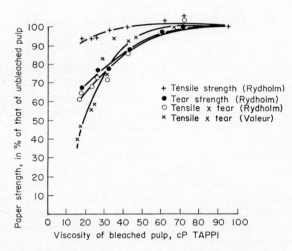

Fig. 14.50. Decrease in paper strength as related to bleached pulp viscosity on bleaching pine kraft pulp (Rydholm, Valeur)

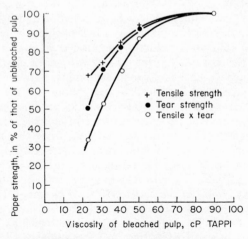

Fig. 14.51. Decrease in paper strength as related to bleached pulp viscosity on bleaching spruce sulfite pulp (Rydholm)

971

In mild hypochlorite bleaching of lignin-rich pulps, such as neutral sulfite semichemical hardwood pulps, an *increase* of the paper strength properties is achieved, which is caused by the improved swelling in water of the delignified fibers (54). A slight degradation of the cellulose and little degradation of the hemicelluloses occurs (54), and even with a fairly complete lignin removal, only small quantities of carbohydrates are lost, provided the pH and temperature are not excessively high (5).

III. Chlorine Dioxide and Chlorite Oxidation

1. GENERAL DESCRIPTION OF PROCESS

Although the benefits of chlorine dioxide bleaching were already realized in the 1920's (37, 115, 115a, 115b), the cost and handling difficulties of the new bleaching agent prohibited technical use until suitable production methods from sodium chlorate had been developed during and after World War II (cf. Chapter 19). Chlorine dioxide, being explosive in the pure state, cannot be handled as chlorine in liquid form for transport and consequently has to be made at the pulp mill.

The original studies used chlorine dioxide for holocellulose preparations from wood, and although its possibilities as a bleaching agent were obvious, the first patents suggesting chlorine dioxide bleaching of a pre-bleached pulp dates from 1938 (99) in acid and (8a) in alkaline medium. The greatest interest for an efficient bleaching agent with mild carbohydrate action naturally came from the kraft industry, whereas it was less needed for the more easily-bleached sulfite pulps. Shortly after the war, production of super-bleached kraft pulps was taken up by three Swedish kraft pulp mills and around 1950 Canadian and American kraft mills began to apply chlorine dioxide. Now chlorine dioxide is used in most bleached-kraft mills, and a few sulfite mills, for both softwood and hardwood pulps. As a rule, it is applied in combination with hypochlorite (19, 38, 89, 144), but some kraft mills have entirely abandoned hypochlorite, a logical development as the costs of chlorine dioxide with more efficient production methods approaches that of hypochlorite plus buffer. Two chlorine dioxide stages, separated by an alkali extraction, are the rule for kraft bleaching, applied as finishing stages on the pre-bleached pulp. For sulfite pulps, some mills use a finishing stage of chlorine dioxide, whereas others prefer to place the chlorine dioxide stage prior to a finishing hypochlorite oxidation, sometimes without intermediate washing.

Sodium chlorite has similar, but not identical, action as chlorine dioxide and was suggested both as single bleaching agent (130) and as a finish of pre-bleached pulps (142) in the early 1930's. However, it is several times more expensive to use, and is only conceivable in small pulp or paper mills desiring a higher brightness finish at some speciality grades, which are manufactured in smaller lots than to necessitate the construction of a chlorine dioxide plant. It has been in some use for this purpose in quite a few mills, but is likely to be eliminated by chlorine dioxide-bleached pulp and by small installations for chlorine dioxide production. For laboratory work, chlorite is often preferred to chlorine dioxide.

Three important differences from hypochlorite bleaching have practical consequences for the bleaching with chlorine dioxide, namely:

(1) it involves a volatile, toxic gas (36);
(2) it requires fairly high temperatures;
(3) it involves a chemical, corrosive in both liquid and vapor phase (131).

The gas hazards are overcome by using vented filter hoods before and after the chlorine dioxide stages, and by preventing leakage in pipe connections etc. The desirability of closed reactors also makes continuous operation in towers more suitable than hollander bleachers. The corrosiveness is a more severe problem. Construction materials used in the chlorination stage are not sufficiently resistant. For the bleaching towers, acid-brick linings cemented with plastics are used, as is occasionally the case for the mixer housing. Stainless steels of increased molybdenum content, Hastelloy C, titanium etc. are used for mixers, filters, pumps, pipes, thermometer pockets and other machinery. Unfortunately, the fairly high reaction temperatures used in the chlorine dioxide stage prevents a more general use of thermoplastics, but PVC, Saran, and modified hard rubber etc. are used in pipes for chlorine dioxide solution, filter hoods and fans.

The high reaction temperature, 60–80°C, necessitates medium consistency operation and suggests high consistency experiments. The lowest consistencies used are around 6% in upflow towers. Improved feeders for upflow towers make 12 or even 16% consistency possible, and downflow towers for chlorine dioxide bleaching run at 15–18% or even 25–30% consistency. In the latter case screw presses are incorporated in the system. Figure 12.21 shows one of the various arrangements in use (10). The towers allow retention times of 2–6 h. In downflow towers, the dilution water at the tower base is sometimes cold mill water, but especially when the stage is followed by a hot alkali or hypochlorite stage, the white water from the washer is recirculated to the tower base and to the filter trough, in order to keep up the temperature of the pulp. With such an arrangement, however, corrosion may be experienced on the impellers, pump, pipes, and filter, unless special construction materials or other precautions are taken, such as additions of alkali or sulfur dioxide to the white water (24, 89).

A combination of chlorine dioxide and hypochlorite oxidation, used for sulfite pulp, was shown in Figure 12.22. Some residual chlorine dioxide is saved for the last stage, and hypochlorite with sufficient alkali quantities are added to the mixer between the two towers. The last stage consequently becomes a combined hypochlorite and alkaline chlorine dioxide bleaching. Generally, however, chlorine dioxide bleaching is practised in acid medium at the pH range, 5–3, set by the acidity of the chlorine dioxide solution and the acids formed during the oxidation. When using alkaline conditions without hypochlorite activation, the full oxidation power of

973

chlorine dioxide is not utilized, and patents have suggested the use of the white water from the washer after an alkaline chlorine dioxide stage by addition to a previous bleaching stage, such as chlorination (135). The use of the white water from a neutral chlorine dioxide stage, pH 6–8, in a subsequent bleaching stage after acidification has also been suggested (16). In the same way a bleaching stage using neutral chlorine dioxide could be continued, without intermediate washing, by acid or chlorine activation of the chlorite ions formed (13, cf. 22), Even without the utilization of the residual oxidant, chlorine dioxide bleaching in less acid medium may be of interest for some pulps, as will be discussed later on in connection with the influence of the reaction variables on the bleaching result.

In the bleaching of hardwood sulfite pulps, it may be an advantage to apply an oxidative initial bleaching stage instead of chlorination, to avoid the formation of sticky chlorinated resins. Hypochlorite oxidation has been used, but some mills also apply chlorine dioxide in the first stage. In that case, the lignin-rich unbleached pulp reacts with chlorine dioxide already at cold water temperature, and the usual conditions of a chlorination stage are then sufficient, i.e. low consistency, low temperature and fairly short reaction period. The pulp leaving this stage has the appearance of an ordinary chlorinated pulp and requires further bleaching.

The chlorine dioxide charge varies with the type of pulp and the result desired. For pre-bleached kraft pulps of around 60% GE brightness, 10 kg ptp active chlorine is a suitable charge for each of the two chlorine dioxide stages. For the brightness finish of a sulfite pulp, 5–10 kg ptp active chlorine is sufficient, but in the combined chlorine dioxide-hypochlorite stage for super-bleached pulp, 15-20 kg ptp is desirable (1 kg ClO_2 corresponds to around 2.6 kg act. Cl). As an initial treatment, the charge should follow the Roe number.

Sodium chlorite is used in corresponding charges, at corresponding temperatures, times and consistencies. To activate the chlorite, addition of sulfuric acid to a pH of around 3 is desirable. Activation by chlorine has also been used (70, 137). *Sodium chlorate*, the raw material used in the preparation of chlorine dioxide, is not an active oxidant at normal pulp bleaching conditions. It can be activated by catalysts (78), especially vanadium pentoxide (95). However, bleaching with activated chlorate gives less good results and higher costs than chlorine dioxide bleaching (95).

2. ˙ REACTIONS

A. Inorganic reactions

The chlorine dioxide obtained from the generation contains 0–30% chlorine, varying with the efficiency and selectivity of the process (cf. Chapter 19), generally below 10% chlorine. It arrives at the bleachery in the form of a solution containing 10–15 g/l act. Cl. Sodium chlorite is sold in solid form containing 75–99 + % $NaClO_2$.

974

Chlorine dioxide is reduced in *acid* medium in the following manner (30), at least in principle and disregarding side reactions:

$$ClO_2 + 4\,H^+ + 5\,e^- = Cl^- + 2\,H_2O$$

and consequently gives 5 oxidation equivalents. Thus, 1 kg ClO_2 corresponds to $1 \times 5 \times 35.5/67.5 = 2.63$ kg act. Cl. In *alkaline* medium the main reaction (22) is

$$ClO_2 + e^- = ClO_2^-$$

involving only one oxidation equivalent, as the chlorite ion does not react further.

Chlorite has consequently to be acidified to become an active bleaching agent, and the chlorous acid formed is reduced according to the reaction (137):

$$HClO_2 + 3\,H^+ + 4\,e^- = Cl^- + 2\,H_2O$$

involving 4 oxidation equivalents. Consequently, 1 kg $NaClO_2$ corresponds to $1 \times 4 \times 35.5/90.5 = 1.57$ kg act. Cl. The strength of chlorous acid corresponds to a pK_a of 2.0 (1a, 49).

One of the intermediate stages at the reduction of chlorous acid is hypochlorous acid, as

$$HClO_2 + 2\,H^+ + 2\,e^- = HClO + H_2O$$

The latter has a higher oxidation potential and can convert chlorous acid into chlorine dioxide in the reaction

$$HClO + 2\,HClO_2 = 2\,ClO_2 + H_2O + H^+ + Cl^-$$

It is thus evident that in chlorine dioxide bleaching, chlorite, or rather chlorous acid, is also involved, and in acid chlorite bleaching chlorine dioxide also takes a part in the reactions. This explains the similarities of the two methods as regards reaction temperatures and times needed, as well as the corrosion troubles occurring. However, as will be demonstrated in a following section, the treatments do not give entirely identical results. It is also obvious that activation of sodium chlorite could be made by the addition of chlorine or hypochlorite instead of an acid, at the same time utilizing the cheaper oxidation equivalents of chlorine, and therefore to be preferred in technical bleaching. Addition of hypochlorite has also been logically suggested as a means of utilizing all 5 oxidation equivalents of chlorine dioxide also in alkaline bleaching (137).

As in the case of hypochlorite bleaching, chlorate formation occurs as an undesirable side reaction, according to the following equation:

$$2\,ClO_2 + 2\,OH^- = ClO_2^- + ClO_3^- + H_2O$$

Evidently, this reaction should become more remarkable at alkaline chlorine dioxide bleaching. Similarly, chlorine dioxide and hypochlorous acid form chlorate in neutral and alkaline medium:

$$2\,ClO_2 + HClO + 3\,OH^- = 2\,ClO_3^- + Cl^- + 2\,H_2O$$

Chlorate is also formed from chlorite in acid medium:

$$4 \ HClO_2 = 2 \ ClO_2 + HClO_3 + HCl + H_2O$$

B. Lignin reactions

The reactions of chlorine dioxide with lignin have been studied with the aid of model compounds, as well as with lignin preparations and wood meal. Aromatic substances containing phenolic groups were early found to be rapidly degraded under the formation of colored quinoid compounds, which are further oxidized to carbon dioxide and organic acids such as oxalic, maleic and formic (115). Chlorine dioxide treatment of diphenols such as pyrocatechol yields small amounts of chlorine-containing compounds in addition to oxalic and maleic acid (115). 'Chlorite lignin' isolated from the solution after a chlorite holocellulose preparation of slash pine (8) and black spruce (56, 86) has been found to contain chlorine in the 6- or 5-position, as well as a reduced methoxyl content. Acid solutions of chlorite react more slowly with model compounds and lignosulfonate (30), but little difference is experienced in the final result, as chlorine dioxide is formed during the reaction through the intermediate formation of hypochlorous acid from chlorous acid and their interaction. The chlorine substituents also indicate that the intermediately formed hypochlorous acid gives chlorine to react with lignin. Chlorine dioxide and chlorite oxidation of lignin have been found to partly eliminate the absorption maximum at 280 mμ, suggesting a destruction of the aromatic system (1b, 92). The same treatments of model compounds, lignin preparations and wood meal (29a, 92a, 113) were found to lead to demethylation and elimination of the aromatic structure by at least three principal mechanisms, namely o- and p-quinone formation as well as ring opening, Figure 14.52. Model compounds containing only etherified diphenol structures, in contrast react only very slowly at room temperature (29a, 92a, 113), which also probably explains the incomplete demethylation experienced with lignin preparations. On the whole, the reaction mechanism closely resembles that outlined for hypochlorite oxidation of lignin in Figure 14.27, i.e. an oxidative peeling starting from the guaiacyl-containing monomers, with the possible exception that chlorine formed during the reaction may help to create new guaiacyl units according to the reactions outlined in Figure 14.12. However, it should be stressed that these conclusions mainly refer to chlorine dioxide reaction at room temperature, with comparatively unchanged lignin, such as applied in the first-stage bleaching of sulfite pulp in special cases. In a finishing bleaching stage for high brightness, the normal application of chlorine dioxide, the residual lignin is probably comparatively condensed and inaccessible, and more severe conditions, 60–70°C, are necessary. This is likely to involve degradation also of molecules containing little free phenolic hydroxyls, a course which can be conceived also for hypochlorite at high temperature. However, it is the great merit of chlorine dioxide, that such severe conditions can be allowed without endangering the carbohydrates.

976

C. Carbohydrate reactions

Chlorine dioxide in acid medium seems to be completely inactive towards carbohydrates (94, 108, 115). Not even their reducing aldehyde end groups are converted to carboxyls at normal bleaching conditions. Technical chlorine dioxide, containing small amounts of chlorine, effects a limited carboxyl formation (108). When applied in large excess and at high temperature, aliphatic compounds have been found to react with chlorine dioxide, and then carbonyl compounds much more readily than alcohols (122). Preoxidized carbohydrate monomers could thus be expected to degrade by chlorine dioxide in the bleaching, but undamaged molecules only to a very slight extent.

In contrast, acid chlorite solution rapidly converts aldehyde groups to carboxyls (57, 80). The active reagent is with all probability chlorous acid, as the oxidation is rapidly diminished on increasing pH. Possibly oxidation is preceded by an esterification similar to that suggested for hypochlorous acid oxidation. Neutral or alkaline chlorite solutions are also inactive towards aldehyde groups.

Alkaline chlorine dioxide solutions are more active towards carbohydrates. The reason for this is not known, possibly there is an intermediate formation of hypochlorite. Anyway, not only aldehyde groups are converted to carboxyls, but new reducing groups are formed and chain degradation occurs (94).

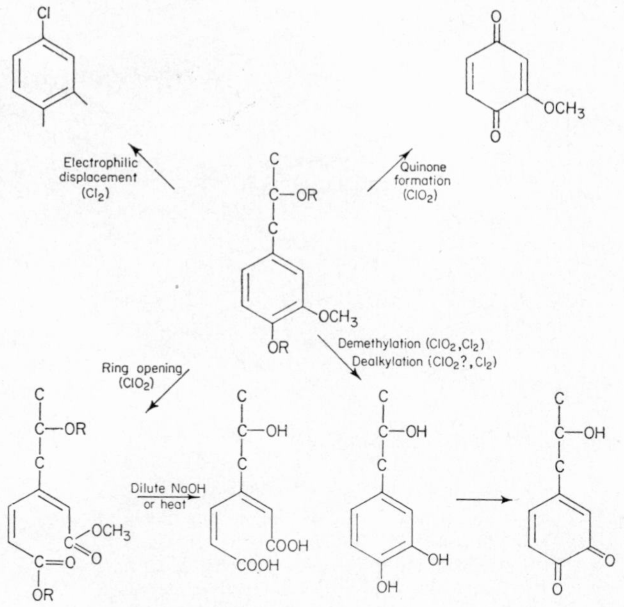

Fig. 14.52. Reactions of lignin with chlorine dioxide (Sarkanen *et al*)

The carboxyl formation from aldehyde groups on acid chlorite treatment causes an apparent slight increase in the viscosity of the pulp. This effect is obtained as the carbohydrate chains are stabilized against the degrading action of the alkaline copper ammonia or amine solutions. When DP is determined by nitrate viscosity this effect is not observed. Chlorine dioxide does not have the same alkali-stabilizing action, as seen from Table 14.5 (30).

The oxidation of aldehyde groups with chlorite also has some interest for the hot alkali purification reactions, cf. Chapter 15.

It is of interest to compare the influence of various oxidants on the carbohydrates with their oxidation potentials at different pH, Figure 14.53 (47, 49, 121, cf. 13a). There is some disagreement in the literature as

Table 14.5. Effect of chlorite and chlorine dioxide oxidation on pulp viscosity

Pulp treatment	Cuoxam viscosity, cP TAPPI	Nitrate viscosity, DP
Periodate oxidation only	26	1,340
ibid., followed by chlorite	51	1,260
ibid., followed by chlorine dioxide	26	1,320
Over-chlorination only	15	820
ibid., followed by chlorite	20	765
ibid., followed by chlorine dioxide	16	815

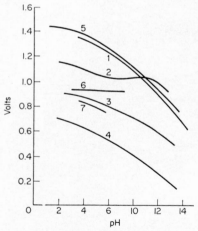

Fig. 14.53. Redox potentials of bleaching agents. (1) sodium hypochlorite (Solvay), (2) chlorine dioxide (Solvay), (3) sodium chlorite (Solvay), (4) sodium peroxide (Solvay). (5) sodium hypochlorite (Hisey–Koon), (6) chlorine dioxide (Holst), (7) sodium chlorite (Holst)

to the absolute levels of the oxidation potentials, as seen in the figure, but the general trends are the same, i.e. a decrease at increased pH for hypochlorite, chlorite and peroxide but a fairly constant value for chlorine dioxide. This is well in agreement with the concept that the acid forms are the active oxidants. However, when comparing the redox potentials with the actual carbohydrate degradation observed during the bleaching of sulfite or kraft pulp, Figures 14.54–55 (94), it is obvious that there is no direct connection between the redox potential and the carbohydrate degradation. Some of the disagreement can be explained by the influence of the lignin, since a constant amount of oxidant was charged. For instance, some of

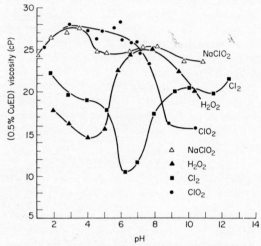

Fig. 14.54. Effect of pH on the viscosity of sulfite pulp with four bleaching agents (Rapson)

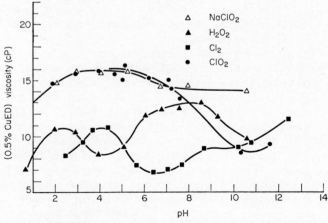

Fig. 14.55. Effect of pH on the viscosity of kraft pulp with four bleaching agents (Rapson)

979

the decrease in degradation on decreasing the pH of the hypochlorite solution below pH 6 may depend on the increased consumption of chlorine in the rapid substitution reaction of lignin and the subsequent oxidation of the chlorolignin, leaving less oxidant to the carbohydrate degradation. Other phenomena need to be explained differently. The degradation of the pulp on chlorine dioxide bleaching at pH 10 does not depend on an increased oxidation potential of chlorine dioxide. The redox potential of chlorine dioxide in acid solution, where no degradation is obtained, is as high as that of a hypochlorite solution at pH 8 (or 10), which causes appreciable degradation. Chlorous acid–chlorite has considerably higher oxidation potential than peroxide, but causes no degradation, whereas the degradation by the peroxides at comparable conditions is appreciable. Obviously, factors such as formation of intermediate compounds prior to oxidation, have to be considered (91). The swelling of the fiber structure at increased pH may also be of consequence, for instance on chlorine dioxide oxidation at the alkaline side, or on hypochlorous acid oxidation in the pH range 4–6, where the maximum degradation occurs at higher pH than the maximum concentration of hypochlorous acid. Redox potentials are therefore a poor guide to the action of an oxidant in pulp bleaching, which is natural, since they refer only to reversible reactions.

3. INFLUENCE OF REACTION CONDITIONS ON PULP YIELD AND PROPERTIES

As in the case of hypochlorite oxidation, chlorine dioxide and chlorite oxidation, as applied in technical bleaching, does not remove much substance, and therefore, the variation in pulp yield is not great on varying the reaction conditions. It has been claimed that the yields obtained with chlorine dioxide are somewhat higher than with hypochlorite, but the difference must be negligible for normal pulps. When applied in the first stage, chlorine dioxide, like chlorine, decreases the yield in an amount slightly exceeding the lignin content.

Fairly little has been published on the influence of reaction conditions on pulp properties in chlorine dioxide and chlorite bleaching. As far as is known, temperature, time and consistency mainly influence the consumption of oxidant, without any specific effects at constant oxidant consumption. The main variables therefore are pH and chemical charge and consumption, with the consistency usually kept at medium level, temperature at 60–70°C and time at 3–4 h, giving substantially complete reaction. At varying pH, but constant chemical charge and other conditions, the variations of oxidant consumption and pulp properties are seen in Figures 14.56–59 for chlorine dioxide and chlorite bleaching of sulfite and kraft pulps (94). For comparison, Figures 14.60–61 for peroxide bleaching are included; compare also Figures 14.47–48 for hypochlorite bleaching. In buffered chlorine dioxide bleaching, maximum brightness is obtained at pH 6, in spite of the consumption of oxidant decreasing at increased pH from pH 3–4 onwards. Degradation is obtained on increasing pH from neutrality. In chlorite bleaching, maximum brightness is obtained at pH 4, brightness and rate of reaction rapidly decreasing at higher pH. It is remarkable that the decrease in bleaching effect does not appear in the range pH 2–4, as the pK_a of chlorous acid is 2.0.

At constant charge (but undetermined consumption) of chlorine dioxide, the brightness increased during the first 3 h at 68°C on the bleaching of a prebleached kraft pulp and then remained almost constant (39). Increased consistency in the interval 8–20% caused a slight increase in

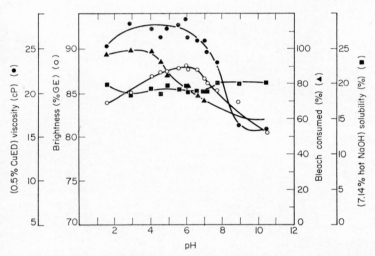

Fig. 14.56. Effect of pH on bleaching chlorinated and extracted sulfite pulp with chlorine dioxide (Rapson)

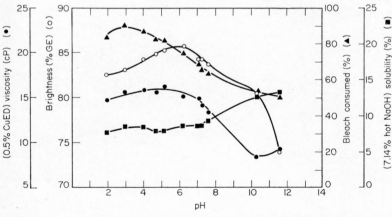

Fig. 14.57. Effect of pH on bleaching with chlorine dioxide a kraft pulp purified in a preliminary stage (Rapson)

981

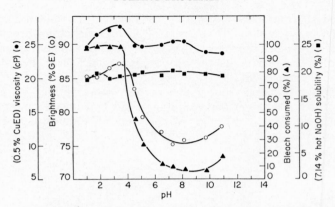

Fig. 14.58. Effect of pH on bleaching sulfite pulp with sodium chlorite (Rapson)

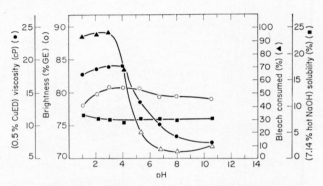

Fig. 14.59. Effect of pH on bleaching kraft pulp with sodium chlorite (Rapson)

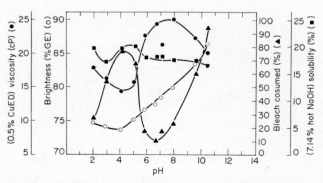

Fig. 14.60. Effect of pH on bleaching chlorinated and extracted sulfite pulp with peroxide (Rapson)

982

brightness up to 15% and then a slight decrease, probably because of unsatisfactory mixing. Increased temperature in the interval 40–100°C caused an increase in brightness up to 82°C and then a slight decrease. Brightness stability, however, was better at 100°C. Most of these effects are probably explained by influenced rate of reaction. There have been claims that pressure would influence the rate of reaction and the bleaching result, as the escaping tendency of the chlorine dioxide from the solution is decreased by increased pressure. However, this is not so in the interval of 0–2 kp/cm² (39). The paper strength was unaffected by the treatment at all the varying conditions mentioned above, with the possible exception of a slight decrease when bleaching at temperatures above 80°C. However, on the addition of sodium hydroxide of more than 1.5 kg ptp (above pH 4), there was a decided decrease in strength, which became serious on the alkaline side. The brightness was at a maximum at around 1.5 kg ptp NaOH and decreased rapidly at higher alkali charges. The influence of the brightness level of the pulp entering the stage on the final brightness was also investigated and found to be small in the range of 67–77% GE, all pulps giving a final brightness of around 88% GE. This may not be generally true, and could be explained as a result of varying consumption at an excess charge, but the very fact that charges in excess of the demand do not damage the pulp makes the chlorine dioxide stage a 'leveler' of quality variations. The chlorite and chlorate formation on kraft pulp bleaching with chlorine dioxide at different pH is seen in Figure 14.62 (16). Oxidant consumption and brightness in this case decreased with increasing pH. However, if the chlorite formed is utilized in a subsequent stage, brightness maximum is obtained at about neutrality.

The influence of the chlorine dioxide charges on the brightness was in the above investigation found to be appreciable up to an amount of around 5.5 kg ptp ClO₂ or 15 kg ptp act. Cl and then negligible. Although further improvement is obtainable by increasing charge and temperature or time simultaneously, it is more effective to divide the chlorine dioxide stage

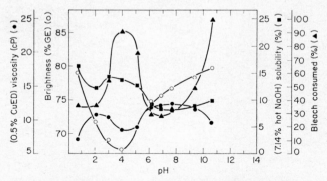

Fig. 14.61. Effect of pH on bleaching with peroxide a kraft pulp purified in a preliminary stage (Rapson)

983

into two, with an intermediate alkali stage to remove some oxidation products and make the remaining traces of coloring matter more accessible to oxidation. The alkali charge and the temperature of that stage noticeably influence the final brightness result. In the case of alkaline chlorine

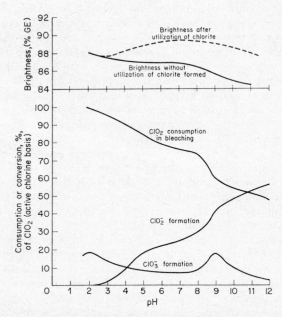

Fig. 14.62. Consumption of chlorine dioxide and formation of chlorite and chlorate when bleaching kraft pulp at varying pH. Brightness results in the same bleaching, as well as after utilization of the chlorite formed in a subsequent stage (Collin–Jonsson)

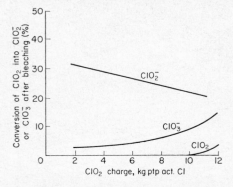

Fig. 14.63. Conversion of chlorine dioxide into chlorite or chlorate during the bleaching of kraft pulp at various charges (Collin–Jonsson)

984

dioxide bleaching, chlorate formation is suppressed by the addition of chlorine dioxide in repeated, small charges (16), as is evident from Figure 14.63, but this is impractical in modern, continuous tower bleaching.

Chlorate and chlorite formation in chlorine dioxide bleaching has been further studied to shed additional light on the question of optimal pH conditions. At otherwise equal conditions, pH 7.0 and pH 5.8 gave more rapid chlorine dioxide consumption than pH 3, but this was essentially due to more chlorate and chlorite formation (85a). These trends were obtained for all types of pulps, rich or poor in lignin or hemicelluloses, as well as with blank experiments without pulp. However, at pH 7.0 and

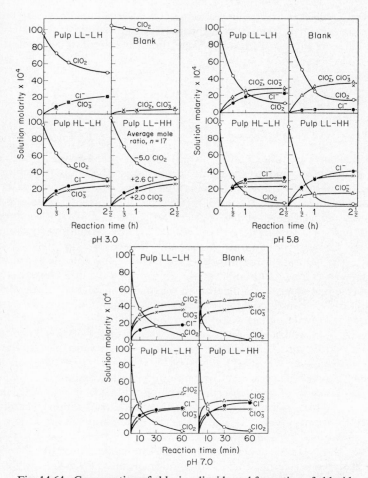

Fig. 14.64. Consumption of chlorine dioxide and formation of chloride, chlorite and chlorate during chlorine dioxide bleaching for 3 hours at 70°C of three different pulp types at three different pH's. LL, low lignin content; HL, high lignin content; LH, low hemicellulose content; HH, high hemicellulose content (Paulson)

pH 5.8, the chlorate and chlorite formation were approximately equivalent, whereas at pH 3 fairly little chlorite but considerable amounts of chlorate were formed, together with the ever-apparent chloride, Figure 14.64 (85a). These results were interpreted to mean that at the two high pH levels, lignin reacts with chlorine dioxide with the formation of chloride and the consumption of all five oxidation equivalents, at the same time as the disproportionation reaction to chlorate and chlorite:

$$ClO_2 + 5\ e^- \xrightarrow{\text{[Lignin]}} Cl^-$$

$$2\ ClO_2 + H_2O \xrightarrow{\text{[OH-]}} ClO_2^- + ClO_3^- + 2\ H^+$$

At low pH, however, the lignin reaction with chlorine dioxide was assumed to give only chlorite, which by disproportionation would regenerate half of the chlorine dioxide and at the same time yield chlorate and chloride:

$$ClO_2 + e^- \xrightarrow{\text{[Lignin]}} ClO_2^-$$

$$10\ ClO_2^- + 4\ H_2O + 3\ e^- \xrightarrow{\text{[H+]}} 5\ ClO_2 + 2\ ClO_3^- + 3\ Cl^- + 8\ OH^-$$

giving the net reaction:

$$5\ ClO_2 + 4\ H_2O + 13\ e^- \xrightarrow{\text{[H+, Lignin]}} 2\ ClO_3^- + 3\ Cl^- + 8\ OH^-$$

Another investigation (120a), working with prebleached sulfite and kraft pulps, after finding the same trends, suggested that the chlorate formation noticed at low pH (and high temperature) during chlorine dioxide bleaching, arises from the interaction of chlorine dioxide and lignin. Anyway, it can be stated that during chlorine dioxide bleaching at low natural pH, slightly less than half of the five oxidation equivalents available are lost in chlorate formation. Increasing the pH will not decrease the chlorate formation but will increase the chlorite formation, Figure 14.65 (120a). Although, therefore, chlorine dioxide bleaching will not represent as efficient a utilization of the oxidation equivalents available, in comparison with hypochlorite bleaching, its mild action on the carbohydrates at low pH makes it still a very valuable tool.

A kraft pulp which previously could not be brought up to a brightness of more than 80–85% GE without severe losses in strength, is, with the aid of chlorine dioxide, bleached to above 90% GE with a slight *improvement* in strength as compared to the corresponding unbleached pulp.

As in the case of hypochlorite bleaching, chlorine dioxide bleaching also gives higher brightness with sulfite than with kraft pulps. Therefore, even if chlorine dioxide has permitted the production of kraft pulps as white as normal hypochlorite-bleached sulfite pulps, there is still a span of 5–10% GE between superbleached grades of sulfite and kraft. Provided the mill water is clean enough, sulfite pulps of above 99% GE brightness can be obtained with the aid of chlorine dioxide though 94–96% GE are more normal values. The viscosity of the sulfite pulp is left almost unaffected, unless pH is increased by alkali addition, which is also the case of the content of oxidized groups.

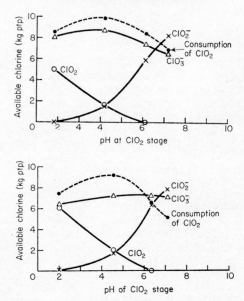

Fig. 14.65. Composition of waste liquor from chlorine dioxide bleaching of prebleached sulfite (above) and kraft (below) pulp at different pH levels (Soila *et al*)

The purity of the chlorine dioxide is only critical for the carbohydrates in the finishing stage with little residual lignin to eliminate the elemental chlorine present. As an initial stage (70a, 125, 136) and also in the bleaching of kraft pulp to a lower brightness (137), approximately corresponding to the first of two finishing chlorine dioxide stages, appreciable amounts of chlorine could be present in the chlorine dioxide, to no disadvantage for pulp quality and appreciable economic benefit. In the latter case, the stage is preferentially kept neutral or alkaline and is consequently a mixed chlorine dioxide–hypochlorite stage. However, one purpose of using chlorine dioxide as an initial stage is to avoid the chlorination of the pulp extractives, and in such a case, the presence of chlorine in the chlorine dioxide liquor must be avoided. This is not particularly difficult with most chlorine dioxide generation processes, cf. Chapter 19.

Additional information on chlorine dioxide bleaching is given in several papers (e.g. 11, 12, 93, 140), including surveys (11, 93) and experimental results. The improved brightness stability of pulps bleached with schedules including both chlorine dioxide and peroxide stages has been demonstrated (12).

Fewer studies have been published on the variables of chlorite bleaching (10, 12, 76, 85a, 120a, 124, 137). To keep the cost of chemicals within reasonable limits, fairly small amounts of chlorite must be charged and fairly small effects are consequently achieved.

987

REFERENCES

1. Arnold, G. C., et al., *Paper Trade J.*, **107**, No. 10, 32 (1938).
1a. Barnett, B., Dissertation, Univ. California, 1935.
1b. Barton, J. S., *Tappi*, **33**, 496 (1950).
2. Bethge, P. O., et al., *Svensk Papperstid.*, **55**, 44 (1952).
3. Bevan, E. J., and C. F. Cross, *J. Chem. Soc.*, **38**, 666 (1880); TAPPI Standard T 17 m.
4. Bhujang, K. S., and G. M. Nabar, *J. Sci. Ind. Res. (India)*, **8 B**, No. 6, 103 (1949).
5. Björkqvist, K. J., et al., *Svensk Papperstid.*, **56**, 734 (1953).
6. Brauns, F. E., *Paper Trade J.*, **103**, No. 6, 36 (1936).
7. Browning, B. L., in L. E. Wise and E. C. Jahn, eds., *Wood Chemistry*, Reinhold, New York 1952, p. 1238.
8. Bublitz, W. J., Dissertation, Appleton, Wis., 1949.
8a. Campbell, J., and L. O. Rolliston, *Swed. Pat.* 89,292 (1937).
9. Carmody, W. R., and J. S. Mears, *Paper Trade J.*, **106**, No. 20, 38 (1938).
10. Carr, R. L., and K. S. MacLeod, *Tappi*, **36**, No. 5, 195A (1953).
11. Casciani, F., *Paper Trade J.*, **136**, No. 10, 21 (1953).
12. Casciani, F., and G. K. Storin, *Tappi*, **33**, 588 (1950).
13. Cederquist, K. N., *U.S. Pat.* 2,502,410 (1950).
13a. Chene, M., and P. Froment, *Papier, Carton et Cellulose*, **10**, No. 6, 135 (1962).
14. Clibbens, D. A., et al., *J. Textile Inst.*, **16**, T13 (1925).
15. Clibbens, D. A., and B. P. Ridge, *Shirley Inst. Mem.*, **6**, 1 (1927); *J. Textile Inst.*, **18**, T 135 (1927).
16. Collin, P. H., and J. H. Jonsson, *Swed. Pat.* Appl. 2346/48.
17. Coster, N. W., and R. I. Thieme, *Tech Assoc. Papers*, **24**, 204 (1941).
18. Curran, C. E., et al., *Paper Trade J.*, **80**, No. 16, 51 (1925); **87**, No. 22, 44 (1928).
19. Dailey, J. D., *Paper Mill News*, **78**, No. 13, 56 (1955).
20. Davidson, G. F., *Shirley Inst. Mem.*, **12**, 1 (1933).
21. Davidson, G. F., and T. P. Nevell, *J. Textile Inst.*, **47**, T439 (1956).
22. Day, G. A., and B. G. Hoos, *Swed. Pat.* 138,540 (1952).
23. Dence, C., and K. Sarkanen, *Tappi*, **43**, 87 (1960).
24. Diedrichs, B. E. J., *Swed. Pat.* 140,997 (1950).
24a. Duncan, E. P., and W. H. Rapson, *Pulp Paper*, **34**, No. 11, 100 (1960).
25. Eriksson, E., and L. Stockman, *Svensk Papperstid.*, **59**, 663 (1956).
26. Erdmann, E., *J. Prakt. Chem.*, **22**, 282 (1880).
27. Fotiev, S. A., *Pulp Paper Mag. Can.*, **39**, 749 (1938).
28. Freudenberg, K., et al., *Ber.*, **62**, 1554 (1929).
29. Genberg, G. P., et al., *Pulp Paper Mag. Can.*, **28**, 167 (1929).
29a. Gianola, G., and J. Meybeck, *Atip Bull.*, **1**, 25 (1960).
29b. Giertz, H. W., *Svensk Papperstid.*, **48**, 317 (1945).
30. Giertz, H. W., Medd. CCL, Stockholm, **B10** (1946); *Tappi*, **34**, 214 (1951).
31. Giertz, H. W., *Svensk Papperstid.*, **46**, 152 (1943); **48**, 485 (1945); *Tappi*, **34**, 209 (1951).
32. Grangaard, D. H., *Tappi*, **39**, 270 (1956).
33. Hägglund, E., *U.S. Pat.* 1,792,009 (1931).
34. Hägglund, E., and H. Urban, *Acta Acad. Aboensis Math. Phys.*, **5**, 4 (1929).

35. Hägglund, E., *et al.*, Medd. CCL, Stockholm, **B7** (1944); *Svensk Papperstid.*, **47**, 226 (1944).
36. Haller, J. F., and W. W. Northgraves, *Tappi*, **38**, 199 (1955).
37. Hamburger, R., and S. Kaesz, *Brit. Pat.* 209,073 (1924), *Ger. Pat.* 413,338 (1925), *U.S. Pat.* 1,580,136 (1926).
38. Harrison, W. D., *Tappi*, **36**, No. 5, 142A (1953); and in TAPPI Monograph No. 10, New York 1953, p. 119.
39. Harrison, W. D., and C. R. Calkins, *Tappi*, **38**, 641 (1955).
40. Hedborg, F., *Svensk Papperstid.*, **46**, 381 (1943).
41. Heiwinkel, H., and E. Hägglund, *Svensk Papperstid.*, **43**, 391 (1940).
42. Henderson, J. T., *J. Am. Chem. Soc.*, **79**, 5304 (1957).
43. Hentola, Y., and J. E. Stone, *Tappi*, **40**, 396 (1957).
43a. Herbst, J. H. E., *Tappi*, **45**, 833 (1962).
44. Herbst, J. H. E., and H. Krässig, *Tappi*, **42**, 660 (1959).
45. Heuser, E., and R. Sieber, *Angew. Chem.*, **26**, 801 (1913).
46. Hibbert, H., *et al.*, *Paper Trade J.*, **113**, No. 24, 33 (1941); *Tech. Assoc. Papers*, **24**, 179 (1941).
46a. Hinrichs, D. D., *Tappi*, **45**, 765 (1962).
47. Hisey, W. O., and C. M. Koon, *Paper Trade J.*, **103**, No. 6, 36 (1936).
48. Hochberger, E., *Papierfabrik.*, **26**, 66 (1929).
49. Holst, G., *Svensk Papperstid.*, **48**, 23 (1945).
50. Ingham, J. W., and J. Morrison, *J. Chem. Soc.*, **1933**, 1200.
51. Ivancic, A., and S. Rydholm, *Svensk Papperstid.*, **62**, 554 (1959).
52. Jackson, E. L., and C. S. Hudson, *J. Am. Chem. Soc.*, **58**, 378 (1936); **59**, 994, 2049 (1937); **60**, 989 (1938).
53. Jakowin, A. A., *Z. Physik. Chem.*, **29**, 613 (1899).
54. Jappe, N. R., *Tappi*, **41**, 224 (1958).
54a. Jayme, G., and L. Rothamel, *Papierfabrik.*, **40**, No. 7/8, 26 (1942).
55. Jayme, G., and L. Rothamel, *Cellulosechem.*, **21**, 7 (1943).
56. Jayne, J. E., *Tappi*, **36**, 571 (1953).
57. Jeanes, A., and H. S. Isbell, *J. Research Natl Bur. Std.*, **27**, 125 (1941).
58. Kauffmann, H., *Papierfabrik.*, **28**, 557 (1930).
59. Keller, E. L., and P. B. Borlew, *Tappi*, **38**, 379 (1955).
60. Kenner, J., *Chem. Ind.*, **1955**, 727.
61. Kenyon, W. O., *et al.*, *J. Am. Chem. Soc.*, **64**, 121, 127 (1942); **69**, 342, 347, 349, 355 (1947).
62. Komarov, F. P., and N. V. Lebedev, *Zellstoff Papier*, **20**, 211 (1940).
63. Kraft, F., *Papierfabrik.*, **36**, 429 (1938).
64. Kress, O., and E. H. Voigtman, *Paper Trade J.*, **97**, No. 7, 29 (1933).
65. Larson, L. L., *Paper Trade J.*, **113**, No. 21, 25 (1941).
66. Lautsch, W., and G. Piazolo, *Ber.*, **73**, 317 (1940).
67. Lekander, K. E., and L. Stockman, *Svensk Papperstid.*, **58**, 775 (1955).
67a. Lewin, M., *Angew Chem.*, **66**, 176 (1954).
68. Lewis, G. N., and M. Randall, *Thermodynamics*, McGraw-Hill, New York 1923, p. 508.
69. Lidman-Safwat, S., and O. Theander, *Svensk Papperstid.*, **61**, 42 (1958).
70. Logan, J. O., *Swed. Pat.* 98,583 (1940).
70a. Logan, J. O., *U.S. Pat.* 2,235,837 (1941).
71. Lorås, V., and F. Löschbrandt, *Norsk Skogind.*, **10**, 402 (1956); **15**, 302 (1961).
72. Löschbrandt, F., *Bleaching of Sulfate Pulp*, TAPPI Monograph, New York 1941.

73. Löschbrandt, F., and C. V. Wetlesen, *Svensk Papperstid.*, **61**, 656 (1958).
74. Lyon, M. G., and A. C. Salisbury, *Tappi*, **43**, 349 (1960).
75. McCarthy, J. L., et al., *Pulp Paper Mag. Can.*, **50**, No. 5, 88 (1949).
76. MacLeod, K. S., *Pulp Paper Mag. Can.*, **51**, No. 3, 156 (1950).
77. MacMillan, J. R., *U.S. Pat.* 1,547,138 (1925).
78. Marpillero, P., *Tappi*, **41**, No. 5, 213A (1958).
79. Meller, A., in TAPPI Monograph No. 10, New York 1953, p. 41.
80. Meller, A., *Tappi*, **38**, 682 (1955).
81. Ohlsson, K. E., 1951 unpublished.
81a. O'Meara, D., and C. E. J. Mair, *Tappi*, **45**, 578 (1962).
82. Opferman, E., *Ger. Pat.* 436,804 (1927).
83. Opferman, E., and E. Hochberger, *Die Bleiche des Zellstoffs*, Berlin 1935–1936, Part I, p. 237.
84. Parsons, S. R., and H. J. Lausman, *Tappi*, **34**, 97 (1951).
85. Paulson, J. C., *Tappi*, **41**, 655 (1958); **42**, 683 (1959).
85a. Paulson, J. C., *Tappi*, **45**, 933 (1962).
86. Pearl, I. A., *J. Am. Chem. Soc.*, **68**, 916 (1946).
87. Phelps, M. W., and J. Schuber, *Paper Trade J.*, **106**, No. 8, 126 (1938).
88. Polcin, J., *Chem. Zvesti*, **10**, 450 (1956); **12**, 60 (1958).
89. Pulp Purification Session, 40th Annual TAPPI Meeting, 1955; *Tappi*, **38**, No. 11, 163A (1955).
90. Purves, C. B., and G. D. Thorn, cited in L. E. Wise and E. C. Jahn, eds., *Wood Chemistry*, 2nd Ed., Reinhold, New York 1952, p. 1049.
91. Purves, C. B., et al., *Tech. Assoc. Papers*, **28**, 178 (1945).
92. Purves, C. B., et al., *Pulp Paper Mag. Can.*, **56**, No. 5, 117 (1955); *Ind. Eng.*
92a. Purves, C. B., et al., *Can. J. Chem.*, **33**, 68, 82 (1955).
Chem., **49**, 1394 (1957).
93. Rapson, W. H., *Paper Mill News*, **77**, No. 34, 15 (1954); *Paper Ind.*, **36**, No. 6, 575, No. 10, 998 (1954/55).
94. Rapson, W. H., *Tappi*, **39**, 284 (1956).
95. Rapson, W. H., et al., *Tappi*, **42**, 642 (1959).
96. Rashback, H., and F. H. Yorston, *Forest Prod. Lab. Can.*, *Quart. Rev.*, No. 7, 12 (1931).
97. Richtzenhain, H., and B. Alfredsson, *Acta Chem. Scand.*, **7**, 1177 (1953); **8**, 1519 (1954); **10**, 719 (1956).
98. Roe, R. B., *Ind. Eng. Chem.*, **16**, 1808 (1924); TAPPI Standard T 202 m-45.
98a. Rollinson, S. M., *Tappi*, **38**, 625 (1955).
99. Rosén, W. O., *Swed. Pat.* 118,790 (1938).
100. Rue, J. D., *Paper Trade J.*, **104**, No. 25, 19 (1937).
101. Rue, J. D., *Trans. Electrochem. Soc.*, **73**, 137 (1938).
102. Rue, J. D., and J. S. Sconce, *Paper Trade J.*, **95**, No. 17, 54 (1932).
103. Rydholm, S. A., unpublished.
104. Samuelsen, S., *World's Paper Trade Rev.*, **106**, 1284 (1936).
105. Samuelsen, S., *Proc. Tech. Sect., Paper Makers' Assoc. Gt. Britain, Ireland*, **17**, No. 11, 293 (1937).
106. Samuelson, O., *Svensk Kem. Tidskr.*, **59**, 105 (1947).
107. Samuelson, O., et al., *Svensk Kem. Tidskr.*, **61**, 234 (1949).
108. Samuelson, O., et al., *Svensk Papperstid.*, **53**, 155 (1950); *Svensk Kem. Tidskr.*, **62**, 197 (1950).
109. Samuelson, O., and C. Ramsel, *Svensk Papperstid.*, **53**, 155 (1950).
110. Samuelson, O., and L. A. Wikström, *Svensk Papperstid.*, **63**, 543 (1960).

111. Sarkanen, K. V., and C. W. Dence, *J. Org. Chem.*, **25**, 715 (1960).
112. Sarkanen, K. V., and R. W. Strauss, *Tappi*, **44**, 459 (1961).
113. Sarkanen, K. V., *et al.*, *Tappi*, **44**, 465 (1961); **45**, 24, 29 (1962).
114. Sarkar, P. B., *Sci. Cult. (Calcutta)*, **2**, 551 (1937).
115. Schmidt, E., *et al.*, *Ber.*, **54**, 1860 (1921); **55**, 1529 (1922); **56**, 25 (1923); **58**, 1394 (1925); *Cellulosechem.*, **11**, 73 (1930); **12**, 201 (1931).
115a. Schmidt, E., *Ger. Pat.* 331,907 (1921).
115b. Schmidt, E., *Brit. Pat.* 191,357 (1923).
116. Schmidt-Nielsen, S., *Papir-J.*, **26**, 83 (1938).
117. Sihtola, H., and R. Gustafsson, *Paperi Puu*, **32**, 295 (1950).
118. Sihtola, H., and E. Kaila, *Paperi Puu*, **36**, 341 (1954).
119. Silov, E. A., and G. V. Kubinskaja, *Bull. Acad. Sci. USSR*, II, No. 3–4 (1935).
120. Smith, J. W., and W. L. Thornburg, *Tappi*, **43**, 596 (1960).
120a. Soila, R., *et al.*, *Svensk Papperstid.*, **65**, 632 (1962).
121. Solvay Process Div., Allied Chem. and Dye Corp., cited in TAPPI Monograph No. 10, New York 1953, p. 110.
122. Somsen, R. A., *Tappi*, **43**, 154, 157 (1960).
123. Stakheva-Kaverzneva, E. D., *et al.*, *Bull. Acad. Sci. USSR, Div. Chem. Sci.*, **1952**, 681; Trans. 13th Int. Congr. Pure Appl. Chem., Stockholm 1953, p. 328; cf. *Tekstilna Prom.*, **14**, No. 3, 31 (1954).
124. Stone, W. A., and J. G. Matarese, *Pulp Paper Mag. Can.*, **52**, No. 1, 85 (1951).
125. Stone, W. A., and J. G. Matarese, *U.S. Pat.* 2,741,537 (1956).
126. Sunesson, E. B. F., *U.S. Pat.* 2,140,863 (1939).
127. Swartz, J. N., *Pulp Paper Mag. Can.*, **47**, No. 3, 203 (1946).
128. Swedish Standard CCA 9.
129. TAPPI Standards T 214 m-50.
130. Taylor, M. C., and J. F. White, *Swed. Pat.* 87,402 (1936).
131. Teeple, H. O., and R. L. Adams, *Tappi*, **38**, 44 (1955).
132. Theander, O., *Svensk Papperstid.*, **61**, 581 (1958); *Svensk Kem. Tidskr.*, **71**, 1 (1959).
133. Trivedi, S. A., *et al.*, *Paper Ind. Paper World*, **28**, 1443 (1948).
134. Valeur, C., *Svensk Papperstid.*, **54**, 613 (1951).
135. Vincent, G. P., *U.S. Pat.* 2,129,719 (1938); *Swed. Pat.* 101,127 (1941).
136. Vincent, G. P., *U.S. Pat.* 2,166,330; 2,235,837; *Swed. Pat.* 127,231 (1949).
137. Vincent, G. P., *et al.*, *Ind. Eng. Chem.*, **32**, 898 (1940); **34**, 782 (1942); *Tech. Assoc. Papers*, **23**, 215 (1940); *Paper Trade J.*, **115**, No. 21, 25 (1942); **121**, No. 20, 25 (1945); **124**, No. 26, 53 (1947).
137a. Virkola, N. E., *et al.*, *Svensk Papperstid.*, **62**, 477 (1959).
138. Voelker, M. H., and M. N. May, *Tappi*, **42**, 514 (1959).
139. Weiss, J. J., *Angew. Chem.*, **44**, 488 (1931).
140. Wenzl, H., *Holzforschung*, **1**, 65 (1947).
141. Whistler, R. L., *et al.*, *J. Am. Chem. Soc.*, **78**, 4704 (1956); **79**, 6460 (1957).
142. White, J. F., *Swed. Pat.* 93,525 (1938).
143. Whitney, R. P., and J. E. Vivian, *Ind. Eng. Chem.*, **33**, 741 (1941).
144. Wiley, A. L., *Paper Mill News*, **78**, No. 13, 64 (1955).

15

CARBOHYDRATE-REMOVING METHODS

I. General Principles of Alkaline Pulp Purification

Carbohydrate removal from wood pulp by alkaline extraction is practised with dissolving pulps and sometimes also with paper pulps. In the latter case, the paper properties are modified in several respects, as the hemicellulose content decreases. By extraction of a pulp in cold alkali lye of increasing strength (26) as well as by hot alkali purification (39), tensile and bursting strength decrease, whereas tear strength in the case of hot alkali treatment increases considerably. Opacity, bulk, softness, and brightness stability to heat also increase by alkaline removal of carbohydrates, and these properties are desired in papers for plastics and for printing. However, some of these characteristics may to some extent be achieved by hydrolytic dissolution of carbohydrates, as occurs on prolonged sulfite cooking, and this is a less expensive method. In those cases where alkaline extraction is to be preferred to hydrolysis, e.g. when tear and folding endurance should be kept at a reasonably high level, alkaline extraction in the *cooking* is less expensive, and kraft cooking or a sodium carbonate cooking stage subsequent to sulfite delignification may be applied. Therefore, the main interest in carbohydrate removal in bleaching operations lies in the purification of dissolving pulps. Naturally, sulfite pulps are more sensitive to alkaline treatment than alkaline-cooked pulps, but prehydrolysis–kraft pulps are also subjected to purification treatments.

The carbohydrates to be removed by alkaline purification are mainly hemicelluloses, although some simultaneous losses of cellulose are unavoidable because of the similarity in structure and reactivity. To a certain extent these losses of easily accessible cellulose are even desired in order to obtain a more homogeneous chain length distribution in the remaining pulp. The carbohydrate removal is often combined with the removal of lignin and resin in the same alkali stage, but may also be carried out as a separate stage subsequent to the lignin removal. More seldom the alkali purification is carried out on the unbleached pulp as the first bleaching stage, but this is sometimes motivated when deresination of hardwood sulfite pulps is combined with the carbohydrate removal. Alkaline purification of the unbleached pulp is otherwise preferentially done in the digester as is the case of kraft or carbonate cooking stages (cf. Chapter 9). In some rare cases, viscosity control is a function of the alkaline extraction stage, either in very high temperature purification (7), or in cold alkali lye extraction using oxidants and possibly oxidation catalysts (4, 48). To affect the reactivity of the fibers by alkaline swelling is another less frequent function of the treatment (44, 55).

However, the main objective is the removal of undesirable carbohydrate molecules, which influence either the processing behaviour of the pulp or the quality of the final product.

The undesirable carbohydrate components are not quite well-defined. Principally they consist of the residual hemicelluloses left after cooking, glu-comannan and glucuronoxylan. However, some hemicellulose components might be tolerated in the pulp-using dissolving process, provided their physical and chemical character is suitable for the particular process and end use. On the other hand, some of the cellulose molecules might be too short to suit the properties of certain final products, mainly cord rayon and high tenacity staple fibers, and should therefore be removed. Purific-ation should thus be adjusted to the need of the dissolving process, and pulp grades of widely varying purity are sold. It thus involves the removal of suitable amounts of intermicellar and short-chain micellar material. Part of the intermicellar material is easily accessible and soluble, whereas other parts are more intimately mixed with the microfibrillar structure and need considerable swelling of the latter for their removal. The same is true for the main part of the fragmented cellulose. As discussed in Chapter 9, adsorption of glucomannan to the cellulose microfibril surfaces in the sulfite processes, and of glucuronoxylan in the kraft process, occurs to a considerable extent, varying with the pulping conditions, and this material is particularly difficult to remove. Determination of the non-cellulosic constituents by chromatography or pentosan analysis prior to and after the treatment is one principal way of judging the result of the purification. The most usual manner of expressing the degree of purification is, however, to report the *alphacellulose content*. The more detailed discussion of this concept is given in Chapter 20 on pulp characterization and in Chapter 9.III on multistage cooking. Originally, the alphacellulose determin-ation was worked out to predict the yield of the viscose process, but as usually carried out, alphacellulose is not the portion insoluble in 18% NaOH but in a lye of a concentration varying from 18 to 0% NaOH, as all intermediate concentrations are passed during the washing after steep-ing in 18% lye. Therefore, similar methods of analysis have also been worked out, which describe the true solubility in 18%, 10% or any other sodium hydroxide concentration. Still, alphacellulose is the main concept used for the designation of the pulp grade of dissolving pulps, and its changes with purification conditions is of the greatest technical and econ-omic interest.

Alkaline purification of pulp can be carried out in two principally different ways, *cold* and *hot alkaline purification*. (The terms cold and hot refining are also used, but the word refining should be reserved for the mechanical fiberizing of untreated or chemically softened chips in refiners.) Cold purification consists of a treatment of the pulp in a fairly concentrated lye at room temperature or slightly higher or lower, whereby intermicellar and some intramicellar swelling takes place, permitting short chain material and microfibril fragments to dissolve. Thus, cold purification mainly involves physical changes, and little alkali is consumed in chemical reactions. Hot alkaline purification on the other hand utilizes chemical reactions as well, in a completely intermicellar process. The more accessible parts of the fiber react in dilute alkali at elevated temperature under formation of organic acids which dissolve in the lye. Both processes have their advantages and disadvantages. Combinations of the two types of treatment are therefore also used.

II. Cold Alkali Purification

1. DESCRIPTION OF PROCESS AND REACTIONS

Figure 4.27b shows a diagram of alkali cellulose formation at room temperature and varying alkali concentration. Obviously, there is a transition to a crystal lattice different from that of cellulose, which is complete in lyes of 17–18% NaOH and commences at around 10% NaOH. This intramicellar swelling is, however, preceded by an intermicellar swelling at somewhat lower concentrations. The latter form of swelling is causing the largest changes of the fiber dimensions and the largest sorption of water, Figures 15.1–2. As the non-cellulosic carbohydrates are almost exclusively

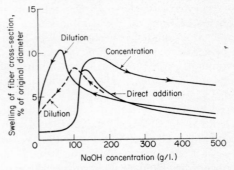

Fig. 15.1. Comparison of effects on the swelling of ramie cellulose obtained by diluting and concentrating of solutions NaOH (Saito)

intermicellar material, they should be removable already at concentrations considerably below that of mercerization. In fact, since intermicellar swelling decreases at above 10–12% NaOH, the removal of short-chain material is likely to be less efficient at concentrations higher than 10–12%, provided washing is done with preserved alkali concentration and followed by immediate neutralization. Figure 15.3 illustrates this for two types of pulp of different viscosity levels. It is seen that a pulp containing much hydrolytically degraded cellulose has a solubility maximum at 10% NaOH

994

at room temperature, whereas the less degraded pulp displays increasing solubility for increasing lye concentration, although with only a slight difference between 10 and 18% NaOH. In the latter case, most of the dissolved matter is hemicelluloses, whereas the solubility maximum of the degraded pulp is mainly caused by microfibril fragments, which pass into solution and can be recovered upon acidification, the *betacellulose* fraction. Finally, if intramicellar swelling is allowed to occur to a more remarkable extent, the cellulose is regenerated in another form, under a simultaneous increase in the amount of non-crystalline regions, which on drying tend to yield hornified and less reactive structures (19).

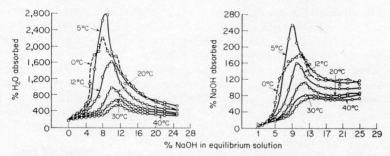

Fig. 15.2. Effects of temperature and concentration on the total alkali and water absorbed by regenerated cellulose (Beadle–Stevens)

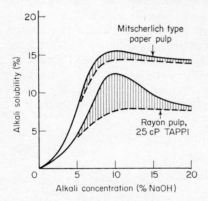

Fig. 15.3. Alkali solubility of sulfite pulp carbohydrates. Shadowed areas correspond to the acid-precipitable fraction (Annergren–Rydholm)

The dissolution of short-chain material by cold alkali purification was only suggested shortly after the invention of the viscose method (6, cf. 18). It is the most selective way of increasing the alphacellulose content of the pulp, giving the highest yields and the highest purity. Still it is seldom used on a technical scale because of the vast amounts of alkali needed.

When working at 5% consistency and 10% NaOH concentration, 2 t ptp NaOH are charged. If this quantity of lye cannot be reused, or utilized in another operation in the pulp mill, the cost of purification will exceed the total other costs of manufacture. In the case of cold alkali purification of prehydrolysis–kraft pulp, or where a kraft mill is localized at the same place as the sulfite mill, the excess lye may be used in the kraft cook (57, 58). If the quantities of lye thus charged to the kraft cooking exceed the sodium losses of the regeneration system, which will be the case if any substantial quantities of purified pulp are produced, it is necessary to use white liquor containing both sodium hydroxide and sulfide for the purification. Although less active than the hydroxide, the sulfide does not seem to produce any harmful effects in the purification, and has even been found to produce a slight improvement (48, cf. 31). However, depending on local conditions, it may be necessary to evaporate the white liquor prior to the purification or prior to use in the kraft cook.

Another means of disposing of the excess lye of purification is to use it for hot alkaline purification, if the production of hot alkali purified pulp considerably exceeds that of cold alkali purified pulp. This has been the general practice for the production of small amounts of cold alkali purified pulp for special nitration grades, but presents no principal solution of the large-scale cold alkali purification.

Even granted that the excess lye can be utilized, there is the problem of expelling the lye from the highly swollen pulp, in order to leave a minimum of alkali in the pulp after purification. This desire coincides with the wish to remove the dissolved impurities. Both screw, drum or disk presses, centrifuges, and press roll filters are used, often several units in series, and sometimes completed with counter-current washing, Figure 15.4 (62), which has to be done carefully to avoid reprecipitation of dissolved matter. More elaborate systems for counter-current treatment have also been suggested (22). To limit the fiber swelling, a slightly elevated temperature, 30–40°C, is often used. In other cases the washing is limited, and

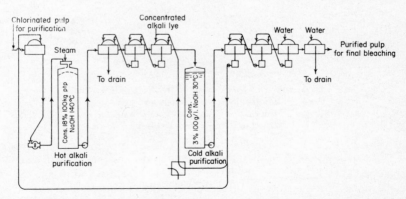

Fig. 15.4. Hot–cold alkali purification system for high-alpha sulfite pulp for acetate (Wayman)

the residual alkali consumed in a subsequent hot purification stage. A retention tower for the cold purification is not always needed, the physical changes occurring very rapidly.

The excess lye from the cold alkali purification can also be used for hot alkali purification in a previous stage. It is also conceivable to re-use the expelled lye for the purification of more pulp. The alkali concentration should thereby be kept up by addition of strong alkali lye, in an amount corresponding to the hydroxide remaining in the pulp after pressing. This necessitates that the water introduced to the system with the concentrated lye and with the pulp (plus possible wash water) should not exceed the amount of water leaving the pressed purified pulp. Therefore, a similar press system is also needed for the pulp entering the purification system or a multistage counter-current washing system previously mentioned. Further, ample devices for disintegrating the pulp press cakes may be needed to ensure a uniform chemical treatment. Therefore, cold alkali purification in all of its conceivable variations involves rather elaborate machinery. As will be seen below, the result of the purification is much deteriorated by recirculation of the lye, because of the accumulation of impurities. It is possible that special treatment of the lye between the purifications, such as dialysis or heating followed by cooling, might remove or destroy some of the impurities and improve the results. At present, however, technical cold alkali purification is mainly limited to operation together with kraft mills or to expensive speciality pulp grades, cord, acetate and nitrate pulps.

2. INFLUENCE OF REACTION CONDITIONS ON PULP YIELD AND QUALITY

Cold alkali purification applies *temperatures* below 40°C and lye *concentrations* below 18% NaOH. At these low temperatures mainly physical changes occur. The *swelling* and *purification effect* at various temperatures are shown in Figure 15.5 (49). Too much swelling causes difficulties in expelling the lye or handling the pulp on filter washers, and 15–20°C is a general minimum for sulfite pulps (25), although a higher temperature, about 35°C, is used for the technical purification of both sulfite and pre-hydrolysis–kraft pulps. Further increase in temperature will decrease the alphacellulose content, 50°C giving the least good results (48). At still higher temperatures, the chemical reactions of hot alkali purification will cause a renewed increase in the alphacellulose content. The lye concentration applied depends on the effect desired, the pulp type, the temperature (16), the reclaiming system and alkali costs, the equipment, etc. In the case of prehydrolysis–kraft pulp, already of high alphacellulose content after the cooking, only a limited swelling in order to improve the reactivity of the fibers may be needed, in which case a 7% NaOH lye is sufficient (44). If a considerable increase in purity is also desired, 9–10% NaOH (61), meaning a white liquor concentration of 12–14% active alkali, is used. An alphacellulose content of around 98% or even 99%

997

is reached. Also one-stage kraft pulps respond to cold alkali purification in a similar way (42), but their purity is still not sufficient to enable their use as dissolving pulps. In the case of sulfite pulps, the increase in purity is considerable in the range 4–7% NaOH at room temperature, as seen in Figure 15.6, whereafter a minor increase is obtained on further increase in lye concentration to around 10–12% NaOH (25), which gives a maximal alphacellulose content of around 98.5% (48). Similar results are obtained for prehydrolysis–kraft pulps (44) It should be pointed out that 100% alphacellulose is not obtained, although conditions are used which are as purifying as those of the alphacellulose determination. This is due to the fact that repeated swelling in alkali will more thoroughly affect the fiber structure than a single one, and some new fragmentation of microfibrils will always occur. The cold alkali purification to very high alphacellulose contents is facilitated by a preceding hot alkali stage, and starting with a hot alkali purified pulp with about 95.5% alphacellulose content, cold alkali treatment at various lye concentrations and temperatures gave the result in Figure 15.7 (63). Thus the optimal concentrations for this pulp were 120–140 g/l NaOH (about 11–12%) and the optimal temperature 10–15°C. 130 g/l and 18°C gave an alphacellulose content of about 99.5%. It is also worth mentioning that cold alkali purified pulps, although very easily bleached, are extremely sensitive to oxidative attacks, whereby the alphacellulose is further decreased. Sometimes therefore it is recommended that cold purification should be carried out on the bleached pulp. In other cases an oxidative degradation is desired to decrease the pulp viscosity, and hydrogen peroxide or other oxidants or oxidation catalysts are added to the lye (4).

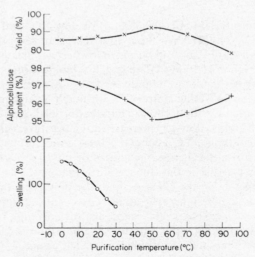

Fig. 15.5. Alkali purification of sulfite pulp at varying temperature in 10% NaOH (Rys–Treka)

The *time* needed for the treatment is short, as the swelling takes place almost instantaneously (25). However, in order to facilitate diffusion of dissolved material from the interior of the fiber wall, retention towers of up to 3 h capacity are in use, though 10–30 minutes can be considered sufficient. The *consistency* used will vary with the equipment from 5–15%, a lower consistency improving the uniformity of the treatment and the effect of purification (48), but increasing the problem of lye disposal.

Figure 15.6 shows the *amounts of alkali* left in the pulp after pressing to 45% consistency, which is about maximal prestation of a screw or disk press for this kind of pulp. Obviously, already at a lye concentration of about 6% NaOH the residual alkali exceeds the maximal amount used in hot alkali purification. Therefore washing of the purified pulp is necessary at higher concentrations. In the same figure the *yields* are shown for varying concentrations of the lye. Those yields are bound to vary also with the type of pulp to be purified, its initial purity and viscosity level, but yields around 85% being generally encountered in cold alkali purification of unpurified sulfite pulps and 95–98% for prehydrolysis–kraft pulps, or sulfite pulps which have had a previous hot alkali purification. The yield losses are normally 1.2–1.5% per 1% increase in alphacellulose content.

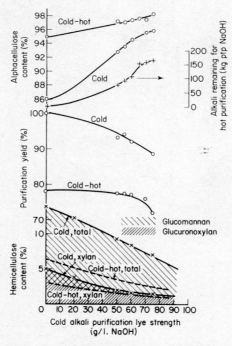

Fig. 15.6. Purification of spruce sulfite pulp (100 cP TAPPI) with cold alkali (20°C) of varying strength, followed by pressing to 45% consistency and heating to 100°C for 2 hours (Rydholm)

999

Although not shown in the figure, the *hemicellulose* content of the pulp decreases as the alphacellulose content is increased. The minimum values obtainable vary with the type of pulp: around 0.5 % glucomannan and as much xylan in softwood sulfite (34, 42) and prehydrolysis–kraft pulp (44, cf. 60), little glucomannan and about 1.5 % xylan in hardwood prehydrolysis–kraft pulps (44, 59), 2 % xylan in one-stage softwood kraft pulps (42) and 8 % xylan in one-stage hardwood kraft pulps (56). Xylan removal in cold alkali after various pretreatments has also been studied (27). In comparison with hot purification to identical alphacellulose level, cold alkali treatment removes more xylan (42, 60) and also more gluco-mannan (60). However, some carbohydrate material of which some less well-ordered cellulose, easily accessible to hot alkaline reaction, remains after cold purification. Therefore combined cold and hot alkali treatment is indicated, although the pulp yield after a combined treatment is neces-sarily low.

Figure 15.6 also shows the results of a subsequent hot purification at 100°C for 2 h in the alkali left after pressing to 45 % consistency. It is seen that the additional effect of hot purification is less pronounced the higher the cold purification effect. However, the combination of cold and

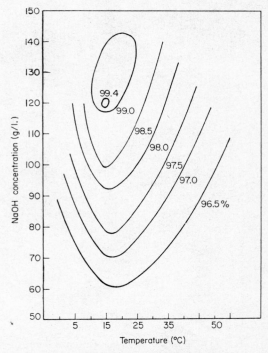

Fig. 15.7. Relation of alphacellulose content to caustic concentration and temperature of extraction starting from a hot-alkali purified sulfite pulp (Wayman–Sherk)

hot purification gives a certain alphacellulose content at 1–2% lower lye concentration than a cold purification alone. Such a system therefore makes alkali recovery from the pulp press cake after the cold stage less important, but does not avoid the need for an economic disposal of the expelled lye. The pulp yields after the double purification are considerably lower than at cold purification alone, and somewhat lower than from only hot purification at corresponding conditions. Such a combination of cold and hot purification has long been suggested (2, 19, 32, 45) and is now in technical operation for both kraft and sulfite pulps. The heating has been assumed to cause such changes in the partially formed alkali cellulose lattice that the original crystal structure is restored, which gives a better reactivity of the cold alkali purified pulp approaching that of hot alkali purified pulps (19). Combinations with hot purification preceding the cold treatment also give good purification results (48, 63) and are applied to large-scale operation.

A very special variant of cold alkali purification is the *freeze purification* (42, 49). This method is based on the phenomen that water will crystallize out of alkali lye on freezing, making the residual lye in the pulp more concentrated. 5% pulp consistency, −15 to −17°C at 5% NaOH concentration is recommended for optimal results, and the pulp slurry is thawed after 15–30 minutes, washed and possibly beaten to remove residual alkali (49). 98% alphacellulose content is reached. Also higher consistency, e.g. with the pulp in sheet form, steeped in lye of much lower concentration, 1–2% NaOH, gives appreciable purification effect on freezing to −10 to −20°C (42). However, the method has not been applied commercially.

III. Hot Alkali Purification

1. DESCRIPTION OF PROCESS

In contrast to cold purification, hot alkali treatment utilizes chemical reactions for purification, although physical effects are obviously also of importance. The swelling is limited, as the concentration of lye in the reaction mixture is only 0.3–3% NaOH. The degree of purification is regulated by the alkali charge, in kg ptp, as well as by temperature, time and consistency, the variables being mentioned in decreasing order of importance. In contrast to cold purification, the treatment leaves no excess lye disposal problem, as the reactions are almost carried to completion. The chief drawbacks of the method are the large amounts of steam used, and the fairly low yields of pulp obtained, in comparison with cold purification. A yield loss of about 3% per 1% increase in alphacellulose content is experienced (e.g. 21). On the other hand, the process could be adjusted to give any desired yield and degree of purification, to a maximum of 96–97% alphacellulose content at 70–75% yield.

The hot alkali purification is ordinarily used only for sulfite pulps, as it involves the same carbohydrate reactions as occur in the alkaline cooks, at less severe conditions, and therefore does not contribute much to the purity of alkaline-cooked pulps. Only preceded by a cold alkali purification, by which new regions of the fiber are opened up for reactions with alkali, is hot purification of interest for the prehydrolysis–kraft pulps. Therefore, the discussion in this section will be limited to sulfite pulps.

The *temperatures* ordinarily used range from 70 to 120°C, in exceptional cases 140°C, and to save steam the consistency is kept at maximum. Downflow towers are therefore almost exclusively used, preceded by equipment for concentrating the pulp and for the introduction of heat and chemicals. Figure 15.8 shows a common system. Hot water at the last showers of a filter equipped with press rolls brings the pulp sheet up to around 50°C, and the remaining heat is supplied by steaming in a mixer. The alkali is added at the filter, either at a shower or in the shredder screw. The mixing of alkali is carried out by a single or double shaft mixer, to which the steam is subsequently introduced. The *consistency* after

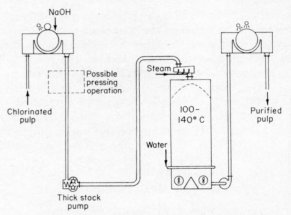

Fig. 15.8. Pressurized hot alkali purification system

mixing is 12–18%. To improve the mixing and to increase the resulting consistency on the filter, a double filtration system is often used between the chlorination and purification towers, where part or all of the alkali is added already at the first filter and the white water from the second filter is returned for dilution of the pulp leaving the first one. To improve the consistency further, thus saving steam and at high-alpha pulps some alkali also, screw, drum or disk presses are sometimes introduced after the filter. The resulting consistency after alkali mixing is 25–35%. When temperatures above 100°C are applied, which is motivated only for high-alpha pulps, a pressure feeder is used between filter and mixer. This is usually a star feeder, but thick stock pumps have recently been introduced for the same purpose.

The *retention time* needed varies for the different grades. For low- and medium-alpha pulps 1–2 h is sufficient, whereas high-alpha pulps need longer times, varying with the temperature applied. Low-pressure towers working at around 120°C need about 3 h, longer times only leading to unnecessary degradation. Towers constructed for atmospheric pressure should allow at least 4 and preferably 5–6 h to give maximum alphacellulose content, around 96.5%.

A recent variation of the hot alkali purification utilizes sodium carbonate and sulfite mixtures at high temperature and pressure. 160°C for 2 h then gives alphacellulose contents above 97% (33). To carry out such a process on a large scale, a digester construction is necessary. Because of the large amounts of steam and chemicals needed, and the difficulty of their recovery in the bleaching operation, this type of reaction should preferably be carried out in the digester house in connection with the delignification, as in the Sivola or similar processes, cf. Chapter 9. Alternatively purification of the unbleached pulp should be performed at high consistency, 25–40%, with recovery of the white water from the subsequent filter for recycling within the stage to increase the solids content of the waste liquor finally sent to the recovery plant (33). It could also be used as a wash liquor of the pulp from the sulfite digester (38).

The *amounts of alkali* added vary from 30–150 kg ptp NaOH. The wish to avoid dilution of the pulp to maintain the consistency must be balanced against the demand for uniform distribution of the alkali and also to avoid partial mercerization of the pulp. The alkali is therefore usually added to the pulp in the filter shredder screw at around 10% NaOH concentration.

The washing of the pulp after purification is done on filters, sometimes two in series to ensure complete removal of dissolved matter, especially resin. The white water is used for dilution at the tower base and in the filter trough.

2. REACTIONS

Recent studies (20, cf. 15) on the reactions of mono- and disaccharides, as well as sugar ethers and glucosides in alkali at room and elevated temperatures have facilitated the understanding of the reactions of hot alkali purification of pulp. The results were dealt with in more detail in Chapter 9 on alkaline cooking processes, which involve essentially the same carbohydrate reactions as hot purification, the difference mainly being that the kraft cook is carried out at considerably higher temperature and therefore also involves reactions which occur very slowly if at all at the normal conditions of hot purification. Thus the cleavage of β-glucosidic bonds of cellulose by alkaline hydrolysis, which occurs to a considerable extent in the kraft cook, as evidenced by the decrease in viscosity of the pulp on prolonged cooking, is not noticed at hot purification, unless the retention time is increased far beyond normal practice (9), or the temperature is brought up to the neighbourhood of kraft cooking temperature. Then there is a rapid decrease in viscosity, which is utilized for DP regulation of cotton linters (7) but which also affects the alphacellulose content. In the same way, transglycosidations, which might complicate the carbohydrate reactions in the kraft cook, are likely to be absent. The dominating reaction is the alkaline *'peeling reaction'* (20), starting at the aldehydic end groups of the carbohydrate chains, as well as at carbonyl groups introduced at other places along the chains during the pretreatments of the pulp, mainly in the chlorination. The peeling reaction is illustrated in the following formulae:

$$
\begin{array}{ccc}
\text{CHO} & & \text{CH}_2\text{OH} \\
| & & | \\
\text{HCOH} & & \text{C}=\text{O} \\
| & & | \\
\text{HOCH} & \rightleftharpoons & \text{HOCH} \\
| & & | \\
\text{HCO–Cell} & & \text{HCO–Cell} \longrightarrow \\
| & & | \\
\text{HCOH} & & \text{HCOH} \\
| & & | \\
\text{CH}_2\text{OH} & & \text{CH}_2\text{OH}
\end{array}
$$

$$
\text{Cell–OH} +
\begin{array}{cccc}
\text{CH}_2\text{OH} & \text{CH}_2\text{OH} & & \text{CH}_2\text{OH} \\
| & | & & |\quad\text{OH} \\
\text{C}=\text{O} & \text{C}=\text{O} & & \text{C}\!\!<\!\! \\
| & | & & |\quad\text{COOH} \\
\text{HOC} & \text{C}=\text{O} & \longrightarrow & | \\
\| \quad \rightleftharpoons & | & & \text{CH}_2 \\
\text{HC} & \text{CH}_2 & & | \\
| & | & & \text{HCOH} \\
\text{HCOH} & \text{HCOH} & & | \\
| & | & & \text{CH}_2\text{OH} \\
\text{CH}_2\text{OH} & \text{CH}_2\text{OH} &
\end{array}
$$

Thus principally the aldehyde group of the C_1 atom is shifted to a carbonyl group on C_2, which causes cleavage of the β-glycosidic bond in the β-position to the carbonyl group and formation of an enol, in equilibrium with the dicarbonyl compound which finally rearranges to an isosaccharinic acid. The new end group formed reacts in an identical way, and the peeling reaction proceeds until by an intramolecular rearrangement a carboxyl end group is formed (as a glucosaccharinic or predominantly gluco*meta*saccharinic acid monomer (23)), which stabilizes the chain towards alkali, the *'stopping reaction'* (23). On the average, 50 glucose units per chain molecule have then been peeled off in the case of cellulose (54). Other experiments indicate that glucomannan is less stable towards hot alkali than glucan, and glucan less stable than xylan (43), cf. Chapter 9. II.

With the knowledge of these reactions, it is not astonishing to find that the loss in yield during the hot alkali treatment is related to the copper number (or carbonyl content) of the unpurified pulp (3, 10, 46, 53), that the copper number decreases during the treatment in proportion to the yield losses, Figure 15.9, and that the maximum hot alkali soluble substance (*perte à la soude*) also bears a direct relation to the copper number, Figure 15.10 (53). It is also natural that a *hypoiodite* (3), *bisulfite* (30) or *chlorite* (1, 28) oxidation as well as a *tetrahydroborate* reduction (1, 28, 43) or an end-group *methylation* (24, 28, 36) of the pulp prior to purification noticeably decreases the amount of hot alkali solubles. Periodate oxycellulose, which is rapidly degraded in alkali, preserves its DP if first oxidized with chlorite (14, 46). Furthermore, it is not astonishing to learn that the alkali consumption during the refining is proportional to the yield losses (3), Figure 15.11. However, the alkali consumption does not correspond to one mole per monosaccharide unit dissolved, but rather to 1.4 (54) or 1.6 (3), showing that the end products of the degradation must be smaller than iso- and metasaccharinic acid, or that the latter change into

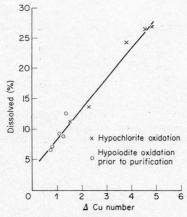

Fig. 15.9. Hot alkali purification loss as a function of the decrease in copper number (Bergek *et al*)

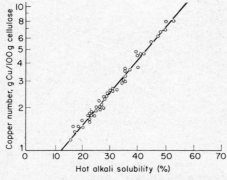

Fig. 15.10. Relation between copper number and hot 7% NaOH solubility (Samuelson–Ramsel)

1005

polybasic or more low-molecular acids. The average consumption of alkali during hot alkali purification, irrespective of the concentration of alkali used (3), but to some extent depending on pulp viscosity, Figure 15.12, and the severity of the conditions, is around 100 kg ptp NaOH for

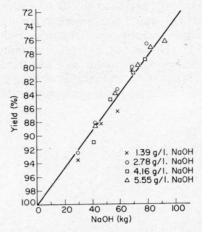

Fig. 15.11. Hot alkali purification yield vs. alkali consumption at varying alkali concentration (Bergek *et al*)

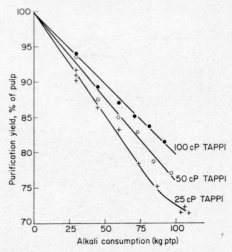

Fig. 15.12. Hot alkali purification yield vs. alkali consumption for prechlorinated spruce sulfite pulps of various viscosity levels. Inclination of curves corresponds to an equivalent weight of dissolved substance of 80, 100 and 120 for 100, 50 and 25 cP pulps respectively (Rydholm)

25% yield losses, corresponding to an average equivalent weight of around 100 for the degradation products. Potentiometric titration of the waste liquors of hot alkali purification of both cotton linters and wood pulps (47) indicated the presence of acids with pK_a 2.4 (33%), 3.7 (67%) and 4.7 (traces). *Pyruvic acid*, $CH_3COCOOH$ (pK_a 2.3, equivalent weight 88) *formic acid* (pK_a 3.7, equivalent weight 46), *glycolic acid* (pK_a 3.7, equivalent weight 76) and *lactic acid* (pK_a 3.8, equivalent weight 90) are possible degradation products, most of which have been indicated, together with β,γ-dihydroxybutyric acid (12, 37, 52). The quantity of acids of low molecular weight tend to increase with temperature, and this is not caused by secondary degradation of isosaccharinic acid (52) but shows a gradual change in the degradation mechanism from the classical peeling rearrangements to various types of *fragmentation* reactions, discussed in more detail in Chapter 9.II. It is obvious, however, that at normal hot alkali purification temperatures, there also occurs considerable fragmentation. A characteristic smell accompanying all hot alkali purifications indicates volatile aldehydes among the degradation products, probably *methyl glyoxal*, CH_3COCHO. Alkaline decomposition of hexoses to *methyl glyoxal, glyceraldehyde* and *dihydroxyacetone* has also been demonstrated (17). From the considerably increased reduction capacity of the waste liquor from hot alkali refining on hydrolysis in mineral acid (3) it is also evident that part of the dissolved matter still preserves polysaccharide structures.

The question of reaction order and whether the reactions are inter- or intramicellar has been discussed (3, 25, 43). The x-ray diagram of the hot alkali resistant part does not deviate from that of the cellulose prior to the treatment (13, 43). Irrespective of variations in lye concentration (2–6 g/l NaOH), there is a rapid reaction, corresponding to a yield loss of 8–9%, or 35–40 kg ptp NaOH, which gives around 91–92% alpha-cellulose content, and subsequently a much slower reaction of probably zero order (3). Considering the dilute lye used, intermicellar material as well as the surface of the ordered regions only, are likely to be accessible to the reactions, the former material contributing to the faster phase of reaction. However, because of the stabilizing 'stopping' reaction of metasaccharinic acid end monomer formation, hot alkali treatment does not remove the intermicellar material quantitatively and can therefore not be utilized as a method for determination of accessibility. Still, the low yields from wood pulps, 70–75%, in comparison with about 95% for cotton linters, at severe alkali conditions, show the importance of crystallinity or molecular order for the hot alkali resistance. At these high yield losses, the alphacellulose content of the wood pulp is increased from 88–89% to around 96%. Whereas initially one per cent increase in alphacellulose content means a yield loss of 2–3%, the losses at the highest alphacellulose levels are 5–6% or more, until finally no further gain in alphacellulose is reached at continued yield losses. Then the remaining low-molecular material is fairly stable towards alkali, and its further dissolution proceeds at a rate which does not much deviate from that of the more ordered long-chain material. The entire reaction also slows down as the points open to alkaline attack decrease.

Obviously, if the short-chain material is to be removed, a stabilization such as that obtained on oxidation of the aldehyde groups to carboxyls is undesirable, and oxidative bleaching stages should be placed subsequent to the purification stage. On the other hand it is undesirable to introduce new carbonyl groups and thereby increase the hot alkali solubility, as such introduction cannot be made selectively to the short-chain material. Chlorination, which is normally preceding the purification, should therefore be carried out with as little oxidative effect to the carbohydrates as possible. No principal objections are against carrying out hot alkali treatment even prior to chlorination, as the purification effect is almost as good on the unchlorinated pulp (48). However, it is desirable to remove small amounts of oxycellulose formed on chlorination, and furthermore an alkali extraction is still needed after the chlorination to remove residual chlorolignin, and hence the two functions of lignin and carbohydrate removal are preferably combined in one stage. Only occasionally is there a real advantage to start the bleaching with the hot alkali purification, such as in the case of resinous hardwood sulfite pulps.

Another risk of oxidative damage occurs in the hot alkali treatment itself, when air is allowed to come into contact with the hot alkaline pulp. The light-brown color then changes into black, and the oxidative degradation shows up in decreased alphacellulose contents and yields. Additions of reductants such as sodium sulfide or sulfite have been suggested (8, 48) but in normal technical operation with a closed purification tower preceded by a steam mixer there is probably little damage of this type. Sometimes an oxidative effect is desired, and the addition of oxidizing catalysts has been suggested to decrease pulp viscosity (35).

3. INFLUENCE OF REACTION CONDITIONS ON PULP YIELD AND QUALITY

A. Pulp type and pretreatment

Figure 9.54 shows the hot alkali solubility of spruce sulfite pulps as a function of pulp viscosity after the cook (51). Obviously, as the hydrolytic degradation introduces new end groups, the points of alkaline attack increase and hence the dissolvable material. The hot alkali solubility is defined as the amount of pulp dissolvable on treatment in an excess of dilute lye at 100°C for a fairly long time. These conditions ensure that the state of ultimate purification is reached, leaving a material essentially stable to further hot alkali treatment (cf. Chapter 20 on methods of characterization).

Obviously the hydrolytic degradation during the cook must lead to decreased yields of high-alpha pulps, as will be discussed further below. On the other hand, the degradation of non-cellulosic components facilitates the purification, and hence the amounts of contaminating hemicelluloses are lower for purified pulps which have been cooked to a lower viscosity, as

1008

is demonstrated for pentosans of spruce sulfite pulps cooked to various viscosities and purified to various yields, Figure 15.13. It is also seen that the decrease in xylan content with increasing aplhacellulose content is rather small, and that removal of glucomannan and low-molecular cellulose therefore accounts for the main yield loss. Another circumstance, however, causes the maximum alphacellulose content obtainable by purification to be constant or even decrease, on decreasing pulp viscosity from around 70 cP Tappi. The hydrolytic attack during the final phase of the sulfite cook is far from uniform, and the fragmentation of microfibrils causes an increasing proportion of cellulose to be soluble in 10% NaOH lye, as was demonstrated in Figure 9.43. This also affects the conventional alphacellulose content, and the deficit cannot be compensated for by hot alkali purification, as the micell fragments are of similar degree of order as the main part of the cellulose, and therefore rather resistant to dilute alkali although soluble in more concentrated

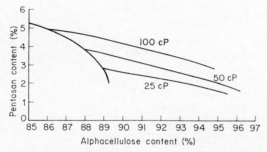

Fig. 15.13. Pentosan removal by hot alkali purification of three spruce sulfite pulps of different viscosity levels (Rydholm)

lye. The main effect of the purification is thus a decrease in the content of material which is soluble in both 18 and 10% NaOH, as seen in Figure 15.14 for three different viscosity levels. In Figure 15.15 the yield of purification versus alphacellulose content, as well as versus R_{18} and R_{10} (the fractions resistant to 18 and 10% NaOH), is seen for three pulps of different viscosity. Obviously with R_{18} as the base of comparison, the purification yield is relatively slightly affected by pulp viscosity. Compared at the same R_{10}, the low-viscosity pulps are obtained in much lower yields, and with alphacellulose as the base of comparison, high- and low-viscosity pulps reach about the same ultimate yields of purification, whereas medium-viscosity pulps give the best results. As is further illustrated in Figure 15.16, this is true for high-alpha pulps, whereas at lower alphacellulose levels the low-viscosity pulps compare more favorably. The figure shows that the ease of purification is increased at decreased viscosities after cooking, until the 50–60 cP level, whereafter the R_{18} is not increased further and R_{10} is decreased because of the hydrolytic fragmentation in the cooking, resulting in a decrease in the alphacellulose content also.

These results should be regarded in the light of the variation of cooking yield with pulp viscosity. As seen in Figure 15.17 there is a higher yield of purified pulp, calculated on wood basis, at any alphacellulose level, the higher the pulp viscosity, but the more remarkable effects occur at the viscosity interval of 20–70 cP Tappi. At very high viscosity levels the pulp

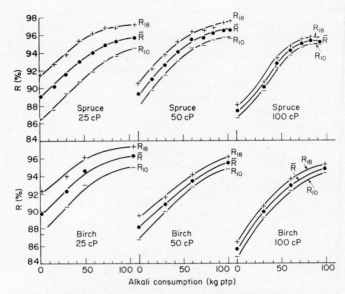

Fig. 15.14. Alkali non-solubilities vs. alkali consumption on the hot alkali purification of spruce and birch sulfite pulps of three viscosity levels. R_{18} and R_{10} denote the non-solubilities in 18 and 10% NaOH respectively; $\overline{R}$ approximately equals alphacellulose content (Rydholm)

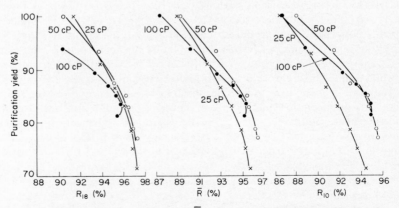

Fig. 15.15. Purification yield vs. R_{18}, $\overline{R}$ and R_{10} on the hot alkali purification of spruce sulfite pulps of three viscosity levels (Rydholm)

cannot be refined to high-alpha pulp. This is in some contrast to the purification at higher temperatures, as occur in the Sivola and similar processes, where fairly high alphacellulose content can also be reached for mildly cooked sulfite pulps, Chapter 9. The temperature effect on the purification result will be dealt with later on.

Apart from the importance of the degree of cooking, the conditions of chlorination will also influence the purification results. Figures 15.18–19 show the hot alkali solubility of sulfite and kraft pulps, chlorinated or oxidized with other bleaching agents at various pH (33a). The results are completely analogous to those shown in Figure 14.23 (53), showing the copper number after the same treatment, Obviously, there is

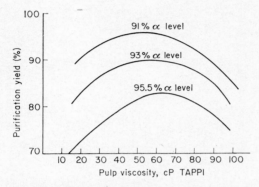

Fig. 15.16. Purification yield vs. pulp viscosity at three alphacellulose levels (before final bleaching) on hot alkali purification of spruce sulfite pulps (Rydholm)

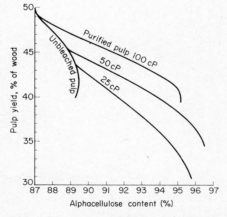

Fig. 15.17. Yield vs. alphacellulose content on hot alkali purification of spruce sulfite pulps of three viscosity levels (Rydholm)

1011

a formation of carbonyl groups, which constitute new points of hot alkali attack. It is most pronounced at neutral pH's, whereas the oxidation is repressed at low pH, and carried to alkali-stable carboxyl groups at high pH (hypochlorite oxidation in the presence of excess alkali), which even decreases the hot alkali solubility (cf. 21). Ordinarily, only chlorination

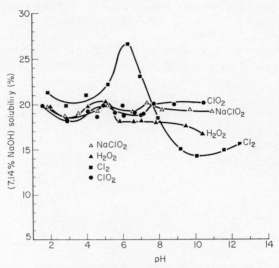

Fig. 15.18. Effect of pH on 7.14% NaOH solubility of sulfite pulp with four bleaching agents (Rapson)

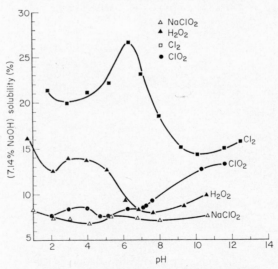

Fig. 15.19. Effect of pH on 7.14% NaOH solubility of kraft pulp with four bleaching agents (Rapson)

at low pH precedes the purification stage, and by proper choice of chlorination conditions, the purification results are not affected.

Different wood species yield pulps of varying ease of purification. Most hardwood pulps, containing more xylan than softwood pulps, are less easy to obtain in a pure form (41), probably because of the greater resistance of xylan to the peeling reaction (cf. 1, 11). It is therefore also less attractive with hardwood pulps to increase the pulp yield by increasing the viscosity of the unbleached pulp, since the hydrolytic degradation of the xylan during the cook is needed to render them sufficiently reactive to hot alkali. Other hardwoods, especially some eucalyptus, are more rich in cellulose, and yield sulfite pulps which can be easily purified by alkali to high purity, Table 15.1 (47).

Table 15.1. Response to hot alkali purification by acid sulfite pulp from various wood species (47)

Wood species	Alphacellulose content, %		Pentosan content, %	
	Unbleached	Purified*	Unbleached	Purified
Picea abies, Scandinavian spruce	89.0	96.0	3.5	1.8
Betula verrucosa, silver birch	88.0	94.8	7.5	3.0
Eucalyptus camaldulensis, red gum	88.9	94.9	4.8	2.8
Eucalyptus globulus, blue gum	90.3	95.2	5.6	2.9
Eucalyptus saligna, Sydney blue gum	92.4	96.6	3.1	1.7
Populus × *euramericana*, hybrid poplar	89.0	95.7	4.2	1.9

* Hot alkali treatment at 100°C for 4 h at 10% consistency with 120 kg ptp NaOH, and mildly bleached. Alphacellulose content determined as the average of the non-solubilities in 18 and 10% NaOH. Unbleached pulps, of viscosity 60 cP TAPPI, were delignified by chlorite prior to analysis.

B. Consistency, reaction time, temperature, and alkali charge

A higher consistency gives a higher alkali concentration in the purifying lye for a constant alkali charge. This increases the rate of reaction, as seen in Figure 15.20 (21) but does not affect the yield loss at a certain alkali consumption (3) and degree of purification. Generally speaking, the choice of consistency is merely a question of retention time available, as well as of heat economy. A thumb rule is that the increase in alphacellulose content is a function of the product of lye concentration time, i.e. at half the consistency twice the retention time is needed at constant alkali charge to achieve a certain degree of purification (21). Provided good mixing of the alkali with the pulp is ensured, satisfactory results are obtained at 12–18% consistency, and even 25–30% is practised in some cases.

The time required varies with the grade of purified pulp. As was pointed out earlier, the reaction of purification can be subdivided into two courses, one rapid reaction, corresponding to an alkali consumption of about 35–40 kg ptp NaOH, a yield loss of 8–9%, and an alphacellulose content of 91–92%, and one slower reaction for further purification (3). This observation was made on keeping the concentration of the purifying lye constant

1013

by additions of strong lye corresponding to the amounts of alkali consumed. In technical operation, all alkali is supplied at a time, and in an amount only slightly higher than the consumption, since a reclaiming of residual alkali

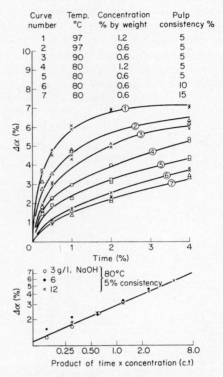

Curve number	Temp. °C	Concentration % by weight	Pulp consistency %
1	97	1.2	5
2	97	0.6	5
3	90	0.6	5
4	80	1.2	5
5	80	0.6	5
6	80	0.6	10
7	80	0.6	15

Fig. 15.20. Influence of reaction conditions on hot alkali purification (Leugering)

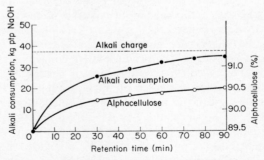

Fig. 15.21. Alkali consumption and development of the alphacellulose content on the hot alkali purification of spruce sulfite rayon pulp. Conditions: 16% consistency, 100°C

1014

is difficult. Therefore, the alkali concentration is continuously decreasing during the purification. Still, a fairly short time is needed for the limited purification mentioned, as seen in Figure 15.21. Retention times of 1–2 h suffice at temperatures of 100°C or slightly lower. As a matter of fact, the limited purification desired for pulps of alphacellulose content 90–91 %, which constitute a large part of the dissolving pulp production, is reached so readily that temperatures below 100°C are frequently used to preserve some residual alkali, which is of benefit in the deresination of pulp (cf. Chapter 16). Around 80°C for 90 % and 90°C for 91 % alphacellulose grades are about normal at 1–2 h retention time. For 100°C and 5 h reaction, alkali charges of up to 60 kg ptp NaOH react wholly, giving alphacellulose contents of 94–95 %. At still higher charges, increasing amounts of residual alkali are left, as seen in Figure 15.22, but increasing

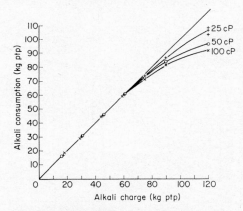

Fig. 15.22. Alkali consumption vs. alkali charge on hot alkali purification of spruce sulfite pulps of various viscosity levels. Conditions: 10% consistency, 100°C, 5 hours (Rydholm)

amounts of alkali are consumed up to more than 100 kg ptp NaOH. Prolonged time or higher temperature will increase the alkali consumption further and decrease the yield still more, but with little effect on alphacellulose content.

The effect of temperature has been studied mainly with regard to the ultimate alphacellulose and pentosan content obtainable (41, 45, 48), and an increase in alphacellulose and a decrease in pentosan content have been noted at the same time as viscosity decrease. The latter indicates a degradation by alkaline hydrolysis, similar to that noticed with cotton linters (7, 9). As seen in Figure 15.23 (47), the degradation is also noticeable as a decrease in R_{10} content, indicating a fragmentation of microfibrils. Obviously, there is not much point in exceeding 140°C in the case of sodium hydroxide purification even for fairly high-viscosity pulps, whereas somewhat higher temperatures than 100°C are motivated for high-alpha pulps, especially if the unpurified pulp is of high viscosity and fairly resistant to purification.

Whereas the degradation of wood pulp is preferably carried out in other stages than the alkali purification, viscosity control of cotton linters is to a certain extent carried out in a high-temperature alkali treatment, often called *kier-boiling*. This is illustrated in Figure 15.24 (7). However, it has been suggested in the case of wood pulp to degrade in the hot alkali purification, following swelling in cold concentrated alkali, in which case the viscosity decrease is especially rapid and leaves a more uniformly degraded pulp (50), if temperatures above 130°C are applied.

The degradation effect of hot alkali purification is fairly limited at temperatures below 120°C and is then overshadowed by the viscosity increase due to the dissolution of short-chain material. This is illustrated by Figure 15.25 for pulps of various unbleached viscosity. The effect is

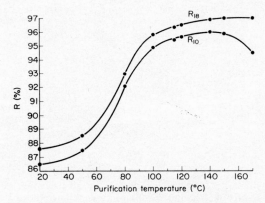

Fig. 15.23. Cold alkali non-solubility in 18 and 10% NaOH of a high-viscosity spruce sulfite pulp upon hot alkali purification at varying temperature for 4 hours with 120 kg ptp NaOH (Rydholm)

Table 15.2. Change in carbohydrate composition of acid sulfite pulps from spruce upon hot alkali purification (47)

Pulp treatment	Viscosity cP TAPPI	R_{18} %	R_{10} %	$\overline{R}$ %	Cellulose, %	Gluco-mannan, %	Glucuron-oxylan, %
Unbleached	25	91.5	87.5	89.5	92.5	4.0	3.5
Purified*	28	97.2	94.8	96.0	97.3	1.7	1.0
Unbleached	90	88.0	87.0	87.5	87.0	8.5	4.5
Purified*	100	96.5	95.5	96.0	96.4	1.8	1.8

* Hot alkali treatment at 100°C for 4 h at 10% consistency with 120 kg ptp NaOH. R_{18} and R_{10} are non-solubilities in 18 and 10% NaOH, and their average, $\overline{R}$, corresponds approximately to the alpha-cellulose content.

1016

further displayed by changes in the chain length distribution diagrams for high- and low-viscosity pulps before and after hot alkali purification to high-alpha pulps (5), since much of the low-molecular material of DP below 200 is removed. Table 15.2 illustrates the simultaneous change in carbohydrate composition (47). The disappearance of most of the non-glucose components is evident, although there are still noticeable quantities of impurities, especially in the high-viscosity pulp.

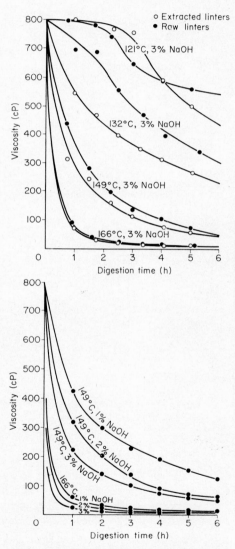

Fig. 15.24. Effect of kiering conditions on cotton linters viscosity (Burdynski–Kobe)

C. Type of alkali

The most active type of alkali is sodium hydroxide, which is also readily available and fairly inexpensive. Sodium hydroxide, pure or mixed with sulfide in the form of white liquor, is therefore the chemical commonly

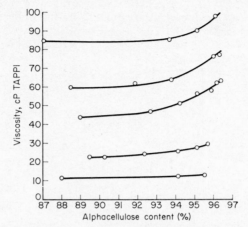

Fig. 15.25. Viscosity increase by hot alkali purification (Rydholm)

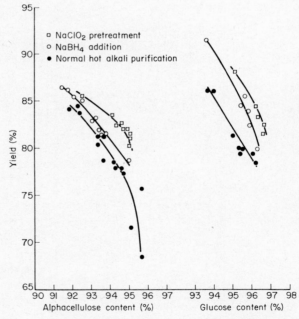

Fig. 15.26. Effect of chlorite pretreatment or tetrahydroborate borohydride addition on the result of hot alkali purification (Assarsson *et al*)

used for the purification. However, a large number of other alkaline chemicals have been investigated for pulp purification, such as sodium carbonate, sulfite, sulfide, borate, phosphate, silicate, calcium hydroxide, and ammonia (e.g. 42, 48). Common to all these compounds is that a higher temperature is needed for the purification than with sodium hydroxide, generally 150–200°C. Table 15.3 gives a list of results obtained at comparable conditions for a large number of chemicals (42). Obviously, quite a few give considerable purification. As mentioned before, oxidation or reduction of the aldehydic end groups of the carbohydrates tends to reduce their reactivity with hot alkali. This can be utilized to increase the pulp yield in the kraft process, where the hot-alkali treatment is needed for delignification and all carbohydrates could be used in the product. Sodium tetrahydroborate and polysulfide have therefore attracted interest as kraft pulping additives, cf. Chapter 9.II. However, in hot alkali purification removal of hemicelluloses is desired, and at the same time cellulose preservation. Therefore, oxidants and reductants of aldehyde groups are of

Table 15.3. Hot alkali purification of spruce sulfite pulp with various types of alkali. 2 hours (42)

Chemical type	Conc., g/l.	Temp. °C	Yield %	Alpha-cellulose, %	Pentosans, %
NaOH	10	125	75.0	96.0	1.2
Na$_2$CO$_3$	10		82.6	94.7	1.6
	20		80.6	95.1	1.5
	30		77.6	96.0	1.3
Na$_2$S	10		79.0	96.0	—
Ca(OH)$_2$	20		84.6	90.9	1.6
NaOH	10	150	73.0	96.2	1.1
Na$_2$CO$_3$	10		77.5	95.8	1.3
Na$_2$SO$_3$	20		87.0	93.1	1.2
	40		82.8	93.4	—
Na$_3$PO$_4$	10		81.9	94.9	—
	20		71.8	96.3	1.2
Na$_2$B$_4$O$_7$	10		81.9	94.6	—
	20		71.8	94.8	—
Ca(OH)$_2$	20		81.5	94.0	1.6
NH$_3$	20		89.0	92.8	1.1
	50		88.6	92.3	1.6
Na$_2$SiO$_3$	10	200	84	94.0	1.5
NaOCOCH$_3$	10		85	95.0	1.4
NaHCO$_3$	10		75	97.0	1.2
Na$_3$PO$_4$	10		76	96.9	1.3
Na$_2$B$_4$O$_7$	10		72	97.0	1.1
Na$_2$CO$_3$	10		72	97.2	1.3
Na$_2$SO$_3$	10		74	95.1	1.4
NH$_3$	10		83	94.3	2.0
MgSO$_3$	10		81	94.4	1.6

1019

interest in pulp purification only if they tend to increase the selectivity of the hot alkali hemicellulose removal. This actually seems to be the case with sodium chlorite or tetrahydroborate (1), since the pulp yield for a given alphacellulose level is improved, Figure 15.26. The effect is, however, rather slight, and has not been utilized in practice, as far as is known.

Mixtures of sodium carbonate and sulfite have proved especially effective (33). Figure 15.27 shows purification of a high-viscosity pulp with mixtures of carbonate and sulfite in different proportions at 160°C.

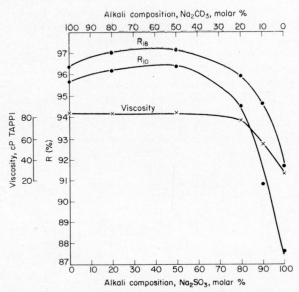

Fig. 15.27. Result of sodium carbonate–sulfite purification of a spruce sulfite pulp at 160°C for 2 hours. 250 kg ptp (Rydholm)

Initial pH is 10–11, and a drop in pH occurs during the period of purification, in the case of sulfite at 160°C down to below 8 and for carbonate to below 10. This is reflected in the degrees of purification, which for sulfite is not very high at the conditions chosen, whereas carbonate as well as mixtures of up to 50% sulfite at 160°C give a high alpha content. The sulfite on the other hand influences the lignin reactions and the presence of sulfite gives a brighter pulp after purification, which to some extent also means a pulp more easily bleached. Figure 15.28 shows the relation of purification degree and amounts of chemicals, for high-temperature carbonate–sulfite mixture in comparison with purification in sodium hydroxide at 100°C. It is seen that more than twice the amount of Na_2O is needed to obtain similar results with the carbonate–sulfite mixture. This, together with the high temperature necessary, is the main drawback of the method, as chemical recovery is somewhat complicated. The yields of purified pulp reached, however, are quite satisfactory, as seen from Figure 15.29. The figure also shows some results from calcium hydroxide purification at comparable conditions, and it is seen that about the same yield against alphacellulose relation is obtained, but that considerably lower degrees of purification are reached.

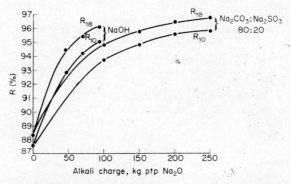

Fig. 15.28. Hot alkali purification of a high-viscosity spruce sulfite pulp with sodium hydroxide (100°C, 4 hours) and sodium carbonate–sulfite mixture (160°C, 2 hours) (Rydholm)

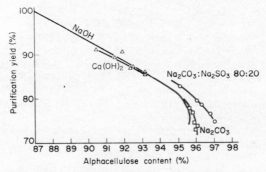

Fig. 15.29. Purification yield vs. alphacellulose content on hot alkali purification of a high-velocity spruce sulfite pulp with various chemicals (Rydholm)

On the whole, although promising from a qualitative point of view, high-temperature purification with various chemicals, particularly sodium carbonate–sulfite mixtures, will be more expensive than treatment with sodium hydroxide, if not carried out as a cooking stage, where there are greater possibilities for the recovery of heat and chemicals. As a bleaching stage, hot alkali purification will continue to use sodium hydroxide, which also fulfills the deresination function of the stage much more efficiently than does sodium carbonate.

1021

REFERENCES

1. Assarsson, A., *et al. Svensk Papperstid.*, **62,** 865 (1959).
2. Bassett, H. P., *U.S. Pat.* 1,733,393 (1929).
3. Bergek, T., *et al.*, *Svensk Papperstid.*, **50,** No. 11B, 22 (1947).
4. Bernstein, A., *Ger. Pat.* 537,846 (1928).
5. Björkqvist, K. J., *Medd.* CCL (Stockholm), **B 36** (1957).
6. Bronnert, E., *et al.*, *Ger. Pat.* 119,099 (1900).
7. Burdynski, R. F., and K. A. Kobe, *Tappi*, **36,** 248 (1953).
8. Busch, H., *U.S. Pat.* 1,991,786 (1935).
9. Christoffersson, K., and O. Samuelson, *Svensk Papperstid.*, **63,** 729 (1960).
10. Clibbens, D. A., *et al.*, *J. Textile Inst.*, **16,** T 13 (1925); **17,** T 145 (1926); **18,** T 277 (1927).
11. Corbett, W. M., and J. Kidd, *Tappi*, **41,** 137 (1958).
12. Corbett, W. M., and G. N. Richards, *Svensk Papperstid.*, **60,** 791 (1957).
13. Davidson, G. F., *J. Textile Inst.*, **34,** T 87 (1943).
14. Davidson, G. F., and T. P. Nevell, *J. Textile Inst.*, **39,** T 102 (1948).
15. Evans, W. L., *et al.*, *J. Am. Chem. Soc.*, **52,** 294 (1930); **53,** 4384 (1931); **58,** 2388 (1936).
16. Faust, O., and V. Hottenroth, *Ger. Pat.* 567,332 (1930).
17. Fischler, F., *Z. Physiol. Chem.*, **157,** 10, 22 (1926); **165,** 57 (1927).
18. Jayme, G., *Papierfabrik.*, **35,** 2 (1937).
19. Jayme, G., and U. Schenck, *Papier*, **3,** 469 (1949).
20. Kenner, J., *et al.*, *J. Chem. Soc.*, **1953-1959;** surveyed *Chem. & Ind.*, **1955,** 727.
21. Leugering, H. J., *Papier*, **7,** 47 (1953).
22. Limerich, J. McK., *U.S. Pat.* 2,592,300 (1952).
23. Machell, G., and G. N. Richards, *J. Chem. Soc.*, **1957,** 4500.
24. Machell, G., and G. N. Richards, *Tappi*, **41,** 12 (1958).
25. Maksimov, V. F., *Mitt. Kirov forsttech. Acad. (U.S.S.R.)*, **1940,** No. 59, 28.
26. March, R. E., *Paper Trade J.*, **127,** No. 17, 51 (1948).
27. Meller, A., *Tech. Assoc. Papers*, **30,** 214, 317 (1947).
28. Meller, A., *Tappi*, **34,** 171 (1951); **36,** 366 (1953); **38,** 682 (1955); **39,** 722 (1956); *Chem. & Ind.*, **1953,** 1204.
29. Meller, A., *The Alkaline Extraction of Wood Pulp*, in TAPPI Monograph Series No. 10, New York 1953, p. 29.
30. Meller, A., *Svensk Papperstid.*, **65,** 307 (1962).
31. Nepenin, Y. N., and A. D. Buervskaya, *Tr. Leningr. Lesotekhn. Akad.*, No. 80, part 2, 19 (1958).
32. Opferman, E., *et al.*, *Ger. Pat.* 539,938 (1929).
33. Parrett, A. N., *U.S. Pat.* 2,823,119; 2,823,120; 2,823,121 (1958); *Swed. Pat.* 163,857 (1958).
33a. Rapson, W. H., *Tappi*, **39,** 284 (1956).
34. Rapson, W. H., and G. K. Morbey, *Tappi*, **42,** 125 (1959).
35. Rayonier Inc., *Swed. Pat.* 152,116 (1955).
36. Reeves, R. E., *et al.*, *J. Am. Chem. Soc.*, **68,** 1383 (1946).
37. Richards, G. N., and H. H. Sephton, *J. Chem. Soc.*, **1957,** 4492.
38. Richter, G. A., *U.S. Pat.* 1,654,603 (1928).
39. Richter, G. A., *Ind. Eng. Chem.*, **23,** 266 (1931).
40. Richter, G. A., *U.S. Pat.* 1,935,129 (1933).
41. Richter, G. A., *Ind. Eng. Chem.*, **33,** 1518 (1941).

42. Richter, G. A., *Tappi*, **38**, 129 (1955).
43. Richtzenhain, H., *et al.*, *Svensk Papperstid.*, **57**, 363, 538 (1954).
44. Rogers, L. N., *et al.*, *U.S. Pat.* 2,878,118 (1959).
45. Rosenberger, N. A., *Zellstoff Papier*, **21**, 184, 210 (1941).
46. Rutherford, H. A., *et al.*, *J. Research Nat'l Bur. Std.*, **29**, 131 (1942).
47. Rydholm, S. A., unpublished.
48. Rys, L., and A. Bönisch, *Zellstoff Papier*, **18**, 573 (1938).
49. Rys, L., and P. Treka, *Zellstoff Papier*, **21**, 6, 35, 80, 112 (1941).
50. Samuelson, H. O., *U.S. Pat.* 2,902,481 (1959).
51. Samuelson, O., *et al.*, *Svensk Kem. Tidskr.*, **61**, 234 (1949).
52. Samuelson, O., *et al.*, *Svensk Papperstid.*, **64**, 694 (1961).
53. Samuelson, O., and C. Ramsel, *Svensk Papperstid.*, **53**, 135 (1950).
54. Samuelson, O., and A. Wennerblom, *Svensk Papperstid.*, **57**, 827 (1954).
55. Schenker, C., and M. A. Heath, *Tappi*, **42**, 709 (1959).
56. Schoettler, J. R., *Tappi*, **37**, 686 (1954).
57. af Schultén, K., *Finn. Pat.* 17,029 (1936).
58. Schur, M. O., and B. G. Hoos, *U.S. Pat.* 1,968,468 (1934).
59. Simmonds, F. A., *et al.*, *Tappi*, **35**, 166 (1952); **36**, 103 (1953); **38**, 178 (1955).
60. Simmonds, F. A., *et al.*, *Tappi*, **39**, 641 (1956).
61. Surewics, W., *Przeglad Papier.*, **8**, 233 (1952).
62. Wayman, M., Paper presented at the TAPPI Pulp Bleaching Conf., Chicago 1960.
63. Wayman, M., and D. L. Sherk, *Tappi*, **39**, 786 (1956).

16

REMOVAL OF IMPURITIES

I. Deresination

1. GENERAL CONSIDERATIONS

The terms *resin* and *pitch* refer to organo-soluble matter which occurs in the pulp and as a deposit on the pulp and paper-making machinery, and which originates from the extractives of the wood. Its chemical nature is not known in every detail, since it represents a mixture of incompletely investigated and fairly reactive substances of the wood, which have undergone a sequence of rather severe chemical treatments. The term resin will be commonly used for this mixture at any stage of processing and for any type of wood origin, although admittedly the term in that way will describe widely varying chemical compounds. *Deresination* will be the term used to describe their removal (75). As an important part of the deresination is done in the alkali stage of the bleaching, this chapter on deresination is placed here, but to make the treatment more comprehensive, other efforts of deresination will also be described briefly here. Surveys of the vast literature of the subject have been given (e.g. 11, 21, 56, 64, 73, 87).

On the whole, resin is an undesirable component of the pulp. There is definite proof that part of the resin in the dissolving pulps may have a beneficial surface activity in the viscose process (82a), whereas excessive amounts of resin affect the processing and product properties of the dissolving pulps adversely. The resin content of dissolving pulps should, therefore, be kept within fairly rigid limits, usually 0.15–0.30%. On the processing of paper pulps, resin deposits on the paper machine, as well as foaming, are experienced from resinous pulps, and also resin specks in the paper. Clogging of filters and screens, deposits on moving metal parts as well as on bleach-hollander linings, causing sudden contamination of the pulp, are among the resin troubles encountered in the pulp mill (3, 61, 91). Another disadvantage of the pulp resin is the phenomenon of self-sizing, which occurs on the storage of paper products through the redistribution of the resin over the entire fiber surface. This impairs the absorptive properties of tissue or the wettability of corrugating medium paper by silicate glue (94). The main weapons used to fight resin troubles are:

(1) Seasoning of the wood.
(2) Efficient washing of the pulp after cooking.
(3) Fiber fractionation.

(4) Alkaline extraction.

(5) Additions of surface active agents and sequestering agents.

An additional important way to fight pitch troubles cannot be placed under the heading of deresination as it aims to fixate the resin to the fibers in a non-tacky form. To this category belongs the use of aluminium sulfate or cation-active agents (36), as described in Chapter 8.I on the groundwood pulping of pine. A similar principle involves the addition of finely dispersed silica, to decrease the tackiness of the pulp resin (17).

2. LOCATION AND CHEMICAL COMPOSITION OF RESINS

As dealt with in Chapter 4.V, the extractives of wood are located in the middle lamella between most cells in small amounts, in large amounts in the medullary rays and other parenchymatic cells, and further, with soft-woods in the resin ducts, and with hardwoods in the partition walls of the vessels (70) and in the tylose tissue forming in the heartwood of some hardwoods. The resin-producing parenchyma cells are the only living cells of the xylem, and their death means the formation of heartwood. The formation of heartwood is in all wood species preceded by an increased resin production for the *protection* of the inner part of the xylem. It must be kept in mind that the felling of the tree leads to the death of all paren-chyma, but not immediately. The manner of storage of the pulpwood is of importance in how far the production of resin will go before the functions of the cells cease. Apart from the protective function, the wood resin also serves as a *food reserve*. The fat content of birch has been found lowest during the winter and maximal in May (71, 72). According to other find-ings, the minimum occurs in the summer.

The composition of the extractives varies with the growth region, the wood species and the location in the trunk. Analytically, the resin is characterized by repeated extractions with different solvents, such as *petrol or ethyl ether* followed by *ethanol or acetone*. The ether-soluble fraction will then contain the less polar compounds and is usually con-sidered to constitute the more troublesome part of the resins. The *alcohol-soluble* fraction after previous ether extraction contains more polar compounds, e.g. the phenols *pinosylvin, lignans, phlobaphenes, tannins*.

The *ether-solubles* can be subdivided into *fatty acids* and *esters, resin acids* and *unsaponifiables*. The latter category contains a number of various compounds, such as *sterols, triterpenes, higher alcohols*, etc. Hardwoods contain more of that category than softwoods, as exemplified by Figure 16.1 (48, 49, cf. 12, 86). The birch resin contains mainly neutral substances and a small fraction of free fatty acids. However, the neutral substance is considerably saponifiable to *fatty acids*, so that two-thirds of the resin consists of fatty acids and esters and only one-third of unsaponi-fiables. The alcohol part of the fatty esters is mainly *glycerol*, but a minor part of the fatty acids is combined with sterols (12). The sprucewood resin, on the other hand, contains two-thirds of neutral substances and one-third of free acids, mainly *resin acids*, and after saponification it consists of 50 % of fatty acids, one-fourth of resin acids and one-fourth of unsaponifiables (20). As one of the main means of deresination is alkali extraction, the above facts explain why resin problems are generally greater with hardwoods than with softwoods, and why some resin is more easily removed than the remainder. Pine contains less neutral resin components than does spruce, only about 10 % of the extractives (8, 33, 35, 45, 58, 84), and this is reflected in the relative ease of deresination of pine sulfite pulps on bleaching, in spite of a relatively high initial resin content of the unbleached pulp (30).

The more detailed *composition of the fatty acids* is also exemplified in Figures 16.1–2. The main part consists of C_{16-18} acids, of which the majority are *unsaturated*. Of the unsaturated fatty acids those with two double bonds, mainly *linoleic acid*, dominate, a minority has one double bond, as in *oleic acid*, and another small part is of the *linolenic acid* type with three double bonds. The proportions of these three acids probably vary with the climate (61a), a lower temperature requiring a lower degree of saturation, and the linolenic acid part has been found to vary between 4 and

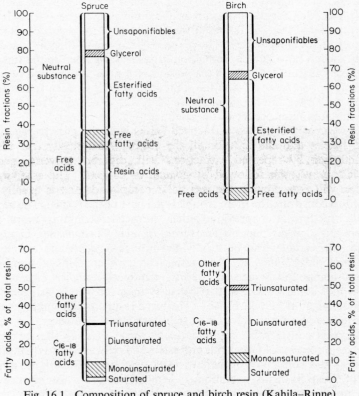

Fig. 16.1. Composition of spruce and birch resin (Kahila–Rinne)

1026

10% in the different investigations, cf. Table 4.32. The *saturated* fatty acids have been further analyzed, with the results given in Table 4.33 (86). *Palmitic* and *stearic acid* dominate.

The resin ducts contain considerably more of the acid and ester fraction than do the medullary rays, in which the unsaponifiables dominate (7).

Investigations on the *composition of the resin acids* of the gum oleoresin of spruce (10a, 13a, 47) and pine (10a, 31) could, therefore, be considered as representative also for the resin acids of sprucewood and pinewood.

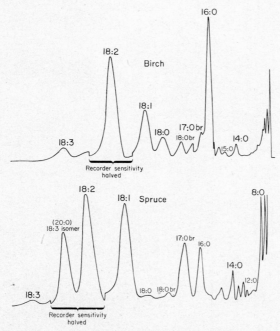

Fig. 16.2. Gas chromatograms of the fatty acid fraction of birch and spruce. 'br' denotes supposedly branched molecules (Donetzhuber)

These results are summarized in Table 4.34 and Figure 16.3. In spruce, *dextropimaric acid*, and in pine *levopimaric acid* dominate, but considerable quantities of several other resin acids are present in both cases. They are readily isomerized to similar resin acids, mainly *abietic acid*.

The *unsaponifiable fraction* has also been studied rather more closely. The dominating components are *phytosterols*, in spruce (20) and pine (8, 33, 84) as well as birch (49, 86). The phytosterols are dominated by β-*sitosterol* together with smaller quantities of the more saturated β-*sitostanol*. Other components, mainly *lignoceryl alcohol*, are also present in the unsaponifiables, together with the glycerol of the fats, which appear to be entirely triglycerides.

1027

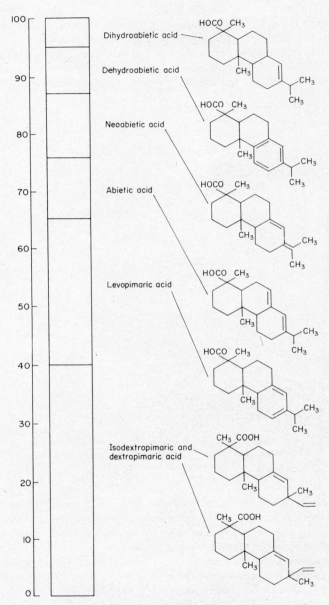

Fig. 16.3. Composition of softwood oleoresin (Harris, Kahila)

3. EFFECT OF SEASONING

It is generally agreed that green wood, if not pulped immediately after felling, will cause considerably more resin troubles than after a long period of storage, *seasoning*. It has been maintained that volatile compounds, which disappear on storage, might polymerize to resinous compounds in the processing of unseasoned wood. Their disappearance might also influence the character of the remainder, especially its *tackiness*. Another explanation is that the wood extractives take up *oxygen* on storage and thereby change their physical character (e.g. 61b). Anyhow, it is generally agreed that the extractives on storage change to a less tacky form, and a decrease of the ether-soluble fraction has been noted (e.g. 10, 64, 74, 77a, 87, cf. however, 35, 95). However, the effect depends on the type of storage. The ether, alcohol and total extracts of sulfite pulps from spruce, stored on land and/or in water for various periods, are seen in Figure 16.4

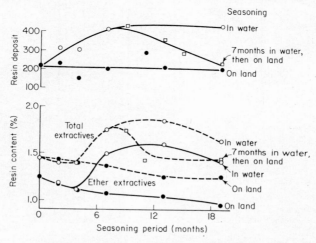

Fig. 16.4. Ether extractives, ether + alcohol (total) extractives and pitch depositing tendency of unbleached sulfite pulp from spruce, seasoned in various ways (Gufstafsson *et al*)

(27), together with index numbers for the tendency of these pulps to form pitch deposits. Such numbers are obtained by empirical methods determining the part of the pulp resin which adheres to moving metal parts (5, 26). Whereas the alcohol extract of the pulps is fairly unaffected by the storage, the ether extract will decrease on land storage of the wood but increase on storage under water. Storage under water should thus be avoided unless preceded by land storage (for instance in the forest) for some months. To decrease pitch troubles caused by wood storage under water, subsequent storage on land for a considerable time is necessary. The effect of water storage is likely to be explained by an increased life-time of the parenchymatic cells, possibly under stimulation of their resin-producing activity.

The changes in the chemical composition of sprucewood resin on storage are demonstrated in Figure 16.5 (48, 64). Obviously the relative concentration of unsaponifiables, as well as that of the free and combined acids taken as an entity, does not change materially, whereas the relative concentration of free acids, especially fatty acids, increases with the period of storage, particularly on storage under water, at the same time as an

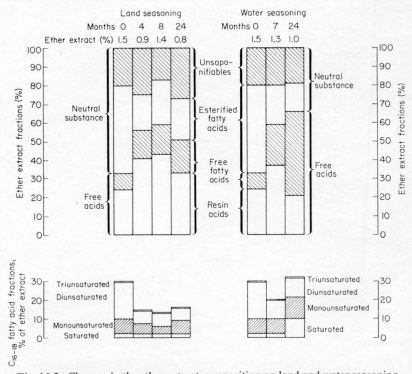

Fig. 16.5. Changes in the ether extract composition on land and water seasoning of spruce (Kahila)

increase in the acid number and decrease in the iodine number. The absolute amount of acids and esters calculated on wood basis, however, decrease on land storage.

As the changes in the fatty acid and ester fraction seem to be the most essential chemical effect of the seasoning, that fraction was analyzed more closely, as demonstrated in Figure 16.5. As was the case for the entire acid and ester fraction, the C_{16-18} fatty acids and esters also decrease on land storage but less so on storage under water. It is mainly the linolenic and linoleic acid fractions which decrease, whereas the saturated fatty acids as well as the oleic acid fraction are largely unaffected by land storage and may even increase in the case of water storage. The changes noted reappear in the sulfite pulps from these wood grades. Figures 16.6–7 demonstrate in a similar manner the changes of the ether-soluble components, particularly the fatty acids, on land seasoning of peeled birch logs (14a). The ester hydrolysis of the fats occurred mainly during the first six months, during which period the free fatty acids logically increased, subsequently to decrease again because of the other main reaction, the oxidation

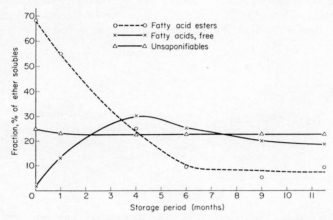

Fig. 16.6. Changes in fractions of ether solubles during seasoning of birch logs (Croon–Assarsson)

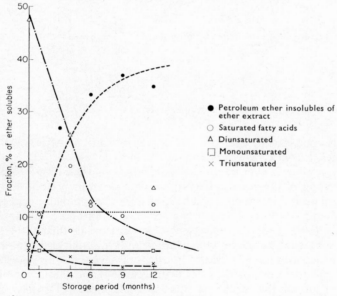

Fig. 16.7. Changes in fatty acids during seasoning of birch logs (Croon–Assarsson)

of linoleic acid, which, however, also occurred mainly during the first six months, accompanied by a corresponding increase in the petroleum ether insolubles ('oxidized acids'). Unsaponifiables, saturated and mono-unsaturated fatty acids are not affected by the seasoning.

Whereas the ester hydrolysis is generally considered to be enzymatic, the mechanism of oxidation and the products formed have not been completely clarified. It has been demonstrated that 10% of the C_9 double bonds of linoleic acid shift to C_8 position upon autoxidation (51), and studies on the autoxidation of fats (e.g. 59a) have led to a concept of the reaction sequence which is summarized in Figure 16.8. Oxygen is added to give hydro-

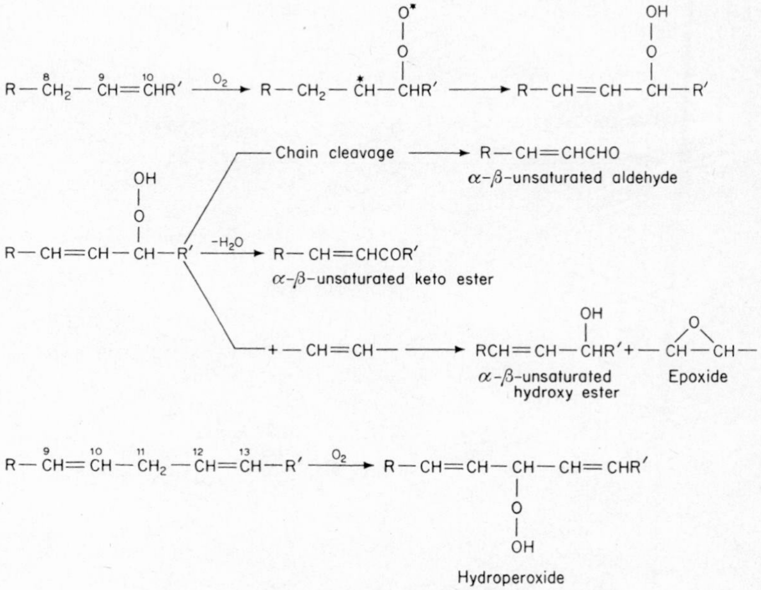

Fig. 16.8. Autoxidation of fats (Lea)

peroxides or peroxide radicals, which give rise to chain cleavage and to aldehydes, ketones, hydroxy compounds and epoxides.

The levopimaric acid fraction of pine resin has been found to decrease on seasoning of the wood, at the same time as an increase in the abietic acid formation, indicating isomerization (67). Levopimaric acid has also been found to oxidize rapidly in the presence of air and catalysts, such as quinones (59). The main effects of wood seasoning thus seem to be a *hydrolysis* of the fats and an *isomerization* and *oxidation* of the unsaturated acids particularly linoleic acid. The effect of *drying* during wood storage seems to be to accelerate the ester hydrolysis (64) and should facilitate the access of air for the oxidation. One possible means of accelerating the expensive storage operation is the exposure of a larger wood surface, such as occurs on chipping. Chip piles are known to develop considerable heat,

1032

possibly an effect of oxidation. Such exothermal effects have been correlated to the resin content of the wood (89). Figure 16.9 (14a) very clearly
demonstrates the acceleration of both the ester hydrolysis and the oxidation of fatty acids when storing sprucewood in the form of chips instead of
logs. Chip storage by still higher temperature than that developed in outdoor piles (50–60°C) has been suggested and shown to bring about further
acceleration of the desirable reactions of the resin (61b).

A further decrease of the amount and a change in the resin composition
connected with the handling of pulpwood is noted in the *wood room*, as
the sawdust fraction (from spruce) contains 3–7 times as much resin as
the main chip fraction (7, 99), presumably from the resin ducts, as it
contains more acids, especially resin acids, than the average.

4. EFFECT OF COOKING

The *cooking process* considerably influences the resin content of the pulp.
In the *kraft* cooking of softwoods, the main part of the resins are dissolved
and obtained in the form of soap skimmings on the evaporation of the black
liquor. The unbleached kraft pulps therefore generally contain only about
0.2% resin. The skimmings contain around 10% unsaponifiables and approximately equal parts of soaps of fatty and resin acids. If the amount of
unsaponifiables increases, as in the case of mixing in hardwoods, the acid
soaps do not finally possess sufficient micellar-forming properties (cf. below)
to carry the less polar compounds into solution, and then even kraft mills
may run into appreciable resin troubles unless softwood soap skimmings
are added to the cook to facilitate the dispersion of the hardwood resin.
The main difficulties with resin, however, occur in the *sulfite* mills and with

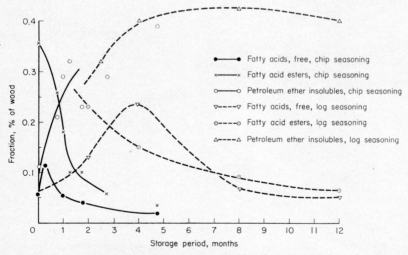

Fig. 16.9. Changes in fractions of ether solubles during seasoning of spruce
logs and chips (Croon–Assarsson)

1033

both softwoods and hardwoods. In the acid cook, the fatty and resin acids are not converted into hydrophilic soaps as in the alkaline pulping processes. Still, a considerable amount of resin, up to around 50%, is dispersed in the cooking liquor, from both softwoods and hardwoods (48, 49, 64, 97, 101).

It has been pointed out (20) that in order to judge which chemical changes occur with the resin during the sulfite cook, it is not sufficient to compare the composition of the resin in the wood with that in the pulp, as certain of the components are dissolved to a higher extent than the others. A correct estimation will therefore require analysis of the total extractives before and after pulping. This has been done on pulping of spruce, enriched on extractives (20). The most remarkable chemical change noted was an acid hydrolysis of fatty acid esters. No oxidation, reduction or polymerization was observed, although the resin became considerably darker by the cook. Not all resin could, however, be accounted for, possibly because chemical changes such as sulfonation during the cook lead to higher hydrophility of some material.

None the less it is of obvious interest to characterize the resin of the pulp and compare its composition with that of the wood resin. Figure 16.10 (48, 49, 64) demonstrates that the changes in the resin composition brought about by the storage of sprucewood, are also noticeable in the

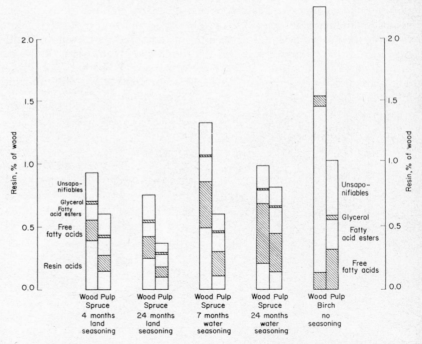

Fig. 16.10. Dissolution and composition changes of ether extractives on acid sulfite pulping of spruce, seasoned by different methods, and of green birchwood (Kahila–Rinne)

resin of the unbleached pulp. Thus, the pulp resin from the water-stored wood is especially rich in fatty acids. It is also evident that 20–50% of the wood resin disappears during the cook, and that the composition of the remainder deviates from the original. As was noted earlier (20, 101), the *resin acids* especially are dispersed during the cook to an extent (60% or more) exceeding the average, whereas the total sum of free and combined fatty acids remains largely unchanged, and the unsaponifiables are dispersed to an extent corresponding to the average. The selective dispersion of resin acids could be explained not only as a chemical effect but possibly also by a greater accessibility of the duct resin as compared to that of the ray cells. In other investigations, an increased proportion of unsaponifiables in the pulp resin, 24 to 44%, has been noted (81).

Figure 16.10 likewise shows the corresponding changes of the *birch* resin. It is evident that the somewhat larger amount of resin is subjected to an absolutely as well as relatively greater dispersion than the spruce resin, in spite of the lack of acids. Fatty acids are thus rather more easily dispersed than the unsaponifiables. The fatty acid esters are hydrolyzed to a very great extent during the cook. Green birchwood, with its higher content of fats and unsaponifiables, gives a less easy resin dispersion during the sulfite cook, as compared with birch stored on land for about 8 months (64).

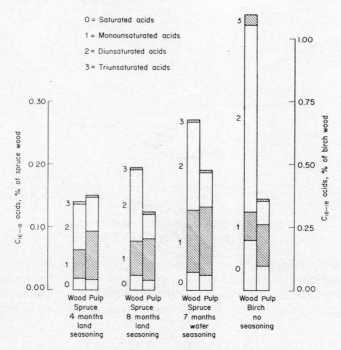

Fig. 16.11. Changes in the C_{16-18} fatty acid composition of spruce and birch on acid sulfite pulping after different types of seasoning (Kahila–Rinne)

1035

On sulfite cooking, the acid and iodine numbers of the fatty acids decrease by some 10–20 units, whereas the acid number of the resin acids remains unchanged. Figure 16.11 (48, 49) shows that the content of unsaturated C_{16-18} fatty acids, containing two double bonds (linoleic acid, etc.), decreases considerably as compared with the oleic acid fraction. That is true for both spruce and birch. The distribution of the saturated fatty acids remains largely unchanged during the cook. Birch, cut in the spring, gives a higher resin content not only in the wood (72) but also in the sulfite pulp (71), as compared to wood cut in summertime. On an *average*, unbleached sulfite pulps contain about 1.5% resin (alcohol extractives) from green wood and about 1.0% resin from stored wood. Corresponding figures for birch sulfite pulps are 3.5 and 2.5% resin. No major changes are obtained by changing the cooking conditions, whereas a decrease is generally experienced with an increased degree of cooking (28).

The changes of the resin during *neutral sulfite pulping* have not been investigated in detail. However, Figure 16.12 (80) demonstrates the importance of keeping a sufficient buffer capacity in the cooking liquor, to avoid reprecipitation of the dispersed resin onto the fibers during the final stages of the cook. The pH dependence clearly indicates the role of the fatty acid soaps as dispersing agents.

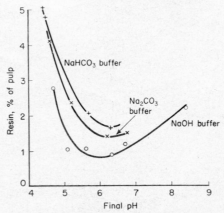

Fig. 16.12. Pulp resin vs. final pH upon neutral sulfite cooking of birch (Rydholm)

The resin removal during the cooking is therefore quite considerable in all processes, in the acid sulfite pulping also. It is therefore naturally very important that the *washing* of the pulp should be carried out carefully and avoid reprecipitation of the dispersed resin by the use of hot water (87).

5. EFFECT OF SCREENING

The resin removal by fiber fractionation in the screening room was mentioned in Chapter 10 (cf. 77, 84a). With modern equipment, the reject leaving the fractionators has a resin content of 20–35%, but some losses of good fibers are still unavoidable, and the economic justification of fiber fractionation is still debated in the case of normal softwood sulfite pulps. However, for sulfite pulping of some hardwoods, fiber fractionation is a valuable complement to other methods of deresination.

6. EFFECT OF THE BLEACHING STAGES

Deresination in the bleachery takes place mainly in the alkali stage, although the treatments before and after the alkali extraction are also important for the ultimate result. Table 16.1 and Figures 16.13 (64) and

Table 16.1. The resin content of wood and sulfite pulp at various stages of processing

Wood species	Spruce	Pine	Birch
Resin content, % of			
green wood	1.5–2.5	4–6	2–4
seasoned wood	1–2	4–6	2–4
unbleached pulp	1.0–1.5	2.5–4	2–4
fractionated pulp	–	–	1.0–1.5
alkali extracted pulp	0.1–0.6	0.1–0.6	0.3–0.8
bleached pulp	0.1–0.5	0.1–0.5	0.2–0.6

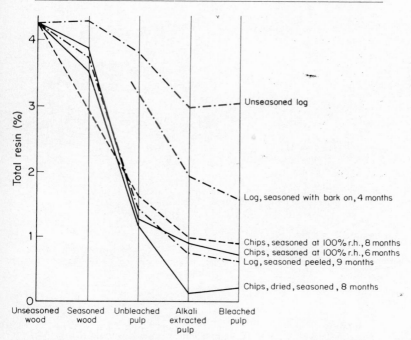

Fig. 16.13. Deresination of white birch after various stages of seasoning (Mutton)

16.14 (1a) give a survey of the resin content of wood and pulp at various stages of processing. The figures are only indicative, wood species and local conditions much influencing the results. It is seen, that some deresination is achieved during storage, considerable deresination occurs in the cooking and hot alkali purification, provided the wood was seasoned, and some additional deresination in the final oxidative bleaching. Unseasoned wood makes a less efficient deresination in all stages. The changes in wood resin composition in seasoning spruce logs and chips (cf. Figure 16.9) are likewise reflected in the resin content of bleached and unbleached pulps. Chip storage appears to shorten the necessary seasoning period from 8–12 to 1–2 months.

As mentioned in the introduction, the resin troubles in connection with paper pulps are of rather different type, as for dissolving pulps. In the former case those parts of the resin, which are comparatively free at the surface of the fibers cause the main difficulties, in the form of resin depositions on the machinery and specks in the paper. In the case of dissolving pulps, the resin remaining within the fibers is also a source of trouble, as it is exposed at the dissolution of the pulp, causes processing difficulties and

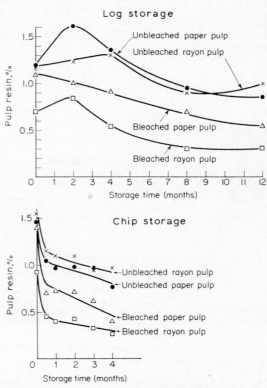

Fig. 16.14. Effect of log and chip seasoning in the production of spruce sulfite pulps (Annergren *et al*)

impairs the final product. In both cases the brightness of the bleached pulp (and the brightness stability) is also affected by the presence of resin.

The troubles caused by the externally located resin are also related, apart from the amount, to its tackiness. Viscosity measurements on the resin give some information. Contact angle measurements have been made against mercury, but the results obtained were incomprehensive (57). Measurements of surface film pressures gave results more in agreement with practical experience (43). The empirical methods measuring the weight of resin deposit on moving copper or steel parts at defined conditions have yielded more valuable results (5, 26). The deposition of the resin particles always occurs on the pressure side of the moving specimen and will be enriched there if the surface is porous. If the surface is hard and smooth, the resin particles tend to travel leewards and may finally leave the specimen in aggregated form, to give resin specks in the paper. These phenomena change with the tackiness and viscosity of the resin, as illustrated by Figure 16.15 (5). It has been found that the tackiness

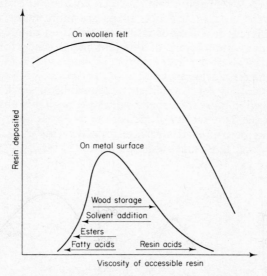

Fig. 16.15. Influence of resin viscosity on pitch deposition on felt and metal surfaces, and factors influencing resin viscosity (Back)

of the resin increases with the pH in the range of pH 5–9, from a fairly low level in acid medium, and with a downward trend at above pH 9, Figure 16.16 (26). In the presence of calcium ions tackiness is considerably increased in addition to the pH effect, but only in the pH range mentioned. Salts of monovalent ions such as sodium bicarbonate, have little effect. Tackiness usually increases with temperature to a maximum at around room temperature and decreases at additional rise in temperature, Figure 16.16 (26). The maximum is reached at higher temperatures for harder

1039

resins (with a higher melting interval) from stored wood (92). Therefore, in a limited temperature interval, the deposit might increase for one type of resin and decrease for another. These phenomena are probably closely related to the viscosity of the resin (92), which decreases with an increase in temperature. At a certain viscosity interval, tackiness is at a maximum. The viscosity increase reached on the storage of the wood, be it an oxidative polymerization or a loss of volatile components, gives resins which are less tacky than from green wood at normal temperature, but which at increased temperature arrive at the critical viscosity interval, whereas the resins from green wood pass out of the same on a temperature increase. However, the rheological properties of the resins being non-newtonian, resin tackiness could hardly be described by a viscosity figure alone. The changes in the flow curve are likely to be quite different for a similar increase in apparent viscosity by storage of the wood and by a temperature decrease. The non-tacky resin in pulp from stored wood is likely to have a higher yield value than a tacky resin of the same apparent viscosity.

The pH effect is probably explained by a conversion of the acid components to soaps, and the calcium soaps are more tacky than sodium soaps. The different tendency of resin deposition on different metals has been explained as monolayers of different metal soaps forming at the interface. The pK_a's of the fatty acids are around 5–6 (18, 44, 68, 90, 100), and those of the resin acids around 5.7 (6), and hence both types of acids, but especially the fatty acids, are likely to contribute to the development of tackiness. Addition of hydrocarbons, which are probably absorbed by the resin and decrease its viscosity, diminish the tackiness (26). The addition of kerosene has been used to decrease resin deposits in the screening of resinous hardwood kraft and sulfite pulps.

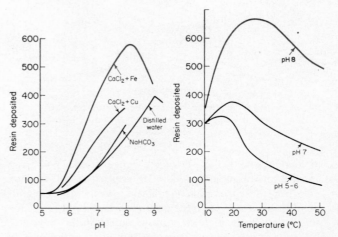

Fig. 16.16. Pitch trouble (illustrated as resin deposit on copper or iron propeller) at varying pH and temperature in the presence or absence of monovalent or divalent metal ions (Gustafsson et al)

The resin deposited on the copper impeller of the method of determining tacky resin was analyzed with the result in Figure 16.17 (48). Obviously the deposited resin has about the same composition as the ether extract of the pulp. The composition of the C_{16-18} fatty acid fraction also agreed with that in the pulp.

The question of which component causes the tackiness of the pulp resin has been debated, and the suggestion that the amount of ethyl or petrol ether extract of the pulp is proportional to the amount of depositable resin has been rejected (48). It was shown instead that the amount of free fatty acids bore a certain relation to the extent of deposition. Three pre-extracted pulps were impregnated with a typical resin fraction in an amount of 1.5%, whereupon the amount of depositable resin was determined in

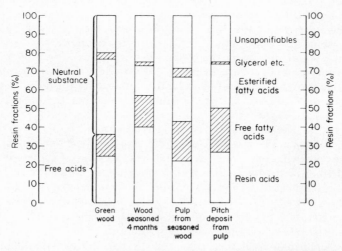

Fig. 16.17. Resin composition of sprucewood, sulfite pulp and pitch deposit (Kahila–Rinne)

the usual way. The results are shown in Table 16.2 together with results from pulps with natural resin content, analyzed for fatty acids. It is obvious that the tackiness is mainly related to the content of free fatty acids. That the latter have not been found to be enriched in the deposited resin must be explained by the fact that the other components will follow the fatty acids to the hydrophobic phase. The tackiness of the different components has also been studied by comparison with model substances, such as saturated and unsaturated fatty acids, abietic acid, fatty acid esters, unsaponifiable substances etc. (67). In the pure form only the fatty acids were noticeably tacky, but a suitable mixture of abietic acid with other, low-viscosity components also gave rise to tackiness.

The mechanism of pitch deposition is visualized as follows. A monolayer of pitch is always formed at an air–water interphase. If the interphase is changed by mechanical means, the behavior of the monolayer will depend on its physical properties. An acid film, especially at higher temperatures, is liquid and dispersible, but as the metal content of the layer increases, the viscosity of the film increases rapidly (93). The metal content of the film varies with pH, analysis showing no calcium present at pH 6, and complete conversion to calcium soaps at pH 9. When the film becomes very viscous and rigid, it tends to collapse on deformation, is 'skimmed off' and forms threads and soft, tacky balls, which tend to agglomerate to deposits and also catch other, less tacky substances, such as lignin and carbohydrate matter. The more air–water interphases, the greater the rate of mono- and multilayer film formation. To avoid pitch troubles, aeration of the pulp suspensions at pumps and backfalls should be avoided. The role of the bicarbonate ion in water to be acidified, has also been pointed out (25). Carbon dioxide is evolved on acidification, causing new interphases and pitch troubles.

Chlorination of the resin adds considerably to the tackiness, especially in the case of hardwood pulps (75, 77), whereas *oxidation* has the reverse effect and yields a more hard and brittle resin. Obviously, these phenomena also have importance for the dispersion of the resins in alkali, because the pretreatment of the pulp is of considerable importance for the efficiency of deresination in the alkali stage. Figure 16.18 shows the resin content after the alkali stage of softwood and hardwood pulps, with constant conditions of deresination and varying amounts of chlorine or chlorine dioxide charged in the preceding stage (75). Obviously, oxidative treatment facilitates deresination, and chlorine charges in excess of those consumed by the lignin of the pulp make resin removal more difficult, especially in the case of hardwoods. An initial oxidative stage is therefore recommended in the case of hardwoods instead of chlorination, with either *hypochlorite* (77) or preferably *chlorine dioxide* (75, 76), unless the alkali stage is placed first in the bleaching sequence. Also with resinous softwood pulps it is wise to avoid chlorination of the resins, e.g. by an intermediate alkali stage

Table 16.2. Content, composition and deposition tendency of resin in spruce sulfite pulps, unextracted, or extracted and subsequently impregnated with typical resin fractions (48)

	Resin content, %	Fatty acid content, % Total fats and fatty acids	Free fatty acids only	Deposited resin at pH 7, 40°C, mg/200 g pulp
Extracted, impregnated with				
unsaponifiables	1.50	0	0	41
resin acids	1.50	0	0	127
fatty acids	1.50	1.50	1.50	693
Unextracted, land-storage wood,				
4 months	1.35	0.60	0.27	165
24 months	1.28	0.65	0.25	45
Unextracted, water-storage wood,				
7 months	1.33	0.69	0.40	420
24 months	1.79	1.13	0.68	637

between two chlorinations, of which the initial is performed with less chlorine than corresponding to the demand of the lignin. The chemical reactions involved at the chlorination have been found (60) to be an addition of chlorine and hypochlorous acid to double bonds of unsaturated fatty acids, resin acids, as well as some of the unsaponifiables, possibly accompanied by a polymerization, since there was an increase in the molecular weight of the chlorinated resin, which was also found to become more hydrophobic than before the chlorination. The following reactions are thus probable:

$$-CH{=}CH- + Cl_2 \longrightarrow -\underset{\underset{Cl}{|}}{C}H-\underset{\underset{Cl}{|}}{C}H-$$

$$-CH{=}CH- + HOCl \longrightarrow -\underset{\underset{Cl}{|}}{C}H-\underset{\underset{OH}{|}}{C}H- \qquad\qquad -CH-\overset{+}{C}H-$$

$$-CH{=}CH- + Cl^+ \longrightarrow -\underset{\underset{Cl}{|}}{C}H-\overset{+}{C}H- \longrightarrow -\underset{\underset{Cl}{|}}{C}H-CH-$$

The oxidation must also involve the double bonds, accompanied by a

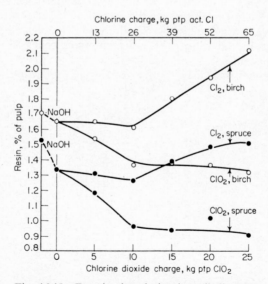

Fig. 16.18. Deresination during hot alkali purification of spruce and birch sulfite pulps after initial chlorination or chlorine dioxide oxidation with various charges. Conditions: stage 1, 3% cons., 25°C, 1 h; stage 2, 15% cons., 95°C, 3 h, 40 kg ptp NaOH (Rapson)

1043

degradation to smaller molecules and formation of carbonyls and ionizable carboxyl groups (60). Chlorination of the double bonds probably prohibits subsequent oxidation, and the slight deresination effected by the final oxidative stages will be counteracted by an initial chlorination of the resins. However, the degradation caused by oxidation must be limited, as even excessive use of oxidants does not appreciably lower the resin content of a pulp. The main disadvantage of initial chlorination of the resin, therefore, is that the dissolution of resin in the alkali stage is impeded.

The dispersion of resin in the alkaline extraction stage of bleaching, as well as in alkaline cooking stages, is in principle a *saponification* of the ester components of the resin, a *dissolution* of the fatty and resin acids in the form of sodium salts (soaps), and a *micellar solubilization* of the more or less hydrophobic constituents of the resins, i.e. the unsaponifiables and the remaining fatty acid esters. The micellar solubilization is effected by surface active agents, either the fatty and resin acid soaps, or added quantities of soaps or synthetic detergents. To improve the action of either category, inorganic compounds, known as *builders* in detergent chemistry, are often also added, such as tetrasodium pyrophosphate, sodium hexametaphosphate, sodium silicate, etc. The mechanism of micellar solubilization of hydrophobic or weakly polar compounds is illustrated by Figure 16.19 (2). The surface active components form micellar particles of a considerable degree of orientation, the hydrophilic parts of the molecules turned outwards into the solution and the hydrophobic parts into the interior of the micelles, enclosing the non-polar constituents of the resin. Weakly polar compounds orientate in the micells as do the molecules of the surface active agents, but are incapable of forming micelles alone. There is a critical concentration of the surface active agents below which micelles are not formed. This concentration is somewhat lowered by the

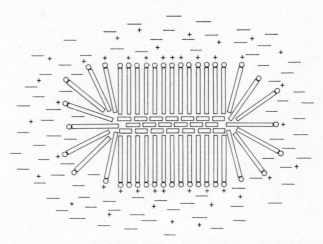

Fig. 16.19. Soap micell containing solubilized non-polar substance
(Back)

addition of builders, which explains why the addition of inorganic compounds alone, such as sodium hexametaphosphate (22) or tetrasodium pyrophosphate (61), will improve deresination. The critical concentration of micelle formation varies with the constitution of the molecules, being around 0.02 moles/l for resin soaps (2, 32) and 0.001–0.002 for fatty acid soaps (14, 55). A mixture of 50% fatty and 50% resin acid soaps has a critical micellar concentration of 0.0025 moles/l (32) and with this figure, it has been calculated (2) that in the kraft cooking of pine micellar concentration is exceeded, in the hot alkali purification half of the soaps are likely to form micelles, whereas in a dilute pulp suspension such as alkaline washing after chlorination, no micelle formation is obtained. The quantity of non-polar substances to be dispersed further determines the amounts of surface active agents needed. In the case of hardwood pulps, the proportion of non-polar or weakly polar constituents is considerably higher than with softwoods, and therefore addition of synthetic detergents is necessary.

Fairly early, additions of fatty acid soaps or oleic acid were used in the alkali stage for deresination. With the development of the synthetic detergents such additions were also patented for deresination of pulp, first the use of turkey red oil or sulfonated castor oil (38), and later non-ionic surface-active agents, consisting of ethylene oxide polycondensates with various organic substances (69, 76, 83), of which nonyl phenol was found to be particularly suitable. The optimum proportion of ethylene oxide varies with the type of co-condensed molecule, but 60–75% ethylene oxide is generally found most active with somewhat more ethylene oxide for softwood pulps than for hardwood pulps (69). These types of agents, sold at around $700 per ton, have to be added in the smallest quantities possible. The amounts necessary vary with the effect desired and the conditions, but are usually around 1–3 kg ptp, as seen in Figures 16.20–21 (75). Mechanical agitation improves the result. Addition of phosphate builders in quantities of 2–3 kg ptp add noticeably to the effect, but also to the costs. Generally speaking, therefore, additions of surface active agents are only used as a complement to cheaper methods of deresination, in cases of resinous pulps such as certain hardwood sulfite pulps, as well as when extremely low resin contents of softwood sulfite pulps are desired (dissolving pulp grades).

On dilution of the pulp suspension from the alkali stage, the critical micellar concentration is passed, and there is a danger of reprecipitation of resin. This may be counteracted by the addition of ethylene oxide polycondensates of a somewhat different type (pure alkyl ethers) in small amounts, down to around 0.1 kg ptp. Such additions are often used not only to prevent deposition on the pulp but also to keep the equipment clean of resin. Even when it is not considered necessary to add such agents, the washing of the pulp after the alkali and hypochlorite stages must be carried out very carefully and with hot water to derive the full benefit of the previous extraction of resin.

An important factor determining the effect of deresination as well as the reprecipitation phenomena is the alkalinity. Initially, pH in the alkali stage is sufficiently high to convert all acids and saponified esters to surface active soaps, thus also aiding the micellar solubilization of the less polar compounds. As alkalinity decreases during the hot alkali treatment in both the kraft cook and the purification stage, there is a danger of reconversion of the soaps into acids with lower hydrophility. As indicated by the pK_a's mentioned earlier, the critical pH range is

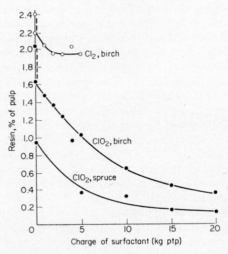

Fig. 16.20. Effect of surfactant (nonyl phenol polyoxyethylene) on the deresination of a hot alkali purification stage (15% cons., 95°C, 3 h, 40 kg ptp NaOH). Spruce and birch sulfite pulp, initial stage Cl_2 or ClO_2 (Rapson)

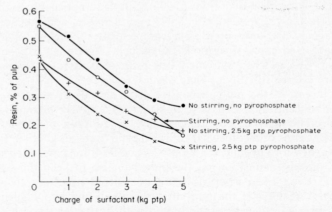

Fig. 16.21. Effect of surfactant (nonyl phenol polyoxyethylene), pyrophosphate and stirring upon deresination in a hot alkali purification stage (15% cons., 95°C, 3 h, 40 kg ptp NaOH) of pretreated spruce sulfite pulp (Rapson)

10–5. The final pH of an ordinary kraft cook is around 12, but in the case of high yield kraft cooks, where considerably less alkali is charged, pH may drop down to 7 or even lower, if not the other cooking conditions are adjusted accordingly. Such kraft pulps are darker in color and more resinous than pulps cooked to equal yield with higher alkali charges and lower temperature or shorter time used. In an analogous way, low-alpha and medium-alpha dissolving pulps, purified by fairly small alkali charges, are threatened with resin reprecipitation if the conditions of the purification stage are not properly chosen. As the period of purification is usually kept constant, maximum temperature and alkali charge should be balanced in a way giving the alphacellulose content desired and, at the same time, sufficient residual alkali to maintain good deresination conditions. Table 16.3 (66) shows some results obtained at low-alpha pulps, purified at three different temperatures to the same alphacellulose content. The addition of surface active agents to improve deresination does not eliminate the pH effects but tends to accentuate them.

Table 16.3. Resin content of spruce sulfite rayon pulps, hot alkali purified to 91.5% alphacellulose content at different temperatures (66)

Alkali charge, kg ptp	50	35	25
Temperature, °C	85	95	105
Final pH	12.5	11.5	8.5
Resin content, %	0.15	0.30	0.45

Thus, in the pH range 5–10, where the tackiness of the pulp resin increases, the solubility changes of the resin also occur. However, although the soap formation at increased pH will cause more tackiness and pitch troubles for paper pulps, soap formation is necessary for the deresination of dissolving pulps. The solubility of lauric and myristic acid at room temperature and varying pH is given in Figure 16.22 (68), and the similarity with the curves for depositable resin in Figure 16.16 is striking. At above

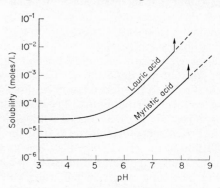

Fig. 16.22. pH dependence of fatty acid solubility (Nyren–Back)

1047

34—PP

pH 8 the soap formation is sufficient to cause micelle formation, which considerably increases the solubility and might also diminish tackiness and the tendency to form deposits.

However, the alkalinity alone does not determine the final result of deresination. The temperature and time effects are also of great importance, possibly because of the saponification reaction of the esters, probably also because of the lowered viscosity and easier accessibility of the resins at increased temperature, as well as increased solubility. Table 16.4 shows that when the temperature is lowered from 100°C to 30°C, the final resin content increases considerably, in spite of a higher final pH at the lower temperature. Sulfite paper pulps will therefore always have a higher resin content than hot alkali purified dissolving pulps, if not specially treated, and high-alpha pulps less resin than low-alpha pulps, as exemplified in Table 16.5.

Table 16.4. Temperature effect in deresination of rayon and paper pulps (spruce sulfite) in the alkali extraction stage

Alkali charge, kg ptp	15	50	50
Residual alkali, kg ptp	7	35	2
Temperature, °C	30	30	100
Final pH	11.5	12.5	10.0
Resin content, %	0.62	0.63	0.27

Table 16.5. Resin content, %, of various bleached spruce sulfite pulp grades

Strong paper pulps	0.6
90% alpha pulp for rayon staple	0.3
92% alpha pulp for filament rayon	0.2
95% alpha pulp for acetate	0.1

The manner of alkali addition to the chlorinated pulp is also of importance. It has been found that the main addition of alkali should be made at such a time that the critical pH range of 5–10 is passed as rapidly as possible. The detailed mechanism to explain that phenomenon is not elucidated, but is probably connected with physical phenomena, such as tackiness increase, as well as the chemical formation of calcium soaps from the calcium ions of the mill water. Calcium soap formation is probably detrimental to both the deresination of dissolving pulps and the avoidance of pitch troubles in paper pulps. The washing of the chlorinated pulp, where a large part of the calcium of a lime-based sulfite pulp is removed, must be carried out thoroughly. Part of the beneficial effect of polyphosphate addition in the alkali stage may be explained by sequestering calcium ions. Calcium soap formation is the cause of resin troubles in the hypochlorite bleaching stages, when using calcium hypochlorite. This is one of the reasons why the rather more expensive sodium hypochlorite is being increasingly used.

1048

Thus, the combined efforts of seasoning, cooking, fiber fractionation, alkali extraction in combination with surfactants, and oxidative degradation will lead to pulps of acceptable resin content. If seasoning is left out, the deresination of sulfite pulps becomes more difficult, and it is only recently, with the aid of surfactants and chlorine dioxide, that unseasoned wood can be used for more qualified pulp grades.

II. Removal of Inorganic Impurities

1. GENERAL DESCRIPTION OF PROCESS

A. Introduction

The inorganic impurities of the pulp, often collectively described as the *ash content*, mainly consist of silicates, sulfates and carbonates, as well as metal ions combined to the acidic groups of the pulp. A common subdivision is *acid-soluble* and *acid-insoluble* ashes, the latter being mainly the silicates. Most of the attention given to the ash content comes from the fact that these impurities affect the processing properties of dissolving pulps. Some impurities, mainly iron, manganese and copper, catalytically accelerate the air oxidation of unbleached sulfite pulp, called 'reddening' (1, 78, 98). Iron and manganese also impair the brightness and brightness stability of unbleached and bleached pulps (65, 78), as well as the rayon color (103), and are thus of interest for both paper and dissolving pulps. The aging of alkali cellulose prepared from dissolving pulps containing iron, manganese, copper, and other heavy metal ions is irreproducibly affected (50, 103). The presence of carbonates and carbonate-forming ions, such as calcium and magnesium, causes trouble in the pressing of the alkali cellulose, the filtration of the viscose and the spinning of the rayon (54). The silicate particles are especially objectionable for viscose filtrability (63, 82). Polyvalent metal ions cause viscosity anomalies and haze in the cellulose acetate prepared from impure acetate pulp (62).

B. Removal of silicates

Silicate enters the pulping process in three different ways, with the fiber raw material, with the chemicals, and with the mill water. Its removal is concerned with suitable treatment of these three categories, as well as of the pulp. As will be described in more detail in a subsequent section, alkaline treatment is more efficient than neutral or acid cooking to remove silica from the fiber raw material, and consequently kraft pulps contain less silica than sulfite pulps. A hot alkali purification is also more efficient in removing silica than an ordinary alkali extraction. However, the methods of pulping must in general be chosen on grounds other than silica removal. The treatment of cooking liquors by clarification (cf. Chapter 11) takes special notice of the silica content of the dissolving pulp to be produced. The mill water quite often requires special filtration to be suitable for dissolving pulp production, and for some rayon pulp mills, seasonal variations in the mill water quality makes it necessary to

1049

turn over to temporary paper pulp production. Considerable amounts of silica are mechanically removed during the thickening and washing operations after screening (104), and in special cases it is an advantage to use fiber fractionators to remove the small silica-rich epidermis cells of grass pulps to achieve a low final silica content.

The cleaning of pulp from mineral particles by rifflers and vortex cleaners (cf. Chapter 10) has a definite influence on the silica content of the pulp, a decrease from around 120 to 50 ppm. being noted upon the installation of vortex cleaners for ordinary spruce rayon pulps. For bamboo rayon pulps the corresponding figures are about 10 times as high.

C. Removal of metal ions

Iron, copper and *manganese,* as well as other metal ions in small quantities enter the system with the wood, cooking liquor, and mill water or from corrosion on the machinery. Manganese especially may be submitted to seasonal variations of the mill water. Manganese is also often concentrated as incrustant of the water purification station by the growth of *manganese-collecting bacteria* (*Chenotrix*), and may then enter the pulping system in widely varying amounts.

Calcium and *magnesium* enter with the wood, the chemicals, and with the mill water. Their concentration is usually much higher than that of the other metal ions. In the sulfite process, calcium and magnesium enter with the cooking acid, and the former precipitates at a certain stage of the cook on the pulp in the form of sulfate dihydrate (cf. Chapter 9). Part of the precipitate is dissolved during the washing of the pulp, and most of the remainder in the subsequent screening operation. Calcium ions are also attached to the sulfonate groups of the residual lignin of the pulps. In the thickening and filtration after screening, considerable amounts of lignosulfonate are removed, together with calcium (104). At the same time as the losses of fines in these operations or special fiber-fractionating equipment (cf. Chapter 10), iron, manganese, and silica are removed to a considerable degree (104). The iron and manganese of the wood are possibly concentrated in the ray cells (103). In the chlorination, most of the metal ions are removed by the acid treatment, and this is a function of the chlorination stage which is mostly disregarded until the chlorination for some reason, such as in the deresination of hardwood sulfite pulps, has to be exchanged for a hypochlorite stage.

However, some metal ions remain even after chlorination, and new ones are introduced with the mill water and the bleaching chemicals, especially by the calcium hypochlorite. As carbon dioxide is one of the oxidation products, calcium and magnesium carbonate precipitate on the pulp in the hypochlorite stage. In the case of sodium hypochlorite bleaching, less precipitate is formed, but nevertheless the mill water calcium is likely to be precipitated. Some metal ions are precipitated on the pulp as hydroxides, others are combined to the pulp by the carboxylate groups formed during the bleaching.

Therefore, unless there is a finishing chlorine dioxide or acid chlorite stage, the pulp leaves the bleaching with a considerable content of inorganics, which should be removed before drying the pulp. This is performed by *acidification*, which dissolves the carbonates and hydroxides and removes those metal ions attached to the carboxylate groups by ion exchange. The latter reaction is generally the most important one, and is very rapid. Therefore, only a short retention time is needed to remove the metal ions by acidification. In some cases, however, a special retention tower is provided to allow some time for diffusion. That is especially desirable if all bleaching stages have been alkaline, so that the metal hydroxides and salts have to be dissolved. Cold water temperature, low consistency, 2–3%, and short retention time, 0.25–0.5 h, are used, which makes the tower needed fairly small and the equipment simple. Upflow towers are used generally. After the acidification stage, the introduction of new metal ions with the mill water must be carefully avoided, and therefore the subsequent water system should be closed, with extensive white water recirculation from the wet end of the drying machine. The pH of this water system will also eventually drop to a fairly low value. If the acidification tower is omitted, the acid is introduced into the machine chest, with or without white water recirculation from the wet end. The removal of metal ions will be more efficient the lower the pH. A practical limit is imposed by the cost of chemicals and the corrosion experienced on the drying machine. A pH of 4 is necessary to get an appreciable effect, and some mills go as far as pH 2.5. The most common acid used in sulfite mills is sulfur dioxide, but hydrochloric or sulfuric acid are also used in both sulfite and kraft mills. When an acid chlorine dioxide stage has finished the bleaching sequence no extra addition of acid is necessary, provided an extra wash water is added on the last filter and the residual chlorine dioxide has been destroyed by sulfur dioxide. To minimize corrosion, some mills have exchanged their bronze wires for stainless steel or nylon. To protect the drying cylinders, as well as the pulp, extra showers are desirable at the suction boxes to wash out the acid, especially if the non-volatile sulfuric acid has been used. Sometimes small amounts of alkali are also added to restore the pH to neutrality. However, these showers should be limited to a minimum, as the metal ion content of the shower water will be immediately fixed to the pulp by ion exchange. Sometimes this water is previously demineralized by passing it through a battery of ion exchangers.

Table 16.6. Inorganic impurities of modern dissolving wood pulps, ppm

Ca + Mg	100
Fe	6
Mn	0.5
Cu	1
SiO_2	40
Total ashes	0.08

1051

The metal ion content of the dried dissolving pulp is in this way kept at a low level, as demonstrated in Table 16.6.

For unbleached and bleached sulfite paper pulps, the following values have been found, Table 16.7 (104), and for kraft pulps, Table 16.8 (24).

Table 16.7. Inorganic components of sprucewood, unbleached and bleached sulfite paper pulps (104)

	Wood		Unbleached pulp		Bleached pulp	
	% of wood	% of ash	% of pulp	% of ash	% of pulp	% of ash
Total ash	0.24	100	0.96	100	0.48	100
Ca	0.08	31	0.33	34	0.27	56
Mg	0.01	4.3	0.03	2.9	0.01	2.3
Fe	0.0008	0.35	0.0031	0.32	0.0015	0.31
Mn	0.0062	2.6	0.0009	0.10	0.0001	0.02
Cu	0.0005	0.2	0.0012	0.12	0.0006	0.12
Pb	0.0000	0.0	0.0002	0.02	0.0001	0.01
SiO_2	0.0149	6.2	0.0340	3.5	0.0182	3.8
SO_3	0.0146	6.0	0.41	43	0.058	12

Table 16.8. Inorganic components of pine kraft pulp at various stages of processing, % (24)

	Brown stock	Stage 1 Cl_2	Stage 2 Cl_2 + $Ca(OH)_2$	Stage 3 CaCl(ClO)	Stage 4 NaOH	Stage 5 CaCl(ClO)	Stage 6 SO_2
Fe	0.0030	0.0009	0.0036	0.0040	0.0084	0.0046	0.0038
Cu	0.0003	0.0002	0.0002	0.0002	0.0048	0.0002	0.0002
Mn	0.0030	0.0002	0.0004	0.0005	0.0014	0.0005	0.0003
Ni	0.0006	0.0006	0.0004	0.0048	0.0096	0.0010	0.0003
Ca	0.15	0.15	0.87	1.4	1.0	0.92	0.44
Mg	0.13	0.020	0.034	0.055	0.048	0.054	0.020

2. REACTIONS AND REACTION VARIABLES

A. Removal of silicates

The ash content of wood is fairly low, 0.1–1.0%, usually about 0.3% (e.g. 29), of which about 6% (104) is silica. More accentuated is the problem when monocotyledone species are used as the fiber raw material, cereal straw, reed, bamboo, bagasse, and *Arundo* grass, which have an ash content of around 3–9%, of which 50–75% is SiO_2 (e.g. 16, 34, 39, 40, 41, 42, 43, 52, 96), varying with species, area of growth, and climatic conditions. The silica is mainly located in the epidermal cells, which are protected by the *cuticula* layer (40, 41). Because of the greater dominance of these cells in the leaves, the latter have been found to have more than twice as high a silica content as the average of the entire plant (40). The silica content of young plants is higher in the stems, but in ripe plants the silica has moved out to the leaves (13). The nature of the silica of the epidermal cells has been suggested to be solid silica gels of varying water content and amounts of organic impurities (23), whereas other investigations indicate the presence of organic silicium compounds (19, 37).

The removal of silica presents a combined chemical and mechanical problem. Part of the silica is water-soluble, part is alkali-soluble. The investigations indicate that on cooking in acid or alkaline water, some of the silica is removed as a turbid, micro-crystalline suspension (40), and it is difficult to discriminate between chemical dissolution of the silica and its mechanical dispersion upon chemical action on the surrounding organic components of the epidermal cells. However, one- to two-thirds of the silica is removed on water digestion at 100°C for 2 h of straw, whereas a corresponding digestion in 5% NaOH removes around 90% (40). This indicates that a kraft cook ought to be more effective on silica removal than a sulfite cook, and that is actually the case. For instance, sulfite cooking of reed (40) gave a pulp containing 3.4% ashes, of which 89% was silica. Kraft cooking on the same material gave an ash content of 0.39%. A three-stage bleaching of the former pulp gave an ash content of 1.7%, containing 98% silica, whereas the latter pulp after bleaching contained 0.2% ashes, of which only 20% was silica. The removal of silica during the bleaching of the sulfite pulp can be increased by a hot alkali purification stage to a final residual ash content of 0.08%, of which 63% is silica. Prehydrolysis–kraft pulping gave a final bleached pulp of 0.13% ashes, of which only 20% was silica. The results, summarized in Table 16.9, show that it is quite possible to reduce the ash content to a level approaching that of ordinary wood pulps. It may be added, that the residual silica content of

Table 16.9. Removal of ashes and silica content on reed pulping (40)

Species	Cooking process	Bleaching	Ashes, %	Silica, %
Reed	Unpulped		2.89	2.31
	Sulfite	Unbleached	3.4	3.05
	Sulfite	Bleached as paper pulp	1.70	1.66
	Sulfite	Chlorinated	3.03	
	Sulfite	Chlorinated, hot alkali purified	0.19	
	Sulfite	Chlorinated, purified and bleached	0.08	0.05
	Kraft	Unbleached	0.39	
	Kraft	Bleached as paper pulp	0.20	0.04
	Prehydrolysis	Unbleached	2.63	2.10
	Prehydrolysis–kraft	Unbleached	0.33	0.22
	Prehydrolysis–kraft	Bleached	0.13	0.02
Spruce	Sulfite	Chlorinated, hot alkali purified, bleached	0.08	0.005

the pulp showed a correlation to the quality of the acetate prepared therefrom (40), and that investigations on the viscose filtering properties of pulps often show a correlation to the silica content, although naturally there is no such correlation when comparing pulps of different types, other qualities of the pulp influencing its processing properties as well. Mechanical removal of silica can be achieved by fiber fractionation or vortex cleaning, and such means are necessary for reducing the silica content of bamboo rayon pulps to acceptable levels.

B. Removal of metal ions

The acidic properties of cellulose have been studied in connection with the methods of determining the content of carboxyl groups (9). The ion-exchange reactions with various cations have then been investigated (15). Figure 16.23 (15) shows the sorption of various cations at varying pH at two concentrations, and Figure 16.24 the amount of cations bound at pH 3.5 on varying concentrations of the salt solution. It is seen that the normal order of affinity with an ion exchanger prevails, except for silver ions, which may be affected by the reductive properties of the pulp. Thus

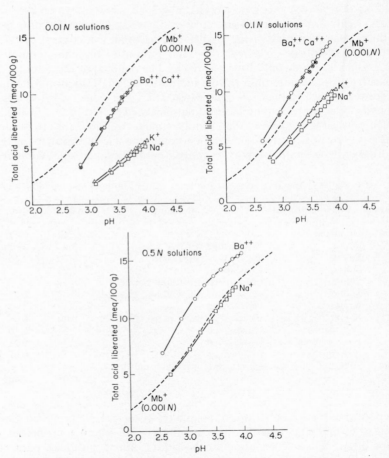

Fig. 16.23. Absorption of monovalent and divalent cations vs. pH. Mb⁺ denotes methylene blue absorption, used to determine carboxylate content of pulp
(Davidson)

polyvalent ions, such as Ca^{2+}, Mg^{2+}, Fe^{3+}, Cu^{2+} and Mn^{2+}, have a great tendency to be fixated on the pulp. However, the tendency is pH-dependent, as the carboxyl groups of the pulp are effective only in carboxylate form. Carboxyl groups of this type normally have a pK_a of 3.5–3.8 (53, 79, 85), and should therefore be in carboxylate form to 50% at that pH level. However, with polyelectrolytes the apparent pK_a value is moved towards higher values (46) by the influence of adjacent groups on the ionization of a certain carboxyl group. This effect disappears only at comparatively high ionic strength. In agreement herewith, it has not been found possible to calculate the exact pK_a value of the carboxyl groups of cellulose because of the extension of the latter half of the neutralization curve towards higher pH (15).

The amount of cations absorbed by the pulp is obviously dependent on the ion concentration of the water. Normal water hardness corresponds to about 10^{-3} to 10^{-4} N solution with respect to calcium and is therefore much below the concentrations indicated in Figures 16.23–24. Approximate figures for the uptake of calcium from such a solution would be around 80% of the carboxyls at pH 4.5, 50% at pH 4.0, 35% at pH 3.5, and around 20% at pH 3.0. With a carboxyl content of 0.004 per glucose unit, this should result in the following calcium contents of the pulp, Table 16.10.

Some experimental results are shown in Figure 16.25 on a low-viscosity sulfite rayon pulp, containing 0.0042 carboxyl groups per glucose unit, corresponding to 520 ppm Ca at saturation. It left the washer after the calcium hypochlorite stage at pH 8 and contained a surrounding liquor of 70 mg/l Ca. Corrected for the calcium of the liquor, the pulp itself contained 585 ppm Ca, thus somewhat more than corresponding to the carboxyl groups and indicating the presence of calcium carbonate precipitate. Curves A and B show the decrease in calcium content on suspending

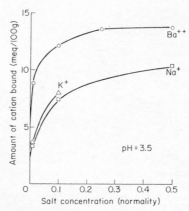

Fig. 16.24. Absorption of monovalent and divalent cations on pulp from solutions of varying concentration at pH 3.5 (Davidson)

this pulp at 2 % consistency in water, acidified with SO₂ to various pH values. Curve *A* indicates the values at immediate filtration and washing with 5 m³ ptp distilled water, curve *B* the corresponding results after 0.5 h retention in the acid liquor. Ion exchange is obviously instantaneous. Curve *C* corresponds to curve *A* with the difference that the wash water was acidified to the same pH as the previous treatment. It is seen that these values are lower throughout and indicates that some of the calcium liberated on acidification will be absorbed again as the pH increases at

Table 16.10. Calcium content of a pulp of normal carboxyl content in equilibrium with water of normal hardness, calculated

pH	Ca, ppm
7.0	500
4.5	400
4.0	250
3.5	175
3.0	100

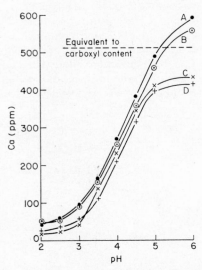

Fig. 16.25. Calcium removal by acidi-fication. Curve (A), acidification and immediate washing with water; (B) acidification and washing with water after 0.5 h; (C) acidification and im-mediate washing with SO₂ water of same pH; (D) saturation of deminera-lized pulp with 0.5 *N* CaCl₂, washing and repeating procedure A (Rydholm)

the subsequent washing, if the wash water is not acidified accordingly. Curve *D* was obtained after the removal of all calcium and subsequent saturation of the pulp by treatment with 0.5 *N* CaCl$_2$ and then repeating the acidification experiments. The general form of the curves closely corresponds to the calculated values mentioned previously.

Figure 16.26 shows the calcium content of the same pulp in equilibrium with water of varying hardness and pH. The importance of a soft wash

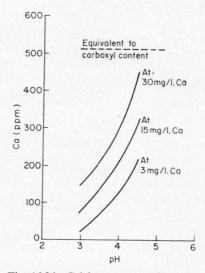

Fig. 16.26. Calcium content of pulp in equilibrium with water of varying hardness and pH (Rydholm)

water is clearly seen, and motivates demineralization of the final shower on the wet end of the drying machine. Obviously the use of sodium hypochlorite, which decreases the original calcium content of both pulp and surrounding liquor, facilitates the calcium removal. Also, the advantage of double acidification treatment, with removal of the main calcium content in the first filtration is clearly seen, as in the case of an acidification tower with subsequent washer and a renewed acidification prior to the drying machine. Several variations of the system are possible.

REFERENCES

1. Adler, E., and S. Häggroth, *Svensk Papperstid.*, **53**, 287, 321 (1950).
1a. Annergren, G. E., *et al.*, *Svensk Papperstid.*, **7**, 125 (1964).
2. Back, E., *Svensk Papperstid.*, **54**, 657 (1951).
3. Back, E., *Svensk Papperstid.*, **56**, 284 (1953).
4. Back, E., *Svensk Papperstid.*, **60**, 905 (1957).
5. Back, E., *Svensk Papperstid.*, **63**, 556 (1960).

6. Back, E., *et al.*, *Acta Chem. Scand.*, **4**, 810 (1950); **12**, 1516 (1958).
7. Back, E., and O. T. Carlson, *Svensk Papperstid.*, **58**, 415 (1955).
8. Bergström, H., *Bihang till Jernkontorets Annaler*, **12**, No. 6, 507 (1911).
9. Browning, B. L., in L. E. Wise and E. C. Jahn, eds., *Wood Chemistry*, 2nd Ed., Reinhold, New York 1952, p. 1249.
10. Browning, B. L., and L. O. Bublitz, *Tappi*, **36**, 418 (1953).
10a. Bruun, H. H., and S. Gåsland, *Åbo Akad. Medd*, No. 185 (Finland).
11. Bryde, Ö., Report, Papirind. Forskningsinst., Oslo, Sept. 1948.
12. Buchanan, M. A., *et al.*, *Tappi*, **42**, 578 (1959); **44**, 576 (1961).
13. Chêne, M., *Le Papier*, **46**, 209 (1943).
13a. Cherches, K. A., *et al.*, *Zhur. Priklad Khim.*, **34**, 938 (1961).
14. Corrin, M. L., *et al.*, *J. Chem. Phys.*, **14**, 480 (1946).
14a. Croon, I., *et al.*, *Svensk Papperstid.*, **66**, 876, 940 (1963).
15. Davidson, G. F., *Shirley Inst. Mem.*, **21**, 69 (1947).
16. Dörr, R. E., *Cellulosechem.*, **21**, 49 (1943).
17. Durand, R. W., *Tappi*, **41**, No. 5, 171A (1958).
18. Ekvall, P., *J. Colloid Sci.* Suppl., **1**, 66 (1954).
19. Engel, W., *Angew Chem.*, **64**, 601 (1952).
20. Enkvist, T., *Paperi Puu*, **25**, No. 7A, 108 (1943).
21. Fitzgerald, L. E., *Paper Trade J.*, **103**, TS 266 (1936).
22. Freeman, H., *Pulp Paper Mag. Can.*, **48**, No. 8, 73 (1947).
23. Frey-Wyssling, A., *Die Stoffausscheidungen der höheren Pflanzen*, Berlin 1935.
24. Gard, A. J., *Tappi*, **44**, No. 10, 162A (1961).
25. Gavelin, G., *Pulp Paper Mag. Can.*, **50**, No. 2, 59 (1949); **51**, No. 5, 87 (1950).
26. Gustafsson, C., *et al.*, *Paperi Puu*, **34**, 121 (1952); **36**, 269 (1954); *Norsk Skogind.*, **8**, 54 (1954).
27. Gustafsson, C., *et al.*, *Paperi Puu*, **39**, 179, 277 (1957).
28. Gustafsson, C., *et al.*, *Paperi Puu*, **40**, 239 (1958).
29. Hägglund, E., *Chemistry of Wood*, Acad. Press, New York 1951, pp. 17, 37, 351.
30. Hägglund, E., and L. Stockman, *Svensk Papperstid.*, **57**, 409 (1954).
31. Harris, G., *J. Am. Chem. Soc.*, **70**, 3671 (1948).
32. Harva, O., Dissertation, Åbo Akademi, Åbo (Finland) 1951.
33. Hasselström, T., *et al.*, *Paper Trade J.*, **118**, No. 16, 30 (1944); **128**, No. 7, 17 (1949); *J. Am. Chem. Soc.*, **63**, 111 (1941).
34. Herig, F., *Cellulosechem.*, **2**, 44 (1921).
35. Hibbert, H., and J. B. Phillips, *Can. J. Research*, **4**, 1 (1931).
36. Holgersson, S., and K. Groth, *U.S. Pat.* 2,932,602 (1960).
37. Holzapfel, L., *Z. Elektrochem.*, **55**, 577 (1951).
38. Jayme, G., *U.S. Pat.* 2,074,473 (1937).
39. Jayme, G., *Papierfabrik.*, **40**, 97 (1942).
40. Jayme, G., *et al.*, *Papier*, **7**, 223, 298, 347, 459 (1953).
41. Jayme, G., and M. Harders-Steinhäuser, *Papierfabrik.*, **40**, 89, 97 (1942).
42. Jayme, G., and W. Mohrberg, *Papierfabrik.*, **39**, 9 (1941).
43. Jufieriew, J., *et al.*, *Zellstoff Papier*, **5**, 445 (1925).
44. Jukes, T. H., and C. L. A. Schmidt, *J. Biol. Chem.*, **110**, 9 (1935).
45. Juvonen, V. V., *Suomen Kemistilehti*, **20A**, 18 (1947).
46. Kagawa, I., and K. Katsuura, *J. Polymer. Sci.*, **7**, 89 (1951).
47. Kahila, S. K., *Paperi Puu*, **39**, 7 (1957).

48. Kahila, S. K., *Paperi Puu*, **39**, 35 (1957).
49. Kahila, S. K., and A. E. Y. Rinne, *Paperi Puu*, **39**, 526 (1957).
50. Kaila, E., *et al.*, *Paperi Puu*, **39**, 1 (1957).
51. Kajanne, P., *Paperi Puu*, **39**, 417 (1957).
52. Karnik, M. G., and D. L. Sen, *J. Sci. Ind. Research*, **9B**, 201 (1950).
53. Karrer, P., and G. Schwarzenbach, *Helv. Chim. Acta.*, **16**, 302 (1933).
54. Kleinert, T., and W. Wincor, *Svensk Papperstid.*, **53**, 638 (1950); **56**, 874 (1953).
55. Kolthoff, I. M., and W. Stricks, *J. Phys. Colloid Chem.*, **52**, 915 (1948).
56. Kress, O., and L. A. Moss, *Paper Trade J.*, **102**, No. 25, 38 (1936).
57. Kress, O., and P. E. Nethercut, *Tech. Assoc. Papers*, **29**, 297 (1946).
58. Kurth, E. F., *Ind. Eng. Chem.*, **25**, 192 (1933).
59. Lawrence, R. V., *Tappi*, **42**, 867 (1959).
59a. Lea, C. H., *Chem. and Ind.*, **1953**, 1303.
60. Leopold, B., and D. B. Mutton, *Tappi*, **42**, 218 (1959).
61. Linehan, D. D., *Tappi*, **35**, No. 6, 119A (1952).
61a. McNair, J. B., *Botan. Rev.*, **11**, 1 (1945).
61b. Malevskaya, S. S., *et al.*, *Zhur. Priklad. Khim.*, **34**, 2535 (1961).
62. Malm, C. J., *et al.*, *Ind. Eng. Chem.*, **42**, 730 (1950).
63. Marschall, A., *Jentgens Kunstseide Zellwolle*, **24**, 188, 462 (1942).
64. Mutton, D. B., *Tappi*, **41**, 632 (1958).
65. Newhall, N., *Pacific Pulp Paper Ind.*, **5**, 33 (1931).
66. Nilsson, E., and S. A. Rydholm, unpublished.
67. Nishida, K., *et al.*, *J. Japan. Forestry Soc.*, Spec. Issue, 294 (1951), **34**, 161, 315 (1952); *Japan. Tappi*, **10**, 125, 597 (1956); *Nippon Ringaku Kaishi*, Spec. Issue, 354 (1954); *Mokuzai Gakkaishi*, **3**, 57 (1957).
68. Nyrén, V., and E. Back, *Acta Chem. Scand.*, **12**, 1516 (1958).
69. O'Meara, D., and R. M. L. Patterson, *Tappi*, **43**, 927 (1960).
70. Perilä, O., *Paperi Puu*, **36**, 213 (1954); **38**, 499 (1956); *Ann. Acad. Sci. Fennicae* A II Chemica, 76 (1956).
71. Perilä, O., *Paperi Puu*, **40**, No. 4a, 159 (1958).
72. Perilä, O., and A. Toivonen, *Paperi Puu*, **40**, No. 4a, 207 (1958).
73. Phillips, J. B., *Pulp Paper Mag. Can.*, **31**, 211 (1931).
74. Potter, G. C. J., *Pulp Paper Mag. Can.*, **29**, 363 (1930).
75. Rapson, W. H., *Pulp Paper Mag. Can.*, **57**, No. 10, 147 (1956).
76. Rapson, W. H., and M. Wayman, *U.S. Pat.* 2,716,058 (1955).
77. Richter, G. A., *Ind. Eng. Chem.*, **33**, 1518 (1941).
77a. Richter, G. A., *Ind. Eng. Chem.*, **33**, 75 (1941).
78. Rollinson, S. M., *Tappi*, **38**, 625 (1955).
79. Rydholm, S. A., Thesis, KTH, Stockholm 1952.
80. Rydholm, S. A., and C. Svensson, unpublished.
81. Samuelsen, S., *Papir-J.*, **27**, 224 (1939).
82. Samuelson, O., *Svensk Papperstid.*, **51**, 15 (1948).
82a. Samuelson, O., *Svensk Papperstid.*, **51**, 317, 331 (1948).
83. Samuelson, H. O., *Swed. Pat.* 150,651 (1955).
84. Sandqvist, H., *et al.*, *Svensk Kem. Tidskr.*, **42**, 106 (1930); *Ber.*, **63**, 1935 (1930); **64**, 2167 (1931); I.V.A. Handlingar, **10**, Stockholm 1932.
84a. Sarten, P., *Papier*, **8**, 376 (1954).
85. Sävenborn, S. A., Dissertation, Uppsala Univ. (Sweden) 1945.
86. Selleby, L., *Svensk Papperstid.*, **63**, 81 (1960).
87. Sieber, R., *Über das Hartz der Nadelhölzer*, Berlin 1925.
88. Sihtola, H., and E. Kaila, *Paperi Puu*, **39**, No. 4a, 143 (1957).

89. Smith, K. N., *Tappi*, **42**, 869 (1959).
90. Stainsby, G., and A. E. Alexander, *Trans. Faraday Soc.*, **45**, 585 (1949).
91. Stocker, F. W., *Pulp Paper Mag. Can.*, **53**, No. 9, 115 (1952).
92. Stockman, L., unpublished.
93. Swanson, J. W., and S. Cordingley, *Tappi*, **38**, 684 (1956).
94. Swanson, J. W., and S. Cordingley, *Tappi*, **42**, 812 (1959).
95. Thommen, E. K., *Svensk Papperstid.*, **56**, 937 (1953).
96. Tomeo, M., and F. Meni, *Anales Real. Soc. Espan. Fis. Quim.* (*Madrid*), **45B**, 111 (1949).
97. Ulfsparre, S., *Norrlandsutredningen*, Stockholm 1942, p. 125.
98. Wahlberg, H. E., *Svensk Papperstid.*, **27**, 38 (1924).
99. v. Weissenberg, B., *Paperi Puu*, **21**, 446 (1939).
100. White, J. R., *J. Am. Chem. Soc.*, **72**, 1859 (1950).
101. Wienhaus, H., *Papierfabrik.*, **35**, 385 (1937).
102. Willamo, H. H., *Paperi Puu*, **33**, 310 (1951).
103. Wultsch, F., *et al.*, *Papierfabrik.*, **42**, 354 (1944).
104. Wultsch, F., and F. Senger, *Tappi*, **38**, 25 (1955).

17

MULTISTAGE BLEACHING

I. General Description of Process (8, 14, 26)

Bleaching was originally carried out as a single-stage process, but around 1920 two-stage hypochlorite bleaching was introduced to the wood pulping industry, after having been developed in rag bleaching. It was found that an intermediate wash decreased the consumption of chemicals. When around 1930 it was found that chlorination followed by hypochlorite bleaching had technical and economic advantages, and that alkaline extraction was a further improvement, multistage bleaching became a necessity. The sequence of chlorination–alkali extraction–hypochlorite bleaching was for a long time found sufficient for sulfite pulps, whereas repeated chlorinations or hypochlorite stages with intermediate alkali extractions were found necessary to achieve fully bleached kraft pulps with preserved strength properties. Gradually the competition forced the brightness levels to increase, necessitating new bleaching agents and more bleaching stages. Special tasks were added to the bleachery functions, such as the removal of resin and calcium and the extraction of a proper amount of carbohydrates, which required special chemicals and in some cases a special technique. Thus, bleaching, originally carried out in comparatively simple equipment, was extended to a process of up to 10 or 11 stages, requiring a great deal of expensive and space-consuming equipment in a separate department, the bleachery, and various chemicals, the manufacture and storage of which needed much extra space and machinery, sometimes in separate buildings or even separate mills.

The machinery used in multistage bleaching has been described in Chapter 12.IV. Only its combination and application will be treated here, as exemplified by the flow sheets of Figures 12.24 and 13.4. The conditions in the various stages were treated in Chapters 13–16, and will only be briefly summarized here. After screening, the pulp is received in a buffer chest prior to the bleachery. The bleaching is nowadays becoming fully continuous; chlorination is always continuous, alkali extraction predominantly so, and the oxidative stages are also made continuous to an increasing extent, although some advantages of a discontinuous final bleach have checked the development at that point. The equipment used for continuous bleaching are *mixers* or various types for the addition of chemicals and heat, followed by *towers* to allow sufficient retention time for the reactions. The washing between the stages is carried out on *filters* of various types. To control levels, consistencies, temperatures and chemical charges, a considerable *instrumentation* is required. The construction materials in a bleachery today are mainly good-quality stainless steel in the machinery, and tile- or rubber-lined steel or concrete in the towers.

Important for the success of a multistage bleachery is the control of the rate of the pulp charged, to which all additions of chemicals should be adjusted. Therefore the consistency and flow rate of the pulp suspension entering the bleachery are measured for example, by magnetic flow meters, and regulated. Then usually the first chemical added is chlorine, which is mixed with the pulp either in a separate mixer or by impellers in the bottom of an upflow tower. Although medium- or even high-consistency chlorination is practised in a few mills (5), chlorination is generally a low-consistency process because of its rapidity, even in dilute suspension. Upflow towers are customary, or downflow towers with an initial, upflow leg. A consistency of around 3%, for 15–60 minutes at cold water temperature are suitable conditions. The chlorine is introduced as a gas via a rotameter, or dissolved to chlorine water, and the charge is generally chosen to leave some residual chlorine at the end of the stage. As the lignin content of the unbleached pulp is bound to vary somewhat, in spite of all control in the cooking department, the chlorine charge has to be accordingly adjusted. Therefore frequent sampling is necessary and a certain excess for safety is usual in the charge. In the downflow chlorination towers with an upflow leg, the pulp color is sometimes determined at the top of the tower, as a measure of the extent of chlorination achieved after the first few minutes of retention (19). This value can be used for manual or automatic adjustment of the chlorine dosage. Also, a determination of the redox potential after a short initial retention has been developed to allow an early adjustment (3). These efforts to keep a correct dosage of chlorine have not only a direct economic motive in the prevention of chlorine waste. Changes in the extent of chlorination will affect the following bleaching stages and also the final pulp quality. Further, too large an excess of chlorine will cause foaming and filtration difficulties in the subsequent washing. The chlorine charges vary, according to pulp type, from 10 kg ptp for the softest dissolving grades, up to 140–180 kg ptp for neutral sulfite pulps. In the latter case, special arrangements are often made to ensure good mixing of the large chlorine quantities with the pulp. The chlorine charge is either automatically determined from the previously mentioned reflectance or redox impulses, or adjusted according to the variations of the chlorine or permanganate number of the unbleached pulp. Methods have been devised involving up to five different chlorine charges on laboratory samples to judge the bleachability of the pulp (9), but for mill control rapid methods are essential and the chlorine charge limited to a large extent by the equipment. The chlorination tower is constructed for a certain retention time and consistency, and much excess chlorine cannot be accepted from a practical and economical standpoint. In this connection, an efficient mixing of chlorine and pulp before the stage has been found essential.

Sometimes it is found desirable to add less chlorine in the first stage than can be consumed, thus leaving no residual chlorine. Thereby

1062

chlorination of the extractives is avoided to some extent. The alkali extraction of some resins is more complete, if they have not been chlorinated, and before continued chlorination an alkali extraction is carried out. In the case of very resinous pulps, such as those from some hardwoods, chlorination should be avoided and exchanged against an oxidative treatment with hypochlorite (25) or chlorine dioxide (22). Then sometimes alkali extraction is the preferred first stage. In contrast with the use of hypochlorite or chlorine dioxide as finishing bleaching agents, their use in an initial stage does not require more than room temperature. To prevent pitch deposition in the screening room, some very resinous pulps, such as pine sulfite, are alkali extracted before screening.

Washing after chlorination is done on one or two filters. In the latter case alkali is added after the first filtration and the white water from the second filter recirculated. This system is used to some extent by the dissolving pulp industry to ensure perfect mixing of larger amounts of chemicals. However, modern double-shaft alkali mixers are sufficiently efficient for this purpose. The alkali is then added to the pulp directly after filtration, sometimes at the final showers. The heat necessary for the alkali stage is supplied by hot water to the filter, with an adjustment of steam in the mixer, if necessary.

The conditions of the alkali stage are entirely different for different types of pulp. In the case of acid and neutral sulfite pulps most lignin dissolves during the chlorination. Therefore, the alkali stage could be considered as a mere neutralization of the pulp, as well as a stage for deresination. On the other hand, the neutral sulfite pulps and acid sulfite pulps of greaseproof and similar type contain much hemicellulose of economic and qualitative value. For this reason the alkali stage should be made with extreme caution to avoid losses. Low alkali charges of 10–20 kg ptp, low temperatures, 10–30°C, and fairly short retention times, 30–60 minutes, are therefore used. This allows fairly low-consistency operation, generally around 5% in simple upflow (or downflow) towers. If sulfite paper pulps with less hemicellulose and higher brightness and opacity are desired, more severe alkaline conditions are applied. However, temperatures above 50°C and alkali charges above 40 kg ptp are seldom used. Higher consistency, 5–12%, and longer retention times, 1–2 h, are then motivated, in downflow or special upflow towers. Similar conditions are used for the alkali extraction stages of kraft pulps. However, since the pulp has just left a much more severe alkaline stage, the cooking, the carbohydrate removal and deresination aspects are less important. The removal of chlorinated lignin, which in the case of kraft pulps is water-soluble only to a minor extent but well soluble in alkali, requires somewhat more severe conditions than those for sulfite pulp. Alkali charges are then 25–40 kg ptp or even higher, and temperatures may be as high as 70°C.

The severest alkali stage is that of dissolving pulp hot alkali purification, where temperatures of 50–140°C, charges of 20–125 kg ptp, and retention times of 1–6 h are used, according to the degree of refining desired. In this case medium to high consistency is required to save space, heat and chemicals, and 15–30% is generally used, in downflow towers. The filter leaving this pulp should have press rolls and is for the highest consistencies completed with a drum, screw or disk press. For temperatures much above 100°C a pressure tower and a pressure feeder are required. For high-alpha pulps the refining with sodium carbonate or carbonate–sulfite has also been suggested and practised. As this requires a temperature of around 160°C, the suitable equipment must be a discontinuous or continuous digester. There is, however, a tendency to carry out extreme high-temperature refining already in the cooking, where it is more favorable from the aspect of heat economy. To save heat it is also general practice to recirculate the white water from the filters after high-temperature stages to dilute the pulp on discharging from the tower.

The hot alkali purification of sulfite pulps is in some mills preceded by an alkali extraction of discoloring matter. To ensure complete removal of dissolved resin, double filtration is often practised after an alkali extraction stage.

Sometimes cold alkali purification is also practised, generally in combination with a previous or subsequent hot alkali purification stage, utilizing the alkali bled off or left after some washing of the cold alkali purified pulp.

After alkali extraction, chlorination may be repeated. This is especially the case for kraft pulps, as the alkali extraction will expose new regions of unchlorinated lignin. However, as the lignin content is decreased, the pulp is getting more sensitive to oxidative attack of hypochlorous acid. Therefore, there is a tendency to leave out the second chlorination for kraft pulps, in favor of a well-buffered hypochlorite stage. Hypochlorite oxidation is performed in bleach hollanders, other types of discontinuous bleachers, mainly of the medium-consistency type, or in low-medium consistency bleaching towers (upflow or downflow). Consistency thus varies from 6 to 20% or sometimes more, temperature is kept around 30–60°C and times from 1–8 h. The chemicals are charged either directly to the batch bleacher or continuously into a mixer. Both calcium and sodium hypochlorite are used, generally in combination with excess alkali to keep pH above 9. Sodium hypochlorite is rather more expensive but often preferred because of easier preparation, and is also preferred in the bleaching of dissolving pulp to avoid introduction of calcium, the traces of which have to be removed subsequently. The amounts of chemicals added depend entirely on the extent of prebleaching, the number of subsequent bleaching stages, the final brightness and viscosity level desired. Normally 3–10 kg ptp of active chlorine are added and sometimes up to 20 kg ptp. Excess alkali used amounts to 1–5 kg ptp.

For further bleaching to higher brightness, another hypochlorite stage may be added, with or without intermediate washing and with or without an intermediate alkali extraction. This is especially practised for kraft pulps and for sulfite dissolving pulps, where a second hypochlorite stage is added to facilitate viscosity control. In many cases, where the first hypochlorite treatment has been considerable, and where paper strength is essential, more selective bleaching agents are preferred, which remove lignin without considerable damage to the carbohydrates. These agents are chlorine dioxide, sodium chlorite and peroxide. Sodium chlorite is more expensive than the other two, and as its action is quite similar to that of chlorine dioxide, it is seldom used, and only in small amounts for a brightness finish. Chlorine dioxide, on the other hand, especially when manufactured at a kraft pulp mill, can be made at about the same cost as sodium hypochlorite or even lower. It is therefore increasingly used as a lignin-removing agent in larger charges, 5–25 kg ptp of active chlorine, thereby substituting for some hypochlorite oxidation. Chlorine dioxide and sodium chlorite react fairly slowly as finishing bleaching agents, and 60–75°C for 2–5 h are necessary. This motivates medium-high consistencies, 10–30%, in downflow or special upflow towers. Peroxide bleaching is practised at similar conditions (4, 6), but is frequently often carried out by peroxide addition to an alkali extraction stage.

To achieve the best effects of chlorine dioxide, it should be carried out in two stages with an intermediate alkali extraction, especially in kraft bleaching. The use of chlorine dioxide in sulfite pulp bleaching is still to some extent a matter of discussion, but is an advantage for super brightness grades and where a low resin content is essential. Peroxide bleaching of dissolving pulps is avoided because of its addition of sodium silicate.

As a final stage in the bleaching of dissolving pulps, after the viscosity-controlling last hypochlorite stage, acidification is practised. As it is mainly a question of exchange of calcium and heavy metal ions against hydrogen ions, the retention time needed is usually short, and many mills add the acid after the final bleach washer, prior to the drying machine. However, in other mills a retention tower is considered of benefit, usually a small upflow tower for low consistency. Sulfur dioxide, sulfuric or hydrochloric acid are all used. If acid chlorine dioxide has been the final bleaching stage, acidification could be omitted. Neutralization at the last wire shower is often practised to limit corrosion on the drying machine and degradation of the pulp on storage.

Quite often the bleached pulp is stored in high- or medium-density downflow towers prior to drying or paper-making. Other mills use low-density chests for the equalization of quality.

Apart from the control of temperatures and chemical charges by the instruments, and of the chlorine demand of the unbleached pulp entering the bleachery, all sorts of additional controls are practised, varying from mill to mill. pH and residual chemicals of the different stages are usually determined, and adjustment of the chemical charges made accordingly. In the same way the pulp is tested for demand of oxidizing agents, viscosity, alphacellulose and brightness at the various stages. The viscosity test, originally developed and used in dissolving pulp bleaching, is nowadays also used in many paper pulp mills as a measure of the degradation of carbohydrates during the bleaching. Although the viscosity test does not measure a property with direct meaning for the paper strength, an indication is obtained which is then confirmed with less frequent and more time-consuming paper strength testing (4, 28).

II. Multistage Bleaching of Mechanical and Semichemical Pulp

The combined effects of peroxide and dithionite bleaching of mechanical and semichemical pulp have also motivated lignin-preservative bleaching in a multistage system. So far, the only active chemicals of technical importance are peroxide and dithionite, and the possible combinations are thus limited to two schedules, both of which are practised. The detailed aspects of this type of bleaching, which is of increasing importance, were dealt with in Chapter 13.

III. Multistage Bleaching of Sulfite Pulps

Sulfite pulps are easier to bleach than pulps from other processes, requiring less stages and usually less chemicals to achieve fairly high brightness. The main reason for this is that the residual lignin is sulfonated to some degree and therefore water-soluble after chlorination to a large extent, dissolves during the chlorination stage and thus exposes the less accessible lignin to chlorination. Unbleached sulfite pulp has a brightness varying from 40–70% GE. Unbleached pulp brightness, however, although of great importance for the final result in the case of lignin-*bleaching* one-stage or two-stage processes, is unimportant in the case of lignin-*removing* multistage bleaching. The final brightness of the bleached pulp is influenced by the following four factors:

(1) Residual lignin.
(2) Residual extractives.
(3) Residual non-cellulosic carbohydrates.
(4) Impurities introduced during and after bleaching, mainly with the mill water.

For brightness stability of different types still another factor is important,

(5) Oxidized groups of the carbohydrates, introduced during the bleaching.

The following will illustrate the relative importance of these factors (27). If the mill water is not too dirty, the dominating factor is residual lignin for semibleached sulfite pulps of 75–80% GE and up to the level of fully bleached pulps around 88% GE. Then mill water purity and residual extractives begin to influence the brightness noticeably. A brightness above 93% GE requires unusually clean mill water or special water purification. With very pure water, 95% GE can be achieved for paper pulps and up to 99% GE for dissolving pulps, where in the latter case the more severe alkali extraction conditions give a more complete deresination, as well as removal of low-molecular carbohydrates. If the extractives are removed with a solvent prior to bleaching, paper pulp brightness can be improved to 97% GE. Some discrepancy still prevails between this figure and that obtained after more severe hot alkali refining to high-alpha pulps, probably showing the effect of low-molecular carbohydrate removal in the latter case. If the oxidation of the carbohydrates has been carried too far, corresponding to a low viscosity level and a high carbonyl group content, the brightness stability is affected, as is seen from the decrease in brightness on storage, on exposure to light or heat, or by alkali steeping of dissolving pulps. The brightness stability will influence the final color of the paper, and the color of the alkali cellulose which is one indication of the color of the final rayon yarn.

These general results have been obtained for *spruce* sulfite pulps on experimental bleaching in the laboratory and mill scale. The same factors are also of importance for the bleaching of other sulfite pulps, but their relative importance changes according to the composition of the unbleached pulp. In the case of birch pulp, deresination is as important as delignification for the final brightness, already in the semibleached range.

In pulp bleaching, not only the brightness improvement, but also the chemical properties of the final bleached product have to be considered, and during the various stages not only the discoloring impurities but also the colorless pulp constituents react. Therefore, the conditions of especially the alkali extraction and the oxidation stages may not be chosen with regard to brightness improvement only. For paper pulps the alkali extraction should be rather mild for most grades in order to preserve the hemicellulose part, which contributes to the burst and tensile strength and to the density of the final paper. Then deresination will be limited, with the aforesaid consequences for the brightness. The main conflict lies, however, in the oxidative bleaching stages, where some brightness improvement has to be sacrificed for the preservation of the strength properties. For rayon pulps similar considerations are to be taken. The conditions of the hot alkali refining must be chosen mainly with regard to the alphacellulose content desired, and less to the requirements of deresination, and the oxidative bleaching must first consider the viscosity level and then pulp brightness.

Therefore, deresination in the alkali extraction sometimes has to be improved by surface active agents and other means rather than by making the conditions more severe, and for the oxidative stages more selective oxidants than hypochlorite, mainly chlorine dioxide and sometimes sodium chlorite and peroxide. Although not without influence on the carbohydrates, these bleaching stages cause less damage to the pulp while removing the remaining impurities. Some improvement is also obtained by choosing proper conditions of the conventional stages, such as improved deresination in the alkali stage at identical alphacellulose level by decreasing the temperature and increasing the alkali charge, or in the hypochlorite bleaching by selecting the proper amount of excess alkali buffer and by dividing the charge of hypochlorite into two stages. Improved deresination is in some cases likewise obtained by double chlorination with intermediate washing and eventually alkali extraction, to avoid chlorination of the resins, or by substituting chlorine for chlorine dioxide.

1067

Therefore, also with the fairly simple bleaching of sulfite pulps, some variants in the bleaching schedules are motivated. In the following, some schedules from actual sulfite mill bleaching practice will be presented, together with some comments. The abbreviations chosen follow one of the suggestions of the literature (4), with the addition that the sign / stands for filter washing. Thus,

C = chlorination
E = alkali extraction, including hot alkali purification
A = cold alkali purification
H = hypochlorite oxidation
D = chlorine dioxide oxidation
S = sodium chlorite oxidation
P = sodium or hydrogen peroxide oxidation.

These abbreviations will also be used in the following sections on kraft and neutral sulfite multistage bleaching.

(1) /C/E/H/. Conventional three-stage bleaching, much used for both paper and dissolving pulps (12, 20, 29).

(2) /C/E/HH/. The former schedule, modified with two hypochlorite additions but no intermediate washing, preferably carried out in an up-flow tower combined with a downflow tower. This permits easier quality control than schedule 1.

(3) /C/E/H/H/. Offers little advantage to schedule 2 and requires an extra filter. Schedules 2 and 3 are often used with the initial hypochlorite stage at low temperature and comparatively high chemical charge, for the bleaching of dirt specks, followed by a temperature adjustment for the second hypochlorite bleaching to the brightness level desired.

(4) /C/C/E/H/. Two initial stages for better control of the chlorination and some chlorine saving by the intermediate washing of dissolved lignin. It is sometimes believed to improve the deresination, and could of course also be varied in the final bleaching stages according to schedules 2–3.

(5) /C/E/C/E/H/. Improved deresination. Caution must be exercised to avoid 'overchlorination', or oxidative attack on the carbohydrates in the second chlorination. However, schedules 4 and 5 are sometimes used for controlled viscosity decrease in the chlorination. This is more danger-ous to quality than viscosity control in the hypochlorite stages and should only be used for very low-viscosity grades.

(6) /C//E/H/. Double filtration for better washing and alkali mixing, to save alkali.

(7) /C/E//H/. Double filtration for better deresination.

(8) /C/E/H/D/. Chlorine dioxide finish for higher brightness.

(9) /C/E/H/P/. Peroxide finish for higher brightness stability.

(10) /C/E/DH/. Combined chlorine dioxide and hypochlorite bleaching without intermediate washing. Superior to schedule 8 in heat economy and brightness results, but requires closer control of chemicals charges. Is preferably carried out in the same equipment as schedule 2.

(11) /D/E/DH/. Similar to schedule 10, but with the initial chlorination

partly or completely exchanged for chlorine dioxide oxidation in the case of resinous pulps.

(12) /H/E/H/. Schedule 1 modified to avoid chlorination of resinous pulps.

(13) /HC/E/H/. Schedule 1 modified to obtain an initial oxidation of resinous pulps prior to chlorination.

(14) /E/H/E/H/. Schedule 12 modified to obtain some deresination in the first stage, which decreases the chemicals consumption in the hypochlorite stage.

(15) /C/E/E/H/. An alkali extraction preceding a hot alkali purification stage to avoid discoloration in the latter at severe conditions.

(16) /C/E/C/E/H/D/. An example of a more advanced bleaching schedule. More than four or five stages should not be necessary in any sulfite bleaching except in very special cases. Sulfite bleacheries of up to nine stages are, however, known.

The influence of reaction conditions on pulp yield and quality in the various stages has been treated in detail in the sections on the separate stages. This section will only compare some results of different types of multistage bleaching. Figure 17.1 shows a compilation of results obtained at the bleaching of an ethanol-preextracted pulp, according to three different schedules, /C/E/H/H/, /C/E/H/D/, and /C/E/DH/ (27). The pulp was a spruce sulfite pulp of soft paper pulp or medium-viscosity rayon pulp type, with an unbleached viscosity of 60 cP TAPPI, a Roe chlorine number of 1.5, alphacellulose content after alcohol extraction and chlorite lignin removal of 88.1 % and a resin content after alcohol extraction of 0.01 %. Obviously, the three schedules are fairly equivalent with respect to brightness, keeping in mind the absence of resin. The brightness of the alkali cellulose is possibly somewhat higher in the last-mentioned bleaching schedule. The effect of the alkali extraction is especially noticeable in the brightness of alkali cellulose and almost negligible in pulp brightness. The figures after the letter E in the alkali stage denote the alkali charge in kg ptp, the 15 kg ptp charge being used at low temperature as a paper pulp alkali extraction, the 50 kg ptp charge at high temperature as a dissolving pulp hot alkali refining. The effects are seen in the figures for alphacellulose content of the bleached pulps. Obviously, in spite of the absence of resin, the conditions of the alkali stage influence the brightness somewhat and brightness stability considerably, which must be attributed to the removal of low-molecular carbohydrates and possibly some resistant residual lignin. The most striking differences between the bleaching schedules are obtained for viscosity changes. Here, the most destructive schedule is shown to be /C/E/H/H/, and the least destructive /C/E/H/D/, as would be expected from the knowledge that chlorine dioxide is mild in action on the carbohydrates, whereas hypochlorite, especially in the absence of considerable quantities of lignin, will oxidize and degrade the carbohydrates. It is also seen that a hot alkali purification tends to render the carbohydrates more sensitive to oxidation.

Similar results are obtained with ethanol-extracted pulps of higher

1069

unbleached viscosities, although the brightness level is then somewhat lower.

These results have shown the influence of residual lignin and low-molecular carbohydrates in multistage bleaching of sulfite pulps, with elimination of the influence of resin and water impurities. (Distilled water should be used in all laboratory bleaching experiments not devoted to the special study of the influence of water impurities.) However, in the production of bleached pulp, the influence of the residual resin content on the brightness cannot be disregarded. Figure 17.1 also shows the results of bleaching of the same spruce pulp without previous ethanol extraction and therefore with an initial resin content of 1.4%. Considerable differences are now observed, not only for the influence of the alkali extraction conditions, which now also affect the resin content of the pulp, but also between the various bleaching schedules. It is seen that the schedules including chlorine dioxide are superior to the conventional /C/E/H/H/ schedule, in respect of

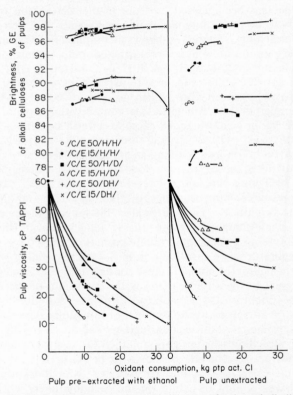

Fig. 17.1. Viscosity of pulp and brightness of pulp and alkali cellulose on bleaching spruce sulfite rayon pulp before and after ethanol extraction. C, chlorine; E, alkali extraction (with 15 or 50 kg ptp); H, hypochlorite; D, chlorine dioxide (Rydholm)

both brightness improvement and limited carbohydrate degradation. Obviously, in the production of bleached sulfite pulp the deresinating effects are as important for the result as the delignifying ones. The conditions and results of a satisfactory sulfite pulp bleaching are shown in Table 12.6.

The improvements over conventional hypochlorite bleaching obtained by chlorine dioxide are also reached by the more expensive sodium chlorite. Good results have also been reported (32) for a finishing peroxide bleach, especially with regard to brightness stability. It is not possible to judge generally between chlorine dioxide and peroxide bleaching of sulfite pulps. Where new installations are made, chlorine dioxide should be preferred because of lower costs of manufacture. Small plants adding an extra bleaching stage may find it less expensive to install peroxide bleaching equipment.

IV. Multistage Bleaching of Kraft Pulps

Kraft pulping not only produces the darkest pulps, 15–30% GE, but also those most difficult to bleach. As in the case of sulfite pulps, unbleached color has little connection with the final brightness of multistage-bleached kraft pulps. Soda pulps have less dark unbleached color, apart from some dense, resin-containing wood species, and have been considered more easy-bleaching. However, a comparison of kraft and soda pulps from the same wood species and similar lignin content shows no principal difference in ease of bleaching. Commercial soda pulps on the other hand are fairly well-cooked hardwood pulps, which contain relatively little lignin. A four stage /C/E/H/H/ or /C/E/H/D/ schedule is therefore considered adequate (7).

The main reason why alkali-pulped fibers are more difficult to bleach is the insolubility in water of most residual lignin even after chlorination. Therefore, the chlorinated lignin does not enter into solution during the chlorination stage as in the case of sulfite pulps, and does not leave the less accessible lignin exposed to the chlorine. Instead, the chlorolignin has to be removed by alkali extraction in a subsequent stage, whereafter the remainder of the lignin can be attacked by chlorination or oxidation. Even then, additional intermediate alkali extractions are necessary to achieve high brightness.

Thus, in the multistage bleaching of kraft pulps, the *residual lignin* plays a dominating role for the final brightness, and more stages and chemicals have to be added than in sulfite pulp bleaching to achieve the same brightness level. *Residual extractives* are generally no problem, partly because the resin-removal in the kraft cook is far more complete than in the sulfite cook, partly because the very highest brightness levels, where the residual extractives might be of importance, are seldom considered in kraft pulp bleaching. The same is true for *residual non-cellulosic carbohydrates*. Only kraft pulp from 'resinous' hardwoods presents a 'resin' problem, if not met by adding tall soap to the digester, and even then the use of chlorine dioxide instead of chlorine in the first stage may be of advantage. That the purity of the water during and after bleaching is also important for kraft pulps is obvious, especially at the highest brightness levels.

The grades desired are *semi-bleached*, *fully bleached*, and *super-bleached* kraft pulps, and the brightness levels of these grades correspond to those of sulfite pulp grades, although one category lower throughout. Thus, semi-bleached kraft pulps have the brightness level—at least according to European nomenclature—of unbleached sulfite pulps, 60–70% GE, although with a more yellowish tinge than the latter, which are usually reddish-gray. Fully bleached kraft pulps are those bleached with additional stages but with conventional chemicals, and have a brightness of about 80% GE, or approximately what could be described as a semi-bleached sulfite pulp brightness. The super-bleached kraft pulp grades have a brightness of about 90% GE, which is obtained with the aid of the new types of bleaching agents, mainly peroxide and chlorine dioxide. Higher brightness than 93% GE is hardly produced in the case of kraft pulps. The development of the kraft bleaching technology tends to change the nomenclature to consider only 90% GE pulps as fully bleached.

Kraft pulp bleaching concentrates on brightness improvement, with the usual necessity of preserved strength properties. Only in the case of prehydrolysis–kraft pulps for dissolving purposes are other effects required at the same time, such as viscosity control, alphacellulose improvement and the removal of metal ions and other impurities. Then additional stages are added, such as cold and hot alkali purification, as well as acidification stages.

Therefore, kraft pulp bleaching requires a considerable number of stages, and some bleaching schedules taken from modern mill praxis will be listed here, together with some comments. The same abbreviations are used as in the previous section.

(1) /C/E/H/. Conventional and sufficient schedule for semi-bleached kraft, when produced from unbleached pulps of normal lignin content, around 5%. The increase in brightness is obtained without a loss in strength properties. Another hypochlorite stage allows better brightness control, or higher brightness but endangers pulp strength (1).

(2) /C/E/C/E/H/. Conventional schedule for fully bleached kraft, produced from unbleached pulps of normal lignin content, or for semi-bleached kraft from high yield pulps. Care should be exercised to avoid strength losses in the second chlorination in the case of fully bleached pulps. The final oxidative stage is also dangerous to pulp strength, if not properly buffered and with well adjusted hypochlorite charge.

(3) /HC/E/C/E/H/. Similar to schedule 2, but with an initial hypochlorite stage, proceeding with a chlorination. If carried out without intermediate washing, addition of an acid, usually sulfuric or hydrochloric is required. The initial stage mainly proceeds as a chlorination of the lignin-rich pulp, although in weakly alkaline medium, and the chlorolignin dissolves directly, exposing less accessible lignin for chlorination. Careful

selection of the conditions of the second chlorination and of the final stage is necessary to limit strength losses.

(4) /C/E/H/E/H/. Similar to schedule 2, but with the second chlorination exchanged for a hypochlorite stage. This is nowadays often preferred as there is less danger of strength losses. For fully bleached pulps, but admits no super-bleaching (17).

(5) /C/E/H/E/H/H/. Similar to schedule 4, but easier adjustment of the final quality possible. The washing between the last two stages could be omitted.

(6) /C/E/H/EP/H/. Similar to schedule 4, but with a peroxide addition in the second alkali extraction, allowing super-bleaching up to about 87% GE (e.g. 18). Peroxide addition could also be added of course in any of the previous schedules with similar result. No extra strength loss is observed.

(7) /C/E/H/E/H/P/. Allows super-bleaching to the same extent as schedule 6 and improved brightness stability (17, 21).

(8) /C/E/H/E/H/D/. Similar in action to schedule 7. Chlorine dioxide could be exchanged for sodium chlorite in small mills avoiding the construction of a chlorine dioxide plant, and used as an alternative for schedule 5 for extra brightness finish in the existing equipment. This was one of the first schedules in America for super-bleached kraft pulp (30).

(9) /C/E/H/D/H/. Less stages but similar results as in schedules 6–8. Last stage involves a risk of strength losses, but gives with a limited hypochlorite charge the desired brightness level with less total oxidant (31).

(10) /C/E/H/D/P/. Gives outstanding brightness stability as well as high brightness (4, 6, 14).

(11) /C/E/H/C/H/D/E/D/. First mill scale production of super-bleached kraft in both Europe and America used this schedule. Two chlorine dioxide stages and an intermediate thorough alkali extraction are essential to real super-bleaching, up to 93% GE. Stage 4 and 5 are dangerous to pulp strength if not properly managed.

(12) /C/E/H/H/D/E/D/. Schedule 11 less second chlorination. Equivalent to the former. Optimal conditions of the chlorine dioxide stages have been studied (10).

(13) /C/E/H/D/E/D/. Schedule 12 less second hypochlorite stage. Equivalent to the former in brightness achievement, almost fool-proof in respect of strength damage, requires less hypochlorite but more chlorine dioxide (17, 27). This schedule represents an optimum for most kraft pulp bleaching with regard to quality, installation and production costs. The first four stages give satisfactory bleaching up to 87–88% GE (18).

(14) /C/E/D/E/D/. Schedule 13 less hypochlorite stage. Compares to 13 as 13 to 12 but is not quite as efficient as 13 for softwood kraft. The schedules 11–14 mirror an historical development in kraft pulp super-bleaching, logical because of the decreased cost of chlorine dioxide in comparison to hypochlorite, and conscious of the increased capital costs of bleaching and washing stages (15).

(15) /C/E/H/P/H/P/. Has been compared to schedule 13 but found

1073

somewhat inferior (17), which is of interest since the comparison concerns chlorine dioxide vs. peroxide.

(16) /C/E/H/E/D/. Almost as expensive as schedule 14 and less good (17, cf. 31).

(17) /C/E/H/D/. Similar comments as to schedule 16 (17). Found superior to schedule 18, at least economically (16).

(18) /C/E/H/P/. Comments above.

(19) /C/E/D/. Adequate for semibleaching, but schedule 1 is preferred.

(20) /C/H/D/. Suggested as the shortest kraft bleaching sequence to give *almost* super-bleached pulps (23), especially with the addition of chlorine dioxide in the first stage.

(21) /C/H/D/E/D/. Discussed in connection with birch kraft bleaching (13) as well as the next schedule.

(22) /D/E/D/E/D/. Which is similar to schedule 14 but avoids chlorination in the first stage to improve the deresination. Conceivable only for low-lignin hardwood pulps from an economic standpoint. Other common hardwood schedules are 1, 17 and 10, depending on the brightness desired.

(23) /C/E/C/E/H/E/H/E/D/E/D/. Exemplifies one of the earliest bleaching schedules for super-bleached kraft pulp, and should be compared to schedule 14, which does essentially the same job with less danger to the pulp strength and, nowadays, probably less cost of chemicals.

(24) /C/H/H/E/D/H/ and

(25) /C/C/E/H/A/E/H/H/D/ are used for the bleaching of prehydrolysis–kraft pulps, which are generally lower in unbleached lignin content and therefore require less initial treatment for lignin removal but should instead give proper viscosity adjustment and to some extent removal of short-chain carbohydrate material. In the case of cold alkali purification, followed by hot alkali purification, it is also claimed that swelling in alkali will improve the reactivity of the pulp in the viscose process (24). The relative positions of the final bleaching stages could be changed. As these pulps are dissolving pulps, a final acidification is necessary for the removal of calcium and heavy metal ions, and this could be done in the bleachery as a separate stage.

The changes in pulp yield and properties for each separate stage are treated in detail in the sections on the various stages. Here, only three examples are given for schedules of fully bleached and super-bleached pulps, Tables 17.1–3 (14, 27). As in the case of sulfite paper pulp bleaching, the yield losses correspond to some 40 % in excess of what is to be expected from lignin removal only, and occur mainly in the chlorination–alkali extraction stages. The strength losses, which to some extent are indicated by the decrease in viscosity, occur mainly in the second chlorination, as well as in the hypochlorite stages. However, no strength loss is generally observed until a viscosity level below 50 cP TAPPI, and becomes serious at 35–20 cP (4, 28). The viscosity units referred to give a normal unbleached kraft viscosity of about 90 cP. Some increase in the beating response is observed after the removal of lignin.

In Table 17.4 (17) the results of various bleaching schedules are compared in terms of the final viscosity and brightness achieved. Obviously, multistage bleaching involves so many variables, that a comparison like this can only be considered as indicative, but it does indicate the ability of chlorine dioxide to give high brightness without carbohydrate degradation.

Table 17.1. Conditions and results on the bleaching of softwood kraft pulp according to the schedule /C/E/H/D/E/D/

Schedule	—	/ C	/ E	/ H	/ D	/ E	/ D /
Consistency, %		3	10	10	10	10	10
Temperature, °C		15	50	30	60	50	70
Time, h		1	1	1	3	1	4
Charge, kg ptp act. Cl		60	—	15	10	—	10
kg ptp NaOH		—	20	15	—	15	—
Residual chlorine, kg ptp		6	—	2	0	—	1
Final pH		2	11	12	3	12	3.5
Viscosity, cP TAPPI	90	85	85	78	77	—	77
Brightness, % GE	25	—	—	55	75	—	91
Mullen, %	100						105
Tear, %	100						105

Table 17.2. Conditions and results on the bleaching of softwood kraft pulp according to the schedule /C/E/H/C/H/D/E/D/

Schedule	—	/ C	/ E	/ H	/ C	/ H	/ D	/ E	/ D /
Consistency, %		3	10	10	3	10	10	10	10
Temperature, °C		15	50	30	20	40	60	50	70
Time, h		1	1	0.5	1	4	4	1	4
Charge, kg ptp act. Cl		55	—	5	8	10	10	—	5
kg ptp NaOH		—	25	5	—	12	—	10	—
Residual chlorine, kg ptp		0	—	0	3	5	0	—	1
Final pH		2	11	10	3	12	3	12	4
Viscosity, cP TAPPI	90	88	88	80	60	40	40	—	40
Brightness, % GE	25	—	—	50	55	65	84	—	91
Mullen, %	100								99
Tear, %	100								90

Table 17.3. Conditions and results on the bleaching of softwood kraft pulp according to the schedule /C/E/H/D/P/

Schedule	—	/ C	/ E	/ H	/ D	/ P /
Consistency, %		3	16	16	14	14
Temperature, °C		30	65	30	70	80
Time, h		1.2	2	2.5	5	5
Charge, kg ptp*		55	18	12	10	2
Brightness, % GE	26	26	29	68	85	89
Mullen %	100					97
Tear %	100					98

* As active chlorine, respectively sodium hydroxide or peroxide.

Table 17.4. Comparison of bleaching schedules for softwood kraft pulps (17)

Schedule	Viscosity, cP	Brightness, % GE Direct	Aged
/C/E/H/D/	92	89	
/C/E/H/E/D/	89	90	
/C/E/H/E/D/	94	91	
/C/E/H/E/H/	40	84	
/C/E/H/E/H/P/	52	85	
/C/E/H/P/H/P/	55	87	
/C/E/H/P/H/P/	91	89	
/C/E/H/P/	—	87	
/C/E/H/P/H/P/	91	89	86
/C/E/H/P/H/P/	73	89	87
/C/E/H/P/H/P/	80	90	88
/C/E/H/P/H/P/	86	88	86
/C/E/H/P/H/P/	55	87	84
/C/E/H/D/E/D/	102	92	88
/C/E/H/D/E/D/	142	92	88
/C/E/H/D/E/D/	171	92	88
/C/E/D/E/D/	188	88	86

V. Multistage Bleaching of Neutral Sulfite Pulps

The main difference of multistage bleaching of neutral sulfite pulps as compared with sulfite and kraft bleaching, lies in the high content of lignin and hemicelluloses. The former constituent necessitates large quantities of bleaching chemicals, the latter special precautions in the alkali extraction and hypochlorite oxidation stages.

Because the main part of the residual lignin of the unbleached neutral sulfite pulp is sulfonated, it has the same tendency as acid sulfite pulp lignin to enter into solution during chlorination, thereby exposing more lignin to chlorination. Therefore, in spite of the large amounts of lignin to be removed, one chlorination is usually sufficient; altogether three stages of the normal /C/E/H/ sequence are adequate for bleaching to brightness 80–85% GE, which is usually enough. However, there is some reason to split the chlorination into two stages, as the lignin dissolved initially during the chlorination tends to consume more chlorine, and therefore an intermediate washing after half or two-thirds of the chlorine charge might reduce the total chlorine consumption by some 5–10 kg ptp. This must not mean an extra tower, as much of the chlorine is consumed during the first 5 minutes, but necessitates an extra pump or chlorine mixer, a wide pipe for retention, and an extra filter. Another advantage of splitting the chlorine charge into two is that less chlorine has to be mixed with the pulp at a time. The large amounts of chlorine otherwise charged often need special arrangements, such as double charge-pipes and double mixing impellers in the bottom of a conventional upflow tower.

The lignin content of the unbleached pulp varies with yield and wood species, a normal value for 70–75% yield being 10–12% lignin,

1076

corresponding to Roe chlorine numbers of 15–17. This suggests a chlorine charge of 150–170 kg ptp. It has been a matter of discussion, how much chlorine should be charged in chlorination and how much should be saved for the final hypochlorite bleach, and proportions of from 95 : 5 to 65 : 35 have been suggested. The former extreme is said to give a better pulp strength, whereas the latter would give a cleaner pulp. It is generally true that the chlorination should be less dangerous to pulp yield and strength than the hypochlorite bleach of a neutral sulfite pulp, and should therefore be carried as far as possible. Furthermore, since the development of the vortex cleaners, there is less need to consider cleanliness as a primary purpose of bleaching, and it is not justifiable to sacrifice strength for that purpose any more. Therefore, mill practice tends to devote some 90% of the total amount of chlorine to the chlorination stage.

The washing after chlorination and also on the subsequent filters depends considerably on the pulp freeness obtained after disk refining. Here, it is important that the refiner will be sufficiently precise to achieve fiber liberation without bruising and cutting the fibers excessively, which will otherwise decrease the freeness, especially after the lignin removal by chlorination. One possible remedy is to limit the refining and remove the coarse fiber bundles in the screening room, for repeated disk refining.

Another factor of importance to the washing efficiency is foaming, which is likewise apt to cause considerable trouble in the case of neutral sulfite pulps. The large amounts of chlorinated lignosulfonic acids in the pulp suspension considerably decrease surface tension, and the resin present, along with the short ray cells of the hardwood pulps, are excellent foam stabilizers. Therefore, the introduction of air through pumps, etc., should be carefully avoided. Another source of gas for foaming is chlorine. Therefore, the mixing of chlorine gas with the pulp prior to chlorination should be made carefully, avoiding local excess, and the charge adjusted to prevent considerable residual chlorine. Foam killers, such as octanols, silicons, etc., are efficient but generally too expensive to be used in current production.

The alkali extraction stage is also influenced by the operations preceding the bleaching. With a uniform penetration of cooking liquor to the chips and a uniform cooking, there is no need to apply alkali extraction conditions from the point of lignin removal. This is important, as there is a considerable content of glucuronoxylan, which is valuable to quality and yield, and which is rather alkali-labile. Therefore, both alkali charges and reaction temperature should be kept at an absolute minimum. Some removal of resin and chlorinated lignin is desirable, however. Usually, cold water temperature is sufficient, and alkali charges of about 20 kg ptp. Insufficient washing of the chlorinated pulp may increase this figure to 25 or even 30 kg ptp. The use of sodium sulfite instead of hydroxide has been recommended for milder action on the carbohydrates. However, if a large excess of alkali is avoided, equally good results are achieved with hydroxide, at less cost.

Caution in the alkali stage is especially required, when the bleached pulp is to be used for greaseproof and glassine papers, for which bleached neutral sulfite pulp is especially suited. Some arguments might be raised against too mild alkaline conditions when fine paper grades are desired, where bulk, opacity and brightness are of greater importance. The suitability of the neutral sulfite process for these grades has not been quite established, and cooking at somewhat lower pH, such as in the bisulfite or even acid sulfite process, is an alternative to produce more opaque pulps

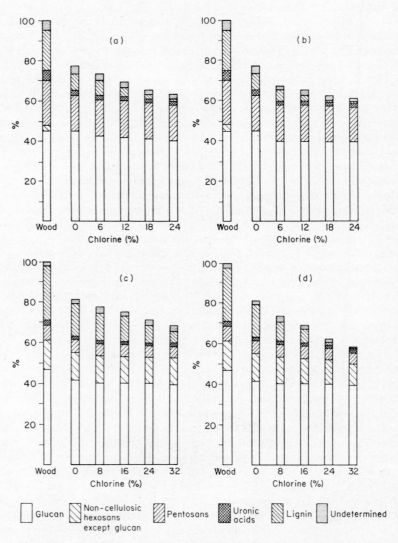

Fig. 17.2. Changes in pulp composition in the bleaching of neutral sulfite pulps (Björkqvist *et al*)

of lower yield. Even choosing the neutral sulfite pulping process, it is likely that it should be carried out to lower yields and lignin content than normally, if the more opaque grades of paper are desired, thus lowering the cost of bleaching chemicals. In both cases, the removal of some carbohydrates to produce more opacity is preferably carried out in the digester and only to a limited extent in the alkali extraction tower. Only so much more severe conditions are employed as are necessary to give satisfactory brightness improvement in the subsequent hypochlorite bleaching stage. Here, of course, not only the pulp grade but also the wood raw material are determining factors.

The hypochlorite stage has to consider the danger of both alkaline and oxidative degradation of the hemicelluloses (11). As a precaution against the former, the initial pH should not be too high, whereas to prevent oxidative attack it is necessary that pH should not drop too low. These two facts suggest batch bleaching with continuous or repeated small additions of alkali, as the reaction proceeds. However, other advantages of continuous hypochlorite bleaching are sufficient to accept the possibility of somewhat less good results. By careful adjustment of the chemicals charges and dividing the stage into two, without washing but with a new addition of chemicals, results almost identical to those of batch bleaching can be obtained. Thus the simple schedule of

(1) /C/E/H/ may be extended to

(2) /C/C/E/H/ to decrease chlorine consumption and to

(3) /C/C/E/HH/ to avoid hemicellulose degradation. Also a chlorine dioxide stage is conceivable for higher brightness, but has hitherto not been found necessary in neutral sulfite bleaching.

The yield losses are considerable during neutral sulfite multistage bleaching, as would be expected from the high initial lignin and hemicellulose content. 15–20% of the unbleached pulp is dissolved leaving a total yield of bleached pulp of about 60%, wood basis, from the hardwoods of intermediate lignin content, such as birch. The detailed course of a birch neutral sulfite multistage bleaching is exemplified in Figure 17.2 (2).

REFERENCES

1. Bishop, F. W., *Paper Trade J.*, **133**, No. 18, 21 (1951).
2. Björkqvist, K. J., *et al.*, *Svensk Papperstid.*, **56**, 734 (1953).
3. Bush, W. H., *Pulp Paper Mag. Can.*, **59**, No. 3, 197 (1958).
4. Casciani, F., and G. K. Storin, *Tappi*, **33**, 588 (1950); *U.S. Pat.* 2,494,542 (1950).
5. Chadeyron, L., *La Papeterie*, **72**, 357 (1950).
6. Chadwick, A. F., *et al.*, *Tappi*, **42**, 308 (1959).
7. Freedman, H., *Tappi*, **40**, No. 3, 74A (1957).
8. Giertz, H. W., *Tappi*, **34**, 209 (1951).
9. Gustafsson, G. R., *Paperi Puu*, **32**, 223 (1950).
10. Harrison, W. D., and C. R. Calkins, *Tappi*, **38**, 641 (1955).
11. Jappe, N. A., *Tappi*, **41**, 224 (1958).
12. Jayme, G., and L. Rothamel, *Wochbl. Papierfabrik.*, **82**, No. 11, 421 (1954).

1079

13. Jensen, W., *et al.*, *Paperi Puu*, **40**, 555 (1958).
14. Kraft, F., *Papier*, **5**, 478 (1951); **15**, 507 (1961).
15. Laler, T. M., and S. M. Rollinson, *Tappi*, **39**, No. 8, 154A (1956).
16. Lindahl, E., *et al.*, *Svensk Papperstid.*, **62**, 308 (1959).
17. Miller, R. L., *et al.*, *Tappi*, **39**, 826 (1956).
18. Nicholls, G. A., *Tappi*, **43**, 910 (1960).
19. Obenshain, D. N., *Tappi*, **41**, 1 (1958).
20. Parsons, J. L., *Paper Trade J.*, **131**, No. 22, 216 (1950).
21. Raaka, C., *et al.*, *Tappi*, **40**, 201 (1957).
22. Rapson, W. H., *Pulp Paper Mag. Can.*, **57**, No. 10, 147 (1956).
23. Rapson, W. H., and C. B. Anderson, *Tappi*, **41**, 486 (1958).
24. Rogers, L. N., *et al.*, *U.S. Pat.* 2,878,118 (1959).
25. Richter, G. A., *Ind. Eng. Chem.*, **33**, 1518 (1941).
26. Rue, J. D., *Tappi*, **40**, No. 11, 207A (1957).
27. Rydholm, S. A., unpublished 1953–55.
28. Valeur, C., *Svensk Papperstid.*, **54**, 613 (1951).
29. Virkola, N. E., *et al.*, *Svensk Papperstid.*, **62**, 477 (1959).
30. Wiley, A. L., *Southern Pulp Paper Mfr*, **18**, No. 4, 64 (1955).
31. Wilson, J. W., and M. Wayman, *Pulp Paper Mag. Can.*, **58**, No. 9, 137 (1957).
32. Wultsch, F., and W. Gärtner, *Die Peroxydbleiche von Zellstoff und Holz-schliff*, Degussa Bull., 1956.

18

FURTHER TREATMENT OF BLEACHED PULPS

I. Wet Operations

Figure 18.1 exemplifies the finishing operations after the bleachery. There are many variations, depending on the type of pulp, the quality of the mill water, etc. In integrated mills the bleached pulp is pumped to the beater room directly after the last bleach washer, and *screening* and *cleaning* is carried out immediately prior to the machines to remove some

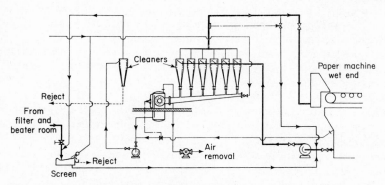

Fig. 18.1. Screening and cleaning of pulp prior to the paper machine (Eie)

impurities which have escaped the cleaning of the unbleached pulp and the bleaching, or which have formed during the bleaching. To the latter category belong fragments of ceramic or rubber linings, pitch lumps and fiber nodules. Because of the various shapes and specific gravities of these impurities, it is an advantage to combine a screening system with a battery of centrifugal cleaners. Both types of machinery have been described in Chapter 10, and only some coupling principles will be mentioned here. In both operations only one single treatment of the main flow is considered necessary, with additional equipment used to minimize the reject losses. The screens are as a rule high-frequency vibratory screens with 0.25–0.35 mm slot width and very little overflow, which can often be discarded without re-screening. Sometimes the overflow is larger and is then passed to secondary and even tertiary screens of the same type. More recent installations apply pressurized centrifugal screens of the Impco, Bird Centriscreen or Selectifier types. The accepted pulp passes to a battery of vortex cleaners, usually

1081

for 3–5 stages to minimize the pulp losses. The rejected pulp may even be recycled to the screening room for unbleached pulp. In integrated mills especially care should be taken to avoid the introduction of air into the stock in the cleaning operation.

The screening and cleaning operations are carried out at a pulp consistency of 0.5–1.0%. In some mills they are directly coupled to the drying machines with no intermediate storage chest. However, it is often desired to carry out the screening and cleaning at a somewhat lower consistency than the preferred headbox consistency of the machines, in which case a final filter or decker and a machine chest are necessary. This is the customary arrangement, and it allows a more undisturbed control of the consistency and flow of pulp to the headbox. The machine chest consistency is then preferably kept at 3–4%, and where *acidification* of the pulp to remove metal impurities is required (dissolving pulps and pulps for photographic paper, cf. Chapter 16), it is usually done here as an automatically controlled addition of sulfur dioxide to give a pH of 3–4.

Immediately prior to the machine are sometimes coupled *refiners* of the conical type. These may be used for paper pulps as a *pre-beating* stage to facilitate the beating operations of the customers. However, since the subsequent drying of pulp destroys much of this effect, beating is usually left to the paper mill entirely. For rayon pulps, where the sheet structure is important, refining may be carried out to improve the subsequent sheet formation by destroying any flocks or fiber nodules formed in previous operations.

One important consideration regarding the finishing wet operations on bleached pulps is how the brightness of the pulp is influenced by the mill water. Several of the brightness units gained in the bleachery are lost again in these operations if the mill water is unsuitable, especially at modern, super-bleached pulp grades. It is therefore necessary to control the quality of the mill water and if necessary purify it. However, the costs of water purification are not negligible, especially as 100–300 m^3 ptp are required for the finishing wet operations, if there are no special precautions taken. Therefore, recycling of the water is often practised, in order to (1) reduce the overall water consumption, (2) reduce the amounts of mill water impurities brought in contact with the bleached pulp, and (3) reduce the cost of the water purification if necessary. The white water from the filter or decker prior to the machine chest may thus be reused to dilute the pulp from the last bleach washer prior to screening, and the white water from the machine wet end may be used to dilute the pulp before and after the machine chest to headbox consistency, as indicated in Figure 18.1. As the pulp leaves the wet end of the drying machine with a higher consistency than that after the last bleach washer, in principle no fresh water is needed. In addition, some fresh hot water is always added on the machine wet end to save steam at the drying, and some fresh water at the showers trimming the edges of the wet sheet, thus ensuring a positive white water balance. A further advantage of a closed system is that heat from the hot water shower on the machine will accumulate and facilitate the heating of the wet sheet. The sulfur dioxide consumption in the case of acidification of the pulp will decrease for similar reasons. On the other hand a marked disadvantage is that none of the dispersable pulp impurities, mainly resin particles, are able to leave the system as is the case with an open water system. This may result in an agglomeration of the particles to show up as dirt specks in the pulp sheet. The water system should consequently be closed only to an extent which eliminates more impurities of mill water than are kept of those entering with the bleached pulp. Obviously, there are some possibilities of increasing the removal of such impurities in the bleaching.

II. Drying Operations

Most bleached pulp of non-integrated mills is delivered dry, at a moisture content of less than 10%. Although it is generally slushed by the customer (with the exception of the viscose mills using sheet steeping), the dominating form of shipment is that of baled sheets, and the dominating pulp drying equipment has been developed from the paper machine, with a sheet-forming wet end (*fourdrinier* or *cylinder* type), a press section and a cylinder dryer section, Figure 18.2 (6), after which the finishing operations on and off the machine are added. Alternatively, the steam-heated cylinders are either enclosed for vacuum drying, the *Minton* dryer, or exchanged for a *flakt dryer* section, where the sheet is dried by hot air while conducted by rolls in a series of horizontal or vertical slings, or more recently airborne at higher speed, Figure 18.3 (1, 5). Combinations of cylinder dryers with flakt dryers are frequent, as added drying capacity to a cylinder machine has been achieved by putting a vertical type flakt dryer at the dry end. Recently several new developments have also been made, which omit the sheet-forming operations and dry the pulp in a fluffy shape, subsequently baling it in equipment developed by the cotton or synthetic fibers industry. Such *flash drying* systems are the *Bauer* (7), *Glomera* (2, 3, 4) and *Courtaulds* systems, as exemplified in Figure 18.4. They apply a slush pulp pressing to high consistency, 40–60%, followed by breaking of the press cake to fluff pulp by various types of shredders and drying by hot flue gases from an oil or gas burner. In spite of the high gas temperature, 200–400°C, this drying in most cases requires a retention chamber of some type, e.g. three vertical drying towers or a cylinder with three concentric pipes, but when the pressing operation is very efficient, the temperature of the flue gases high enough, and the latter introduced directly in the shredder, as in the Courtaulds system, the drying takes place almost instantly and the dry fluff pulp is separated in a cyclone immediately after the shredder. These drying systems have now been tested on a large scale for some time, with chemical as well as mechanical pulp, and appear to have considerable merits, since they require less investments than a sheet dryer and may also decrease the costs of operation.

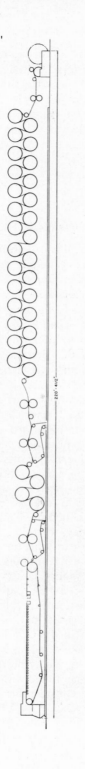

Fig. 18.2. Sandy Hill–Kamyr cylinder pulp driers with fourdrinier or cylinder wet ends

The conventional pulp drying machines have some features which require comments, and are especially important in the production of rayon pulp for sheet steeping. In order to obtain a uniform sheet of good formation, some of the same precautions have to be taken at the wet end as for a paper machine. Although normally run at a headbox consistency of 1 %, there is a trend towards lower consistency, which will diminish fiber flocculation prior to sheet formation. The headbox should be properly designed to give an even flow of pulp across the entire width of the wire. A few machines even have the closed air-cushioned headbox of a high-speed paper machine. The slice should be adjusted to give a linear speed of the flow not far from that of the wire, from about 10 up to 100 m/min,

Fig. 18.3. Svenska Flaktfabriken airborne pulp web flakt drier

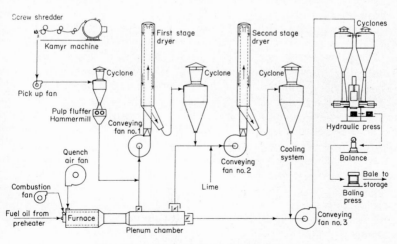

Fig. 18.4. Glomera flash-drying system

varying with the load and width of the machine and with the desired basis weight of the sheet. The basis weight is seldom above 1,000 g/m², normally about 600 g/m², and the machine width seldom exceeds 6 m. The wire may be of bronze, stainless steel or even polyamide fibers, or a combination of metal warp and polyamide weft. On the wire one or more showers are applied for washing, sometimes neutralization, and heating by hot water. In rayon pulp production the last shower is sometimes designed to give stripes in the sheet in a manner considered to facilitate the lye penetration in sheet steeping. The same effect can be achieved with a dandy roll. That last shower can also be used for application of wetting agents or aging catalysts sometimes delivered with the rayon pulp. In rare cases hydrogen peroxide is also added for a bleach finish.

To drain the water off the wet end, the machine is equipped like a paper machine with table rolls, suction boxes, rotabelt and a couch roll, the description of which machinery is outside the scope of this book. To increase the temperature of the wet sheet and thereby the pressing and drying capacity, there are several arrangements in addition to the hot water shower. A steam box is sometimes placed over a suction box, or a preheater hood for exhaust air from a flakt dryer is put in immediately after the wire section. In the press section there are generally three pairs of press rolls, one or two sometimes placed after a couple of cylinder dryers in order to ensure full effect of pressing by lowering the viscosity of the water. The consistency of the pulp sheet is thus increased from about 18% when leaving the wire to about 44% after the press section. The last wet press is sometimes a riffling press. For rayon pulps, one further pair of press rolls, a smoothing press, is placed in the dryer section at a dry content of the sheet between 60 and 80%, in order to compress the sheet further at a stage where a compression will still have an irreversible effect but with as much water as possible removed. Such pressing gives a denser sheet with less entrapped air and hence less tendency to float in the alkali steeping presses of the viscose mill.

A comparison of cylinder and flakt dryers depends to some extent on local factors such as the relative costs of fuel and power, but in most cases the flakt dryer gives lower costs of operation as the steam consumption is about 1.3 t ptp as compared to about 1.5 t ptp for cylinder drying and to about 80 kg ptp bunker oil and 70 kWh ptp for flash drying. On the other hand a flakt dryer gives a less nice sheet structure owing to bending of the sheet over smaller cylinder radii. This is unimportant for paper pulps, especially as customs regulations in many countries require that the pulp exporter should destroy the pulp sheet structure in a way which prevents its use as a board. This is done by a pair of perforating rolls at the dry end of the machine.

Sometimes the last one or two cylinders especially of rayon pulp drying machines operate as sheet coolers to eliminate color reversion and viscosity reduction of the slightly acidic, hot pulp on storage. The quality questions of color reversion and paper strength changes on drying are treated in Chapters 12 and 21, respectively.

III. Finishing Operations

The dried pulp emerges from the dryer as a continuous sheet, which is cut in the machine direction to desired width and trim-cut at the two edges of the original sheet. Some machines, especially for dissolving pulp, are equipped for roll handling, where huge, 10 t rolls of the full machine width are removed to storage and subsequently cut to desired sheet sizes and baled. Some pulp consumers, such as acetate mills, prefer their pulp delivered in rolls, but this requires more shipping volume and is avoided for other purposes. Normally the sheet cutters are located directly at the machine, cutting the pulp sheet in sizes of about 60 × 80 cm for rayon pulp and somewhat larger for paper pulp. The piles of sheet are then weighed, wrapped and baled to units of about 200 kg. These operations have been very labor-consuming but are now becoming increasingly automated. At the baling, the piles of sheets are compressed by a hydraulic press together with the wrapping, and subsequently stringed without much expansion, to reduce the shipping volume. The density of an ordinary bale is about 0.6–0.8. Baling of fluff-dried pulp can be allowed to apply higher pressures, and densities of up to 1.0 can be reached. Such bales are, however, as hard as bricks and require special, though not very complicated, breakers ahead of the slusher in the paper or viscose mill. The appearance

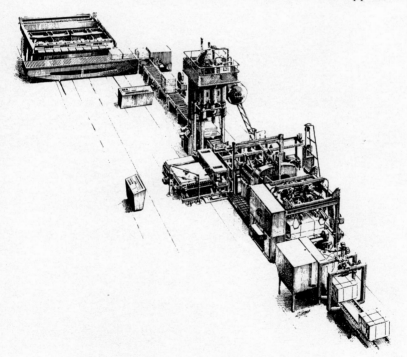

Fig. 18.5. Cutting and baling of pulp sheets (Nordströms)

of so-called fish-eyes or unslushable hard fiber lumps is a problem in the operation occurring with flash-dried pulp. Figure 18.5 shows a layout of the finishing room. The bales are finally marked with a current number and the grade, and delivered by truck or conveyor to storage or to rail, road or sea transport.

REFERENCES

1. Diehl, W. F., *Pulp Paper International*, **1,** No. 12, 48 (1959).
2. Dunbar, T. W., *Tappi*, **42,** No. 9, 133A (1959).
3. Evans, J. C. W., *Paper Trade J.*, **142,** No. 16, 26 (1958).
4. Gagnon, L., and K. Stangl, *Pulp Paper Mag. Can.*, **59,** No. 10, 164 (1958).
5. Grindrod, J., *Pulp Paper Mag. Can.*, **60,** No. 8, 76 (1959).
6. Sandy Hill Tech. Bull.
7. Sternberger, R. M., *Pulp Paper Mag. Can.*, **59,** No. 10, 167 (1958).

19

PREPARATION OF BLEACHING
CHEMICALS

The bleaching operations require a number of chemicals, which are not recovered but have to be purchased, mainly from the electrochemical industry, for either direct use or conversion in the pulp mill to useful bleach liquors. It is beyond the scope of this book to enter into the details of the electrochemical processes. Only the basic principles will be mentioned, and the handling of the chemicals in the pulp mill described, together with a more complete treatment on the preparation of hypochlorite and chlorine dioxide, which is usually done at the pulp mill. In addition to chemicals, the bleaching operations need water of a higher purity than other pulp mill operations. An introduction to the water purification methods was recently given in a TAPPI Monograph (29b), and a more detailed treatment is considered outside the scope of this book.

I. Preparation and Handling of Chlorine, Alkali, Sodium Chlorate, Chlorite, Peroxide and Dithionite

The manufacture of these chemicals is a large-scale industry mainly concentrated in regions with cheap electrical energy, since the latter is one of the dominant cost items of the production. If the pulp industry is located in such regions, as is the case in, for example, Sweden, Norway and Canada, it may find it economic to invest in its own chlorine–alkali plants, but seldom in the manufacture of the other chemicals. A few mills also have chlorate electrolysis.

1. CHLORINE AND ALKALI

Chlorine and *sodium hydroxide* are made by electrolysis of sodium chloride. To avoid complications in the electrolysis, the brine has to be purified by precipitation of contaminating cations. It is then fed to electrolytic cells, which are either of the mercury or diaphragm type. These terms refer to the means of keeping the anode and cathode products apart to prevent interaction, which leads to hypochlorite formation and a decrease in current efficiency. The anode of the cell is graphite, and the cathode steel screen or wire in the case of diaphragm cells or mercury in the mercury cells. The diaphragm separating the electrodes is made of asbestos. Chlorine is formed at the anode and hydrogen and sodium hydroxide at the steel cathode. The mercury cathode instead forms an amalgam with

1089

sodium, which is continuously removed to react with water in a separate chamber to hydrogen and sodium hydroxide. Each cell requires 3.5–4.5 V, and therefore a large number of cells are coupled in series. Currents of 600–1,000 amp are used. Current efficiencies run 95–97%, and 1.0 t Cl_2 and 1.1 t NaOH are produced from 1.8 t NaCl and 3,150 kWh. The hydrogen by-product is either wasted or used for the production of other chemicals, such as ammonia. The caustic from the mercury cells is obtained at a concentration of 40% and is usually sold as such, whereas the 10% NaOH, brine-containing lye of the diaphragm cells is evaporated to 50 or 70% NaOH, with separation of sodium chloride.

The strong lye is delivered at the pulp mills in tank cars or wagons of 20–40 m³. They are preferably equipped with steam coils to facilitate unloading in wintertime, as the strong lye tends to solidify in cold weather. Steam coils should also be installed in the outdoor storage tanks of the mill, although some dilution is generally done upon unloading. Other mills dilute the caustic from the storage tank to an intermediate tank, usually to 10–15% NaOH concentration. The dilution is sometimes automatically controlled by means of impulse from a conductivity cell or a specific gravity controller, as illustrated in Figure 19.1.

The hot chlorine gas from the anode carries much water. The water is removed by a cooler-condenser, and a final drying is accomplished in a

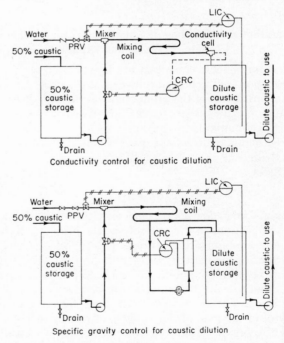

Fig. 19.1. Methods of diluting 50% caustic to the concentration required for mill use (Rue)

sulfuric acid scrubber. After drying, the chlorine can be handled in iron equipment. The chlorine gas is compressed to 2.5 to 5 atm and cooled as it liquefies. It is then stored and transported as a liquid. It arrives at the pulp mill in special tank wagons of 25–50 t. These may be the only chlorine storage at the mill, but often there are intermediate pressure tanks to receive and weigh liquid chlorine. The transfer from the wagon is done through extra-heavy steel pipes, with excess air pressure attached to the top of the wagon. The empty car is vented by air to a caustic tank. The air used should be dry to avoid corrosion. The usual contaminant of liquid chlorine is sulfuric acid from the compressors of the electrolysis plant, and iron compounds from the corrosion of pipes when moisture has been introduced to the system. These contaminants are removed, as the chlorine is gasified in specially designed evaporators, heated by hot water, pressure controlled and equipped with sediment traps and filters of coke and glass wool. The filtered gas is metered under passage to the chlorination stage or hypochlorite preparation. Figure 19.2 illustrates the chlorine handling system.

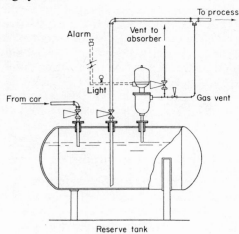

Fig. 19.2. Chlorine handling at pulp mill

2. SODIUM CHLORATE

Whereas the overall reaction of chlorine–alkali electrolysis is

$$2\,NaCl + 2\,H_2O \longrightarrow 2\,NaOH + H_2 + Cl_2$$

the corresponding overall reaction for chlorate production is

$$NaCl + 3\,H_2O \longrightarrow NaClO_3 + 3\,H_2$$

The electrolysis is carried out in steel cells with no diaphragm to separate the reaction products. The purified brine is acidulated with hydrochloric acid and some sodium dichromate is added as a corrosion inhibitor. A cooling coil keeps the temperature at 40°C. The hypochlorous acid formed by electrolysis is further oxidized with formation of chlorate and more hydrogen. The chlorate solution is steam stripped, barium chloride added to precipitate the chromate, and the barium chromate and graphite mud from the electrodes are allowed to settle before evaporation of the solution and separation of the sodium chlorate crystals. The crystals are centrifuged and dried and the mother liquor returned to the process. The chlorate electrolysis cells require 3–3.5 V each, and a large number are therefore coupled in series. The current efficiency is somewhat lower in the chlorate electrolysis, which consumes about 0.56 t NaCl and 5,600 kWh per t $NaClO_3$, as well as 5.5 t steam. To allow a comparison with the above figures for chlorine–alkali, it may be added that after conversion of the chlorate to chlorine dioxide (see below) with an efficiency of 90%, 1 t of active chlorine in the form of chlorine dioxide corresponds to a consumption of 3,800 kWh and 0.38 t NaCl, to which other chemical costs must also be added, however.

Sodium chlorate is transported in bulk in carloads or large moveable containers or drums, or in special cases as a concentrated solution. At the mill, the drums or containers are handled by a telfer and emptied into a storage tank for dissolution. Carloads are discharged by recirculating hot water between the car and the dissolver-storage tank. The crystal slurry leaving the car is completely dissolved in the tank by increasing the temperature or adding more water. At the freezing point, the saturation point is about 600 g/l, at 80°C about 1,000 g/l. Certain precautions in handling sodium chlorate must be observed. Contamination with organic matter must be avoided, and clothes in contact with chlorate solution should be immediately soaked and washed.

3. SODIUM CHLORITE

Similar in bleaching action to chlorine dioxide, sodium chlorite can be transported in pure form and is hence used by small pulp mills or mills desiring a brightness finish only occasionally, and therefore not wishing to install a chlorine dioxide generator. However, chlorite is much more expensive, since it is made from chlorate via chlorine dioxide under consumption of 20% of the oxidation capacity and with use of extra chemicals, e.g. by the reaction

$$4\ NaOH + Ca(OH)_2 + C + 4\ ClO_2 \longrightarrow 4\ NaClO_2 + CaCO_3 + 3\ H_2O$$

The product is purified by filtration and evaporated to yield crystals or flakes of 90–98% purity, which are sold in drums. Similar precautions as with chlorate are necessary in handling sodium chlorite at the mill.

4. SODIUM PEROXIDE AND OTHER PEROXIDES

Sodium peroxide is produced by oxidation of sodium, made by electrolysis of fused sodium chloride:

$$2\ NaCl \longrightarrow 2\ Na + Cl_2 \qquad 2\ Na + O_2 \longrightarrow Na_2O_2$$

The cell is a closed, refractory-lined steel box, having an iron cathode and a carbon anode. The anode and cathode are arranged in separate chambers to facilitate the recovery of sodium and chlorine. The cell operates at 600°C, at which temperature the chloride is made to melt through the addition of other salts. The energy consumption is about 15,000 kWh per t Na.

The oxidation of sodium is carried out in an excess of air at 300°C. The resultant product is packed in iron drums and is a yellow, hygroscopic powder or granules with a purity of about 95%. In contact with organic matter, the powder absorbs water and is thereby heated sufficiently to cause ignition. It must therefore be handled with the same care as sodium chlorate and, in addition, be protected especially against moisture.

Calculated per t of 'active chlorine' in order to compare the raw material consumption with the other oxidants, sodium peroxide corresponds to about 10,000 kWh and 1.65 t NaCl (in addition to which 1 t Cl_2 is produced as a by-product, however). Thus it represents a less efficient way of converting electrical energy to bleach oxidant and is about as expensive. Its use is motivated by its milder action for specific purposes, such as brightening lignin-containing pulps without substance losses. Similar in use, but generally more expensive to produce, is *hydrogen peroxide*. The classical methods are the electrolytical oxidation of sulfuric acid to *persulfuric acid*, which is then hydrolyzed with steam to give hydrogen peroxide, or the treatment of *ammonium persulfate* with sulfuric acid, or by oxidation of barium oxide at 600°C to *barium peroxide* and decomposing the latter with sulfuric acid. Hydrogen peroxide is also used for the production of *sodium perborate*, which has found wide use as a mild oxidant in the detergent industry but is not used in pulp bleaching. *Peracetic acid* is a compound made by the electrolytic oxidation of acetic acid and has attracted interest as a pulp bleaching agent, although it is still too expensive for industrial use.

The preparation of stabilized peroxide liquor, including the additives of magnesium sulfate and sodium silicate, was described in Chapter 13.

5. SODIUM DITHIONITE

Sodium dithionite, sometimes called hyposulfite or hydrosulfite, $Na_2S_2O_4$, has a similar use to sodium peroxide as a brightening agent for lignin-rich pulps, and is sometimes used in combination with peroxide in a two-stage process. It is a reducing agent made from zinc dust and sulfur dioxide and sodium sulfite or carbonate, according to the principal reactions

$$Zn + 2 SO_2 \longrightarrow ZnS_2O_4$$
$$ZnS_2O_4 + NaCO_3 \longrightarrow ZnCO_3 + Na_2S_2O_4$$

The zinc salt is filtered off and the sodium dithionite salted out with sodium chloride. As zinc is to a considerable extent produced electrolytically, with lead anodes and aluminium cathodes, requiring 2,400 kWh per t, it might be of curiosity interest to find the electrical energy needed to convey reductive equivalents to pulp bleaching by this path. Calculated in the same, somewhat irrational unit of t active chlorine, this would correspond to about 2,200 kWh. Alternatively to sodium dithionite, zinc dithionite is also sometimes used.

II. Preparation of Hypochlorite and Chlorine Dioxide

1. HYPOCHLORITE

The principal reactions involved in hypochlorite production are

$$Cl_2 + 2\ NaOH \longrightarrow NaClO + NaCl + H_2O \text{ and}$$
$$Cl_2 + 2\ CaO \longrightarrow Ca(ClO)_2 + CaCl_2$$

Chlorine is thus absorbed by alkali or lime. In the latter case, the solid compound obtained has the approximate composition (9):

$$CaO \cdot 3\ Ca(ClOCl) \cdot 4\ H_2O$$

corresponding to 42% chlorine and 11% excess lime. Additional lime is added to bind the water, which tends to make such *bleach powders* unstable on storage, especially in the tropics, whereby oxygen and calcium chloride are formed. The excess lime added decreases the chlorine content to about 35%. Calcium chloride can be removed from the mixture to make the powder less hygroscopic and leaves a calcium hypochlorite of a higher content of active chlorine, as seen from the analysis of two commercial bleach powders, Table 19.1.

Table 19.1. Composition of bleach powders

	Normal	High
Active chlorine, %	35.0	62.5
$Ca(ClO)_2$, %	35.2	63.0
$CaCl_2$, %	33.0	9.0
$Ca(ClO_3)_2$, %	1.9	0.4
$Ca(OH)_2$, %	22.8	22.0
$CaCO_3$, %	4.9	3.0
H_2O, %	1.5	1.1

The chlorate content of the bleach powders originates from the reaction

$$3\ HClO \longrightarrow 3\ H^+ + 2\ Cl^- + ClO_3^-$$

which takes place at elevated temperatures, especially above 50°C (13). As the preparation of hypochlorite is an exothermic reaction, care must be exercised to suppress the temperature of the reaction mixture.

Bleach powders were more important before methods and facilities were developed to transport liquid chlorine. Central production from dilute 'waste chlorine' gas in combination with other industries is still some motivation for bleach powder manufacture. However, mills with any considerable consumption of hypochlorite make their own bleach solutions from lime and chlorine. This is also the case for mills using sodium hypochlorite. Equipment and methods have been designed for an automatically controlled, continuous production (10, 12, 16a, 27, 28) the principle of which is outlined in Figure 19.3 for calcium hypochlorite solution. Lime is slurried in a tank and the slurry passed to a level-controlled feed tank, from which it is pumped to an injection reactor. There,

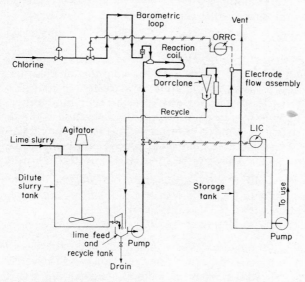

Fig. 19.3. Hooker automatic calcium hypochlorite system
(Rue)

chlorine is introduced via a control valve receiving an impulse from a redox instrument after the mixing with the lime. Between the reactor and the redox electrode flow assembly, there is a retention coil, and a vortex separator to remove excess lime, which is recycled to the feed tank. The flow of lime slurry is controlled from a level impulse of the hypochlorite solution storage tank. A continuous production of sodium hypochlorite has the same principal design, less the vortex separator. If the sodium hydroxide concentration has not been carefully adjusted in the previous lye system, this has been done prior to the feed pump. Alternatively to the redox impulse, a pH impulse could be used. Instead of the retention coil, a vertical double-tube reactor can be used (12), where chlorine gas is introduced to the inner tube, inducing a rapid internal upward flow, and a corresponding downward flow between the tubes. This continually introduces hypochlorite to the reaction zone of alkali and chlorine, which eliminates the initial lag of reaction occurring in a mixture of pure alkali and chlorine. The reaction is exothermic and causes a temperature rise

1095

of about 10°C at the production of a 30 g/l active chlorine solution. The cost of the installation including instruments is estimated to be about $10,000.

2. CHLORINE DIOXIDE

A. Principles

Although direct oxidation with ozone or peroxy compounds has been suggested (8), all commercial methods for chlorine dioxide preparation start from sodium chlorate (3, 23, 32, 33). In mills using purchased sodium chlorite, the chlorine dioxide generation is in the *bleaching*,

$$2 \text{ NaClO}_2 + \text{HClO} + \text{HCl} \longrightarrow 2 \text{ NaCl} + 2 \text{ ClO}_2 + \text{H}_2\text{O}$$

where either the chlorite is acidified and after initial reduction to hypochlorous acid the latter reacts with the chlorite, or chlorine (or hypochlorite) is added from the beginning to 'activate' the chlorite. The latter is obviously the less expensive way of using sodium chlorite. However, the only economic way to chlorine dioxide generation is the reduction of chlorate. Variations in the reaction conditions and in the choice of reactant have led to a considerable number of processes, which will be discussed in some detail here. They can be subdivided into the following groups:

(1) Reduction with SO_2 (*Griesheim, Holst, Mathieson, C.I.P.* processes).
(2) Reduction with $Cr_2(SO_4)_3$ (*Persson, Columbia–Southern* processes).
(3) Reduction with CH_3OH (*Solvay* process).
(4) Reduction with HCl (*Kesting, Day, Rapson* processes).

The use of sulfur dioxide was early patented (5), but the necessity of using concentrated sulfuric acid to get a rapid reaction was discovered somewhat later (14, 15, 19). In the *Griesheim* method, solid chlorate was dissolved in fairly dilute sulfuric acid prior to reduction, whereas the *Holst* method utilizes strong sulfuric acid and a strong solution of chlorate and the *C.I.P.* method (22, 26) does not add any sulfuric acid but instead utilizes the sulfuric acid formed in the reactions, although this leads to a higher consumption of chlorate in side reactions. The *Mathieson* method like the Holst process makes use of a concentrated sulfuric acid but applies a fairly dilute chlorate solution (16b, 34) so that it operates at conditions similar to those towards the end of the Holst process (33). Hence, the former process can be operated continuously without excessive losses of chlorate, whereas the Holst process is operated batchwise. Recently the reaction efficiency of the Mathieson process has been found to increase by the addition of sodium chloride (1). The C.I.P. process is also continuous.

In the *Persson* process (18, 20, 21, cf. 4), the sulfur dioxide instead of reducing the chlorate directly, is used for the reduction of chromic acid, and the chromic sulfate formed is then mixed with the chlorate to yield chlorine dioxide and chromic acid, which is recirculated. Thus, no addition of sulfuric acid is used except in the upstart, and the sodium sulfate formed in the net reaction is separated in the form of crystals. This is an advantage in comparison with the methods mentioned earlier, which present an effluent problem because of the highly acidic waste liquor. In the kraft mills, this is partly overcome by using the waste liquor instead of sulfuric acid to produce tall oil from the soap skimmings. Recirculation of the acidic waste liquor is also conceivable in the Holst method, but the separation of the crystals is a complication to be avoided. In the Persson method, however, it is a necessity, and that has limited the success of this principally elegant process, where the use of chrome salts as a redox buffer avoids excessive reduction of the chlorate and of chlorine dioxide which can occur in the direct contact with sulfur dioxide.

A novel reductant, methanol, was applied in the more recently developed *Solvay* process (6, 11, 29). This is also a continuous method, and the concentrations of chlorate and sulfuric acid used are similar to those of the Mathieson process. The chlorine dioxide formed is carried from the reactors by a stream of air, which serves to dilute it to about 16% by volume in order to avoid explosive concentrations. The same caution is necessary in the Persson process as well as in the direct-reducing processes using 100% SO_2. However, it is customary to produce the SO_2 gas in the mill by sulfur burning, which automatically reduces the concentration to the desired level.

Another important reductive agent in the manufacture of chlorine dioxide is hydrochloric acid. The recent *Rapson R2* process (25) produces chlorine dioxide from chlorate, chloride and strong sulfuric acid and passes an air stream through the reactor to carry away the chlorine dioxide formed. This process deviates from the improved Mathieson process only in the absence of sulfur dioxide, and as a result, considerable quantities of chlorine are formed at the same time, about one mole for every second mole of chlorine dioxide. More complicated are the *Kesting* (17) and *Day* (7) processes, which also involve the electrolytical oxidation of the chloride of the residual liquor to chlorate. Only chlorate and hydrochloric acid are present in the reactor, chlorate in high, the hydrochloric acid in low concentration. The process is continuous and the liquor flowing to the electrolytical department is far from exhausted of chlorate, which is permissible in this process. As in the Rapson R2 process, considerable quantities of chlorine are unavoidably formed. The hydrochloric acid is the only chemical consumed, and it is purchased or produced by reacting chlorine and hydrogen in special burners. As there is no addition of salts, there is consequently no problem of crystal separation in spite of a completely closed system.

Figure 19.4 schematically illustrates the equipment in use for most processes applying sulfur dioxide as a reductant. From thermostated stirrer tanks, where the concentrated reaction liquors of sodium chlorate and sulfuric acid are prepared, pipes lead to one or more reactors. These are plastic-, ceramic- or glass-lined vessels, equipped with coils or jackets for temperature regulation and safety lids which release the pressure at the mild explosions or 'puffs' which sometimes occur in the reactors for various reasons. In the bottom of the reactors gas distributors are placed, lead spargers or preferably carborundum diffuser plates, to introduce the dilute sulfur dioxide gas in bubbles of suitable size. The dilute chlorine dioxide gas leaves at the top of the reactor for an absorption tower, where cool water is introduced at the top and chlorine dioxide water leaves at the bottom for buffer tanks. Because of its lower solubility in water, contaminating chlorine gas is dissolved to a much less extent. Chlorine and residual chlorine dioxide are absorbed in lye or sulfite waste liquor in a subsequent tower or vessel. The reacted waste liquor is discharged from the reactor either to a sewer at the end of a batch reaction or continuously by overflow to a secondary reactor to diminish the residual chlorate content. Two or more reactors are thus coupled in parallel in the batch methods and in series for continuous operation. Some of the waste liquor may be recycled for diluting the reactants and decrease the need of free sulfuric acid. The recycling is limited by the crystallization tendency of sodium bisulfate and sulfate. Co-current and counter-current reactor operation has also been investigated but does not offer any particular advantages. The retention time is about 30 h and the reaction temperature of the sulfur dioxide reduction is kept between 30 and 40°C and of the methanol reduction at about 55°C. For the hydrochloric acid reduction of the Kesting and Day processes a continuous counter-current operation in a series of six reactors is maintained, whereby steam and air are introduced in the last units, which are kept at 100°C, and the first unit is kept at 20°C, where chlorate solution and hydrochloric acid enter and dilute chlorine dioxide leaves the system, Figure 19.5.

Numerous comparisons of the economy of the various processes have been made (e.g. 23, 25, 29a, 32), and of the processes not including electrolysis, the differences between the lowest and highest production cost figures are only about 15 %, with the Mathieson process as the least expensive. The Kesting and Day processes require much higher investment for both generators and especially for the electrolysis, but have the lowest operating costs. In general, however, the pulp mills find that pay-out time for the capital invested is too long to be acceptable and the additional operating

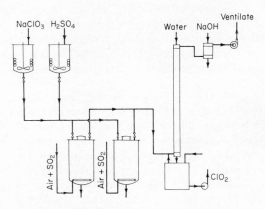

Fig. 19.4. Holst chlorine dioxide process

difficulties too high. With the increased use of chlorate by the pulp industry, central production of chlorate has been increased and rationalized considerably, leading to substantial reduction in the market price of sodium chlorate. In fact, the operating costs of chlorine dioxide from purchased chlorate are now lower than those of sodium hypochlorite and approach that of calcium hypochlorite, compared at the same basis of available chlorine. Table 19.2 gives an indication of the relative costs of the various bleaching agents in use. The investment is about $150,000 for a unit producing 3 t/d ClO_2 without electrolysis.

Table 19.2. Approximate cost figures for various bleaching
agents, expressed in $/kg act. Cl

Chlorine	0.07
Calcium hypochlorite*	0.13
Sodium hypochlorite*	0.20
Chlorine dioxide	0.16
Hypochlorous acid	0.11
Sodium chlorite	0.65
Sodium peroxide	0.35

* Including 50% excess alkali (0.5 kg NaOH).

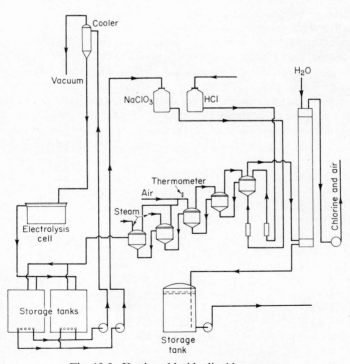

Fig. 19.5. Kesting chloride dioxide process

1099

B. Reactions

The overall reaction for the sulfur dioxide processes is

$$2\,NaClO_3 + SO_2 + H_2SO_4 \longrightarrow 2\,ClO_2 + 2\,NaHSO_4,$$

in the Persson process subdivided into two stages and yielding sulfate instead of bisulfate:

$$6\,NaClO_3 + Cr_2(SO_4)_3 + H_2O \longrightarrow 6\,ClO_2 + H_2Cr_2O_7 + 3\,Na_2SO_4$$
$$\underline{H_2Cr_2O_7 + 3\,SO_2 \longrightarrow Cr_2(SO_4)_3 + H_2O}$$
$$6\,NaClO_3 + 3\,SO_2 \longrightarrow 6\,ClO_2 + 3\,Na_2SO_4$$

For the methanol reductant, a similar reaction takes place:

$$6\,NaClO_3 + CH_3OH + 6\,H_2SO_4 \longrightarrow 6\,ClO_2 + CO_2 + 6\,NaHSO_4 + 5\,H_2O$$

with formaldehyde and formic acid as intermediate oxidation products. In the case of chlorate reduction with hydrochloric acid, the reaction could be written:

$$NaClO_3 + 2\,HCl \longrightarrow NaCl + ClO_2 + 1/2\,Cl_2 + H_2O$$

with the side reaction

$$NaClO_3 + 6\,HCl \longrightarrow NaCl + 3\,Cl_2 + 3\,H_2O$$

This reductant yields a considerable quantity of chlorine as a by-product, which has to be utilized for either the production of hypochlorite or the generation of hydrochloric acid with hydrogen. Side reactions also occur with sulfur dioxide reductant, but the chlorine dioxide gas leaving the generator on well-chosen reaction conditions only contains about 2% chlorine, and this content is further reduced in the selective water absorption, so that the chlorine dioxide water produced can be considered free of chlorine for all practical purposes.

The above reactions only correspond to the overall result. The detailed mechanism of the chlorine dioxide generation has been subjected to several investigations and speculations (2, 16, 24, 30, 33). The following reactions are possible in the system of chlorate, sulfur dioxide and strong sulfuric acid:

$$HClO_3 + SO_2 \longrightarrow HClO_2 + SO_3 \tag{1}$$
$$HClO_2 + SO_2 \longrightarrow HClO + SO_3 \tag{2}$$
$$HClO + SO_2 \longrightarrow HCl + SO_3 \tag{3}$$
$$HClO_2 + HClO_3 \longrightarrow 2\,ClO_2 + H_2O \tag{4}$$
$$HClO + HCl \longrightarrow Cl_2 + H_2O \tag{5}$$
$$Cl_2 + H_2O + SO_2 \longrightarrow 2\,HCl + SO_3 \tag{6}$$
$$ClO_2 + H_2O + 3\,SO_2 \longrightarrow 2\,HCl + 3\,SO_3 \tag{7}$$
$$HClO_3 + HCl \longrightarrow HClO_2 + HClO \tag{8}$$
$$2\,HClO_3 \longrightarrow HClO_2 + HClO_4 \tag{9}$$
$$2\,HClO_2 \longrightarrow HClO + HClO_3 \tag{10}$$
$$2\,HClO \longrightarrow HCl + HClO_2 \tag{11}$$
$$HClO + HClO_2 \longrightarrow HCl + HClO_3 \tag{12}$$
$$HClO + HClO_3 \longrightarrow HCl + HClO_4 \tag{13}$$
$$2\,ClO_2 \longrightarrow Cl_2 + 2\,O_2 \tag{14}$$

The chlorine dioxide production thus assumingly (2, 16, 24, c.f however, 17a, 30) arises from chloric and chlorous acids according to reaction (4). In order to produce the chloric acid, the chlorate has to be strongly acidified, e.g. with sulfuric acid. To obtain chlorous acid, the reduction of chloric acid with sulfur dioxide is a possible reaction, although it is believed, that sulfur dioxide tends to react further with chlorous acid to hypochlorous and hydrochloric acid according to reactions (2), (3) and (6). Therefore, the main reductant yielding chlorous acid is thought to be hydrochloric acid, according to reaction (8), which is also the only possible reaction for the *Rapson, Kesting* and *Day* processes operating without sulfur dioxide. The hypochlorous acid subsequently forms chlorine and water with hydrochloric acid, reaction (5), which explains why these processes yield one mole of chlorine for every second mole of chlorine dioxide. When sulfur dioxide is used as the reductant, it has been suggested (5) and is likely that its main function is to reduce hypochlorous acid to hydrochloric acid according to reaction (3), which prevents chlorine formation. This also explains why an initial addition of sodium chloride improves the yield of chlorine dioxide from chlorate, as the initial stepwise reduction of chloric acid to hydrochloric acid is not needed to start the reaction sequence. Of the other various possible reactions between the chlorine compounds, (9), (10), (11), (12), (13), those leading to perchloric acid decrease the chlorine dioxide yield, whereas the others only slow down the overall reaction. Reduction of chlorine dioxide by sulfur dioxide to hydrochloric acid and sulfur trioxide (7) requires the presence of water but may occur above the liquid phase of the reactor at condensed water vapor droplets. This is a fairly slow reaction. The decomposition of chlorine dioxide to chlorine and oxygen, reaction (14), requires light and high temperatures.

With the reaction conditions well chosen, most of the processes yield 85–90% of the theoretical amount of chlorine dioxide from the chlorate. The C.I.P. process, which must produce some extra sulfuric acid instead of those added in the other processes, gives a lower yield, about 75%, and the Mathieson process with extra sodium chloride added is said to reach yields of 95%. A critical variable in the generation is the bubble size of the dilute sulfur dioxide introduced in the bottom of the reactor. The ideal size gives complete reaction of the sulfur dioxide just when the bubble reaches the liquid surface. Larger bubbles will not allow time for all sulfur dioxide to react, causing a corresponding reduction in the final chlorine dioxide solution. Too small bubbles will be depleted of sulfur dioxide too early, and therefore chlorine gas diffusing from the liquid phase into the bubble will not be reduced but will leave the reactor as a loss and a contaminant. The pores of the diffuser plates must therefore be dimensioned in relation to the gas throughput, the height of the reactor and the reaction temperature chosen. The concentration of the sulfuric acid in the reaction mixture of the batch process is about 3.8 molar and that of the chlorate 3.3 molar, with a change in the concentrations during the reaction period illustrated in Figure 19.6 (33). The continuous chlorine dioxide generation must choose a lower chlorate concentration to allow continuous removal of reaction mixture. Usually, 4.5 molar sulfuric acid and 0.2 molar chlorate concentration is chosen, corresponding to the state of the batch operation towards the end of the reaction. Those concentrations must be adjusted to the reactor design and desired production, to yield complete reaction of sulfur dioxide and a minimum of chlorine in the gases leaving the reactor.

The hazards of chlorine dioxide are *toxicity* and *explosiveness*. The odor of chlorine dioxide is apparent at 15 ppm and irritating at 45 ppm. Guinea pigs were dead after less than an hour at 150 ppm (31). Continued exposure to even very dilute concentrations produces an effect on the human body for at least one day. Headache, stomach troubles and irritation of the mucous membranes are typical effects. Pure chlorine dioxide has a melting point of $-59°C$ and a boiling point of $11°C$. The density of the liquid is 2.4. The solid, liquid and gaseous states are all violently explosive. Chlorine dioxide decomposes at a measurable rate at $30–40°C$ and explosively above $50–60°C$. High temperatures, as well as contaminants, light or sparks, are the main causes of explosion, and this will be more violent the higher the concentration. Gas concentrations below 20% by volume only cause fairly mild explosions, known as 'puffs', and these just cause the safety lids of the reactors to rise. The most common cause of puffing is contaminants, such as oil, paper, wood, etc., introduced with the raw materials. Leaks on the strong sulfuric acid pipe causing dropping in the vapor phase of the reactor have also been found to cause puffing. The actual compound causing the violent decomposition is the radical $\langle ClO \rangle$, which above a certain concentration starts a chain reaction with chlorine dioxide (19). The radical is neutralized by compounds such as nitrogen dioxide, and a theoretical possibility exists for the safe handling of liquid chlorine dioxide in the presence of small amounts of compounds which slowly decompose under nitrogen dioxide formation. However, for

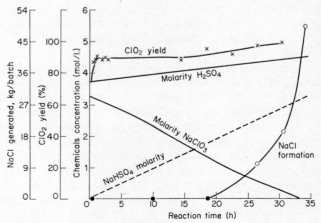

Fig. 19.6. Reaction conditions on batch production of chlorine dioxide (Wiesner)

1102

understandable reasons no attempts have been made in this direction so far.

However, with increased experience, accidents in chlorine dioxide preparation and use are now rare. The chlorine dioxide water has a greenish color, as has the dilute gas, and colorimetric analysis can be used in the instrument control of the concentration. Usually, iodometric titration in neutral and then acid medium is used to determine the content of chlorine dioxide and chlorine. Chlorine dioxide is thereby reduced to chlorite and chloride respectively, and only one of its five oxidation equivalents is active in neutral medium. One kilogram of chlorine dioxide equals $5 \times 35.5/67.5 = 2.63$ kg active chlorine, a unit which is preferred in the bleacheries in giving the charge figures.

REFERENCES

1. Anon., *Paper Trade J.*, **140**, No. 24, 36 (1956).
2. Bray, W., *Z. Anorg. Allorg. Chem.*, **48**, 217 (1906).
3. Casciani, F., *Paper Trade J.*, **135**, No. 10, 22 (1952).
4. Conrad, P., and G. Carlson, *Pulp Paper Mag. Can.*, **58**, No. 11, 160 (1957).
5. Cunningham, G. L., *U.S. Pat.* 2,089,913 (1937).
6. Dailey, J. D., *Paper Trade J.*, **138**, No. 51, 34 (1954).
7. Day, G. A., *et al.*, *U.S. Pat.* 2,484,402 (1949).
8. Degussa, *Swed. Pat.* 108,068 (1942).
9. Dietz, H., cited in F. Wultsch and W. Gärtner, *Die Peroxydbleiche von Zellstoff und Holzschliff*, Degussa Bull., 1956.
10. Duncan, E. P., *Pulp Paper*, **30**, No. 2, 124 (1956).
11. Ernest, F. M., *Paper Trade J.*, **143**, No. 34, 46 (1959).
12. Fisher, H. S., and R. E. Carlson, *Paper Trade J.*, **140**, No. 19, 24 (1956); *Tappi*, **38**, No. 10, 154 A (1955).
13. Förster, F., *et al.*, *J. Prakt. Chem.*, **59**, 60 (1899); **63**, 141 (1901).
14. Gardiner, W. C., and E. H. Karr, Off. Tech. Services Report, PB 33: 218 (1946).
15. Heitman, J. B., *Tappi*, **36**, 419 (1953).
16. Holst, G., *Svensk Papperstid.*, **47**, 537 (1944); **50**, 472 (1947); *Paper Trade J.*, **128**, No. 1, 21 (1949); *Swed. Pat.* 110,488; 129,235 (1943); *U.S. Pat.* 2,373,830 (1945).
16a. Jack, W. Q., and A. H. Dowsley, *Pulp Paper Mag. Can.*, **61**, No. 10, T490 (1960).
16b. Jalkanen, M. G., *Norsk Skogind.*, **14**, 520 (1960).
17. Kesting, E., *Papier*, **6**, 155 (1952); *Tappi*, **36**, 166 (1953); *Ger. Pat.* 831,542 (1948).
17a. Lenzi, F., and W. H. Rapson, *Pulp Paper Mag. Can.*, **63**, No. 9, T442 (1962).
18. Lundberg, A. H., *Pulp Paper*, **24**, No. 5, 78 (1950).
19. Martin, H., *et al.*, Trans. XIII. Int. Congress of Pure and Applied Chem., Stockholm 1953, cf. *Z. Elektrochem.*, **59**, 740 (1952); **60**, 959 (1953).
20. Pechukas, A., *U.S. Pat.* 2,765,214; 2,765,215 (1956).
21. Persson, S. H., *Swed. Pat.* 116,363 (1942); 123,419; 128,625 (1943); *U.S. Pat.* 2,376,935 (1945).
22. Rapson, W. H., *Can. Pat.* 466,815; 466,816 (1949); *Pulp Paper Mag. Can.*, **55**, No. 5, 92 (1954).

23. Rapson, W. H., *Tappi*, **37,** 129 (1954).
24. Rapson, W. H., *Tappi*, **39,** 554 (1956).
25. Rapson, W. H., *Can. Pat.* 543,589 (1957); *Tappi*, **41,** 181 (1958).
26. Rapson, W. H., and M. Wayman, *U.S. Pat.* 2,598,087 (1953).
27. Rue, J. D., *et al.*, Hooker Bull. No. 200, Niagara Falls, N.Y., 1957.
28. Schmidt, G. A., *Wochbl. Papierfabrik.* **87,** 616 (1959).
29. Schuber, J., and W. A. Kraske, *Pulp Paper*, **27,** No. 10, 104 (1953).
29a. Serafin, J. G., and H. C. Scribner, *Pulp Paper Mag. Can.*, **62,** No. 10, T473 (1961).
29b. TAPPI Monograph No. 18, *Water Technology in the Pulp and Paper Industry*, New York 1958.
30. Taube, H., and H. Dodgen, *J. Am. Chem. Soc.*, **71,** 3331 (1949).
31. Taylor, M. C., *et al.*, *Ind. Eng. Chem.*, **32,** 901 (1940).
32. Tydén, H., *Svensk Papperstid.*, **57,** 583 (1954).
33. Wiesner, W., *Pulp Paper Mag. Can.*, **58,** No. 2, 83 (1957).
34. Woodside, V., and K. S. MacLeod, *Paper Trade J.*, **137,** No. 8, 26 (1953).

PART IV

PULP PROPERTIES AND USES

20

CHARACTERIZATION OF PULP PROPERTIES

The characterization of pulp properties is vital for both internal control purposes and as a means of describing the pulp grade for sale. An enormous amount of work has been devoted to this task, and is currently needed as long as new pulping methods, new pulp grades and new pulp uses are developed. As will be further stressed in the following chapter on pulp properties and uses, the task of characterizing these properties is very difficult. Although pulp is admittedly a heterogeneous product in several respects, it is relatively easy with modern methods of analysis to describe the *chemical composition* and some *physical properties* of a pulp. The real difficulties start with a statement of how this pulp will perform in the pulp consumer's mill, its *processing properties*, and most difficult, of all, what will be the *quality of the end product*.

Several of the methods used to characterize pulps are the same as those used to analyze the wood raw material. Methods of wood analysis are beyond the scope of this book and are thoroughly discussed in monographs on wood chemistry (e.g. 19). Complete descriptions of wood and pulp analyses can be found in the monographs on control methods of the pulp industry (87, 119) and also in the standardized method charts edited by the technical associations of the pulp industry in various countries such as the U.S.A. (TAPPI Standards), Sweden (CCA Standards), Germany (Merkblatt des Vereins der Zellstoff- und Papier-Chemiker und -Ingenieure), Scandinavia (Scan-C Standards), and recently by the International Committee for Cellulose Analysis (ICCA Standards). The work on international standardization of the methods of characterization is important in supplying a common basis to evaluate not only commercial pulps, but also the results published in the enormous literature in the pulping field. It must, however, be emphasized that once a method of characterization has been generally accepted and become integrated in the conceptions of those working in the field and in the literature, thereby becoming tied up in correlations with other properties, it should be preserved quite conservatively and not changed unless very material improvements have been achieved. Even then it is necessary to give a clear correlation between the values of the old and new method. However, obviously the ultimate goal of the analytical work must be methods determining the strict chemical composition of the pulp in terms of content of well-defined chemical compounds, as well as their physical and mechanical properties in well-defined fundamental units.

I. Chemical Composition

In all pulps, the dominant component is *cellulose*, and although some of the high-yield pulps contain much of other components, the analysis of the chemical composition of pulps can be regarded as a determination of non-cellulosic impurities, with cellulose as the undetermined remainder to make up the 100%. Those impurities are partly of the same nature as the non-cellulosic *wood* components, *hemicelluloses*, *lignin* and *resin*, although changed by the processes, partly also like those introduced by the pulping processes, *modified carbohydrate groups*, *inorganics*, and *water*. Other changes brought about, although related to these properties, such as average molecular size and size distribution, brightness and brightness stability and opacity, must be called physical properties and are treated in Section II.

1. DETERMINATION OF RESIDUAL HEMICELLULOSES

The nature of the pulp hemicelluloses has become known only recently and knowledge is still lacking in several details. The main components are *glucomannan, 4-O-methylglucurono(arabino)xylan*, and *arabinogalactan*. The first category may include some galactoglucomannan and in the second category varying amounts of 4-O-methylglucuronic acid groups and arabinose units have been split off during the pulping processes, leaving a more or less straight *xylan* molecule in the pulp. Hardwood xylan does not contain arabinose even in the native state. Acetyl groups occur in softwood glucomannan and hardwood xylan in the native state and in some pulps.

The main methods of determination of these compounds are indirect and some were developed before their constitution was known. Therefore, it has become customary to speak of the various monomers, regardless of their mode of coupling: glucose, mannose, galactose, arabinose, xylose and glucuronic acid, which is natural, or of hypothetical pure polymers; glucan, mannan, galactan, arabinan, xylan and polyuronides, which is less satisfactory and should be avoided. Arabinan and xylan were both included in the determination of *pentosans*, which together with *uronic acid* determination was for a long time the only routine method available for estimating the residual hemicelluloses of pulp. That has partly connected the concept of pentosans too closely with that of hemicelluloses and tended to disregard the other constituents, which are of equal importance in softwood pulps. The alkali solubility and beta–gamma cellulose determination is also unsatisfactory as a method of characterizing the hemicellulose fraction or even defining it, which has caused much confusion, and hence alkali solubility methods will here be treated among the methods for characterizing physical properties rather than chemical composition. More satisfactory methods were developed through *paper chromatography*, which is now becoming a standard method in all advanced pulping research

1108

and sometimes even as a mill control. Some of the chromatographic methods make it possible to separate all hemicellulose monomers in one single chromatogram, and with the present knowledge of the native constitution of the various types of hemicelluloses it is possible to estimate the actual content of glucomannan, substituted xylan and arabinogalactan, as well as cellulose, in the pulps. The functional groups of *acetyl* and *O–methyl* are determined according to standard methods with sufficient accuracy. The former is, however, present only in unbleached sulfite pulps in some quantity, and the latter occurs in the residual lignin as well and could not be taken as representative for the carbohydrates in unbleached pulps.

In spite of the progress of the chromatographic methods, they are still too laborious for too frequent routine work, and the pentosan and uronic acid determinations are therefore still of some importance.

The *pentosan determination* (19, 63, 180) involves boiling the pulp sample in hydrochloric (159) or hydrobromic (60) acid, whereby pentose monomers are formed by hydrolysis and in turn converted to furfural according to the reaction

$$C_5H_{10}O_5 \longrightarrow C_5H_4O_2 + 3\ H_2O$$

The furfural distills with the acid to be analyzed. In order to maintain the hydrochloric acid concentration, 12% (155) or 13.5% (137), during the hydrolysis, fresh acid is added continuously (77), or else sodium chloride is added to the original solution (76). The distillation is continued for about 1.5–2 h to a certain distillate volume and the furfural is determined by precipitation with barbituric acid (10, 137, 167), titration with bromide–bromate (10, 54, 99, 155), or spectrophotometer after the addition of orcinol (63, 142), which gives a blue color with furfural, or other reagents (e.g. 135), or without reagent in the ultraviolet (10, 125). The furfural determination is complicated by some formation of hydroxy-methyl furfural from hexoses, according to an analogous but slower reaction during the distillation. This compound has a very similar UV absorption spectrum (10), is titrated quantitatively together with furfural by bromide–bromate (10) and interferes with the barbituric acid precipitation of furfural (10, 39, 72). Fortunately, its formation is fairly limited, about 3–4 mg/g of pulp or 0.5% expressed as pentosan, and it is constant independent of the pulp type (10), whereas the furfural formation is almost quantitative. This allows the application of certain corrections, especially after redistillation of the condensate. In the case of dissolving pulps with a low content of pentosans, the determination is more disturbed, and the orcinol method is then preferred, since the blue color developed is specific to furfural (63). The formation of formaldehyde from the residual lignin (36) tends to give slightly high pentosan values for unbleached pulps, and very pentosan-rich pulps, such as kraft or neutral sulfite hardwood pulps, appear to be somewhat more difficult to analyze correctly, probably because of irregularities in the distillation technique (63). It is also worth mentioning that uronic acids yield furfural to about

40% of the theoretical amount at the conditions of the pentosan determination.

The *determination of uronic acid* is carried out by distillation with 12% HCl, whereby uronic acids decompose according to the equation

$$C_6H_{10}O_7 \longrightarrow C_5H_4O_2 + 3\,H_2O + CO_2 \quad (78)$$

The carbon dioxide evolved is carried by nitrogen through a condenser and a trap to remove hydrochloric acid and water, and finally to an absorption tube to be determined gravimetrically. The trap may contain 85% phosphoric acid with silver phosphate (18). Boiling is accomplished by a glycerol bath and carried on for a certain time, about 3 h. There are several complications, such as a slow carbon dioxide evolution from hexoses and pentoses (174), and decarboxylation of oxycellulose (69).

The *chromatographic determination of the sugar monomers* applies the following principal operations (e.g. 107):

(1) Complete hydrolysis of the pulp sample, e.g. by dissolution in 72% H_2SO_4 followed by dilution to 3% and boiling, as in the Klason lignin determination (see below).
(2) Removal of lignin residues by filtration and of inorganic ions by exchange.
(3) Evaporation of the sugar solution in vacuum to a given volume.
(4) Application of a metered, small volume of the solution to a chromatographic paper by means of a syringe, parallel to control samples of exact quantities of known sugars.
(5) Separation of the sugars by partition chromatography in a closed, thermostated vessel with a solvent mixture, such as butanol: acetone:water (4:5:1) for a given time.
(6) Development of the chromatogram by spraying the dried paper with a color reagent for qualitative or some types of quantitative analysis, or elution of the sugars at the located spots and quantitative sugar determination by classical copper and arsenomolybdate reagents (94, 127).

The paper, preferentially Schleicher and Schüll 2043a or Whatman no. 1 and 3MM, may be specially impregnated in advance by a phosphate buffer to facilitate the separation of the sugars (58). The accuracy of the determination may be about $\pm 5\%$ for the hemicellulose components of the pulp. A modified technique has been developed, allowing the analysis of fiber samples as small as 0.1–0.2 mg (86).

2. DETERMINATION OF RESIDUAL LIGNIN (44)

Determination of residual pulp lignin is the most important of all pulp analyses. It indicates the degree of delignification obtained by the cook and forms the basis of comparison for many of the cooking results, such as the yield, screenings, pulp brightness, etc. It is the figure on which the charge of bleaching chemicals is based, especially for the initial chlorination, but sometimes also for following treatments in a multistage bleaching. It is used as a control method in laboratories and mills, and as a quality figure in the sales of unbleached pulp. It has been used almost since the start of the chemical pulp industry in a variety of forms, of which only the most important ones will be mentioned here. There are *direct* and *indirect* methods. In the former, the carbohydrates are removed and the lignin determined gravimetrically. The most important of these is the *Klason* lignin determination (70, 104, 140) with sulfuric acid. The indirect methods are based on measurement of either a physical property of lignin, such as its *light absorption*, or a chemical reaction, such as *chlorination* or *permanganate oxidation*. These methods are more rapid but have the drawback of giving only a relative figure for the lignin content and not an absolute value. As a rule they are not even linearly related to the lignin content. Especially difficult is the determination of the small amounts of lignin in bleached pulps.

Klason lignin determination is carried out as standardized for wood (60, 140, 159). The sample is treated with 72% H_2SO_4 at room temperature for 2 h, diluted to 3% H_2SO_4 and boiled for 4 h. The residue is isolated, washed, dried and weighed. The major difficulty with the direct determination of lignin in *pulps* is that some lignin goes into solution with the carbohydrates during the hydrolysis. Pulp lignin is modified by the chemical reactions of the cook, and especially the sulfonated lignin of sulfite pulps tends to dissolve during the hydrolysis and gives about 20% too low values for Klason lignin (81). The hydrolyzate should therefore be analyzed for lignin spectroscopically after dialysis (81). This also applies to hardwood lignin, which even in the native state dissolves to some extent in the sulfuric acid (98). Kraft pulps are better suited to the determination.

Spectroscopical determination can be carried out in various ways. The yellow color of a solution of the pulp sample in 76% H_2SO_4 has been used as a measure of the lignin content (40). An improvement represents the measurement of ultraviolet light at the absorption maxima of 280 or 210 mμ (81, 82). A variation of the method is to dissolve the pulp sample in 80% H_3PO_4 and measure the absorbency at 280 mμ (9). It is possible to establish a conversion factor, or to give the lignin content in terms of absorbency. This method is useful only for chemical pulps, as semi-chemical pulps do not dissolve in phosphoric acid at room temperature, whereas they do in sulfuric acid, at least upon the hydrolysis.

Chlorine numbers are obtained by measuring the chlorine which reacts with lignin in substitution and oxidation reactions. The *Roe* chlorine number (38, 65, 105, 140, 149) indicates the grams of chlorine, absorbed in 15 minutes at 20°C by 100 g pulp containing 55 g water. The analysis is carried out in an apparatus of standardized design, containing a reaction flask and a gas burette connected to a chlorine tube. It has a world-wide use and is an important method for production control and research. It also has the advantage of telling directly how much per cent chlorine should be charged in the bleaching. It is applicable on pulps in the semi-chemical as well as the chemical range and has a good reproducibility, provided the equipment is kept in good order and the sample correctly prepared. Its correlation with the lignin content of the pulp is fairly straight-lined, with a factor of about 0.9 for sulfite and 0.8 for kraft pulps to give the lignin content in per cent (68a, 157). Other modifications, such as the *Küng* and the *Tingle* number, have also been in use. The somewhat different factors may be caused by the different chlorination tendency for sulfite and kraft pulp lignin.

Permanganate numbers are based on the fact that lignin is rapidly oxidized by potassium permanganate. At standardized conditions the excess permanganate can be determined after a certain reaction period. A figure for the permanganate consumption can thus be obtained, which is a rapid and accurate measure of the lignin content of the pulp, at least in the chemical and lower semichemical yield range. At higher yields some difficulties for the oxidant in penetrating the fibers appear, to a higher degree than for chlorine, and this results in too low values. The conditions chosen for the standardization determine the figure obtained. The earlier Swedish standard methods (64) choose to express the result as a Roe chlorine number, after converting the permanganate consumption by means of empirically established correlation curves, one for sulfite and one for kraft pulps. The American standard method (175) gave a *permanganate number* corresponding to the number of ml $0.1 N$ $KMnO_4$ solution reduced by 1 g pulp at standard conditions. Two volumes of permanganate charge were standardized, 25 and 40 ml, to suit pulps of lower and higher lignin content, which in itself demonstrates the weakness of the method and has given rise to confusion. An international standard (55) based on extensive investigations (157, 169, 173) is now accepted, which eliminates the uncertainty. It applies the principle that the amount of pulp tested should be adjusted to leave 50% of the standardized permanganate charge unreacted. Variations between 30 and 70% are tolerated but corrections are applied to correspond to 50% unreacted. The number thus defined is called the *Kappa number* and is related to the Klason lignin content in per cent by a factor of 0.13 (157), and to the Roe chlorine number by a factor of 0.20 for sulfite and 0.16 for kraft pulp. It may well be that the agreement of the factors for lignin of sulfite and kraft pulps is coincidental, since the Klason lignin determination gives too low results on sulfite pulps. Conversion diagrams between the earlier methods for lignin determinations in pulp have also been published, and one is shown in Figure 20.1 (1).

3. THE DETERMINATION OF PULP RESIN

The pulp resin is a complex mixture of wood extractives which have undergone structural changes during the cooking and bleaching but have remained undissolved. A similar technique is used as in the quantitative determination of wood extractives. Ethyl ether, methylene dichloride, acetone, ethanol–benzene or ethanol are the solvents most commonly used. The former two extract predominantly fats, waxes, fatty and resin acids, sterols and non-volatile hydrocarbons, whereas the others also

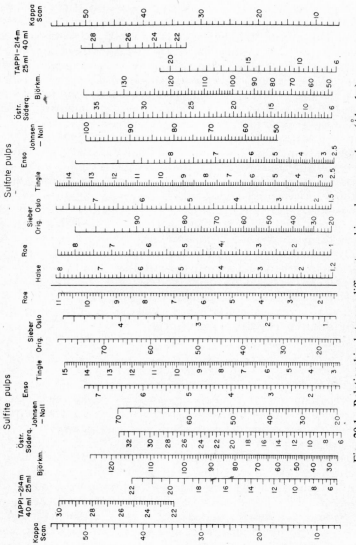

Fig. 20.1. Relationship between different cooking degree numbers (Ålander)

remove tannins, phlobaphenes, etc. The extraction is preferably carried out in a Soxhlet extractor, where the solvent is refluxed and the condensate passes the pulp sample on the way back to the flask. After a standardized refluxing period, the solvent is evaporated and the resin residue dried to constant weight (88, 118, 136, 148). The reflux time is generally quite long, 6 h or overnight, and the evaporation and drying takes additional time. Although this standard analysis is a very important and much used method in mill control, especially in dissolving pulp mills, it is too slow in urgent situations, and various short-cuts have been tried, without any complete success. Ethanol extraction time has been brought down to 5 minutes (68), and attempts have been made to measure the resin content of the extract colorimetrically, after the addition of dyestuff (e.g. 68, 124). Though such modifications may be useful in some situations, they are not sufficiently reliable for a current quality control.

Paper pulp mills are faced with a resin problem different from that of the dissolving pulp mills. More important than the total resin content of a paper pulp is the quantity which tends to deposit on metal surfaces or else aggregate to pitch lumps. This is called *harmful* or *depositable* resin. No method is accepted as a standard, but some are in use and have been described (5, 45). In principle, they apply an impeller with copper or stainless steel blades, which is rotated in a suspension of the pulp sample at standardized conditions. The deposited resin is determined gravimetrically by weighing the impeller before and after the test. The blades are interchangeable, and prior to the test they should be thoroughly cleaned and etched. Although the method has been useful in studying the variables which influence the deposition of resin, such as pH and temperature, the reproducibility is hardly sufficient to allow more than a coarse classification of pulps in this manner.

4. MODIFIED GROUPS

When carbohydrates are oxidized, the hydroxyl groups are converted to either *carbonyls* or *carboxyls*. Both are of interest to determine, partly as a check on the bleaching performed, partly because the groups may influence some of the properties of the pulp, such as brightness reversion or cation adsorption.

Carbonyls are of two kinds, aldehyde and keto groups. The former can be estimated by chlorite oxidation to carboxyl and determination of the increase in carboxyl content by carboxyl analysis before and after the oxidation (49, 179). To determine total carbonyl, the reaction with hydroxylamine has been suggested (42), with a determination of the quantity of hydrochloric acid liberated from the hydroxylamine hydrochloride reagent after the reaction. A still more sensitive method involves the reaction with the Girard reagent followed by colorimetric determination (37). For oxidized pulps rich in carbonyl, a sodium tetrahydroborate reduction method has been employed (80). An indirect indication of the amounts of carboxyl groups of a pulp sample give the *copper number* and

1114

the *hot alkali solubility* determinations. The copper number is expressed as the weight of cupric ions reduced to cuprous ions by 100 g pulp. The figure varies with the conditions standardized. The *Braidy* copper number determination employs a copper sulfate solution and an alkaline sodium carbonate–bicarbonate buffer, heating for 3 h at 100°C and titration of the residual solution after washing of the pulp (16, 20). The *Hägglund* copper number determination applies *Bertrand's* solution and limits the boiling to 3 minutes (46). The copper number methods are still widely used as a measure of the reducing capacity of a pulp, although they have no direct stoichiometrical meaning. They are likely to include not only aldehyde groups but also the potentially reducing keto groups, since the treatment is hot alkaline. There is a different, though linear correlation between copper number and carbonyl content for each type of oxidized cellulose (79). The *hot alkali solubility* is related to the copper numbers and the carbonyl groups of a pulp, since the hot alkali peeling reaction starts at carbonyls of the carbohydrate molecules and proceeds at a rate approximately proportional to the number of starting points. The yield loss on boiling in an excess of alkali, usually a 7.14% NaOH or a 10% KOH solution, is measured (46, 110). This figure obviously has no stoichiometrical significance either, which would allow a calculation of the number of oxidized groups per monomer.

Carboxyl determination methods are based on ion exchange. They generally start with an acid treatment, with HCl (109) or CO_2 (3) to remove all metal cations and transfer the carboxyl groups to the acid form. After washing with distilled water, the sample is treated with an inorganic salt solution, such as NaCl (26, 92), NaCl + $NaHCO_3$ (176), Na_2SO_4 (181), $Ca(OAc)_2$ (69, 83, 126) or $Zn(OAc)_2$ (28), and the amount of liberated protons determined by titration. Alternatively, the quantity of cations adsorbed by the sample after the ion exchange is determined by difference measurements, such as silver from silver *o*-nitrophenolate (128) solution by titration or methylene blue cation from a methylene blue solution (25, 26) by colorimetric analysis. Even other colorimetric reagents have been used (e.g. 102). A comparison between several methods for a variety of pulps (181) shows that any of the methods (28, 126, 176) give accurate results after some training. An alkalimetric method (109) tends to give higher carboxyl values than the calcium acetate method with alkali cooked pulps and pulps degraded by aging of alkali cellulose (111), which was ascribed to the opening of lactone rings. A qualitative test for lactones is the reaction with hydroxylamine and detection of the hydroxamic acids formed by addition of iron(III)chloride (130). Lactones can be approximately estimated from an alkalimetric carboxyl determination prior to and after the reduction with sodium tetrahydroborate (111).

5. INORGANICS

The inorganic constituents are of interest in pulping research, as well as in the mill control, especially of dissolving pulps. They are partly present as contaminating free salts or particles, and partly cations adsorbed to the anionic groups of the fiber. The following analyses are usually applied: *ash content* (112), *acid-insoluble ash* or *silica* (115), *calcium* (113), *iron* (146), *manganese* (114), *copper* (147) and *sodium*.

In the ash analyses, ashing temperatures are specified. It is customary to use direct ashing technique with no addition of sulfuric acid. The weighed ash is then treated with hydrochloric acid to give acid-insoluble ash, which is determined gravimetrically or colorimetrically (with molybdate). Calcium and magnesium were formerly determined gravimetrically after precipitation of the acid-soluble part with oxalate and pyrophosphate. A complexometric titration with EDTA is now recommended (123, 160), preferably using the cal-red indicator. Iron is determined colorimetrically in the acid-soluble part with *o*-phenanthroline as the reagent, and copper in the same manner with diethyldithiocarbamate. Manganese is determined colorimetrically after oxidation to permanganate. Sodium is determined with conventional methods, either gravimetrically or preferably with a flame spectrophotometer.

The *moisture content* of pulp is normally determined by drying to constant weight at 105°C (153).

II. Physical Properties

Of the physical properties of pulp, two types are tested by analysis, namely *molecular size and solubility*, and *optical properties of the pulp fibers*. To the former type belong *viscosity* and *alkali solubility* methods, to the latter *brightness*, *opacity* and *color reversion*. The tests for the *mechanical properties* of the carbohydrate molecules and of pulp fibers are still very special and not included in the more common types of pulping investigations and control. They have a counterpart in some tests of product properties, such as paper strength and rayon fiber strength, which are very much influenced by the pulp type, but where a conversion operation is intermediate between the pulp and the test. Such tests will therefore be treated in a subsequent section.

1. ALKALI SOLUBILITY (2, 96, 166, 177)

Alkali solubility tests at room temperature were originally developed to describe the quality of *rayon pulps* and are still of decisive importance in that respect. In the viscose process, the pulp is treated with alkali lye, and the final yield and some operations are greatly influenced by the content of alkali-soluble matter in the pulp. However, the tests are also used for *acetate* and *paper pulps*, which will not be alkali treated. That the tests are still useful shows that the alkali solubility also gives information about other qualities, such as the amount of hemicelluloses present, and the extent of cellulose degradation. As was stressed previously, alkali solubility tests as such give little accurate information on the *hemicellulose content* and they cannot be used to give exact figures for the content of cellulose or hemicelluloses. Still, in general, the solubility of a sulfite pulp in 18% NaOH gives a fair indication of the hemicellulose content, though some degraded cellulose may go into solution and some hemicelluloses always remain undissolved. The deviations are more pronounced for kraft pulps, especially from hardwoods. In pulps containing much *degraded cellulose*, this portion tends to dissolve in lye at about 10% NaOH concentration, where cellulose fibers have a swelling maximum. Only limited amounts are dissolved in 18% NaOH, and the difference in alkali solubility in 10 and 18% NaOH, sometimes called 'rest-hemi' (4, 7) may be taken as a rough measure of the state of degradation. There are methods to increase the solubility by *decreasing the temperature* or by adding *zinc* or *beryllium oxide* (73, 161) or to use *lithium* instead of sodium hydroxide, but little further information is obtained thereby. A more complete determination of the state of degradation requires a *chain length distribution analysis*, to be described subsequently.

The alkali solubility is generally determined at three concentrations, 5, 10 and 18% NaOH. The 5% NaOH determination gives a xylan-rich fraction with fairly little glucomannan. It was earlier referred to as 'wood gum' (89). There is little modern use of the method. The 10 and 18% solubilities (139) have more recently become widely used, especially to characterize dissolving pulps. They involve the dispersion of the pulp at a consistency of 1.5% in the lye at 20°C, allowing 1 h of swelling, filtering off the residue and determining the amount of dissolved matter by oxidation with acid dichromate and analyzing the dichromate consumption volumetrically or spectrophotometrically.

The classical determination of the *alpha-, beta- and gammacellulose content* (62) of pulp is a similar analysis, although it is less precisely defined. The pulp sample is treated (138, 150) with 17.5% NaOH lye, which is added at intervals and the pulp repeatedly macerated with a stirring rod. After a defined swelling period, an equivalent volume of water is added, the pulp suspension filtered and the filter cake washed with water, acetic acid and water again before drying and weighing. This insoluble fraction is called the *alphacellulose*. The combined filtrate and washings are acidified with sulfuric acid and the precipitate, or *betacellulose*, allowed to settle, leaving the *gammacellulose* in solution. The former can be determined volumetrically or gravimetrically, the latter always volumetrically by dichromate oxidation as described above. The outcome of the analysis is very dependent on the manner of maceration, since it affects the extent of swelling, as well as the method of washing, since the filter cake will pass through the swelling maximum at 10% NaOH during the washing. Consequently, during the washing additional amounts will dissolve, and the alphacellulose content thus corresponds to an intermediate of the non-solubilities in 18 and 10% NaOH (called R_{18} and R_{10}). The betacellulose analysis will be similarly affected. Furthermore, the porosity of the filter used will influence the quantity of highly swollen fiber fragments, which pass into the filtrate and appear in the beta fraction. This phenomenon is particularly pronounced with hardwood rayon pulps. In spite of these deficiencies, the alphacellulose analysis is the deciding quality criterion for rayon pulps all over the world and cannot very well be substituted with alkali solubility in 10 *or* 18% NaOH alone, since it is a combined measure of purity and degradation state.

The alphacellulose analysis was originally intended to indicate the *rayon yield*. However, not all the alkali-soluble matter is lost on pressing off the steeping lye, and the main part of the betacellulose fraction remaining in the pulp after pressing will be precipitated in the acid spinning bath and thus add to the rayon yield. Another test for rayon yield has been developed (21, 33), the *RC* value of *Charles*, which is the non-solubility in 21.5% NaOH. This does not deviate considerably from that in 18% NaOH.

The alkali solubility of *unbleached* pulps is sometimes of interest to determine. However, the residual lignin affects the accuracy of the determination and should be removed by chlorite oxidation, which does not affect the carbohydrates and their alkali solubility (24).

2. VISCOSITY

One of the most important methods of pulp analysis for both research and control work is the *viscosity* test, which measures the average DP of the pulp sample, mainly that of cellulose. The viscosity test makes it possible to check the extent of degradation caused by the cooking and bleaching processes, which greatly influences the quality of both paper and rayon pulps. In principle, the pulp sample is dissolved in a suitable solvent at a certain concentration, usually 1 or 0.5%, and the viscosity of the solution determined at standardized conditions in a capillary viscometer. However, there are many complications encountered when precise measurement is desired. The *sample has to be brought entirely into solution*, or else gel particles will clog the capillary or give false viscosity values. Strong paper pulps, especially those in the region of semichemical or high yield chemical pulps, are particularly difficult in this respect, even after chlorite delignification. This is true for all types of solvents tested so far, and limits the applicability of the method appreciably. The two solvents most widely used are cuprammonium hydroxide and cupriethylenediamine hydroxide solution. *Oxidative degradation of the sample* during dissolution and measurement must be avoided. Since the solvents are all alkaline, and those commonly used also contain copper, this is a serious complication. The dissolution of the sample is therefore performed in closed bottles, where all air is excluded. Some copper pieces are added to aid the stirring on shaking, which is done in a mechanical shaker for a defined period. An interesting new solvent is cadoxene (52, 59), which is colorless and necessitates less precaution against oxidation. The *temperature* must be constant, usually $20 \pm 0.1°C$, and this requires the viscometer to be thermostated. *Different velocity gradients* give different viscosity results with the same pulp. Pulps of different viscosity levels give different velocity gradients when using the same capillary. Two

1118

capillaries, used for high- and low-viscosity pulps, will give different results for a pulp of intermediate, border-line viscosity. This is the disadvantage with previously standardized viscosity methods (152, 156), which have stipulated 1.0 or 0.5% pulp concentration and a certain viscometer. For more accurate measurements over the whole viscosity range (145), corrections have to be applied with the viscosity value to correspond to a constant velocity gradient, and the pulp concentration should be adjusted approximately to suit the viscosity level of the pulp to avoid too large corrections for deviating velocity gradients. From the value of relative viscosity, obtained from the efflux time of the analysis, the intrinsic viscosity is calculated from *Martin's* formula (122)

$$\log \eta_{sp}/C = \log [\eta] + K[\eta]C$$

whereby the correction for deviating velocity gradient is found in a table. The intrinsic viscosity value can be used as such, or converted to DP by means of the equation (56)

$$DP^{0.905} = 0.75 [\eta]$$

This sounds more complicated than is actually the case and the revised method is already widely used for routine control purposes. However, as sales conventions, etc., are normally tied up with a certain, older TAPPI standard method, conversion curves have been established. The approximate relation between some of the many various viscosity methods is shown in Figure 20.2 (97b) where an approximate DP scale is also attached.

The DP thus established is a viscosity average value, which has no exact meaning, but comes closer to the weight average than the number average. To obtain the entire *DP distribution curve*, which is of interest especially for rayon pulps, an entirely different technique must be applied. The sample is then nitrated by a method avoiding degradation (48, 91) and the nitrate dissolved and subjected to fractional precipitation (67, 97a) by means of adding increasing quantities of a non-solvent and separating the precipitated materials in fractions, which are refractionated with the same technique. Each sub-fraction is determined quantitatively and its DP established by viscosity measurements. On the basis of all sub-fraction values, the DP distribution curve is then constructed. This analysis is tedious work, and only used in special investigations.

3. BRIGHTNESS

Brightness is a measure of the colorimetrical possibilities of a pulp to be used in the production of colored or uncolored paper or rayon (170). It is a physical concept, but it is measured at conditions which allow the closest connections with the physiological reactions of the human eye. The eye is sensitive to yellow shades, and brightness is measured as the reflectivity at 457 mμ with the light passing a standard blue filter. The effective wavelength of the reflection meter should be 457 $\pm$ 0.5 mμ with a half-intensity band width of maximum 45 mμ. The brightness is expressed in

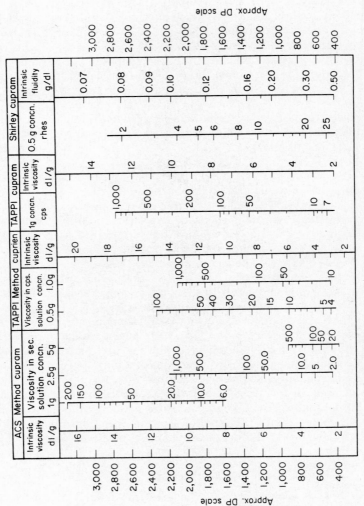

Fig. 20.2. Relationship between commercial pulp viscosity methods and intrinsic viscosity, compiled by Harpham *et al* (Ott)

per cent of the reflectivity of magnesium oxide, using a master instrument of defined construction (154). This is located at the Institute of Paper Chemistry in Appleton, Wisconsin, U.S.A., which regularly distributes papers of carefully measured brightness for the control of master instruments of other countries. These are in turn used for the standardization of other instruments, often of a different construction. The master instruments are *General Electric* constructions, and the brightness unit is therefore called % GE. For routine work, the *Hunter* and especially the *Zeiss Elrepho* instruments are used. The latter has a particularly advanced construction (53, 132). Whereas the master instruments measure the reflectivity at 45° angle to the light beam, the Elrepho instrument applies an integrating sphere for radiation of light at all angles onto the paper, which therefore reflects the light to the photocell at all angles.

Brightness can be measured on pulp sheets from the drying machine. However, the surface of a machine sheet has received influences from several sources, such as drying cylinders, drying felts, baling etc. (168). It is therefore recommended, either to split the sheet and measure the insides, or to make laboratory sheets just as from slush pulp. The laboratory sheets should be carefully prepared in clean equipment from distilled water at standardized conditions (143), which give them a basis weight of about 150 g/m². The brightness of the top side is measured. Four sheets are placed under each other to give the correct background, and measurements are made on two sheets, at five places on each, avoiding the edges (144).

The brightness range measured goes from about 10% GE for the darkest high yield kraft pulps to about 98% GE for the brightest bleached sulfite pulps. In the higher brightness range, yellow is the dominant shade for most pulps. In the lower range, all sorts of color influences occur. At about 60% GE, semibleached kraft pulps are yellowish, unbleached sulfite reddish grey and groundwood pulps still another shade. Unbleached kraft pulps in the 25% GE range are brown but vary considerably in shade, sometimes even at the same brightness level. This necessitates another optical classification than brightness. The Elrepho instrument is equipped with tristimulus-filters, allowing *colorimetric measurements* and classification according to the C.I.E. coordinate system (47a, 66, 133).

4. OPACITY

Opacity properties are measured with the brightness meter. *Printing opacity* is defined by the brightness figure of the sheet measured against a black background, divided by the normal brightness value. From these figures and the basic density of the sheet the *specific scattering coefficient* can also be computed. The opacity properties are not measured on brightness pulp sheets but only on the comparatively thin hand-sheets made in connection with the testing of paper properties. The specific scattering coefficient is a definite pulp characteristic but is also very much dependent on the degree of beating and should be compared at a certain beating state.

5. COLOR REVERSION

The brightness level of a pulp is not stable, but is influenced by several factors, such as light, heat and air oxygen. The measurement as such is not complicated, because it involves the same operations as in the brightness and opacity determinations, but after aging. However, there is no agreement on the mode of aging and reporting the result. The most widely used method so far, the p.c. (post color) method, uses too high an aging temperature, 120°C (41). A revised method applying 90°C is under consideration. The time and the moisture conditions must also be standardized. It is questionable whether the difference in k/s or in k only, should be reported, as discussed in Chapter 12. Color reversion on treatment with mercerizing lye of a rayon pulp has also attracted attention, but there is no commonly accepted standard method with a proven value. Methods tested are the brightness of the pressed alkali cellulose, absorbency of a cadoxene solution of the sample, or brightness of the regenerated rayon silk.

III. Processing and Product Properties

It is vital to be able to determine the influence of the pulp on the converting process and on the quality of the final product. This can be judged only to a limited extent by the analytical figures for chemical composition and physical properties. Therefore, *simulation procedures* have to be used for the conversion properties, whereafter the product properties are tested with the same methods as are used for the actual converted product. Thus, paper pulp is tested by beating in laboratory beaters, and testing of the hand-sheets prepared from the beaten pulp. Similarly, rayon pulps are tested by mercerization, shredding, xanthation, viscose preparation, filtration and sometimes spinning, and acetate pulps are tested by a similar sequence of operations.

1. PAPER PULP TESTING

The following principal procedure is used (141, 151). The pulp is *slushed* in a standard disintegrator, conveyed to a laboratory beater and diluted to a standardized consistency (e.g. 1.6%). *Beating* is performed at a standardized temperature, e.g. 23°C, during a period which varies for various pulp types (30–90 min.). During the beating, samples are removed at intervals, diluted to low consistency (e.g. 0.15%) and used for the formation of a sheet. Five or six samples per beating is normal. At the same time, the beaten pulp is *tested for freeness* by either the *Canadian Standard freeness tester* or the *Schopper–Riegler tester*. The hand-sheet preparation is also standardized and includes *dilution*, *sheet-making* by drainage on a wire of a standardized sheet form, *couching* by placing two blotting papers on the wet sheet and moving a couch roll over them, *pressing* between two blotting papers or between a blotting paper and a mirror-polished plate at standardized conditions, and *drying*. After conditioning at usually

65 % relative moisture and 20°C, the sheets are subjected to the convention-al paper tests, such as *tensile, burst, tear* and *folding* strength tests, as well as *basis weight, density, porosity* and *opacity*. The results are reported in the form of *beating curves*, where the test figures are plotted against either freeness or beating time (beating revolutions). In the curves, values representative for one or two specified degrees of beating, e.g. 25 or 45°SR (Schopper–Riegler), are interpolated. Those figures are used in the com-parison between pulps. Beating curves with interpolations are shown in Figure 20.3. Another manner of comparing the beating results of pulps is to plot the beating curves in the form of tensile strength against tear strength, since those characteristics are controversial and their interrelation fairly well describes the pulp type. In that case, the rate of beating and the drainage properties will not appear in the diagram, Figure 20.4, but must

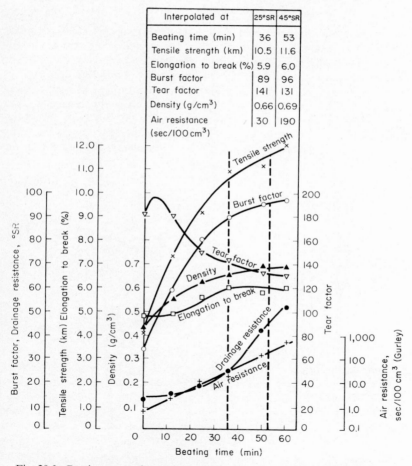

Interpolated at	25°SR	45°SR
Beating time (min)	36	53
Tensile strength (km)	10.5	11.6
Elongation to break (%)	5.9	6.0
Burst factor	89	96
Tear factor	141	131
Density (g/cm³)	0.66	0.69
Air resistance (sec/100 cm³)	30	190

Fig. 20.3. Beating curves from Valley standard testing of the paper properties of an unbleached Scots pine kraft pulp

1123

be neglected or indicated on the curves. On the other hand, the rate of beating is difficult to keep reproducible for a laboratory beater, and the drainage tests only give a poor indication of the drainage properties of the pulp on the machine in actual practice.

The equipment and standardized conditions vary from one laboratory to another. Among the beaters now in use are those of *Lampén* (22, 93, 117), *Jokro* (32), *P.F.I.* (134), *Valley, Aylesford* (23), *Banning–Seybold* and *Noble–Wood*. Most widely accepted is the Valley beater. Of the sheet-forming procedures in use, the British standard is the most widespread.

As with all simulation procedures, three important questions arise, namely:

(*1*) Is the method reproducible within the laboratory?
(*2*) Are results from different laboratories comparable?
(*3*) Does the method give results comparable with actual mill experience?

To keep the method reproducible within the laboratory (8), standard pulps are tested with intervals (84), and the beater corrected at intervals by grinding (101) and frequently washing with solvents to remove resin deposits which influence the rate of beating. The results from different laboratories deviate because of a number of differences in equipment as well as procedure (17). Therefore, it is not possible to discuss the tensile or tear strength of a pulp in the same absolute terms as its viscosity or alpha-cellulose content (not that those two analyses are by any means any absolute concepts). Still, a comparison between several beaters within the

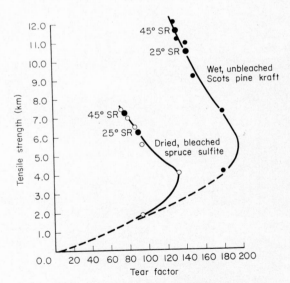

Fig. 20.4. Principal method for plotting the development of two essential strength properties during beating

same laboratory (30), or between several beaters in different laboratories using the same or different sheeting methods (31), showed that the pulps were classified in much the same way. Furthermore, comparison with a mill beater followed by hand-sheet formation or even machine-made paper gave a fair agreement in the classification (23, 30). The general experience is also, that the standardized Valley beating procedure (151) is especially useful for research and control work, although not adequate to permit a general grade specification in the sales of paper pulp. A thorough recent comparison between several types of laboratory beaters gave the result that they gave the same correlation between strength properties and sheet density, but different correlations between strength properties and density on one hand and drainage properties and air resistance on the other (85a), Figures 21.5-13. The shear forces created in the various beater types, including mill refiners, are obviously not identical, and the amounts of drainage-retarding debris therefore different. A very considerable drawback is that the method is time-consuming and expensive compared with analytical methods. Much information is still lacking on the fundamentals of the various paper-making operations involved, and much work is still needed to establish the correlation between the laboratory method and mill results in specific cases, such as the behavior of pulp mixtures, etc. A recent investigation demonstrated the effect of electrolytes (158), another demonstrated the changes in fiber length for unbleached and bleached softwood and hardwood pulps on beating in four different beaters (95).

Apart from the standard testing, many other tests on the hand-sheets are used for special characterization, such as *stiffness, softness, impulse, stress-strain diagram, greaseproofness, compressibility, printability,* etc. On the beaten pulp, other drainage tests may also be carried out in order to establish more fundamental properties, such as the specific surface and specific volume developed during the beating of the particular pulp. For the testing of paper board, a different sheeting technique is required, to give sheets of sufficient size and basis weight. For still closer simulation of the paper and board manufacture, pilot paper machines of various sizes are operated at the more advanced laboratories, though predominantly in connection with paper rather than paper pulp research.

2. VISCOSE RAYON PULPS

The complicated problem of characterizing the processing and product properties of rayon pulps cannot be solved with chemical and physical analysis alone, although these methods give valuable information. For rayon pulps simulation procedures also become necessary, which are still more complicated, tedious, expensive and uncertain than those for paper pulps. The methods are therefore used mainly for research, and are applied as a complementary quality control for the rayon pulp mills with much lower frequency than the normal control analyses.

The simulation methods (120) include the *behavior of the pulp sheet* in the sheet steeping (103, 116, 165) (*swelling, floating tendency, pressing resistance*) and in slurry steeping (*dispersibility*), and the *behavior of the pulp fibers* in the *aging, shredding, xanthation, dissolution, ripening* and *viscose filtration*, as well as the *properties of the molecules* upon *spinning to rayon* at standardized conditions (*brightness, tensile strength, elongation* and *fatigue testing,* etc.). At some mills, the tests are confined to analytical methods, others also include the behavior of the pulp sheet, the majority go as far as viscose filtration, often with the testing centralized to a research laboratory, and the most advanced laboratories also include rayon spinning and evaluation of the product properties. These laboratories also have the character of service laboratories for customer problems and have contributed to the development of the viscose industry.

Several laboratory techniques for the simulation of the viscose process have been described and the complications demonstrated (6, 27, 34, 47, 50, 57, 120a, 164, 172). The scale of testing varies from 10 g of pulp to 1 kg or even more. Steeping is performed either in slurry or in sheet form at specially designed small-scale sheet steeping presses. Normal lye concentration is 18 or 19% NaOH. The lye may or may not contain carbohydrates from previous use. Temperature is normally kept at 20°C, but is sometimes as high as 40°C. Pressing is done in the steeping presses or in slurry presses of special design. The alkalicellulose after pressing should normally contain 33% cellulose and 16% NaOH, with a press ratio of about 2.9. The shredding is done in sigma-blade batch or continuous disk shredders. Aging is performed in thermostated bottles at 25–35°C, to a controlled viscosity level, usually about 6 cP TAPPI, which takes 16–24 h. Xanthation is performed in thermostated rotating churns of special and varying design, aiming at a homogeneous access of carbon disulfide in the vapor phase to the shredded alkalicellulose. The temperature is generally kept at about 25°C, and normal charges of CS_2 are 30, 32, or, for cord pulps, 36% of the cellulose. Alternatively but less used, emulsion xanthation is carried out, in an excess of alkali and water, in which the pulp and carbon dioxide are mixed by shaking. Dissolution of the xanthate is a critical operation requiring thermostated vessels with carefully designed stirrers. The amount of alkali added is normally kept at two levels, since that is a critical figure for the degree of dissolution as well as for the economy of the viscose process. The lower concentration, about 5%, is taken to represent the staple fiber industry, whereas the higher concentration, e.g. 6% NaOH, is chosen for the conditions of continuous filament manufacture. The cellulose concentration is kept at about 8%. After ripening of the viscose at standardized conditions, usually 20°C for about 18 h, to an end point sometimes controlled by salt addition, the viscose viscosity is measured and the viscose filtered at 20°C and standard pressure in a carefully designed filter device with selected filter materials (51, 163). The filtering operation is particularly critical and has been the subject of many studies (e.g. 108, 163, 171). The filtered viscose is weighed at intervals or at the end of a predetermined period, and plugging constants, k_w, or filterability constants, R_v, calculated as a measure of the degree of dispersion. This

1126

property, which is influenced by all the previous operations, is an important quality characteristic of the pulp, since it determines the capacity of the filtering department of the rayon mill and is also reflected in the behavior of the viscose in the spinning. The filterability determination is of sufficient accuracy for internal control when running two or more tests in parallel, but cannot be used as a quality figure for sales. Other studies on the gel particles of the viscose, such as electrical (75) or optical counting (15, 74, 100, 162) or turbidity studies (43), are complementary to the filterability test and may also develop into standard methods. The spinning tests have so far been little discussed in the literature and must be regarded as special investigations, as much concerned with the customer problems as with the pulp quality. The testing of the final product is also advanced and special (178), although correlations have been established with the pulp quality (4) as well as with the performance of the product in use (71).

3.   ACETATE PULPS

The determination of processing and product properties of acetate pulps is complicated by the fact that the commercial acetylation process has so many variants, which stress somewhat different properties. As with paper and rayon *analytical methods* are insufficient, and a simulation procedure is necessary. As with rayon, this procedure can be more or less advanced. The simplest tests involve *measurements on the reaction mixture* after a suitable acetylation period. More complicated are tests also involving *hydrolysis to secondary acetate*, precipitation and *testing of the product*. This testing can be limited to direct physical properties, such as solubility, etc., but could also involve *spinning in special equipment* and *yarn testing*, or *conversion to plastic* test specimens, followed by *measurement of their quality*.

To the first category of tests belong those of *reactivity, filterability*, content of *undissolved residues, color, turbidity* and *viscosity* of the reaction mixture. Reactivity can be easily measured by the temperature rise in adiabatic acetylation (29, 85), which has a direct correlation with the degree of substitution, or by the change in electrical conductivity (14). Reactivity as related to degradation tendency is obtained by sampling during the latter part of the reaction period and testing for filterability and viscosity (12), as compared with standard pulps. The haze and color of the acetylation dope are also generally measured (13, 61, 106, 121) or estimated by visual comparison with standards in a viewing box (90). Spreading experiments of acetate solutions on water or urea solutions and surface tension measurement have also been suggested as a measure of the state of aggregation (14). In most cases, an activation of the pulp in acetic acid prior to the addition of anhydride is involved in the test method, as well as in mill practice. If the sulfuric acid catalyst is added directly in the activation, it becomes absorbed in the fibers to a varying extent, which is a pulp property to measure, since the treatment of pulp–linters mixtures has been found to react anomalously because of different catalyst absorption (106). Finally, the haze of acetone solutions of the secondary acetate may be measured, and it has been demonstrated to have a correlation with the discoloration of acetate plastics (129), as well as with some pulp properties, such as mannan and xylan content (e.g. 61, 131) and the extent of drying, especially of cold alkali purified pulps. Thus, as in the case of viscose pulp characterization, all methods contribute to establish an evaluation of the processing and product properties. Because of the complexity of the simulation methods, the current effort of the characterization research must be to connect the analytical methods closer to the service properties of the pulp.

REFERENCES

1. Ålander, P., *Paperi Puu*, **33**, 201, 229 (1951); **45**, 403 (1963).
2. Améen, W., and B. Karlsson, *Svensk Papperstid.*, **43**, 302, 314 (1940).
3. Ant-Wuorinen, O., *et al.*, *Paperi Puu*, **34**, 195 (1952); **38**, 327, 479 (1956); **39**, 229 (1957).
4. Bachlott, D. D., *et al.*, *Tappi*, **38**, 503 (1955).
5. Back, E., *Svensk Papperstid.*, **59**, 319 (1956); **63**, 556 (1960).
6. Bartunek, R., *Cellulosechem.*, **22**, 56 (1944); cf. ref. 119, p. 709, *Papier*, **9**, 254 (1955).
7. Bartunek, R., *Papier*, **4**, 451 (1950); **6**, 120 (1952).
8. Bauer, T. W., *Tappi*, **40**, 84 (1957).
9. Bethge, P. O., *et al.*, *Svensk Papperstid.*, **55**, 44 (1952).
10. Bethge, P. O., *et al.*, *Svensk Papperstid.*, **59**, 372, 535 (1956); **61**, 267, 565 (1958).
11. Björkman, C. B., *Paper Trade J.*, **85**, No. 18, 59 (1927).
12. Blume, R. C., *et al.*, *Tappi*, **37**, 28 (1954).
13. Borgen, G. L., *Norsk Skogind.*, **11**, 522 (1957).
14. Borgin, K., *Norsk Skogind.*, **5**, 69 (1951); **6**, 373 (1952); **7**, 210 (1953).
15. Boryniec, A., *Prom. Chem.*, **22**, 278 (1938).
16. Braidy, H., *Rev. Gén. Matier. Color.*, **25**, 35 (1921).
17. Brandon, C. E., *Tappi*, **40**, No. 12, 178A (1957); **41**, No. 7, 120A, No. 9, 129A (1958).
18. Browning, B. L., *Tappi*, **32**, 119 (1949).
19. Browning, B. L., *The Chemical Analysis of Wood*, in L. E. Wise and E. C. Jahn, eds., *Wood Chemistry*, Vol. 2, Reinhold, New York 1952, Part VII.
20. Burton, J. O., and R. H. Rasch, *J. Res. Natl Bur. Std.*, **6**, 603 (1931); TAPPI Standard T 215 m, Swedish Standard CCA 5.
21. Charles, F. R., *Tappi*, **37**, 148 (1954).
22. Cohen, W. E., APPITA Proc. 2 (1948), Div. Forest Prod. Report No. 110.
23. Cottrall, L. G., *Svensk Papperstid.*, **41**, 175 (1938).
24. Cundy, P. F., and M. M. Beck, *Paper Trade J.*, **124**, No. 18, 36 (1947).
25. Davidson, G. F., *J. Textile Inst.*, **39**, T 65 (1948).
26. Davidson, G. F., and T. P. Nevell, *J. Textile Inst.*, **39**, T 102 (1948).
27. Dean, W. L., *et al.*, *Svensk Papperstid.*, **63**, 570 (1960).
28. Doering, H., *Papier*, **10**, 140 (1956).
29. Dyer, E., and H. D. Williams, *Tappi*, **40**, 14 (1957).
30. Ekstam, T., *Svensk Papperstid.*, **53**, 484 (1950); *Paperi Puu*, **32**, 275 (1950).
31. Ekstam, T., *Svensk Papperstid.*, **57**, 204 (1954).

32. Ekstam, T., *Paperi Puu*, **39**, 309 (1957).
33. Ellefsen, Ö., *Norsk Skogind.*, **9**, 264 (1955).
34. Ellefsen, Ö., *et al.*, *Norsk Skogind.*, **7**, 12 (1953); **9**, 322 (1955); **10**, 38 (1956); **12**, 255 (1958).
35. Finnish Standard A 4044, cf. K. Lekander and L. Stockman, *Svensk Papperstid.*, **58**, 777 (1955).
36. Freudenberg, K., and M. Harder, *Ber.*, **60**, 581 (1927).
37. Geiger, E., and A. Wissler, *Helv. Chim Acta*, **28**, 1638 (1945).
38. Genberg, G. P., *et al.*, *Paper Trade J.*, **82**, No. 22, 50 (1926); **88**, No. 17, 71 (1929).
39. Gierisch, W., *Cellulosechem.*, **6**, 61 (1925).
40. Giertz, H. W., *Svensk Papperstid.*, **48**, 485 (1945).
41. Giertz, H. W., *Svensk Papperstid.*, **48**, 317 (1945).
42. Gladding, E. K., and C. B. Purves, *Paper Trade J.*, **116**, No. 14, 26 (1943).
43. Golben, M., *Tappi*, **38**, 507 (1955).
44. Gustafsson, G. R., *Paperi Puu*, **32**, 104, 145, 177 (1950).
45. Gustafsson, C., *et al.*, *Paperi Puu*, **34**, 121 (1952); **36**, 269 (1954); *Norsk Skogind.*, **8**, 54 (1954).
46. Hägglund, E., *Cellulosechem.*, **11**, 1 (1930); Swedish Standard CCA 3.
47. Hara, H., *et al.*, *Tappi*, **43**, 871 (1960).
47a. Hardy, A. C., *Handbook of Colorimetry*, Technology Press, Cambridge, Mass. 1936.
48. Harland, W. G., *Shirley Inst. Mem.*, **28**, 167 (1955); *J. Textile Inst.*, **45**, T 678 (1954); cf. C. F. Bennett and T. E. Timell, *Svensk Papperstid.*, **58**, 281 (1955).
49. Harris, M., *et al.*, *J. Res. Natl Bur. Std.*, **27**, 449 (1941); **29**, 131 (1942).
50. Hartler, N., and E. Ringström, *Svensk Papperstid.*, **63**, 641 (1960).
51. Hembree, E. E., *Tappi*, **39**, 91 (1956).
52. Henley, D., *Svensk Papperstid.*, **63**, 143 (1960).
53. Höfert, H. J., *Z. Instrumentk.*, **67**, 119 (1959).
54. Hughes, E. E., and S. F. Acree, *Ind. Eng. Chem., Anal. Ed.*, **6**, 123 (1934); **9**, 318 (1937).
55. ICCA Standard 1 : 59, SCAN-C Standard 1 : 59.
56. Immergut, E. H., *et al.*, *Monatsh Chem.*, **84**, 219 (1953).
57. Jayme, G., and K. Chen, *Zellwolle, Kunstseide, Seide*, **48**, 47 (1943).
58. Jayme, G., and H. Knolle, *Angew. Chem.*, **68**, 243 (1956).
59. Jayme, G., and K. Neuschäffer, *Makromol. Chem.*, **23**, 71 (1957).
60. Jayme, G., and P. Sarten, *Biochem. Z.*, **308**, 109 (1941).
61. Jayme, G., and U. Schenck, *Melliand Textilber.*, **31**, 153, 230 (1950).
62. Jentgen, H., *Kunststoffe*, **1**, 161 (1911); cf. Cross, C. F., *et al.*, *Cellulose*, Longmans, London 1895.
63. Johansson, A., *Svensk Papperstid.*, **55**, 820 (1952).
64. Johansson, D., *Svensk Papperstid.*, **35**, 656 (1932); Swedish Standard CCA 9.
65. Johansson, D., *Paper Trade J.*, **101**, No. 13, 101 (1935).
66. Johansson, T., *Färg*, Natur och Kultur, Stockholm 1952.
67. Jörgensen, L., *Studies on the Partial Hydrolysis of Cellulose*, Dissertation NTH Trondheim 1950.
68. Jullander, I., and B. Olsson, *Svensk Papperstid.*, **57**, 151 (1954).
68a. Keller, E. L., and P. B. Borlew, *Tappi*, **38**, 379 (1955).
69. Kenyon, W. O., *et al.*, *J. Am. Chem. Soc.*, **64**, 121, 127 (1942); **69**, 347 (1947).

70. Klason, P., *Ber. Hauptversammlung des Vereins der Zellstoff-u. Papier-chem.*, **52**, Berlin 1908; *Cellulosechem.*, **4**, 81 (1923).
71. Klein, W. G., *et al.*, *Tappi*, **43**, 657 (1960).
72. Kleinert, T., *Monatsh. Chem.*, **80**, 356 (1950).
73. Kleinert, T. N., *Tappi*, **41**, 134 (1958).
74. Koblitz, W., *Reyon Zellwolle Chemiefasern*, **30**, 343 (1952).
75. Kolos, F., *et al.*, *Svensk Papperstid.*, **64**, 533, 577 (1961).
76. Kullgren, C., and H. Tydén, I.V.A. Handl. (Stockholm), No. 94 (1929).
77. Launer, H. F., and W. K. Wilson, *J. Res. Natl Bur. Std.*, **22**, 471 (1939).
78. Lefèvre, K. U., and B. Tollens, *Ber.*, **40**, 4513 (1907).
79. Lidman-Safwat, S., and O. Theander, *Svensk Papperstid.*, **61**, 42 (1958).
80. Lindberg, B., *et al.*, *Svensk Papperstid.*, **55**, 13 (1952); **57**, 83 (1954).
81. Lorås, V., and F. Löschbrandt, *Norsk Skogind.*, **10**, 402 (1956); **15**, 302 (1961).
82. Löschbrandt, F., *Norsk Skogind.*, **4**, 130 (1950).
83. Lüdtke, M., *Angew. Chem.*, **48**, 650 (1935); *Biochem. Z.*, **285**, 78 (1936).
84. McEwen, J. M., and E. G. Guetlin, *Tappi*, **41**, No. 7, 134A (1958).
85. Malm, C. J., *et al.*, *Ind. Eng. Chem.*, **46**, 557 (1954); **49**, 763 (1957).
85a. Malmberg, B., *Svensk Papperstid.*, **65**, 911 (1962); **67**, 69 (1964).
86. Meier, H., *Svensk Papperstid.*, **62**, 687 (1959).
87. Merck A.-G., E., *Chemisch-Technische Untersuchungsmethoden für die Zellstoff- und Papierfabrikation*, Verlag Chemie, Weinheim 1957.
88. Merkblatt Zell. Chem. Ing. (Germany) 5–6.
89. Merkblatt Zell. Chem. Ing. (Germany) 9, Swedish Standard CCA 6.
90. Mitchell, J. A., *Tappi*, **40**, 713 (1957).
91. Mitchell, R. L., *et al.*, *Ind. Eng. Chem.*, **45**, 2526 (1953); *Anal. Chem.*, **21**, 1497 (1949).
92. Neale, S. M., and W. A. Stringfellow, *Trans. Faraday Soc.*, **33**, 881 (1937).
93. van Nederveen, G., *Vezelinstituut*, T.N.O., V.I.P., **34** (1952).
94. Nelson, N., *J. Biol. Chem.*, **153**, 376 (1944).
95. Nordman, L. S., and J. A. Niemi, *Tappi*, **43**, 260 (1960).
96. Ohlsson, K. E., *Svensk Papperstid.*, **55**, 347 (1952).
97. Ott, E., and H. M. Spurlin, eds., *Cellulose and Cellulose Derivatives*, *Part III*, Interscience, New York 1955, (a) p. 1176 ff., (b) p. 1432.
98. Pearl, I. A., and L. R. Busche, *Tappi*, **43**, 961 (1960).
99. Pervier, N. C., and R. A. Gortner, *Ind. Eng. Chem.*, **15**, 1167, 1255 (1923).
100. Pohl, E., and W. Seefeldner, *Chem.-Ing.-Tech.*, **27**, 22 (1955).
101. Poole, V. H., *Tappi*, **43**, 248 (1960).
102. Rebek, M., *et al.*, *Kolloid-Z.*, **92**, 217 (1940); *Papier*, **10**, 91 (1956); **12**, 201 (1958); **13**, 1 (1959); **14**, 175, 510 (1960).
103. Ringström, E., and N. H. Apler, *Svensk Papperstid.*, **51**, 501 (1948); **53**, 127 (1950); **58**, 145 (1955).
104. Ritter, G. J., *et al.*, *Ind. Eng. Chem.*, *Anal. Ed.*, **4**, 202 (1932); TAPPI Standard T 13 m.
105. Roe, R. B., *Ind. Eng. Chem.*, **16**, 808 (1924).
106. Rosenthal, A. J., and B. B. White, *Tappi*, **43**, 69 (1960).
107. Saeman, J. F., *et al.*, *Tappi*, **37**, 336 (1954).
108. Samuelson, O., *Svensk Papperstid.*, **53**, 397 (1950).
109. Samuelson, O., *et al.*, *Svensk Papperstid.*, **58**, 713 (1955); **60**, 706 (1957); **63**, 749 (1960).
110. Samuelson, O., and C. Ramsel, *Svensk Papperstid.*, **53**, 155 (1950).

111. Samuelson, O., and B. Törnell, *Svensk Papperstid.*, **64**, 198 (1961).
112. Scandinavian Standard SCAN-C 3x–4x, Swedish Standard CCA 19.
113. Scandinavian Standard SCAN-C 7x, Swedish Standard CCA 19.
114. Scandinavian Standard SCAN-C 8x, Swedish Standard CCA 19, CCA 32:59; *Svensk Papperstid.*, **62**, 123 (1959).
115. Scandinavian Standard SCAN-C 10x, Swedish Standard CCA 19.
116. Scandinavian Standard SCAN-C 21x.
117. Schönberg, E., and K. Wilbrink, *Svensk Papperstid.*, **57**, 872 (1954).
118. Schwalbe, C. G., *Wochbl. Papierfabrik.*, **45**, 2286 (1914); *Papierfabrik.*, **28**, 183 (1930); **29**, 598, 609 (1931); **30**, 151 (1932).
119. Sieber, R., *Die Chemisch-Technischen Untersuchungsmethoden der Zellstoff- und Papierindustrie*, 2nd Ed., Springer, Berlin 1951.
120. Sihtola, H., *Paperi Puu*, **37**, 455 (1955).
120a. Sihtola, H., *et al.*, *Paperi Puu*, **44**, 295 (1962).
121. Sihtola, H., and E. Kaila, *Paperi Puu*, **39**, No. 4a, 143 (1957).
122. Signer, R., *Makromol. Chem.*, **17**, 39 (1955).
123. Sjölin, L., *Svensk Papperstid.*, **59**, 623 (1956).
124. Smirnov, V. S., *Bumazhn. Prom.*, **16**, No. 5, 53 (1938).
125. Smith, E. D., and L. N. Rogers, *Tappi*, **36**, 390 (1953); *Anal. Chem.*, **25**, 931 (1953).
126. Sobue, H., and M. Okobo, *Tappi*, **39**, 415 (1956); cf. M. A. Millet, *et al.*, *Tappi*, **41**, 560 (1958).
127. Somogyi, M., *J. Biol. Chem.*, **195**, 19 (1952).
128. Sookne, A. M., and M. Harris, *J. Research Natl Bur. Std.*, **26**, 205 (1941).
129. Sperling, L. H., *Tappi*, **44**, 280 (1961).
130. Stakheva-Kaverzneva, E. D., and A. S. Salova, *Zh. Analit. Khim.*, **8**, 365 (1953).
131. Steinmann, H. W., and B. B. White, *Tappi*, **37**, 225 (1954).
132. Stenius, Å. S:son, *Svensk Papperstid.*, **62**, 829 (1959).
133. Stenius, Å. S:son, *Svensk Papperstid.*, **63**, 1 (1960).
134. Stephansen, E., *Norsk Skogind.*, **2**, 207 (1948).
135. Stillings, R. A., and B. L. Browning, *Ind. Eng. Chem., Anal. Ed.*, **12**, 499 (1940).
136. Swedish Standard CCA 2.
137. Swedish Standard CCA 4.
138. Swedish Standard CCA 7 and CCA 10.
139. Swedish Standard CCA 8:55; *Svensk Papperstid.*, **59**, 188 (1956).
140. Swedish Standard CCA 9.
141. Swedish Standard CCA 17:44.
142. Swedish Standard CCA 24.
143. Swedish Standard CCA 26:55; *Svensk Papperstid.*, **59**, 12 (1956).
144. Swedish Standard CCA 27:58; *Svensk Papperstid.*, **61**, 358 (1958).
145. Swedish Standard CCA 28:57; *Svensk Papperstid.*, **60**, 513 (1957).
146. Swedish Standard CCA 30:57; *Svensk Papperstid.*, **60**, 808 (1957); SCAN-C 9x.
147. Swedish Standard CCA 31:57; *Svensk Papperstid.*, **60**, 852 (1957); SCAN-C 11x.
148. TAPPI Standard T 5 m.
149. TAPPI Standard T 202 m.
150. TAPPI Standard T 203 m.
151. TAPPI Standards T 205 m, T 220 m.
152. TAPPI Standard T 206 m, Swedish Standards CCA 13 and CCA 16.

153. TAPPI Standard T 210 m, Scandinavian Standard SCAN-C 12x.
154. TAPPI Standards T 217 m, T 452 m.
155. TAPPI Standards T 223 m, T 450 m.
156. TAPPI Standard T 230 m.
157. Tasman, J. E., and V. Berzins, *Tappi*, **40**, 691, 695, 699 (1957); *Pulp Paper Mag. Can.*, **58**, No. 10, 145 (1957).
158. Thomas, B. B., *Tappi*, **43**, 447 (1960).
159. Tollens, B., *Ann.*, **249**, 247 (1888).
160. Tötterman, H., *et al.*, *Paperi Puu*, **40**, 501 (1958).
161. Treiber, E., *Svensk Papperstid.*, **59**, 157 (1956); *Paperi Puu*, **38**, 145 (1956).
162. Treiber, E., *Svensk Papperstid.*, **61**, 794 (1958).
163. Treiber, E., *et al.*, *Svensk Papperstid.*, **58**, 67, 471 (1955).
164. Treiber, E., *et al.*, *Svensk Papperstid.*, **58**, 287, 605 (1955); **59**, 838 (1956); **60**, 524 (1957); *Papier*, **11**, 133 (1957).
165. Treiber, E., and V. Holta, *Svensk Papperstid.*, **61**, 926 (1958).
166. Tydén, H., *IVA Handl. (Stockholm)*, **175**, 1 (1943).
167. Unger, E., and R. Jäger, *Ber.*, **36**, 1222 (1903).
168. Valeur, C., *Svensk Papperstid.*, **62**, 915 (1959).
169. Valeur, C., and I. Törngren, *Svensk Papperstid.*, **60**, 829 (1957).
170. Van den Akker, J. A., *et al.*, *Paper Trade J.*, **114**, No. 5, 34 (1942).
171. Vosters, H., *Svensk Papperstid.*, **53**, 29, 59, 613, 771 (1950); **57**, 122 (1954); **58**, 443, 699 (1955).
172. Wannow, H. A., *Reyon, Zellwolle Chemiefasern*, **29**, 135 (1951).
173. Watson, A. J., and C. Stamp, *Appita*, **10**, 4 (1957); **12**, 137 (1959).
174. Whistler, R. L., *et al.*, *J. Research Natl. Bur. Std.*, **24**, 13 (1940).
175. Wiles, R. H., *Paper Trade J.*, **98**, No. 11, 34 (1934); TAPPI Standard 214 m.
176. Wilson, K., *Svensk Papperstid.*, **51**, 45 (1948).
177. Wilson, K., *et al.*, *Svensk Papperstid.*, **55**, 31 (1952).
178. Wilson, M. W., *Tappi*, **43**, 129 (1960).
179. Wilson, W. K., *et al.*, *J. Research Natl. Bur. Std.*, **51**, 537 (1953); *Tappi*, **38**, 292 (1955).
180. Wilson, W. K., and J. Mandel, *Tappi*, **43**, 998 (1960).
181. Wilson, W. K., and J. Mandel, *Tappi*, **44**, 131 (1961).

21

PULP PROPERTIES AND USES

I. General Considerations

1. PULP PROPERTIES

The pulp industry has developed in an empirical way. After the fundamental problem of separating the wood fibers had been overcome by mechanical or chemical means, the pulp qualities were developed by observing the change in properties of the final product on changing the pulping conditions. Some of these properties are fairly well defined and could even be measured quantitatively, and thus the analytical control methods of the pulp quality were developed. Eventually, a large body of experience was collected, giving the interrelation between pulping conditions and the analytical data of the pulp produced. More recently, most of the physical and chemical courses of the pulping processes have been elucidated, facilitating the efforts to make pulp grades specially suited to a certain end use. The development of better machinery for pulping and of large production units has been of great importance for ensuring a high and uniform quality for each pulp grade.

As in the case of most intermediates, however, it is more difficult to elucidate the detailed mechanism for the processes accompanying the conversion and the final use of the end product, than it is to clarify the mechanism of the processes involved in the production of the pulp. Therefore it is still necessary to resort to empirical methods in the evaluation of the pulp quality, to observe the customers' reactions and to work out test methods which simulate the conversion procedure and the stresses of the use of the end product. The customers' reactions are often difficult to correlate with the process conditions of the pulping or the analytical data of the pulp because of the multitude of unknown or largely uncontrollable variables. Laboratory test methods simulating the conversion procedure must usually for practical reasons be modified at vital points, which introduces doubts on the general validity of the test result. For instance, deficiencies in the conversion equipment originating from the size of the production scale cannot be properly simulated in the laboratory. The stresses in the use of the final product are generally difficult to define, and the test methods simulating them run the risk of distorting the whole development, if the tests neglect essential demands of the use and concentrate on properties which, although quantitatively measurable, have only minor importance for the quality of the final product. Often, the closer the test methods approach the real application of the product,

1133

the more time-consuming they become, and measures to accelerate the test often exaggerate variables of less real importance. If the end uses are many small ones, it is not even economic to work out specially designed tests for all. Finally, many of the qualities of the end product are of the kind which require physiological and psychological investigations rather than mechanical and physico-chemical ones.

In spite of these difficulties, it is necessary to rely on some control methods, and it is desirable that continued research on the basic processes of conversion procedures and end uses will give a clearer picture of what is required of the pulp in terms of chemical composition and physical state.

2. PULP USES

The two dominating fields in which pulp is used are *paper and board* production, where the pulp fibers are mechanically modified to give a coherent sheet, as well as for '*dissolving purposes*', i.e. the chemical conversion of the fiber components, mainly cellulose, to textiles, films, lacquers plastics, etc. Production and consumption statistics will be given in Chapter 22, where Tables 22.2 and 22.5 give an approximate picture of the relative importance of these fields of application. It is seen that dissolving pulp production is only a comparatively small fraction, about 3 M t/year, of the total production of pulp, about 63 M t/year. The dominating fields are those of paper and board, and it is observed that there is a considerable production using waste paper as a raw material. As is also seen from Table 22.6, newsprint is the largest category of papers, followed by coarse papers for wrapping, bag and sack purposes. Container board dominates among the board products, of which most are used in the packaging industry. A large quantity of special boards, produced mainly by the Asplund and Mason processes, is also consumed by the building industry. Of the other products, newsprint uses mainly groundwood with 10–30% chemical pulp, unbleached sulfite or semibleached kraft. Printing papers of increasing quality contain increasing amounts of chemical pulps. Magazine papers contain 30–50% sulfite or kraft, book papers 30–70% and 'wood-free' printing and writing papers 70–100% bleached chemical pulp. These paper categories represent the major uses for sulfite and groundwood pulps. Tissue and sanitary papers also consume large quantities of these pulp types, in admixture with, for example, cold caustic pulp and waste paper. Cold caustic and neutral sulfite semichemical pulps are also used for newsprint. The packaging papers and boards require to a large extent the strong unbleached kraft pulp, predominantly for sack, bag and wrapping papers and liner board. Unbleached sulfite pulp is also used for some bag and wrapping paper, and bleached kraft for an increasing quantity of white packaging paper and food board. Boxboard grades from cylinder wire or Inverform machines use groundwood or waste paper in the bottom or middle plies and bleached sulfite or kraft in the top or outer layers. Neutral sulfite semichemical pulp is used for corrugating medium board, competing mainly with straw pulp and waste paper.

Table 21.1 illustrates the various applications of dissolving pulps. Textile purposes dominate, a large proportion is converted to cellophane, and the remainder is used in plastics and lacquers. Most of the textile production is made by the viscose process, and some specialities are produced by the acetate process. Acetate and nitrate dominate the plastics and lacquers, whereas cellulose ethers are of minor importance. Regular-tenacity rayon and acetate filament yarn are still important, but are increasingly overshadowed by the production of high-tenacity yarns and staple fiber. Sulfite pulp of varying degrees of purification is the dominant raw material, but prehydrolysis–kraft pulps have conquered the important sector of high-tenacity viscose products.

Table 21.1 Approximate world consumption of cellulose for chemical conversion 1960, M t

Process	Textile fiber purposes	Non-fiber purposes	Total
Viscose	2.40	0.40	2.80
Acetate	0.16	0.04	0.20
Nitrate	—	0.07	0.07
Cuprammonium	0.06	0.01	0.07
Etherifications	—	0.07	0.07
Total	2.62	0.59	3.21

II. Paper Pulps

1. BRIEF DESCRIPTION OF PAPER-MAKING OPERATIONS

To obtain a paper or board sheet from a pulp suspension, a series of operations are performed, which could be classified as *stock preparation*, *sheet formation* and *drying*, Figures 21.1–2. Further operations, *finishing* and *converting*, yield a final product to be used in a wide variety of fields. The converting is sometimes made in connection with the paper mill, but especially if the latter is integrated with a pulp mill, it is closely tied up with the wood- and water-supplying areas, whereas the diversified converting is preferably located in the consuming districts and therefore, as a rule, independent of the paper mill.

The stock preparation involves *mixing* of various types of pulps and additives, and *beating* of the pulp fibers. The mixing operations are often carried out by the beaters but the charging is preferably done via measuring wheels or flow meters. It is customary to mix several types of pulp in order to obtain the paper properties desired and to be able to vary them by mixing in various proportions. For instance, in newsprint production, the groundwood pulp is always mixed with 10–25 % of unbleached sulfite

1135

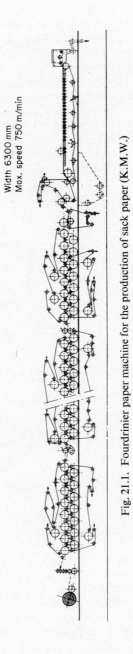

Width 6300 mm
Max. speed 750 m/min

Fig. 21.1. Fourdrinier paper machine for the production of sack paper (K.M.W.)

or semibleached kraft pulps in order to obtain sufficient wet web strength, etc. Bleached hardwood kraft pulps are added to bleached softwood pulps to improve paper formation, and some softwood kraft pulp to unbleached hardwood neutral sulfite semichemical pulp to improve some board properties. Bleached sulfite and bleached kraft pulps from both soft-woods and hardwoods are mixed to give the desired mechanical and optical properties to the various types of fine papers, etc.

Beating serves to make the fibers more flexible and to give them a 'fibrillated' surface, in order to enlarge the contact areas between the fibers in the final paper and to increase its strength. Another effect of beating is the fragmentation of long fibers, which is sometimes considered to improve the sheet formation and the uniformity of the paper but usually impairs some of its strength properties. Some loose fiber debris is also formed on beating, which does not contribute to the paper strength but impairs the drainage properties. Not all pulps are beaten. Groundwood pulp contains sufficient quantities of fibrillated fibers already after the grinding operation to meet the limited demands for strength in the newsprint paper and the strength is not improved by conventional beating. Un-bleached semichemical pulp for board often receives most of its mechanical treatment in the refiners needed for fiberizing. As a rule, however, the pulp is beaten before the paper formation, either in batch *hollander beaters* or in continuously operating beaters of the *conical refiner*, or *jordan*, type. The pulp fibers are thereby exposed to shear forces as the suspension is passed between the bars of the rotating beater roll or refiner plug and the bars of the beater bedplate or refiner shell. The bar interdistance can be closely adjusted and varied according to the amount of beating desired. The type of beating, predominantly bruising or predominantly cutting, can be influenced by the speed of rotation and by the design of the bars. In extreme cases, such as in beating pulp for grease-proof and glassine paper, the bars may be exchanged for lava stones to minimize the cutting action. As a rule, hollander beating is now carried out in series with jordan beating, the latter being placed immediately prior

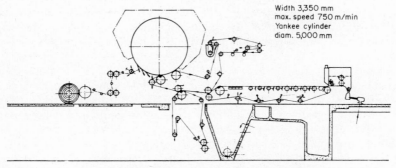

Width 3,350 mm
max. speed 750 m/min
Yankee cylinder
diam. 5,000 mm

Fig. 21.2. Yankee paper machine for the production of MG packaging paper or tissue paper (K.M.W.)

1137

to the machine and having the function of uniforming the prebeaten pulp by small adjustments in the degree of beating. It is operated at headbox consistency, 0.5%, whereas hollander beating works at about 5% consistency.

Dyes or *pigments* are added in the beaters, not only for colored papers but also for white papers, where especially blue dyes are charged to eliminate the yellow tint of some pulps. Unbleached kraft paper is often given a deep green color to cover the original brown, whereas most of the lightly colored papers require bleached pulps or unbleached sulfite. Subsequently, *sizes* are added to the beater. The dominating size is rosin, essentially abietic acid, converted to the sodium salt, but recently, modified or synthetic resins have been applied with improved result. The size, which mainly influences the hydrophility of the sheet and its wet strength properties, is adjusted according to the properties desired. Blotting paper is unsized ('waterleaf'), towelling, tissue and printing papers lightly sized, writing papers medium sized, coarse papers medium to hard sized. Papers requiring special wet strength, e.g. coarse papers for outdoor uses, are sized with synthetic resins, such as melamin–formaldehyde resins. Other sizes, often used in fine papers, are starch, gums, animal glue, casein, etc. The size is completed by *alum*, aluminium sulfate, in a certain proportion to give a slightly acidic pulp suspension and a colloidal aluminium abietate with the rosin size. Finally, a wide variety of *fillers* are often added to impart special properties to the paper, such as improved brightness, opacity, surface smoothness, etc. Such fillers are china clay, blanc fixe, chalk, and titanium dioxide, the latter being esteemed because of its high refractive index.

After stock preparation, the stock is pumped to the paper machine prior to which it is diluted to the right consistency and metered to the correct flow in a stuff box. The dilution is done with white water from the machine wet end. The consistency is kept at about 0.5%, which means that around 200 m³ of water have to be removed from every ton of paper produced. The large dilution is needed to avoid 'bad formation' of the paper involving excessive flocculation. The stock is then introduced to the wet end of the paper machine at the *headbox*, which consists of a series of chambers, separated by distributing pipes or baffles and containing perforated rectifier rolls. In the headbox, the stock is de-aerated and excessive turbulent flow eliminated, whereas sufficient movement is maintained to avoid flocculation phenomena. From the headbox, the flow is uniformly distributed across the wire by careful adjustment of the slice at the opening slot of the headbox. The uniform distribution of the flow is important for obtaining a uniform paper web, and presents an intricate hydrodynamic problem, especially in the modern wide and fast-running machines. The linear speed of flow, which should match that of the machine wire, is adjusted by the slice, whereby a corresponding pressure head is built up in the headbox. Closed, air-cushioned headboxes are now the general rule. On the *wire*, most of the water-removal takes place, and a wet web is formed. The wire is driven by the *couch roll*, where the web leaves for the presses with a water content of about 80%, or 4 m³ ptp, whereas the removed water, almost 200 m³ ptp, is recirculated to dilute beaten stock. The drainage, which is enhanced by the *table rolls*, supporting the wire, and the *suction boxes* and *rotabelts*, is very much influenced by the type of pulp and its degree of beating. The fines developed on grinding or beating of pulps rich in hemicelluloses cause the largest resistance to drainage. An increase in temperature facilitates the drainage. Machines making paper from a highly beaten stock, such as for greaseproof paper, therefore run at a comparatively low speed, around 100–150 m/min, whereas the production of kraft paper and board, which uses a much less beaten stock, can use high speeds, up to or even above 600 m/min. Newsprint machines run even faster. Naturally, in some cases the dry end of the machine may also limit the machine speed. Because there is a preferential alignment of the fibers in the direction of the flow, the tensile strength of the paper in the machine direction is always higher, generally almost twice that of the cross direction, whereas cross direction tear is higher than machine direction tear. Some board machines, instead of using a flat fourdrinier wire, form the web on a series of *cylinder wires*. A recent construction is the *Inverform* wet end, also used to build up a board web from several pulp layers but utilizing as well a flat wire with repeated units of furnish additions and drainage of the water upwards.

The wet web leaving the wire is received by the press felt and passed through the presses, where additional water is removed, down to a residual content of 2.0–1.5 m³ ptp or a dry content of 33–40% in the web. The remaining water has to be removed by evaporation in the dryer sections, usually two to five, each consisting of several drying cylinders, which are kept in contact with the paper by the dryer felts. The dryer sections run with slightly different speeds, adjusted according to the dimensional changes in the paper during the drying. Due to the stretch in the machine direction, created by the *reel*, onto which the dry web is rolled, the shrinkage of the paper is larger in the cross direction. That is another of the main causes of the different properties in the two directions of the paper. By special *compacting units*, consisting of rubber blankets or rolls, such as the *Clupak* and *Expanda* processes, a higher stretch can be obtained in the machine direction, thus improving the rupture resistance of the paper, which is particularly valuable for sack and bag papers. *Machine-creped* paper is produced by a doctor blade at the last press, and by slowing down the reel and dryer sections to maintain the crepe so created. *Machine-finished* (M.F.) paper is produced by passing the dry paper web through smoothing calender stacks prior to the reel. Thereby a smooth and somewhat glossy surface is ensured. A one-sided improved gloss is produced by drying the paper on a huge dryer called a Yankee cylinder. The paper is then kept in contact with its mirror-polished surface during the entire drying process. Such paper machines are called *Yankee machines* and the paper produced *machine-glazed* (M.G.). An oscillating doctor blade applied to the paper when leaving the Yankee cylinder will produce

1139

thin, creped *tissue* paper. The multicylinder machines are called *Fourdriniers*, and there are also *combined* machines containing both types of drying cylinders.

Although there are exceptions, the dry paper web is normally wound up on the reel in its full machine width and is subsequently cut into less wide rolls in the *winder*. There are paper machines from 1 to more than 8 m wide. Cutting to sheets, if required, is done subsequently by special machines in the *finishing room*. The standard sizes vary with the type of paper. The sheets are counted into piles of generally 500 or 1,000, called a *ream*, and packed. In most cases, however, the paper is sent in rolls for *conversion*. That word covers a multitude of operations, such as bag and sack manufacture, coating, printing, waxing, super-calendering, laminating, corrugating, etc., all making the paper ready for its final, many-sided use.

2. MECHANISM OF BEATING AND FIBER BONDING

A dried sheet of unbeaten pulp has a comparatively low mechanical strength. A light mechanical treatment in the presence of water greatly improves the strength of the dried sheet, and further treatment leads to further considerable increase in most strength properties. The mechanism of beating and fiber bonding in the dried paper has been the subject of an immense amount of research and several theories have been advanced (14, 25, 32, 39, 100, 165, 177). It is now generally agreed that the strength of a paper is not derived purely from frictional forces in an entanglement of fibers and fibrils, but that *the main interfiber cohesion arises from hydrogen bonds* developed between hydroxyl groups of the carbohydrates in adjacent fibers. Beating serves the purpose of *increasing the area of contact* between the fibers *by increasing their surface* through 'fibrillation' and *by making them more flexible*. The elements of adjacent fibers have to approach one another quite closely, as the distance between two oxygen atoms of a hydrogen bond is of the order of 2.7–2.9 Å. The forces bringing the fiber elements into contact are those of surface tension as water disappears from the sheet on drying (25). Compression of the wet sheet prior to drying serves to overcome some resilience of the fibers and bring them closer together, thus facilitating the action of the surface tension forces and leading to higher paper density and strength (46, 127).

In order to result in increased surface area capable of hydrogen bonding, the mechanical treatment must be carried out in a manner which facilitates *swelling* of the fibers and *imbibition* of the liquid. Beating in non-polar media, such as hydrocarbons, or in the weakly polar higher alcohols, does not lead to an increase in the strength of the sheet formed, whereas beating in polyalcohols, water, and still better formamide, which are all strongly polar, results in papers of good strength (100). Beating in water at alkaline conditions favors rapid strength development, in comparison with neutral or acid medium (e.g. 176), which is in agreement with the greater swelling tendency of pulp fibers in alkali. The presence of potentially water-

1140

soluble hemicelluloses in the pulp fibers increases their swelling tendency and hence causes a rapid strength development during the beating. However, there are other factors which restrict the swelling and retard the beating effect. In unbleached pulps, especially those of high yield, lignin which is predominantly located in the outer parts of the fiber walls considerably constrains swelling and retards beating, being essentially a non-polar compound. This effect will be discussed further in a subsequent section. However, also in the case of delignified pulps, the outermost parts of the cell wall, the P and $S1$ layers (cf. Chapter 3), restrict fiber swelling because of their peculiar ultra-structure. The initial effect of beating is therefore to remove these layers partly or entirely. It is believed that the initial increase in all strength properties on a very light beating occurs as a consequence of the removal of the primary wall (23, 32, 59), if it has not already disappeared during the pulping operations. The transition lamella, $S1$, which is more persistent (50), will likewise constrain swelling even at higher degrees of beating. Damage to the outer layers can be detected by accelerated swelling in e.g. phosphoric acid (174), in which 'balloon' swelling of the fibers occurs at the points of damage.

As the beating action allows the fibers to imbibe water more freely, a plasticizing of the intermicellar matter occurs, which makes the fibers more flexible (54). At the same time, other mechanical deformations occur at the surface of the fibers. Besides the loosening of the transition lamella, the main part of the secondary wall, $S2$, is also affected. The changes appear in the light microscope as a formation of fibrils at the fiber surface, and by a special technique of metal-shadowing these fibrils appear to be thin layers, loosely attached to the fiber wall and curling up at the free sides to resemble fibrils (49). Electron microscopy reveals an irregular splitting of the fiber wall, as well as flake debris originating from both the $S1$ and $S2$ layers (6). The mechanical action also leads to fragmentation of entire fibers, which is observed as a reduction of the average fiber length, especially in the case of the long softwood fibers, whereas the shorter hardwood fibers are astonishingly intact. This fragmentation has been shown to occur primarily at disturbances of the native tracheid structure caused by crossing ray cells (54a), although it is quite likely that the pulping chemicals, particularly the sulfite cooking acid, emphasize these weak spots by degradation.

The large amount of 'fines', 'crill' or debris produced on prolonged beating results in a decrease in the drainage properties of the pulp, as well as decreased opacity and porosity. However, the debris contributes little to the strength of the paper (36, 176), and an ideal beating action will develop a maximal fiber flexibility and fiber surface area with a minimum of disruption of the fiber elements to loose fragments. The shortening of the long-fibered fraction on prolonged beating, or beating carried out under special 'cutting' conditions, affects the strength properties of the paper adversely but may be desired to improve the uniformity of paper formation in the case of extremely long-fibered and resilient pulps. The morphological phenomena just described occur during the beating of chemical pulps, and also semichemical pulps of the low yield range. The refining of chemimechanical and mechanical pulps likewise results in fragmentation and fibrillation of fibers. However, the phenomena will appear in principle to deviate in some respects from those of beating, probably because of the presence of the large amounts of lignin, which restrict the fiber swelling. The fibrillation appears to occur partly as a splitting of the entire fibre wall in the spiral planes of the $S2$ layer, in extreme cases leading to development of ribbon-like structures with fringed ends, c.f. Figure 7.6b-c (54b). Furthermore, the debris formed does contribute to the strength, at least to some extent, and in contrast to the debris formed on beating chemical pulps it is the main opacity-contributing factor. This property makes the groundwood pulp an important component of printing papers, together with the bulkiness and absorptivity of groundwood-containing sheets.

Thus, the plasticizing of the pulp fibers, as well as the enlargement of their surface area, leads to improved interfiber contact on drying. Electron microscopical studies (6) have revealed contact areas of all morphologically possible combinations, $S1$–$S1$, $S1$–$S2$, $S2$–$S2$, as well as contact in lumen, whereby the $S2$–$S2$ contacts occur more frequently at the more highly beaten samples. The contact regions appear to be of an intimate sort, indicating that definite forces have been in action, which produce a pressing and 'welding' of adjacent fiber elements. Free-pending thin cellulose membranes after drying form ring net structures in the case of random direction of microfibrils, and strings in the case of parallel orientation of microfibrils (86). The contact area may assume sizes ranging from almost point contact up to around 100 μ^2, where the fewer but more important large contact regions occur between fibers which are little damaged apart from surface 'fibrillation'. The smaller contact areas are especially frequent between the fines. The thin-walled springwood fibers will collapse when being dried. They do not flatten out quite like a ribbon, but are shaped more like a double T-support. Thick-walled summerwood fibers as well as most hardwood fibers generally preserve their original pipe-like shape. The former category will contribute considerably more to the interfiber bonding of the paper.

It is naturally of great interest to possess a method of quantitatively estimating the area of interfiber bonding. One method, employing a silvering technique, determines the pulp surface area prior to and after paper formation and drying (21, 131). The silvering technique, even in its improved form, is not considered to give correct values (cf. 113), and air permeability methods (19, 26, 37, 51, 79, 150, 151) as well as absorption methods of dyestuff (180) or nitrogen (70) have been suggested as alternatives. To measure the unbonded area in a paper sheet, opacity measurements have also been used (131). Opacity in a paper is caused by multiple reflections from surfaces inside the sheet, and as the number of these is diminished by the fibers becoming merged into one another, the whole must become more transparent. Wet pressing prior to drying will decrease the final opacity, and likewise increase the strength of the paper (127).

However, the whole bonded, or optical contact area does not contribute to the strength properties (127). Therefore, instead, the increase in opacity on subjecting a paper to stress has been taken as a measure of the ruptures occurring within the paper (126). There is a good correlation between the increase in opacity at a loading–deloading cycle, and the energy lost in the same cycle, as calculated from the stress–strain curve, Figure 21.3 (126). The correlation is the same for a given pulp at any degree of beating, which means that the increase in tensile strength during beating is achieved as a consequence of an increased bonded area, not in an increased bond

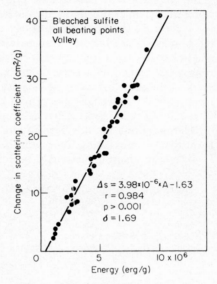

Fig. 21.3. Quantitative relationship between change in scattering coefficient and energy loss in a straining/destraining cycle at various degrees of beating (Nordman)

strength per unit area. From the investigation of the bond strength of different pulps it was concluded that a high content of hemicellulose will increase the bond strength, and not only the bonded area. The rôle of the hemicelluloses in paper pulps will be further discussed in the subsequent section, but it must be touched upon here in the discussion of bonded area and bond strength. Obviously, not all of the area in optical contact must contribute to the mechanical strength of the paper, and some of it will involve weaker bonds or structures than the remainder. The hemicellulose portion of the fiber elements in contact, being much more accessible to solvation than the microfibrils of cellulose, is likely to fill out minor void spaces at the contact areas, in short, act as a glue between the fiber elements at certain places. The existence of a glue in paper bonding has

1143

been much debated in the past, but could be accepted in this restricted sense. The addition of polar polymers, such as locust bean gum (34, 92, 124, 177a), guar gum (153, 177a), starch (28) or carboxymethyl cellulose (75, 194), as well as extracted hemicellulose (128, 134), has a definite positive effect on the paper strength. A slight acetylation, methylation, ethylation or carboxymethylation (1, 13, 85, 178, 190) of the fiber surface also improves the mechanical properties of the paper, whereas intermediate or high degrees of esterification decrease the interfiber bonding (72, 108). It is not easy to discriminate between the glueing effect achieved at the surface of the fibers and the improved plasticizing, produced by the substituents at the surface of the microfibrils in the interior of the fibers. The former effect would increase the bond strength per unit contact area, the latter increase the bonded area. It could also be questioned whether or not all the increase in opacity on a loading–deloading cycle originates from ruptures in strength-bearing contact areas, considering among other things the fines. The close relation between the opacity phenomena, the density of the dried paper, and its mechanical strength has, however, frequently been found (58, 106a, 126, 127), as further demonstrated in Figures 21.3 and 4 (58, 126). The same relation has been found between bursting strength and other means of measuring the interfiber bonding area, such as porosity (151) or by the silvering method (22). Further evidence of

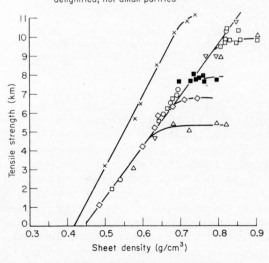

Fig. 21.4. Tensile strength vs. sheet density for various pulp types on beating to a varying extent (Giertz)

the dominating rôle of the hydrogen bond for the strength of the paper, as compared with the rôle of fibrillar entanglement is the strong cohesion of two plane sheets of cellophane, which have been wetted, pressed and dried together (32), as well as the lack of cohesion between normally beaten and sheet-formed pulp fibers, which have been freeze-dried (111, 188). In the latter case, surface tension forces, which normally increase the contact area, are also absent. When the interfiber bonding has been achieved, through the action of wet pressing and surface tension of the disappearing water, the density of the structure is increased, as compared to the wet paper web. Increased degree of beating will give an increased density of the final paper. The density can be expressed in terms of porosity as well as volume weight. The latter varies from about 0.3 g/cm^3 in a paper made from resilient hardwood groundwood fibers to about 0.9 g/cm^3 for a grease-proof paper made from extremely beaten flexible spruce sulfite fibers. The strength properties of the paper are closely related to the volume weight, or rather the increase in volume weight from that of a paper with no strength and no intimate interfiber contact. This concept, d_o, has a numerical value, which varies with the type of pulp, normally between 0.25 and 0.45 g/cm^3, and has obvious morphological aspects (109b). That it is also influenced by the pulping process is seen from the fact that d_o was found to be 0.45 for sulfite and 0.40 for kraft pulps from Scandinavian softwood, and 0.35 for Douglas fir kraft and birch kraft. Most mechanical paper properties have been found to be functions of the increase in volume weight, $d-d_o$, on paper production (109b), Figures 21.5–13. Thus:

$$y = \text{const.}\ \frac{d - d_o}{d^n}, \text{ where}$$

$n = 0$ for $y =$ modulus of elasticity and rupture energy (and, less rigidly, for tensile strength)

$n = 1$ for $y =$ ring crush and CMT resistance

$n = 2$ for $y =$ flat crush resistance

$n = 3$ for $y =$ bending rigidity

$n = 5$ for $y =$ tear strength (softwood pulps, and slightly modified for hardwood pulps).

Most of these functions have their rational explanation in mechanical considerations.

Many of these tests have been initiated by the demands of the packaging industry, especially for boards and sack paper. The development of suitable stress–strain instruments has facilitated the measurement of such fundamental properties as modulus of elasticity and rupture energy, which give, together with the registered load-elongation curve, more information on the visco-elastic behavior of paper than the classical tensile, burst and tear tests. However, the mass of data collected on the influence of the wood and pulping variables still concern mainly the latter three tests, and much of the subsequent discussion will have to refer to these tests. It is unfortunate, that the conventional tensile strength testers normally

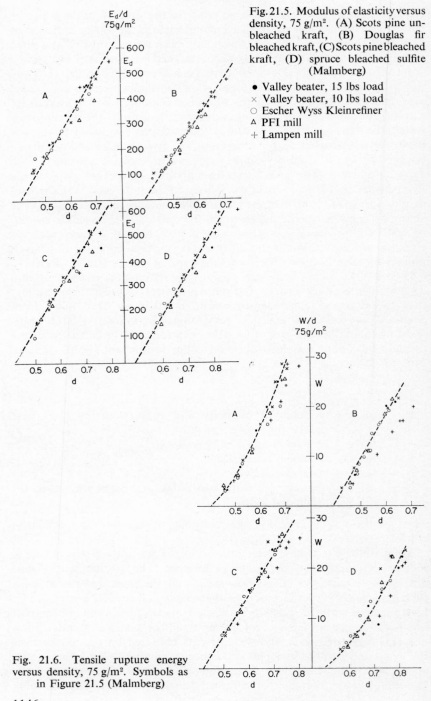

Fig. 21.5. Modulus of elasticity versus density, 75 g/m². (A) Scots pine unbleached kraft, (B) Douglas fir bleached kraft, (C) Scots pine bleached kraft, (D) spruce bleached sulfite (Malmberg)

● Valley beater, 15 lbs load
× Valley beater, 10 lbs load
○ Escher Wyss Kleinrefiner
△ PFI mill
+ Lampen mill

Fig. 21.6. Tensile rupture energy versus density, 75 g/m². Symbols as in Figure 21.5 (Malmberg)

1146

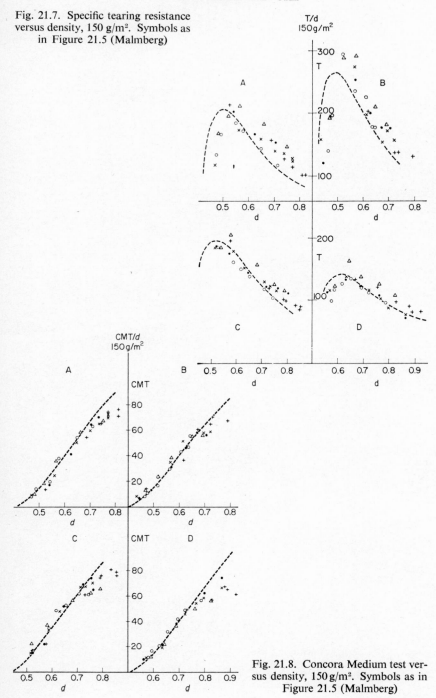

Fig. 21.7. Specific tearing resistance versus density, 150 g/m². Symbols as in Figure 21.5 (Malmberg)

Fig. 21.8. Concora Medium test versus density, 150 g/m². Symbols as in Figure 21.5 (Malmberg)

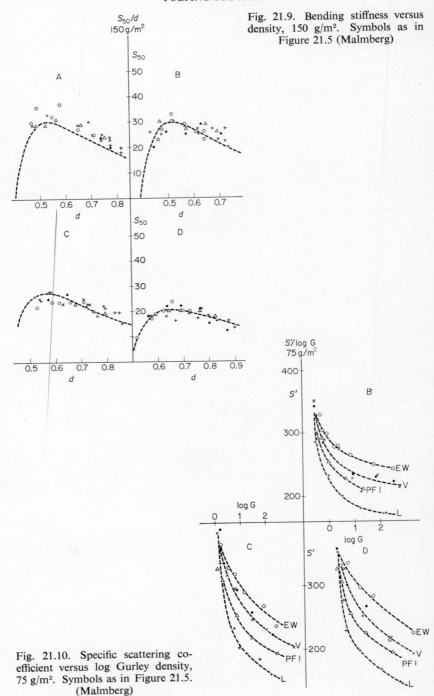

Fig. 21.9. Bending stiffness versus density, 150 g/m². Symbols as in Figure 21.5 (Malmberg)

Fig. 21.10. Specific scattering co-efficient versus log Gurley density, 75 g/m². Symbols as in Figure 21.5. (Malmberg)

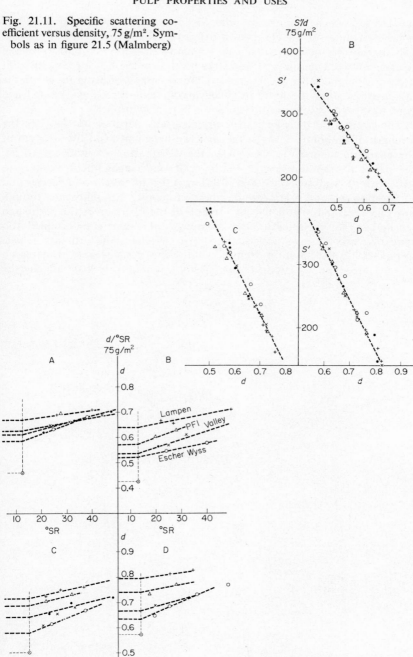

Fig. 21.11. Specific scattering coefficient versus density, 75 g/m². Symbols as in figure 21.5 (Malmberg)

Fig. 21.12. Density versus °SR, 75 g/m². Symbols as in Figure 21.5 (Malmberg)

involve too much slippage or other disturbance at the clamps to allow reliable readings of the elongation to break, which would otherwise be a valuable complement to the tensile strength values. A comparison of the relation between tensile and tear strength during the beating for different pulps is now probably the most satisfactory method of using the available information, until the more qualified instruments for paper testing have been more extensively devoted to pulp characterization.

The strength of the paper structure naturally depends not only on the strength of the joints between the structural elements, but the strength of the elements themselves, as well as the distribution of weak spots, i.e. the paper formation. The strength of the individual fibers is likely to vary with the wall thickness and is different for different wood species and for springwood and summerwood fibers, cf. below. An indication, though not very clear-cut, of the tensile strength of the fibers gives the zero span tensile test (35), in which the tensile strength of a sheet is determined at a span between the jaws approaching zero. Whereas the ordinary tensile test as well as the bursting strength will increase considerably at increased bonded area, the zero span tensile strength is relatively little affected by

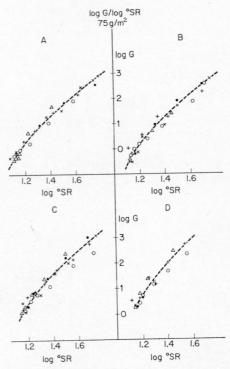

Fig. 21.13. Log Gurley density versus log °SR, 75 g/m². Symbols as in Figure 21.5 (Malmberg)

beating, Figure 21.14 (55). In the strength tests which admit an orientation of the strength-bearing elements in the direction of the stress, the failures are likely to occur between these elements to a large extent. Therefore, such tests as tensile and bursting strength are considered to express largely the strength of the interfiber bonding rather than that of the elements, although studies have revealed that once failure occurs a large number of fibers are ruptured (63a). Tearing strength, on the other hand, applies a stress of local character, where only a few structural elements are loaded. As an increased degree of fiber bonding tends to fix the elements, an orientation of the latter to take up the local stress is made less easy, and rupture

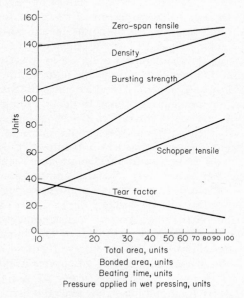

Fig. 21.14. Principal relationship of strength
properties and interfiber bonding (Forman)

will occur to an increasing extent within the strength-bearing elements instead of between them and so the paper tends to be brittle. Even granted that the *force* to cause a rupture within those elements is higher than that causing a failure *between* the fibers at a lower degree of beating, the work required to tear the fiber fragment out of the structure will be less than that used for an undamaged fiber, which is less rigidly anchored in the paper but has to be freed of additional contacts with hydrogen bonds or frictional forces (4). The tearing strength of softwood paper therefore, after an initial increase at the earliest stages of beating, will continually decrease throughout the beating, and although it will be a function of both the strength of the paper structural elements and the degree of bonding, the former will appear to a larger extent in tearing strength than in the tensile and bursting strengths. Hardwood papers behave somewhat differently,

1151

in that the short and less flexible types of hardwood fibers require considerable beating before the interfiber bonding will reach a stage where the tear work has a maximum.

3. RELATIONSHIP OF PULP AND PAPER PROPERTIES

The relationship of the origin and analytical composition of the pulp and the properties of the paper is of the utmost technical importance as it determines what wood species and pulping process should be used, as well as the conditions of the latter, to achieve a pulp suited for the production of a certain type of paper. The variables of paper-making allow considerable adjustments of the paper properties even using one and the same type of pulp, but basically the pulp puts definite limits to what paper properties can be achieved.

One of the most striking differences observed in comparing the properties of papers from different pulp types is the influence of the *fiber dimensions* (34, 62). Hardwoods generally produce pulps of lower strength than softwoods, a phenomenon closely related to the difference in *fiber length*. Tearing strength is especially inferior in the short-fibered pulps. Some particularly long-fibered softwood species give pulps of unusually high tear, even compared with average softwood pulps. However, a classification of paper pulps according to fiber length alone is misleading, since other fiber dimensions, as well as the chemical composition, are important. To achieve a pure measure of the influence of the fiber length, some experiments have been carried out with rayon staple fibers, chopped to well-defined lengths and beaten together with locust bean gum (34). Tensile strength was then found to be proportional to $L^{0.5}$, bursting strength to $L^{1.0}$ and tearing strength to $L^{1.5}$. However, investigations on the influence of fiber length, using wood pulp samples of varying average fiber length, achieved either by changes in the wood used, the pulping process, the beating process, or by fractionation, have generally arrived at somewhat different relationships, because other factors have automatically varied as well. A more rigid technique has been applied to *Araucaria klinkii*, an Australian softwood with unusually long tracheids (192a). Chips, delignified with chlorite, were cut in 1–7 mm lengths and then fiberized by treatment in cold dilute alkali. Hand-sheets made after beating of these pulps were found to have a tear strength, which had a linear correlation with the fiber length. Also properties associated with fiber bonding tended to increase with fiber length, but more slightly. This is in agreement with the experience that there is a larger difference in tear than in tensile strength between hardwoods and softwoods. The inner (core) wood of both hardwoods and softwoods has shorter fibers and also gives pulps of lower strength, especially lower tear, than does the outer wood. One of the most interesting questions in this connection is why kraft pulps of Scandinavian and certain North-American softwoods give a different type of paper to Douglas fir and southern pines (30, 42, 73). The former category gives a higher degree of fiber bonding, a higher tensile and bursting strength but a considerably lower tearing strength than kraft pulp of Douglas fir and some southern pines, which constitute the main part of the North-American kraft pulp production. A series of investigations revealed that whereas the chemical composition between the pulps of the two categories did not vary considerably (104), the DP of the cellulose fractions did not show differences corresponding to the behavior of the papers (71), nor did the crystalline orientation as judged from x-ray measurements (31), but the fiber dimensions showed certain characteristic deviations (63). The average fiber length and weight was considerably higher for the pulps of high tear, and the summer fibers of Douglas fir especially showed a remarkable cell wall thickness as compared with its spring fibers and the fibers of most other species. It was also demonstrated how paper made from the summer fibers was extremely low in fiber bonding, tensile and bursting strength, and high in tear, whereas the opposite was true for the spring fiber paper (18, 41, 74, 192). A high proportion of long and resilient fibers will lead to a pulp which requires much beating and still yields paper of low strength, excepting tear. Scandinavian softwoods as well as some northern North-American ones have a summer fiber content of less than 30%, whereas some of the subtropical and tropical pines contain as much as 50% or even more (122a). Tables 9.28 and 9.30 give a comparison between commercial kraft pulps from different wood species to demonstrate the difference in paper properties between softwoods and hardwoods, and between Douglas fir and Scandinavian pine pulps.

It is clearly seen, that although there is a large difference between the strength properties, especially tear strength, of softwoods and hardwoods, with average fiber lengths of 3 and 1 mm, there are significant deviations from the general pattern. Thus, young-growth slash-pine has rather short fibers and yet a higher tear than e.g. Engelmann spruce, and *Eucalyptus saligna*, properly cooked and fairly-well beaten, gives a tear strength comparable to that of softwood pulp, in spite of its short fibers. The correlation between wood density and paper properties is particularly obvious for the softwood pulps.

As described in Chapter 2, not only fiber length but the width of the fibers and of the fiber lumen, as well as the thickness of the fiber walls vary considerably for different species, for different growing conditions and age, and within a growth ring. The differences between springwood and summerwood fibers are more pronounced in softwoods than hardwoods. In most hardwoods, the fibers approach the softwood summerwood fibers in type, i.e. with comparatively thick walls and narrow lumen, although the dimensions of the hardwood fibers are smaller throughout. Such fibers to a large extent preserve their pipe-like shape during the beating and sheet-forming processes, and are therefore less plastic and give rise to less fiber-bonding area than the thin-walled fibers of the softwood springwood type, and consequently the strength properties of hardwood papers are also for this reason lower than for softwood papers. The extremely thin-walled fiber species are generally those with a low basic density, such as the umbrella tree, *Musanga smithii* (West Africa) or the balsa

1153

tree, *Ochroma lagopus* (South America), with a wall thickness of about $1.5\,\mu$ and a density of 0.2 and 0.1, respectively (154), whereas extremely thick-walled fiber species are those with a high density, such as *Rhizophora mangle*, mangrove, or *Lophira procera*, with basic densities of about 1.1 and an average wall thickness of 6 or 10 μ. The lumen diameters of these species are, respectively, 40, 20–55, 6 and 2 μ, indicating the varying degree of fiber stiffness. However, mainly due to a varying volume fraction of vessel elements, there is no general relationship between wood density and wall thickness, or better of *wall fraction*, in per cent of the total fiber cross section. The wall fraction in the cases mentioned is about 7 % for the thin-walled extremes and 67–91 % for the thick-walled extremes. Of the more common hardwoods, *Populus*, *Betula*, and *Tilia* species belong to an intermediate class with about 40 % wall fraction (some poplars down to 25 %), whereas in *Quercus* and *Fagus* species the wall fraction amounts to 55–85 % (122). Some *Eucalyptus* species, such as *E. camaldulensis* (161) *E. globulus* and *E. saligna* belong to the intermediate class, whereas others, especially *E. gomphocephala*, are much more thick-walled. There is also a considerable spread in the values for wall fraction within a pulp sample for hardwoods, but there is generally only one peak in the distribution curve, whereas for softwoods there is one peak for the springwood fibers at around 30 % and another for the summerwood fibers at around 85 %. Consequently there is a wide spectrum of softwood fibers of 10–95 % wall fraction, and the average wall fraction value for softwoods thus depends on the proportions of springwood and summerwood fibers, and is about 35 % for Scandinavian and some North-American softwoods and 65 % for some western and southern North-American softwoods and some subtropical softwood species. In the former type, there is only 5–30 % summerwood fibers (66, 122a), whereas in the latter the summerwood fraction amounts to 50–75 %. It is generally considered that the most favorable paper properties are obtained when the summerwood fibers are below 50 % (43) and the average value of the wall fraction below 50 % (154). For hardwoods, the dense species having fiber wall fractions much above 50 % are less suitable for pulping. In an effort to establish the morphological influence on the paper properties, a large number of American hardwoods of widely varying density were pulped by the kraft process and compared at equal lignin content (178a). Thereby the influence of the pulping process and the chemical composition was minimized, and more than 80 % of the variations could be related to some basic morphological features, such as fiber length, wall fraction and fiber strength (the latter measured as *zero span tensile strength*, or as the tensile strength of handsheets with no distance between the clamps, a measure fairly independent of the interfiber bonding). The wall fraction is often expressed also in terms of lumen width : fiber width, or twice the wall thickness : lumen width (the Runkel ratio (154)). The paper strength was found to improve with increasing (zero span) fiber strength, with increasing fiber length and with decreasing wall fraction. Tear strength improved with decreasing wall fraction only to a certain extent, and as pointed out above in the discussion on the paper properties of springwood and summerwood fibers, the more thick-walled fibers with a high wall fraction give the highest tear strength for *softwood* pulps.

Thus, in addition to fiber length, fiber width and wall thickness, sometimes expressed as *fiber coarseness* in decigrex (dg., or mg/100 m), decide the paper properties. In experiments with viscose filaments of varying length and coarseness (36a), the latter was found to influence bulk with an exponent of -0.3, burst with -1.0, tensile with -0.6 and tear with -0.3.

Although a high basic density is desirable from the economic point of view, as long as pulpwood is bought by volume, it is not a very desirable property from the paper-making point of view. The tensile strength of kraft pulps from *Pinus radiata* and *P. taeda* were shown to decrease with increasing wood density, and the bulk and tear to increase (192), in accordance with the experience from comparing species of different density, as well as paper made from springwood and summerwood fibers. Selection of trees with the highest density for seed production is therefore somewhat questionable (43, cf. 117), especially as a high rate of growth does not necessarily mean a high density of the wood (117).

The rôle of the '*fines*' fraction has been discussed earlier. Fragments produced by fiber cutting give paper of low strength (20), the native short fibers originating from the same wood, on the other hand, give fairly good paper strength excepting tear (47), but the long fibers of chemical pulps mainly decide the strength properties of a paper (176). On the other hand, the fines of groundwood pulp are important for the fiber bonding and the strength of the paper, provided the fines have been obtained by the right type of mechanical action (33, 101, 162).

The rôle of the *pulping process* for the paper properties is shown in Table 21.2, showing typical values for unbleached and bleached spruce pulp hand-sheets beaten to the same freeness. Obviously, groundwood pulp gives the lowest strength figures and kraft pulp the highest, whereas sulfite pulp, although it has a good response to beating and gives an extensive fiber bonding, is decidedly weaker than the kraft pulp, which on the other hand requires more beating energy. Bisulfite pulping means an improvement in most respects, whereas a subsequent carbonate cook modifies the paper properties of an acid sulfite or bisulfite pulp in the same direction as a prehydrolysis prior to the kraft cook does to the properties of the kraft pulp, i.e. towards less fiber bonding and higher tearing strength. In both cases, hemicelluloses are removed in the extra cooking stage. The groundwood pulp, although giving a weak paper, has the important quality of giving a very resilient and absorbent paper of very good printability, and is thus suited to the purpose of newspaper printing in fast presses, whereas the strong kraft pulp is ideally suited for most packaging papers and boards, and the easy-beating sulfite and bisulfite pulps for dense papers such as greaseproof and glassine. The semichemical pulps are generally intermediate in strength properties, but the interdependence of strength and pulp yield are quite different for different processes, and bisulfite pulping gives especially good paper strength already at rather high yields.

1155

Table 21.2. Paper properties of spruce pulps, showing the effect of various pulping processes and treatments (155)

Process and treatment	Yield, % u.	b.	Pulp composition, % Lig-nin	Cellu-lose	Gluco-man-nan	Glucu-rono-xylan	Paper properties, at 45° SR Beat-ing time, min	Tensile strength, km	Tear strength
Groundwood, u.w.	95	—	27	42	19	12	—	2.5*	40*
Acid sulfite, u.w.	85	—	25	50	19	6	50	6.2	60
	75	—	22	56	16	6	35	7.5	60
	70	—	20	60	15	5	30	8.5	60
	65	—	17	65	13	5	25	9.3	60
	60	—	12	71	12	5	20	9.8	63
	55	—	6	77	11	6	20	9.5	70
	50	—	3	84	8	5	23	9.4	75
	45	—	1	90	6	3	40	6.0	50
Acid sulfite–carbonate, u.w.	45	—	3	92	2	3	70	8.0	140
Neutral sulfite–acid sulfite, u.w.	70	—	16	60	19	5	20	8.0	55
	65	—	13	65	17	5	16	8.2	60
	60	—	8	71	16	5	15	8.5	65
Bisulfite, u.w.	90	—	28	47	18	8	36	2.8	43
	85	—	27	50	15	7	79	5.9	59
	80	—	25	54	15	6	65	7.9	62
	75	—	22	58	14	6	45	9.8	70
	70	—	20	61	14	5	40	10.0	70
	65	—	17	65	13	5	28	10.9	72
	60	—	12	71	12	5	25	11.0	75
	55	—	6	77	11	6	22	10.7	85
	50	—	3	84	8	5	25	9.5	95
Bisulfite–carbonate, u.w.	55	—	10	81	5	4	47	10.3	96
	45	—	2	90	4	3	56	8.8	133
Neutral sulfite–bisulfite, u.w.	70	—	16	60	19	5	30	10.0	60
	65	—	13	65	17	5	25	9.9	60
	60	—	8	71	16	5	20	9.7	63
Kraft, u.w.	70	—	20	56	15	9	—	7.0	100
	60	—	13	66	12	9	120	9.5	110
	55	—	8	72	11	9	95	10.9	120
	50	—	4	79	8	9	85	11.5	130
Prehydrolysis–kraft, u.w.	45	—	2	91	3	4	125	9.5	180
Kraft tetrahydroborate, u.w.	60	—	6	67	21	6	80	10.5	100
	55	—	2	72	20	6	56	10.8	100
Kraft polysulfide	55	—	3	73	18	6	82	12.0	110
Acid sulfite, b.w.	55	50	0	82	12	6	25	10.0	70
b.d.	55	50	0	82	12	6	30	8.9	85
Bisulfite, b.w.	55	50	0	82	12	6	40	10.5	85
Kraft, b.w.	50	47	0	82	8	10	77	11.5	130
b.d.	50	47	0	82	8	10	80	11.0	145

u. = unbleached, b. = bleached, w. = wet, d. = dry

* At 70° SR, as produced.

Obviously, the great changes in paper properties obtained with pulps of the same wood origin by varying the process reflect the changes taking place in the various types of pulping processes. The changes are physical as well as chemical. The changes in fiber dimensions, the influence of which has already been dealt with, are greatest at the groundwood process and least important in the kraft process. Whereas only about 25% of the ground-wood pulp fibers are retained on a 35 mesh screen on fractionation, the corresponding figures are 85–90% for sulfite and 90–95% for kraft pulps. Although the differences in fiber dimensions may well explain some of the differences in paper properties between groundwood pulp and the chemical pulps, they are not sufficiently large to account for the differences between sulfite and kraft pulps. The explanation for them has been often sought but not yet entirely found, and before entering into that discussion, some more obvious chemical differences have to be examined, namely the influence of the *lignin* and *hemicellulose* contents.

As lignin is essentially hydrophobic, it is natural to expect it to decrease the possibilities of interfiber bonding in paper. One of the pulp fibers giving the lowest paper strength is *Defibrator* or *Asplund* fiber (which is not used for paper but for construction boards after heat pressing, giving a special type of bonding). In contrast with groundwood pulp, the fibers of the *Asplund* process are isolated with little fragmentation and 'fibrilla-tion', although with almost all lignin preserved. Delignification of *Asplund* fiber with chlorine considerably increases the strength of the paper pre-pared therefrom, until the lignin content has decreased to around 4% (121). In a similar manner, delignification of groundwood pulp with chlorine dioxide (81) or neutral sulfite pulp with chlorine (131a, 186) continuously improves the paper properties in proportion to the lignin removed. In the case of *Asplund* fiber and groundwood pulp, delignification is too expensive, but an increasing proportion of the neutral sulfite pulps pro-duced from hardwoods are being bleached to yield pulps of interest in the more qualified paper fields, although the main production is still unbleach-ed pulp for corrugating medium board. Kraft (139) and sulfite (91) pulps have also been delignified with mild agents (sodium chlorite) with improved paper strength as the result. Microdissection experiments have revealed the expected effect of decreased adhesion between the fiber surfaces in the presence of lignin (56). There has been some speculation on how much lignin can be tolerated without any interference with the fiber bonding. It has been stated that for kraft pulps up to about 9% may be present (103), as at lower contents most of the lignin is located in the interior of the secondary wall. Other investigations maintain that both sulfite and kraft pulps show a maximum tear at around 5% lignin and a maximum tensile and burst at around 7% lignin (69), or 4–6% lignin at pulps of maxi-mum 'average' strength (83, 88). A strength maximum at 6.5% lignin was found in kraft cooked groundwood pulp (81), and sulfite pulps were found to have a maximum tensile and bursting strength at Roe number 5–6 and a tear maximum at Roe number 3–4 (57), i.e. at lignin contents of around 5 and 3%, respectively. However, in all the cases mentioned, the lignin content figures for maximal paper strength cannot be regarded as measures of the lignin effect only, but also, and in some cases predominantly, changes in the carbohydrate fraction, which occur during the delignification. As also clearly seen from Table 21.2, the sulfite and especially bisulfite processes develop the paper strength at a higher yield level than does kraft cooking. This is likely to be caused by the sulfonation of the lignin, which will improve the hydrophility of the lignin. Another contributing factor is the preservation of a larger fraction of amorphous hemicelluloses in the sulfite processes as compared to kraft cooking. To sum up, lignin has been shown to restrict swelling and decrease the adhesion forces between the fibers because of its hydrophobic nature and its dominant location at the fiber surfaces. In removing the lignin, swelling of the fiber during beating occurs more rapidly, the fibers become more flexible, surface enlargement can occur and interfiber bonds of good strength can be formed. The manner in which the lignin is removed during the chemical pulping processes to eliminate its negative influence will determine how the strength-bearing elements are affected and show up as differences between pulps of different processes, or from the same process but pulped under different conditions.

The *carbohydrate* fraction, both cellulose and hemicelluloses, is sensitive to most delignifying agents, partly dissolves, is partly reprecipitated or adsorbed, and partly degrades during the pulping. Therefore, the *quality* as well as the *quantity* of the carbohydrates has to be considered. Interest has been focused on the *hemicelluloses* as the part of the carbohydrates which is most readily attacked by pulping agents, and at the same time likely to take an active part in interfiber bonding due to its location in the outer part of the fiber walls and its easy accessibility to water. One of the points of interest has been the optimal content of hemicelluloses in a pulp. In the above-mentioned model experiments on staple fiber cuts (34), it was found that appreciable quantities, around 20%, of amorphous material, a galactomannan, had to be added to the cellulose fibers in order to get good interfiber bonding. The addition of extracted xylan to rag stock had a positive influence on all strength properties up to 6% and additional quantities gave a further increase in interfiber bonding, as indicated by increase in tensile and decrease in tearing strength (128). The same trends were noted for purified sulfite pulp, and even for regular sulfite paper pulp there was an increase in paper strength up to 20% xylan addition. Alkaline extraction of pulp holocellulose usually displays optimal strength properties of the resultant pulps at a hemicellulose content of around 20% (e.g. 110, 134). For some reason, untreated holocellulose does not give a very strong paper. It has been pointed out (e.g. 68), that changing the content of hemicelluloses in a pulp and then comparing the strength of hand-sheets on the same basis weight means that the number of fibers in the sheets is then lower at a higher hemicellulose content of the pulp, which must be of consequence to the strength, especially as the differences in the fiber quantity in most comparisons are considerable.

1158

Since the hemicelluloses occur to a fairly large extent in the analytical gammacellulose fraction, there is a fair correlation between gamma-cellulose content and paper strength, expressed as tensile or bursting strength (38, 58). That is especially so when comparing sulfite pulps. The alkali-soluble fraction is sometimes considered to give a better measure of the potential paper bonding than the entire hemicellulose fraction, as part of the hemicelluloses are less accessible to water. The more accessible hemicelluloses are responsible for the ease of beating of a pulp (67). It is of special interest to note, that the strong, but slow-beating kraft pulps contain a particularly large amount of hemicelluloses which do not dissolve on treatment of the pulp with alkali. It should also be pointed out, that although an increase in the hemicellulose content of a sulfite pulp by neutral sulfite precooking does cause an increased beatability, a corresponding increase in the kraft pulp hemicellulose content by tetrahydoborate or polysulfide addition will not materially influence the rate of beating.

The influence of the hemicelluloses, which is partly a swelling effect in the secondary wall making the fibers more flexible, to increase the area of interfiber contact, partly a direct participation in the interfiber bonds (cf. Section II.2), in most cases improves only the interfiber bonding and those strength properties which mainly depend on it, such as tensile and burst strength. The strength of the structural elements is probably unaffected or may even be adversely affected by the presence of hemicelluloses. Tearing strength generally decreases with an increase in the hemicellulose content, and in some cases it is desirable to remove some of the hemicelluloses to obtain paper types where high tear, sheet softness and opacity are essential. Medium- and high-alpha pulps produced by hot alkali purification of sulfite pulps have been investigated for that purpose (144), although it is more general practice to remove hemicelluloses by prolonged acid sulfite cooking, in case tear is not essential but softness and opacity are desired. It is even practical to achieve similar effects by the use of *dried* pulps, and some fine-paper producers with integrated mills prefer to dry even their own pulp production prior to its conversion to paper. By drying the pulp, hydrogen bonding occurs within the pulp fibers, especially in the outer, amorphous parts, and although those phenomena are not irreversible (100), a considerable soaking time would be required to restore the original condition of the slush pulp. Therefore, predried pulps tend to give softer and more opaque papers of higher bulk and tear and lower tensile and bursting strength. The phenomenon is especially noticeable in the case of sulfite pulps, and also means that greaseproof pulp, which in contrast should contain a large amount of hemicelluloses capable of imbibing much water and then drying to a transparent paper of high density, must be converted to paper at the place of pulp production, or else shipped in a wet or semi-dry condition, around 70% dry content.

There are other means of achieving opacity in printing papers than reducing the hemicellulose content of a softwood sulfite pulp. In printing papers where *groundwood* can be allowed, the addition of groundwood gives the desired opacity effect at a lower cost. The same is true for *clay* addition. Since beating will reduce opacity as well, *less beating* is also often a practicable method. The addition of inexpensive *hardwood pulps* is also a means of opacity improvement, which is increasingly practiced. The improvement of opacity and sheet formation is a field in which pulps from high-density hardwoods have a part to play. Apart from the morphological contribution to opacity, i.e. the stiff rod-like fibers having low flexibility and low fiber-bonding capacity, the hardwoods of medium density also give especially high opacity when pulped by the acid sulfite process. Thereby, relatively little xylan is left, and thus the swelling tendency and flexibility of these fibers are reduced, in spite of a relatively low wall fraction. On the other hand, kraft pulps of medium-density hardwoods contain relatively large amounts of hemicelluloses and give good paper bonding and only limited opacity. These effects are demonstrated for some typical market pulps in Table 21.3. The influence of the hemicellulose content on the paper properties of both sulfite, bisulfite and kraft pulps was clearly demonstrated in Tables 9.31, 9.33 and 21.2. A higher content will increase the fiber bonding and hence the tensile and burst strength but decrease the tear strength.

The condition of the *cellulose* fraction, although it is the back-bone of the paper, is generally not critical. A large amount of work has been done to compare the paper strengths of pulp with the DP of the cellulose (83, 84, 102, 123, 130, 133, 164, 173), and it is generally found that all strength properties, especially tearing and folding strength, decrease with decreasing DP of the cellulose. However, it is not easy to decide whether that correlation is a primary or secondary phenomenon. When decreasing the DP of the cellulose by cooking or by bleaching, other phenomena occur, which are likely to be more important. The DP of the similarly reacting and more accessible hemicelluloses is likely to be reduced in a manner which parallels, or slightly precedes, the average decrease in DP of the entire carbohydrate fraction. Furthermore, the degradation during cooking and bleaching being far from uniform, large amounts of fiber fragments are formed, and still more fragmentation will occur during the beating of the degraded pulps, reducing especially the tearing and folding strengths. That the DP of the cellulose fraction as such should be high enough to give high strength even at fairly low-viscosity pulps is obvious from the fact that 20–25 cP TAPPI (which is lower than for most paper pulps) corresponds to a DP of 1,000, whereas the critical DP range for most polymers as regards mechanical strength occurs at around DP 0–400, with the most important changes at DP 0–200 (112). This general law has been confirmed for cellulose products by measuring the tensile strength of acetate films (171), and is demonstrated in Figure 21.15. It is interesting to note, that the DP of native glucomannan has been found to be about 80–100, and of glucuronoxylan around 130–200 (40a, 134, 181), and that this DP is largely preserved in kraft pulps but reduced to less than half that value at a fairly early stage of sulfite cooking (134 155). Therefore, one likely reason for some of the differences in strength

1160

Table 21.3. Commercial types of dried bleached paper pulp and their properties (155)

Pulping process	Sulfite				Kraft					
Wood species	Spruce	Spruce	Birch	Beech	Eucalypt	Spruce	Pine	D. fir	Birch	Beech
Pulp, type	Strong	Soft	Soft	Soft	Soft					
Chemical composition, %										
Cellulose	85	89	89	88	91	82	81	81	72	75
Glucomannan	10	7	3	3	5	8	8	12	1	1
Glucuronoxylan	5	4	8	9	4	10	11	7	27	24
Paper properties at 25° SR										
Beating time, min	22	20	24	21	18	48	37	35	20	21
Tensile strength, km	6.8	4.2	3.5	2.2	2.5	9.9	8.8	6.3	5.8	2.8
Tear strength	103	88	74	45	78	160	125	180	93	37
Sheet density, g/cm³	0.74	0.66	0.64	0.56	—	0.66	0.68	0.64	0.70	0.55
Spec. scattering coeff.	240	304	375	455	460	230	235	—	320	415
Paper properties at 45° SR										
Beating time, min.	40	36	45	42	36	77	60	50	36	40
Tensile strength, km	8.2	4.9	4.8	3.5	3.6	11.0	10.2	7.3	7.6	4.1
Tear strength	77	72	75	47	34	140	108	140	83	46
Sheet density, g/cm³	0.82	0.70	0.72	0.63	—	0.70	0.73	0.66	0.78	0.62
Spec. scattering coeff.	175	305	320	395	420	205	200	—	235	375

properties between kraft and acid sulfite pulps lies in differences in the *quality* of the hemicelluloses rather than in the *quantity*. By prolonged kraft or sulfite cooking, as well as by oxidative bleaching, the hemicellulose DP is further reduced, and the changes are noted in the reduced inter-fiber bond strength and conventionally recorded as a viscosity decrease in the pulp, although viscosity is strictly speaking a measure of the DP of the cellulose. Naturally, only the average chain length is indicated, and as the degradation is distinctly heterogeneous, a considerable portion of the strength-bearing *cellulose* elements are also likely to have become degraded to a critical DP and this may be an equally large or even more important cause of the strength decrease. In some mills the viscosity test is used to control the quality of both cooking and bleaching operations, and investigations indicate that in kraft pulp bleaching, a TAPPI viscosity of about 35 cP should not be gone below (27, 187). A further indication of the relative insignificance of average cellulose DP to the paper strength is the fact that strong sulfite pulps show a higher DP and viscosity than kraft pulps, although they give a considerably weaker paper (e.g. 7).

The differences in paper strength properties between sulfite and kraft pulps have often led to speculation as to the relative value of hemicelluloses of different chemical composition (e.g. 93). The DP of native xylan is higher than that of glucomannan, and probably remains so after pulping. Generally kraft pulps contain more xylan and less glucomannan than sulfite pulps, especially from softwoods (94), excepting Douglas fir kraft, which has a composition similar to that of spruce sulfite pulp. An investigation of birch pulps, on the other hand, where the dominating hemicellulose component is xylan in both kraft and sulfite pulps, shows virtually the same differences in paper strength properties as in the case of softwoods (155). One possible reason for that is the different DP's of the hemicellulose fractions mentioned above, but it is believed that there are more reasons. As the fiber dimensions of the birch pulps were the same for kraft and sulfite both before and after beating (155), it is suggested that the differences in strength properties are caused by differences in the

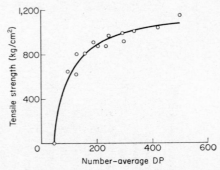

Fig. 21.15. Effect of molecular weight on the strength of cellulose acetate film (Sookne–Harris)

microfibrillar structure. The interesting changes noted in the adsorption of xylan by the cellulose during the kraft cook, sometimes described as an intercrystallization (194), cause a decreased alkali solubility of the xylan fraction, and also less swelling tendency in the fiber, whilst the dissolution of glucomannan and the more accessible portions of the *cellulose* during the alkaline cook are likely to have a similar effect. They cannot, however, be held responsible for the slower beating properties of kraft pulp, since the preservation of glucomannan and accessible xylan by tetrahydroborate addition does not improve the beatability radically, and therefore the slower beating response of kraft pulps must be explained by a better preservation of the morphological structure. The microfibrillar structure, as indicated by electron micrographs (87), becomes less easily dispersed on beating, becomes less fixed in a rigid position during drying, and will therefore retain a greater ability to orientate in the direction of stresses. That will be especially valuable where local high stresses occur, i.e. in the tearing strength test.

The potential paper strength-bearing structural elements in the wood fibers are extremely sensitive to degradation when exposed during the cook, cf. Chapter 9.I–II. Bruised ends of wood chips, as formed in normal chipping, and especially with dull knives, cause the pulps from the kraft, and particularly from the sulfite process to have inferior paper strength properties. Such compressive damage is likely to involve loosening of the transition lamella from the main part of the secondary wall or even destroy the hydrogen bonding locally in so-called slip planes of the main secondary wall. Thereby the latter is allowed to swell more freely, and chemical degradation will occur on the paper strength-bearing elements thus exposed. Similarly, subjecting either Asplund or groundwood pulp to either kraft or acid sulfite cooking leads to excessive degradation and low paper strength, and mechanical damage to the soft chips during the cooking, e.g. by using tumbling digesters, also decreases the strength properties of the resultant pulp. These phenomena have caused considerable difficulties in achieving an acceptable paper pulp quality by continuous cooking of kraft (98, 146, 155a), neutral sulfite (82) and acid sulfite (155b) pulp. The problem of discharging an undamaged pulp can only be solved by decreasing the discharge temperature, not by limiting the mechanical treatment, as obviously already fairly small forces cause sufficient exposition of the fiber walls to chemical damage. No analytical differences in the pulps before and after such damage could be detected, which indicates that only very concentrated local damage to the strength-bearing elements occurs.

The individual fiber strength average was, however, shown to decrease significantly for sulfite pulps when the wood was compression-damaged before cooking (69a), whereas the interfiber bonding strength and bonded area remained unchanged for the papers prepared. This represents direct experimental evidence for the theory that the compression damage phenomena involve very local weakening of the fiber wall, which cannot be expected to show up in any average figures for chemical composition, DP etc. However, the individual fiber strength of undamaged sulfite and kraft fibers was shown to be equal, which means that the differences in paper strength between sulfite and kraft, which exists also for undamaged wood, has to be sought in bonding strength, bonding area and fiber flexibility differences. An investigation on the shear strength of individual fiber–fiber contacts indicated roughly the same unit shear stress at failure, 30 kp/cm², for sulfite as for kraft fibers (114a). Since the average bonded area per interfiber contact was higher, $2.1.10^{-5}$ cm², for kraft as compared to $1.3.10^{-5}$ cm² for sulfite, the average shearing load per interfiber contact was about 50% higher for kraft. Beating only slightly influenced these results. The bond strength for kraft pulps cooked to different yields and then delignified was on the other hand found to decrease linearly with the yields of the delignified pulps, from about 70 kp/mm² for summerwood holocellulose fibers to 30 kp/mm² for summerwood kraft fibers of the lowest yield (107a). The corresponding figures for springwood fibers were 27–18 kp/mm². The fiber strength was also found to decrease with the yield, when measured in absolute terms, but to remain constant in specific terms, about 85 kp/mm² for summerwood and 40 kp/mm² for springwood fibers of loblolly pine, until the very last stages of cooking, where (probably because of over-cooking) the fiber strength values decreased. Thus, there is a definite influence on the bond strength from the hemicellulose content, as also previously indicated by opacity measurements (126), which corroborates the vast literature on the influence of the hemicellulose content on the paper strength. The influence of beating on the bonding is likely to be considerably larger for summerwood fibers, which are stiffer than the springwood fibers (159a). Kraft fibers are about as flexible as sulfite fibers, when well delignified, but much stiffer in the semichemical region, probably because the sulfonated lignin of the sulfite semichemical pulps allows far better access for the water molecules to the carbohydrates (150a).

The causes of summerwood fibers being twice as strong as springwood fibers, also per unit area, are probably morphological (102a), such as the more well-developed pits in springwood fibers. An interesting observation is the decrease in individual fiber strength upon the successive extraction of hemicelluloses (102a), which may indicate that the hemicellulose content of a fiber is important not only for its paper-bonding ability but also for its internal strength. However, the phenomenon may also be caused by a weakening of the fiber structure by swelling in the extracting lye, especially since the specific fiber strength is not materially affected by hemicellulose removal in kraft cooking, as discussed above.

To conclude, the paper strength properties of pulps depend on the morphological, physical and chemical character of the raw material and on the changes in these characters occurring in the various pulping processes as well as in the subsequent beating process. Of these characters, fiber length and wall thickness, the fragmentation or weakening of the fibers and microfibrils, the DP's of the cellulose and especially the hemicelluloses, the residual content of hydrophobic lignin and hydrophilic hemicelluloses, are the most essential. Figures 21.16–17 show some of the conventional paper

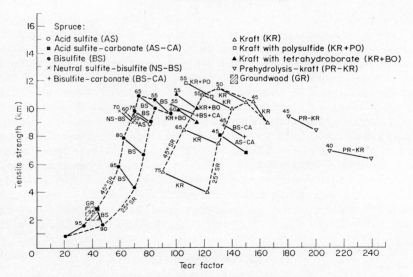

Fig. 21.16. Tensile–tear strength relation in the 25–45 °SR region for spruce pulps of various degrees of delignification from various processes. Numbers indicate pulp yield (Rydholm *et al*)

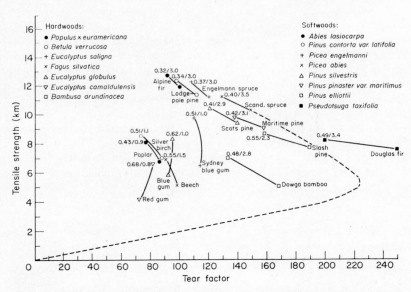

Fig. 21.17. Tensile–tear strength relation in the 25–45 °SR region for kraft pulps of various wood species. Numbers at each curve indicate basic density/average fiber length for the respective wood species (Rydholm *et al*)

1165

characteristics for a series of pulps of various yields, wood species and processes, to indicate what can be achieved with the materials and methods at our disposal. The superiority of the kraft process for the production of strong papers is clearly seen, but it is obvious that there are modifications of the conventional acid sulfite process which might be suited to the production of special grades of paper. The particular properties of the kraft pulp hemicelluloses and microfibrils make it more difficult to obtain transparent and low-porosity papers from kraft pulps. However, especially after satisfactory bleaching methods for kraft pulps have been developed, their outstanding rôle as the main paper raw material has been clearly borne out. The resilience and good printability of papers from groundwood pulp have been pointed out, as well as the stiffness and flat crush resistance of neutral sulfite semichemical pulp, which make these two pulp types suited to the special uses for newsprint paper and corrugating medium board respectively.

III. Dissolving Pulps

1. PROCESSES AND OPERATIONS USING DISSOLVING PULPS (129, 137, 147)

The most important consumer of dissolving pulps is the *viscose* process, which is an esterification carried out in alkaline medium. The *etherification processes* are also alkaline, whereas other *esterifications*, mainly *nitration* and *acetylation*, are performed in acid medium.

The alkaline processes (60, 61, 65, 76, 80, 169) involve *steeping* of the pulp in strong sodium hydroxide lye, followed by charging of the substituting reagent and a reaction period. In the case of some ethers, the reaction mixture may be sold as such, wet or dried, and other grades require further purification from the sodium salts of the reaction mixture. However, in the viscose process, the cellulose derivative, the xanthate, is not isolated as such but dissolved in lye and subsequently decomposed by sulfuric acid under *regeneration of unsubstituted cellulose*.

In order to make the cellulose hydroxyls accessible to the reagents, the cellulose is steeped in lye to form *alkali cellulose*. The chemistry of this process, which involves an intracrystalline swelling and the formation of an addition compound between cellulose, sodium hydroxide and water, according to the reaction:

$$R-OH + NaOH \longrightarrow R-OH-OH^- Na^+$$

has been dealt with in detail in Chapter 4.II. The activated cellulose hydroxyls are then able to react with carbon disulfide to xanthate:

$$R-OH-OH^- Na^+ + CS_2 \longrightarrow R-OCS_2^- Na^+ + H_2O$$

with sodium chlorocetate to carboxymethyl cellulose

$$R-OH-OH^- Na^+ + ClCH_2COO^- Na^+ \longrightarrow R-OCH_2COO^- Na^+ + NaCl + H_2O$$

with ethylene oxide to hydroxyethyl cellulose

$$R–OH–OH^- Na^+ + CH_2CH_2O \longrightarrow R–OCH_2CH_2OH + NaOH$$

and with alkyl chlorides to alkyl ethers, such as methyl or ethyl cellulose

$$R–OH–OH^- Na^+ + CH_3Cl \longrightarrow R–OCH_3 + NaCl + H_2O$$

At the same time, there are corresponding side reactions with sodium hydroxide and water:

$$NaOH + CS_2 \longrightarrow HOCS_2Na$$
$$NaOH + ClCH_2COONa \longrightarrow HOCH_2COONa + NaCl$$
$$HOH + CH_2CH_2O \longrightarrow HOCH_2CH_2OH$$
$$NaOH + CH_3Cl \longrightarrow HOCH_3 + NaCl$$

Of the substituting agent, 50–75% is utilized in the reaction with cellulose, whereas the rest is lost in the side reactions or remains unreacted after the reaction period. The cellulose ether groups are quite stable to hydrolysis, but the xanthate groups are hydrolyzed by both alkalis and acids:

$$R–OCS_2Na + HOH \longrightarrow R–OH + HOCS_2Na$$

under regeneration of cellulose. The sodium bidithiocarbonate is in alkali neutralized to dithiocarbonate, which is further decomposed, leaving trithiocarbonate, sulfide, and carbonate as the end products. In acid, carbon disulfide and hydrogen sulfide are formed during the xanthate decomposition, as well as sodium bisulfate from the alkali.

Flow sheets of the viscose process are presented in Figures 21.18–19. Alkali steeping, or mercerization, requires 18% NaOH concentration of lye, and is carried out either as *sheet steeping* in hydraulic presses with perforated steel plates in batches of up to 1 ton of cellulose sheets, vertically inserted, or as *slurry steeping*, where a slurry of fibers in lye is prepared. The former operation is batchwise, and the excess lye is removed by draining, followed by expelling with a plunge. The slurry steeping operation is continuous and is followed by continuous pressing of the slurry in various

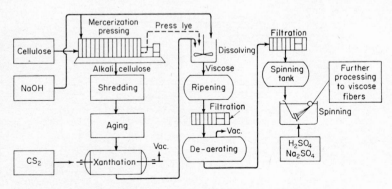

Fig. 21.18. 'Classical' viscose process (Rånby–Rydholm)

types of machinery, such as perforated-roll presses or vacuum filters equipped with press rolls. A small amount of carbohydrates dissolve in the lye and leave the system with the press lye. A large part of the steeping lye is recirculated for re-use.

After steeping and pressing, the alkali cellulose contains about 30% cellulose and 15% NaOH. It is then shredded, either batchwise in cooled sigma-blade shredders, or continuously in disk shredders, to small crumbs, a suitable form for the *aging* and *xanthation* operations. Aging is a controlled degradation of the cellulose molecules by air oxygen at 15–40°C (in exceptional cases up to 60°C) for a few hours or a few days. The reaction mechanism of aging was dealt with in Chapter 4.II. The DP is reduced from 1,000–1,500 in the pulp to about 400–600 in the aged alkali cellulose. Xanthation is then performed in rotating drums, called churns or barattes, or in a modified type of sigma-blade shredder, whereby 300–350 kg ptp CS_2 are charged. About 3 hours are required at 20–35°C to give a DS (degree of substitution) of 0.4–0.5 in the cellulose xanthate, which is colored yellow from thiocarbonate by-products. The product, still in fiber crumb form, is then dissolved in lye to give *viscose*, orange in color, which contains about 5–8% NaOH and 6–9% cellulose in the form of xanthate. Dissolution is performed in vessels equipped with paddle stirrers. The viscose is *ripened, filtered* and *de-aerated* prior to the regeneration. Ripening is controlled by measurements of the changes in viscosity and salt tolerance and interrupted at a definite stage. During the ripening the dissolution of the xanthate is completed and a certain uniformation of the distribution of the substituents is likely to occur through hydrolysis and re-xanthation. However, because of the side reactions the DS will slowly decrease until finally gelation of the cellulose molecules occurs. Well before that stage, the viscose must be used. To remove gel particles and impurities, the viscose is filtered two or three times through cotton or PVC cloth in filter presses. This operation is one of the bottle-necks of

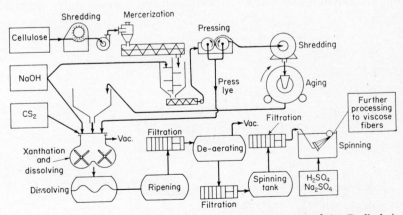

Fig. 21.19. Continuous (or semi-continuous) viscose processes (Rånby–Rydholm)

any viscose plant and is very sensitive to pulp quality. De-aeration is accomplished during the ripening period by applying vacuum to the storage tanks. Finally, the viscose is filtered through ceramic candle filters immediately prior to extrusion.

Regeneration of the cellulose is then obtained by extrusion of the viscose into coagulation baths, one or two in series, containing sulfuric acid and salts, such as sodium sulfate, bisulfate, and bisulfite, magnesium sulfate, ammonium sulfate and zinc sulfate. The composition of the baths varies with the effects desired. A fairly normal bath contains about 130 g/l H_2SO_4, 280 g/l Na_2SO_4, 15 g/l $ZnSO_4$ and 60 g/l of added glucose. Other components are frequently present in small amounts, such as quaternary ammonium salts, cyclohexylamine, etc. If two baths are used in series, the second one is acidic to complete the hydrolytic regeneration, whereas the first can be either acidic or mainly a salt bath, in which case the initial coagulation is predominantly a salting-out of cellulose xanthate. In the case of high-tenacity yarn spinning, a retarded coagulation of the core is desired, giving a possibility of stretching the filaments more extensively and thereby achieving a more uniform crystallinity of the final product. Heavy-metal salts, such as zinc sulfate, are thereby especially active as they form a skin of less soluble metal cellulose xanthate on the filament surface. The temperature of the coagulation baths is kept at around 50°C. The speed of spinning is around 100 m/min and the bath travel normally about 25 cm but may be considerably longer. The spinneret holes vary in diameter from 0.05 to 0.30 mm, normally 0.07 mm. The diameter of the filaments will also depend on the stretch applied. The number of filaments per thread varies from 10 to 1,000, in the case of rayon staple fiber up to 10,000.

Emerging from the coagulation bath, the yarn is stretched by godet wheels driven at the desired speed differential. The yarn is subsequently wound on a rotating bobbin or collected as a centrifugal cake in a rotating bucket. The bobbins or cakes are then subjected to finishing treatments, involving *washing* with water to remove spin bath components, *desulfuring* by sodium sulfide which is then removed by a new water wash, *bleaching* with sodium hypochlorite, additional water wash, drying, oiling and finally twisting and winding to cones for delivery. More recently, methods have been developed which involve continuous operation at all the finishing treatments of the moving yarn, until it is finally packaged onto a bobbin for delivery. The advantages are several, especially a more uniform drying of the yarn, which eventually results in a more uniform dyeing. The delivery of entire yarn beams has also been made possible, thus eliminating the warping operation for the textile mills and ensuring higher uniformity of the warp. In the production of staple fiber, the untwisted yarn from a number of spinnerets is collected to form a large bundle, or *tow*, which is then mechanically crimped and cut to short lengths, up to 60 mm but normally only about half, which will be used either alone or in mixture with other short fibers, to form *spun yarns*.

The manufacture of *cellophane* follows the same pattern as that of the textile yarns up to the stage of coagulation, although with small modifications in the lye handling system. The viscose is extruded through a slit, into one or two coagulation baths, the first of which may contain only salts and none of them zinc sulfate. The casting machines are generally only about 1 m wide but resemble in many ways a paper machine. The cellophane web passes through the usual finishing baths, one of which also contains glycerol or other plasticizers, and finally enters a dryer section. The thickness of a standard cellophane sheet of a basis weight 32 g/m^2 is about 0.02 mm. The speed of the casting machines is about 100 m/min. To decrease the hydrophility of the cellophane, it is subsequently dip coated into a solution of cellulose nitrate and wax, and dried. The rolls are thereafter rewound and cut to smaller rolls, for further modifications in the converting industry, such as laminating, printing, and combination with plastic films, metal foils, paper or board.

The production of *cellulose ethers* deviates in many respects from the operations of the viscose process. The reactor for the substitution process has to be specially adjusted according to the nature of the substituting agent. Chloracetic acid and ethylene oxide react with alkali cellulose at about the same conditions as does carbon disulfide, but the alkyl chlorides require higher temperatures and pressure vessels. As there is no possibility of redistributing the substituents in a more uniform manner as in the viscose process, a very intimate mixing of the etherifying agent with the alkali cellulose is vital. Sigma-blade shredders are sometimes used, but more radical deviations from the standard viscose operations are frequent, such as spraying a solution of the reagent to a fine-powdered cellulose, or adding a diluent such as ethanol or isopropyl alcohol to facilitate mixing. In such cases the conventional steeping stage is omitted and mixing of cellulose, diluent, lye and etherifying agent is carried out in one piece of equipment, a steam-jacketed stirring vessel.

Of the *acidic esterification processes* (53, 60, 105, 115, 116, 132, 169, 172), nitration yields products for explosives, lacquers, and plastics, and acetylation products for textiles, lacquers, and plastics. A water-soluble sulfate ester for thickening purposes, detergent additive, etc., has also been tried on a semi-commercial scale. In the nitration, the fibrous structure of the cellulose is virtually retained, although in a swollen state, whereas acetylation involves the dissolution of the cellulose acetate in the reaction mixture. Because the solubility of the ester in various technical solvents is highly dependent on the DS, the latter is carefully controlled. As maximal solubility in the less expensive solvents is obtained in the neighborhood of DS 2.0 rather than 3.0, the triesters are prepared only in exceptional cases. For nitrates, this can be done by adjusting the composition of the nitration bath, whereas in the acetylation an even distribution of the acetate groups can only be achieved by carrying the esterification to the triester stage and then hydrolyzing the dissolved product to the diester stage, after the addition of some water. The difference between the two processes may depend on the fact that acetylation proceeds more heterogeneously in the earlier stages, making the solubility properties of

1170

the directly prepared diester inferior. Details of the esterification reactions are given in Chapter 4.II. They probably involve the formation of nitronium and acetylium cations through dehydration of the charged chemicals by sulfuric acid, and subsequent reaction with the cellulose hydroxyls

$$R\text{–}OH + NO_2^+ \longrightarrow R\text{–}ONO_2 + H^+$$
$$R\text{–}OH + CH_3CO^+ \longrightarrow R\text{–}OCOCH_3 + H^+.$$

The operations of *nitration* involve: preparation of the dry cellulose, nitration, removal of spent acid, stabilization and viscosity control, washing and, finally, replacement of the water by alcohol. The operations are influenced by the fact that cellulose nitrate is highly inflammable in the dry state. Small units for the operation of the more dangerous stages are necessary. Batches of 15–20 kg cellulose, disintegrated by hammer-milling and dried to a controlled moisture content, are mixed in small vessels with about 1 ton of nitration acid, a mixture of sulfuric acid, nitric acid and water in the approximate proportions of 3 : 1 : 1. The reaction temperature is 10–30°C, depending on the viscosity grade desired. Nitrate for explosives requires low temperature to preserve a high DP. The main esterification is complete in a few minutes, but the reaction period is usually prolonged to 30–40 minutes to ensure uniformity. The spent acid is removed by centrifugation and recirculated after adjustment of its composition. After centrifugation, the cake of cellulose nitrate is dumped into water for washing and then boiled with water to remove sulfate ester groups which otherwise tend to make the nitrate unstable. If low-viscosity lacquer grade nitrates are desired, the digestion with water is carried out at 150°C to achieve hydrolytic degradation of the glucosidic bonds. A slight hypochlorite bleach is then performed and the bleached nitrate pressed to blocks, through which ethanol is forced to displace the water.

Processing of cellulose nitrate to the final products is carried out in various ways. For lacquers, the nitrate is dissolved in ester solvents, eventually extended with inert diluents such as aromatic hydrocarbons. In the case of explosives, the alcohol-moist nitrate is gelatinized with ether, acetone or nitroglycerin, and pressed through a macaroni press. For celluloid plastics, especially films, the usual plasticizer is camphor, added to about 25% along with an alcohol and kneaded in a mixer. Afterwards, the dough is pressed into blocks, sliced and dried.

The operations of *acetylation* involve disintegrating the cellulose to flocks, drying and then pretreating them with acetic acid, esterification to 'primary' or triacetate on the addition of a diluent, acetic anhydride and a catalyst, usually sulfuric acid, further hydrolysis to 'secondary' acetate on the addition of water to the reaction mixture, precipitation of the secondary acetate by further water addition, and washing of the flakes obtained. After hammer-milling of the cellulose, the flocks are dried and conditioned to a controlled moisture content and then wetted with acetic acid, up to 1 t ptp, in a mixer for 1–2 hours. The diluent subsequently added is either more acetic acid or methylene dichloride, 2.5–5 t ptp, and the amount of acetic anhydride is about 3 t ptp. The reaction mixture is stirred together with 10 kg ptp sulfuric acid catalyst in reactors taking batches of up to 3.5 t cellulose. The reaction temperature is about 40°C and the esterification time about 6 hours. During the reaction, all hydroxyl groups are esterified mainly to acetate, but small amounts of sulfate groups are formed from the catalyst as well. These have to be removed in the subsequent hydrolysis together with some of the acetate groups, to produce a stable cellulose acetate of desired DS, usually about 2.3. The hydrolysis is usually carried out in the same reactor as the esterification, whereafter the mixture is further diluted with water in a precipitator stirring tank. The precipitated flakes are then counter-currently washed on a band filter, centrifuged and dried. The dilute acetic acid is recovered for regeneration of concentrated acetic acid and anhydride.

Cellulose acetate is either delivered in the flake form or further processed to fibers, foils, lacquers or plastics. It is thereby usually dissolved in acetone to a solution containing about 25 % polymer, which is filtered and spun or cast to its final form. During the latter operations, the acetone is evaporated and subsequently recovered for re-use. In the case of films, plasticizers such as dialkylphthalate are added to the acetone solution before casting. Plasticized cellulose acetate is also delivered in the form of powder, rods or sheets for further processing to plastics. The spinning operations, so-called dry spinning, deviate from those described for the viscose process. The spinnerets are enclosed in a hot-air cabinet. The candle filters prior to the spinnerets are heated to supply part of the heat required for the evaporation of the solvent. The hot air is introduced at the bottom of the cabinet and leaves at the top for the acetone recovery unit, enriched with acetone. The yarn, somewhat stretched in the cabinet, leaves at the top at a speed of 100–1,000 m/min, thus considerably faster than in viscose spinning. It is then lubricated and finally received by a bobbin, or collected to a tow for cutting to acetate staple fiber. In special cases, such as for certain films and textiles, a higher DS, up to 3, gives more desirable properties. The solvent used for spinning or casting of such products cannot be acetone. Methylene dichloride or other chlorinated hydrocarbons, sometimes mixed with other solvents, are then used.

2. RELATIONSHIP OF PULP COMPOSITION TO PROCESSING AND PRODUCT PROPERTIES

A. Alkaline processing of dissolving pulp

The processing properties of dissolving pulps for the viscose and etherification processes depend on the physical state and chemical composition of the pulp. The problem of characterization of a rayon pulp is complicated, and there are several approaches to solve it, varying in the degree of exactitude and the costs involved in the characterization. One is that of *chemical analysis*, not only of the main components but also of the impurities. Directly related to the viscose process is the *alphacellulose determination* (cf. Chapter 20), which is always carried out on market dissolving pulp and frequently used for quality gradation and price fixation. Related to that analysis are *alkali solubility* at well-defined lye concentrations, and *rayon process yield* determination. To characterize the solubles further, the separation into *beta-* and *gammacellulose* fractions is often used. The main components are further characterized by *viscosity determination* for average DP and *copper number* (or alternatively *hot alkali solubility* or *perte à la soude*) and *carboxyl content* for reducing and acidic groups respectively. An extended characterization, seldom used for routine control, is *chromatographic analysis* of the sugar components (or more frequently only *pentosan determination*), and dissolution followed by fractional precipitation to determine the *DP distribution*. As the quality of dissolving pulps is closely related to some of its impurities, even routine control involves the determination of *ash content*, *silica*, traces of *metals*, such as *Ca, Mg, Fe, Cu, Mn, Na*, and *extractives* (or *resin*) content.

In addition to chemical analysis, a considerable number of rayon pulp producers also control some of the processing properties of the pulp by simulating the operations of the viscose plant on a small scale. It is fairly common to carry the conversion of the pulp as far as viscose filtration, with standardized conditions of steeping, shredding, aging, xanthation, dissolution, viscose ripening and filtration. As quality figures from such tests usually emerge *swelling capacity* and *floating tendency* of the sheet, *brightness* and *speed of aging* of the alkali cellulose, and *filtrability of the viscose* at one or two compositions.

To carry the testing beyond the viscose filtrability stage involves considerable labor and capital expenditure. Some of the largest manufacturers, however, test their new pulp grades by extensive *spinning experiments* and *testing the properties of the final yarn*. The results are then obtained in the form of various figures for *spinnability of the viscose* and *optical and mechanical properties of the yarn*.

Even the most elaborate testing is not sufficient to predict the performance of a pulp in a specific viscose plant, and the introduction of a pulp to the large scale has to be followed up carefully. Because of that and the expensive nature of some of the laboratory tests, a great deal of study has been devoted to the correlations between the behavior of the pulp in the viscose plant and its chemical composition and physical state as given by analysis. These correlations will now be considered in some detail.

Although lately fluff pulp drying has also been developed for rayon pulps used in continuous *slurry steeping*, most rayon pulps are still delivered in the sheet form. In the case of slurry steeping, the dominating demand on the pulp sheets is ready dispersibility in the mercerizing lye with no formation of nodules or fiber knots (24). Alkali *steeping in the sheet form*, which is still the dominating steeping operation, requires the fulfilling of several conditions (148, 149, 191, cf. 2):

(1) *Uniform absorption of mercerizing lye*, for which good sheet formation is a prerequisite.

(2) *Optimal and uniform rate of lye absorption*, which means that the sheet should be easily wetted by the lye (no hornified surface structure due

to overdrying, etc.) and a linear vertical rate of absorption, which is not too low and not excessively high in comparison with normal filling rate of lye to the steeping press. Too low a rate will decrease the capacity of the press, and a very high rate of absorption will cause excessive 'wicking', which means that the rising front of lye in the sheet will be much in advance of the rising lye level outside the sheet. Thereby the sheets will be penetrated by a lye which will eventually become weaker owing to preferential absorption of alkali in the previous regions. That will increase the danger of incomplete mercerization of the pulp. If the rate of lye absorption is non-uniform due to non-uniform sheet formation, there may occur areas of incomplete penetration and entrapped air. Incomplete mercerization will cause 'yellow spots', which are detrimental to the viscose filtrability.

(3) *Efficient displacement of air from the individual sheets* by the entering lye. If less than about 70% of the air is displaced, the sheet tends to float in the steeping press, with excessive wicking as a result (148, 149). Some presses are equipped to keep such sheets down in the lye, but incomplete penetration and mercerization are not entirely prevented. The most efficient way of eliminating sheet floating tendency is to compact the sheet by pressing. Both pressing at the wet end and bale pressing of the dry pulp sheets help to compact the sheet (15), but the best effect is achieved by smoothing press rolls in the drying section, at around 60–80% dry content (191).

(4) *Satisfactory penetration of lye between the sheets.* Excessive swelling will cause adjacent sheets to touch each other too compactly, and prevent the flow of lye between them. This leads to entrapped air pockets and the formation of yellowing areas (11, 148, 149). Decrease in the number of sheets will decrease the capacity of the press and is therefore no solution to the problem. An embossed pattern, especially of the continuous stripes type made at the wet end by ribbing rolls or showers, facilitates the flow of lye between the sheets.

(5) *Satisfactory mechanical behavior of the sheets in the press and on discharging the press.* Sheets which are too thin, or non-uniform, or contain too many short fibers, tend to slump and split in the press, produce uneven pressing, wet edges, break on handling after pressing, etc. Non-uniform sheet dimensions also cause wet sheet edges on pressing. Short-fibered hardwood pulps tend to give more handling problems than long-fibered pulps, partly because of the lower strength of the mercerized sheets (183).

In order to control the steeping properties of pulp sheets, their weight, bulk, floating tendency at various lye filling rates, swelling tendency, mechanical strength before and after steeping, etc., are determined. It is often stressed that the behavior of the pulp during steeping will greatly influence the subsequent operations (148, 149, 183, 191). Some non-uniformities are unavoidable, e.g. that summerwood fibers are more resistant to pressing after steeping than springwood fibers (77). In a few respects, sheet steeping is less sensitive to the fiber properties than slurry steeping.

Thus, the capacity of some slurry steeping presses is adversely affected by the small-fiber fraction of the pulp (179).

The *shredding* properties of the steeped pulp are significantly dependent on the type of fiber (especially softwood–hardwood), which will influence the time required for optimal density of the shredded pulp. That in turn will affect the aging and xanthation operations.

Aging to a controlled DP level is naturally influenced by the average DP of the original pulp, i.e. pulp viscosity, as well as by its DP distribution. Sulfite pulps age more rapidly than prehydrolysis–kraft pulps of the same viscosity, and sulfite pulps which have been predominantly degraded in the cooking age somewhat faster than those degraded in the bleaching. As aging seems to give the most uniform degradation (12, 159, 167), a trend has appeared for sulfite pulps especially to be delivered at a higher viscosity (up to 60 cP TAPPI) than normally (20 cP) (140). To accelerate the aging of such pulps, as well as of the slower-aging kraft pulps, oxidation catalysts have been applied (119), such as Ni, Co (40), and Mn (141). They are usually added to the shredder in amounts of about 0.5 p.p.m. In exceptional cases they have been added to the pulp already at the drying machine by the pulp manufacturer. The occurrence of such metals as impurities in the pulp has to be carefully controlled, as well as the content of iron and copper, which also, although to a less extent, act as aging catalysts (96). Contaminating calcium and magnesium ions do not influence the rate of aging but are detrimental to sheet pressing and some subsequent operations, partly because of the formation of insoluble carbonates (5, 97). The metal impurities of the pulp are normally combined to the carboxylate ions of the carbohydrates and are virtually removed in the last stage of pulp processing by acidification to pH 3–4, immediately prior to the sheeting machine (cf. Chapter 16).

Xanthation and dissolution are influenced by the reactivity of the pulp, whereby deficiencies in these operations, as well as in the previous stages (especially alkali steeping), are discovered predominantly in the *filterability* of the prepared and ripened viscose. Macroheterogeneities in the substitution are caused by ball formation and clogging of the xanthate to the walls of the reaction vessels, whereby some of the pulp properties, such as response to the previous shredding operation or excessive resin content, are of importance. Some hardwood pulps have given rise to difficulties in that respect. The amount of carbon disulfide applied in the xanthation (185, 189) as well as of sodium hydroxide (99, 106, 183) added to the dissolvers, determines the ease of filtration of the viscose. However, different pulps require different amounts of chemicals to give a satisfactory viscose, and some pulps never will, despite excessive additions of chemicals. Apart from the influence of some impurities, such as resin and silica, which greatly affect the filterability and have to be closely controlled (cf. below), this depends on the reactivity of the carbohydrates and the alkali solubility of the corresponding xanthates. The formation of 'hornified' structures on drying of pulps rich in hemicelluloses is often assumed to be the reason for decrease in reactivity, whereas suitable preparations of mannan and xylan have been found to xanthate readily (134a). Such components are especially undesirable, which become sufficiently affixed not to be dissolved in the mercerizing lye, such as some of the xylan of kraft paper pulps (195) or glucomannan of specially prepared sulfite pulps (3). They cause decreased reactivity in the viscose (as well as acetate) processes. Excessive amounts of hemicelluloses which do dissolve in the mercerizing lye are also undesirable as they accumulate there and cause steeping troubles (114, 156). Further consequences of too high a hemicellulose content of the pulp are contamination of the spinning bath and inferior end product qualities. Dissolving pulps therefore generally contain less than 10% hemicelluloses, the removal being achieved by a combined treatment of acid hydrolysis and alkaline 'peeling off' reaction. On the other hand, processing properties are not improved by an extreme removal of hemicelluloses, and cotton linters, the dissolving pulp with the highest cellulose purity, does not have very good processing properties. These difficulties are probably related to the physical state of the pulp, and a fair amount of low-molecular components aid the swelling of the pulp in the mercerization. However, the lye swelling of a pulp can also be improved by additions to the lye, as well as by temperature adjustment.

The influence of resin extractives on the pulp quality is pronounced. Too much resin will cause clogging in the xanthation, haze in the viscose, filtration and spinning troubles, as well as a yellowish yarn, but when the resin content falls below about 0.15%, filtration troubles occur because of lowered surface activity (158). Addition of small amounts of synthetic surface active agents overcomes that deficiency (95, 142). Viscose pulp normally contains 0.15–0.40% extractives, the content being regulated mainly in the bleachery. Often the short parenchymatic cells, which contain a large part of the pulp resin, are removed by fractionation (48), to some benefit for the viscose filtrability (9, 160, 166, 184). The influence of silica on the processing properties is most important (157, 189) and requires special attention in pulp mills with inferior water supplies. The content is regulated mainly by water treatment and to some extent by vortex cleaners, and should be kept in the range of 20–200 ppm.

The pulp qualities will have to consider not only the viscose processing properties but also the *properties of the final products* and the closely related *spinning properties*. Thereby various end products require widely differing pulp grades. In some cases, pulp brightness, or rather purity from colored contaminants in the final product, is important, especially for textile purposes, whereas e.g. high-tenacity rayon for cord webs is less sensitive to discoloration. On the other hand, to allow for the stretch necessary in the spinning of high-tenacity yarns, as well as to achieve a high-quality end product, it is important to have a pulp of a very special molecular composition (8, 10, 29, 44, 45). The amount of low-molecular hemicelluloses has to be very limited, and the molecular weight distribution of the cellulose fraction should be such as to give a virtually homogeneous DP distribution in the rayon, with a minimum of low- and high-molecular chains. As pointed out previously, the hydrolytic degradation during the sulfite cook is thereby the least satisfactory degradation method, and the most suitable DP distribution in the final yarn is obtained with either highly purified high-viscosity sulfite pulps or preferably pre-hydrolysis–kraft pulps, the latter thereby being sometimes subjected to cold alkali purification in the bleachery.

The chemical reactivity of the various hemicelluloses, disregarding accessibility, in the viscose and etherification processes has not been studied sufficiently, but can be assumed not to deviate widely from the reactivity of cellulose. Some differences have been noticed. For instance, in the carboxymethylation of beech xylan to various degrees of substitution in the range 0.1–0.9, no doubly-substituted xylose unit was found (163). No primary hydroxyl is present, and a considerable quantity of the 2–hydroxyls are substituted by uronic acid groups.

In the production of cellophane and low-tenacity yarns and staple fiber, pulp grades of 89–91% alphacellulose content are usually sufficient, normally supplied at a viscosity of 20 cP TAPPI (DP about 1,000). These are mainly sulfite pulps from both softwoods and hardwoods. To produce high-tenacity yarns and wet-strength staple fiber, the alphacellulose content has to be higher, 93–95% for intermediate grades and 96–98% for the highest grades. The viscosity of such pulps is less standardized and frequently below 20 cP in the case of prehydrolysis–kraft pulps (from softwoods as well as hardwoods) and much higher, 50–70 cP, for the purified sulfite pulps. The pulp brightness is often below 90% GE for a cord or cellophane pulp but normally 92–95% GE in pulps for textile purposes. Table 21.4 gives some examples of the analytical data of some commercial

Table 21.4. Commercial types of viscose and acetate pulp and their properties

Pulping process	Sulfite						Prehydrolysis–kraft			
Purification	Hot	Hot	Hot	Hot	Hot–cold	Hot	No	Cold	Cold	No
Wood species	Spruce					Birch	Pine	Pine	Gum	Gum
Pulp type	Celloph. and staple	Reg. ten. yarn	Poly-nosic fiber	High ten. yarn	Ace-tate	Celloph. and staple	High ten. yarn	High ten. yarn	High ten. yarn	Staple fiber
Viscosity, cP T.	20	20	20	55	40	20	20	20	20	9
Alphacellu-lose, %	90	92	94	96	97.5	91	96	97	98	94
R_{18}, %	92.5	94.2	96.1	97.0	98.5	93.3	97.4	98.4	98.7	97.6
R_{10}, %	87.5	90.0	91.8	95.1	96.7	88.7	95.4	97.6	97.0	96.0
R, %	90.0	92.1	94.0	96.0	97.6	91.0	96.4	98.0	97.9	96.8
Cellulose, %	92.5	94.0	96.0	96.5	98.0	93.0	97.0	98.5	98.0	97.0
Glucomannan, %	4.0	3.5	2.0	1.5	1.2	3.0	1.0	0.5	0.5	0.5
Glucuron-oxylan, %	3.5	2.5	2.0	2.0	0.8	4.0	2.0	1.0	1.5	2.5
Resin, %	0.30	0.20	0.20	0.15	0.05	0.25	0.02	0.05	0.15	0.11
Brightness, % GE	93	93	92	92	94	94	88	87	91	89

rayon pulps of various grades. The etherification processes generally seem to be less sensitive to pulp quality than the viscose process, partly because of less sensitive end uses.

B. Acid processing of dissolving pulp

A considerable amount of work has been devoted to determining the quality of nitrate and acetate pulps and correlating the results with the analytical data of the pulp. As the technical versions of the acetate process vary considerably more than those of the viscose process, it is difficult to develop a test method which yields a generally significant evaluation of acetate pulps. Several methods have been published (e.g. 16, 89, 118, 135, 168). They involve pretreatment of the pulp, acetylation with anhydride diluted with acetic acid or methylene dichloride, and usually sulfuric acid catalyst in small amounts, followed by an evaluation of the color, clarity and viscosity of the triacetate dope. A more complete evaluation includes the preparation of the secondary acetate and determination of the properties of its acetone solution or of the yarn spun from it, or of plastics prepared from the acetate. The most severe criticisms of a pulp concern *discoloration, haze* or *bad filtrability*, and *'false viscosity'* of the solution. The latter term applies to a phenomenon frequently encountered where the concentrated acetone solution displays a higher viscosity than is to be expected from the DP of the acetate and its viscosity in dilute solution. In nitrate pulps containing low-molecular carbohydrates, their oxidation will increase the consumption of nitric acid and thus the cost of manufacture.

Acid processing generally requires pulps of higher purity than the alkaline processes. On the whole, the nitrate process, at least for most end uses, seems to be less critical to pulp quality than the acetate process, and pulp grades down to 92% alphacellulose content are used. Nitrate pulps for explosives, however, demand an extremely pure pulp, usually cotton or cotton linters or cold-alkali refined wood pulps of 98% alphacellulose content. Acetate pulps normally have an alphacellulose content of 95.0–96.5%, of the hot-alkali refined sulfite pulp type. In most respects apart from economic considerations, however, cotton linters is the preferred raw material for acetate (e.g. 16, 89, 109, 118, 145), especially for acetate plastics, which are particularly sensitive to discoloration and haze.

The cause of the inferiority of wood pulps is complex, as is evident from the simple fact that a kraft paper pulp of 86% alphacellulose content, a prehydrolysis–kraft pulp of 97% alphacellulose content and a cold-alkali refined sulfite pulp of 98% alphacellulose content are all inferior to both cotton linters and normal acetate wood pulp. There is an influence from the *non-cellulosic components* as well as from the *physical state of the cellulose*. Inorganic components are undesirable. The silicate content of prehydrolysis–kraft pulps from straw has been correlated to the haze of the acetate prepared (90). At very hazy acetates, the isolated haze fractions were found to contain much calcium and magnesium, combined to residual sulfate ester groups and especially to uronic acid groups (17), causing

1178

filtration troubles. Calcium has also been found to cause false viscosity in nitrates (152) and acetates (52, 109a), probably by interconnecting carboxyl or sulfate ester groups of separate polymer chains. For the same reason, uronic acid groups as well as excessive amounts of carboxyl groups formed during the bleaching should be avoided. Haze and false viscosity in acetate and nitrate are also produced by the two dominating hemicellulose components, xylan and glucomannan (17, 89, 138, 170, 175, 193), of which small amounts are very persistent through the cooking, purification and esterification processes (52, 64, 120). It is interesting to note that the diesters of xylan alone have been indicated to be insoluble in the usual solvents (78, 136), which should be a logical explanation for some of the difficulties, e.g. haze and filterability. However, in the case of false viscosity, mannan but not xylan has been found to be the cause, as judged from both correlating the mannose content of pulps with the viscosity anomalies (175), and by adding mannan to pulps before acetylation (193). Xylan added in the same manner did not lead to false viscosity. Glucomannan esters are, however, very soluble in the usual solvents.

The color of the acetate is influenced by many factors, such as the reaction conditions. The pulp quality is also important in this respect, and residual lignin, resin and degradation products of hemicelluloses and cellulose all contribute to the discoloration (125). Through the introduction of chlorine dioxide bleaching, a great improvement has been achieved in these respects.

The influence of the physical state of the cellulose on the reactivity in the acetylation process is considerable. First of all, the cellulose sheet has to be soft in order to facilitate disintegration. The latter does not aim at complete separation of the individual fibers, as this would increase the amount of diluent necessary in the process, and it is therefore important that the sheet fragments left after disintegration are fluffy enough to allow complete and rapid penetration. The sheet structure is regulated at the press section of the drying machine. The state of the fiber wall also has to be considered. Satisfactory penetration of the fiber wall by the esterification baths is necessary. In the case of nitration, the swelling power of the acid is sufficient, but for acetylation non-uniformities often occur in this respect. The pretreatment with acetic acid to wet the pulp serves to eliminate them, but satisfactory activation is not always achieved. Cold-alkali purified sulfite pulps, which have been strongly swollen and subsequently dried, seem to develop a more dense structure of the fiber wall due to formation of more hydrogen bonds. They turn out to be inferior as acetate pulps in spite of their high purity (e.g. 89), unless the pretreatment is prolonged, or the cold-alkali purification preceded or followed by a hot alkali stage, which seems to decrease the possibilities of intrafiber contacts, probably by removing some of the less well-ordered cellulose. Wetting agents have been suggested to improve the behavior of wood pulps in the pretreatment and acetylation stages (143), preferably added to the pulp prior to drying. It is also important that the accessibility of the hydroxyl groups in the fiber wall is sufficient to give a comparatively rapid acetylation, because of the acetolytic degradation of the cellulose at the glucosidic bonds occurring during the reaction period. This degradation, which is followed in its later course by viscosity control tests, must be interrupted at a definite stage by the addition of dilute acetic acid. At the same time, esterification is interrupted and should therefore have reached the triester stage well before the acetolysis has come to the critical point. To some extent, this problem can be solved by increasing the pulp viscosity, and a definite trend has occurred towards higher viscosities from, previously, 20–30 cP TAPPI to 40–60 cP. However, a good reactivity of the pulp is imperative for many other reasons.

Table 21.4 gives the analytical data of a commercial acetate pulp.

REFERENCES

1. Aiken, W. H., *Ind. Eng. Chem.*, **35,** 1206 (1943).
2. Anderson, A. W., and R. W. Swinehart, *Tappi*, **39,** 548 (1956).
3. Annergren, G. E., and S. A. Rydholm, *Svensk Papperstid.*, **62,** 737 (1959); **63,** 591 (1960).
4. Anon., *Paper Trade J.*, **118,** No. 5, 13 (1944).
5. Anthoni, B., and H. Sihtola, *Paperi Puu*, **38,** 521, 571 (1956).
6. Asunmaa, S., and B. Steenberg, *Svensk Papperstid.*, **61,** 686 (1958).
7. Atchison, J. E., *Paper Trade J.*, **116,** No. 22, 243 (1943).
8. Bachlott, D. D., *et al.*, *Tappi*, **38,** 503 (1955).
9. Bandel, W., *Papier*, **11,** 238 (1957).
10. Bartunek, R., *Papier*, **4,** 451 (1950).
11. Beaudry, J. P., *Pulp Paper Mag. Can.*, **57,** No. 8, 109 (1956).
12. Björkqvist, K. J., Medd. CCL (Stockholm), **B 36** (1957) and unpublished.
13. Bletzinger, J. C., *Ind. Eng. Chem.*, **35,** 471 (1943).
14. Bolam, F., ed., *Fundamentals of Papermaking Fibres*, St. Winifred's, Kenley, Surrey, England, 1958.
15. Borgen, G. L., *Norsk Skogind.*, **9,** 437 (1955).
16. Borgin, K., *Norsk Skogind.*, **5,** 69 (1951); **6,** 373 (1952); *Tappi*, **36,** 284 (1953).
17. Bradway, K. E., *Tappi*, **37,** 440 (1954).
18. Bray, M. W., and C. E. Curran, *Tech. Assoc. Papers*, **21,** 458 (1938).
19. Brown, J. C., *Tappi*, **33,** 130 (1950).
20. Brown, R. B., *Paper Trade J.*, **95,** No. 13, 145 (1932).
21. Browning, B. L., *Tappi*, **33,** 410 (1950).
22. Browning, B. L., and P. S. Baker, *Tappi*, **33,** 99 (1950).
23. Bucher, H., and L. P. Widerkehr-Scherb, *Morphologie und Struktur von Holzfasern*, Attisholz 1947.
24. Buurman, A., and M. J. Maurice, *Svensk Papperstid.*, **58,** 35 (1955).
25. Campbell, W. B., *Paper Trade J.*, **95,** No. 8, 29 (1932); **100,** No. 7, 35 (1935); *Tappi*, **32,** 265 (1949).
26. Carroll, M., and S. G. Mason, *Can. J. Technol.*, **30,** 321 (1952).
27. Casciani, F., and G. K. Storin, *Tappi*, **33,** 588 (1950).
28. Casey, J. P., *Pulp and Paper*, Interscience, New York 1960, Vol. 1, p. 407.
29. Charles, F. R., *Tappi*, **37,** 148 (1954).

30. Chidester, G. H., et al., Paper Trade J., **107**, No. 4, 36, No. 13, 24 (1938); **109**, No. 13, 36 (1939).
31. Clark, G. L., Tappi, **33**, 108, 384 (1950).
32. Clark, J. d'A., Paper Trade J., **97**, No. 26, 25 (1933); Paper Ind. Paper World, **25**, 382, 507 (1943); and in E. Ott and H. M. Spurlin, eds., Cellulose and Cellulose Derivatives, 2nd Ed., Interscience, New York 1954, Part II, p. 621.
33. Clark, J. d'A., Paper Trade J., **110**, No. 9, 122 (1940).
34. Clark, J. d'A., Paper Trade J., **115**, No. 26, 328 (1942); Pulp Paper Mag. Can., **44**, No. 2, 92 (1943).
35. Clark, J. d'A., Paper Trade J., **118**, No. 1, 29 (1944); TAPPI Standard T 231 m.
36. Clark, J. d'A., Pulp Paper Mag. Can., **49**, No. 10, 101 (1948).
36a. Clark, J. d'A., Tappi, **45**, 628 (1962).
37. Corte, H., Tappi, **35**, 124 (1952).
38. Cottrall, L. G., Paper-Maker, **105**, No. 5, T.S. 25 (1943).
39. Cottrall, L. G., Tappi, **33**, 471 (1950).
40. Courtaulds' Inc., U.S. Pat. 2,542,492 (1951).
40a. Croon, I., and B. Enström, Tappi, **44**, 870 (1961); Svensk Papperstid., **65**, 595, 693 (1962).
41. Curran, C. E., Paper Trade J., **103**, No. 11, 36 (1936).
42. Curran, C. E., Paper Trade J., **106**, No. 23, 40 (1938).
43. Dadswell, H. E., and A. B. Wardrop, Pulp Paper, **33**, No. 4, 117 (1959).
44. Davis, W. E., Ind. Eng. Chem., **43**, 516 (1951).
45. Dörr, R. E., Angew. Chem., **53**, 292 (1940).
46. Doughty, R. H., Paper Trade J., **93**, No. 15, 44 (1931).
47. Doughty, R. H., Paper Trade J., **94**, No. 9, 114 (1932).
48. Dubach, M., and M. Rutishauser, Papier, **11**, 37 (1957).
49. Elston, R., unpublished.
50. Emerton, H. W., in F. Bolam, ref. 14, pp. 35, 431.
51. Emerton, H. W., et al., Tappi, **37**, 55 (1954).
52. Engelmann, H., Papier, **5**, 149 (1951).
53. Fabel, K., Nitrocellulose, Herstellung und Eigenschaften, Enke, Stuttgart 1950.
54. Forgacs, O. L., et al., in F. Bolam, ref. 14, p. 447.
54a. Forgacs, O. L., Tappi, **44**, 112 (1961).
54b. Forgacs, O. L., Pulp Paper Mag. Can., **64**, No. C, T89 (1963).
55. Forman, L. V., Tappi, **33**, 444 (1950).
56. Fowler, W. F., and W. M. Harlow, Paper Trade J., **114**, No. 14, 161 (1942).
57. Genberg, G. P., and E. O. Houghton, Paper Trade J., **88**, No. 17, 71, No. 18, 53 (1929).
58. Giertz, H. W., Svensk Papperstid., **55**, 72 (1952).
59. Giertz, H. W., in F. Bolam, ref. 14, p. 389.
60. Givens, J. H., et al., Continuous and Staple Fibre Plants of Germany, P.B. 377, Washington, D.C. 1945.
61. Götze, K., Chemiefasern nach dem Viskoseverfahren, Springer, Berlin 1951.
62. Graff, J. H., and R. W. Miller, Paper Trade J., **109**, No. 6, 31 (1939).
63. Graff, J. H., and I. H. Isenberg, Tappi, **33**, 94 (1950).
63a. Graham, D., Tappi, **39**, 147 (1956).
64. Haas, H., and E. Regelin, Wochbl. Papierfabrik., **75**, No. 3, 45 (1947).
65. Hader, R. N., et al., Ind. Eng. Chem., **44**, 2803 (1952).
66. Hägglund, E., Papierfabrik., **29**, 557 (1931).

67. Hägglund, E., and B. Webjörn, *Svensk Papperstid.*, **52**, 131 (1949).
68. Hägglund, S. E., *Svensk Papperstid.*, **57**, 465 (1954).
69. Hall, G. A., *World's Paper Trade Review*, **91**, No. 16, 1340, 1396 (1929).
69a. Hartler, N., *et al.*, *Svensk Papperstid.*, **66**, 301, 309, 412 (1963).
70. Haselton, W. R., *Tappi*, **37**, 404 (1954); **38**, 716 (1955).
71. Heuser, E., *et al.*, *Tappi*, **33**, 101 (1950).
72. Higgins, H. G., *et al.*, *Tappi*, **41**, 193 (1958).
73. Holzer, W. F., and K. G. Booth, *Tappi*, **33**, 95 (1950).
74. Holzer, W. F., and H. F. Lewis, *Tappi*, **33**, 110 (1950).
75. Horsey, E. F., *Tech. Assoc. Papers*, **30**, 294 (1947); *Paper Trade J.*, **125**, No. 4, 40 (1957).
76. Hoyt, L. F., *Report on Tylose HBR*, P.B. 3865, Washington, D.C. 1945.
77. Imamura, R., *J. Soc. Textile Cellulose Ind. Japan*, **9**, 14 (1953).
78. Immergut, B., and B. G. Rånby, *Svensk Papperstid.*, **60**, 573 (1957).
79. Ingmanson, W. L., *Tappi*, **35**, 439 (1952).
80. Inskeep, G. C., and P. van Horn, *Ind. Eng. Chem.*, **44**, 2511 (1952).
81. Jahn, E. C., and C. V. Holmberg, *Paper Trade J.*, **114**, No. 17, 203 (1942).
82. Jansson, L., *et al.*, *Pulp Paper Mag. Can.*, **59**, No. 10, 217 (1958).
83. Jayme, G., *Papierfabrik.*, **40**, 137, 145 (1942).
84. Jayme, G., *Cellulosechem.*, **21**, 73 (1943).
85. Jayme, G., and D. Froundjian, *Cellulosechem.*, **18**, 9 (1940).
86. Jayme, G., and G. Hunger, *Holz Roh Werkstoff*, **13**, 212 (1955); *Naturwissenschaften*, **42**, 290 (1955); *Monatsh. Chem.*, **87**, 8 (1956); *Papier*, **11**, 140 (1957); *Zellstoff Papier*, **6**, 341 (1957); *Wochbl. Papierfabrik.*, **85**, 900 (1957); *Mikroskopie*, **13**, 24 (1958); *Holzforschung*, **13**, 1 (1959).
87. Jayme, G., and G. Hunger, in F. Bolam, ref. 14, p. 263, figures 2–3.
88. Jayme, G., and E. Lochmüller-Kerler, *Papierfabrik.*, **42**, 223 (1944); *Holz Roh Werkstoff*, **5**, 11, 377 (1942).
89. Jayme, G., and U. Schenck, *Melliand Textilber.*, **31**, 153, 230 (1950).
90. Jayme, G., and L. Scheuring, *Papier*, **7**, 223, 298, 347 (1953).
91. Jayme, G., and R. Wettstein, *Papierfabrik.*, **36**, No. 49, 519 (1938).
92. Jayne, J. E., *et al.*, *Tappi*, **33**, 32 (1950).
93. Jones, K. G., and E. Rieth, *Wochbl. Papierfabrik.*, **64**, 853 (1933).
94. Jörgensen, L., in F. Bolam, ref. 14, p. 107.
95. Kaila, E., *Paperi Puu*, **38**, 451 (1956).
96. Kaila, E., *et al.*, *Paperi Puu*, **39**, 1 (1957).
97. Kleinert, T., and W. Wincor, *Svensk Papperstid.*, **53**, 638 (1950); **56**, 874 (1953).
98. Knutsson, T., and L. Stockman, *Svensk Papperstid.*, **61**, 424 (1958).
99. Koblitz, W., *et al.*, *Z. Elektrochem.*, **58**, 874 (1954).
100. Kress, O., and H. Bialkowsky, *Paper Trade J.*, **93**, No. 20, 35 (1931).
101. Kress, O., and F. W. Brainerd, *Paper Trade J.*, **98**, No. 13, 163 (1934).
102. Landt, G. E., and S. A. Rulon, *Paper Trade J.*, **111**, No. 4, 44 (1940).
102a. Leopold, B., and D. C. McIntosh, *Tappi*, **44**, 235 (1961).
103. Lewis, H. F., *et al.*, *Paper Trade J.*, **109**, No. 14, 188 (1939).
104. Lewis, H. F., *et al.*, *Tappi*, **33**, 92 (1950).
105. Lipscomb, A. S., *Cellulose Acetate*, Ernest Benn, London 1933.
106. Lottermoser, A., and F. Wultsch, *Kolloid-Z.*, **83**, 180 (1938).
106a. Luner, P., *et al.*, *Tappi*, **44**, 409 (1961).
107. McEwen, J. M., Dissertation, Appleton, Wis., 1941.
107a. McIntosh, D. C., *Tappi*, **46**, 273 (1963).

108. McKenzie, A. W., and H. G. Higgins, *Australian J. Appl. Sci.*, **6**, 208 (1955).
109. Malm, C. J., *Svensk Papperstid.*, **50**, No. 11B, 135 (1947).
109a. Malm, C. J., *et al.*, *Ind. Eng. Chem.*, **42**, 730 (1950).
109b. Malmberg, B., *Svensk Papperstid.*, **65**, 911 (1962); **67**, 69 (1964).
110. March, R. E., *Paper Trade J.*, **127**, No. 17, 51 (1948).
111. Marchessault, R., *et al.*, *Svensk Papperstid.*, **59**, 859 (1956).
112. Mark, H., in E. Ott, ed., *Cellulose and Cellulose Derivatives*, 1st Ed., Interscience, New York 1943, p. 1007, cf. 2nd Ed., New York 1954, p. 1329.
113. Mason, S. G., *Tappi*, **33**, 407 (1950).
114. Matthes, W., *Faserforsch. Textiltech.*, **6**, 398 (1955).
114a. Mayhood, C. H., *et al.*, *Tappi*, **45**, 69 (1962).
115. Miles, F. D., *Cellulose Nitrate*, Oliver & Boyd, London 1955.
116. Milliken, M. G., *Ind. Eng. Chem.*, **22**, 326 (1930).
117. Mitchell, H. L., *U.S. Dep. Agr.*, *Forest Prod. Lab. Report* No. 1993 (1954); *Pulp Paper*, **33**, No. 5, 144 (1959).
118. Mitchell, J. A., *Tappi*, **40**, 713 (1957).
119. Mitchell, R. L., *Ind. Eng. Chem.*, **47**, 2370 (1955).
120. Mitchell, R. L., *et al.*, *Tappi*, **39**, 571 (1956).
121. de Montigny, R., and O. Maass, Dominion Forest Service Bull. 82, Ottawa 1935.
122. Mühlsteph, W., *Papierfabrik.*, **36**, 341 (1938); **38**, 109 (1940); *Holz Roh Werkstoff*, **3**, 45 (1940); *Cellulosechem.*, **18**, 132 (1940); *Wochbl. Papierfabrik.*, **72**, 201, 219 (1941).
122a. Murray, C. E., and B. B. Thomas, *Tappi*, **44**, 625 (1961).
123. Musser, D. M., and H. C. Engel, *Paper Trade J.*, **113**, No. 2, 13 (1941).
124. Musser, D. M., and H. C. Engel, *Paper Trade J.*, **115**, No. 8, 33 (1942).
125. Nicolaysen, V. B., and K. Borgin, *Norsk Skogind.*, **7**, 134 (1953).
126. Nordman, L., *et al.*, *Paperi Puu*, **36**, 315 (1954); and in F. Bolam, ref. 14, p. 333.
127. Nordman, L., and C. Gustafsson, *Paperi Puu*, **33**, 36 (1951).
128. Obermanns, H. E., *Paper Trade J.*, **103**, No. 7, 109 (1936).
129. Ott, E., and H. Spurlin, eds., *Cellulose and Cellulose Derivatives*, 2nd Ed., Interscience, New York 1954, Part II.
130. Parsons, J. L., *Paper Trade J.*, **93**, No. 1, 42 (1931).
131. Parsons, S. R., *Tech. Assoc. Papers*, **25**, 360 (1942).
131a. Parsons, S. R., and H. J. Lausman, *Tappi*, **34**, 97 (1951).
132. Partridge, E. P., *Ind. Eng. Chem.*, **21**, 1044 (1929).
133. Pascoe, T. A., *Tech. Assoc. Papers*, **30**, 422 (1947).
134. Pettersson, S. E., and S. A. Rydholm, *Svensk Papperstid.*, **64**, 4 (1961).
134a. Philipp, B., *Faserforsch. Textiltech.*, **8**, 21 (1957).
135. Proffitt, J. R., *et al.*, *Tappi*, **37**, 28 (1954).
136. Purves, C. B., in E. Ott, ed., *Cellulose and Cellulose Derivatives*, 1st Ed., Interscience, New York 1943, p. 107, cf. 2nd Ed. New York 1954, p. 668.
137. Rånby, B. G., and S. A. Rydholm, in C. E. Schildknecht, ed., *Polymer Processes*, Interscience, New York 1956, p. 837.
138. Rassow, B., and E. Dörr, *J. Prakt Chem.*, **108**, 113 (1924).
139. Ratcliff, F. T., *Tappi*, **32**, 357 (1949).
140. Rayonier Inc., *Rayocord X*.
141. Rayonier Inc., *U.S. Pat.* 2,542,285 (1951).
142. Rayonier Inc., *U.S. Pat.* 2,541,558 (1951).
143. Rayonier Inc., *U.S. Pat.* 2,393,817 (1946).
144. Richter, G. A., *Ind. Eng. Chem.*, **23**, 266 (1931).

145. Richter, G. A., *Tappi*, **39**, 668 (1956); **40**, 429 (1957).

146. Richter, J., *Svensk Papperstid.*, **61**, 741 (1958).

147. Riley, J. L., in C. E. Schildknecht, ed., *Polymer Processes*, Interscience, New York 1956, p. 837.

148. Ringström, E., *Svensk Papperstid.*, **58**, 145 (1955); Medd. CCL (Stockholm), **B 35**.

149. Ringström, E., and N. H. Apler, *Svensk Papperstid.*, **51**, 501 (1948); **53**, 127 (1950).

150. Robertson, A. A., in F. Bolam, ref. 14, p. 411.

150a. Robertson, A. A., *Svensk Papperstid.*, **66**, 477 (1963).

151. Robertson, A. A., and S. G. Mason, *Pulp Paper Mag. Can.*, **50**, No. 13, 103 (1949).

152. Rogovin, Z. A., and M. Shyakhover, *Kolloid-Z.*, **78**, 228 (1937).

153. Rowland, B. W., *Paper Ind.*, **27**, 1398 (1945).

154. Runkel, R. O., *Wochbl. Papierfabrik.*, **71**, 93 (1940); *Holz Roh Werkstoff*, **5**, 413 (1942); *Zellstoff Papier*, **21**, 139 (1941); *Tappi*, **35**, 174 (1952).

155. Rydholm, S. A., *et al.*, *Svensk Papperstid.*, **66**, 196 (1963) and unpublished.

155a. Rydholm, S. A., *et al.*, *Svensk Papperstid.*, **66**, 110 (1963).

155b. Rydholm, S. A., unpublished.

156. Samuelson, O., *et al.*, *Svensk Papperstid.*, **50**, 21 (1947).

157. Samuelson, O., *Svensk Papperstid.*, **51**, 331 (1948); **52**, 1 (1949).

158. Samuelson, O., *Svensk Papperstid.*, **51**, 331 (1948).

159. Samuelson, O., *Svensk Kem. Tidskr.*, **59**, 105 (1947).

159a. Samuelsson, L. G., *Svensk Papperstid.*, **66**, 541 (1963).

160. Sarten, P., *Papier*, **10**, 554 (1956).

161. Scaramuzzi, G., in A. de Philippis, ed., *Publ. Centro di Sperimentzione Agricola e Forestale*, Vol. I, Rome 1957.

162. Schafer, E. R., *et al.*, *Paper Trade J.*, **91**, No. 3, 57 (1930); **97**, No. 19, 224 (1933).

163. Schmorak, J., and G. A. Adams, *Tappi*, **40**, 378 (1957).

164. Schur, M. O., and H. F. Lewis, *Tappi*, **33**, 392 (1950).

165. Schwalbe, C. G., *Paper Trade J.*, **72**, No. 5, 58 (1921).

166. Sihtola, H., *et al.*, *Paperi Puu*, **38**, 221 (1956); **39**, 383 (1957).

167. Sihtola, H., and E. Kaila, *Paperi Puu*, **36**, 341 (1954).

168. Sihtola, H., and E. Kaila, *Paperi Puu*, **39**, No. 4A, 143 (1957).

169. Smith, L. H., *Synthetic Fiber Development in Germany*, P.B. 7416, New York 1946.

170. Sobue, H., *et al.*, *J. Soc. Textile Cellulose Ind. (Japan)*, **8**, 79 (1952); **9**, 565 (1953).

171. Sookne, A. M., and M. Harris, *Ind. Eng. Chem.*, **37**, 478 (1945).

172. Stannett, V., *Cellulose Acetate Plastics*, Temple Press, London 1950.

173. Staudinger, H., and F. Reinecke, *Papierfabrik.*, **36**, 489 (1938); *Holz Roh Werkstoff*, **3**, 321 (1939).

174. Steenberg, B., *Svensk Papperstid.*, **50**, No. 11 B, 155 (1947).

175. Steinmann, H. W., and B. B. White, *Tappi*, **37**, 225 (1954).

176. Stephansen, E., *Norsk Skogind.*, **2**, 207 (1948).

177. Strachan, J., *Proc. Tech. Sect. Brit. Paper Board Makers' Assoc.*, **6**, 139 (1926); **13**, 61 (1932); **14**, 447 (1933); **19**, 171 (1938).

177a. Swanson, J. W., *Tappi*, **33**, 451 (1950); **39**, 257 (1956).

178. Talwar, K. K., *Tappi*, **41**, 207 (1958).

178a. Tamolang, F. N., and F. F. Wangaard, *Tappi*, **44**, 201 (1961); **45**, 548 (1962).

179. Tengquist, E., *Svensk Papperstid.*, **55**, 176 (1952); *Papier*, **8**, 479 (1954).

180. Thode, E. F., *et al.*, *Tappi*, **35**, 379 (1952).

181. Timell, T. E., *et al.*, *Pulp Paper Mag. Can.*, **59**, No. 10, 242 (1958).

182. Treiber, E., *et al.*, *Svensk Papperstid.*, **58**, 287 (1955).

183. Treiber, E., *et al.*, *Svensk Papperstid.*, **59**, 838 (1956); *Papier*, **11**, 133, 194 (1957).

184. Treiber, E., *et al.*, *Svensk Papperstid.*, **61**, 55 (1958), cf. *Paperi Puu*, **38**, 145 (1956).

185. Treiber, E., and O. Fex, *Svensk Papperstid.*, **58**, 605 (1955).

186. Trivedi, S. A., *et al.*, *Paper Ind.*, **29**, 1443 (1948).

187. Valeur, C., *Svensk Papperstid.*, **54**, 613 (1951).

188. Van den Akker, J. A., *Tappi*, **35**, 13 (1952).

189. Vuori, R., Dissertation, Helsinki 1947, Centrallab. Bull. No. 51, Helsinki 1947.

190. Walecka, J. A., *Tappi*, **39**, 458 (1956).

191. Walker, F., *Paper Trade J.*, **139**, No. 17, 22 (1955); **140**, No. 36, 21 (1956); *Pulp Paper Mag. Can.*, **57**, No. 8, 127 (1956).

192. Watson, A. J., *et al.*, *Australian Pulp Paper Ind.*, *Tech. Assoc. Proc.*, **6**, 243 (1952); **8**, 290 (1954).

192a. Watson, J. K., and H. E. Dadswell, *Australian Pulp Paper Ind.*, *Tech. Assoc. Proc.*, **14**, 168 (1961).

193. Watson, J. K., and D. R. Henderson, *Tappi*, **40**, 686 (1957).

194. Wurz, O., *Wochbl. Papierfabrik.*, **87**, 567 (1959).

195. Yllner, S., and B. Enström, *Svensk Papperstid.*, **59**, 229 (1956); **60**, 549 (1957).

22

PULP INDUSTRY OF THE WORLD

I. Location

This book on pulping processes started with an introduction to the forests of the world, to show the location and nature of the pulping raw materials. In conclusion, a short description should be given of the location and structure of the pulp industry.

The location of the forests reflects the climatic conditions of the globe. The fairly humid, cold–temperate regions of the northern hemisphere are covered with conifer forests, south of which occurs a belt of mixed conifer–broadleaf forests. Then follow regions of increasing aridity, poorly forested, and in the wet regions around the equator the tropical broadleaf forests appear. The southern hemisphere follows a similar pattern, although the smaller land masses at the latitudes of cold–temperate climate limit the forest areas extremely.

The location of the pulp industry reflects not only the location of the forests but also their varying usefulness as pulping raw materials, as well as the industrialization of the various regions. Thus, North America and Europe, containing one-third of the world population and land area, and less than half the forest area, produce 90% of the pulp, as seen by Table 22.1 (U.S.S.R. production is still mainly located to Europe). Although considerable interest is now displayed by Asiatic, African and South-American countries in developing their own pulping industry, the picture is not going to change radically within the next few decades. These countries produce somewhat more paper, as they import some pulp, but as much as 85% of the paper production is still within North America and Europe, as shown in Table 22.2. The paper consumption is also mainly concentrated in those two regions, about 83% of the total, which is reflected by the per capita consumption shown in Table 22.3.

Therefore, although bamboo pulp from south-east Asia and pulp from tropical hardwoods as well as from planted eucalypts and pines in Africa and South America are of future importance, a description of the present pulping industry can concentrate on the countries of North America and Europe, together with Japan, which has the most important pulp industry of Asia.

II. Description by Raw Materials, Processes and Products

Although short-fibered pulps gain in importance, softwood is the dominating raw material for pulping. As seen by Table 22.4, only 20% of pulp

1186

production is based on hardwood and other short-fibered plants, as compared with 50% of the forest area. In Table 22.5, the approximate proportions of mechanical, semichemical and chemical kraft and sulfite pulp production of the world is shown, and how much is bleached. It is seen that mechanical pulps and chemical kraft pulps dominate, whilst semichemical neutral sulfite pulp constitutes a considerable and growing quantity, and chemical sulfite pulp, once a dominating grade, still

Table 22.1. Wood pulp production by regions and countries, 1960, M t

Region	Country*	Production		%
North America	U.S.A.†	22.8		
	Canada	10.3	33.1	56
Europe	Sweden	5.0		
(excluding U.S.S.R.)	Finland	3.7		
	Norway	1.5		
	Germany (W.)	1.5		
	Germany (E.)	0.6		
	France	1.3		
	Austria	0.7		
	Czechoslovakia	0.5		
	Poland	0.5		
	Italy	0.5		
	Switzerland	0.2		
	United Kingdom	0.2		
	Yugoslavia	0.2		
	Belgium	0.1		
	Netherlands†	0.1		
	Portugal	0.1		
	Rumania	0.1		
	Spain	0.1	17.0	29
U.S.S.R.	U.S.S.R.	3.1	3.1	5
Asia	Japan	3.5		
(excluding U.S.S.R.)	China†	0.6	4.1	7
Pacific Area	Australia	0.4		
	New Zealand	0.2	0.6	1
Latin America	Brazil	0.3		
	Mexico	0.2	0.5	1
Africa	Republic of South Africa	0.2	0.2	0
All regions		58.8	58.8	100

* Countries having a pulp production of less than 0.1 M t have been included in the summative figures.
† In addition a straw (or bamboo, etc.) pulp production of about 0.4 M t in the Netherlands, 0.5 M t in the U.S.A. and 1.6 M t in China.

Table 22.2. Production of paper and board by regions and countries, 1960. M t

Region	Country	Newsprint M t	Printing, writing paper M t	Other paper M t	Paper board M t	Total paper and paper board		Fiber board M t
						M t	%	
North America	U.S.A.	1.8	5.9	7.5	14.3	29.5		1.7
	Canada	6.1	0.4	0.5	0.9	7.9		0.2
	Total	7.9	6.3	8.0	15.3	37.4	51	1.9
Europe	U.K.	0.7	1.0	1.1	1.1	4.1		0.1
(excl. U.S.S.R.)	Germany (W.)	0.2	0.8	1.5	0.9	3.4		0.1
	Germany (E.)	0.1	0.2	0.3	0.3	0.8		
	France	0.6	0.6	1.1	0.4	2.6		0.1
	Sweden	0.6	0.3	1.0	0.3	2.2		0.5
	Finland	0.8	0.2	0.4	0.5	2.0		0.1
	Italy	0.3	0.4	0.6	0.2	1.5		
	Netherlands	0.1	0.2	0.3	0.4	1.0		
	Norway	0.2	0.2	0.3	0.1	0.8		0.1
	Poland	0.1	0.1	0.2	0.1	0.6		0.1
	Czechoslovakia	0.0	0.1	0.3	0.2	0.6		
	Austria	0.1	0.2	0.2	0.1	0.6		0.1
	Switzerland	0.1	0.1	0.1	0.1	0.5		
	Belgium	0.1	0.1	0.1	0.1	0.4		0.1
	Spain	0.0	0.1	0.1	0.1	0.3		
	Denmark					0.2		
	Rumania					0.2		
	Yugoslavia					0.2		
	Hungary					0.1		
	Portugal					0.1		
	Bulgaria					0.1		
	Greece					0.1		
	Ireland					0.1		
	Total	4.2	4.9	8.2	5.1	22.4	30	1.5
U.S.S.R.	U.S.S.R.	0.4	0.6	1.4	0.8	3.2	4	0.2
Asia	Japan	0.7	0.9	1.0	1.3	3.8		0.2
(excl. U.S.S.R.)	China	0.3	0.2	1.3	0.4	2.1		
	India		0.2	0.1	0.1	0.4		
	Taiwan					0.1		
	Total	1.1	1.3	3.3	2.4	8.1	11	0.1
Pacific Area	Australia	0.1	0.1	0.1	0.2	0.5		0.1
	New Zealand	0.1		0.1		0.2		
	Total	0.2	0.1	0.1	0.2	0.6	1	0.1
Latin America	Argentina			0.2	0.1	0.4		
	Brazil	0.1	0.1	0.2	0.2	0.6		
	Mexico		0.1	0.1	0.2	0.4		
	Total	0.2	0.3	0.7	0.5	1.7	2	0.1
Africa	Total	0.0	0.1	0.1	0.1	0.3	0	0.1
All regions		14.0	13.5	21.8	24.6	73.9	100	4.3

Table 22.3. Consumption of paper and paper board, 1962. Kg per capita

Region	Country	Consumption Newsprint	Other	Total
North America	U.S.A.	40	165	205
	Canada	27	107	134
	Average	39	159	198
Europe	Sweden	32	98	128
(excl. U.S.S.R.)	Switzerland	17	88	105
	United Kingdom	27	78	105
	Netherlands	17	88	105
	Finland	25	75	100
	Norway	13	76	89
	Germany (W.)	11	73	84
	Denmark	18	60	78
	Belgium	15	54	69
	France	16	48	64
	Iceland	10	38	48
	Austria	8	38	46
	Ireland	14	29	43
	Germany (E.)	5	37	42
	Italy	7	33	40
	Czechoslovakia	2	30	32
	Rumania	3	22	25
	Poland	3	20	23
	Hungary	3	19	22
	Bulgaria	3	13	16
	Portugal	5	10	15
	Yugoslavia	3	12	15
	Spain	3	11	14
	Greece	3	10	13
	Average	11	44	55
U.S.S.R.		2	14	16
Asia	Japan	11	46	57
(excl. U.S.S.R.)	Hong Kong	9	24	33
	Israel	4	26	30
	Taiwan	1	10	11
	China			3
	India			1
	Average	2	5	7
Pacific Area	Australia	32	50	82
	New Zealand	35	55	90
	Average	26	48	74
Latin America	Argentina	10	22	32
	Venezuela	7	22	29
	Uruguay	9	10	19
	Mexico	2	13	15
	Brazil	3	7	10
	Average	3	9	12
Africa	Republic of South Africa	5	13	23
	Average	1	2	3
All regions	Average	5	22	27

represents a large, although rather stagnant, portion of the entire production. The quantities of unbleached and bleached grades are less easy to estimate accurately, but somewhat more than one-fourth of the entire production or almost half the chemical grades are bleached. Production of bleached mechanical and semichemical pulps is as yet unimportant, but approximately 1 M t/year of groundwood pulp is bleached with dithionite and about as much groundwood and cold caustic pulp is bleached with peroxide in the U.S.A. The difference between the total paper production of 74 M t and the total pulp production of 63 M t (or 60 M t paper pulp) in 1960 is explained by the incorporation of waste paper and pigments in the production of some papers. Waste paper recovery is as high as 20–25% of the total paper consumption.

This production pattern is determined by the raw material situation as well as by the market. Some of the pulpwood grades are better suited to mechanical pulping or sulfite pulping, others should preferably be kraft cooked. However, as has been shown in the chapters on the pulping processes, this influence from the raw material is gradually diminishing as technical improvements are being introduced.

Table 22.4. World production of pulp by raw materials, percentage of 63 M t, 1960

Softwood pulps	79
Hardwood pulps	15
Other (bamboo, bagasse, straw)	6
	100

Table 22.5. World production of pulp by grades, percentage of 63 M t, 1960

Special alpha and dissolving pulps	5 (of which 4 bleached sulfite)
Sulfite pulps	21 (of which about 9 bleached)
Soda pulps	1
Kraft pulps	34 (of which about 13 bleached)
Total chemical wood pulps	61
Semichemical pulps	4
Defibrated or exploded pulps	5
Groundwood pulps	24
Total semichemical and mechanical wood pulps	33
Other (bamboo, bagasse, straw) pulps	6
All pulps	100

	Sulfite	Kraft	All chemical
Unbleached	12	21	33
Bleached	13	14	27
	25	35	60

1190

Table 22.6 lists the end uses of the pulp produced and their relative importance. The dominating consumption of pulp fibers is in paper and paper board, whereas dissolving pulps represent only a small, high-grade fraction (as indicated in Table 22.5). The two largest categories are *printing papers* and *container boards*, consuming largely unbleached pulps, mechanical and sulfite, and kraft and neutral sulfite semichemical respectively.

Table 22.6. End products of paper pulps, percentage of 39 M t, produced in North America 1960. Figures in brackets give % of world production 1960, 78 M t, for same category

Newsprint	20 (18)
Book	11
Fine	5 (17)
Coarse	10
Tissue and sanitary	5
Building paper	4
Other paper	1
Total paper	56 (63)
Liners	15
Corrugating	7
Chip and filler	1
Total container board	23
Folding	8
Set-up	1
Special food board	4
Total boxboard	13
Compressed building board	2
Non-compressed building board	3
Other board	3
Total board	44 (37)
Total paper and board	100

Another large sector for unbleached pulps, kraft and some sulfite, is *coarse papers*, including sack, bag and wrapping paper. Important markets for bleached grades are *tissue*, writing and printing *fine papers*, as well as *food board*. The qualitative trends are towards *more mechanical and semichemical pulps* and less chemical pulp in newsprint and some other printing papers, *more short-fibered pulps* in fine papers and bleached board, more semichemical kraft and neutral sulfite pulps in container boards, more hardwood dissolving pulps. All these trends emphasize the search for less expensive pulps, and the technical advances of the pulp-consuming industries to utilize those pulps. The quantitative trends are towards more paper of all categories, but especially of newsprint and

1191

Table 22.7. A tentative forecast of pulp, paper and board demand, M t (FAO, 1960)

Region	Pulp demand			Newsprint			Printing and writing			Other paper			Paper board			Total paper and board		
	1955	1965	1975	1955	1965	1975	1955	1965	1975	1955	1965	1975	1955	1965	1975	1955	1965	1975
North America	25.2	34.2	46.9	6.4	8.2	10.6	5.1	6.7	8.9	7.2	9.6	12.9	12.9	18.3	26.2	31.5	42.8	58.6
Latin America	1.6	3.0	5.6	0.5	1.0	1.8	0.3	0.6	1.2	0.6	1.2	2.2	0.4	0.7	1.4	1.8	3.5	6.5
Western Europe	10.7	17.3	24.5	2.6	4.6	6.5	2.8	4.4	5.9	4.4	6.7	9.2	3.3	5.6	8.6	13.2	21.3	30.2
Eastern Europe	1.6	3.4	5.9	0.2	0.5	1.0	0.4	0.8	1.3	0.8	1.4	2.4	0.5	1.2	2.4	1.9	3.9	7.1
U.S.S.R.	2.3	5.6	11.1	0.3	0.8	1.8	0.5	1.2	2.4	1.1	2.4	4.4	0.6	1.7	3.8	2.5	6.1	12.3
Africa	0.5	0.9	1.5	0.1	0.1	0.3	0.1	0.2	0.3	0.2	0.4	0.7	0.1	0.1	0.3	0.5	0.9	1.6
Near and Middle East	0.1	0.3	0.5	0.0	0.1	0.1	0.0	0.0	0.1	0.0	0.1	0.2	0.0	0.1	0.1	0.1	0.3	0.5
Far East (excluding China)	2.3	5.7	11.3	0.7	1.5	2.9	0.8	1.7	3.1	0.8	1.6	3.1	0.8	2.0	4.7	3.0	6.9	13.8
China (Mainland)	0.8	2.9	8.1	0.1	0.5	1.6	0.3	1.0	2.7	0.3	0.9	2.4	0.2	0.7	2.2	0.9	3.1	8.8
Oceania	0.7	1.2	1.7	0.3	0.5	0.6	0.1	0.2	0.3	0.1	0.3	0.4	0.2	0.4	0.6	0.8	1.3	1.8
World total	45.9	74.4	117.1	11.3	17.8	27.2	10.4	16.8	26.1	15.5	24.6	37.8	18.9	30.8	50.3	56.1	90.0	141.4

magazine paper and of packaging papers and boards. Making use of the established correlation between gross national income and per capita consumption, illustrated in Figure 22.1, projections have been made for the world pulp and paper demand till 1975, Table 22.7. It is obvious, that under an assumed peaceful development, an enormous increase in the pulp production must take place.

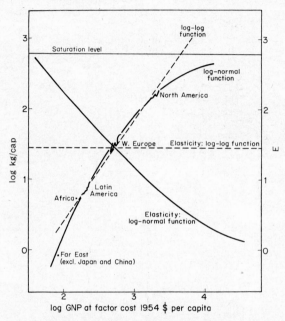

Fig. 22.1. Total paper and board consumption vs. gross
national product for different regions (F.A.O.)

III. Description by Regions

1. CANADA

In the Canadian forests, spruces and firs are dominant, whereas hardwoods and pines occur to only a limited extent. This makes Canada the typical and traditional groundwood and sulfite pulp producer of the world. Only in the Douglas fir–Sitka spruce region in British Columbia, has the kraft industry more recently achieved major importance. More than half the production is groundwood pulp, as seen by Table 22.8, and about half the chemical pulp is sulfite. Of the sulfite pulp, the larger portion is unbleached and used together with the groundwood pulp for newsprint. An important production of dissolving pulps also takes place. Table 22.9 shows that Canadian pulp production has developed rapidly during the last four decades.

1193

The total production makes Canada second only to the United States, and a leader in groundwood pulp production. A large part of the pulps produced is converted to paper in Canadian mills, especially to newsprint, but more than 20 % is exported, which makes Canada one of the leading pulp exporters of the world. The pulp export mainly goes to the United States, together with the bulk of the newsprint. There are more than a hundred pulp mills, two-thirds of which are integrated with paper production, and their location is seen by Table 22.10. The provinces of Quebec,

Table 22.8. Canadian pulp production 1960, M t

Mechanical	5.6
Unbleached kraft	0.9
Bleached kraft	1.3
Unbleached sulfite	1.5
Bleached sulfite	0.6
Dissolving and spec.	0.3
Other chemical	0.2
Total wood pulps	10.3

Table 22.9. Evolution of the Canadian pulp industry 1920–1960, M t

	1920	1930	1940	1950	1960
Mechanical	1.0	2.0	3.0	4.5	5.6
Sulfite	0.6	1.0	1.3	1.9	2.4
Alkaline	0.2	0.2	0.4	1.0	2.3
Total	1.8	3.2	3.7	7.4	10.3

Table 22.10. Location of Canadian pulp production, 1958

Province	Production, M t	Pulp mills	Pulp and paper mills	Paper mills	Total mills
Quebec	3.8	12	34	9	55
Ontario	2.5	9	19	15	43
British Columbia	1.3	8	6	—	14
Manitoba		—	3	—	3
Alberta		1	—	—	1
Newfoundland	1.5	1	2	—	3
Nova Scotia		2	2	—	4
New Brunswick		4	3	—	7
Canada	9.1	37	69	24	130

Ontario and British Columbia contain the major part of the mills. As the Canadian pulp industry is comparatively old, many of the units are fairly small. However, there are also modern mills, especially at the West coast, with capacities of up to 500 t/d of mechanical as well as chemical

1194

pulp. New units will produce up to 900 t/d. Among the most important producers are Abitibi Power & Paper Co, Canadian International Paper Co, Consolidated Paper Co and Powell River–MacMillan Bloedel Co.

2. UNITED STATES OF AMERICA

This large and industrialized country is well forested and has a dominant position in the world's pulp and paper industry. It produces almost half the entire pulp and paper quantity of the world, predominantly for its own use. Formerly a large importer of pulp, the U.S.A. has in recent years become an exporter of considerable quantities.

The forests of the U.S.A. have greatly influenced the location and type of its pulp industry. The oldest part of the industry is located in the 'North', the Lake and north-eastern states of the country. Here, originally a similar production pattern developed as in eastern Canada, but eventually the supply of spruces and firs diminished. This has limited the development of the pulp industry of the North and necessitated the use of hardwoods, in groundwood and sulfite pulping, as well as in new processes such as cold caustic, neutral sulfite and chemigroundwood. The small quantity of (hot) soda pulp produced in the U.S.A. is also located in the North, and is traditionally based on hardwoods. Some kraft mills use local pines, such as jack pine. The second region to develop an important pulp industry was in the West. Here, the use of Douglas fir and western hemlock dominates, whereas hardwoods are in short supply. The large tree dimensions of virgin forests have led to a saw-mill industry of enormous importance in this region, and the pulp industry has developed partly as a complement hereto, utilizing also logs of smaller dimensions, damaged logs and saw-mill waste. Hemlock and some fir is used for groundwood and sulfite pulping, Douglas fir together with hemlock and some pines is the raw material for large kraft pulp mills. Coastal Alaska has recently begun to develop a pulp industry. Sitka spruce being one of the dominant species, the first mills to start were sulfite mills. In the South, growing conditions are much different. The broad pine belt stretching from eastern Texas to the Atlantic has favored the kraft industry, which has grown enormously. In recent years a groundwood pulp industry from pine has also emerged, after solving the technical problems involved. The absence of sulfite mills has also caused another change from the conventional newsprint production there, in that the chemical pulp of the furnish is semibleached pine kraft. Even glassine paper is produced from bleached kraft in the South. Intermixed with the pine forests and increasing in the northern parts of the region occur hardwoods of various types. They are still utilized to only a very limited extent and constitute one of the pulpwood reserves of the continent. Gums and oaks are now pulped by both kraft and neutral sulfite mills for use in various board types, unbleached as well as bleached, and new methods, such as cold caustic pulping, are also being applied.

This regional production pattern influenced by the forest types is reflected in the production pattern by processes and products, Table 22.11. About 80% of the pulp produced is chemical or semichemical, and there is five times as much kraft as sulfite pulp produced. Half the chemical pulp quantity is 'semibleached' or bleached, among which is a considerable amount of dissolving pulp (sulfite as well as prehydrolysis–kraft pulp). In addition to the large quantity of virgin pulp produced, there is also a large quantity of waste paper, about 8 M t, reused in the paper mills. Table 22.12 shows the rapid growth of the U.S. pulp industry, especially during the last 10 years.

Tables 22.11. U.S. pulp production by grades 1960, M t

Mechanical (groundwood)	2.9
Mechanical (other)	1.1
Semichemical	1.8
Unbleached kraft	8.2
Semibleached kraft	0.6
Bleached kraft	4.4
Soda	0.4
Unbleached sulfite	0.5
Bleached sulfite	1.8
Dissolving and special alpha	1.0
Total	23.2
Total kraft	13.8
Total sulfite	2.7
Total chemical	17.0
Total bleached	8.2

Table 22.12. Evolution of the U.S. pulp industry 1899–1959, M t

1899	1909	1919	1929	1938	1949	1959
1.0	2.2	3.2	4.4	5.3	11.0	22.0

Most of the pulp mills are integrated with paper production, although there is some market paper pulp produced in addition to the dissolving pulp. The paper mill production is equally divided between paper and paper board, Table 22.13. The development of the modern distribution techniques and sales in self-service supermarkets has initiated the remarkable growth of the packaging papers and especially boards. Of the paper categories, sanitary and facial tissues have had a more rapid development than most other large groups, of which book, wrapping, newsprint and fine papers are all very substantial. There are about 350 pulp mills and about 800 paper mills responsible for this enormous production, truly the biggest in the world. The older mills, especially those located in the North, are comparatively small, but the modern units of the West and South normally produce at least 300 t/d, and some between 1,000 and 2,000 t/d. Among the most important producers are International Paper Co, Crown–Zellerbach Corp., Scott Paper Co, Weyerhaeuser Timber Co, St. Regis Paper Co, West Virginia Pulp and Paper Co, Union Bag–Camp Paper Co, Champion Paper and Fiber Co. Some of these companies also include lumber operations and a very noticeable recent trend of a large number of firms is to include the converting industry, especially in the packaging field. This development facilitates the efforts towards an improved overall economy in the production. Most of the large companies have production units and forest holdings in all the important regions. As seen by Table 22.14, more than half the pulp production is in the South, although Washington is the leading state. The paper industry has a somewhat different location, with more emphasis in the North. This partly reflects the influence of the consumption areas.

Table 22.13. U.S. paper production by grades 1960, M t

Newsprint	1.8	
Book	4.2	
Fine	1.6	
Coarse	3.5	
Tissue and sanitary	2.0	
Building paper	1.2	
Other paper	0.7	15.0
Liner	4.9	
Corrugating	2.3	
Chip and filler	0.2	
Folding	2.6	
Set-up	0.6	
Special food board	1.4	
Other paper board	2.3	
Fiber board	1.7	16.0
Total paper and board		31.0

Table 22.14. U.S. pulp and paper production by regions, 1958 M t

Region	Pulp	Paper	State	Pulp	State	Paper
North	5.2	13.2	Washington		Wisconsin	1.8
West	3.5	3.4	(incl. Alaska)	2.3	Florida	1.6
South	11.2	11.0	Georgia	1.9	New York	1.6
			Florida	1.9	Georgia	1.6
Total	19.9	27.6	Louisiana	1.3	Louisiana	1.5
			Maine	1.3	Michigan	1.5
			Alabama	1.0	Maine	1.4
			Virginia	1.0	Pennsylvania	1.4
					Ohio	1.3
					Washington	1.3
					New Jersey	1.1
					Virginia	1.0
					California	1.0

3. U.S.S.R.

Russia holds more than half the coniferous forests of the world, and should accordingly be one of the leading pulp producers. That this is not quite so yet, is to a large extent explained by the fact that the largest part of the forests is in Siberia, which is still sparsely populated, has little industry and few possibilities of transportation. However, great efforts are being made in the industrialization of Siberia, and a very impressive scheme is under development in the Bratsk district near Lake Baikal, where around 0.5 M t annually is going to be produced, together with a wide variety of other forest products. Other large production centers will be in Kotlas, Arkhangelsk and Astrakhan. Today, there are only three mills in Siberia, and with the exception of some at South Sakhalin, acquired from Japan during the last war, all pulp mills are located in the Baltic and Karelia provinces. About 50 pulp mills are in operation and another 20 planned or under construction. The localization of the pulp mills to a region with abundant spruce forests has emphasized the groundwood and sulfite pulp industries, as seen by Table 22.15, but it is

Table 22.15. U.S.S.R. pulp and paper production by grades, 1960. M t

Mechanical	0.9	Newsprint	0.4
Sulfite	1.9	Book	0.4
Kraft	0.4	Fine	0.2
	—	Coarse kraft	0.4
Total pulp	3.2	Other papers	1.0
		Paper board	0.8
		Building board	0.2
		Total paper and board	3.4

Table 22.16. U.S.S.R. paper and board production 1938–1959. M t

1938	1949	1959	1965 (target)
1.0	1.2	3.1	7.8

likely that large tonnages of kraft pulp will appear as the industry moves east into the pine and Siberian larch districts. The target for 1965 is a pulp production of 6.2 M t, paper 4.2 M t and paper board 3.6 M t, as compared to the present production of about 4 M t pulp and as much paper and paper board. As seen by Table 22.16, this marks the entrance of the Russian pulp industry into an expansive period, not unlike the recent one in the U.S.A. Most of the pulp is to be consumed within the country.

4. JAPAN

World War II left Japan with an insignificant pulp industry. About half the previous production capacity, 1.1. M t 1940, and the main supply of pulpwood was located in Sakhalin, which was lost to Russia. Today, Japan is one of the leading nations in both pulp and paper production, and the rate of industrial growth is similar to that of the U.S.S.R., as seen by Table 22.17. The problem of how this expansion can be supplied with raw material is met by rapid forestal as well as technical initiatives. The conifer species available are sugi (*Cryptomeria*), which resembles spruce, and further pine and larch. Reforestation and aforestation schemes are being carried out on a large scale, predominantly with sugi. New forest areas are being made available through rapid road construction, and the hardwood forests, which constitute about half the forest area, are beginning to be utilized by the pulp industry. The table shows that emphasis is placed equally on mechanical, sulfite and kraft pulping. A considerable part of the sulfite pulp is used for dissolving purposes, and Table 22.18

Table 22.17. Japanese pulp production by grades, 1940–1960. M t

	1940	1946	1950	1955	1957	1960
Mechanical	0.4	0.1	0.3	0.7	0.8	0.9
Semichemical	—	—	—	—	0.1	0.3
Kraft	0.1	—	0.1	0.4	0.6	1.4
Sulfite	0.4	0.1	0.2	0.5	0.5	0.5
Dissolving and spec.	0.2	—	0.1	0.3	0.4	0.4
Total pulp	1.1	0.2	0.7	1.9	2.4	3.5

Table 22.18. Japanese paper and board production by grades, 1960. M t

Newsprint	0.7
Book	0.8
Fine	0.4
Coarse	0.2
Other paper	0.7
Liner	0.8
Other board	0.8
	4.5

shows the end uses of the paper pulps. There are 60 pulp and above 600 paper mills, located mainly on the islands of Hokkaido, Honshu and Kyushu. The equipment of most of the pulp mills is advanced and modern, and the unit capacities are often high, in exceptional cases as much as 900 t/d. Most of the paper mills are very small, but there are also several large and modern units, e.g. for newsprint and linerboard. Japanese

1199

pulp and paper is expected to play an important part in the future Asiatic economy. The Japanese pulp industry has also recently gone beyond the borders of the country and started a sulfite pulp mill in Alaska.

5. NORTHERN EUROPE

The main European pulp production is located in the coniferous forest belt of Scandinavia and Finland. Spruce dominates in the western parts and pine in the eastern parts, and birch is more abundant towards the East. Thus, the Norwegian pulp industry makes groundwood and sulfite but very little kraft pulp, whereas the kraft pulp industry of Sweden and Finland is important and expanding. Table 22.19 shows the production structure of the region, which is equal in importance to Canada and only surpassed by the United States. Its pulp *export*, about 4.5 M t mainly to Europe, is by far the largest of the world.

Table 22.19. Pulp production of Northern Europe, 1960. M t

	Norway	Sweden	Finland	Total
Mechanical (groundwood)	0.8	1.1	1.0	2.9
Sulfite	0.6	1.9	1.2	3.7
Kraft	0.2	2.0	1.3	3.5
Mechanical (defibrated)	0.1	0.6	0.2	0.9
Total	1.7	5.6	3.7	11.0
Pulp mills	62	82	60	204

The Scandinavian pulp industry is an old one, and most units were built before World War II and the majority before 1930. They are therefore in general fairly small, or have been expanded from a relatively small production to units of 300–500 t/d. The largest pulp mill of the region is Kaukopää in Finland, with a capacity of 1,000 t/d kraft pulp for liner. In proportion to the total production, the manufacture of dissolving pulp, 0.7 M t, and defibrated pulp, 0.9 M t, is considerable. The development of the industry is seen by Table 22.20. After steady progress before the war, the Scandinavian and Finnish pulp industry had a serious set-back during the 1940–45 period and reached prewar figures

Table 22.20. The evolution of the North European pulp industry, 1925–1960. M t

	1925	1937	1946	1951	1955	1960
Norway	0.6	1.1	0.5	1.1	1.4	1.7
Sweden	1.3	3.6	3.0	3.6	4.2	5.6
Finland	0.6	2.3	1.6	2.2	2.7	3.7
Total	2.5	7.0	5.1	6.9	8.3	11.0

only comparatively slowly. Recent years have again been marked by an increased activity, particularly for kraft pulp production, whereas the groundwood and especially sulfite pulp production has been rather stagnant. New forest inventories have indicated that raw material for further expansion is available in Sweden and Finland, partly as a result of advanced silvicultural efforts, and as market surveys have indicated an ever-growing demand for pulp in Europe, considerable new capacity has been announced for the 1960's. One of the new features is the utilization of birch and other hardwoods, especially for kraft pulping, another is the change in the log transportation pattern, which is gradually taking place. Except for the main river districts, where the traditional river-driving is still the most economic means of transportation, new forest roads are continually being constructed, making new forest areas accessible.

At the same time as the fairly modest quantitative expansion there is a trend towards the production of higher grades. An increasing quantity, now almost half the chemical pulp, is bleached, and an increasing fraction is converted to paper, although the region will in the foreseeable future remain predominantly a pulp exporter. The paper production is shown in Table 22.21. Two-thirds of it is exported, mainly to Europe. Among the leading pulp producers in the three countries are Borregaards A/S, Norway, Svenska Cellulosa AB, Sweden, and Enso–Gutzeit Oy, Finland.

Table 22.21. Paper production of Northern Europe, 1937–1960. M t

	1937			1951			1960		
	Paper	Board	Total	Paper	Board	Total	Paper	Board*	Total
Norway	0.4	0.1	0.5	0.4	0.2	0.6	0.7	0.2	0.9
Sweden	0.8	0.3	1.1	1.1	0.5	1.6	1.8	0.9	2.7
Finland	0.6	0.1	0.7	0.7	0.3	1.0	1.5	0.7	2.2
Total	1.8	0.5	2.3	2.2	1.0	3.2	4.0	1.8	5.8

* Of which about half is fiber boards from defibrated wood pulp.

6. CENTRAL AND SOUTHERN EUROPE

This part of Europe is less homogeneous than Northern Europe in respect of the pulp industry. A feature in common for most countries is the lack of pulpwood and especially of coniferous pulpwood. As the region is heavily populated and industrialized, it has a considerable demand for pulp and paper, which are both imported to a large extent, especially from Scandinavia and Finland. However, some countries, mainly France and Germany, but also Austria, Czechoslovakia, Poland and Italy, have developed their own pulp industry, producing about 5 M t of pulp annually, Table 22.22. Groundwood and sulfite pulping predominate, and kraft pulp is produced in remarkably small quantities, half of which in France. Raw materials are spruce, fir, Scots pine and in France also maritime pine, and an increasing quantity of hardwoods, especially beech.

The short-fibered pulps, in which are included the straw pulp of Holland (0.4 M t annually), Italy, etc., the eucalypt pulp of Portugal and Spain (0.1 M t) and some esparto pulp, are the main hope for future expansion of these pulp industries, together with pine-based mills connected with reforestation schemes. The proper combination of short-fibered pulp of Central and Southern Europe with softwood pulp from Northern Europe will be one of the main lines of development for the European pulp and paper industry. As regards dissolving pulps, beech has already been successfully processed in France, Germany and Italy, and eucalypts in Spain and Italy.

Table 22.22. Pulp production of Central and Southern Europe, 1960. M t

	France	West Germany	East Germany	Austria	Czecho-slovakia	Poland	Italy	Total
Mechanical	0.4	0.7	0.3	0.2	0.1	0.2	0.2	2.1
Sulfite	0.3	0.8	0.3	0.4	0.4	0.1	0.2	2.5
Kraft	0.3	0.0	0.0	0.1	0.0	0.1	0.1	⸴ 0.6
Mechanical (defibrated)	0.1	0.1						0.3
Total	1.1	1.6	0.6	0.7	0.5	0.4	0.5	5.5

IV. Costs of Pulp Manufacture

The economic aspects are essential in most problems involved in the pulping processes. A technical book cannot enter into any details on this subject, but a few fundamentals may be added. In the manufacturing costs of pulp, the wood costs enter with about 50–75%. The pulpwood prices as well as the wood consumption are therefore important considerations. The pulpwood prices are widely varying over the world, and it is difficult to get comparable figures, since they are quoted in different currency, different wood measures, at different stages of woods operation and transportation. The decisive price figure is that *delivered at mill*. Of the wood measures, cord, cunit, 1,000 board feet, cubic foot, solid cubic meter, loose cubic meter, stacked cubic meter, wet ton, dry ton, long, metric or short, the most rational one for comparisons is *dry metric ton* of wood. This is because bark volume, crookedness, water content and wood density all vary and give incomparable volume units. Thus, Table 22.23 tries to give a fair estimation of the situation in 1960 in the main pulp-producing regions, expressing the price figures in U.S. $ per metric ton of dry wood, delivered at mill. The enormous variation reflects partly the supply–demand situation, partly the location of the industry in relation to the markets, partly also the forest labor rates, the ease of transportation, the rate of forest growth, and the land value in competition with other crops, etc. There is also a considerable variation in the pulpwood prices with the pulp market situation over the years, but the long-term trend is invariably towards increasing wood prices. Finally, the custom of measuring pulpwood by volume often tends to favor the lighter-weight woods. The differences between hardwoods and softwoods are to some extent a result of this, although the major reason is that technical methods have not yet advanced to make hardwood as popular as softwood in pulping and pulp use, compared with the often abundant supply. The difference often met in the prices of spruce and pine, or of hemlock and Douglas fir, originates from the fact that the use of pines and Douglas fir for groundwood and sulfite pulp is limited for technical reasons.

The factor next in importance to pulpwood prices is wood consumption. For the same reasons as those mentioned for quoting prices, it is preferred in this comparison to list the wood consumption in *tons of dry wood per ton of 90% dry pulp*. The reason for expressing the weight of pulp as air-dry is that all pulp production figures and prices are quoted per air-dry ton. The mechanical losses in the handling of wood and pulp are in a well-managed mill limited to about 5%, which has been allowed for in the calculation for all processes. Table 22.24 shows that the wood consumption varies between the extremes of 1 and 3 tons. The conversion costs will vary according to the pulp grade. Of the total factory costs, the wood costs are therefore in Scandinavia at present about three-fourths for unbleached and two-thirds for bleached grades and groundwood pulps from softwood, and the corresponding values for regions with a less tense pulpwood situation are two-thirds and one half. The capital costs

Table 22.23. Pulpwood prices, delivered at mill, U.S. $ per metric ton of bone dry wood

Region	Species	Price $/t
Canada, eastern	Spruce, fir	30
western	,, ,,	22
U.S.A., north	,, ,,	26
,,	Pine	22
,,	Hardwoods	17
west	Spruce, hemlock	24
,,	Douglas fir	20
,,	Saw-mill waste	15
,,	Hardwoods	17
south	Pines (longleaf, slash)	16
,,	Pines (loblolly, shortleaf)	18
,,	Gum	16
,,	Oak	14
Scandinavia	Spruce	36
	Pine	33
	Birch	24
Central Europe	Beech	18
	Poplar	25
Southern Europe	Eucalypt	13
South Africa	Pine	12
	Eucalypt	8
South America	,,	5

for pulp mills vary considerably with the process, the location and the size of the mill. Roughly speaking, a mill with an annual capacity of 100,000 t will involve an investment of $5 M for groundwood, $10 M for unbleached sulfite, $15 M for unbleached kraft or bleached sulfite, and $20 M for bleached kraft. The final differences in the manufacturing costs of various pulp grades are comparatively well reflected in the prices paid for market pulp in a normal year, Table 22.25, although the supply–demand situation may have caused minor deviations.

Table 22.24. Pulpwood consumption, t of dry wood per t of 90% pulp

Pulp type	Wood consumption, t/t_{90}
Groundwood, unbleached	1.0
,, bleached	1.0
,, bleached, poplar	1.2
Chemigroundwood, hardwoods	1.2
Cold caustic, hardwoods	1.2
Neutral sulfite, unbleached, hardwoods	1.3
,, ,, bleached, hardwoods	1.7
Kraft, unbleached, pine	2.0
,, ,, hardwoods	1.8
,, bleached, pine	2.2
,, ,, hardwoods	2.0
Sulfite, unbleached, spruce	1.8
,, ,, hardwoods	1.8
,, bleached, strong, spruce	2.1
,, ,, soft, spruce	2.2
,, ,, strong, hardwoods	2.0
,, ,, soft, hardwoods	2.1
,, ,, rayon, spruce	2.4
,, ,, acetate, spruce	2.8
,, ,, rayon, hardwoods	2.5
Prehydrolysis–kraft, bleached, cord, pine	2.7
,, ,, ,, ,, hardwoods	2.8

Table 22.25. Approximate prices for market pulps 1959, U.S. $/metr. t_{90}

Pulp type	Price $/t
Groundwood, unbleached	91
,, bleached	108
Kraft, unbleached	130
,, semibleached	155
,, bleached	173
,, bleached, hardwoods	168
Soda, bleached	163
Sulfite, unbleached	150
,, bleached	171
,, bleached, hardwoods	166
,, rayon	175
,, rayon, hardwoods	166
,, acetate	207

Author Index

Aaltio, E., 517, 709
Aarsrud, N., 613, 700
Abrahamsson, B., 192, 233, 481, 495, 693
Acree, S. F., 1109, 1129
Adams, A. H., 738, 761
Adams, G. A., 104, 160, 162, 165, 219, 233, 251, 1177, 1184
Adams, R. L., 973, 991
Adamson, G. A., 692, 693
Adkins, H., 152, 233
Adler, E., 166, 174, 177, 178, 180, 184, 187, 189, 190, 194, 195, 198, 201, 207, 211, 213, 215, 216, 217, 218, 233, 234, 246, 520, 522, 525, 548, 592, 693, 706, 821, 830, 853, 882, 895, 913, 1049, 1057
Aflenzer, F. A., 329, 363
Ahlén, L., 522, 693
Ahlfors, S. E:son, 746, 760
Ahlm, C. E., 161, 175, 234, 609, 638, 646, 647, 693
Ahlm, E., 592, 693
Aiken, W. H., 1144, 1180
Aitken, K. G., 888, 913
Akamatsu, K., 548, 693
Åkerman, R., 232, 234
Akhtar, M., 447, 449, 693
Ålander, P., 1112, 1128
Alexander, A. E., 1040, 1060
Alexander, W. J., 105, 234
Alfredsson, B., 189, 199, 200, 205, 206, 207, 210, 211, 239, 250, 590, 591, 592, 593, 594, 604, 693, 697, 699, 948, 950, 990
Algvere, K. V., 41
Alhojärvi, J., 585, 693, 741, 744, 760
Allgulander, O., 652, 693
Alm, A. A., 302, 304, 363, 640, 649, 713
Alm, N. O., 882
Almin, K. A., 739, 749, 751, 760
Alsfeld, M., 692, 693
Améen, W., 1116, 1128
Ancker, C., 382, 384, 399
Anderson, A. B., 223, 234
Anderson, A. W., 1173, 1180
Anderson, C. A., 271, 272, 274, 295, 363, 507, 543, 586, 651, 693
Anderson, C. B., 853, 883, 1074, 1080
Anderson, E., 94, 98, 99, 100, 160, 162, 234
Anderson, O. E., 815, 830
Andersson, P. E., 789, 830
Andersson, T., 781, 834
Anderzén, O., 175, 207, 213, 234, 591, 693
Andress, K. R., 114, 117, 139, 143, 234

Andrews, H., 374, 399
Andrews, I. H., 886, 913
Anker-Rasch, O., 143, 234, 651, 693
Annergren, G., 158, 164, 234, 264, 274, 505, 510, 514, 522, 574, 612, 617, 641, 642, 649, 651, 655, 656, 671, 693, 1038, 1057, 1176, 1180
Ant-Wuorinen, O., 1115, 1128
Anthis, A., 160, 161, 234
Anthoni, B., 585, 586, 693, 1175, 1180
Apler, N. H., 1126, 1130, 1173, 1174, 1184
Arend, J. L., 261, 274
Aries, R. S., 805, 830
Arldt, H. G., 186, 234, 643, 693
van Arsdel, W. B., 718, 760
Armstrong, B., 870, 883, 889, 915
Armstrong, N., 888, 913
Arnborg, T., 258, 275
Arnold, G. C., 938, 944, 988
Arnold, H. E., 153, 237
Arnold, K., 610, 713
Arnold, S., 500, 700
Aronovsky, S. I., 233, 234, 411, 422, 432, 433, 663, 664, 672, 681, 682, 684, 685, 688, 689, 691, 692, 693
Arreguin, B., 219, 234
Ashorn, T., 206, 208, 234, 593, 594, 694
Asoka, H., 108, 234
Aspinall, G. O., 156, 160, 161, 162, 234
Asplund, A., 286, 294, 332, 343, 363, 395, 399
Asplund, G., 395, 399
Assarsson, A., 604, 694, 1005, 1013, 1020, 1022
Asunmaa, S., 72, 73, 75, 84, 88, 111, 157, 171, 234, 285, 312, 313, 315, 316, 317, 363, 508, 694, 1141, 1142, 1180
Atack, D., 372, 373, 374, 379, 394, 399
Atchison, J. E., 106, 234, 432, 433, 678, 684, 688, 694, 1162, 1180
Aulin-Erdtman, G., 167, 177, 181, 182, 183, 184, 187, 199, 234, 522, 694
Aurell, R., 304, 305, 363, 561, 603, 638, 642, 649, 694

Bache-Wiig, C., 404, 433
Bachlott, D. D., 1117, 1127, 1128, 1176, 1180
Back, E., 224, 231, 232, 235, 1024, 1027, 1029, 1033, 1039, 1040, 1044, 1045, 1047, 1057, 1058, 1114, 1129
Back, S., 887, 913
Backman, A., 258, 271, 275

1205

Bäckström, C. H., 542, 548, 550, 651, 694
Badehuizen, N. P., 117, 247
Bailey, A. J., 81, 84, 88, 157, 171, 192, 235, 285, 312, 672, 693
Bailey, E. L., 651, 662, 694
Bailey, I. W., 60, 68, 69, 88
Bain, A. M., 341, 363
Baird, P. K., 415, 433
Baker, P. S., 1144, 1180
Baker, R. E., 568, 694, 711, 725, 760, 779, 803, 830
Bakken, J. F., 343, 365
Baldwin, N., 350, 363
Ball, D. H., 161, 162, 235
Bandel, W., 1176, 1180
Bandelin, C. E., 404, 433
Bandurski, R. S., 69, 88
Banerjee, S. K., 161, 235
Bannan, M. W., 69, 88, 220, 235
Barber, G. A., 219, 252
Barker, E. R., 815, 830
Barnes, F., 222, 223, 235
Barnett, B., 975, 988
Barry, A. J., 117, 139, 235
Barsalou, M., 568, 569, 571, 694, 815, 830
Barton, J. S., 976, 988
Barton, R. W., 886, 887, 888, 889, 891, 893, 903, 904, 906, 911, 914
Bartunek, R., 142, 242, 1117, 1126, 1128, 1176, 1180
Bassett, H. P., 1001, 1022
Bassham, J. A., 69, 88, 100, 101, 235
Bath, J., 111, 237
Battista, O. A., 112, 127, 235
Bauer, E., 456, 704
Bauer, T. W., 781, 788, 830, 1124, 1128
Baum, M., 821, 831
Baumann, E., 694
Bayer, A., 197, 235
Beall, G., 126, 235
Beath, L. R., 394, 400, 418, 419, 437
Beaudry, J. P., 1174, 1180
Beaujean, J., 413, 433
Beazley, W. B., 456, 467, 468, 478, 559, 561, 674, 694, 813, 831
Beck, M. M., 1118, 1128
Becker, E., 167, 222, 223, 251
Beckman, E., 166, 235
Beeman, L. A., 886, 887, 889, 894, 901, 904, 907, 908, 910, 911, 914
Beevers, H., 219, 244
Behr, E. A., 363
Bellak, F., 610, 698
Bender, F., 94, 99, 236
Benedicks, C., 342, 363
Benjamin, L. R., 545, 694
Benko, J., 192, 235

Bennett, C. F., 1129
Benny, J., 846, 882
Benoist, S., 103, 235
Benson, H. K., 568, 694
Bergek, T., 525, 545, 604, 694, 1004, 1005, 1006, 1007, 1013, 1022
Bergholm, A., 789, 790, 791, 808, 831
Bergling, K., 680, 704
Bergson, C. R., 817, 831
Bergström, H., 227, 232, 235, 587, 694, 772, 821, 828, 831, 1026, 1027, 1058
Bergström, R. E., 725, 730, 732, 763, 769, 770, 823, 831
Berklund, B. L., 261, 275
Berl, E., 145, 146, 148, 235
Bernardin, L. J., 657, 694
Bernstein, A., 993, 998, 1022
Berry, L. R., 805, 831
Berthier, R., 610, 642, 694
Bertrand, G., 103, 235, 683, 694
Berzins, V., 1112, 1132
Bethge, P. O., 940, 988, 1109, 1111, 1128
Beuschlein, W. L., 815, 816, 831
Bevan, E. J., 944, 988
Beveridge, J. B., 347, 363
Bhat, R. V., 415, 433, 615, 694
Bhujang, K. S., 965, 988
Bialkowsky, H. W., 568, 694, 772, 773, 830, 831, 1159, 1182
Bickell, L. K., 795, 831
Biggs, W. A., 429, 433, 768, 831
Bilberg, E., 642, 694, 772, 773, 831
Bildt, O., 272, 275, 295, 319, 363, 507, 543, 694
Billwiller, J., 651, 694
Binger, H. P., 514, 694
Bishop, C. T., 104, 219, 233
Bishop, F. W., 161, 162, 235, 694, 1072, 1079
Bisset, I. J. W., 53, 67
Bittner, F., 167, 169, 177, 238
Bixler, A. L. M., 313, 314, 315, 363
Björk, C. F., 105, 249
Björkman, A., 167, 174, 175, 176, 177, 178, 180, 182, 186, 192, 193, 199, 235, 287, 363, 482, 500, 590, 694, 789, 805, 823, 830, 831
Björkman, C. B., 213, 240, 519, 531, 700, 725, 726, 727, 760
Björkman, E., 257, 262, 275, 542, 695
Björkqvist, K. J., 158, 164, 235, 970, 988, 1017, 1022, 1078, 1079, 1175, 1180
Björnhaug, A., 114, 116, 235
Björnstad, P. L., 402, 433
Bland, D. E., 192, 235
Bletzinger, J. C., 1144, 1180
Blikstad, F., 791, 831

Bloomberg, W., 674, 675, 695
Bloomen, T., 817, 831
Blume, R. C., 1127, 1128
Blundell, M. J., 179, 252
Boadway, J. D., 747, 748, 760, 761
Bodenheimer, V. B., 413, 433
Boedecker, H., 517, 700
Boehm, R. M., 294, 363, 398, 399
Boesen, C. E., 682, 692, 695
Bois, P. J., 264, 275
Bolam, F., 1140, 1180
Bölviken, A., 418, 433
Bonavia, M., 676, 691, 692, 695
Bönisch, A., 993, 996, 997, 998, 999, 1001, 1008, 1015, 1023
Bonnier, H., 688, 713
Booth, K. G., 568, 695, 1152, 1185
Boozer, R. F., 354, 363
Borchers, E., 302, 363
Borgen, G. L., 1127, 1128, 1174, 1180
Borgin, K., 1127, 1128, 1178, 1179, 1180, 1183
Borišek, R., 651, 695, 821, 831
Borlew, P. B., 585, 586, 587, 695, 917, 989, 1112, 1129
Boryniec, A., 1127, 1128
Bosshard, H. H., 58, 67, 76, 88
Botto Micca, G., 692, 695
Bouchayer, H., 421, 434
Bouchonnet, A., 148, 235
Bouveng, H. O., 99, 159, 160, 161, 162, 163, 235
Boyer, R. Q., 805, 806, 831, 833
Braconnot, H., 103, 235
Bradley, L., 422, 434, 888, 914
Bradway, K. E., 165, 235, 1178, 1179, 1180
Braidy, H., 1115, 1128
Brainerd, F. W., 1155, 1182
Brandon, C. E., 1124, 1128
Brasch, D. J., 160, 161, 235
Braun, C. A., 422, 434
Brauns, F. E., 162, 174, 175, 186, 205, 235, 236, 610, 695, 900, 914, 929, 988
Brauns, O., 166, 235, 390, 399, 548, 695
Braunscheid, F., 545, 703
Brax, A. J., 725, 726, 760
Bray, M. W., 420, 421, 427, 429, 434, 576, 585, 610, 612, 613, 615, 618, 620, 621, 623, 624, 635, 636, 648, 695, 706, 708, 711, 1153, 1180
Bray, W., 1100, 1101, 1103
Brecht, W., 259, 275, 325, 326, 350, 363, 368, 374, 385, 386, 399, 402, 404, 407, 434, 741, 745, 746, 748, 757, 760, 761, 904, 911, 914
Brenner, F. C., 109, 235

Briggs, B. T., 555, 651, 658, 665, 695, 702
Briggs, D. A. E., 615, 695
Brink, D. L., 673, 674, 675, 695
Brissaud, L., 106, 235
Bristow, O. J., 826, 827, 831
Brodsky, A. E., 527, 695
Bromley, W. S., 261, 275
Bronnert, E., 995, 1022
Brookbank, E. B., 548, 695
Brötz, A., 139, 242
Brown, H. P., 42, 49, 50, 54, 67
Brown, J. C., 1142, 1180
Brown, K. J., 354, 363, 413, 415, 416, 417, 434, 610, 614, 615, 616, 695, 706
Brown, R. B., 1155, 1180
Brown, R. W., 791, 833
Brown, S. A., 102, 169, 236
Brown, W. F., 271, 276
Browne, C. A., 166, 236
Browning, B. L., 173, 222, 223, 224, 236, 965, 988, 1029, 1054, 1058, 1107, 1109, 1110, 1128, 1131, 1142, 1144, 1180
Brumley, G. W., 719, 732, 761
Brune, K., 853, 883
Brunes, B. T., 717, 719, 723, 761, 774, 776, 779, 789, 790, 791, 831
Bruun, C. E., 615, 703
Bruun, H. H., 615, 695, 1027, 1058
Bryde, Ö., 102, 106, 108, 236, 302, 363, 508, 516, 695, 1024, 1058
Bublitz, L. O., 173, 223, 224, 236
Bublitz, W. J., 976, 978, 1029, 1058
Buchanan, M. A., 175, 182, 186, 205, 223, 224, 225, 228, 235, 236, 623, 695, 1025, 1058
Bucher, H., 72, 75, 79, 80, 88, 291, 297, 313, 314, 315, 317, 363, 540, 695, 1141, 1180
Buckman, S. J., 297, 298, 363
Buervskaja, A. D., 996, 1022
Bugg, E. J., 413, 434
Bunton, C. A., 509, 695
Burch, G., 826, 828, 831
Burchhardt, Ö., 336, 363
Burdynski, R. F., 604, 695, 993, 1003, 1015, 1016, 1022
Burgeni, E., 117, 236
Burns, I. G., 678, 695
Burr, H. K., 298, 363
Burton, H., 236
Burton, J. O., 1115, 1128
Busch, H., 1008, 1022
Busche, L. R., 183, 185, 186, 248, 1111, 1130
Bush, W. H., 1062, 1079
Buurman, A., 165, 236, 1173, 1180
Byerrum, R. U., 169, 236

Byrne, J. R., 413, 415, 434
Byström, S., 651, 695

Cabella, S., 415, 436
Cable, D. A., 271, 275
Cabott, I. M., 201, 203, 236, 497, 499, 592, 695
Cady, L. C., 298, 299, 363
Calhoun, J. M., 478, 479, 497, 500, 559, 561, 574, 695
Calhoun, T. B., 725, 730, 761
Calkin, J. B., 153, 236, 597, 695
Calkins, C. R., 981, 983, 989, 1073, 1079
Calkins, D. L., 746, 761
Callin, G., 262, 275
Calvin, M., 69, 88, 100, 101, 235
Campbell, J., 806, 807, 831, 972, 988
Campbell, W. B., 372, 373, 374, 376, 377, 399, 457, 695, 846, 882, 1140, 1180
Campbell, W. G., 162, 174, 236
Cameron, E. P., 385, 399
Canadian Standard CPPA, 587, 588, 695
Cann, E. D., 610, 696
Cannon, J. J. R., 310, 363, 478, 559, 561, 696
Cape, G., 341, 363
Captain, H. A., 674, 675, 689, 696, 714
Carlberg, G. L., 222, 236
Carlsmith, L. A., 351, 353, 363
Carlson, G., 823, 824, 831, 1096, 1103
Carlson, O. T., 224, 235, 1027, 1033, 1058
Carlson, R. E., 1095, 1103
Carmody, W. R., 209, 236, 922, 948, 960, 988
Carnap, A., 126, 243
Carpenter, C., 615, 696
Carr, R. L., 973, 987, 988
Carroll, C. W., 618, 628, 696
Carroll, M., 1142, 1180
Carter, M. O., 160, 234
Casciani, F., 888, 907, 913, 914, 970, 987, 988, 1065, 1066, 1068, 1073, 1074, 1079, 1096, 1103, 1162, 1180
Casey, J. P., 677, 696, 715, 761, 1144, 1180
Cederquist, K. N., 429, 430, 434, 791, 807, 831, 974, 988
Cellulose Development Corp., 676, 696
Centola, G., 139, 236, 545, 696
Ceragioli, G., 413, 415, 430, 431, 434, 436
Chadeyron, L., 610, 696, 853, 882, 1062, 1079
Chadwick, A. F., 888, 907, 913, 914, 1065, 1073, 1079
Chambers-Allison, R., 402, 434
Chandler, J. B., 725, 732, 761
Charles, F. R., 1118, 1128, 1176, 1180

Chédin, J., 139, 236
Chen, C. L., 179, 239
Chen, K., 1126, 1129
Chêne, M., 978, 988, 1052, 1058
Cherches, K. A., 1027, 1058
Chesley, K. G., 368, 399, 430, 434, 610, 648, 696
Chidester, G. H., 271, 276, 295, 300, 365, 420, 421, 430, 431, 434, 543, 545, 548, 553, 559, 568, 572, 611, 613, 692, 696, 702, 706, 886, 914, 1152, 1181
Chittenden, A. E., 687, 696
Chollet, J. L., 646, 696
Chowdhury, J. K., 146, 246
Christensen, G. N., 363
Christenson, T., 429, 434
Christiani, W., 797, 801, 802, 831
Christiansen, C. B., 342, 363, 427, 434, 610, 625, 636, 639, 646, 647, 649, 650, 696
Christoffersson, K., 600, 696, 1003, 1015, 1022
Cittadini, A., 676, 687, 696
Claeson, S., 105, 236
Clark, G. I., 114, 240
Clark, G. L., 139, 195, 236, 1153, 1181
Clark, J. C., 175, 236
Clark, J. d'A., 295, 363, 844, 882, 1140, 1141, 1144, 1145, 1150, 1152, 1155, 1158, 1181
Clark, T. F., 347, 353, 363, 685, 687, 691, 696
Clayton, D. W., 605, 608, 696
Clerk, J. F., 676, 696
Clermont, L. P., 92, 94, 99, 100, 120, 223, 236
Clewell, D. H., 848, 882
Clibbens, D. A., 953, 960, 965, 988, 1004, 1022
Cliff, W. R., 801, 831
Cochrane, J. A., 385, 399, 402, 422, 434
Coenen, M., 146, 236
Cogan, E., 886, 903, 914
Cohen, W. E., 106, 125, 237, 252, 615, 616, 704, 1124, 1128
Cole, E. J., 354, 363
Collicut, S. A., 374, 376, 385, 386, 399
Collin, P. H., 549, 551, 651, 665, 696, 974, 983, 985, 988
Collins, R. E., 429, 434
Collins, T. T., 772, 831
Colombo, P., 354, 364, 413, 414, 415, 434, 586, 613, 635, 696, 738, 761
Coma, J. G., 827, 828, 833
Conner, W. P., 192, 236
Conrad, C. C., 109, 127, 236
Conrad, C. M., 137, 236
Conrad, F. H., 815, 816, 831

Conrad, P., 1096, 1103
Converse, C. W., 732, 738, 761
Cooper, F. P., 161, 162, 235
Coppens, N., 219, 236
Coppick, S., 106, 117, 237
Corbett, W. M., 600, 602, 603, 604, 663, 696, 828, 831, 1007, 1013, 1022
Cordingley, R. H., 520, 696
Cordingley, S., 1024, 1042, 1060
Corey, A. J., 479, 485, 497, 500, 574, 696, 817, 831
Cornell, C. F., 801, 833
Correns, E., 76, 88, 651, 665, 696
Corrin, M. L., 232, 237, 1045, 1058
Corte, H., 739, 749, 761, 1142, 1181
Coster, N. W., 940, 988
Coté, W. A., 849, 882, 901, 914
Cottrall, L. G., 1124, 1125, 1128, 1140, 1159, 1181
Courtaulds Inc., 1175, 1181
Cowan, W. F., 272, 275, 613, 696
Cox, B. D., 623, 696
Craig, K. A., 888, 914
Crandall, H. C., 628, 696
Crooks, K. L., 341, 364
Croon, I., 111, 116, 151, 152, 153, 154, 158, 159, 161, 162, 165, 166, 237, 248, 429, 436, 522, 597, 598, 603, 605, 606, 607, 608, 642, 651, 655, 693, 696, 897, 898, 901, 914, 1031, 1033, 1058, 1160, 1181
Cross, C. F., 422, 434, 461, 553, 697, 944, 988
Cross, R. H., 746, 761
Crotogine, H. F., 420, 437
Croup, A. H., 744, 747, 748, 754, 762
Crowe, G. A., 568, 697
Cundy, P. F., 1118, 1128
Cunningham, G. L., 1096, 1101, 1103
Curran, C. E., 418, 420, 434, 544, 610, 612, 613, 615, 636, 648, 697, 960, 988, 1152, 1153, 1180, 1181

Dadswell, H. E., 53, 60, 62, 67, 84, 89, 94, 99, 192, 234, 254, 260, 264, 275, 320, 367, 412, 413, 415, 438, 1152, 1155, 1185
Dahm, H. P., 651, 655, 697
Dahlén, A., 223, 237
Dailey, J. D., 972, 988, 1097, 1103
Dall, K., 167, 174, 239
Darmstadt, W. J., 779, 803, 831
Davenport, D. A., 147, 242
Davidson, G. F., 130, 133, 135, 237, 600, 697, 920, 951, 988, 1005, 1007, 1022, 1054, 1055, 1058, 1115, 1128
Davis, B. D., 170, 237
Davis, M. N., 842, 844, 882

Davis, W. E., 139, 237, 1176, 1181
Day, G. A., 974, 975, 988, 1097, 1103
De Carufel, G., 418, 434
De Haas, G. G., 772, 773, 830, 831
De la Roza, J. J., 351, 364, 651, 684, 692, 709
Dean, W. L., 1126, 1128
Decker, N. N., 404, 434
Dedert, W. G., 725, 730, 761
Degussa, 1096, 1103
Delagrange, L. A., 342, 364
Delcroix, P., 674, 697
Delga, J., 683, 694
Dence, C., 208, 209, 237, 251, 930, 938, 988, 991
Denham, W. S., 103, 237
Dentremont, A. E., 404, 434, 746, 761
Derksen, J. C., 139, 244
Desch, H. E., 42, 67
Deshpande, P. R., 688, 697
Desorbay, G., 674, 697
Detcher, T. E., 429, 436, 568, 697
Dhingra, D. R., 692, 697
Dickerscheid, J. L., 610, 623, 625, 697
Dickey, E. E., 103, 237
Diedrichs, B. E. J., 973, 988
Diehl, W. F., 760, 761, 1083, 1088
Diehm, R. A., 413, 434
Dietrich, G., 177, 186, 239
Dietz, H., 1094, 1103
Dietzel, R., 456, 457, 697
Dignam, M., 517, 711
Dillén, S., 823, 831
van Dillewijn, C., 680, 697
Diwald, J., 174, 239
Dixon, H. P., 271, 276
Dobry, A., 104, 237
Dodgen, H., 1100, 1101, 1104
Doering, H., 1115, 1128
Donetzhuber, A., 142, 237
Donofrio, C. P., 692, 703, 899, 900, 915
Doriswamy, K., 576, 697
Dorland, R. M., 302, 364, 394, 395, 399, 420, 434, 504, 561, 563, 568, 697, 781, 788, 830
Dorman, K. W., 258, 275
Dörr, R. E., 651, 662, 664, 692, 697, 1052, 1058, 1176, 1179, 1181
Doty, P. M., 104, 237
Doughty, R. H., 844, 882, 1140, 1155, 1181
Dowsley, A. H., 1095, 1103
Dozier, E. L., 732, 761
Drefahl, G., 123, 246
Dreher, E., 192, 252
Drewsen, V., 422, 434
van Drunen, V., 648, 708
Dryselius, E., 119, 120, 165, 237

Du Rietz, C., 477, 494, 697
Dubach, M., 745, 748, 757, 761, 1176, 1181
Dunbar, T. L., 651, 658, 697
Dunbar, T. W., 1083, 1088
Duncan, E. P., 940, 988, 1095, 1103
Dunlop, F., 66, 67
Dunning, J. W., 732, 738, 761
Durand, R. W., 1025, 1058
Durant, L. G., 347, 352, 364, 424, 434
Durfee, W. H., 126, 237
Durkess, C. L., 349, 366
Dürr, W., 210, 239
Dutton, G. G. S., 160, 237
Duvall, T. C., 411, 435
Dyer, E., 153, 237, 1127, 1128
Dyfverman, A., 123, 124, 238

Easley, L. T., 258, 275
Easterwood, M., 166, 252
Eastwood, P. R., 427, 434, 576, 695
Eber, G., 673, 702
Eberhardt, G., 169, 237
Eberhardt, L., 290, 294, 328, 330, 332, 351, 364, 392, 393, 399, 413, 434
Ebersole, W. M., 746, 761
Edhborg, A., 195, 237
Edling, G., 772, 776, 777, 831
Edlund, E., 610, 712
Edwardes, V. P., 262, 270, 275
Eftring, K. E.. 555, 651, 655, 697
Egerton, G. S., 137, 237, 854, 882
Eggert, J., 651, 697
Eidem, I., 613, 700, 717, 761, 819, 831
Eie, R., 744, 746, 747, 748, 754, 755, 761
af Ekenstam, A., 125, 126, 139, 143, 237
Eklund, R., 261, 275
Ekman, K., 592, 697, 772, 832
Ekman, U., 561, 700
Ekstam, T., 1124, 1125, 1128, 1129
Ekvall, P., 1040, 1058
Eliaschberg, M. G., 200, 237, 461, 484, 697
Ellefsen, Ö., 116, 139, 185, 234, 244, 253, 1118, 1126, 1129
Ellis, J. W., 111, 237
Ellmer, L., 177, 233
Elsner, J. G., 402, 434
Elston, R., 1141, 1181
Emerton, H. W., 72, 75, 76, 79, 88, 1141, 1142, 1181
Emery, C., 106, 237
Enderlein, G. F., 628, 696
Enebo, L., 823, 832
Eneroth, O., 59, 67
Enge, L., 404, 434
Engel, H. C., 1144, 1160, 1183
Engel, O., 175, 237, 672, 697

Engel, W., 233, 238, 1053, 1058
Engelmann, H., 1179, 1181
Engelstad, A., 461, 553, 697
Englis, D. T., 162, 238
Enkvist, T., 175, 177, 185, 192, 195, 205, 206, 207, 208, 222, 224, 227, 238, 246, 586, 587, 589, 590, 591, 592, 593, 594, 623, 697, 698, 702, 705, 772, 828, 829, 830, 832, 1027, 1034, 1035, 1058
Enström, B., 158, 161, 164, 237, 254, 429, 436, 597, 605, 606, 607, 608, 696, 714, 1160, 1176, 1181, 1185
Enthwistle, D., 136, 238
Erdmann, E. J., 930, 988
Erdtman, H., 167, 175, 177, 186, 194, 195, 196, 197, 198, 204, 220, 227, 230, 238, 457, 480, 489, 490, 520, 542, 548, 654, 698, 821, 832
Erickson, A. E., 817, 832
Ericsson, L., 342, 366
Eriksson, E., 516, 518, 698, 920, 940, 941, 988
Eriksson, I., 462, 555, 556, 573, 574, 575, 698
Ernest, F. M., 1097, 1103
Ernsberger, F. M., 192, 238
Ernst, A. J., 412, 435, 682, 683, 685, 686, 687, 688, 691, 698
Esau, K., 42, 67
Esilä, A. J., 721, 725, 730, 761
Eslyn, W. E., 264, 276
von Essen, C. G., 342, 364
Evans, J. C. W., 294, 354, 364, 413, 424, 435, 1083, 1088
Evans, W. L., 1003, 1022
Eymery, A., 673, 713

FAO Monographs, 41, 42, 67, 258, 275, 678, 679, 690, 691, 698
Fabel, K., 1170, 1181
Fahey, D. J., 430, 435
Fahlgren, S., 746, 761
Falck, M., 457, 698
Falck, R., 63, 67
Faldner, J., 678, 698
Falk, H., 826, 828, 832
Farebrother, T. H., 844, 883
Faust, O., 997, 1022
Fedorishcheva, I. P., 610, 698
Feischl, O., 623, 714
Felicetta, V. F., 494, 495, 698
Fells, H. A., 894, 914
Fengel, D., 72, 89
Fennell, F. L., 886, 887, 888, 891, 892, 903, 904, 914
Feola, J. A., 223, 238
Ference, G. M., 264, 275

Ferguson, D. M., 889, 910, 914
Fex, O., 1175, 1185
Field, J. L., 427, 435
Finck, F., 92, 96, 243
Findley, M. E., 310, 364, 427, 435, 828, 829, 832
Fineman,O. 350, 355, 365, 582, 698, 878, 880, 883
Finnish Standard Method, 587, 588, 698
Firth, J. B., 894, 914
Fischer, E., 602, 687, 698
Fischer, E. W., 116, 238
Fischler, F., 602, 698, 1007, 1022
Fisher, D. G., 139, 238
Fisher, H. S., 1095, 1103
Fitzgerald, L. E., 1024, 1058
Flamm, E., 610, 698
Fleck, L. C., 94, 98, 223, 250
Flindt-Kruse, E., 682, 692, 695
Flinn, E. S., 424, 435
Flodén, I., 429, 435
Fones, R. E., 772, 773, 832
Fordyce, C. R., 146, 238, 246
Foreman, E. L., 162, 238
Forgacs, O. L., 60, 67, 78, 88, 320, 364, 379, 394, 395, 399, 1141, 1142, 1181
Forman, L. V., 615, 616, 698, 854, 883, 1151, 1181
Forni, P. A., 855, 857, 883
Forsaith, C. C., 42, 67
Forss, K., 517, 518, 698, 773, 774, 776, 832
Förster, F., 525, 527, 698, 1094, 1103
Foster, D. H., 160, 161, 162, 252
Foster, J., 745, 746, 750, 761
Fotiev, S. A., 817, 832, 922, 973, 988
Fowler, W. F., 1157, 1181
Fox, E. C., 354, 363
France, W. G., 192, 238
Frank, A., 219, 238
Frank, G., 145, 238
Frank, M. B., 106, 246
Frankel, T., 429, 435
Franzon, O., 600, 604, 698
Franzreb, J. P., 687, 698
Fraser, R. L., 746, 761
Freedman, H., 651, 698, 1071, 1079
Freeman, H., 744, 747, 748, 760, 761, 1045, 1058
Freeman, R. D., 223, 238
Frei, E., 76, 88
Freudenberg, K., 103, 124, 125, 167, 169, 173, 174, 175, 177, 179, 186, 187, 188, 190, 192, 193, 199, 201, 208, 210, 228, 495, 508, 520, 525, 698, 821, 822, 823, 832, 929, 988, 1109, 1129
Frey-Wyssling, A., 58, 67, 71, 72, 78, 80, 88, 102, 111, 112, 115, 239, 1053, 1058

Friedrich, A., 174, 239
Friele, L. F. C., 843, 883
Friese, G., 813, 832
Friese, H., 193, 239
Friis-Hansen, J., 801, 832
Frilette, V. J., 109, 239
Frisch, H. L., 514, 698
Froment, P., 978, 988
Froundjian, D., 1144, 1182
Fry, G., 410, 435
Fukuda, Y., 651, 702
Fukutome, T., 165, 248
Furman, K. E., 672, 698

Gabriel, H., 672, 708
Gagnon, L., 1083, 1088
Gajdos, J., 662, 698
Galanos, S., 456, 457, 697
Gard, A. J., 1052, 1058
Gardiner, W. C., 1096, 1103
Gardner, W. S., 746, 761
Gardon, J. L., 494, 699
Garegg, P. J., 161, 239
Garland, H., 76, 88, 285, 364
Garretson, H. H., 456, 471, 712
Garrett, G. A., 296, 364
Gärtner, W., 870, 884, 886, 887, 888, 889, 891, 901, 902, 903, 904, 907, 908, 911, 914, 915, 1071, 1080
Gary, W. T., 160, 161, 251
Gasche, U., 501, 542, 569, 571, 699
Gåsland, S., 1027, 1058
Gaslini, F., 207, 239
Gauvin, W. H., 781, 791, 808, 832
Gavelin, G., 748, 761, 1042, 1058
Geiger, E., 1114, 1129
Genberg, G. P., 917, 950, 988, 1111, 1129, 1157, 1181
Georgi, E. A., 146, 151, 246
Ghoneim, A. F. M., 687, 705
Gianola, G., 212, 239, 966, 976, 988
Gibbs, R. D., 66, 67
Gierer, J., 177, 180, 188, 189, 199, 200, 205, 206, 207, 208, 215, 233, 240, 591, 592, 593, 594, 699
Gierisch, W., 1109, 1129
Giertz, H. W., 72, 75, 89, 209, 212, 239, 418, 433, 563, 672, 699, 844, 846, 847, 848, 852, 853, 854, 855, 883, 901, 903, 914, 922, 923, 924, 927, 928, 940, 962, 976, 978, 988, 1061, 1079, 1111, 1122, 1129, 1141, 1144, 1159, 1181
Giese, E., 403, 435
Giguère, P. A., 457, 698
Gilles, T. L., 264, 275, 725, 730, 761
Gillespie, D. C., 799, 802, 832
Gillespie, R. J., 147, 239

Gilmont, P. L., 610, 648, 696
Ginaven, M. E., 738, 761
Givens, J. H., 1166, 1170, 1181
Gladding, E. K., 1114, 1129
Gläser, H., 265, 275
Glaudemans, C. P. J., 160, 161, 239
Glennie, D. W., 257, 262, 275, 610, 614, 710
Gloor, W. E., 146, 240
Gocke, W. A., 315, 326, 364
Godard, H. P., 179, 240
Goddard, R. E., 64, 67
Gohel, V. P., 662, 692, 699
Golben, M., 1127, 1129
Goldfinger, G., 131, 240, 309, 310, 364,
    503, 573, 699
Goldschmid, O., 177, 240
Goldsmith, V., 75, 88
Goliath, M., 114, 128, 199, 207, 240, 246,
    502, 699
Goodspeed, T. H., 233, 253
Goodwin, L. F., 799, 832
Goodwin, R. G., 347, 349, 351, 353, 364,
    424, 429, 435
Gordon, L. J., 568, 699
Goning, D. A. I., 107, 108, 160, 192, 240
Gortner, R. A., 411, 422, 432, 433, 663,
    664, 672, 673, 693, 1109, 1130
Goss, M. J., 166, 249, 673, 705
Göthner, K. F., 727, 761
Götze, K., 146, 240, 1166, 1181
Grace, N. H., 302, 364
Graff, J. H., 51, 52, 64, 67, 1152, 1153, 1181
Graham, D., 1151, 1181
Graham, J. A., 549, 651, 699
Gralén, N., 192, 242, 590, 699
Granath, M., 179, 240
Grand, L., 392, 399
Grandis, E., 692, 695
Grangaard, D. H., 209, 240, 922, 923, 924,
    925, 926, 988
Grangård, G., 815, 832
Grant, J., 678, 692, 695
Gravel, J. J. O., 781, 791, 808, 832
Green, H., 272, 275, 295, 364, 507, 543,
    544, 545, 613, 699
Green, H. V., 298, 367, 427, 437
Green, J. W., 603, 699, 828, 832
Greenwalt, J. E., 805, 832
Greminger, G. K., 146, 240
Gremler, E. R., 415, 435
Grewin, F. W., 775, 832
Grieve, J. R., 717, 719, 725, 730, 732, 761
Griffee, D., 815, 832
Grimes, W. S., 610, 695
Grindrod, J., 1083, 1088
Grögaard, L., 272, 275, 294, 295, 318,
    364, 507, 543, 550, 574, 613, 699, 703

Grohn, H., 174, 240
Grondal, B. L., 295, 364, 672, 699
Gross, S. T., 114, 240
Groth, K., 1025, 1058
Grotjohn, H., 146, 242
Guetlin, E. G., 1124, 1130
Guide, R. G., 792, 834
Guha, S. R. D., 662, 699
Gundermann, J., 117, 118, 139, 241
Gustafsson, C., 92, 94, 96, 97, 98, 99, 163,
    203, 210, 240, 499, 509, 602, 699, 710,
    1029, 1036, 1039, 1040, 1058, 1114,
    1129, 1140, 1142, 1143, 1144, 1183
Gustafsson, G. R., 1062, 1079, 1110, 1130
Gustafsson, R., 960, 965, 967, 991
Gustafsson, S., 542, 694
Gustavson, K. H., 822, 832

Haarmann, W., 167, 252
Haas, H., 106, 165, 240, 1179, 1181
Hachihama, Y., 548, 699
Haden-Guest, S., 41
Hader, R. N., 1166, 1181
Haegland, B., 342, 364
Hägglund, E., 42, 53, 54, 59, 65, 66, 67, 68,
    92, 94, 96, 99, 159, 163, 166, 174, 175,
    177, 178, 181, 192, 195, 196, 197, 201,
    203, 205, 209, 213, 215, 218, 240, 248,
    252, 260, 271, 276, 295, 299, 302, 310,
    364, 450, 457, 461, 463, 477, 479, 480,
    481, 489, 500, 504, 507, 517, 519, 520,
    523, 527, 531, 538, 541, 542, 543, 545,
    547, 548, 549, 555, 556, 559, 561, 562,
    563, 586, 587, 590, 591, 593, 603, 610,
    613, 618, 624, 628, 639, 645, 647, 649,
    651, 654, 698, 699, 700, 769, 774, 821,
    822, 828, 832, 922, 923, 928, 929, 930,
    988, 989, 1026, 1052, 1058, 1115, 1129,
    1154, 1159, 1181, 1182
Hägglund, S. E., 420, 435, 1158, 1182
Häggroth, S., 200, 217, 218, 233, 240, 477,
    479, 481, 490, 494, 552, 559, 700, 853,
    882, 895, 913, 1049, 1057
Haglund, G., 548, 550, 651, 700, 815, 832
Hakkarainen, N. H., 720, 725, 730, 761
Hale, J. D., 42, 50, 53, 67
Hall, G. A., 1157, 1182
Hall, L., 821, 822, 832
Haller, A. K., 827, 832
Haller, J. F., 973, 989
Haller, R., 130, 240
Hamada, T., 517, 518, 712
Hamaguti, E., 692, 700
Hamburger, R., 972, 989
Hamilton, J. K., 156, 158, 160, 161, 162,
    240, 241, 605, 606, 608, 701
Hamilton, R. P., 350, 355, 365, 582, 701

Han, S. T., 468, 704, 817, 834
Hannan, P. J., 349, 364
Hannunkari, L., 719, 725, 727, 732, 761
Hansel, S., 267, 275
Hansen, L. A., 64, 68
Hanson, F. S., 585, 624, 701
Happey, F., 146, 241
Hara, H., 1126, 1129
Harada, H., 80, 89
Harder, M., 1109, 1129
Harders-Steinhäuser, M., 99, 243, 679, 703, 1052, 1058
Harding, S. A., 418, 435, 517, 545, 556, 568, 704
Harland, W. G., 105, 148, 241, 1119, 1129
Harlow, W. M., 1157, 1181
Harnist, G., 302, 364
Harper, E. A., 730, 761
Harris, D. W., 563, 709
Harris, E. E., 174, 179, 201, 209, 241, 252, 643, 664, 701, 711, 823, 832
Harris, G., 227, 241, 1027, 1058
Harris, G. C., 644, 701
Harris, G. R., 568, 571, 701
Harris, M., 1114, 1115, 1129, 1131, 1160, 1184
Harrison, V. G. W., 842, 844, 847, 883
Harrison, W. D., 972, 981, 983, 989, 1073, 1079
Hart, J. S., 303, 364, 418, 421, 435, 545, 559, 560, 562, 563, 568, 574, 576, 610, 614, 615, 618, 624, 625, 628, 629, 635, 645, 646, 647, 648, 701, 705
Hartler, N., 135, 165, 211, 241, 250, 270, 271, 272, 273, 274, 275, 307, 320, 364, 461, 462, 507, 508, 516, 527, 530, 531, 542, 543, 553, 555, 603, 606, 613, 629, 630, 632, 634, 635, 640, 642, 644, 701, 893, 894, 895, 914, 1126, 1129, 1163, 1182
Hartmuth, R., 175, 241, 527, 672, 701
Harva, O., 232, 241, 1045, 1058
Hasche, R. L., 664, 701
Haskins, J. F., 123, 241
Haselton, W. R., 1142, 1182
Hasner, L., 192, 251
Hasselström, T., 227, 241, 1026, 1027, 1058
Hassler, J. W., 342, 364
Hästbacka, K., 199, 206 241 594, 701
Hasted, J. B., 142, 241
Hata, K., 548, 610, 701
Hatch, R. S., 553, 568, 701
Haworth, W. N., 103, 104, 160, 161, 241
Hazelquist, S. E., 779, 803, 832
Head, F. S. H., 640, 701
Hearon, W. M., 827, 832

Heath, M. A., 662, 710, 993, 1023
Hedborg, F., 651, 700, 940, 944, 989
Hedlund, I., 500, 501, 701
Hedlund, R., 310, 364, 618, 624, 639, 700
Hedström, B., 769, 770, 832
Heese, F., 753, 761
von Heideken, F., 261, 275
Heidt, L. J., 124, 241
Heitman, J. B., 1096, 1103
Heiwinkel, H., 203, 209, 240, 241, 520, 701, 922, 923, 929, 930, 989
Helferich, B., 146, 241
Hella, R. P., 888, 914
Hellenberg, G. H., 692, 707
Hembree, E. E., 1126, 1129
Henckel, N. N., 404, 435
Henderson, D. R., 165, 254, 1179, 1185
Henderson, J. T., 951, 989
Hendry, I. F., 754, 755, 762
Henley, D., 105, 116, 142, 241, 1118, 1129
Henning, T., 402, 437
Hentola, Y., 585, 701
Herbert, W., 347, 364
Herbst, J. H. E., 428, 435, 955, 957, 960, 989
Hergert, H. L., 901, 914
Herig, F., 1052, 1058
Heritage, C. C., 411, 418, 435
Hermans, P. H., 109, 110, 139, 241
Hernestam, S., 522, 693
Herty, C. H., 403, 435
Herzog, R. O., 109, 181, 241
Hess, K., 103, 114, 117, 118, 139, 143, 145, 146, 152, 161, 174, 241, 242, 253
Hessler, L. E., 109, 242
Hestrin, S., 102, 242
Heuer, J. H., 332, 364, 404, 435
Heuman, H. E., 174, 242
Heuser, E., 106, 108, 139, 142, 178, 242, 828, 832, 929, 930, 989, 1153, 1182
Hibbert, H., 178, 179, 180, 181, 194, 208, 209, 210, 224, 242, 248, 253, 672, 701, 822, 823, 832, 929, 930, 947, 960, 989, 1026, 1029 1058
Higgins, H. G., 111, 143, 247, 286, 364, 1144, 1182, 1183
Higuchi, T., 194, 244
von Hildebrandt, P. G., 732, 761
Hiley, W. E., 258, 275
Hilf, H. H., 259, 275
Hiller, L. A., 155, 242
Hillmer, A., 181, 241
Hilpert, R. S., 175, 242
Hilton, R. D., 354, 363
Hilz, H., 562, 701
Hinrichs, D. D., 676, 689, 690, 701, 702, 940, 941, 989

Hirschkind, W., 402, 435, 886, 914
Hirst, E. L., 103, 156, 160, 242, 243
Hisey, W. O., 920, 922, 978, 989
Hochberger, E., 960, 970, 989, 990
Hock, C. W., 117, 242
Höfert, H. J., 1121, 1129
Hofmann, R., 145, 242
Hoge, W. A., 525, 548, 549, 550, 702
Hogsed, M. I., 123, 241
Hoholik, F. S., 369, 399
Holgersson, S. P., 341, 364, 1025, 1058
Holl, M., 386, 399
Hollabaugh, C. B., 146, 242
Holland, W. W., 385, 400
Holmberg, B., 174, 175, 186, 192, 197,
    198, 205, 207, 213, 234, 242, 591, 693
Holmberg, C. V., 1157, 1182
Holmberg, J., 195, 240
Holst, G., 975, 978, 989, 1100, 1101, 1103
Holt, J. J., 580, 648, 711
Holta, V., 1126, 1132
Holtzer, A. M., 105, 242
Holzapfel, L., 233, 242, 1053, 1058
Holzer, W. F., 332, 364, 392, 393, 394,
    400, 542, 568, 610, 611, 615, 646, 702,
    704, 849, 883, 1152, 1153, 1182
Homans, R., 746, 761
Honeyman, J., 153, 242
Hönig, M., 178, 242
Hooper, H. S., 651, 702
Hooper, J. F., 555, 651, 658, 702
Hooper, S. W., 757, 761
Hoos, B. G., 974, 975, 988, 996, 1023
Höpner, T., 517, 518, 523, 687, 692, 702
Hopper, E. W., 342, 364
Horio, M., 158, 164, 171, 242, 545, 547,
    651, 662, 692, 702
van Horn, P., 1166, 1182
Horsey, E. F., 1144, 1182
Horton, J. L., 568, 702
Horton, P. M., 681, 702
Horváth, E., 673, 702
Hosaka, H., 415, 435
Hossfeld, R., 643, 707
Hottenroth, V., 997, 1022
Hougberg, B., 207, 238, 586, 587, 592,
    593, 698, 702
Houghton, E. O., 1157, 1181
Houwink, R., 105, 242
Howard, E. J., 301, 302, 364
Howard, G. C., 821, 832
Howsmon, J. A., 109, 110, 117, 127, 242
Hoyt, L. F., 1166, 1182
Hrubesky, C. E., 572, 702
Hsiung, W., 260, 276
Huber, B., 49, 67
Hudson, C. S., 130, 243, 951, 989

Hughes, E. D., 147, 242
Hughes, E. E., 1109, 1129
Hughey, G. B., 799, 833
Hull, J. H., 793, 833
Hull, W. Q., 568, 702
Hultsch, K., 594, 702
Humm, W., 817, 833
Hunger, G., 1142, 1163, 1182
Hunt, G. M., 296, 364
Hunt, K., 160, 237
Hunt, M. L., 104, 105, 243
Husain, S., 895, 914
Husband, R. M., 431, 435, 471, 472, 545,
    563, 702
Huseby, R. A., 342, 364
Husemann, E., 126, 130, 243, 254
Hussey, L. E., 103, 251
Hutino, K., 139, 243, 250
Hutton, F., 568, 694, 725, 760, 779, 803,
    830
Hyland, F., 51, 52, 67
Hyttinen, A., 404, 435

ICCA Standards, 1112, 1129
Ichikawa, S., 418, 435
Il'in, N. A., 375, 702
Imamura, R., 1174, 1182
Immergut, B., 114, 128, 158, 161, 165, 243,
    606, 702, 1179
Immergut, E. H., 105, 119, 243, 1119, 1129
Ingalls, E. G., 568, 711
Ingham, J. W., 920, 989
Ingmanson, W. L., 1142, 1189
Ingold, C. K., 146, 243, 483, 702
Ingruber, O. V., 447, 449, 456, 463, 466,
    650, 702
Inskeep, G. C., 1166, 1182
Irvine, J. C., 103, 243
Isbell, H. S., 122, 124, 130, 211, 243, 977,
    989
Isenberg, I. H., 51, 52, 64, 67, 222, 223,
    236, 243, 680, 702, 1153, 1181
Ivancic, A., 177, 181, 182, 185, 203, 209,
    243, 447, 448, 449, 536, 538, 539, 702,
    930, 931, 935, 937, 989
Ivanow, H. I., 662, 692, 702
Ivarsson, B., 192, 197, 217, 243
Ivnäs, L., 199, 243

Jack, W. Q., 1095, 1103
Jackson, D. T., 429, 435, 791, 833
Jackson, E. L., 130, 243, 951, 989
Jackson, G. E., 548, 550, 702
Jacques, H., 888, 914
Jäger, R., 1109, 1132
Jahn, E. C., 92, 93, 106, 158, 217, 220, 237,
    253, 254, 1157, 1182

Jahne, J. F., 892, 914
Jakobson, T., 828, 833
Jakowin, A. A., 920, 989
Jalkanen, M., 1096, 1103
Jancke, W., 109, 241
Jane, F. W., 42, 67
Jansson, L., 425, 435, 1163, 1182
Jansson, L. B., 342, 350, 364, 580, 582, 702
Jappe, N. A., 1079
Jappe, N. R., 972, 989
Jayme, G., 62, 67, 72, 89, 92, 96, 99, 108,
    130, 142, 146, 158, 162, 165, 243, 294,
    295, 313, 318, 364, 365, 397, 400, 427,
    435, 507, 543, 545, 574, 590, 610, 613,
    614, 615, 625, 642, 643, 647, 651, 664,
    679, 692, 702, 703, 928, 929, 995, 1001,
    1022, 1045, 1052, 1053, 1058, 1068,
    1079, 1109, 1110, 1111, 1118, 1126,
    1127, 1128, 1129, 1142, 1144, 1157,
    1160, 1163, 1178, 1179, 1182
Jayne, B. A., 57, 67, 259, 260, 275
Jayne, J. E., 976, 989, 1144, 1182
Jeanes, A., 124, 130, 211, 243, 977, 989
Jeanloz, R., 124, 243
Jenness, L. C., 420, 435
Jensen, W., 92, 96, 173, 223, 243, 406, 435,
    508, 514, 545, 547, 614, 615, 616, 703,
    1074, 1080
Jenssen, G. D., 815, 833
Jentgen, H., 1117, 1129
Joglekar, H. H., 692, 703
Johann, I., 297, 365
Johansson, A., 463, 700
Johansson, A., 1109, 1129
Johansson, D., 51, 52, 54, 64, 67, 541, 542,
    611, 612, 703, 1111, 1112, 1129
Johansson, O. S., 386, 388, 400, 911, 914
Johansson, S., 547, 703
Johansson, T., 843, 883, 1121, 1129
Johnson, E. H., 321, 365, 368, 400
Johnson, T., 196, 197, 240, 461, 700
Johnson, T. R., 748, 762
Johnsson, H., 260, 261, 275
Johnston, H. W., 297, 298, 365
Johnstone, H. F., 456, 703
Jolley, L. J., 139, 243
Jonas, K. G., 553, 703, 1162, 1181
Jones, E. A., 185, 186, 207, 208, 223, 243,
    590, 591, 592, 703
Jones, E. J., 181, 185, 192, 243
Jones, G. W., 212, 213, 244, 900, 914
Jones, J. B., 385, 400
Jones, J. K. N., 158, 160, 161, 162, 243,
    254
Jones, K. G., 553, 703
Jones, R. M., 429, 436, 568, 697
deJong, J. J., 497, 703

Jonson, H., 429, 434
Jonsson, J. H., 974, 983, 985, 988
Jönsson, S. E., 721, 732, 762
Jopp, J. M., 340, 365
Joransson, P. N., 260, 275
Jörgensen, L., 106, 108, 109, 112, 125, 126,
    127, 128, 129, 235, 242, 244, 508, 509,
    514, 516, 703, 1119, 1129, 1162, 1181
Jovanovic, V., 188, 239
Joyce, C. S., 447, 448, 704
Judd, D. B., 843, 844, 846, 883
Jufieriew, J., 1039, 1052, 1058
Jukes, T. H., 231, 244, 1040, 1058
Jullander, A., 117, 244
Jullander, I., 104, 146, 244, 853, 883, 1114,
    1129
Junker, E., 174, 244
Jurbergs, K. A., 317, 365
Juslén, C., 206, 244
Juvonen, V. V., 224, 244, 1024, 1058

Kaesz, S., 972, 989
Kagawa, I., 1055, 1058
Kahila, S. K., 139, 224, 225, 226, 227, 244,
    1025, 1027, 1030, 1034, 1036, 1041, 1042,
    1058, 1059
Kaila, E., 133, 136, 251, 970, 991, 1049,
    1059, 1127, 1131, 1175, 1178, 1182, 1184
Kailan, A., 155, 244
Kajanne, P., 1032, 1059
Kalb, L., 173, 244, 254
Kalbfleisch, H., 374, 382, 400
Kalinina, T. I., 568, 703
Kampf, G. A., 675, 703
Kanamaru, K., 117, 245
Karlsson, B., 1116, 1128
Karnik, M. G., 678, 692, 703, 1052, 1059
Karr, E. H., 1096, 1103
Karrer, P., 1055, 1059
Katsuura, K., 1055, 1058
Katz, J. R., 139, 192, 244, 254
Katzen, R., 672, 703
Kauffmann, H. O., 895, 914
Kauffmann, H., 947, 989
Kaufmann, Z., 310, 365, 447, 448, 449,
    456, 458, 462, 467, 490, 503, 553, 555,
    573, 703
Kavanagh, K. R., 179, 244
Kawamura, I., 194, 244
Kehoe, R. D., 347, 363, 365
Kellenberger, E., 111, 244
Keller, A., 116, 244
Keller, A. G., 681, 702, 703
Keller, E. L., 427, 428, 429, 430, 435, 436,
    917, 989, 1112, 1129
Keller, R., 854, 883
Kelsall, D. F., 747, 762

Kenetti, A., 815, 833
Kenner, J., 122, 244, 600, 602, 703, 951, 989, 1004, 1022
Kenyon, W. O., 130, 244, 951, 989, 1110, 1115, 1129
Kerp, W., 456, 523, 704
Kerr, W. D., 418, 421, 435, 517, 545, 557, 568, 610, 645, 704
Kertesz, Z. I., 126, 237
Kesler, R. B., 343, 365, 468, 704
Kesting, E., 1097, 1103
Kiato, N., 615, 704
Kibrick, A. C., 642, 704
Kidd, J., 1013, 1022
Kilander, K., 261, 275
Kilpper, W., 320, 365, 404, 434
Kin, M., 146, 254
Kindron, R. R., 887, 888, 889, 892, 903, 913, 914
King, E. G., 175, 244
Kingsbury, R. M., 886, 887, 903, 913, 914
Kircher, H. W., 161, 241
Kirchner, E., 548, 704
Kirmreuther, H., 218, 244
Kitibatake, T., 155, 250
Kittelsen, E., 404, 435
Kittelsen, T., 404, 435
Kivimaa, E., 273, 275
Kjaer, A., 170, 245
Klason, P., 167, 173, 174, 175, 192, 244, 497, 525, 527, 590, 602, 704, 1111, 1129
Klauditz, W., 106, 158, 172, 244, 286, 365, 410, 435, 615, 680, 704
Klein, A., 545, 704, 725, 762
Klein, M., 717, 719, 730, 762
Klein, R., 147, 244
Klein, W. G., 1127, 1130
Kleinert, T. N., 181, 182, 199, 244, 447, 448, 536, 537, 613, 615, 672, 704, 1049, 1059, 1109, 1117, 1130, 1175, 1182
Klemm, K. H., 321, 332, 365, 368, 372, 373, 374, 376, 377, 380, 381, 382, 385, 386, 390, 392, 399, 400, 403, 404, 436, 757, 762
Klinga, I., 744, 747, 762
Klingstedt, F. W., 181, 240, 605, 704
Klug, E. D., 149, 244
Knapp, S. B., 680, 681, 682, 684, 685, 687, 688, 689, 691, 704
Knecht, E., 139, 244
Knechtges, R. G., 424, 436
Knight, C. H., 797, 801, 833
Knight, R. G., 429, 436
Knolle, H., 1110, 1129
Knutsson, T., 582, 614, 704, 1163, 1182
Kobe, K. A., 604, 695, 993, 1003, 1015, 1016, 1022

Koblitz, W., 1127, 1130, 1175, 1182
Koch, H., 651, 664, 692, 697
Koch, R. O., 610, 704
Koehler, A., 55, 67
von Koeppen, A., 260, 275, 313, 318, 349, 350, 36,5 415, 436, 615, 616, 704
Koester, H., 146, 241
Kolboe, S., 185, 244
Kollmann, F., 42, 50, 67, 286, 365
Kolos, F., 1127, 1130
Kolthoff, I. M., 232, 244, 1045, 1059
Komarov, F. P., 940, 942, 989
König, E., 456, 457, 705
König, J., 103, 251
König, W., 143, 244
Koon, C. M., 623, 695, 920, 922, 978, 989
Kopantsev, M. H., 810, 833
Korchemkin, F. I., 662, 704
Kornberg, H. L., 212, 244
Koshijima, T., 161, 244, 610, 704
Kotani, K., 675, 711
Kraemer, E. O., 104, 105, 245
Kraft, F., 209, 245, 922, 989, 1061, 1073, 1074, 1080
Kraft, M. S., 374, 380, 400
Kraft, R., 192, 239
Krais, P., 674, 704
Krantz, T., 166, 237
Kraske, W. A., 1095, 1097, 1104
Krässig, H., 955, 957, 989
Kratzl, K., 169, 178, 199, 201, 245
Kress, O., 542, 624, 704, 922, 989, 1024, 1039, 1059, 1140, 1155, 1159, 1182
Kringstad, K., 162, 243
Krohnstad, W., 826, 833
Kroupa, R., 651, 652, 704
Krüger, A., 817, 818, 833
Krüger, H., 692, 703
Kubat, J., 739, 741, 762
Kubelka, P., 845, 883
Kubinek, V., 757, 762
Kubinskaja, G. V., 921, 991
Kubo, T., 117, 245
Kudzin, S. F., 185, 245
Kuhn, W., 126, 245
Kulkarni, G. R., 310, 365, 618, 620, 630, 704
Kullgren, C., 176, 179, 245, 477, 704, 1109, 1130
Küng, A., 447, 704
Kürschner, K., 179, 245
Kurth, E. F., 158, 220, 222, 223, 224, 236, 245, 250, 610, 614, 704, 1026, 1059
Kurzhalls, N. N., 545, 704

La Fond, L. A., 568, 571, 704
La Forge, F. B., 651, 705

Lagergren, S. E., 76, 89, 199, 200, 250, 272, 275, 286, 288, 289, 290, 293, 309, 320, 365, 366, 413, 436, 477, 481, 483, 484, 485, 486, 490, 491, 492, 493, 494, 507, 550, 555, 651, 705, 710, 807, 810, 833
Laler, T. M., 1073, 1080
Lamb, G. E. R., 372, 400
Lambert, J. E., 332, 365, 419, 436
Landmark, P., 642, 694, 772, 773, 831
Landt, G. E., 1160, 1182
Lange, P. W., 72, 73, 82, 83, 84, 87, 89, 157, 170, 171, 182, 233, 234, 285, 291, 312, 313, 315, 316, 317, 365, 508, 694
Lansing, W. D., 104, 245
Larinkari, G., 92, 96, 245
Laroque, G. L., 618, 619, 705
Larsen, A. D., 805, 831
Larson, L. L., 922, 929, 938, 944, 989
Larsson, A., 186, 245
Larsson, S., 199, 204, 245
Lathrop, E. C., 681, 682, 685, 688, 705
Lathrop, J. B., 342, 363
Latimer, W. M., 584, 705
Lau, H., 673, 705
Laue, H. C., 447, 705
Lauer, K., 615, 687, 705
Launer, H. F., 137, 245, 853, 883, 1109, 1130
Lausman, H. J., 913, 915, 962, 970, 990, 1157, 1183
Lautsch, W., 179, 195, 208, 245, 502, 651, 705, 823, 833, 929, 989
Lawrence, R. V., 226, 245, 1032, 1059
Le May, P. V., 261, 275
Lea, C. H., 1032, 1059
Lea, D. C., 428, 429, 436, 517, 705
Leavitt, E. M., 420, 436
Lebedev, N. V., 940, 942, 989
Lee, H. N., 42, 50, 53, 67
Lee, J. A., 762, 789
Leech, J. G., 161, 245
Lefèvre, K. U., 1110, 1130
Legg, G. W., 610, 614, 615, 625, 629, 635, 636, 645, 649, 650, 696, 705
Leijonhufvud, A. C:son, 261, 275
Lekander, K. E., 853, 883, 960, 962, 966, 967, 989
Lenel, P. O., 657, 712
Lengyel, A., 615, 705
Lengyel, P., 687, 688, 705, 713
Lenzi, F., 1101, 1103
Leopold, B. E., 55, 67, 173, 179, 188, 192, 197, 198, 208, 238, 245, 286, 365, 480, 481, 482, 609, 638, 646, 647, 693, 705, 822, 833, 1043, 1044, 1059, 1164, 1182
Leppla, P. W., 456. 703

Leugering, H. J., 1001, 1011, 1013, 1022
Leupold, E. O., 103, 253
Levitin, N., 677, 705
Levitt, L. S., 213, 245
Lewin, M., 615, 705, 960, 989
Lewis, G. N., 920, 989
Lewis, H. F., 854, 883, 1153, 1157, 1160, 1182, 1184
Lewis, S. J., 218, 245
Ley, H., 456, 457, 705
Liang, C. Y., 116, 158, 159, 245
Libby, C. E., 223, 238, 300, 301, 302, 367, 404, 436, 676, 713
Licht, W., 614, 615, 625, 646, 703
Lidman-Safwat, S., 951, 989, 1115, 1130
Lientz, J. R., 342, 365, 717, 725, 732, 762
Liese, W., 59, 67, 79, 89, 297, 365
Lieser, T., 173, 244
Limerick, J. Mc K., 420, 421, 422, 436, 996, 1022
Lindahl, E., 888, 891, 901, 904, 907, 908, 910, 911, 913, 914, 1074, 1080
Lindau, N., 673, 705
Lindberg, B., 119, 120, 123, 135, 156, 158, 159, 160, 161, 162, 165, 199, 204, 237, 239, 243, 245, 246, 516, 604, 605, 705, 1114, 1130
Lindberg, J. J., 185, 246, 593, 705
Lindberg, S. G., 775, 789, 790, 791, 832
Lindblad, R., 717, 744, 746, 762
Linderoth, J., 110, 127, 246
Lindgren, B. O., 114, 128, 158, 159, 177, 189, 193, 194, 196, 198, 199, 204, 207, 234, 240, 246, 480, 481, 483, 502, 550, 655, 699, 705
Lindgren, K., 744, 746, 752, 762
Lindgren, R. M., 264, 275, 276
Lindner, C., 456, 705
Lindsey, J. B., 175, 195, 253
Lindsley, C. H., 106, 246
Linehan, D. D., 1024, 1045, 1059
Linkhart, R., 347, 353, 365, 611, 706
Linnert, G. E., 341, 364
Lipscomb, A. S., 1170, 1182
Littmann, E., 176, 242
Ljubitsch, N., 103, 241
Ljungbo, S., 287, 365
Lochmüller-Kerler, E., 545, 703, 1157, 1182
Locus, A. H., 651, 662, 692, 705
Logan, J. O., 974, 987, 989
Logan, K. C., 272, 273, 276, 543, 705
Lorand, E. J., 146, 151, 246
Lorås, V., 173, 246, 291, 365, 940, 989, 1111, 1130
Lorenz, F., 130, 240

Löschbrandt, F., 173, 246, 291, 365, 928, 938, 940, 942, 943, 989, 990, 1111, 1130
Lottermoser, A., 1175, 1182
Lougheed, E. H., 404, 436, 810, 883
Love, D. V., 276
Lovell, E. L., 106, 246
Loving, J. M., 349, 353, 365
Lowgren, U., 346, 347, 365, 395, 400
Lucas, R., 300, 301, 365
Lüdtke, M., 161, 242, 1115, 1130
Luhde, F., 325, 326, 363, 374, 381, 383, 399
Lund, A., 607, 644, 701
Lundberg, A. H., 562, 705, 817, 833
Lundén, B., 550, 651, 705, 807, 810, 833
Lundquist, K., 216, 234, 895, 913
Luner, P., 298, 299, 302, 365, 854, 883, 899, 900, 905, 914, 915, 1144, 1182
Luotonen, L. I., 651, 652, 658, 708, 808, 834
Lusby, G. R., 298, 365, 618, 705
Lüthgens, M. W., 808, 833
Lynch, D. F. J., 673, 692, 693, 705
Lyon, M. G., 970, 990

Maass, O., 271, 275, 295, 297, 298, 301, 302, 303, 309, 310, 311, 364, 365, 366, 457, 479, 485, 497, 500, 569, 574, 618, 619, 695, 696, 705, 844, 883, 1157, 1183
MacAdam, D. L., 843, 883
MacClaren, R. H., 658, 709
MacGregor, J. H., 146, 241, 624, 704
MacGugan, I. C., 887, 914
MacLaurin, D. J., 420, 429, 436, 615, 616, 705
MacLeod, K. S., 973, 987, 988, 1096, 1104
MacMillan, J. R., 928, 990
Machell, G., 123, 246, 600, 602, 604, 672, 705, 1004, 1005, 1022
Madsen, F., 757, 762
Magruder, R. S., 347, 365, 424, 436
Mahoney, J. F., 153, 246
Mainguet, H., 673, 705
Mair, C. E. J., 967, 990
Makarowa-Semljarskaja, N., 102, 103, 251
Maksimov, V. F., 997, 998, 999, 1007, 1022
Malevskaya, S. S., 1029, 1033, 1059
Malm, C. J., 146, 155, 246, 1049, 1059, 1127, 1130, 1178, 1179, 1183
Malmberg, B., 1125, 1130, 1145
Manchester, D. F., 810, 833, 900, 914
Mandel, J., 1109, 1115, 1132
Mann, A. A., 732, 762
Mann, J., 111, 116, 139, 238, 246
Mannbro, N. V., 651, 705, 726, 727, 762, 768, 795, 833
Manner, P., 219, 249

Manskaya, S. M., 158, 169, 246
Marathon Corp., 821, 833
March, R. E., 606, 705, 992, 1022, 1158, 1183
Marchessault, R. H., 116, 158, 159, 164, 245, 246, 695, 706, 1145, 1183
Marchlewska-Szrajerowa, J., 447, 706
Marian, J. E., 100, 246, 266, 276
Mariani, E., 517, 518, 706
Mark, H. F., 119, 126, 143, 144, 243, 246, 249, 286, 365, 1160, 1183
Markant, H. P., 806, 807, 817, 833
Markila, L., 727, 726, 760
Marpillero, P., 974, 989
Marrinan, H. J., 111, 116, 246
Marsaudon, A., 139, 236
Marshall, A., 1049, 1059
Marshall, H. B., 175, 246, 428, 435
Marsoni, S., 412, 436, 688, 706
Marteny, W. W., 421, 436
Marth, D. E., 191, 200, 246, 428, 436
Martin, A. R., 130, 246
Martin, D. M., 894, 908, 914
Martin, G. E., 585, 706
Martin, H., 1096, 1101, 1103
Martin, H. C., 623, 706
Martin, J. S., 421, 429, 434, 610, 611, 614, 615, 623, 624, 695, 706
Marton, J., 177, 184, 188, 207, 234, 246, 592, 706
Marton, R., 849, 882, 883, 901, 914
Marum, E. B., 853, 883
Marx, M., 105, 106, 108, 109, 246
Masak, E., 886, 902, 903, 914
Mason, S. G., 494, 699, 1142, 1144, 1180, 1183, 1184
Mason, W. H., 398, 400
Matarese, J. G., 987, 991
Matthes, W., 1176, 1183
Mattsson, V. F., 603, 706
Maurer, K., 123, 130, 246
Maurice, M. J., 1173, 1180
Max, K. W., 224, 246
May, M. N., 427, 429, 436, 438, 530, 576, 610, 620, 621, 639, 642, 648, 706, 708, 713, 788, 833, 962, 991
May, W. D., 372, 374, 379, 394, 399
Mayer, W. C., 899, 900, 915
Mayhood, C. H., 1164, 1183
Mazzeno, L. W., 146, 249
McCarthy, J. L., 143, 192, 234, 246, 970, 990
McColl, B. J., 261, 276
McCorry, A. C., 350, 366, 580, 711
McElwee, R. L., 64, 68
McEwen, J. M., 888, 893, 894, 914, 1124, 1130

McEwen, R. L., 886, 887, 888, 901, 904, 914
McGinn, E. P., 757, 762, 812, 833
McGovern, J. N., 223, 246, 264, 271, 276, 300, 332, 365, 411, 415, 416, 420, 427, 428, 430, 434, 435, 436, 543, 548, 553, 559, 561, 562, 568, 572, 576, 665, 692, 696
McGregor, G. H., 223, 246, 812, 815, 833
McIlhenny, N., 692, 706
McIntosh, D. C., 55, 67, 286, 365, 646, 647, 706, 1164, 1182
McIntyre, J. W., 853, 883
McKay, J. E., 160, 161, 234
McKee, R. H., 175, 246, 673, 706
McKeefe, E. P., 422, 434, 888, 914
McKenzie, A. W., 111, 143, 247, 1144, 1183
McKibbins, S. W., 728, 762
McKinney, J. W., 605, 706
McNair, J. B., 1026, 1059
McPherson, J., 672, 699, 853, 883
Mears, J. S., 209, 236, 922, 948, 960, 988
Mehta, M. M., 175, 247
Meier, H., 72, 76, 79, 80, 81, 83, 84, 85, 86, 87, 89, 94, 98, 99, 157, 158, 159, 161, 162, 163, 194, 245, 247, 285, 313, 315, 317, 366, 505, 522, 605, 706, 1110, 1130
Melander, K., 192, 247
Meller, A., 135, 136, 247, 604, 605, 640, 651, 662, 706, 928, 977, 990, 1000, 1005, 1022
Meni, F., 1052, 1060
Menges, R. A., 341, 366
Mentser, M., 147, 244
Menzinsky, G., 519, 706
Merck, A. G., E., 1107, 1130
Merewether, J. W. T., 193, 247, 592, 593, 706, 829, 833
Merkblatt Zell. Chem. Ing., 1114, 1117, 1130
Merler, E., 160, 161, 162, 247
Merlo, L., 886, 902, 904, 915
Messing, H. S., 347, 349, 366
Meybeck, J., 212, 239, 976, 986, 988
Meyer, K. H., 114, 117, 139, 247
Meyer, W. G., 827, 828, 833
Migita, N., 548, 549, 706
Mikawa, H., 177, 198, 208, 246, 247, 590, 593, 594, 706
Miklukhin, G. P., 527, 695
Milbourn, M., 146, 247
Miles, F. D., 146, 247, 1170, 1183
Milks, J. E., 161, 247
Millar, R. E., 754, 762
Miller, R. L., 888, 914, 1073, 1074, 1076, 1080

Miller, R. N., 477, 478, 559, 573, 574, 665, 706, 707
Miller, R. W., 1152, 1181
Millet, M. A., 114, 127, 247
Milliken, M. G., 1170, 1183
Mills, A. R., 162, 247
Mills, R. T., 886, 915
Minor, F. W., 102, 247
Misch, L., 114, 139, 247
Mitchell, H. L., 64, 67, 257, 260, 276, 1155, 1183
Mitchell, J. A., 1127, 1130, 1178, 1183
Mitchell, R. L., 105, 106, 148, 157, 162, 165, 234, 247, 662, 707, 1119, 1130, 1175, 1179, 1183
Mithel, B. B., 130, 247
Mitra, D. N., 651, 662, 707
Mitscherlich, A. M., 404, 436
Moelwyn-Hughes, E. A., 126, 247
Mohrberg, W., 1052, 1058
Moilanen, M., 592, 593, 594, 698
Moltedo, G., 676, 692, 708
Monier-Williams, G. W., 103, 247
Monnberg, R., 822, 833
Monsson, W. H., 354, 363, 415, 417, 434, 544, 545, 707
Montano, J., 643, 707
Montgomery, R., 159, 252
de Montigny, R., 301, 302, 366, 572, 707, 1157, 1183
de Montmorency, W. H., 330, 332, 366, 369, 382, 383, 400, 418, 419, 436
Montroll, E. W., 126, 247
Moore, T. R., 542, 707
Mörath, E., 289, 366
Morbey, G. K., 104, 249, 1000, 1022
Morehead, F. F., 111, 112, 247, 320, 366
Morgan, H., 271, 276
Morris, W. S., 368, 400
Morrison, H. A., 725, 728, 762
Morrison, J., 920, 989
Morton, D., 687, 696
Morud, B., 484, 707
Mosimann, H., 162, 247
Moss, L. A., 1024, 1059
Most, D. S., 514, 707
Mühlethaler, K., 84, 89
Mühlsteph, W., 49, 50, 51, 52, 53, 54, 67, 1154, 1183
Müller, F. M., 678, 679, 681, 682, 689, 707
Müller, H. F., 651, 657, 662, 707
Müller, W., 374, 385, 399
Munk, F., 845, 883
Murray, C. E., 55, 68, 1153, 1154, 1183
Murray, F. E., 623, 707, 773, 833
Murray, G. E., 155, 247
Murray, M. L., 158, 254

Murtfeldt, L., 424, 436
Murto, J. O., 270, 271, 272, 276
Musser, D. M., 1144, 1160, 1183
Mutton, D. B., 223, 224, 247, 1024, 1029, 1030, 1032, 1034, 1035, 1037, 1043, 1044, 1059

Nabar, G. M., 965, 988
Naffziger, T. R., 651, 662, 681, 682, 688, 692, 707
Nagel, S. C., 615, 709
Nahum, L. Z., 207, 239
Nakano, J., 178, 216, 247
Nakao, M., 651, 658, 662, 664, 707
Neale, F. R., 886, 915
Neale, S. M., 104, 153, 247, 597, 707, 1115, 1130
van Nederveen, G., 691, 692, 707, 1124, 1130
Neill, M. T., 394, 400
Neish, A. C., 102, 169, 236
Nelson, B., 450, 538, 700
Nelson, G. H., 432, 433
Nelson, N., 1110, 1130
Nelson, R., 158, 159, 247
Nepenin, N. N., 263, 266, 276
Nepenin, Y. N., 462, 555, 556, 707, 722, 739, 762, 996, 1022
Nethercut, P. E., 1039, 1059
Neubauer, L. G., 160, 248
Neuberg, C., 673, 707
Neuschäffer, K., 1118, 1129
Nevell, T. P., 130, 133, 248, 951, 988, 1005, 1022, 1115, 1128
Newcombe, A. G., 179, 248
Newhall, N., 1049, 1059
Newman, S., 105, 248
Nicholls, G. A., 1073, 1080
Nickerson, A. W., 347, 366
Nickerson, R. F., 109, 114, 127, 146, 248
Nicolaysen, V. B., 1179, 1183
Nicoll, W. D., 894, 915
Nicolson, A., 162, 234
Niedercorn, F., 201, 239
Niemi, J. A., 1125, 1130
Nihlén, H., 504, 519, 531, 561, 651, 700, 707
Nikoliew, N., 165, 243
Nilsson, E., 878, 880, 883, 1047, 1059
Nilsson, O., 655, 707
Nilsson, T., 717, 719, 723, 762
Nischk, R., 642, 643, 703
Nishida, K., 219, 248, 1032, 1041, 1059
Nishikawa, S., 109, 248
Noble, J. H., 721, 725, 732, 762
Noe, R. W., 116, 249
Nokihara, E., 479, 494, 495, 530, 544, 707

Nolan, P. A., 854, 883
Nolan, W. J., 271, 274, 276, 295, 309, 310, 364, 365, 366, 427, 429, 435, 436, 615, 618, 620, 624, 630, 631, 632, 646, 704, 707, 709, 870, 883, 889, 915
Nord, F. F., 169, 173, 174, 179, 182, 183, 185, 186, 245, 248
Nordman, L. S., 846, 883, 1125, 1130, 1142, 1143, 1144, 1164, 1183
Nordstrand, A., 374, 400
Norén, I., 593, 594, 699
Noreus, R. E., 888, 914
Norman, A. G., 193, 248, 514, 694
Norman, N., 114, 116, 248
Northgraves, W. W., 973, 989
Nowak, P., 674, 710
Noyess, A. A., 462, 470, 707
Nugent, R. A., 805, 806, 833
Nuttall, G. H., 754, 755, 762
Nylinder, P., 65, 68, 94, 248, 260, 276, 541, 542, 707
Nyrén, V., 1040, 1047, 1059
Nyström, G. L., 420, 435

O'Dwyer, M. H., 160, 161, 248
O'Meara, D., 123, 135, 248, 563, 604, 707, 714, 967, 990, 1045, 1059
O'Neil, F. W., 404, 436
Obenshain, D. N., 649, 707, 1062, 1080
Obermanns, H. E., 1144, 1158, 1183
Oddo, B., 302, 366
Ogiwara, Y., 429, 436
Ohlsson, K. E., 931, 990, 1116, 1130
Öhrn, O. E., 159, 248, 429, 436, 506, 522, 606, 608, 707
Okada, H., 208, 247, 590, 706
Okamura, S., 126, 250
Okawa, T., 165, 248
Okobo, M., 1115, 1131
Olson, G., 547, 703
Olson, K. E., 421, 436
Olsson, B., 1114, 1129
Olleman, E. D., 192, 248
Omeis, E., 49, 54, 68
Onaka, F., 60, 68
Onisko, W., 632, 634, 701
Ono, K., 109, 248
Opferman, E., 953, 970, 990, 1001, 1022
Oppenheimer, H. R., 71, 89
Orr, W. L., 725, 732, 762
Osawa, Z., 677, 707
Ost, H., 103, 248
Otis, B., 392, 400
Ott, E., 1119, 1130, 1166, 1183
Ottar, H., 393, 400, 405, 436
Overbeck, W., 651, 657, 662, 707
Oxley, H. F., 149, 252

Packard, R. A., 676, 707
Pacsu, E., 126, 248
Palczewski, T., 545, 707
Palmrose, G. V., 447, 449, 709, 793, 833
Pamén, L., 418, 436
Pancirolli, F., 415, 436
Pancoast, L. H., 461, 462, 490, 502, 553, 555, 709
Paranyi, N. I., 299, 302, 303, 366
Parck, C., 522, 707
Park, F. A., 342, 366
Parker, E. A., 139, 195, 233, 236, 248
Parrett, A. E., 404, 436
Parrett, A. N., 651, 659, 708, 1003, 1020, 1022
Parsons, J. L., 1068, 1080, 1160, 1183
Parsons, S. R., 417, 436, 805, 833, 848, 883, 913, 915, 962, 970, 990, 1142, 1157, 1183
Partridge, E. P., 1170, 1183
Pascoe, T. A., 585, 586, 587, 695, 808, 833, 1160, 1183
Patel, G. M., 848, 883
Paterson, H. A., 390, 400
Patterson, R. F., 181, 248, 447, 537, 708
Patterson, R. M. L., 1045, 1059
Paul, B. H., 260, 276
Paul, F. C., 730, 761
Paulson, J. C., 954, 985, 986, 987, 990
Pauly, H., 192, 248
Payen, A., 90, 248
Pearl, I. A., 173, 174, 178, 179, 183, 185, 186, 187, 192, 248, 822, 833, 976, 990, 1111, 1130
Pearson, A. J., 415, 436
Pechukas, A., 1096, 1103
Peckham, J. R., 429, 430, 436, 530, 615, 616, 642, 648, 705, 706, 708
Pedersen, K. O., 104, 252
Pedersen, N., 175, 195, 248
Pelipetz, M. G., 175, 248, 673, 708
Peniston, Q. P., 193, 248
Penner, S. S., 894, 915
Pennington, D., 192, 248
Peoples, R. S., 342, 366
Pepper, J. M., 179, 244, 248, 822, 833
Perilä, O., 49, 68, 157, 219, 223, 224, 226, 248, 249, 651, 662, 708, 1025, 1036, 1059
Perkins, J. K., 720, 725, 732, 762
Perronoud, H., 174, 249
Perry, H. J., 390, 400
Perry, T. O., 64, 65, 68, 260, 276
Person, B., 287, 363
Persson, S. H., 1096, 1103
Pervier, N. C., 1109, 1130
Petering, W. H., 300, 366
Peterson, F. C., 103, 162, 223, 238, 248, 249

Petitpas, T., 114, 249
Pettersson, G., 447, 449, 708
Pettersson, S. E., 272, 276, 430, 437, 606, 608, 641, 649, 671, 708, 1144, 1158, 1160, 1183
Pettersson, T., 386, 400
Pew, J. C., 167, 188, 193, 204, 249, 374, 385, 400, 548, 549, 708
Phelps, M. W., 938, 940, 944, 990
Philipp, B., 145, 165, 249, 1176, 1183
Philipp, H. J., 105, 249
Phillips, E. W. J., 60, 68
Phillips, J. B., 224, 242, 1024, 1026, 1029, 1058, 1059
Phillips, M., 166, 236, 249
Piazolo, G., 208, 245, 929, 989
Pickard, J., 223, 254
Pickens, A. L., 827, 834
Pictet, R., 461, 553, 708
Pierce, L. A., 887, 915
Pigman, W. W., 94, 98, 99, 100, 234, 249
Pillow, M. Y., 612, 708
Pinder, A. R., 220, 249
Pineo, M. B., 725, 730, 746, 761
Ploetz, T., 173, 239
Podder, V., 678, 679, 708
Poggianti, U., 676, 692, 708
Pohjola, A., 525, 709, 821, 834
Pohl, E., 1127, 1130
Polçin, J., 209, 249, 930, 990
Polglase, W. J., 161, 249
Poljak, A., 677, 708
Pollak, A., 805, 830
Polyani, M., 114, 249
Pomilio, U., 676, 708
Poole, V. H., 1124, 1130
Porphire, P., 651, 708
Porphyre, J. A., 403, 437
Possaner von Ehrenthal, B. S., 404, 437
Potter, G. C. J., 545, 548, 708, 1029, 1059
Praill, P. F. G., 236
Pratt, K. F., 401, 437
Premo, R. A., 413, 437, 887, 915
Preston, R. D., 54, 68, 76, 680, 708
Price, C. E., 892, 914
Profitt, J. R., 1178, 1183
Prütz, G., 49, 67
Pulst, S., 404, 407, 434
Purves, C. B., 130, 153, 155, 160, 165, 174, 201, 203, 212, 213, 236, 237, 246, 247, 248, 249, 250, 252, 497, 499, 592, 695, 948, 951, 976, 980, 990, 1114, 1129, 1179, 1183

Quick, R. H., 428, 429, 430, 437, 517, 708
Quimby, G. R., 161, 241

Raaka, C., 1073, 1080
Rabinovitch, W., 299, 302, 303, 366, 781, 791, 833
Rainio, P., 508, 514, 547, 703
Raitt, W., 650, 678, 679, 687, 708
Ramsel, C., 133, 250, 941, 951, 953, 960, 965, 967, 990, 1004, 1005, 1011, 1023, 1115, 1130
Rånby, B. G., 71, 89, 105, 109, 110, 111, 112, 114, 116, 117, 125, 126, 127, 128, 138, 143, 144, 145, 146, 158, 161, 164, 166, 243, 244, 249, 508, 516, 606, 695, 702, 706, 708, 1166, 1179, 1182, 1183
Randall, M., 920, 989
Ranhagen, G., 741, 744, 746, 752, 757, 762
Rapson, W. H., 104, 249, 853, 883, 907, 913, 915, 940, 953, 960, 962, 974, 977, 979, 980, 987, 988, 990, 1000, 1011, 1022, 1024, 1042, 1045, 1059, 1063, 1074, 1080, 1096, 1097, 1098, 1100, 1101, 1103, 1104
Räsänen, R. H., 585, 651, 652, 658, 701, 708, 808, 834
Rasch, R. H., 853, 883, 1115, 1128
Rashback, H., 948, 990
Rassow, B., 167, 249, 672, 708, 1179, 1183
Rastatter, E. L., 744, 747, 748, 754, 762
Ratcliff, E. K., 165, 254
Ratcliff, F. T., 1157, 1183
Rawling, F. G., 422, 427, 437
Rayonier Inc., 795, 834, 1008, 1022, 1175, 1176, 1179, 1183
Rebek, M., 1115, 1130
Reese, E. T., 137, 250
Reeves, R. E., 1005, 1022
Regelin, E., 1179, 1181
Regestad, S. D., 502, 529, 708
Regnfors, L., 585, 588, 610, 611, 613, 625, 643, 646, 708, 710
Reichert, J. S., 886, 887, 889, 893, 894, 901, 904, 907, 908, 910, 911, 914, 915
Reid, H. A., 611, 708
Reid, J. D., 146, 249
Reid, S. G., 179, 248
Reiff, G., 130, 246
Reinecke, F., 1160, 1184
Reinhardt, L., 139, 143, 234
Rentz, A., 94, 97, 250
Reyerson, L. H., 675, 708
Reynolds, V. T., 747, 762
Rhodes, P. R., 260, 261, 276
Ribi, E., 111, 249, 250, 508, 708
Rich, J. P., 721, 725, 732, 762
Richards, G. N., 121, 123, 135, 136, 246, 248, 250, 508, 600, 602, 603, 604, 663, 672, 696, 705, 707, 708, 828, 831, 1004, 1005, 1007, 1022

Richardson, C. A., 420, 437, 887, 888, 915
Richardson, R., 844, 883
Richardson, R. W., 608, 708
Richter, G. A., 223, 250, 461, 462, 490, 497, 502, 543, 545, 547, 553, 555, 556, 568, 651, 658, 659, 662, 664, 665, 708, 709, 992, 998, 1000, 1001, 1003, 1013, 1015, 1019, 1022, 1023, 1029, 1036, 1042, 1063, 1080, 1159, 1178, 1183
Richter, J., 350, 366, 580, 709, 721, 762, 881, 883, 1163, 1184
Richtzenhain, H., 135, 136, 167, 188, 193, 198, 201, 202, 210, 211, 213, 238, 250, 495, 592, 600, 603, 604, 640, 709, 948, 950, 990, 1004, 1005, 1007, 1023
Ridge, B. P., 133, 250, 953, 960, 988
Rieth, E., 1162, 1181
Riley, J. L., 1166, 1184
Ringström, E., 591, 700, 1126, 1129, 1130, 1173, 1174, 1184
Rinman, E. L., 828, 834
Rinne, A. Y. E., 224, 225, 226, 227, 244, 1025, 1027, 1034, 1036, 1059
Ritchie, P. F., 174, 213, 250
Ritman, E. L., 681, 682, 709
Ritter, D. M., 192, 248
Ritter, G. A., 347, 366, 615, 696
Ritter, G. J., 94, 98, 158, 162, 247, 250, 253, 1111, 1130
Rivise, C. W., 399, 400
Roald, B., 341, 342, 364, 366, 367
Roberson, W. B., 610, 696
Robert, A., 673, 713
Roberts, I., 146, 250
Robertson, A. A., 1142, 1144, 1164, 1184
Robertson, J. D., 721, 762
Robinson, M. D., 563, 709
Robson, H. T., 726, 727, 761
Roe, R. B., 447, 709, 917, 990, 1111, 1130
Roelfsen, P. A., 680, 709
Rogers, C. N., 349, 366
Rogers, L. N., 993, 997, 998, 1000, 1023, 1074, 1080, 1109, 1131
Rogovin, Z. A., 1179, 1184
Rollinson, S. M., 852, 853, 854, 883, 962, 963, 990, 1049, 1059, 1073, 1080
Rollinson, R. R., 157, 250
Rolliston, L. O., 972, 988
Ronssin, S., 106, 235
Root, E. M., 432, 437
Roschier, R. H., 139, 250, 447, 517, 709
Rosebush, F. J., 887, 888, 889, 892, 903, 913, 914
Rosén, G. E., 651, 709
Rosén, W. O., 972, 990
Rosenberger, N. A., 207, 250, 477, 490, 491, 500, 555, 568, 569, 709, 1001, 1015, 1023

Rosenblad, C., 817, 834
Rosengren-Forsblad, K., 161, 249
Rosenqvist, T., 174, 240
Rosenstock, K. H., 692, 703
Rosenthal, A. J., 1127, 1128, 1130
Roseveare, W. E., 109, 127, 250
Ross, J. H., 337, 366, 557, 568, 649, 709
Rossini, F. D., 781, 834
Roth, W. A., 456, 709
Rothamel, L., 928, 989, 1068, 1079
Rothrock, C. W., 264, 276, 624, 709, 799, 801, 834
Roudier, A., 160, 250
Routala, O., 525, 674, 709, 821, 834
Rowen, J. W., 111, 250
Rowland, B. W., 1144, 1184
Rowley, H. J., 672, 701
van Royen, A. H. H., 692, 709
Rue, J. D., 401, 422, 423, 427, 437, 542, 544, 545, 615, 709, 713, 928, 960, 990, 1061, 1080
Rueff, G., 148, 235
Rulon, S. A., 1160, 1182
Runius, S., 175, 242
Runkel, R. O., 51, 52, 68, 260, 276, 401, 410, 411, 437, 677, 709, 1154, 1184
Running, K. D., 544, 545, 547, 709
Russell, J. K., 901, 915
Russell, R., 725, 762
Rusten, D., 574, 709
Rutherford, H. A., 130, 250, 1004, 1005, 1023
Rutishauser, M., 745, 748, 757, 761, 1176, 1181
Rutkowski, J., 545, 707
Rutz, G., 675, 703
Ruus, L., 342, 366, 744, 745, 747, 748, 763
Ruziczka, W., 178, 242
Rydholm, S. A., 138, 145, 146, 153, 158, 161, 164, 175, 177, 181, 182, 185, 199, 200, 203, 209, 217, 223, 234, 249, 272, 276, 309, 351, 366, 420, 430, 431, 437, 447, 448, 449, 455, 456, 459, 461, 462, 463, 464, 475, 477, 481, 483, 484, 485, 486, 490, 491, 492, 493, 494, 505, 510, 511, 512, 514, 520, 522, 524, 533, 535, 536, 537, 538, 539, 541, 546, 547, 551, 553, 554, 555, 558, 563, 564, 574, 582, 602, 606, 608, 612, 613, 616, 641, 643, 649, 651, 652, 654, 655, 659, 662, 663, 665, 671, 673, 693, 702, 708, 827, 834, 855, 856, 883, 930, 931, 935, 937, 958, 967, 970, 990, 1007, 1013, 1015, 1016, 1017, 1019, 1023, 1036, 1047, 1055, 1059, 1066, 1069, 1073, 1074, 1080, 1144, 1156, 1158, 1160, 1161, 1162, 1163, 1166, 1176, 1180, 1183, 1184

Rys, L. J., 272, 276, 677, 710, 993, 996, 997, 998, 999, 1001, 1008, 1015, 1023

Saarnio, J., 160, 161, 250, 602, 606, 710
Sadler, H., 304, 366, 545, 710, 776, 834
Saeman, J. F., 657, 662, 664, 692, 710, 1110, 1130
Saito, G., 140, 145, 250
Sakurada, I., 126, 139, 155, 243, 250
Salisbury, A. C., 970, 990
Salova, A. S., 1115, 1131
Sammet, C. F., 844, 883
Samson, T., 270, 271, 276
Samuels, R. M., 430, 437, 610, 614, 710
Samuelsen, S., 928, 942, 990, 1035, 1059
Samuelson, L. G., 1164, 1184
Samuelson, O., 130, 133, 136, 151, 199, 211, 250, 295, 366, 450, 502, 507, 516, 518, 519, 520, 521, 522, 525, 529, 538, 543, 600, 604, 651, 693, 696, 698, 707, 708, 710, 774, 775, 821, 834, 941, 951, 953, 954, 960, 965, 967, 970, 977, 990, 1003, 1004, 1005, 1007, 1008, 1011, 1015, 1016, 1022, 1023, 1024, 1045, 1049, 1059, 1115, 1126, 1130, 1175, 1176, 1184
Sandberg, E. S., 651, 710, 806, 834
Sandborn, L. T., 822, 834
Sandelin, O., 177, 240, 480, 700
Sander, A., 562, 710
Sandermann, W., 219, 225, 251
Sandqvist, H., 227, 251, 1026, 1027, 1059
Sands, L., 160, 161, 251
Sandy Hill Tech. Bull., 1083, 1088
Saner, W. R., 139, 143, 251
Sanio, K., 53, 68
Sanyer, N., 614, 651, 655, 662, 672, 710
Saponitskii, S. A., 491, 710
Sapp, J. E., 421, 424, 437, 772, 773, 832
Sarie, S. P., 153, 251, 597, 710
Sarkanen, K. V., 177, 208, 209, 212, 237, 251, 592, 710, 930, 938, 976, 988, 991
Sarkar, P. B., 929, 930, 991
Särnström, C. G., 232, 234
Sarten, P., 175, 251, 651, 664, 703, 711, 1036, 1059, 1109, 1111, 1129, 1176, 1184
Sätre, K., 374, 400
Saunderson, H. H., 298, 301, 366, 569, 710
Sävenborn, S. A., 1055, 1059
Scandinavian Standards Scan-C, 1116, 1126, 1130, 1131
Scaramuzzi, G., 51, 52, 68, 1154, 1184
Scarth, G. W., 297, 298, 366
Schaarschmidt, A., 674, 710
Schacht, W., 422, 437
Schafer, E. R., 374, 385, 400, 404, 435, 1155, 1184

Scheil, M. A., 342, 366
Schenck, H., 152, 251
Schenck, U., 995, 1001, 1022, 1127, 1128, 1129, 1178, 1179, 1182
Schenk, H. F., 745, 746, 761
Schenker, C., 662, 710, 993, 1023
Scherer, P. C., 103, 251
Scherrer, P., 109, 251
Scheuring, L., 692, 703, 1178, 1182
Schieber, W., 651, 710
Schippel, H. W., 720, 762
Schlüter, H., 167, 239
Schmeil, W., 678, 710
Schmidt, C. L. A., 231, 244, 1040, 1058
Schmidt, E., 67, 124, 131, 158, 161, 212, 251, 548, 710, 972, 976, 977, 991
Schmidt, G. A., 1095, 1104
Schmidt, J., 545, 710
Schmidt, U., 520, 710
Schmidt-Nielsen, S., 922, 991
Schmorak, J., 165, 251, 1177, 1184
Schöberl, A., 590, 710
Schoeller, P., 677, 709
Schoettler, J. R., 605, 606, 710, 1000, 1023
Schofield, R. K., 153, 251, 597, 710
Scholander, A., 717, 718, 719, 723, 762, 775, 779, 807, 834
Schollin-Borg, G., 628, 649, 700
Scholz, E. K., 342, 366
Schönberg, E., 1124, 1131
Schöön, N. H., 502, 530, 532, 534, 535, 710
Schopmeyer, C. S., 219, 251
Schorger, A. W., 223, 251
Schorigin, P., 102, 103, 251
Schorning, P., 651, 665, 672, 696, 711
Schröter H. 745, 746, 761
Schuber, J., 938, 940, 944, 990, 1095, 1097, 1104
Schubert, W. J., 169, 179, 182, 183, 185, 237, 248
Schuerch, C., 158, 177, 179, 240, 247, 251, 590, 643, 644, 711
Schuler, K., 405, 437
Schulte, H., 404, 437
af Schultén, K., 550, 651, 711, 996, 1023
Schultze-Dewitz, G., 53, 68
Schulz, G. V., 106, 108, 109, 126, 251
Schulze, E., 90, 156, 251
Schulze, F., 91, 251
Schur, M. O., 568, 711, 996, 1023, 1160, 1184
Schüssler, F., 545, 711
Schütz, F., 176, 251, 651, 664, 711
Schwab, E., 119, 251
Schwabe, K., 192, 251
Schwalbe, C. G., 167, 222, 223, 251, 404, 437, 674, 711, 1114, 1131, 1140, 1184

Schwalbe, K., 402, 437
Schwartz, H., 92, 94, 99, 100, 120, 223, 236, 257, 262, 275, 677, 705
Schwartz, R., 402, 437
Schwarz, S. L., 618, 620, 621, 635, 636, 711
Schwarzenbach, O., 1055, 1059
Schwarzkopf, O., 140, 145, 251
Schwerin, G., 99, 251
Sconce, J. S., 928, 990
Scopp, I. W., 642, 704
Scribner, H. C., 1098, 1104
Scroggie, A. G., 109, 127, 236
Seborg, R. M., 286, 366
Sederholm, P., 342, 363
Seefeldner, W., 1127, 1130
Seek, W., 130, 251
Segerfeldt, B., 175, 244, 525, 590, 602, 704
Segring, S. B., 746, 757, 762
Seiler, H., 174, 235
Selleby, L., 223, 224, 225, 227, 251, 1025, 1027, 1059
Selling, H. J., 843, 883
Sen, D. L., 692, 703, 1052, 1059
Senger, F., 233, 254, 1050, 1052, 1060
Sephton, H. H., 136, 250, 600, 708, 1007, 1022
Serafin, J. G., 1098, 1104
Setterholm, V. C., 430, 435
Sevón, J., 674, 709
Sharples, A., 110, 114, 126, 127, 128, 251
Shaw, A. C., 517, 711
Shaw, M. B., 687, 711
Sheldon, F. R., 887, 888, 915
Shelow, W. S., 827, 834
Shema, B. F., 264, 276
Shepherd, D. M., 146, 254
Sherk, D. L., 998, 1001, 1023
Sherrard, E. C., 223, 224, 245, 643, 711
Shick, P. E., 806, 807, 831
Shimoda, I., 675, 711
Shook, R. E., 760, 762
Shrikhande, S. G., 193, 248
Shriner, R. L., 849, 884, 901, 915
Shyakover, M., 1179, 1184
Sidhu, G. S., 174, 186, 190, 239
Sieber, R., 929, 930, 989, 1024, 1029, 1036, 1059, 1107, 1131
Siegel, S. M., 169, 251
Sihtola, H., 133, 136, 251, 517, 518, 711, 853, 883, 960, 965, 967, 991, 1125, 1126, 1127, 1175, 1176, 1178, 1180, 1184
Sihtola, H., 429, 437
Sikström, L., 748, 761
Silbernagel, H., 201, 245
Sillén, L. G., 468, 471, 711, 774, 775, 781, 834
Silov, E. A., 921, 991

Silver, F. P., 418, 419, 437
Simha, R., 126, 246, 247, 251
Simionescu, C., 662, 692, 711
Simmonds, F. A., 545, 547, 651, 660, 662, 664, 711, 1000, 1023
Simmons, T., 779, 834
Simmons, W. B., 746, 761
Simon, A., 456, 457, 471, 711
Simonsen, J. L., 220, 251
Sindall, R. W., 678, 679, 711
Singer, R., 1119, 1131
Singh, K., 680, 708
Sirakoff, G., 651, 711
Sisson, W. A., 139, 143, 251
Sitzmann, L., 260, 275
Sivola, Y. (G.), 651, 658, 661, 711, 806, 808, 834
Sjölin, L., 1116, 1131
Sjöström, E., 651, 711
Skark, L., 651, 652, 654, 704
Skelton, C. H., 744, 747, 761
Sköldkvist, H. N., 651, 665, 696
Skraup, Z. H., 103, 251
Slávik, I., 520, 711
Sloman, A. R., 355, 366, 583, 650, 651, 711, 728, 762
Smedberg, G. E., 888, 915
Smirnov, V. S., 1114, 1131
Smith, A. F., 894, 915
Smith, D., 350, 366, 580, 711
Smith, D. C. C., 178, 252
Smith, D. M., 212, 252
Smith, E. D., 1109, 1131
Smith, F., 159, 161, 252
Smith, J. H. C., 100, 252
Smith, J. W., 958, 991
Smith, K. N., 1033, 1060
Smith, L. H., 146, 252, 662, 664, 674, 711, 1166, 1170, 1184
Smith, R. W., 615, 711
Snyder, K. L., 413, 437
Sobolev, I., 643, 644, 711
Sobue, H., 139, 143, 165, 252, 1115, 1131, 1179, 1184
Söderquist, R., 549, 550, 651, 655, 711, 774, 779, 807, 808, 834
Sohn, A. W., 657, 712
Soila, R., 203, 210, 240, 499, 699, 986, 987, 991
Solechnik, N. Y., 674, 712
Soltau, G., 817, 834
Solvay Process Div., 978, 991
Somer, V., 651, 712, 811, 818, 834
Somerville, J. L., 545, 676, 694, 712
Somogyi, M., 1110, 1131
Somsen, R. A., 124, 252, 264, 276, 977, 991
Sookne, A. M., 1115, 1131, 1160, 1184

Sönnerskog, S., 146, 252
Spaak, G., 410, 437
Spalding, C. W., 817, 834
Sparrow, D. B., 887, 910, 915
Spear, J. D., 297, 298, 366
Spencer, C. C., 103, 249
Sperling, L. H., 166, 252, 1128, 1131
Spinner, I. H., 853, 884
Spitz, R. D., 886, 895, 915
Sponsler, O. L., 114, 252
Sproull, R. C., 687, 692, 712
Spur, S. H., 260, 276
Spurlin, H. M., 151, 165, 252, 1119, 1130, 1166, 1183
Squillace, A. E., 65, 68
Stacie, J. H., 792, 834
Staidl, J. A., 422, 427, 437
Stainsby, G., 1040, 1060
Stakheva-Kaverzneva, E. D., 130, 252, 951, 953, 966, 991, 1115, 1131
Stalter, N. J., 888, 915
Stamm, A. J., 64, 68, 125, 201, 252, 295, 297, 298, 299, 300, 301, 302, 363, 366
Stamp, C., 1112, 1132
Stangeland, G. E., 479, 712
Stangl, K., 1083, 1088
Stanik, V., 821, 831
Stannett, V., 1170, 1184
Starborg, E., 757, 762
Staudinger, H., 103, 104, 106, 192, 252, 1160, 1184
Stauffer, W. O., 886, 915
Steele, F. A., 845, 846, 847, 853, 884
Steenberg, B., 374, 385, 389, 400, 739, 741, 749, 751, 760, 1141, 1142, 1180, 1184
Stefansson, E., 258, 276
Stegmann, G., 261, 276
Steinmann, H. W., 165, 252, 1128, 1131, 1179, 1184
Stemsrud, F., 58, 68
Stenius, Å. S:son, 842, 843, 846, 847, 884, 1121, 1131
Stephansen, E., 842, 884, 1124, 1131, 1140, 1141, 1155, 1184
Stephenson, J. N., 263, 266, 276, 320, 366, 424, 437, 715, 722, 739, 762, 797, 833
Sternberger, R. M., 1083, 1088
Stevens, R. H., 678, 712
Stevens, R. J., 550, 568, 569, 678, 712
Stevens, W. C., 746, 762
Stewart, C. M., 105, 160, 161, 162, 173, 252
Stewart, D. L., 395, 400, 420, 437
Stewart, R., 462, 470, 707
Stillings, R. A., 1109, 1131
Stobo, W. E., 901, 915

Stocker, F. W., 1024, 1060
Stockman, L., 92, 96, 163, 252, 257, 262, 276, 302, 304, 342, 363, 366, 462, 520, 525, 541, 548, 549, 555, 556, 563, 564, 573, 574, 575, 582, 585, 588, 610, 611, 612, 613, 614, 618, 619, 625, 639, 646, 648, 652, 655, 662, 693, 698, 700, 704, 707, 708, 712, 744, 745, 747, 748, 763, 853, 883, 920, 940, 941, 960, 988, 989, 962, 966, 967, 1026, 1040, 1058, 1163, 1182
Stockman, N., 219, 251
Stoeckeler, J. H., 258, 276
Stone, J. E., 179, 191, 252, 272, 276, 286, 288, 294, 295, 296, 298, 299, 366, 367, 404, 427, 428, 437, 507, 543, 597, 712, 713
Stone, W. A., 987, 991
Storin, G. K., 888, 907, 913, 914, 970, 987, 988, 1065, 1066, 1068, 1073, 1079
Strachan, J., 1140, 1184
Strapp, R. K., 362, 367, 418, 437, 494, 559, 560, 562, 568, 571, 574, 576, 610, 618, 624, 628, 645, 646, 647, 648, 701
Strauss, R. W., 209, 251, 930, 991
Streyffert, T., 41
Strickland, R. K., 64, 67
Stricks, W., 232, 244, 1045, 1059
Stringfellow, W. A., 1115, 1130
Studney, J., 548, 712
Stumpf, P. K., 219, 252
Stumpf, W., 175, 186, 252, 823, 834
Suida, H., 673, 674, 712
Sultze, R. F., 167, 252
Sundberg, O., 507, 516, 613, 701
Sundkvist, E., 618, 619, 639, 648, 712
Sundman, J., 464, 517, 518, 520, 524, 525, 712, 821, 824, 834
Sundstedt, N. J., 548, 712
Sunesson, E., 928, 991
Supka, R., 899, 900, 905, 914
Surewics, W., 618, 712, 997, 1023
Sutherland, D. M., 420, 437
Sutherland, J. H., 297, 302, 367
Svedberg, T., 104, 162, 247, 252, 508, 712
Svensson, A. Å., 72, 76, 89, 111, 252
Svensson, C., 1036, 1059
Svensson, S., 302, 334, 367
Swan, B., 897, 898, 901, 914
Swanson, J. W., 1024, 1042, 1060, 1144, 1184
Swanson, W. H., 477, 559, 572, 573, 574, 665, 706, 707, 712
Swartz, J. N., 801, 817, 834, 940, 991
Swedish Standards CCA, 173, 236, 587, 588, 712, 917, 940, 991, 1109, 1111, 1114, 1116, 1117, 1119, 1121, 1122, 1131

Swenson, R. S., 746, 761
Swinehart, R. W., 1173, 1180

Takahama, M., 651, 662, 692, 702
Takehara, S., 136, 252
Talwar, K. K., 1144, 1184
Tamolang, F. N., 615, 616, 680, 712, 1154, 1185
Tank-Nielsen, T., 332, 367, 420, 437
Tanner, W. L., 146, 252
TAPPI Monographs, 1089, 1104
TAPPI Standards, 173, 252, 447, 587, 588, 712, 842, 845, 884, 917, 940, 991, 1109, 1111, 1114, 1116, 1117, 1119, 1121, 1122, 1125, 1131, 1132
Tarkkonen, O., 334, 367
Tartar, H. V., 456, 471, 712
Tasman, J. E., 1112, 1132
Tatsumi, M., 662, 664, 707
Tatsuyama, B., 545, 547, 712
Taube, H., 1100, 1101, 1104
Tayenthal, K., 672, 704
Taylor, M. C., 972, 991, 1102, 1104
Teclaff, E. M., 41
Teeple, H. O., 973, 991
Tengquist, E., 1179, 1185
Termini, J. P., 810, 833
Teves, D., 106, 240
Textor, C. K., 327, 329, 332, 367, 392, 400, 411, 437
Theander, O., 121, 123, 124, 133, 135, 246, 252, 516, 705, 951, 953, 989, 991, 1115, 1130
Theiss, B., 615, 712
Thickens, J. A., 404, 437
Thickens, J. H., 385, 400
Thieme, R. I., 940, 988
Thiesmeyer, L. R., 257, 276
Thode, E. F., 1142, 1185
Thomas, B. B., 55, 68, 1125, 1132, 1153, 1183
Thomas, E. B., 149, 252
Thommen, E. K., 1029, 1060
Thompson, A., 119, 254
Thompson, N. S., 156, 158, 160, 161, 240, 606, 701
Thoresen, G., 341, 367
Thoria, L., 662, 692, 699
Thorn, G. D., 948, 990
Thornburg, W. L., 958, 991
Tiemann, F., 167, 252
Tilghman, B., 553, 712
Timell, T. E., 92, 94, 95, 96, 102, 105, 106, 107, 108, 109, 127, 131, 146, 152, 153, 154, 156, 158, 160, 161, 162, 164, 165, 235, 239, 240, 246, 247, 252, 253
Toda, H., 517, 518, 712

Todd, M., 354, 363
Toivonen, A., 223, 224, 226, 249, 1025, 1036, 1059
Tollens, B., 175, 195, 253, 1110, 1130, 1132
Tomeo, M., 1052, 1060
Tomlinson, G. H., 777, 828, 829, 834
Tomlinson, G. H., 178, 253, 563, 618, 713, 744, 747, 748, 754, 755, 763, 773, 776, 779, 803, 828, 829, 831, 834
Tompa, H., 105, 253
Tongren, J. C., 851, 853, 884
Tönnesen, B. A., 116, 253
Töppel, O., 822, 834
Törnell, B., 1115, 1130
Törngren, I., 1112, 1132
Torraca, G., 517, 518, 706
Tötterman, H., 1116, 1132
Touey, G. P., 145, 146, 253
Trantina, O., 304, 366, 545, 710
Traube, W., 139, 146, 152, 154, 253
Traynard, P., 175, 193, 253, 673, 713
Treiber, E., 1117, 1126, 1127, 1132, 1174, 1175, 1176, 1185
Treka, P., 997, 1001, 1023
Tremaine, B. K., 830, 834
Trendelenburg, R., 42, 49, 50, 64, 66, 68
Tretheway, G. D., 795, 831
Trivedi, S. A., 944, 991, 1157, 1185
Trobeck, K. G., 586, 587, 694, 713, 772, 773, 830, 831, 834
Trogus, C., 139, 140, 241, 253
Trost, E., 683, 713
Trotter, P. C., 901, 915
Trout, P., 431, 432, 437
Tsuboi, M., 116, 253
Tuck, N. G. M., 744, 747, 748, 754, 755, 763
Tucker, E. F., 342, 367
Tudder, T., 347, 353, 365
Turner, C. H., 615, 713
Turner, G. B., 462, 526, 527, 713
Tydén, H., 512, 545, 548, 550, 651, 654, 655, 713, 1096, 1098, 1104, 1109, 1116, 1130, 1132
Tyminski, A., 161, 253

Uber, F. M., 233, 253
Udenfriend, S., 169, 253
Ulfsparre, S., 541, 542, 574, 713, 717, 718, 719, 763, 774, 775, 776, 835, 1034, 1060
Ullman, E. V., 887, 889, 915
Ullman, U., 334, 367
Unger, E., 1109, 1132
Urban, H., 103, 177, 192, 193, 213, 240, 253, 545, 928, 988

Urey, H. C., 146, 250

Valeur, C., 613, 646, 713, 970, 991, 1066, 1074, 1080, 1112, 1121, 1132, 1162, 1185
Vamos, G., 688, 713
Van Beckum, W. G., 158, 253
Van Bergen, J. M., 830, 835
Van Buijtenen, J. P., 65, 68, 71, 88, 610, 611, 695
Van den Akker, J. A., 372, 400, 842, 843, 845, 846, 848, 884, 1119, 1132, 1145, 1185
Van Derveer, P. D., 349, 367, 420, 429, 437, 438, 732, 761
Varshney, M. C., 899, 915
Vassie, J. E., 623, 713
Venemark, E., 613, 623, 625, 642, 713, 717, 720, 725, 726, 763, 770, 772, 835, 878, 884
Vethe, A., 512, 651, 655, 713
Vidal, I. P., 688, 713
Vilamo, E., 304, 335, 367
Vilars, J., 415, 438
Villiger, V., 197, 235
Vincent, G. P., 677, 713, 974, 975, 987, 991
Vink, H., 105, 253
Virkola, N. E., 640, 649, 713, 853, 884, 940, 991, 1068, 1080
Vivian, J. E., 920, 991
Voelker, M. H., 413, 415, 434, 962, 991
Voigtman, E. H., 922, 989
Vorreiter, L., 42, 55, 68
Voss, W., 160, 161, 253
Vosters, H., 1126, 1132
Vranian, H., 719, 732, 763
Vroom, K. E., 618, 713
Vuori, R., 1175, 1176, 1185

von Wacek, A., 169, 204, 253
Wadman, W. H., 162, 253
Wagner, R., 746, 757, 763
Wahlberg, H. E., 1049, 1060
Wald, W. J., 174, 175, 213, 253
Walecka, J. A., 1144, 1185
Walker, F., 1173, 1174, 1185
Walkup, J. H., 223, 224, 253
Waller, A., 820, 835
Waller, R. C., 137, 254
Walt, P. C., 672, 698
Walter, P., 553, 703
Walters, A. J., 146, 254
Walters, W. Z., 427, 438, 576, 713
Walton, H. F., 477, 713
Wangaard, F. F., 615, 616, 712
Wannow, H. A., 1126, 1132
Ward, K., 158, 254

Wardrop, A. B., 54, 60, 62, 68, 72, 73, 75, 76, 79, 84, 89, 94, 99, 111, 112, 172, 192, 254, 260, 264, 275, 285, 291, 313, 320, 367, 412, 413, 415, 438, 1155, 1181
Waters, H. K., 719, 725, 730, 732, 761, 763
Watson, A. J., 260, 261, 276, 415, 438, 1112, 1132, 1152, 1155, 1185
Watson, J. K., 165, 254, 1153, 1179, 1185
Wayman, M., 568, 571, 701, 996, 998, 1001, 1023, 1042, 1045, 1059, 1073, 1074, 1080, 1096, 1104
Weber, E. A., 562, 680, 713
Weber, O. H., 130, 243, 254
Weber-Marshall, J., 674, 713
Webjörn, B., 1159, 1182
Wedekind, E., 175, 192, 237, 254, 672, 697
Weidhaas, A., 757, 761
Weidinger, A., 139, 241
Weishaupt, K., 748, 761
Weiss, H., 402, 407, 434
Weiss, J. J., 947, 991
von Weissenberg, B., 1033, 1060
Weisshuhn, C., 404, 438
Wells, S. D., 420, 438, 544, 545, 610, 649, 688, 713, 828, 835
Welte, C. T., 676, 713
Wennerås, S., 651, 713
Wennerblom, A., 295, 366, 507, 543, 710, 1004, 1023
Wenzl, H., 987, 991
Werking, L. C., 342, 367
Werle, F. A., 402, 438
Wershing, H. F., 60, 68
West, C. J., 401, 438, 673, 676, 677, 713
West, P. H., 719, 725, 730, 732, 763
Westcott, D. B., 649, 714
Westlin, E. A., 525, 529, 651, 710
Wetlesen, C. V., 938, 990
Wettstein, R., 397, 400, 1157, 1182
Whalen, J. F., 420, 436
Whistler, R. L., 123, 163, 254, 951, 991, 1110, 1132
White, B. B., 165, 252, 1127, 1128, 1130, 1131, 1179, 1184
White, C. K., 813, 835
White, E. V., 162, 254
White, J. F., 677, 713, 972, 991
White, J. R., 1040, 1060
Whitcomb, E. M., 429, 435
Whitman, F. A., 902, 903, 915
Whitney, R. P., 781, 806, 835, 920, 991
Widerkehr-Scherb, L. P., 291, 313, 314, 315, 363, 540, 695, 1141, 1180
Wieland, H., 210, 254
Wienhaus, H., 1034, 1035, 1060
Wiesner, W., 1096, 1100, 1101, 1104

Wieters, J. D., 722, 732, 763
Wikman, S. A., 746, 757, 763
Wikström, L. A., 954, 990
Wilbrink, K., 1124, 1131
Wilcox, H. E., 232, 254
Wilcoxson, L. S., 568, 694
Wiles, R. H., 1112, 1132
Wiley, A. L., 744, 747, 748, 757, 763, 972, 991, 1073, 1080
Wilhelmsen, L. A., 826, 827, 828, 835
Willamo, H. H., 227, 254
Williams, H. D., 1127, 1128
Williams, J. W., 298, 299, 363
Willstätter, R., 103, 173, 254
Wilson, J. W., 274, 276, 563, 610, 714, 1073, 1074, 1080
Wilson, K., 1115, 1116, 1132
Wilson, M. W., 1127, 1132
Wilson, T. R. C., 289, 367
Wilson, W. K., 137, 245, 853, 883, 1109, 1114, 1115, 1130, 1132
Wincor, W., 1049, 1059, 1175, 1182
Winsvold, A., 178, 242
Wirpsa, V. J., 300, 301, 302, 367
Wise, L. E., 92, 93, 157, 160, 161, 162, 165, 218, 220, 223, 235, 250, 254
Wissing, A., 100, 246, 266, 276
Wissler, A., 1114, 1129
Wither, R. P., 674, 675, 714
Wohl, A., 651, 714
Wolf, R. B., 553, 714
Wolfrom, M. L., 103, 119, 238, 254, 509, 714
Wood, D., 123, 246
Woodhouse, H., 103, 237
Woods, J. M., 292, 367, 418, 435, 437, 563, 568, 701
Woods, N. I., 301, 303, 367
Woodside, V., 1096, 1104
Working, E. C., 342, 367
Wörner, G., 642, 643, 703
Worster, H., 274, 276
Wright, J. K., 41
Wright, R. H., 772, 835
Wu, W. C., 64, 65, 68, 260, 276
Wultsch, F., 233, 254, 404, 438, 870, 884, 886, 887, 888, 889, 891, 901, 902, 903, 904, 907, 908, 910, 911, 915, 1049, 1050, 1052, 1060, 1071, 1080, 1175, 1182
Wurz, O., 545, 676, 677, 681, 682, 687, 692, 714, 1144, 1185

Yankowski, A. A., 886, 888, 891, 901, 907, 915
Yllner, S., 87, 89, 158, 164, 211, 233, 254, 313, 315, 317, 366, 429, 438, 520, 597, 606, 607, 608, 636, 714, 1176, 1185

Yorston, F. H., 272, 275, 295, 309, 311, 364, 367, 467, 478, 479, 483, 485, 501, 504, 507, 542, 543, 544, 545, 548, 559, 561, 568, 574, 613, 699, 708, 714, 948, 990
Young, A. E., 146, 254
Yundt, A. P., 158, 164, 254, 420, 438, 606, 714

Zacharias, A., 404, 438
Zaitseva, A. F., 610, 714
Zapf, F., 106, 254

Zebbs, F. L., 610, 714
Zechmeister, L., 103, 173, 254
Zemplen, G., 103, 254
Zenczak, P., 672, 699
Zentner, T. G., 591, 593, 594, 714
Ziegelmeyer, F., 623, 714
Zimmermann, B., 404, 438
Zimmermann, E., 719, 732, 763
Zimmermann, F. J., 791, 835
Zimmermann, W. P., 580, 648, 714
Zobel, B. J., 64, 68, 260, 261, 276
Zschenderlein, A., 167, 249

Subject Index

Abbreviations
  general, see preface
  used in multistage bleaching 1068
Abietic acid,
  occurrence in wood 225
  resin component 1027
Abitibi-Permutit recovery system 810
Absorption of sulfur dioxide in acid
  towers, theory 815
Accept, in screening 739
Accessibility,
  of carbohydrates to degradation in
    sulfite cook 509
  of cellulose to hydrolytic degradation
    109, 127
Accumulator, for hot sulfite cooking acid
  818
Acetaldehyde, formation of in sugar
  fermentation 525
Acetate pulp,
  analytical data of 1180
  characterization and testing of 1127,
    1178
  grades of 1135
  purity of 1178
Acetate staple fiber 1172
Acetate yarn 1172
Acetic acid, cf. Deacetylation,
  formation of in sulfite cook 522
  ionization of at elevated temperature
    471
  recovery from neutral sulfite waste
    liquor 429
  recovery from sulfite waste liquors 820
Acetoguaiacone,
  degradation product of lignin 179
  formation of in kraft cook 593
Acetyl groups, cf. Deacetylation,
  occurrence in glucomannan 162
  occurrence in wood 94, 96
  occurrence in xylan 161
Acetylation,
  of cellulose 145
  process 1171
Acid celluloses 138
Acid hydrolysis,
  of carbohydrates, mechanism 509
  of cellulose, heterogeneous 127
  of cellulose, homogeneous 124
  of cellulose 109, 112
  of glycosidic bonds 119
  of glycosidic bonds in sulfite cook 503
  of lignin 200

Acid sulfite process cf. Sulfite process
  439
  effect of cooking liquor composition in
    556
  temperature range used in 552
  using little base 553
Acid sulfite semichemical pulping 418
  flow sheet 419
  yield and pulp properties 420
Acid towers 814
  absorption efficiency of 817
  design for calcium, magnesium or
    sodium base 817
Acid-alkaline pulping processes,
  comparison of 660
  for high-alpha pulp 655
Acid-insoluble ash, determination of in
  pulp 1116
Acidic oxidized cellulose 951
Acidification, of pulp for metal removal
  1051
Acidity,
  of bisulfite cook 470
  of carbohydrate hydroxyls 153, 597
  of monosulfite cook 472
  of neutral sulfite cook 474
  of solid phase of sulfite cook 477, 494
  of sulfite cook 458, 465
  of sulfurous acid cook 470
Activated chlorate, in bleaching 974
Activation energy,
  of kraft cook reactions 618
  of sulphite cook reactions 503, 573
Active alkali, in kraft cooking 587
Active chlorine,
  definition of 861, 947
  in various bleaching agents 861
Addition compounds, of cellulose 137
Adenosine triphosphate, in growth
  mechanism of trees 69
Adsorption, of hemicelluloses to cellulose
  514
Aging, of alkali cellulose 1168
  catalysts for 1175
Ahlfors screen 746
Air pollution, by kraft industry 830
Air-removal,
  from chips 301
  from wood by pressure variations 302
Airplanes, in forestry 262
ALB Semicell process 405
Alcohol lignin 174

Alcohol production from sulfite waste
    liquor   820
  plant for   824
  yield of alcohol   823
Aldehydes, volatile, in condensates from
    sulfite waste liquor evaporation   775
Aldonic acids,
  formation of as terminating monomers
    of carbohydrates   516
  formation of in sulfite cook   519
  mechanism of formation   519
  in bisulfite cook   519, 531
Alkali,
  production of   1089
  transport and handling of   1090
Alkali cellulose,
  aging of   136, 1168, 1175
  crystalline structure of various types of
    138
  formation of as followed by phase
    transition phenomena   143
  formation of at varying alkali concen-
    tration   141, 142
  industrial production of   1166
Alkali extraction (in bleaching),
  alkali charge required in   942
  as initial stage   1063
  deresination in   1047
  general description of   918
  hemicellulose removal from kraft pulp
    by   605
  properties of chlorolignin dissolved by
    938
  pulp yield after chlorination and   944
  reactions of chlorolignin in   930
  solubility of lignin of chlorinated pulps
    in   859
  spectral changes of chlorolignin upon
    934
  temperature and time required in   943
  type of alkali used in   944
Alkali lignin,
  as a by-product   829
  definition of   175
  precipitation of   829
Alkali solubility of pulp,
  decrease in by hot alkali purification
    1009
  determination of   1116
  increase in by degradation in sulfite
    cook   506
  increase in by oxidative degradation in
    bleaching   970
Alkaline hydrolysis,
  of cellulose   136
  of cellulose in prehydrolysis–kraft cook-
    ing   666

of glycosides   604
of glycosidic bonds   120
of glycosidic bonds in kraft cooking
    604
Alkaline pulp purification, objectives of
    993
Alkaline pulping, cf. Kraft process,
  energy of activation of   310
  of straw   412
  rate of with wood meal or chips   309
Alphacellulose, definition of   91
Alphacellulose content,
  decrease in by degradation in sulfite
    cook   506
  decrease in by oxidative degradation in
    bleaching   967
  determination of   1117
  increase in by hot alkali purification
    1009
  increase in by prehydrolysis prior to
    kraft cook   665
Alum, for sizing   1138
Amine celluloses   138
Amines, reactions of with lignin   539
Ammonia buffer, in neutral sulfite cook
    473, 426
Ammonium-based sulfite cook   455, 568
  waste liquor combustion from   779
  waste liquor evaporation from   776
Ammonium ion, reactions of in sulfite
    cook   539
Ammonium sulfamate, in chemical de-
    barking   261
Anderson debarker   265
Anglo drum chipper   273
Annual increments, of pulpwood species
    259
Anodic polarization, in digester corrosion
    342
Apical growth   69
Arabinogalactan, occurrence and struc-
    ture of   92, 162
Arabinonic acid, formation of in sulfite
    cook   519
Arabinose,
  dissolution of in sulfite cook   505
  role in degradation mechanism of xylan
    in kraft cook   603
Arbiso process   563
Arsenite, in chemical debarking   261
Ash,
  acid-insoluble   1049
  composition in wood   232
  content in wood   87
  determination of content in pulps   1116
Aspen, sulfite pulping of   545

Asplund process   395
    development of   281
    energy consumption in   397
    raw materials for   397
    semichemical pulping variant of   347
AST recovery process   781, 809
Åström debarker   265
Atomized suspension technique, recovery
    process   781, 809
Attis filter, fiber fractionator   749
Attrition mills   326
Available chlorine, definition of   947
Available combined sulfur dioxide, con-
    cept of   459
Aylesford laboratory beater   1124

Back-pressure evaporation system   776
Bag paper, pulp grades used for   1134
Bagasse,
    cell dimensions of   680
    depithing of   681
    morphological composition of   680
    production of   679
    pulping of   677
    pulping processes for   679
Baling,
    bale density   1087
    of wet pulp   760
    operation   1087
    press for   760
Balloon swelling,
    of beaten fibers   1141
    of fibers   75
Bamboo,
    cultivation of   679
    dissolving pulp from   692
    kraft pulping of   687
    preparation for pulping   683
    pulp properties and uses   692
    pulping   697
    rate of growth   678
    species of   678
Banning–Seybold laboratory beater   1124
Barattes   1168
Bark   45
    chemical composition of   99
    content of trunk   62
    disposal of   266
    effect of in kraft cook   614
    removal of fragments from in screening
        744
    structural elements of   62
    thickness of   62
Bark pockets, formation of in the trunk
    62
Barker milk-of-lime system   815
Barking drums   264

efficiency of, factors influencing   265
Base in sulfite cooking,
    concept of   455
    effect of type on yield, composition and
        properties   571
Basic density of wood species   64
Bast fragments, removal of in screening
    744
Batch cooking,
    digesters for   336
    operations in   331
    pressure and temperature schedules for
        338
Bauer,
    cleaners   747
    flash dryer   1083
    Rapid-Cycle digester   351
    refiners   328
Bauer–Grenco continuous digester   349
Beater additives   114
Beaters,
    for laboratory testing of paper pulp
        1124
    in paper mills   1137
Beating,
    as compared to refining of mechanical
        pulps   1142
    curves describing paper strength de-
        velopment   1124
    in non-polar media   1140
    mechanism of   1140
    of paper pulp for production   1135
    of paper pulp for testing   1122
Beech, sulfite pulping of   545
von Behrend, pioneer in groundwood
    pulping   278, 403
Bellmer bleacher   280
Bending rigidity, as related to paper
    density   1145
Benzenecarboxylic acids, oxidation pro-
    ducts of lignin   203
Benzyl alcohols, model compounds for
    lignin sulfonation   197
Bergvik, pioneering sulfite pulp mill   279
Berthollet, pioneer in chlorine bleaching
    278
Beryllium oxide, in alkali solubility deter-
    mination   1117
Betacellulose, determination of   1117
Bevan, inventor of the viscose process, cf.
    Cross   280
Bicarbonate,
    buffer in neutral sulfite pulping   426
    pulping process with   422
Biffar screen   746
Billerud, pioneering sulfite pulp mill   426
Billerud–SCA recovery process   809

Biosynthesis, of aromatic amino acids from glucose 170
Birch,
  kraft pulping of 615, 617, 636
  sulfite pulping of 545
Bird screen 746
Bisulfate, ionization of 462
Bisulfite,
  as lignin preservative bleaching agent 886, 887
  ionization of 470
  oxidation of cellulose by 135
  oxidation of pulp by, for improved purification yield 1005
Bisulfite cooking liquor preparation 814
Bisulfite ion,
  as sulfonating agent 484
  autocatalytic decomposition of 525
  concentration changes during sulfite cook and causes 461
  concentration of during sulfite cook 458
  concentration of influencing extent of lignin condensation 553
  concentration of influencing selectivity of delignification 552
Bisulfite process,
  acidity of 470
  aldonic acid formation in 519
  cooking conditions of 445
  cooking liquor composition in 469
  delignification in 486
  effect of temperature and pH in 563
  oligosaccharide and polysaccharide occurrence in 517
  oxidation of carbohydrates in 516
  pine pulped by 549
  pulp quality 564
  semichemical pulping by 418
  stability of cooking liquor for 527
  sulfonation of lignin in 488
  temperature range of 552, 576
Bisulfite–carbonate process 661, 671
Bisulfite–monosulfite cooking,
  liquor composition in mixed 469
  pulp from mixed 431
Bjerrum diagram,
  for neutral sulfite cooking liquor 473
  for the system chlorine–alkali–water 920
Björkman lignin 174
Black cook, in sulfite pulping 497
Black liquor,
  combustion furnace for 776
  combustion thermodynamics of 781
  composition of 768
  concentration of 589, 768
  content of polysaccharides and organic acids in 602
  dry distillation of for by-products 828
  effect of charging to kraft cook 628
  heat recovery from 772
  oxidation of 623, 772, 830
  pressure heating of for by-products 828
Black stock screening 746
Blandin Paper Co, pioneers in chemimechanical pulping 420
Bleach powder, production of 1094
Bleachable sulfite pulp 452
Bleachery,
  costs of 882
  equipment disposition in 877
  operations of multistage 1062
Bleaching,
  agents, relative costs of 1099
  chemical aspects on 857
  chemicals, preparation and handling of 1089
  chemicals used in lignin-preservative 886
  classification and purpose of 839
  consistency in 873
  control methods for lignin removal 940
  controls in multistage 1065
  counter-current 882
  deresination during 1038
  development of 278, 280, 840
  effect of pH in 978
  equipment for 863
  heat economy in 883
  hollander, origin of 280
  lignin-preservative 885
  of kraft pulps 1072
  of neutral sulfite pulps 423
  of semichemical kraft pulps 421
  of sulfite pulps 1068
  packing density of pulp in 877
  presentation of conditions and results of 863
  principal reactions of 860
  principles for applying various agents in 860
  reactors 870
  technical aspects on 861
  terms used in 861
  water economy in 881
Bleaching schedules 863
  for multistage kraft pulp bleaching 1072
  for multistage sulfite pulp bleaching 1068
Bleaching towers 872
  combined upflow–downflow 876

flow pattern in 879
introduction of 280
Blow pit washing 723
Blow tank 732
Blow-down 338
Blowing 338, 578
Board feet 263
Bonding,
    area of per interfiber contact 1163
    strength, influence of compression
        damage of 272
    strength, of sulfite pulp 507
Book papers, pulp for 357, 1135
Boom, of pulpwood 261
Bordered pit 58
Borneol, in sulfite cymene 820
Borohydride, cf. Tetrahydroborate 640
    in-lignin preservative bleaching 886
Boxboard, pulp for 1134
Bramah, inventor of the cylinder-wire
    machine 278
Brauns' native lignin 174
Breaker trap, for semichemical pulp 735
Bridged acid sulfite cook 650
Brightness 842
    changes in on delignification by cook-
        ing 849
    demands for 885
    determination of 1119
    effect of chlorine dioxide on 980
    effect of hypochlorite on 962
    factors controlling ultimate 1066
    levels of for various pulp types 850
    of ammonium-based sulfite pulp 572
    of kraft pulps 635
    stability, cf. Color reversion 851
Brobeck circulation system 336
Brown groundwood pulp 403
Brown stock washing 732
B.T., system 772
Buffer, for pH in neutral sulfite pulping
    426
Buffer storage, of wet pulp 757
Building board, pulps for 360
Bulk transport, of pulp 760
Bull screens, for groundwood 368
Butanol pulping 672
Burgess, inventor of soda pulping of wood
    279
Burnt cook, in sulfite cooking 497
Burr, grinder 323
Burst strength test 1122
By-products, general survey on 765

Cadinene 221
Cadoxen,
    solution of cellulose in 142

viscosity determination in 1118
Calcium,
    determination of in pulp 1116
    removal of 1050
Calcium base,
    in sulfite pulping 568
    of sulfite process 455
Calcium hydroxide, in hot alkali purifica-
    tion 1021
Calcium hypochlorite, production of
    1095
Calcium losses, in kraft recovery cycle
    802
Calcium soap formation, in pitch troubles
    1048
Calcium sulfate, solubility of 774
Calcium sulfite, solubility of in sulfite
    cook 467
Calcium-based sulfite process,
    combustion thermodynamics of waste
        liquor from 781, 788
    recovery of calcium oxide and sulfate
        in 803
Calender stack 1139
Cambial growth 69
Cambio debarker 265
Cambium 45
Canada,
    forests of 12, 14
    pulp industry of 1193
Canadian Standard Freeness Tester 1122
Capillaries,
    dimensions of in wood 297
    resistance to flow in wood 297
Capillary,
    forces in springwood and summerwood
        301
    rise of liquid into wood 297
    system of wood 295
Carbohydrates,
    degradation of in acid cooking 307
    degradation of in alkaline cooking 308
    dissolution of in kraft cook 597
    dissolution of in sulfite cook 504
    distribution of in fiber wall of pulps
        318
    distribution of in native cell wall 84
    DP and DP distribution of in sulfite
        pulps 508, 514
    hydrolysis of, as influenced by sulfite
        cooking variables 459
    hydrolysis of, as influenced by wood
        damage 508
    hydrolytic degradation phenomena of
        505
    reaction mechanism on hydrolysis of
        509

reactions of in chlorine dioxide bleaching   977
reactions of in kraft cook   596
reactions of in lime water   602
reactions of in pulping   307
reactions of in sulfite cook   503
stabilization of against alkaline degradation   604
Carbohydrate composition,
of kraft pulps at various yields   360,
609, 637
of sulfite pulps at various yields   359,
504
Carbon brick linings   340
Carbon dioxide, formation of in prehydrolysis cook   664
Carbonate,
buffer in neutral sulfite cook   426
hot alkali purification with   1020
pulping with   422
Carbonation, of green liquor   807
Carbonic acid,
formation of in sulfite cook   520
temperature dependence of acidity of
476
Carbonyls,
content of in pulp on multistage bleaching   954
determination of in pulp   1114
formation of in hypochlorite oxidation
of carbohydrates   951
importance of in color reversion   853
Carboxymethyl cellulose   149
Carboxyls,
content of in pulp on multistage bleaching   954
determination of in pulp   1115
formation of in hypochlorite oxidation
of carbohydrates   953
Carene,
in wood   221
in turpentine   827
skin-toxic effect of hydroperoxide of
826
Carvestrene   221
Cascade coupling principle in screening
751
Cascade evaporators   770
Cation exchange, in pulps   1054
Cation uptake, by presulfonated wood
477
Cathodic polarization, in digester corrosion   262
Caustic soda, production and handling of
1090
Causticizing,
efficiency of   798

system of in kraft mills   797
CCA Standards   1107
Cedrene   221
Celdecor–Pomilio process   676
Cell formation, in wood   69
Cell wall,
carbohydrate distribution in   84
chemical composition of   80
layers of   79
lignification of   172
lignin content of   171
lignin distribution in   80
microstructure of components in   79
thickness, influenced by genetical
methods   260
Celleco fiber fractionator   749
Cellobiose   103
Celloheptaose   103
Cellohexaose   103
Cellopentaose   103
Cellophane,
production of   1170
pulp grades for   1135
Cellotetraose   103
Cellotriose   103
Cellulose,
I, II, III, and IV   116
accessibility of   109
acetylation of, cf. Acetylation   103,
145
acid hydrolysis of,
heterogeneous   127
homogeneous   124, 125
in studies of lateral order   109, 112
to glucose   103
acidity of hydroxyl groups   153
addition compounds of   137
adsorption of hemicelluloses to   514
aging of alkali, cf. Alkali cellulose
135
alkaline degradation of in kraft process
604
alkaline degradation of in prehydrolysis–
kraft process   666
alkaline hydrolysis of   136
crystallinity of   109
definition of   91
degradation of   119
degradation of during nitration   105
degradation of in alkali at high temperature   1001
degradation of on hypochlorite oxidation   951
degree of polymerization in native   106
deuterium exchange kinetics of   109
dissolution of in polar solvents   142
dissolution of in sulfite cook   504

distribution of in cell wall   84, 312
distribution of substituents on   150
electron microscopy studies on   111
elementary cell dimensions of native
    and regenerated   114, 116
esterification of   145
etherification of   148
formation of   102
glucometasaccharinic and groups of
    alkali-cooked   604
grafting of   119
hydrogen bonding in   115
hydrolysis of, cf. Acid and alkaline
    hydrolysis of hygroscopicity of
    109
importance of for paper properties
    1160
infrared absorption of   111
isolation of   102
lateral order of, methods for determin-
    ing   109
methylation of for structural elucida-
    tion   103
microbiological degradation of   137
microfibrils of   111
molecular constitution of   103
molecular weight distribution of,
    cf. DP   106
    at varying stages of hydrolysis   129
molecular weight of, methods for
    determining   104
nitration of   145
oxidation by bisulfite   135
oxidative degradation by aging or
    bleaching   970
oxidative degradation of   130
oxidized   130
photolysis of   136
photosensitization of   137
rate of hydrolysis of   126
reaction with sodium in liquid ammonia
    103
reactivity of   118
reactivity of hydroxyl groups of   152
regeneration of from viscose   1169
shape of molecules in solution   105
substitution reactions of   145
sulfation of   145
supermolecular structure of   109
swelling of in alkali   994
thermal degradation of   137
weak linkages in   126
x-ray diffraction of   109
xanthation of   149
Cellulose acetate,
    causes of haze and false viscosity in
        1179

production of   1171
Cellulose ethers, production of   1170
Cellulose nitrate, production of   1171
Cellulose sulfate   1170
Celotex process   399
Centrifugal cleaners   746
Centrifugal screens,
    for groundwood   369
    in chemical pulp screening   740
Ceramic brick linings   339
Chain length distribution, cf. DP distri-
    bution
Channel-switching method in evaporation
    775
Characterization,
    methods for pulp   1107
    of processing and product properties
        1122
Chelating agents, for stabilizing peroxide
    894
Chemical pulping,
    definition of   283
    equipment for   331
    history of   279
Chemicals recovery, purpose of   764
Chemifiner, Black–Clawson refiner   330
Chemigroundwood process   404
    pulp properties and uses from   406
    wood consumption in   409
Chemimechanical pulping process   420
    pulp yield and properties from   430
Chemipulp–Kimberley Clark SO$_2$ cooler
    812
Chemipulper, continuous digester system
    347
Chip,
    bin   267
    charge, weighing of   334
    crusher   267
    damage and its influence on pulp
        quality   271
    dimensions   470
    feeders for continuous cooking   353
    filling   334
    packing   302, 334
    packing density in digester   334
    screening   267
    shredding prior to pulping   295
    silo   267
    size and its influence on pulping results
        266, 271, 543, 633
    storage, and its effect on deresination
        264
    thickness, and its effect on kraft pulping
        630
Chippers, construction of   266
Chipping   266

compression damage of wood in 271, 272
energy consumption in 270
fiber cutting in 271
geometry of 270
mechanism of 269
speed of 270
Chlorate,
  activated for bleaching 974
  formation of,
    in chlorine dioxide bleaching 983, 975
    in chlorite bleaching 975
    in hypochlorite bleaching 947
  production of 1091
  transport and handling of 1092
Chlorate–hydrochloric acid pulping 677
Chloride, in kraft digester corrosion 343
Chlorination,
  acids and chloride addition in 922
  carbohydrate degradation in 940
  changes in lignin spectrum on 931
  chlorine demand of technical pulps in 917
  chlorine gas or chlorine water in 921
  combined with hypochlorite stage 928
  effect of consistency in 941
    on pulp resin 1042
    pH on rate of 922
    pulp type on 924, 925
    temperature and time in 940
  equipment for 917
  factors influencing delignification by 929
  general description of 916
  lignin reactions in 929
  methods of assessing proper charge in 1062
  optimal charge of chlorine in 923, 940
    as related to hypochlorite charge 928
  pH during 921
  pulp yield of in combination with alkali stage 944
  rapid and slow phases of 931
  rate of at varying temperature 924
  ratio of substitution to oxidation in 922
  reaction kinetics of 922
  reaction mechanism of 938
  repeated, in multistage bleaching 1064
  solubility of pulp lignin in 859, 924
Chlorine,
  consumption of by various pulp types 857
  hydration constant of at varying temperature 920

introduction of in pulp bleaching 280
oxidation of cellulose by 133
oxidation of glycosides by 123
production of 1089
system of with alkali and water 919, 920
transportation and handling of 1090
Chlorine mixer 867
Chlorine number,
  determination of 1111
  of technical pulps 917
Chlorine pulping, cf. Celdecor–Pomilio 673
Chlorine dioxide,
  equipment for generation of 1097
  gas hazards and corrosion with 973, 1102
  introduction of in pulp bleaching 280
  oxidation of lignin by 211
  oxidation of sugars by 124
  process variables in generation of 1101
  processes for generation of 1096
  reactions of in generation of 1100
  reactions of with low-molecular compounds 212
Chlorine dioxide bleaching,
  as initial stage 974, 1063
  carbohydrate reactions in 977
  chlorine addition in 987
  combination with hypochlorite stage 973
  conditions and equipment used in 973
  effect of pH on carbohydrate degradation in 978
  effect of reaction variables in 980
  formation of chlorate and chlorite in 983
  history of 972
  inorganic reactions in 975
  lignin reactions in 976
Chlorine dioxide pulping 673, 677
Chlorine–methanol pulping 672
Chlorite,
  formation of in chlorine dioxide bleaching 983
  oxidation by for improved pulp yield in purification 1005
  oxidation of aldehyde groups by 124
  oxidation of lignin by 211
  reactions of with low molecular compounds 212
Chlorite bleaching 972, 974
  carbohydrate reactions in 977
  effect of pH in 980
  inorganic reactions in 975
  variables of 987

Chlorolignin,
  chlorine content of 208
  heterogeneity of 938
Chlorous acid, ionization constant of 980
Chops,
  in mechanical refiner pulp 349
  removal of in screening 744
Chromatography, used for sugar analysis of wood and pulp 1110
Chromophors, of lignin and their reactions 895
Churns 1168
C.I.E., system used for pulp color measurement 843, 1121
C.I.P. process for chlorine dioxide generation 1096
Circulation rate of in batch cooking 336
Clad steel digesters 340
Clarifier, for green and white liquor 799
Claus furnace for sulfur recovery 807
Clay filling, of paper 1138
Cleaning,
  effect of vortex 748
  efficiency of multistage vortex 754
  of bleached pulp 1081
  of various pulp types 748
Cleaners, vortex 746
Clear cutting, tree harvesting system 259
Clearance, of disk refiners 328
Climates, global distribution of 3
  influence of in forestry 260
Clupak process for extensible paper 1139
C.M.T., crush resistance, as related to paper density 1145
Coarse grinding 368
Coarse papers, pulp for 357
Coarseness, of fibers, and its effect on paper properties 1154
Cohesive rating method for interfiber bond strength evaluation 292
Cold alkali purification,
  at freezing temperatures 1001
  effect of temperature and lye concentration 997
  hemicelluloses left in pulp after 1000
  hot alkali purification in combination with 998, 1000
  practice of 996
  principles of 994
  yield of as related to effect 999
Cold alkali solubility,
  changes of
    upon hot alkali purification 1009
    upon hypochlorite bleaching 970
    upon sulfite cooking 506

determination of 1116
  of pulp at varying lye concentration 994
Cold blow, of continuous kraft digesters 583
Cold caustic pulps,
  brightness increase on bleaching 904
  brightness of 416
  hypochlorite bleaching of 913
  peroxide bleaching of 888
  properties and uses of 413
Cold caustic pulping process,
  equipment and conditions of 413
  impregnation in 413
  influence of reaction variables on pulp yield and properties 416
  raw materials for 415
  reactions of 417
  swelling of hardwood fibers in 412
  using straw and bamboo 688
Cold grinding 369
Cold steep peroxide bleaching 870, 889
Color,
  of cooking liquor in sulfite cook 449
  of pulp, measurement of 843, 1121
  of pulp, sources of 849
Color reversion of pulp 851
  caused by low pH in hypochlorite bleaching 962
  determination of 853, 1122
  factors influencing 853
  of bleached groundwood 902, 907
  of groundwood on irradiation 854
  of prebleached chemical pulps 907
Colorimetry, trichromatic 843
Columbia–Southern process for chlorine dioxide generation 1096
Combined paper machines 1139
Combined sulfur dioxide,
  concept of in sulfite pulping 455
  demand for in sulfite cook 467
Combustion, thermodynamics of waste liquor 781
Combustion furnace, for waste liquor 776
Compacting units for paper webs 1139
Compression damage, of wood,
  fiber wall changes on 272
  influence on kraft pulp quality 613
  influence on sulfite pulp quality 543
  on chipping 271
Compression wood,
  chemical composition of 94
  kraft pulp from 612
  occurrence of 61
  sulfite pulp from 541

Concentration quotient, in pulp washing 718

Condensation,
of lignin in kraft cook 592
of lignin in sulfite cook, influence of liquor composition on 472

Conductivity, of cooling liquor during sulfite cook 449

Conidenrin, occurrence of in spruce and hemlock 229

Coniferous forests, distribution of 5

Coniferyl alcohol,
enzymatic condensation of 201
in the biogenesis of lignin 167

Consistency, of pulp 862
from presses and filters 881
packaging density at varying 877

Continuous bleaching, introduction of 280

Continuous cooking 343
conditions of 354
kraft process 580

Continuous digesters, chip flow in 355

Contrast ratio 845

Cooking curve,
of batch cooking 336
of kraft process 578
of sulfite process 575

Cooking cycle 333, 338

Cooking liquor, cf. Sulfite cooking acid and White liquor
charge of 334, 335
composition of for various types of sulfite cooks 469
recycling of 335

Cooking operations 333

Copper,
determination of in pulp 1116
disadvantage of in pulp 1049

Copper number,
changes of on chlorination and bleaching 941
determination of in pulp 1114, 1116

Coppice treatment, of eucalypts 259

Cord, pulpwood measure 262

Cord, viscose rayon,
DP distribution in pulps for 1176
pulp grades used for 1135

Cork bark 62

Corrosion,
by chloride, polysulfide and sulfite in digester 343
intergranular 341
of evaporator tubes 769
of kraft digesters 342
of neutral sulfite digesters 343
rate of in kraft digesters 342

Corrugating medium paper, pulp grades used for 1134

Costs of pulp manufacture 1202

Cotton, degradation by hot alkali of 602

Cotton linters,
as a raw-material for cellulose esters 1178
kier-boiling of 1016

Cottrell electro-precipitator 779, 812

Couch roll 813

p-Coumaric acid, degradation product of lignin 178

Counter-current cooking in continuous digesters 355, 583

Counter-current washing in continuous digesters 355, 583

Courtaulds' flash dryer system 1083

Cowan screen 746

Crill, formation of in beating 748

Cross, inventor of the viscose process 280

Cross recovery 768, 795

Cross-linkages, hypothetical formation of in kraft cook 605

Cuam (cuoxam, cuproxam),
lignin 173
solution of cellulose 142
viscosity determination 1118

Cubic meter, loose and solid, pulpwood measures 263

Cuen (cuoxen, cuproxen),
solution of cellulose 142
viscosity determination 1118

Cunit, pulpwood measure 263

Cuprammonium cellulose process 138

Curlator 418

Cyclone evaporator 770

Cylinder dryer 1083

Cylinder wire 1139

m-Cymene, formation from carene 820

p-Cymene, formation in sulfite cook 525, 820

Cymene,
production of from turpentine 827
recovery of from sulfite cook 818

Dahl, inventor of kraft pulping 279

Dam, in grinders 321

Day process 1096

De la Roza continuous digester 351

De Vains process 676

Deacetylation,
in kraft cook 597
in neutral sulfite cook 429, 474
in sulfite cook 5101, 514
in glucomannan 510
of xylan 429

Debarking,
  chemical 261
  in forest 261
  mill-stationed 264
Debarkers,
  Cambio 265
  drums 264, 265
  movable 261
Decay of wood,
  effect of in kraft pulping 611
  effect of in sulfite pulping 542
  nature of 63
  on storage 264
Decigrex, fiber coarseness unit 1154
Decker, for screened pulp 758
Deculator–Cleaner 748
Definition of pulping types 282
Defibrator,
  disk refiner 327
  process of continuous thermomechanical pulping 343, 395
  pulp, properties of 397
Degree of polymerization, cf. DP
  determination of in pulp 1119
  of cellulose 106
  of hemicelluloses 161, 162
  of pulp carbohydrates as related to paper strength 1160
Degree of substitution, of cellulose derivatives 152
Dehydrodiabietic acid, occurrence of in wood 225
Delbay process 673
Delignification,
  effect of on paper properties 1157
  effect of temperature on rate of in sulfite cook 479
  in fiber wall, course of 291
  in variants of sulfite process 486
  mechanism of alkaline 306
  mechanism of in bleaching 306
  mechanism of in kraft cook 545
  mechanism of in sulfite cook 306
  of presulfonated wood by hot water 477
  rate of with wood meal and with chips 309
Demethylation,
  of glucuronoxylan in kraft cook 608
  of lignin in kraft cook 592
Density,
  determination of in paper and handsheets 1122
  of paper, as related to opacity 1144
  of wood species 64
  of wood substance 64
  pulp 862

Depositable resin, determination of in pulp 1114
Deresination,
  by alkali extraction 1047
  by fiber fractionation 1037
  during cooking 1033
  during neutral sulfite pulping 1036
  effect of chlorination and oxidation on 1042
  effect of detergents in 1045
  effect of various processing stages on 1038
  effect of wood seasoning on 1029
  general aspects on 1024
  measures to improve 1024
  of pine sulfite pulp before screening 549
  solubilization mechanism in 1044
Desforges–McLaughlin process 673
Detergents, in deresination 1045
Deterioration, of wood on storage 264
Dextropimaric acid, in resin and wood extractives 225
Diaphragm flat screen 745
Diazomethane,
  effect of on peroxide bleaching and pulp brightness 900
  effect of on ultraviolet light absorption of lignin 184
Diffuser washing,
  batch-wise 723
  continuous 727
  of kraft pulp 725
  results of 726
  variables of 720
Diffusion,
  of gas into wood 295, 299
  of liquid into wood 295
  of solutes into soaked wood 295, 298
  of various cations into wood in sulfite process 569
  of water vapor into air-filled wood 300
  ratio of longitudinal to transversal, of solutes into wood 298
Diffusion coefficients, temperature dependence in pulp washing 727
Digester,
  circulations, study of by radioactive tracers 336
  corrosion 339
  cycle 333
  for straw pulping 684
  linings 339
  operations 333
  pressure, effect of on sulfite pulping rate 559
  types for batch cooking 331

washing in   723, 728
Dihydroquercetinol,
  in sulfite process   549
  occurrence in douglas fir   229
α,δ-Dihydroxy-γ-sulfovaleric acid, from
  xylose in neutral sulfite cook   520
Dilution curve, in pulp washing   730
Dilution factor, in pulp washing   718
Dimethyl sulfide,
  by-product from kraft industry   826
  formation of in kraft cook   592
Dimethyl sulfoxide
  for hemicellulose extraction   159
  production of   827
2,4-Dinitroguaiacol, degradation product
  of lignin   203
Dioxane lignin   174
Dioxane pulping   672
Dipentene   221
Dirtec   747
Discharge of continuous digesters   353
Discontinuous cooking, operations of
  331
Disk evaporators   770
Disk press in pulp washing   723
Disk refiners   320, 326, 328
Disk refining of chips at atmospheric
  pressure   392
Displacement factor, in pulp washing
  721
Displacement ratio, in pulp washing   721
Displacement washing   718, 735
Dissociation constants of,
  acetic acid, temperature dependence of
    471
  bisulfate ion   462
  bisulfite ion   470
  carbonic acid, temperature dependence
    of   476
  carboxyl groups in pulp   1055
  chlorous acid   980
  fatty and resin acids   1040
  hypochlorous acid   919
  sulfurous acid, temperature dependence
    of   456
Dissolving pulps,
  aging properties of   1175
  analytical composition and processing
    properties of   1172
  analytical data of   1177
  content of inorganics in   1052
  development of   280
  effect of hemicelluloses on quality of
    1175
  from hardwoods by the sulfite process
    547

influence of resin and silica content on
    quality of   1176
  processes using   1166
  qualitative and economical aspects of
    356
  sheet qualities of   1173
  testing of   1126
  uses for   1135
  viscose filtrability of   1175
Dithionite,
  effect of in soda kraft cooking   642
  production of   1093
  in lignin–preservative bleaching   886
  introduction of in bleaching   280
Dithionite bleaching,
  brightness increase at varying chemica
    charge in   904
  color reversion upon   902
  combination with peroxide bleaching
    906
  conditions of   887
  inorganic reactions of   892
  pH influence on   908
  temperature effect on   911
Donnan effects, on delignification in
    sulfite cook   477, 492
Dorr causticizing system   797
Dorrco pyrite roaster   811
Double screening   749
Double-disk refiners   328
Douglas fir,
  sulfite pulping of   549
  kraft pulping of   610
DP,
  determination of in pulp   1119
  of acetate films as related to strength
    1160
  of cellulose in wood   106
  of cellulose and hemicelluloses, as
    related to paper strength   1160
  of hemicelluloses in wood   161, 162
  of hemicelluloses in pulping processes
    429
DP distribution,
  determination of   1119
  effect of hot alkali purification on   107
  of carbohydrates in sulfite pulps   506
  of cord pulps   1176
  of sulfite and kraft pulps   318
Dregs   799
Drewsen process   422
Driving of pulpwood   261
Drum chipper   273
Drum press, in pulp washing   723
Dry spinning, of cellulose acetate   1172
Drying,
  cylinders   1139

effect of on pulp opacity 855
machine speed 1085
of pulp as related to paper properties 1159
of pulp, process of 1083
of unbleached pulp 760
steam consumption in pulp 1086
D.S., of cellulose derivatives 151
Dumping, of batch cooks 338
Dust collectors, for calcium base sulfite ash 803
Dyeing, of paper stock 1138

Earlywood
chemical composition of 94
Easybleaching sulfite pulp 452
Eductor tank 818
Effective alkali, in kraft cooking 588
Effective capillary cross-sectional area of wood 491
Eimco causticizing system 801
Ekman, pioneer of sulfite pulping 279
Electron microscopy, in cellulose super-structure research 111
Elementary fibrils 71, 111
End-group stabilization of pulp carbo-hydrates 1005
End-point determination, of sulfite cook 446
Energy,
balance, of pulp mills 776
of activation in pulping 310
of fiberizing 330
Environmental influence, in tree-breeding 260
Episulfide formation, in lignin on kraft cooking 594
Epoxide formation, in lignin on alkaline cooking 594
Equalizing, of pulp quality by mixing 757
Erkensator 746
Escher–Wyss continuous digester 350
Esparto,
pulp properties and uses 692
pulping 677, 687
Esterification processes, for cellulose 1170
Ethanol,
production of from sulfite waste liquor 823
yield of from sulfite waste liquor 823
Ethanol pulping 665
Ether-solubles in wood, composition of 1025
Etherification of cellulose, reactions in 1166

Ethyl cellulose 149
Eucalypt plantations 39
Eucalyptus, pulping of 545
Europe,
central and southern pulp industry 1201
forests of 28
northern pulp industry of 1200
Evacuation, for air-removal from wood 301
Evaporation,
of waste liquors 768
of white liquor 772
multi-effect 770
sulfur losses in black liquor 772
Evaporators,
cascade 770
disk 770
types of 769
Excess alkali, in hypochlorite bleaching 861, 960
Expanda process 962
Extractives,
definition of 91
determination of in pulp 1112
formation of in wood 218
location of in wood 188, 218
reactions of in pulping 309

Failure zone in the fracture and fiberizing of wood 286, 288, 290, 291
False viscosity, causes of in cellulose acetate 1179
Fast-growing wood species 259
Fats, hydrolysis of on wood seasoning 1031
Fatty acids,
composition of 1026
from tall oil 827
occurrence in wood of 224
Fenerty, inventor of groundwood 278
Fermentation, of sulfite waste liquor 823
Fertilizing, in forestry 260
Ferulic acid, degradation product of lignin 178
Fiber bonding, mechanism of 1140
Fiber bundles, removal of from pulp 744
Fiber dimensions 47
factors influencing 53
improvement by genetical methods 260
paper properties as related to 1152
Fiber flexibility, influence of wood struc-ture and pulping process on 1163
Fiber fractionation,
deresination by 748
silica removal by 1053

Fiber fragmentation in beating 1141
Fiber length 51
  distribution, effect of sulfite pulping on
    506
  distribution, of sulfite and kraft pulp
    319
  effect of pulping process on 1157
  paper properties as related to 1152
Fiber liberation,
  point of 282
  progress of in pulping 319
  requirements for 285
Fiber strength 55
  effect of kraft pulping on 647, 1163
  effect of on paper properties 1154
  effect of sulfite pulping on 507, 1163
  effect of wood compression damage on
    272, 507, 1163
Fiber wall,
  carbohydrate distribution in 84, 312
  changes in layers of on pulping 314
  changes in on grinding 379
  chemical composition of 80
  cross-sectional area of 55
  growth of 71
  layers, relative thickness of 72
  lignin content of 171
  lignin distribution in 80
  mass distribution in 311
  strength of on sulfite pulping 506
  structure of 285
  thickness of 51
  thickness of as related to paper pro-
    perties 611, 1153
Fiberizing,
  energy of 293, 330
  of wood prior to chemical pulping 294
Fibers 47
  collapse of on delignification 292
  structure of 71
Fibril formation in beating 1141
Fibrilplasma fines of groundwood 386
Filaments, number of per viscose rayon
    yarn 1169
Filter washing 725, 732
Filters,
  capacity of in bleaching 881
  in bleaching 880
  in screening 758
  in washing 723
Filterability constants, of viscose pulp
    1126
Filtration, of viscose 1168
Fine papers, pulp grades for 357, 1134
Fines,
  effect of on paper properties 1155
  formation of in beating 1141

  in groundwood pulp 386
Finishing operations 1081
Finishing room 1140
Finland, pulp industry of 1200
Fire breaks 262
Fish eyes, in flash-dried pulp 1140
Flakt dryer 1083
Flash drying 1083
Flat crush resistance, as related to paper
    density 1145
Flavanones, occurrence in wood 228
Flexibility, of springwood and summer-
    wood fibers 1163
Flour fines in groundwood pulp 386
Flow rate, of pulp entering the bleaching
    1062
Fluidity, of pulp in hypochlorite bleach-
    ing 954
Fluorescence, of sulfite pulp and ligno-
    sulfonate 214, 218, 539
Foaming, in washing of chlorinated pulp
    1077
Fodder yeast, production of 824
Folin, pioneer in sulfite pulping 280
Folding endurance test 1122
Food board, pulp grades used for 1134
Forest operations 261, 262
Forest plantations 39
Forests, distribution of 8
Formaldehyde,
  formation of in kraft cook 593
  formation of in sulfite cook 464, 520
Formic acid,
  formation of in hot alkali purification
    1007
  formation of in kraft cook 600
  formation of in sulfite cook 520
Fourdrinier, pioneers in paper machine
    construction 278
Fourdrinier paper machine 1139
Fourdrinier wire 1139
Free acid tower 788
Free SO_2, concept of in sulfite process 455
Freeness, determination of 1122
Freeze purification, of pulp with alkali
    1001
Fresk system of chip packing 334
Friction aspects on grinding 380
Friction debarkers, stationary 264
Frottator 419
Fuelwood consumption 8
Fungi, sap stains and rot 63
Furanosidic bonds, hydrolysis of 509
Furfural,
  formation of in sulfite cook 464, 520
  production of from pentoses 824
Fusel oil 824

Galactoglucomannan acetate,
   occurrence of in wood 92
   structure of 161
Galactonic acid, formation of in sulfite
   cook 519
Galactose, fermentation of 823
Galacturonogalactan 99, 163
Gammacellulose, determination of 117
Gammacellulose content, as related to
   paper properties 1159
Gas diffusion, into wood 295, 299
Gas flow, into wood 295
Gel particle counting 1127
General Electric brightness tester 842,
   119
Genetics in forestry 260
Giersdorf pioneering groundwood mill
   278
Glomera flash dryer 1083
Glucan, non-cellulosic 92
Glucomannan 92
   adsorption of by cellulose 510
   adsorption of alkali-resistant, to cellu-
      lose in kraft cook 609
   deacetylation of in sulfite cook 510,
      522
   dissolution of in sulfite cook 504
   distribution of in cell wall 86
   DP of in kraft pulp 1160
   DP of in sulfite pulp 511, 1160
   DP of in wood 1160
   residual, in pulp after cold alkali
      purification 1000
   stabilization of in one- and two-stage
      sulfite pulping 510, 655
   structure of 161
Glucometasaccharinic acid, formation of
   in kraft cook 600
Gluconic acid,
   formation of by hypochlorite oxidation
      of celloulse 951
   formation of in sulfite cook 519
Glucose,
   fermentation of 823
   formation of by hydrolysis of cellulose
      103
Glucuronic acid 597, 606
   demethylation of in kraft cook 604,
      608
   influence on xylan degradation in kraft
      cook 603
Glucuronoxylan, DP of in wood, sulfite
   and kraft pulp 1160
Glycerol,
   occurrence of in wood 225
   pulping with 672
Glycol, pulping with 672

Glycolic acid,
   formation of in hot alkali purification
      1007
   formation of in kraft cook 600
Glycosidation, of aldehyde end groups
   for stabilization 604
Glycosides, oxidation of by various
   oxidants 123
Glycosidic bonds, cleavage of,
   by acid hydrolysis 119, 503
   by alkaline hydrolysis 119, 120
   by chlorine or hypochlorous acid 951
Gould Paper Co, pioneers in cold caustic
   pulping 413
Grasses,
   pulping of 677
   silica content of 1052
Greaseproof pulp, cooking conditions of
   in sulfite process 494
Green liquor, composition of 797
Griesheim process 1096
Grits,
   in kraft recovery systems 800
   of grinder stones 323, 376
Grinder bleaching, with dithionite or
   peroxide 888
Grinder pit 368
Grinder stone,
   action of on wood 377
   artificial 321
   conditioning of 370
   drilling of 376
   friction coefficient of 380
   grits of 376
   self-conditioning of 376
   sharpening cycle of 376
   sharpness of, gypsum image studies on
      386
   sharpness of, relation to friction co-
      efficient 385
   stone, steel brushes for 383
Grinders 320
   capacity of 370
   control of load and wood consumption
      371
   data of modern 281
   operation of 368
   output of modern 385
   power consumption of 383, 659
   production equation for 384
   types of 321
Grinding, cf. Groundwood process
   alkali and alum addition in when using
      pine 403
   burning or charring of wood in 374
   conditions of and their influence on
      production and quality 380

effect of consistency on energy consumption in 382
effect of freeness on energy consumption in 382
effect of peripheral speed on production and quality in 385
effect of stone condition on fiber fractions and freeness in 386
effect of stone material on pulp quality in 386
effect of stone sharpness, power consumption and peripheral speed on grinder production in 386
effect of temperature on pulp quality and energy consumption in 381, 386
effect of wood species on energy consumption in 382
friction aspects on 380
friction coefficient in 385
friction force in 383
grinder power consumption in 383
grinder production equation in 384
high-load 382
mechanism of 371
morphological effects in 379
peripheral speed in 384
pit-less 382
pressure variation frequency in wood on 377
purpose of 380
specific energy consumption in 389
specific pressure in 380, 384
with steel wheel 379
Grinding factor, initial 380
Grinding zone,
consistency of 373
hydraulic pressure of 374
temperature of 373
Gross national income, as related to paper consumption 1193
Groundwood process, cf. Grinding, and Groundwood pulp
addition of chemicals to grinder showers in 402
boiling or steaming in 403
description of 368
energy consumption in 370, 372
history of 278
mechanism of 278
modification of for pine pulping 403
production phases of 376
pulpwood for 368
regrinding in 374
specific energy consumption in 381
theoretical energy consumption in 372
stone consumption in 370

variables of and their effect on production 380
variables of and their effect on pulp quality 386
wood consumption in 370
wood species used in 391
Groundwood pulp,
alkali treatment of from poplar 417
annual production of 368
bleaching of with various types of chemicals 904
brightness and color reversion of 370
brightness increase of on peroxide bleaching 901
brown 403
color reversion of 854
color reversion of peroxide bleached 902
drainage characteristics of 370
effective surface energy of 372
fines fraction of 386
freeness of as related to production and sharpness 389
grades of 368
hypochlorite bleaching of 913
influence of wood on quality of 390
peroxide bleaching of 888
printability of papers containing 370
properties of 391
quality characteristics of 370
quality equation of 389
quality of as related to grinding variables 386
screening of 757
sheet density of 370
strength properties of 370
surface area of 373
tensile strength as related freeness 390
uses of 368
visual quality control of 371
wet web strength of 370, 389
wood consumption of from various species 390
yellowing of 214, 218, 895, 899
yield of 370
Growth mechanism of wood 69
Growth rate,
of forests in various parts of the world 17ff, 40, 259
of pulpwood species 259
of straw and bamboo 259
of trees and genetical improvement of 42, 60
Growth ring 46
Guillet cutter, for thin wood chips 273
Gypsum,
incrustations of in sulfite cook 523
solubility of 774

H-factor 618
Handsheet preparation for paper pulp testing 1122
Hansel chipper 267
Hardboard pulp, screening of 757
Hardwoods,
in kraft pulping 615
in neutral sulfite pulping 429
in sulfite pulping 543
in cold caustic pulping 415
penetration difficulties with 544
water driving of 261
Hauling of trees to road 261
Haze, in cellulose acetate 1178, 1179
Headbox,
of paper machines 1138
of pulp drying machines 1085
Heartwood,
chemical composition of 94
deposition of extractives in the formation of 220
formation of 58
in sulfite pulping 542, 548
penetrability of 274
Heat balance of pulp mills 776
Heat consumption, in lime kiln 802
Heat exchangers,
in bleacheries 882
in digesters 336
Heat recovery from black liquor, efficiency of 772
Heat transfer, factors governing 769
Heat value, of pulping waste liquors 776
Heating,
systems for direct and indirect cooking 336
time in batch cooking 337
Heavy metals, disadvantage of as pulp impurities 1049
Heidenheim, pioneering groundwood mill 278
Hemicelluloses,
acid hydrolysis of 164
adsorption of to cellulose 514
alkaline degradation of 163, 164
changes in accessibility of during sulfite cook 510
characterization of 159
classification of 156
definition of 91
degradation and dissolution of in neutral sulfite pulping 428
degradation of in prehydrolysis 657
dissolution of and eventual degradation in kraft cook 597
dissolution of and eventual degradation in sulfite cook 518
distribution of in fiber wall of wood and pulp 86
effect of on dissolving pulp properties 1175
effect of on fiber strength 1163
effect of on paper properties 116, 1158
effect of on pulp color reversion 853
effect of on pulp opacity 854
esterification of 165
hornification of on drying 165
infrared absorption of 159
isolation of 158
location of in wood 157
occurrence of alkali-resistant, in kraft pulp 605
oxidative degradation of 163
reactivity of 163
residual, after cold alkali extraction 1000
secondary crystallization of 164
structure of 159
substituents of in kraft pulps 607
xanthation of 165, 1177
Herreshoff étage roaster 811
Hexosans, definition of 92
High-tenacity yarn, pulp grades used for 1135
High-yield chemical pulping 410, 418
History of pulp and paper making 277
Holgersson linings 341
Hollander beater 278
Hollander bleacher 870
Holocellulose,
definition of 91
methods of preparation of 158
sulfite cooking of 508
Holst process of chlorine dioxide generation 1096
Horkel system of bagasse depithing 681
Hot acid system in sulfite process 441, 818, 819
Hot alkali purification,
acids formed in 1007
alkali consumption in 1005
alkali types for 1019
carbonate-sulfite mixtures for 1003
combination with cold alkali purification 998
deresination in 1047
effect of chlorite and tetrahydroborate 1019
effect of consistency and temperature 1013
effect of pulp type 1013
effect of pulp viscosity on yield after sulfite cook and 1010
end-group stabilization in 1005

of cold alkali purified pulp 1000
oxidation catalysts in 1008
peeling and stopping reactions in 1004
practice of 1002
pulp viscosity changes in 1003, 1017
reaction order of and crystallinity aspects on 1007
reductants used in 1008
sequence of chlorination and 1008
yield and purity of at various viscosity levels 1009
yield of as compared to alphacellulose content 1001, 1009
Hot alkali solubility,
as influenced by chlorination or oxidation 914, 1012
as related to copper number 1005
as related to pulp viscosity 516, 1008
determination of in pulp 1114
Hot grinding 369
Howard process 821
Hunter brightness tester 1119
Hybridization, in tree breeding 260
Hydrapulper 320, 351
in mechano-chemical pulping 432
Hydraulic debarkers 265
Hydraulic pressure impregnation of wood chips 304
Hydrochloric acid, in prehydrolysis–kraft process 665
Hydrogen, effect of in alkali cooking 643
Hydrogen bonding,
in paper 1140
principles of 140
Hydrogen ion and bisulfite ion concentrations, during sulfite cook 458, 462
Hydrogen peroxide,
in lignin-preservative bleaching 886
ionization constants of 893
production of 1093
Hydrogen sulfide, ionization constants of 584
Hydrolysis,
of carbohydrates, mechanism 509
of carbohydrates in kraft cook 596
of carbohydrates in sulfite cooks of varying acidity 472
of cellulose, 109, 112
of cellulose, acid 124, 127
of cellulose, alkaline 136
of glycosidic bonds 119
of lignin 200
of lignin in kraft cook 592
of lignin in sulfite cook 483
of wood in thermal softening 334
of wood with water 410

Hydrolytic damage to the fiber wall in pulping 318
Hydrosulfide,
effect of on kraft pulping rate 624
formation of in kraft cook 584
ion consumption in kraft cook 585
pulping process 591
reaction of with lignin 204
Hydrosulfite, cf. Dithionite 886, 908
Hydrothermal injection cooking 337, 587
Hydrotropic pulping process 673
Hydrotropic solutions, for lignin isolation 175
p-Hydroxybenzaldehyde, degradation product of lignin 178
p-Hydroxybenzoic acid, degradation product of lignin 178
Hydroxychloroquinone configurations of alkali-treated lignin 931
Hydroxyethylcellulose 149
Hydroxymercaptan groups, in thiolignin 592
Hydroxymethyl furfural, formation of in sulfite cook 520
Hydroxypyruvic acid, formation of in kraft cook 602
α-Hydroxysulfonates,
decomposition of in sulfite cook 464
formation of in sulfite cook 466, 523
α-Hydroxysulfonic acids, in evaporation condensates 775
Hygroscopicity, of wood 65
Hypobromite bleaching, pH dependence of 960
Hypochlorite,
oxidation of cellulose by 133
oxidation of glycosides by 123
oxidation of lignin by 210
production of 1095
Hypochlorite bleaching,
as initial stage 1063
brightness achieved by 962
carbohydrate oxidation mechanism of 951
catalysts for 960
cellulose degradation in 955
chlorate formation in 947
cleavage of glycosidic bonds on 951
combined stage with chlorination 928
development of 278
deresination during 1048
excess alkali in 948, 960
general description of 945
in one or two stages 945
influence of drying prior to 962

influence of prebleaching on brightness in 962

influence of reaction conditions on brightness in 962

influence of reaction conditions on carbonyl and carboxyl formation in 964

influence of reaction conditions on rate of 958

influence of reaction conditions on viscosity and alphacellulose content of 967

inorganic reactions of 946

lignin reactions of 948

lignin removal by 950

machinery used in 946

of lignin-rich pulps in one stage 913

oxidation products formed in 950

paper strength loss in 970

pH conditions in 947, 962

rate of lignin reaction in as compared to chlorination 948

relation of delignification and carbohydrate degradation in 954

yield loss caused by oxidation of carbohydrates in 954

Hypocholorous acid, formation of from chlorine and water 919, 920

Hypoiodite,
oxidation for improved yield in hot alkali purification 1005

oxidation of aldehyde groups by 124

Hyposulfite, cf. Dithionite 886

ICCA Standards 1107

Impco continuous digester 350

Impco screen 746

Impco thick stock pump 864

Impregnation,
equipment for in continuous cold caustic pulping 354

of chips in continuous cooking 354

of wood, purpose of prior to pulping 394

period of cooking 300

Indole-3-acetic acid, role in growth mechanism 69

Indophenol color reaction of lignin 199

Infrared absorption,
of cellulose 111

of hemicelluloses 159

of lignin 181, 185

Initiating layer, in cambial growth 69

Injection cooking, in kraft process 649

Inner secondary wall 72

Inorganics, content of in pulp 1052

Insect damage, in forests 262

Institute recovery method 806

Interfiber bonds of wood,
nature and strength of 283

principal ways for weakening of 286

Intermicellar carbohydrate material, removal of 1007

Intrinsic viscosity,
calculation of 119

in molecular weight determination 105

Inverform paper machine 1139

Ion exchange, chemicals recovery by 795

Ion-exchange properties of pulp 1054

Ionization constants,
of bisulfate ion 462, 555

of bisulfite ion 468, 471

of carboxyl groups in pulp 1055

of chlorous acid 980

of fatty and resin acids 1040

of hydrogen peroxide 893

of hydrogen sulfide 584

of hydrosulfide ion 584

of hypochlorous acid 919

of sulfurous acid 456

Iron,
determination of in pulp 1116

disadvantage of in pulp 1049

Isodextropimaric acid, occurrence of in wood 225

Isogrand process 392

Isohemipinic acid,
degradation product of lignin 178

oxidation product of methylated lignin 201

Isosaccharinic acids,
formation of in hot alkali purification 1004

formation of in kraft cook 602

Japan, pulp industry of 1199

Jenssen sulfur dioxide cooler 812

Jenssen tower system for cooking acid system 815

Jokro mill 1124

Jones refiner 328

Jordan refiner 1137

Kamyr,
continuous cooking system 350, 580

counter-current washing system 355, 583

wet machine 758

Kappa number, determination of 1112

Keebra process 422

Keller, inventor of groundwood pulp 278

Kellner, pioneer in sulfite pulping 280

Kesting process of chlorine dioxide generation 1096
Ketosulfonates, of sugars 519
Kiering, of cotton linters 604
Kinetics,
of kraft process 616
of pulping reactions 309
Klason lignin 173
determination of 1111
Knecht compound 141
Knife debarkers 265
Knots, formation of in wood 63
Knoxville, pioneering mill in neutral sulfite semichemical pulping 423
Koops, pioneer in pulping 278
Kopparfors digester linings 341
Kraft lignin,
as a by-product 829
content of phenolic groups in 592
low-molecular and water-soluble fraction of 593
sulfur content of 590
Kraft process 576
active alkali in 587
air pollution of and reactions leading to it 830
alkali consumption of, as distributed on different reactions 603
alkaline hydrolysis of glycosidic bonds during 604
batch cooking cycle in 578
blowing of digesters in 578
by-products of 828
carbohydrate reactions in 596
cause of the severe cooking conditions used in 590
cellulose degradation in 604
continuous cooking in 580
continuous injection into batch cook 649
cooking liquor composition in 583
critical pH for swelling and xylan precipitation in 597
decrease of DP on prolonged cooking by 646
deresination during 1033
description of 578
delignification mechanism of 594
diffusion of alkali in 629
dissolution of hemicelluloses in 608
dissolution of organic substance in 589
effect of alkali and sulfide charges on pulp properties 647
effect of alkali charge and concentration on pulp yield 635
effect of alkali concentration on pulping rate in 619

effect of bark in 614
effect of black liquor charge in 628
effect of chip shredding in 631
effect of chip thickness in 630
effect of dithionite in 642
effect of maximum temperature on pulp yield 639
effect of polysulfide in 642
effect of sulfide on pulp yield in 639
effect of sulfide on pulping rate in 621
effect of tetrahydroborate (borohydride) on pulp yield of 640
effect of wetting agents in 635
effect of wood moisture content in 613
effect on fiber wall layers of 313-15
effective alkali in 588
energy of activation of 310
fiber strength and cross-sectional area on cooking by 647
formation and consumption of hydrosulfide ions in 584, 585
formation of organic acids in 602
glucuronic acid removal in 606
hardwoods in 614
hydrothermal injection cooking by 587
influence of reaction conditions in 610
influence of wood species and conditions in 610
interrelation of alkali charge, chip thickness and maximum temperature needed in 632
kinetics of 616
lignin reactions in 589
liquor-to-wood ratio in 621
pulp yield from hardwoods in 614
pulp yield from softwoods in 611
pulp yield-lignin content relation in 635
pulping of chip fragments by 613
pulping of green wood by 613
reactions of 583
removal of glucuronic acid substituents from xylan in 604
removal of silica in 1052
role of sulfide in 590
roll press squeezing of chips prior to pulping by 613
solids content of black liquor from 589
straw pulping by 684
sulfide charge in 588, 648
sulfidity in 588, 623
sulfur consumption in 586
temperature effect in 618
Kraft pulp,
bond strength and fiber strength of at various yields 1163

causes of superior paper strength properties of 1162
content of alkali-resistant hemicelluloses in 605
decisive factors determining the quality of 645
distribution of lignin in fiber wall 291
effect of alkali and sulfide charges on properties of 647
effect of maximum temperature on properties of 648
effect of tetrahydroborate on yield and properties of 640
effect of wood damage on quality of 613
effect of wood density on properties of 611
hemicellulose composition of 360, 609, 637
hemicellulose DP of 1160
metal content of 1052
multistage bleaching of 1071, 1074
optimal lignin content of 1157
paper properties of from various wood species 362, 546, 612, 617, 1153
peroxide bleaching of 888
response to beating of at varying lignin content 645
screening of 757
uses of from hardwoods 616
uses of from softwoods 358
yield and color of at varying lignin content 635
yield of from hardwoods and softwoods 611, 614
Kraft pulping, progress of in fiber wall 313
Kraft semichemical pulping 420
Kubelka–Munk theory 845
Küng number, determination of 1111

Labor, used in forest operations 262
Laboratory beaters 1124
Lactic acid,
  formation of in alkaline degradation of cellulose 602
  formation of in hot alkali purification 1007
  formation of in kraft cook 602
  occurrence in black liquor 602
Lampén ball mill for laboratory beating 1124
Larch, sulfite pulping of 549
Latewood 46
  chemical composition of 94
Latitude, influence of on density of Scots pine 612

Lauric acid, occurrence of in wood 224
Leucoanthocyanidin, as a cause of pulp color development 901
Levopimaric acid,
  in resins 1027
  isomerization of on wood seasoning 1031
  occurrence of in wood 225
Levulinic acid, formation of in sulfite cook 520
Libriform fibers 47
Light scattering coefficient 845
Light scattering measurements, for determination of cellulose DP 104
Lignans, occurrence of in wood 229
Lignification, of cell wall 172
Lignin,
  absorption of visible light by 181
  acid hydrolysis of 181
  acidity of phenolic groups in 185
  acidolysis of in dioxane 180
  alkali fusion of 178
  alkali solubility of 590
  alkaline hydrolysis of 207, 208
  as a by-product from the kraft process 829
  bromination of 208
  chemical and physical changes in on heating wood 499, 500
  chemistry of in sulfite process 481
  chlorination of 208
  chlorination of and changes in ultraviolet spectrum of 931
  chlorite and chlorine dioxide oxidation of 211
  chromophors in condensed 538
  color effect on condensation of 502, 849
  color reactions of 214, 215
  color reversion source in pulp 853
  combination with organic excess sulfur 530
  condensation of 201
  condensation of in kraft process 522
  condensation of in prehydrolysis 658
  condensation of in presulfonated wood 500
  condensation of in pretreated wood prior to sulfite cook 497
  condensation of in sulfite cook 472, 495, 533
  condensation of in wood pulping 306
  condensation of with phenols 204
  condensation of with pinosylvin 204
  condensation of with tannin 204
  condensation, oxidation and degradation as sources of pulp color 897

content, as related to Roe number 719
content in various wood species 166
content of phenolic groups after kraft cook 592
content of pulps as influencing paper properties 1157
definition of 91
degradation products of 178
demethylation of in kraft process 592
determination of in pulp 1110, 1111
discoloration of in alkaline cooking 218
discoloration of in ammonium-based sulfite cook 217
discoloration of on condensation 214, 502
distribution of in cell wall and middle lamella 80, 312
distribution of in fiber wall of sulfite and kraft pulps 291
elementary composition of 176
enzymatically liberated 174
episulfide group formation in 206
ethanolysis of 179
formation of during plant growth 166
functional groups of 176
groups reacting in the condensation of 201
halogenation of 208, 929
hydrogenation of 179, 822
hydrolysis and sulfitolysis of in sulfite cook 483
hydrolysis of in kraft cook 592
hydrophility of in sulfite pulps as compared to kraft pulps 859
hypochlorite oxidation of 210
indophenol color reaction of 199
influence of on pulp opacity 855
infrared absorption of 181, 185
isolation of 172
location of in wood 171
loosely combined SO_2 in 195
mechanism of sulfonation of 483
methylation of as related to brightness 900
methylation to pentamethylphenol 822
model substances of and their reactions 593
molecular structure of 185, 190
molecular weight of 192
molecular weight of kraft 208
nitration of 209
nitrobenzene oxidation of 178
oxidation of 210
oxidation of for by-products 822

oxidation of on irradiation in groundwood yellowing 854
oxidation of to benzenecarboxylic acids 203
periodate oxidation of 213
permanganate oxidation of 213
peroxide oxidation of 212
reactivity of 194
shape of molecules in 192
silver oxide oxidation of 178
softening of on heating 287
spectrochemistry of 181
structure of 176
structure of angiosperme 190
structure of monocotyledone 191
structure of reaction wood lignin 192
sulfidation of presulfonated 593
sulfonatalbe groups in 198, 481
sulfonate groups in 198
sulfonate groups of distribution of in solid phase of a sulfite cook 477
sulfonation of 194
sulfonation of and condensation in sulfite pulping 194
sulfonation of and dissolution in neutral sulfite cook 428
sulfonation of borohydride-treated 199
sulfonation of in variants of sulfite cook 488
sulfonation of methylene quinone groups 199
sulfonation of milled-wood 199
sulfonation of presulfidized 593
sulfonation of, topochemical aspects 480
sulfur content in kraft 206
ultraviolet light absorption 181
ultraviolet light absorption, effect of alkali on 184
ultraviolet light absorption, effect of diazomethane on 184
ultraviolet light absorption, effect of sulfonation on 183
ultraviolet light absorption, effect of tetrahydroborate on visible light absorption of 185
yellowing of on chlorination 214, 218
yield of degradation products on oxidation of methylated 201
Lignin-bleaching methods 885
Lignin–carbohydrate bond, possible cleavage of in kraft cook 604
Lignin–carbohydrate complex 193
Lignin–degradative bleaching 857, 916
Lignin–degradative pulping 673

Lignin-preservative bleaching,
  equipment for 888
  organic reactions involved in 895
  production volume of pulps with 886
  pulp yield and properties after 913
  pyrocatechol and quinoid configurations in 895
  reaction mechanisms of 900
  reasons for 885
Lignoceric acid, occurrence of in wood 224
Lignoceryl alcohol,
  in resins 1027
  in wood 224
Lignosulfonates 175
  degree of sulfonation of 197, 495
  diffusion rates of with various cations 491
  fluorescence of 539
  further sulfonation of low-sulfonated 197
  isolation and utilization of 821
  hydrogen sulfide formation on reduction 200
  hydrolytic degradation of 495
  α-hydroxysulfonate formation by in sulfite cook 464
  hypochlorite oxidation of 210
  molecular weight of from softwoods and hardwoods 495
  molecular weight of on delignification in sulfite cook 494
  organic excess sulfur of 502
  solubility and viscosity of with various cations 491, 570
Lignosulfonic acid 175
Limbing of trees 262
Lime,
  composition of reburned 802
  kiln 801
  pulping of straw 683
  recovery in kraft process 802
  slaker 800
  sludge or mud, filtration of 801
  sludge, reburning of 801
Liming-up, of sulfite digesters 467
Limonene 221
Lindblad screen 746
Lindgreen screen 746
Liner board, pulp grades for 1139
Linings, of digesters 340, 341
Linoleic acid,
  in resins 1026
  in wood 224
  oxidation of in wood seasoning 1031
Linolenic acid,
  in resins 1026

in wood 224
Liquid flow,
  in soaked wood 298
  into wood 295
  ratio of longitudinal to transversal in wood 298
Liquid penetration, of air-filled wood 300
Liquor charging, to digester 334
Liquor-to-wood ratio of batch digesters 334
Loddby burner for sulfite waste liquor 779
Loosely combined sulfur dioxide,
  formation of in sulfite cook 520, 523
  in lignin 195
Loosely combined thiosulfate, in lignosulfonates 502
Loose sulfur dioxide, concept of in sulfite process 455
Low-pressure feeder 869
Lumber, wood consumption for 8
Lumen 55
Lumen width, as related to paper properties 1154
Luminosity 843
Lurgi burner for sulfite waste liquor 779
Lurgi pyrite roaster 811

Machine-creped paper 1139
Machine-finished paper 1139
Machine-glazed paper 1139
Machinery,
  for bleaching 863
  for cooking 331
  for drying 1083
  for grinding 320
  for refining 326
  for screening 739
  for tree-harvesting 262
  for washing 722
  for wood preparation 263ff.
Magazine papers, pulp grades for 1134
Magnefite process 431, 563
Magnesium,
  base in sulfite cook 455, 568
  base recovery 793, 803
  base waste liquor combustion 779, 781, 787
  removal of from pulp 1050
  sulfite, solubility of 468
Manganese,
  determination of in pulp 1116
  disadvantage of in dissolving pulp 1049
Manganese-collecting bacteriæ 1050

Mannonic acid, formation of in sulfite cook 519

Mannose, fermentation of 823

Marathon process for lignosulfonate production 821

Markila–Brax diffuser system 726

Marsoni process for straw pulping 412, 688

Martin's formula for DP calculations 1119

Mason process for hardboard production 281, 398, 399

Masonite guns 398

Mass distribution in fiber wall and middle lamella 311

Mathieson process for chlorine dioxide generation 1096

Maximum temperatures of batch cooking 337

Mayh, pioneer in steamed groundwood pulping 403

Mead recovery process for sulfite cooking chemicals 806

Mechanical properties of paper, as related to density 1145

Mechanical pulping, cf. Grinding and Groundwood process
definition of 283
equipment for 320
history of 278

Mechanical pulping of chips 392
energy consumption of 393
mechanism of 394
optimal conditions of 393
plate wear in 394
pulp production in 392

Mechanical refiner pulp, cf. Mechanical pulping of chips

Mechano-chemical pulping process for straw 432, 685

Mercaptan groups in thiolignin 592

Mercapto lignin 175

Mercerization 144

Merkblatt des Vereins der Zell.Chem.Ing. (Germany) 1107

Messing–Durkee (M–D) continuous digester 349

Metabisulfite ion, as sulfonating agent in sulfite cook 485

Metahemipinic acid, oxidation product of methylated lignin 203

Metals, content of in pulp 1052

Metasaccharinic acids, formation of in kraft cook 602

Methanol,
formation of in kraft cook 592
formation of in sulfite cook 522

from kraft digester condensates 828
from sulfite waste liquor 820

Methyl cellulose 149

Methyl glyoxal,
formation of in hot alkali purification 1007
formation of in kraft cook 602
formation of in sulfite cook 520
α-hydroxysulfonate formation of in sulfite cook 464

Methyl mercaptan, formation of in kraft cook 592

Methylation for improved yield in hot alkali purification 1005

Methylene quinone, theory of lignin sulfonation 199

4-O-Methylglucuronoarabinoxylan,
in softwoods 92
structure of 160

4-O-Methylglucuronoxylan acetate,
in hardwoods 92
structure of 160

Micellar-heterogeneous reaction, of cellulose 151

Micelles, formation of from cellulose in sulfite cook 508

Microfibrils, of cellulose, 71, 111
helix angles of in various cell wall layers 76

Middle lamella 72
lignin content of 171
structure of 73

Mill water, for finishing operations 1082

Milled wood lignin 174

Millinocket, pioneer mill in chemiground-wood pulping 404

Mineral constituents,
location of in wood 233
occurrence and composition 232

Mineral particles, removal of in screening 745

Minton dryer 1083

Mixed forests, distribution of 6

Mixers, in pulp bleaching 865, 867

Mitscherlich, pioneer in sulfite pulping 279

Mitscherlich test, end-point determination in sulfite cook 449

Modulus of elasticity of paper, as related to density 1145

Modulus of rupture of wood, as influenced by heating or swelling 286, 289

Molecular weight, methods for determining cellulose 104

Monosulfite process, acidity and cooking liquor composition of 469, 472

Morterud circulation system 336
Multi-log barkers 264
Multiple-effect evaporation 770
Multistage bleaching,
  brightness demand and other pulp quality factors in 1067
  chemical background for 858 ·
  introduction of 280
  of mechanical and semichemical pulps 1066
  of kraft pulp 1071
  of neutral sulfite pulp 1076, 1079
  of sulfite pulps 1066
  operations of 1062
  purpose of 1061
  schedules used in 1066, 1072
Multistage cooking processes 650–52
Müntzing, pioneer in kraft pulping 279
Mutations, in forestry 260

N.A.F.–Haglund system for cooking acid preparation 815
N.A.F.–Schauffelberger digester circulation system 336
Native lignin 174
Neoabietic acid, occurrence of in wood 225
Neutral sulfite semichemical pulping process,
  acidity in 747
  buffering in 426
  cooking conditions of 425
  cooking liquor composition in 473
  deresination during 1036
  dissolution of wood components in 428
  effect of thiosulfate in 429
  effect of wood species in 429
  energy of activation of 210
  formation of acids in 475
  flow diagram of continuous 424
  of straw and bagasse 688
  process description of 424
  reactions and reaction conditions of 426, 427
  refining in 425
  temperatures used in 552
Neutral sulfite semichemical pulps,
  bleaching of 423
  effect of bleaching on paper strength 972
  end uses of 424
  multistage bleaching of 1076
  peroxide bleaching of 888
  yield and properties of 430
Newsprint, pulp grades for 357, 1134

Nichols–Freeman flash-roaster for pyrite 811
Nitrate pulps, purity of 1178
Nitration,
  of cellulose 145
  of wood in isolating cellulose 102
Nitration process, for cellulose 1171
Nitric acid pulping process 673
Nitric acid–ethanol pulping 672
Nitrogen dioxide, oxidation of cellulose by 130
Nitrolignin, nitro group content of 210
Nitrosodisulfonate, color reaction of with lignin 215
Noble–Wood laboratory refiner 1124
Nodulizing, of wet pulp 760
Norman chipper 267
Norway, pulp industry of 1200

Odor abatement, for gases from kraft process 830
Oleic acid,
  in resins 1026
  in wood 224
Oleoresin, formation of 220
Oligosaccharides,
  DP of in sulfite cook 517
  formation of in sulfite, bisulfite and neutral sulfite cook 517
Önan, pioneering groundwood mill 278
Opacity,
  as related to paper bonding 1143
  concept of 844
  measurement of pulp 1121
  of various pulp types 847, 854
  papermaking factors contributing to 1160
Opener, for pulp in screening 752
Optical properties of pulp 841
Organic excess sulfur, of lignosulfonates 502
Ormell debarker 265
Osmometry, for determination of cellulose DP 104
Ottersland chipper 267
Outer secondary wall 72
Overscreening percentage 741
Oxidants for bleaching 210
Oxidation of carbohydrate end groups for alkali stability 604
Oxidized cellulose, structure of 130, 951
Oxycellulose, cf. Oxidized cellulose
Oxygen, effect of in alkaline cooking 644
Ozone pulping 677

Packaging papers, pulp grades used for 1134

Packing density,
  of chips in silos   267
  of chips in digesters   334, 441
  of middle lamella and cell wall   311
  of pulp in bleach towers   877, 879
Palmitic acid,
  in resins   1026
  in wood   224
Pandia, continuous digester system   347
Paper,
  consumption of as related to gross
    national income   1193
  consumption of by countries   1186
  density of as related to capacity   1144
  forecasts of consumption of   1193
  invention of   278
  mechanical properties of as related to
    density   1145
  production of by countries   1186
Paper board, pulp grades for   358
Paper bond,
  area involved in   1142
  area of as related to opacity   1143
  contact areas   1142
  morphological aspects on   1142
  strength of for kraft pulps of various
    yields   1163
  strength of for sulfite pulp from
    damaged wood   272, 1173
Paper industry,
  development of   281
  location of   1186
Paper machine,
  invention of   278
  speed of   1139
Paper properties,
  as related to cellulose and hemicellulose
    DP   1160
  as related to pulp properties   1152
  bonded area per interfiber contact and
    its effect on   1163
  causes of differences in with kraft and
    sulfite   1162
  changes of on alkaline removal of
    carbohydrates   992
  effect of hypochlorite bleaching on   970
  effect of pulp hemicelluloses on   1158
  effect of pulp lignin on   1157
  fiber flexibility variables and   1163
  influence of mechanical wood damage
    on   1163
  influence of pulping process and wood
    species on   1155
  of typical market pulps   1160
  of various pulp types   1164
Paper pulp,
  DP of sulfite   515

qualitative and economical aspects of
  356
quality of hardwood   546
sulfite cooking conditions for   444
testing of   1122
uses for   1134
Paperboard industry, development of
  281
Papermaking,
  history of   277
  process of   1135
Papyrus   277
Parchment   278
Parenchyma cells   47, 60
Parent trees, selection of in forestry   260
Partial volume concept in pulp washing
  718
Patterson diagram for groundwood   390
p.c. value   852
Pectic substances, in cell wall   86
Peeling reaction of carbohydrates,
  in hot alkali purification   1004
  mechanism of in kraft cook   596, 600
  in alkali   123, 602
  in lime water   602
  influence of xylan substituents   603
Pelletizing of pulp for bulk handling   760
Penetrability of wood,
  effect of moisture content   298
  effect of species   296
Penetration of wood,
  forced, of gas and liquid   295
  natural, of liquid   295
  of air-filled wood   300
  of cooking liquor as influenced by wood
    density   544
  pretreatment for   335
  ratio of longitudinal to transversal   297
  factor for various wood species   296
  paths in with hardwoods and softwoods
    295
Pentamethyl phenol, from lignin   822
Pentathionate, formation of by decomposition of bisulfite   527
Pentosans,
  definition of   92
  determination of   1109
Peracetic acid pulping   677
Perforations, of pit membranes   58
Periodate lignin   174
Periodate oxidation of cellulose   131, 951
Permanganate number,
  as a measure of lignin removal in
    bleaching   940
  as related to Roe number   917
  determination of   1112
Permutoid reactions of cellulose   151

Peroxide,
  decomposition of 893
  enzymatic decomposition of 904
  introduction of in bleaching 280
  oxidation of lignin by 159
  preparation of bleach solution with
    887
  production of 1092
  redox potential of 893
  stabilizers for 894
Peroxide bleaching,
  alkali and peroxide consumption in
    908
  brightness increase in 901, 904
  color reversion on 902
  combination with dithionite bleaching
    906
  conditions of 887
  consistency in 911
  effect of pH in 907, 980
  effect of pulp type 888, 903
  effect of stabilizers 908
  effect of temperature on 911
  inorganic reactions of 893
  lignin reactions of 899
  pulp yield and properties on 913
  time required in 911
  viscosity changes in 913
Persson process for chlorine dioxide
    generation 1096
Perte à la soude 1005
P.F.I. mill 1124
pH,
  effect of in bleaching with various
    agents 978
  of bisulfite cook 470
  of monosulfite cook 472
  of neutral sulfite cook 427, 474, 475
  of kraft cook 584
  of sulfite cook 449, 463
  of sulfurous acid cook 470
Phenol lignin 175
Phenol pulping 672
Phenolic extractives, reactions in pulping
    232
Phenolic groups, acidity of in lignin 185
Phenylalanine, precursor of lignin 170
Phenylpropane monomer, building unit
    of lignin 185
Phenylpyruvic acid, precursor of lignin
    170
Phlobaphenes, occurrence of in wood
    228
Phloem 45, 62
Phloroglucinol, color reaction of with
    lignin 215
Phosphates, deresination effect of 1044

Phosphoric acid, hydrolysis of cellulose by
    125
Photolysis, of cellulose 136
Photosensitization, of cellulose 137
Photosynthesis, mechanism of 69, 100
Phytosterols, in resins 1027
Piles, of pulpwood 263
Pine,
  heartwood, sulfite pulping of 48, 655
  plantations of 40
Pinene,
  in turpentine 768
  in wood 221
Pinosylvin,
  condensation of with lignin 204
  occurrence of in pine 229
  rôle in sulfite pulping of pine 548
Pit, grinder 321
Pit membrane, perforation of 297
Pits, in fibers and tracheids 58
Pitch,
  definition of 1024
  troubles in pine grinding 403
  troubles with sulfite pulp 1024, 1036
Pitting, in digester corrosion 341
Plant nurseries 258
Plantations of fast-growing wood species
    40, 41
Plate wear, in disk refining of chips 394
Plugging constants, of viscose pulp 1126
Plunger type of chip feeder 353
Pocket type of chip feeder 353
Point of fiber liberation 282, 291, 418
Point of fiber saturation 65, 300
Poiseulle equation, for flow in soaked
    wood 298
Poix, pioneering groundwood mill 278
Polishing, of white liquor 800
Polyglycol pulping 672
Polyploids, production of in forestry 260
Polysulfide,
  effect of in kraft cook 642, 649
  formation of in black liquor oxidation
    773
  formation of in oxidation of white and
    black liquor mixtures 642
  in kraft digester corrosion 262
Polythionates, formation of by bisulfite
    decomposition 427
Pomilio process for straw pulping 676
Poplar,
  in groundwood production 391, 902
  in sulfite pulping 545
  plantations of 39
Porosity test for paper 1122
Post color value for color reversion 852,
    1122

Power saws 261
Powell River process 402
Prebeating 1082
Precoat filtration technique, for lime sludge 802
Prehydrolysis–kraft process,
    acidity and buffers in prehydrolysis of 663
    development of 281
    effect of kraft cooking variables in 666
    effect of prehydrolysis on tertiary wall in 317
    effect of sulfur dioxide or bisulfite additions to prehydrolysis in 109, 658
    kinetics of prehydrolysis in 664
    lignin condensation during prehydrolysis in 665
    pulp viscosity in 668
    pulp yields and purity in 657, 665
    purpose of prehydrolysis in 664
    substances dissolved in prehydrolysis 665
    temperatures used in 665
    wood species in 662
Prehydrolysis–kraft pulp,
    cold alkali purification of 997
    yield and composition of 657, 665
Prephenic acid, precursor of lignin 170
Press rolls, of paper machine 1139
Press washing of pulp 722, 732
Pressure of batch cooking 338
Presulfonated wood,
    cation uptake and delignification of 477
    sulfurous acid delignification of 490
Prices,
    of pulp grades 1204
    of wood in different regions 1202
Primary screening 749
Primary wall, 72
    changes of on pulping 314
    removal of on beating 1141
    structure of 73
Print-through 845
Printing and writing papers, pulp grades used for 1134
Printing opacity 844
Processing properties of pulp, characterization of 1122
Product properties of pulp, characterization of 1122
Propioguaiacone, formation of in kraft cook 593
4-n-Propylcyclohexanediol-1,2, degradation product of lignin 179

Protocathecuic acid, degradation product of lignin 178
Protolignin 172
Pruning 259
Pulp,
    characterization,
        of acetate 1127
        of chemical composition of 1108
        of physical properties of 1116
        of processing properties of 1122
        of viscose properties of 1126
    color, changes of in multistage bleaching 849
    color, sources of 849
    composition and properties of, as related to yield, process and species 355
    definition of 91
    determination,
        of alkali solubility of 1116
        of brightness of 1119
        of hemicelluloses in 1108
        of inorganics in 1116
        of lignin of 1619
        of oxidized groups in 1114
        of resin in 1112
        of viscosity of 1118
    end products of and their relative importance 1191
    forecast of consumption of 1193
    optical properties of 841
    paper properties of, as influenced by wood species, process and yield 1164
    properties of as related to paper properties 1152
    price of for various grades 1204
    reflexion of visible light by 841
    standard procedure for determination of paper properties of 1125
    uses of 1134
    yield, properties and composition of 360
Pulp industry, location of 1186
Pulp production,
    by countries, grades and raw materials 356, 1186
    costs of investment of 1204
    operating costs of 355
Pulp properties and uses, general considerations 1133
Pulp sheets, basis weight of 1085
Pulping,
    changes in fiber wall layers during 314
    economical aspects on 355
    effect of on wood structure 311
    energy of activation of 310

history of 277
principles and purpose of 277, 306
progress during for fiber liberation 313
qualitative aspects of 355
rate of 309, 311
reaction order of 304
selectivity of delignification chemicals in 308
temperatures used in 311
Pulping processes,
classification of 282
influence of on pulp composition and properties 362, 1155
Pulping reactions,
classification and nature of 306
kinetics and thermodynamics of 309
Pulpwood,
consumption of 8
deterioration of on storage 264
measurement and classification of 262
species chosen for forest planting 258
species used as 42
storage in chips 264
storage in logs 263
storage under water 264
transportation of 261
Pumps, for pulp transport 863
Purifications, objectives of alkaline pulp 993
Pyranosidic bonds, acid hydrolysis of 509
Pyrite roasters 811
Pyrocatechol configurations, pulp color source 895
Pyrosulfite, formation of in bisulfite solutions 457
Pyruvic acid, formation of in hot alkali purification 1007

Quaternary ammonium bases, for cellulose dissolution 142
Quinoid configurations, of lignin in pulp bleaching 896, 898

Radial mixer 867
Radioactive tracers,
in the study of batch digester circulations 336
in the study of continuous digester flow 353
Raffinator refiner 328
Rafts, of pulpwood 261
Raitt process of bamboo pulping 650, 687
Ramén evaporation system 774
Rapson process for chlorine dioxide generation 1096

Rate of pulping 309, 310
Raw-acid tanks 818
Raw materials for pulping 362
Ray cells,
occurrence of in wood 60
removal of in screening 744
weak points of fibers in crossings with 1141
Rayon pulps
analytical data of 1177
cooking conditions for in sulfite process 441
development of 280
DP of sulfite 515
prehydrolysis–kraft process for 665
pulp grades used for 1135
testing of 1126
Rayon yield, determination of 1118
Reaction order of pulping 309
Reaction wood 60
Reactivity, of cellulose hydroxyl groups 152
Ream of paper 1140
Recovery, of cooking chemicals, principles and purpose 764, 768, 791
Recovery cycle,
for digester sulfur dioxide gas 795
of sodium and magnesium based sulfite process 793, 803
Reddening of sulfite pulp 895
Redox potential,
in pulp bleaching 860
measurement of for chlorine charge control 1062
of peroxide 893
of various oxidants at varying pH 978
Reducing oxidized cellulose 951
Reduction, of carbohydrate end groups for alkali stability 604
Reduction zone, of combustion furnace 779
Reed,
demineralization of by various pulping processes 1053
for dissolving pulp 692
Reel 1139
Refiner bleaching 892
Refiners,
conical for beating 1137
disk 320, 328
Refining 329
Reflectivity 842
Reflexion, of visible light by pulps 841
Reforestation techniques 334
Refractive index, of cooking liquor in sulfite process 447
Regenerated cellulose 116

Regeneration, of cellulose from viscose 1169

Regrinding 374

Reject, in screening 739

Relative liquor volume, in pulp washing 718

Residual extractives as related to pulp brightness 1066

Residual lignin,
as related to pulp brightness 1066
determination of in pulp 940, 1110
distribution of in fiber wall of pulps 291

Resin acids
composition of 1027
in tall oil 827
in wood 225

Resin content, effect of on wood permeability 298

Resin ducts 60

Resin removal, cf. Deresination 1024

Resin troubles,
character of 1024
effect of wood seasoning on 1029
methods of characterization of 1039

Resins,
biological function of 1025
chemical changes of on wood seasoning 1030–38
classification of in pulping chemistry 229
composition of 1025–29
definition of 1024
deposition mechanism of 1040, 1042
determination of in pulp 1112
fixation of to pulp by alum or cationic detergents 1024
formation and extrusion of in wood 220
importance of for color reversion 1019
influence of on processing of dissolving pulps 1176
location of in wood 88
reactions and removal of in pulping 231, 309
tackiness of 1039

Reyerson process 675

Rice straw 678

Ricks, of pulpwood 263

Rietz system of bagasse depithing 681

Riffling 746

Ring crush resistance, as related to paper density 1145

Ripening, of viscose 1168

Risör technique of grinding 382

Ritter, pioneer in sulfite pulping 279

River driving, of pulpwood 261

Robert, inventor of the paper machine 278

Roberts grinder 321

Rod mill, for fiberizing 326

Roe number,
determination of 1111
of technical pulps 917

Roll handling 1087

Rosenblad, evaporation system 774

Rosin, for sizing 1138

Ross diagram 362

Rot 63

Rotary burners 776

Rotation, of forest plantations 259

Rotopulper 869

Roundwood felling statistics 8

Runkel ratio 1154

Rupture energy, of paper, as related to density and bonding 1143, 1145

Russia,
forests of 20
pulp industry of 1198

Rye straw 678

Saccharinic acids,
from sugars on alkali treatment 122
in kraft black liquor 602

Saccharomyces cerevisiae Hansen, yeast 823

Sack papers, pulp grades for 1134

Salt celluloses 138

Sap stains 63

Sapwood,
chemical composition of 94
occurrence of in wood 45
sulfite pulping of 542

Saw dust, for kraft pulp 611

Saw kerf chips, for kraft pulp 613

Saw mill waste, for kraft pulp 611

Scaling,
in evaporator tubes 770
in sulphite waste liquor evaporation 774
removal of gypsum by nitric acid in evaporators 775

Scan-C Standards 1107

Scandinavia,
paper production of 1201
pulp industry of 1200

Schäffer, pioneer in pulping 278

Scheele, discoverer of chlorine 278

Schopper–Riegler wetness tester 1122

Screening,
black or hot stock 746
concepts of charge, accept and reject in 739
coupling principles in multistage 749

geometry and nature of impurities in 744

influence of variables of on capacity 744

of bleached pulp 1081

of chips 267

symbols used in pulp 739

Screens, types of 745

Screw feeder, for chips 353

Screw press, in pulp washing 1723

Seasoning of wood, to facilitate deresination 1024

Secondary screening 749

Secondary wall,
    changes in on pulping 315
    outer, removal of in beating 1141
    structure of 73

Sedoheptulose, precursor of lignin 170

Seed cones, ripening of 173

Selection, of parent trees in forestry 175

Selectivity, of pulping chemicals in delignification 308

Selenium dioxide,
    effect of on bisulfite decomposition 527
    removal of in cooking acid preparation 812

Self-sizing 1024

Semibleached kraft pulp 1072

Semichemical pulping,
    acid sulfite 418
    bisulfite 418
    definition of 283, 401
    development of 281
    kraft 420
    neutral sulfite, cf. Neutral sulfite semichemical pulping process
    of bolts 402
    water hydrolysis in 410

Semichemical pulps,
    comparison of pulps from various processes 430
    end uses for 410
    from bolts, comparison of various processes 407
    properties and uses of kraft 421
    screening of 757

Semiquinone configurations, in discoloration of lignin 895

Sequestrants, in lignin-preservative bleaching 886

Sharpness, of grinder stone 323

Shear strength,
    of interfiber bonds in kraft and sulfite papers 1163
    of wood, decrease of on heating 286

Sheet steeping 1167

Sheets, quality demands on dissolving pulp 1173

Shikimic acid, precursor of lignin 170

Shives, removal of in screening 744

Shock pyrolysis 791, 809

Show through 845

Shower wash factor, in pulp washing 721

Showers,
    grinder 323
    pulp machine 1086
    washer 732, 881

Shrinkage, of wood on drying 66

Side relief, of batch sulfite cook 335, 443

Silfate system 795

Silfite system 795

Silica,
    addition of against pitch troubles 1024
    determination of in pulp 116
    disadvantage of in dissolving pulps 1049, 1176
    in straw 232, 681
    in wood 232
    removal 1049, 1052

Silicate, effect of in peroxide bleaching 908

Simulation procedures, for pulp characterization 1122

Single-disk refiners 328

Single-log barkers 264

Site class,
    forest land classification 260
    influence of on wood density 260

β-Sitostanol,
    in resin 1027
    in wood 227

β-Sitosterol,
    in resin 1027
    in tall oil 827
    in wood 227

Sivola,
    pulping process 659
    recovery process 808

Sizing, of paper stock 1138

Slaker, for lime 800

Slip planes,
    in cell wall structure 76
    regions of hydrolytic damage during pulping 320

Slivers, in groundwood 368

Slot width, of screens 744

Slurry steeping 1167

Smelt separation of carbonate from sulfide 806

Smoothing press 1086

Soap skimmings 770

Soda process 576
    delignification of softwoods and hardwoods by 628

pulps of and their bleaching 1071
Söderhamn chipper 267
Sodium,
   base in sulfite pulping 455, 568
   base, recovery of 793, 805
   bicarbonate, buffer in neutral sulfite
      cook 474
   carbonate, buffer in neutral sulfite cook
      474
   chlorate, in bleaching 974
   chlorate, production of 1091
   chlorite, in bleaching 972, 974
   chlorite, production of 1092
   determination of in pulp 116
   dithionite, production of 1093
   hypochlorite, production of 1095
   losses, in a kraft mill recovery cycle
      717, 791, 801
   losses, in a sulfite mill recovery cycle
      810
   peroxide, in lignin preservative bleach-
      ing 886
   peroxide, production of 1092
   recovery, in kraft process 791
   recovery, in sulfite process 805
   recovery, of causticizing cycle 801
   tetrahydroborate, for carbohydrate end
      group reduction 1005
   tetrahydroborate, in lignin-preservative
      bleaching 886, 904
Sodium sulfate–sulfur dioxide pulping
   process 462, 555
Sodium-based sulfite process,
   combustion thermodynamics of waste
      liquor from 781, 788
   recovery cycle for chemicals in 793
Soft sulfite pulp 452
Soil,
   conditions of and growth rate 260
   desiccation, in silviculture 262
Soluble bases, definition of in sulfite
   process 468
Solute diffusion, into wood 261
Solvay process 1096
Solvent pulping 672
Spacing, in tree planting 259
Specific absorption coefficient 846
Specific scattering coefficient,
   definition of 846
   determination of for pulp 1121
   of various pulp types 854
Specific heat, of wood 66
Specks, counting of in pulp sheets 745
Speed of paper machines 1139
Spin bath, composition of in viscose
   process 1169
Spinning of viscose 1169

Spinning tests, of viscose pulp 1127
Splinters, in groundwood 368
Springwood,
   definition of 46
   delignification of in sulfite process 540
   fiber strength of in pulps 1163
Sprout–Waldron,
   continuous digester 349
   refiners 328
Stack-piles, of pulpwood 263
Stainless, or acid resistant steel
   for bleaching 280
   for sulfite cooking 441
   linings in digesters 341
Stampworks for beating 278
Staple fiber,
   production of 1169
   pulp grades used for 1135
Star feeder 869
Steam consumption in pulp drying 1080
Steam hydrolysis, in prehydrolysis kraft
   process 665
Steamed groundwood pulp 403
Stearic acid,
   in resin 1026
   in wood 224
Steel, acid-resistant 215, 441
Steel brushes, for grinder stone 324
Steeping 116
Stere, pulpwood measure 263
Stimuli 843
Stock preparation, for papermaking
   1135
Stopping reaction, in alkaline carbo-
   hydrate degradation 123, 596, 600
Stora recovery process 807
Storabrite semichemical pulping system
   349
Storage,
   of wet pulp for buffering and equalizing
      757
   of wood 1029
Stowing density of pulp bales and bulk
   pulp 760
Strainers, of batch digesters 336
Straw,
   alkaline pulping of 684
   cell dimensions of 680
   chemical composition of 92
   countries producing 678
   mechano-chemical pulping process for
      432
   morphological composition of 679
   neutral sulfite pulping of 688
   preparation of for pulping 683
   pulping processes for 683
   rate of growth of 678

Straw pulp,
  bleaching and cleaning of 689
  for dissolving purposes 692
  properties and uses of 690
Straw pulping 677
  alkaline 412
  economics of 690
  mechano-chemical process of 685
  Pomilio process of 676
Stress–strain curve 1143
Stripping, of sulfur dioxide solutions 820
Strong sulfite pulp 452
Structural elements of wood 47
Substance yield factor, in pulp washing
  718
Substitution, of fiber surface 1144
Suction boxes 1139
Sugar,
  alcohols, oxidation of at bisulfite cook-
    ing conditions 516
  cane, cultivation and harvesting of 679
  composition of wood and pulp, deter-
    mination of 1110
  sulfonates, formation of in sulfite cook
    520
Sugar-bisulfite compounds 519
Sugars,
  destruction of 823
  fermentation of in sulfite waste liquor
    820
  formation of in sulfite cook 517
  α-hydroxysulfonate formation with bi-
    sulfite 464
  oxidation of in sulfite cook 519
Sulfamate, in chemical debarking 261
Sulfate,
  formation of in sulfite cook 523, 531
  losses, in kraft pulp washing 718
  losses, savings in by stack gas treatment
    779
Sulfate process, cf. Kraft process 576
Sulfonation, of cellulose 140
Sulfide,
  balance, in kraft process 621
  charge of in kraft cook 588
  effect of in kraft pulping 590, 647, 687
  groups, in thiolignin 592
  pulping 422
Sulfidity,
  effect of on kraft pulp properties 647
  in kraft cooking 588
Sulfite,
  effect of on kraft pulp properties 648
  in hot alkali purification 1020
Sulfite cooking acid,
  accumulator for 818
  fortification of 817

mechanism of formation of 815
  preparation of 814
Sulfite process,
  acid formation during 458
  acidity of 465
  acidity and bisulfite ion concentration
    in 458
  acidity and side reactions in 533
  acidity of solid phase in 477, 494
  aldonic acid formation in 519
  attempts at improving the competitivity
    of 440
  base charge as related to pulp yield
    504, 550
  base concept in 455
  buffering in 458, 462
  burnt or black cook in 497
  by-products from 820
  carbohydrate reactions in 502
  carbonyl formation by carbohydrate
    hydrolysis in 516
  carbonyl formation by carbohydrate
    oxidation in 516
  causes of hydrolytic degradation in
    damaged wood 508
  changes in cooking liquor properties in
    447
  changes in fiber length distribution
    during 506
  chip damage effects in 543
  color reactions in ammonium-based
    539
  color phenomena in as caused by lignin
    condensation 502
  combined sulfur dioxide demand in
    467
  competitive situation of 439
  composition of cooking liquor in 455
  concepts of total, combined, free and
    loose SO$_2$ 455
  consequences of the condensing ability
    of lignin in 497
  cooking acid composition and prepara-
    tion 819
  cooking conditions of in modern prac-
    tice 441
  cooking curves 575
  cooking liquor composition, effect of
    551
  cooking liquor composition in variants
    of 469
  deacetylation and stabilization of
    glucomannan in 510
  deacetylation of xylan in 514
  degree of lignin sulfonation in 495
  dehydration and decomposition of
    sugars in 520

delignification in by hydrolysis and sulfitolysis 483
delignification in variants of 486
delignification of presulfonated wood in 490
delignification rate and liquor composition in 478
delignification studies at higher pH 480
deresination in 1033
development of fiber damage 318
diffusion in as cooking rate determining factor 479
diffusion rates of various cations 569
dissolution of carbohydrates in 504
dissolution of carbohydrates from fiber wall in 441
Donnan effects in 492
DP and DP distribution of carbohydrates during 508
DP decrease in 313
effect of base type on pulp yield and properties in 567, 571
effect of bisulfite ion concentration in 552, 553
effect of cation valency in 490
effect of chip size in 542
effect of cooking liquor composition in 472, 556
effect of digester pressure in 463
effect of liquor ratio on 561
effect of pH on pulp yield and properties in 562
effect of reaction conditions in 540
effect of sulfate in 556
effect of temperature and pressure in 572
effect of wood species in 543
effect of wood structure and conditions in 540
end-point determination in 446
energies of activation in 310, 573
flow sheet of 441
hardwoods in 543
hemicellulose dissolution and degradation in 518
holocellulose pulping by 320
hydrolytic degradation of mechanical pulp in 507
hydrolytic degradation phenomena in 505, 506
impregnation temperature, optimal, in 494
α-hydroxysulfonate formation in 464
lignin chemistry in 481
lignin condensation in 495

lignin condensation of presulfonated wood in 500
lignin reactions in 478
lignin sulfonation, condensation and hydrolysis in 495
liquor colour changes in 536
mechanism of pulping pine 551
molecular weight of lignosulfonates in 494
pH of at high temperature 463
phenol-rich wood species in 547
pretreatments leading to lignin condensation in 497
process nomenclature of 440
progress of in fiber wall 313
rate of as influenced by cooking liquor in 557
rate of as influenced by digester pressure 557
rate of carbohydrate removal in 503
rate of heating in 572
rate of with wood meal or chips in 309
reaction of thiosulfate with lignin in 502
reactions of 452
reduction of glucomannan DP in 511
relationship of liquor and pulp viscosity in 450
side reactions during 522
size of lignosulfonate molecules in 479
solubility of calcium sulfite in 467
soluble bases in 468, 562
stability of cooking liquor for 527
submicroscopical changes in 508
sugar formation in 517
suitability of variants of for different pulp grades 473
sulfate, tetrathionate and thiosulfate formation in 531, 534
sulfonating agent in 484
sulfonation of lignin in variants of 488
technical improvements of 441
temperature effect on delignification rate in 479
top gas condensate from 444
total sulfur dioxide variations in 468
two-stage mechanism of delignification in 479
two-stage variant of for improved sugar yield 519
two-stage variants of for improved yield and pine pulping 651
ultraviolet light absorption of liquor in 536
versatility of 505
Sulfite pulp,
bonding strength of 507

brightness of ammonium-based 572
brightness of at varying yield 361
carbohydrate composition of at varying yield 504
carbohydrate distribution of in fiber wall 508
carbonyl content and hot alkali solubility of 516
causes of inferior strength properties of 1162
classification of unbleached 452
cold alkali purification of 997
composition of resins in 1034
distribution of lignin in fiber wall 291
DP and DP distribution of 506, 509
effect of cooking liquor composition on yield and quality of 561
effect of hemicellulose content on quality of 562
fiber length distribution of 506
fiber strength of 507
from pine, deresination of 549
hemicellulose DP of 1160
metal content of 1052
multistage bleaching of 1066, 1069
optimal lignin content of 1157
peroxide bleaching of 888
quality of hardwood 546
reddening of 214, 895
relationship of yield, viscosity and lignin content of 452
resin content of unbleached 549, 1066
screening of 757
yield, composition and properties of, obtained with various base types 571
Sulfite waste liquor,
combustion thermodynamics of 781
composition of 517, 768, 773, 820
concentration of 793
fermentation of 823
sealing of on evaporation 774
thiosulfate content of 534
Sulfite–carbonate process 658
effect of carbonate cooking conditions in 671
Sulfite–kraft process 658
yield and composition of pulps from 670
Sulfitolysis, of lignin in sulfite cook 200, 483
Sulfocarboxylic acid, from xylose in sulfite cook 520
Sulfonating agent in sulfite cook 484
Sulfonation of lignin,
effect of on ultraviolet absorption 183

in variants of sulfite cook 481, 488
mechanism of 199, 482
Sulfox process of sodium base recovery 805
Sulfur,
addition of to kraft cook 623
burner for 811
consumption of in kraft cook 586
critical content of in kraft cook 625
formation of elemental in sulfite cook 525
in digester corrosion 343
losses of in black liquor evaporation 772
organic excess, formation of in sulfite cook 529
recovery of in magnesium-base operation 803
recovery of, in sodium-base operation 810
Sulfur dioxide,
absorption media for in sulfite process 793
absorption of in alkaline solution 814
as sulfonating agent in sulfite cook 484
content of in various combustion gases 813
coolers for 812
hydration and ionization equilibria of 456
liquefaction of 811, 818
liquid, use of 810
partial pressure of as related to liquor composition 819
recovery cycle for from digesters 815, 819
recovery of from combustion gases 810
stripping of for concentrating 820
water solubility of at varying temperature 812
Sulfur dioxide pulping process 462, 553
Sulfur dioxide–alcohol pulping 672
Sulfur dioxide–dimethyl sulfoxide pulping 672
Sulfur trioxide, formation of from sulfur dioxide 812
Sulfurous acid,
hydration and ionization equilibria of 456
hydrolysis with in prehydrolysis–kraft process 665
Sulfurous acid pulping process 462, 553
acidity of 470
Summerwood 46
delignification of in sulfite process 540, 541

effect of on kraft pulp properties 611,
1082
strength of in pulps 1163
Sund debarker 265
Super-bleaching, of kraft pulp 885, 894
Supergroundwood 394
Surface active agents, deresination effect
of 1045
Surface tension, effect of in papermaking
1140
Sustained yield basis, forest policy of 258
Sutherland refiners 328
Svensson chip packing system 302, 334
Sweden, pulp industry of 1200
Swelling,
effect of in beating and fiber bonding
1140
of hardwood in alkali lye 412
of wood by chemicals 289
of wood in alkali 597
Sylvestrene 221
Syringaldehyde, degradation product of
lignin 178
Syringic acid, degradation product of
lignin 178

Table rolls 1139
Tackiness, of resins 1039
Tall oil,
composition of 827
recovery conditions for 770, 827
world production of 826
yield of from kraft process 826
yield reduction on chip storage 264
Tannin-damage of spruce, for sulfite
pulping 261, 550, 655
Tannins,
condensation of with lignin 204
condensed, in wood 228
hydrolyzable, in wood 228
TAPPI Standards 1107
Tarkkonen system of chip liquor charging
334
Taxifolin 229, 549
Tear strength,
as related to paper density 1145
nature of 1151
testing 1122
Temperature range of pulping 310, 311
Tensile strength,
of paper testing 1122
of wood, as influenced by alkali, heat,
or delignification 286, 289, 290
Tension wood 62, 94
Terpenes,
classification of 220
reactions of in pulping 230

Terpineol 221
Tertiary screening 749
Tertiary wall 72
changes in on pulping 315
Tetrahydroborate, cf. Sodium tetrahydro-
borate,
effect of on hot alkali purification 1020
effect of on kraft pulping 640, 649
Tetrathionate, formation of by decomposition of bisulfite 527
Thermo-compression evaporators 776
Thermodynamics of pulping reactions
309
Thermomechanical pulping 393
Thick stock pump 864
Thinning of forest 259
Thiocyanate, reaction of with lignin 207
Thioglycolic acid, reaction of with lignin
205
Thiolignin 175
hypochlorite oxidation of 210
molecular weight of 208
phenol groups in 207, 592
sulfur content 206, 592
Thiosulfate,
formation and consumption of in
sulfite cook 528
formation of by decomposition of
bisulfite 527
formation of on black liquor oxidation
773
in neutral sulfite cook 429
in sulfite waste liquor 534
pulping 422
reaction of with lignin in sulfite cook
502
Thujaplicins, occurrence of in western
red cedar 229
Thujic acid, occurrence of in western red
cedar 229
Tilghman, inventor of sulfite pulping 279
Tingle number, determination of 1111
Tissue papers, pulp grades for 1131
Tomlinson, pioneer in kraft recovery 279
Tomlinson furnace,
for black liquor combustion 776
for magnesium-based sulfite waste
liquor 779
for sodium-based sulfite waste liquor
779
Top gas relief, in batch cooking 338, 443
Torulopsis utilis yeast 824
Torus, of bordered pits 58
Total sulfur dioxide,
concept of in sulfite process 455
variations of in sulfite cook 468
Tower acid, composition of 817

Trace elements, occurrence in wood 232
Tracheids 47
Transition lamella 75
    removal of on beating 1141
Transparency 844
Tree-harvesting machines 262
Trichromatic indices 843
Trioses,
    formation of in sulfite cook 520
    α-hydroxysulfonate formation of in
        sulfite cook 464
Triphenylcarbinol, sulfonation of 197
Tristimulus filters 1121
Trithionate, formation of by decomposi-
    tion of bisulfite 527
Tropical forests,
    description of 32
    distribution of 6
Ts'ai-Loun, inventor of paper 278
Turbidity, determination of viscose 1127
Turpentine,
    skin-toxic effect of 826
    yield of in kraft process 826
Two-stage bleaching,
    introduction of 280
    with dithionite–peroxide 888
    with peroxide–dithionite 906
'Two-stage neutral process,' on mag-
    nesium base 661
Two-stage sulfite cooking,
    quality effects of 655
    pH conditions of first stage in 655
    pine in 549
    reactions of 654
Tylose formation 60
    effect of on wood penetrability 297,
        544

Ultracentrifugation, for cellulose DP
    determination 104
Ultra high-yield pulp 420
Ultraviolet light absorption,
    of lignin 181
    of sulfite cooking liquor 447, 537
Unsaponifiables, composition of in resins
    1027
Uronic acid, determination of 1110
United States,
    forests of 15, 18
    paper production of 1196, 1197
    pulp industry of 1195
    wood species of 15
U.S.S.R., pulp industry of 1198

Vacuum evaporation system 776
Valley laboratory beater 1124

Valleyfield, pioneering groundwood mill
    278
Valveless filters 880
Vanillic acid,
    degradation product of lignin 178
    production of from lignin 822
Vanillin,
    degradation product of lignin 178
    production of from lignin 822
    yield of from lignin of various degrees
        of condensation 203
Vanillin-5-carboxylic acid, degradation
    product of lignin 178
Vanillyl alcohol,
    reactions of at kraft cooking conditions
        594
    sulfonation of 198
Vapor phase cooking 305, 336
Vaporsphere 830
Va-purge process for air-removal from
    wood 303
Vegetation types, distribution of 3
Vessel elements 47
Vessels 59
Veratric acid, degradation product of
    lignin 178
Veratrylglycerol-β-guaiacyl ether 187
Vertical bleacher 870
Vilamo method for air-removal from
    wood 304
Viscometry in determining cellulose DP
    104
Viscose,
    composition of 1168
    filtrability and spinnability of 1173
Viscose process,
    description of 1167
    history of 280
Viscose pulp,
    analytical data of 1177
    development of 280
    processing properties of 1173
    testing methods for 1126
Viscosity,
    of cooking liquor during sulfite cook
        447
    of pulp,
        as related to paper strength 970,
            1162
        hypochlorite bleaching effect on 967
        interrelation of methods of analysis
            1119
        reduction of as related to liquor
            colour in sulfite cook 480
    of resins 1040
Voelter, pioneer in mechanical pulping
    278

Voith, pioneer in mechanical pulping 278
Vorject 748
Vortex cleaners 746
Vortex cleaning 748, 1053
Vortrap 747
Vorvac 748
VW bleacher 870

Wall fraction,
  definition of 53
  effect of on paper properties 1154
Wallboard, production of 395
Wart structure, of tertiary wall 80
Washers, in pulp bleaching 879
Washing,
  concepts in pulp 718
  counter-current, in continuous digester 583, 727
  flow rate in diffuser and filter 721
  fundamental principles of 717
  historical development of 716
  machinery for pulp 723
  multistage filter 730
  multistage press 732
  objectives of 716
  on filters in pulp bleaching 881
  of semichemical pulp 735
  substance yield factor, as related to concentration quotient in 718
  variables of diffuser 720
Waste liquor,
  composition and heat value of various types of 776
  specific gravity of at various temperatures 719
  thermodynamics of combustion of 781
  viscosity of as a function of temperature 720
Waste paper, recovery of 1190
Water,
  for bleaching and finishing operations 1082
  quality of as related to pulp brightness 1066
  purification of 1089
Water hydrolysis of wood,
  as a semichemical pulping process 410
  conditions of in prehydrolysis–kraft process 665
  end uses of semichemical pulps from 411
  reactions in 410
Waterous debarker 265
Watt, inventor of soda pulping of wood 279

Western Precipitation recovery process 805
Wet combustion 791
Wet-end equipment, of pulp dryers 1086
Wet lapping 758
Wet-strength resin 1138
Wheat straw 678
White liquor,
  clarifyer for 800
  composition of 583, 799
  evaporation of 772
White point 843
Whiteness 842
Willstätter lignin 173
Winder 1140
Wire,
  of drying machine 1086
  of paper machine 1139
Wolf bleachers 870
Wolfen, pioneering mill in nitric acid pulping 674
Wood,
  acid-susceptible 506
  analytical composition of 92
  ash content of 87
  capillary system of 295
  cell formation in 69
  chemical components in 92
  chemical composition of 90
  consumption of for various pulp grades 1203
  density of, effect on kraft pulp properties 611
  density of various species of 64
  deterioration of on storage 264
  diffusion of gas, liquid and solute into 295, 297
  fiberizing of prior to chemical pulping 294
  food-conducting system of 60
  genetical influence on composition of 260
  growth mechanism of 69
  hygroscopicity of 65
  impregnation of by hydraulic pressure 304
  impregnation of by steaming 304
  impregnation of prior to pulping 294
  influence of growth rate on pulping behavior of 541
  influence of moisture content on pulping behavior of 542
  ion-exchange properties of sulfonated 197
  location of extractives in 88
  methods of air-removal from 301

mineral constitutents of, occurrence, location and composition of 232

modulus of rupture of, decrease on heating or swelling 286, 289

moisture content of in various conditions 300

morphological disturbances in on chipping 507

nitration of for isolation of cellulose 102

penetrability of as influenced by moisture content 298

penetrability of various wood species 296

penetration of air-filled 300

penetration of by gas and liquid 295

phenol-rich, in sulfite process 547

plastic deformation of in fracture 372

price of in different regions 1202

reserve food components of 88

seasoning of 1029

shear strength of, decrease on heating 286

shrinkage of on drying 66

specific heat of 66

steaming of for air removal 302

structural changes of on pulping 311

surface free energy of 372

swelling of in chemicals 289

tensile strength of, decrease by delignification, heating or swelling 286, 289, 290

sulfonation of, as a function of pH 196

water-conducting system of 58

water content of 65

Wood costs, in relation to total costs of pulp manufacture 257

Wood density,

effect of in pulping 544

genetical influence on 260

influence of altitude and latitude on 260

influence of site class on 260

tree selection with regard to 1155

Wood extractives,

formation and location of 218

Wood gum, determination of 1117

Wood properties,

improvement by genetical methods 260

relationship to age of tree 260

Wood room 263

Wood species,

biological classification 42

genetical development of 260

geographical distribution of 8ff.

influence of in kraft process 610

influence of in sulfite process 543

influence of on pulp yield and properties 546, 612, 617

Wood storage 263

Wood yard 263

Wrapping paper, pulp grades for 1134

X-ray diffraction of cellulose 109

Xanthation,

of cellulose 149

of hemicellulose 1177

operations of 1168

Xylan,

alkali extraction of from kraft pulp 605

carboxymethylation of 165

crystallization or adsorption of in kraft cook 606

deacetylation of in neutral sulfite cook 429

deacetylation of in sulfite cook 522

degradation of in neutral sulfite cook 429

degradation of in sulfite cook 506

dissolution of in kraft cook 597

dissolution of in sulfite cook 504

distribution of in cell wall 86

dominance of in tertiary wall 312

DP of in wood, kraft pulp, neutral and acid sulfite pulp 1160

DP reduction of in sulfite cook 506

influence of arabinose and glucuronic acid substituents on alkaline degradation of 603

residue of after cold alkali purification of pulp 1000

Xylem 45

Xylenesulfonate, in hydrotropic pulping 673

Xylobiouronic acid, formation of in sulfite cook 522

Xylonic acid, formation of in sulfite cook 519

Xylose, sulfonation of in neutral sulfite cook 429

Yankee machine 1139

Yeast, for fermentation of sulfite waste liquor 823

Yellowing,

of groundwood pulp 895

of pulp 851

Zeiss Elrepho brightness tester 842, 1121

Zero span tensile test 1150

Zinc dithionite, production of 1093

Zinc oxide, in alkali solubility determination 1117